Third Edition

Basic Theory and Practice of

QUANTITATIVE
CHEMICAL ANALYSIS

ROBERT B. FISCHER
California State College, Dominguez Hills

DENNIS G. PETERS
Indiana University

W. B. SAUNDERS COMPANY
Philadelphia London Toronto 1968

W. B. Saunders Company: West Washington Square
Philadelphia, Pennsylvania 19105

12 Dyott Street
London W.C.1

1835 Yonge Street
Toronto 7, Ontario

Quantitative Chemical Analysis

Preface

Analytical chemistry is one of the active areas of chemical research, and workers in every field of chemistry, in other physical and biological sciences, and in many branches of engineering rely heavily upon the results of chemical analyses. These reasons alone are sufficient to justify a prominent place in the chemistry curriculum for a course in analytical chemistry. Nevertheless, another important reason for the study of analytical chemistry is even more fundamental—chemical analysis provides an avenue for teaching and emphasizing the truly quantitative thinking and approach to problem solving which underlie all of chemistry.

This book is written as a text and is intended to present the basic theory and practice of analytical chemistry. Discussions of gravimetric, volumetric, optical, and electrochemical methods of analysis, as well as those dealing with the important techniques of separation, are included, but we have avoided any sharp division of the subject matter into these traditional categories. Likewise, we have deliberately avoided the common, but quite ambiguous, classifications of *chemical* and *instrumental* methods of analysis, trying instead to integrate the material within the broader framework of analytical chemistry.

We have not attempted to treat analytical chemistry in an exhaustive manner, but rather to present detailed discussions of a relatively few examples as a means of demonstrating the applicability of each analytical method. In this way, we believe that the student can appreciate the rationale of a particular method of analysis. Understanding a few situations thoroughly, he should be better prepared to attack new problems of his own. It is because of this decision to be selective that some of the major methods of analysis receive greater attention than others. For example, descriptions of potentiometric, conductometric, coulometric, and polarographic methods of analysis in Chapters 17 and 18 are more detailed than the discussions of gas chromatography in Chapter 7 and of radiant energy methods in Chapters

15 and 16. One of the several factors we have considered in making these selections is the form and the extent to which various analytical methods can be and typically are encountered elsewhere in the modern chemistry curriculum.

The level of presentation is geared primarily to the advanced student who is already knowledgeable in the subject matter of the average course in general chemistry. In addition, a prior familiarity with the basic concepts and terminology of organic and physical chemistry is helpful, but by no means essential. We recognize that circumstances vary widely from one university or college to another, perhaps even more so now than a few years ago. Therefore, both the content and the organization of this book are intended to permit ready adaptation to different situations.

In recent years the theory and practice of analytical chemistry have been undergoing rapid development; and, in addition, the place of analytical chemistry in the college curriculum has been changing. In recognition of these facts, we have chosen to make the present edition a virtually complete revision of previous versions. Among the more profound changes from earlier editions are the heavy emphasis upon the use of equilibrium calculations to explain and to justify analytical procedures, the considerable expansion of the discussions of methods of separation, the addition of a thorough chapter on nonaqueous acid-base titrimetry, and the more complete and rigorous discussions of the basic principles and applications of oxidation-reduction reactions and of electrochemical phenomena.

Questions and problems found at the end of each chapter play a very important role in this book. In certain instances, problems have been purposely chosen to illustrate techniques and applications of analytical chemistry not discussed in the text itself. Some of the problems are relatively simple and straightforward, a number can be classed as challenging, and a few are very difficult to solve. Answers to all the numerical problems are collected together in an appendix.

Laboratory procedures are stressed throughout this text, because experimental work is in a real sense the very heart of analytical chemistry. Each experiment is prefaced with a specific statement of its purpose, and these purposes extend far beyond simply obtaining the amount of a constituent in a particular unknown sample. More than enough experiments are included for a one-semester or two-quarter course in analytical chemistry. However, it is suggested that some laboratory assignments involve procedures which the student obtains from the original chemical literature; specific, as well as general, references to relevant sources are included in several chapters.

Appreciation is expressed to a number of friends and associates for advice and assistance in preparing this book. Valuable suggestions concerning the various chapters were contributed by Dr. Earl L. Wehry and Dr. Donald L. McMasters, both of Indiana University; Dr. Harry L. Pardue of Purdue University; and Dr. Thomas R. Blackburn of Hobart and William

Smith Colleges. Photographs showing the tools and operations of analytical chemistry were prepared by Dr. Henry P. Longerich, now at the University of Alaska. Mr. Charles P. Land prepared many of the new drawings. To these colleagues and to many others, we owe a debt of gratitude.

In the hope that this book will be helpful to many persons and that a future revision may sometime be desirable, we invite comments, criticisms, and suggestions from students and from professors.

ROBERT B. FISCHER

Dominguez Hills, California

DENNIS G. PETERS

Bloomington, Indiana

Contents

Chapter Three

Chapter Four

Chapter Eight

Contents   **xiii**

Chapter Fourteen

OXIDATION-REDUCTION METHODS INVOLVING

Chapter Seventeen

POTENTIOMETRIC AND CONDUCTOMETRIC METHODS OF ANALYSIS

Chapter Eighteen

COULOMETRIC AND POLAROGRAPHIC METHODS OF ANALYSIS

List of Experiments

xxiii

Chapter One

The Nature of
Analytical Chemistry

Analytical chemistry is the science of chemical characterization. The practice of analytical chemistry consists of all methods, measurements, and techniques for obtaining information about the structure and the composition of matter.

A complete chemical characterization of the composition of any portion of matter must include both qualitative and quantitative information. In a **qualitative analysis,** the chemist is concerned with the detection or identification of the constituents which comprise the sample being analyzed. The results of a qualitative analysis are expressed in words, names, or symbols of the particular kinds or groupings of atoms, ions, or molecules. In a **quantitative analysis,** the relative or absolute amounts of one or more of the constituents are determined. The information obtained in a quantitative analysis is expressed in numbers, along with designation of the units which the numbers represent.

A qualitative identification ordinarily must precede a quantitative determination, because the results of the former serve as a necessary guide for the selection of the method and procedure for the latter. However, the same experimental procedures and apparatus are often similar for both, and a good qualitative analysis generally yields information which is semi-quantitative as well as qualitative.

Analytical chemistry plays a very significant role in the broader field of chemistry. Chemistry is, in essence, that branch of science which deals with chemical reactions, and a chemical reaction is any process in which a bond between atoms is broken or formed, or both. The subject matter of chemistry comprises the vast body of knowledge which deals with the structural properties of all species involved in chemical reactions, the equilibrium conditions for the reactions, and the mechanisms of these reactions. This knowledge has been obtained, and is being continuously refined and expanded, in large measure, by the chemical characterization of substances prior to, during, and after chemical reaction has occurred. For this reason every experimental research problem in chemistry involves some aspect of analysis. This is not to say that every research chemist is an analytical chemist; any classification as all-inclusive as that would be of no real value. Rather, it is to say that every research chemist relies quite directly, in one way or another, upon the data obtained by application of the methods and techniques of analytical chemistry.

An **analytical chemist** is a chemist whose primary interest is in the development of experimental methods of measurement and in their full exploitation to gain information for the chemical characterization of matter. Virtually every conceivable type of chemical reaction and physicochemical property is of real or potential interest to the analytical chemist, as are many principles and techniques in such diverse fields as optics, electronics, and statistics.

Modern science and technology are placing tremendous demands upon analytical chemists. Many naturally occurring materials are chemically very complex, and synthetic materials are becoming more and more so; it is necessary that methods of chemical characterization be available for all of them. Trace components, the presence of which was hitherto considered insignificant or not even suspected, must now be determined quantitatively. Complete analytical data are often required when only a small amount of the bulk material can be spared for use in the analytical laboratory, and in some instances the sample must be returned, literally unchanged, at the completion of the analysis. Speed is often of considerable significance. The desire to automate the analyses, and often to combine the automated analyses with automatic or remote control of processes and industrial operations, presents tremendous challenges in the field of analytical chemistry.

An understanding of the attitudes of the analytical chemist and of the means whereby he approaches problems is an important by-product of the study of analytical chemistry. The analytical chemist must recognize and evaluate alternative approaches to a particular analytical problem. He must consider the interactions of interfering substances. He must decide what precision and accuracy are necessary in achieving the desired information, and he must assess what factors limit the precision and accuracy of each method. All of these are attitudes well worthy of cultivation and application in other areas of study and activity, as well as in analytical chemistry.

THE METHODS OF QUANTITATIVE ANALYSIS

A complete quantitative determination generally consists of four major steps: obtaining a sample for the analysis, separation of the desired constituent in a measurable form, measurement, and calculation of the results and drawing conclusions from the analysis. Of these four steps, measurement is the central one. The first two steps are designed to prepare a sample for the measurement, and the fourth is to make meaningful the results of that measurement. Thus, every quantitative determination rests fundamentally on the measurement of some property which is related, either directly or indirectly, to the amount of the desired constituent present in the sample. Ultimately, the only things which the laboratory chemist can measure directly are physical, or structural, properties. Even when he obtains information on chemical, or reactive, properties, the chemist is really measuring physical properties prior to, during, or following the reaction.

One convenient means of classifying analytical methods is on the basis of the type of physical quantity which is measured. On this basis, most quantitative procedures may be classified into four groups: gravimetric, volumetric, optical, and electrical.

The term *gravimetric* signifies a measurement of weight, but the meaning in quantitative chemical analysis is a bit more restrictive. A **gravimetric determination** involves the separation of the desired constituent in a form that is of known percentage composition and that may be weighed accurately. Gravimetric methods may be further subdivided as precipitation methods, electrodeposition methods, and volatilization methods — depending upon how the desired constituent is separated into a weighable form prior to its measurement. Some selected volatilization and precipitation methods of analysis are discussed in detail in Chapter 6 and electrodeposition methods are considered in Chapter 18.

Each **volumetric determination** includes, as the term implies, one or more measurements of volume. The most common types of volumetric procedures are titrimetric methods, in which measurement is made of the volume of a solution of known composition required to react quantitatively with the unknown constituent. The chemical reaction involved in the titration provides a source of selectivity, frequently making any prior step of separation unnecessary. Titrimetric methods may be further subdivided on the basis of the type of chemical reaction which occurs between the desired constituent and the standard solution. Thus, there are four major categories of titrimetric methods: acid-base methods, which are considered in Chapters 8 and 9; precipitation titrations, as described in Chapter 10; methods in which the reaction consists of forming a complex ion or molecule, Chapter 11; and oxidation-reduction methods, as discussed in Chapters 12, 13, and 14. The analysis of gaseous mixtures can often be accomplished by one or more measurements of gas volume. This category of volumetric methods of analysis is now of relatively little importance, from both pedagogical and practical viewpoints, so it will not be discussed further in this book.

Every **optical method** of analysis involves one or more measurements of the wavelength or of the intensity of radiant energy. Underlying the analytical applications of these measurements are the several mechanisms whereby radiant energy interacts with matter. On the basis of the type of interaction, optical methods may be categorized as, for example, absorption methods, emission methods, diffraction methods, and refraction methods. Alternatively, optical methods of analysis can be designated in terms of the wavelength range of the radiant energy which is employed — infrared methods, visible methods, ultraviolet methods, and x-ray methods. Chapters 15 and 16 consist of discussions and descriptions of analytical methods based upon these several mechanisms of interaction of radiant energy with matter.

The category of **electrical methods** of analysis includes all those methods in which the primary measurement is one of a fundamental electrical quantity, such as voltage, resistance, or current. Methods of analysis based upon these measurements, singly and in combination, are described in Chapters 17 and 18.

In addition to the types of quantities measured in gravimetric, volumetric, optical, and electrical methods of analysis, there are other properties which can usefully be measured for analytical purposes. Among them are mechanical properties, such as specific gravity, surface tension, and viscosity; thermal properties, including thermal conductivity and heat of reaction; other electrical properties, such as dielectric constant and magnetic susceptibility; and nuclear properties of radioactive species. References are made to some of these methods, in conjunction with other topics, throughout the chapters in this book.

Up to this point we have considered the classification of analytical methods according to the mode of carrying out the primary measurements. It should be stressed that any one of several methods of separation may precede a single type of measurement and, conversely, that a given kind of separation may be useful in conjunction with several types of measurement. Thus, for example, separation by precipitation is useful in gravimetric analysis as well as in volumetric and electrical methods of analysis, and separation by ion-exchange chromatography may be useful prior to virtually any type of measurement. Chapter 5 consists of a discussion of the separation of chemical species by precipitation. Extraction and several chromatographic methods of separation are grouped together for discussion in Chapter 7. These and other methods of separation are also mentioned, in conjunction with various methods of measurement and categories of complete determinations, in other chapters of this book.

The methods of quantitative chemical analysis may alternatively be classified according to some aspect of the nature of the unknown sample for which they are most useful. Thus, it is possible to classify quantitative methods on the basis of the size of sample taken for the analysis. In general, the designation **macroanalysis** is applied to determinations involving 0.1 gm or more of the sample. When the sample falls within the approximate range of 0.01 to 0.1 gm, the method is called **semimicro.** The term **microanalysis** generally denotes that the sample weighs between 0.001 and 0.01 gm, and an **ultramicro** method is for a sample weighing less than 0.001 gm. These dividing lines are quite arbitrary, and the experimental techniques useful within one range are often applicable within other ranges as well. Although it is difficult to generalize, it has been found that gravimetric methods are most useful for macro and semimicro determinations, and volumetric titrimetric procedures for macro, semimicro, and micro determinations. Most, but not all, determinations on the ultramicro scale are accomplished by means of instrumental methods for the measurement of optical or electrical properties; these methods are useful for other ranges of sample size as well.

The approximate relative quantity of the desired constituent within the sample is often as significant in the selection of an analytical method as the total amount of sample itself. A **major constituent** is, generally speaking, one that comprises 1 per cent or more of the sample. A **minor constituent** is 0.01 to 1 per cent of the sample, and a constituent present in quantities of less than about 0.01 per cent is called a **trace constituent.** Most titrimetric and gravimetric procedures are best suited for the determination of major or minor constituents, although there are exceptions. Many of the electrical and radiant energy methods are adaptable to the determinations of trace, minor, or major constituents.

In addition to the classification of analytical methods on the basis of the type of primary measurement or on the basis of some characteristic of the sample to be analyzed, analytical methods can be classified in terms of the type of information which is desired. For example, the goal of an **elemental analysis** is the characterization of the sample as to the identity and the amount of each element that it contains. **Functional group analysis** consists of the determinations of certain groupings of atoms in the sample, for example, carboxyl groups ($-\overset{\overset{\text{O}}{\|}}{\text{C}}-\text{OH}$) or hydroxyl groups ($-\text{OH}$), in an organic material. **Molecular analysis** and **crystal structure analysis** involve determinations of the molecules and crystal forms, respectively, that comprise the sample. As we consider various analytical procedures throughout this book, we shall encounter methods which lead to the characterization of matter in each of these kinds of terms.

Analytical methods may be evaluated with respect to any of a number of factors. Among the important criteria are selectivity, sensitivity, precision, accuracy, range, and speed. The overall degree to which a given analytical method meets any of these criteria may be limited by any step in the complete analytical procedure. Sometimes the primary measurement is the factor that limits the overall accuracy, or sensitivity, of the determination. At other times the separation is the limiting factor. No determination can be any more accurate than the degree to which the analytical sample faithfully represents the larger body of matter for which analytical data are desired.

Titrimetric and gravimetric methods are usually precise and are accurate to within one or two parts per thousand. Only rarely is greater accuracy obtained in analytical laboratories, and this accuracy is seldom approached by other methods of analysis. Radiant energy methods are typically precise to within a few parts per hundred.

THE LITERATURE OF ANALYTICAL CHEMISTRY

Analytical chemistry can properly be considered as the oldest field in the science of chemistry. It has continued to be a significant and active field, not only in application but also in research and development. A tremendous amount of literature already exists in analytical chemistry, and more is being added at a rapid rate. For example, a survey revealed that about 10,000 articles were published during one recent year in journals and other periodicals dealing directly with research and development in analytical chemistry. The topics included virtually all conceivable aspects of the subject, including methods of sampling, separation, measurement, and calculation and interpretation of data.

Every student of chemistry should become familiar with some of the periodicals in which new information is reported and summarized. The following three publications, in particular, should be consulted by every student of quantitative chemical analysis:

1. The journal *Analytical Chemistry* is published monthly by the American Chemical Society. Each issue contains reports of new research on the principles and the practice of analytical chemistry. A series of review articles is issued every April.

2. The *Journal of Chemical Education*, published monthly by the Division of Chemical Education of the American Chemical Society, frequently contains articles related to the subject matter of quantitative chemical analysis. Topics discussed in the monthly feature sections, as well as in regularly contributed articles, include gravimetric and volumetric procedures and optical and electrical methods of analysis.

3. *Chemical Abstracts*, a biweekly publication of the American Chemical Society, consists of short abstracts of virtually all chemical articles, patents, and books published throughout the world. Subject and author indexes are issued regularly.

Among the other important periodicals devoted specifically to the field of analytical chemistry are *Talanta, Analytica Chimica Acta, The Analyst,*

Zeitschrift für Analytische Chemie (German), *Chimie Analytique* (French), and *Journal of Analytical Chemistry* (Russian, but available in English translation).

Many textbooks and reference books deal with one or more areas of analytical chemistry. Some of these are listed as specific suggestions for additional reading at the ends of the chapters in this book. Among the books and series of books of general interest throughout many areas of analytical chemistry are the following:

1. *Standard Methods of Chemical Analysis*, sixth edition, D. Van Nostrand Company, Princeton, New Jersey. Volume I, The Elements, was edited by N. H. Furman and appeared in 1962. Volume II, Industrial and Natural Products and Noninstrumental Methods, and Volume III, Instrumental Methods, were both edited by F. J. Welcher and were published in 1963 and 1966, respectively. Throughout the six editions, this book has served as a source of reliable analytical information for general use in the chemical laboratory.

2. *Handbook of Analytical Chemistry*, edited by L. Meites, McGraw-Hill Book Company, New York, 1963. This one-volume compendium provides analytical chemists with concise summaries of fundamental data and practical procedures.

3. *Treatise on Analytical Chemistry*, edited by I. M. Kolthoff and P. J. Elving, Interscience Publishers, New York (Volume 1 of Part I in 1959 and others subsequently). This multivolume series provides a thorough, comprehensive coverage of virtually all phases of analytical chemistry, including theory and practice, analytical chemistry of the elements, and analysis of industrial products.

4. *Comprehensive Analytical Chemistry*, edited by C. L. Wilson and D. W. Wilson, Elsevier Publishing Company, Amsterdam (Volume I-A in 1959 and others subsequently). This is another multivolume series covering many phases of the theory and practice of analytical chemistry.

Chapter Two

Operations and Tools
of Analytical Chemistry

It is the purpose of this chapter to provide introductions to the laboratory work of analytical chemistry and to the general laboratory operations which are common to most quantitative analytical methods. The complete procedure for an analysis usually consists of a series of separate operations. Four general laboratory operations which are common to the gravimetric, volumetric, radiant energy, and electrical methods of analysis are: obtaining a representative sample, drying the sample, weighing the sample, and dissolving the sample. In addition to these four operations, this chapter includes a consideration of several others: precipitation, which is encountered in most gravimetric methods and in some others as well; drying and ignition of precipitates; weighing of precipitates; and titration, which is encountered in many electrical and radiant energy methods of analysis, as well as in volumetric methods. Other operations will be considered in conjunction with the various methods of analysis in subsequent chapters.

THE LABORATORY NOTEBOOK

The student of quantitative analysis must keep several points in mind in order to achieve success in his laboratory work. The average student can

8

acceptably master the exacting experimental techniques necessary in analytical work, but considerable careful practice is necessary. The student who does not consistently develop and practice habits of cleanliness, neatness, and orderliness right from the start of his laboratory work cannot achieve the level of manual dexterity required to perform analyses successfully.

The development of speed and accuracy in laboratory work will also be facilitated if the student has a thorough understanding of the experiment or determination before entering the laboratory and if he has carefully planned the laboratory work in advance. The student should understand the basic principles of the method involved and prepare an outline of the procedure in his laboratory notebook before starting the actual laboratory work. Without this advance preparation, the student is likely to make careless mistakes and to be forced into time-consuming and otherwise unnecessary repetition of the work.

A laboratory notebook which is well planned and carefully and faithfully maintained is of extreme importance. A permanently bound notebook with numbered pages should be used. The first few pages should be reserved for a table of contents and should be filled in as the work of the course progresses. The first page for each experiment should be used for an outline of the procedure and a mathematical statement of the method of calculation; both should be prepared in advance. The procedure should not be copied from elsewhere into the laboratory notebook, but rather should be written in your own words to suit your own particular situation. A reference to the appropriate pages in the textbook or other source of information should be included.

The numerical data of the experiment should be entered on the next page or pages as needed, and the date of every observation should also be included. A form or table for summarizing these data can be prepared, even before beginning the laboratory work, with blank spaces for the insertion of all necessary items. With the form for these data before him, the chemist is constantly reminded of the data required and is not likely, for example, to use a crucible before weighing it or to neglect to measure and record some other equally important quantity.

The laboratory notebook is the permanent record of the experiments; consequently, all notations must be made in ink as neatly as feasible. All data must be recorded immediately and directly into the notebook. The most carefully designed experiment cannot yield the desired result if any part of the data essential for the calculations is mislaid or is not recorded. Recording data first on scratch paper is a nonscientific procedure and may easily lead to loss or error in transcribing essential data. Should it become necessary to alter a figure, the incorrect entry should be crossed out with a single line (not erased or otherwise obliterated) and the corrected value entered above it. When a figure is crossed out, an accompanying explanation is desirable. Erasures and missing pages in laboratory notebooks are not to be tolerated under any circumstances.

SAMPLING

During a course in quantitative analysis, the student almost invariably receives each sample ready for drying and weighing or in a solution ready for subsequent work. Therefore, he seldom needs to be concerned in his laboratory work with the operation of sampling. In practical situations, however, obtaining a sample suitable for analysis is often a source of major difficulty and frequently limits the validity of the final result. The analytical chemist must be very concerned about the origin of his samples and, insofar as is possible, should exercise some control over how samples are obtained.

Two types of situations are encountered: the determination of the composition of a pure substance and the determination of the average composition of a mass of material. The former is encountered, for example, in the analytical division of a laboratory engaged in synthesizing hitherto unknown compounds. It may be necessary to subject crude samples to distillation, crystallization, and other means of purification in preparing final samples suitable for analysis.

If it is desired to perform an analysis of a large body of material, it is essential that the sample taken be truly representative. The importance of this rather obvious statement can hardly be overemphasized. Relatively little difficulty is encountered when the larger bulk of material is so thoroughly homogeneous that any portion of it which is of sufficient mass for analysis exhibits the same composition as any other portion. Such is the case with properly mixed gases and thoroughly agitated liquids and true solutions, but considerable difficulty is frequently encountered with less homogeneous materials.

Sampling errors may be classified into two groups, systematic and random. Systematic errors are those that result from repeated preference for one component of the body of material. Examples are the taking of each sample of a quiescent body of liquid from near the surface when, in fact, concentration gradients may exist at various levels or the favoring of large pieces of a mixture of solid particles when, in fact, the large and small pieces may differ considerably in composition. Coal ash, for example, is generally more predominant in fine particles of coal than in large chunks.

Random errors are those that have just as much tendency to make results high as to make them low. This type of error is less dangerous than a systematic error for two reasons: The results of the analyses of a series of replicate samples can reveal directly something about the magnitude of random errors but give no indication whatever of the presence of systematic errors; furthermore, random errors in sampling can be minimized by taking more samples or larger samples, but this procedure would not necessarily minimize a systematic error.

A statistical basis for the operation of sampling has been devised, based in large part upon the concepts to be introduced in Chapter 3. The full theoretical treatment is not presented in this book, but three general conclusions are of particular significance:

1. For absolute accuracy of sampling, the sample must consist of the entire body of material. However, absolute accuracy is seldom desired and is, in fact, never attainable in other parts of the analysis anyway.

2. The size of the sample that should be taken is determined by (a) the maximum tolerable error or uncertainty, the latter being determined by the accuracies of other operations in the complete analysis and/or the use to which the results are put; and by (b) the extent of heterogeneity of the material.

3. The statistical approach is largely void if a systematic error exists, although statistical concepts are of value in devising totally independent methods of sampling to minimize the possibility of a systematic error.

Gases and Liquids.   Gases are generally homogeneous, and samples may be collected in evacuated bottles or by the displacement of the air initially present in a bottle. A one-phase liquid may be assumed to be homogeneous after it is moderately agitated. Sampling of a quiescent body of liquid is generally to be avoided but, when it is necessary, portions should be taken from several depths.

Solids.   Solid materials which are composed of large numbers of individual pieces often exhibit much variation from piece to piece, as well as within the same piece. It is usually necessary to take a gross sample larger than that which can be subjected to analysis in the laboratory and then to reduce it systematically both in particle size and in overall mass to yield the final analytical sample. In order to minimize the danger of an undetected systematic error in sampling, the gross sample should preferably be taken while the larger bulk of material is in motion, as during the unloading of a carload or while the material passes along a conveyor belt. If the material is stationary in one big pile, those portions which have "filtered" down to the base of the pile and become inaccessible may differ in composition from those portions which are left in more accessible positions. The required mass of the gross sample is determined jointly by the expected variations in composition from one particle to another and by the size of the individual pieces. For coal in lumps greater than 1 inch average dimension, the gross sample should be as large as 1000 lb to yield results of typical quantitative accuracy. For materials which are in smaller pieces and of greater homogeneity, smaller gross samples are acceptable.

The conversion of the gross sample to a sample suitable for analysis in the laboratory requires reduction of particle size along with reduction of mass. Formal procedures have been developed for various types of materials, all designed to minimize the danger of a systematic error at each step and to render random errors as small as possible. A final particle size of about 100 mesh is usually satisfactory.

Various types of crushers, pulverizers, mills, and mortars are useful for the grinding operations. The jaw crusher contains two steel plates, one of which moves back and forth against the other one, which is stationary. This crusher is useful for reducing pieces of material down to pea size. The disk pulverizer contains two plates, one concave and one convex, rotating near each other. The particles encounter diminishing spacing between the two plates as they proceed so that further reduction in particle size results. In a ball mill, the particles to be pulverized are rotated along with some sort of hard pellets in a revolving jar. The continual striking of the pieces results in the sample being broken down into smaller particles. Porcelain and agate mortars are useful for final grinding operations. The proper motion to use with a mortar is circular and grinding, not pounding.

Precautions must be taken to ensure that the sample is not contaminated by the grinding apparatus. The surfaces which come into contact with the specimen must be of harder material than the sample. Some materials undergo chemical change during grinding. For example, iron in the ferrous state may be oxidized to the ferric state, or the water content of a sample may be altered during grinding and crushing operations.

In sampling, as in other operations in the analytical process, attention must be given to adequate labeling of all containers and materials.

It has been assumed in this discussion of sampling and in most of the analytical methods described in this book that it is permissible to "destroy" the sample. In other words, the sample need not be unchanged after the completion of an analysis. Surprisingly, however, it is possible to accomplish nondestructive sampling and analysis in some instances. For example, some of the x-ray methods described in Chapter 15 need not alter the object being analyzed in any way. Furthermore, some methods of analysis require such a small sample that the bulk object is virtually unchanged by removal of a tiny portion. For example, spectrographic analysis of an ancient coin can be accomplished, by special modification of the techniques described in Chapter 15, with no change of that coin except for a tiny hole or indentation which is barely discernible without a microscope. This procedure is, of course, highly susceptible to error due to nonrepresentative sampling of the bulk object.

DRYING AND IGNITION

The role of water in quantitative analysis is particularly significant because of the possible exchange of water between the atmosphere and the sample, which may markedly affect the composition of the sample regardless of what method of analysis is subsequently used. Similarly, in a quantitative determination by a gravimetric precipitation method, exchange of water between the atmosphere and a precipitate can cause error.

Analytical results secured with a perfectly dry sample may be significantly different from the values obtained when the same sample contains a quantity of moisture at the time it is weighed out for the determination.

Consequently, the water content must be a known factor if the analytical results are to be meaningful. Then, if a wet sample is used, the results can be converted to a dry basis, or the results obtained with a dried sample can be modified to represent the analysis of the original wet substance.

Absolute and Reproducible Dryness. Some analytical samples may be brought to a condition of absolute dryness by prolonged heating. Then the sample in its container is put into a desiccator and cooled in contact only with dried air. The dried sample can then be weighed rapidly on the analytical balance in the state of dryness which is, for all practical purposes, absolute. However, the severe conditions required for the complete expulsion of tightly bound water are apt to produce secondary effects, such as loss of carbon dioxide from carbonates or oxidation of sulfides. A sample which has undergone such indeterminate secondary changes is no longer representative of the original material. Therefore, when dealing with samples which can undergo secondary reactions during extensive drying, one must relinquish the goal of absolute dryness in favor of a goal of reproducible dryness. It is essential to attain at least this condition. Otherwise, the water content will vary with time, place, and circumstances such as atmospheric humidity, so that analyses made by different analysts or by the same analyst on different occasions will fail to agree.

Drying by Heating: Ovens, Burners, and Furnaces. The commonest method of achieving reproducible dryness is to heat the sample for one or more hours at 105 to 110°C in a well ventilated oven. This treatment is often insufficient to expel tightly bound water, but it does remove the loosely bound water. The latter is the water fraction most likely to show variations with atmospheric conditions, so its elimination generally yields samples of an adequately reproducible state of dryness. However, this temperature is high enough to cause undesirable secondary reactions with some substances. The selected drying temperature must always be a compromise between requirements for complete drying and prevention of secondary reactions.

The sample should be placed in the drying oven in such a manner that air can have free access to essentially all of the sample. One good method is shown in Figure 2-1.

Either an electric furnace or a burner is used in quantitative analysis when higher temperatures are required for drying or for other purposes. Three types of burners are commonly used. The Tirrill burner is of the basic Bunsen type and provides regulation of both gas and air intake. The flame is cone shaped and consists of three fairly distinct zones. The innermost zone consists of gas emerging from the barrel of the burner. The middle zone consists of gas reacting with oxygen admitted through the burner. The outermost zone is formed by the gas which remains from the middle zone and reacts with oxygen from the surrounding air. The hottest part of the flame is at the junction of the middle and outermost zones and may be about 1500°C. No crucible or other similar object can be situated entirely within this

FIGURE 2-1.   A weighing bottle in a beaker covered with a watch glass supported on glass hooks. The beaker is now ready for insertion in the drying oven. The cover of the weighing bottle may be laid alongside the bottle in the beaker.

hottest part of the flame. The maximum temperature attainable in a covered porcelain crucible in a Tirrill burner is about 650°C, whereas the interior of a covered platinum crucible may reach about 1000°C.

The Fisher-Meker burner has a grating across the orifice at the top of the barrel that splits the single set of cones of the flame into a series of smaller ones (Fig. 2-13). This permits the air which is admitted through the burner to get at the gas more effectively than in a Tirrill burner, so relatively little of the gas burns with oxygen from the surrounding air. Higher temperatures, about 800 and 1200°C, respectively, are attainable in covered porcelain and platinum crucibles.

The blast burner is designed to permit air or tank oxygen to enter from the base of the burner along with the fuel in such a way that more efficient mixing occurs and somewhat higher temperatures are attainable. Fuels other than natural or bottled gas, including hydrogen and acetylene, can also be used for special purposes.

Desiccators.   A **desiccator** is a vessel used to achieve and maintain an atmosphere of low humidity for the storage of samples, precipitates, crucibles, and weighing bottles. The common form consists of three parts: a ground glass cover which slides onto the body of the desiccator to form an airtight seal, a perforated plate upon which the articles to be stored are placed, and a lower portion in which a desiccant may be placed, as illustrated in Figure 2-2.

Aluminum desiccators are also commercially available. They possess the advantages of light weight, relative durability, and rapid cooling but have the disadvantages that certain desiccants must not be placed directly against the floor and lower walls of the desiccator and that the walls are not transparent. Some desiccators are equipped with side arms by which they can be connected to a vacuum pump so that the contents can be kept under a vacuum rather than merely in an atmosphere of dry air. The same connector can also be used to introduce an atmosphere of nitrogen or other special gas to provide an inner atmosphere for special purposes.

Care is required even in the use of such a simple piece of equipment as a common desiccator. A hot crucible or other hot vessel should be allowed to cool in air for at least 60 seconds prior to insertion into the desiccator. Otherwise, the air within the desiccator will be hot when the desiccator is closed and a partial vacuum will develop as it cools. Upon subsequent opening of the partially evacuated unit, a sudden inrush of air can easily result in spilling the samples within. However, the hot crucible must not be permitted to stand in room air any longer than necessary, lest the interaction of crucible and contents with moist air be excessive.

Weighing bottles and crucibles should not be handled directly with the

FIGURE 2-2. A desiccator.

FIGURE 2-3.   A strip of lint-free filter paper wrapped around a weighing bottle. The ends of the paper may be grasped with the thumb and forefinger, thus permitting handling of the bottle without touching it directly with the fingers.

fingers after drying or ignition. One simple, yet effective method of handling them for insertion into and withdrawal from the desiccator, as well as for any handling necessary in the weighing operation, is shown in Figure 2-3. Crucible tongs should, of course, be used with hot objects and may be used in any case.

A desiccator should be opened no more often than absolutely necessary, as each opening permits the entry of moist room air. The action of the desiccant in removing moisture from the air is a rather slow process, and the desiccator must remain closed for an appreciable period of time before the inner atmosphere is made dry. Without doubt, the usual and overly frequent openings of the desiccator in student laboratories limit the efficiency of the desiccator much more seriously than does the inherent lack of an ideally perfect desiccant.

Desiccants.   A **desiccant** is a chemical substance which has the property of combining with moisture from the surrounding atmosphere. No desiccant is ideally perfect; that is, no desiccant can make and keep the air within a closed desiccator perfectly dry. Some desiccants are more effective than others, as indicated in Table 2-1. The smaller the amount of moisture remaining per liter of air, the more effective the desiccant can be. Calcium chloride is a commonly used desiccant, but is clearly one of the less effective ones. Sulfuric acid is a good desiccant, but the danger of its splashing and spilling presents a practical drawback. Porous barium oxide is satisfactory; however, this material swells as it absorbs moisture so that sufficient space must be provided for this expansion. Phosphorus pentoxide may be effective, yet it is not convenient to handle and its effectiveness is limited by an insulating film of phosphoric acid formed early in use. Anhydrous magnesium perchlorate and calcium sulfate are two modern, effective desiccants. Some commercially available desiccants include a colored substance along with the desiccant itself, the hue of the color changing as the water content increases. Thus the analyst can tell at a glance when replacement of the desiccant is needed. Some desiccants are reversible; the spent material can be dried in an oven and then used over again. Others are best discarded after a single use.

TABLE 2-1. RELATIVE EFFECTIVENESS OF SOME DESICCANTS

Desiccant	Milligrams of H_2O in 1 Liter of Air at Equilibrium
P_2O_5	0.00002 or less
BaO	0.0007
$Mg(ClO_4)_2$	0.002
H_2SO_4	0.003
$CaSO_4$	0.004
$CaCl_2$	0.36

Drying by Evaporation. When analytical specimens undergo secondary changes even under mild conditions of oven drying, the method of evaporation must be used. In this method the finely ground sample is simply exposed to air at room temperature so that any excess water can evaporate. The surrounding air itself may be dried by a desiccant or may be maintained at a constant level of humidity. Vacuum drying is occasionally employed, but it has little or no advantage over air drying. Sometimes drying by evaporation cannot be avoided and the so-called "air-dry" material is usually somewhat uncertain in composition, showing substantial variations with changes in the relative atmospheric humidity. Metal samples may be dried rapidly and conveniently by rinsing them with pure acetone or other water-miscible volatile solvent and then air drying them for a short time.

Drying the Container. The same possibilities of absolute or reproducible dryness are involved in the preparation of containers for weighing. A porcelain crucible may be brought to a condition of absolute dryness, but this condition is difficult to attain with glass vessels which cannot withstand a high-temperature ignition. Even if absolute dryness were attainable, it would be practically impossible to weigh glassware in this condition because it readily adsorbs moisture from the air. Thus, a condition of reproducible dryness is the goal in preparing glass containers for weighing, the weight of the equilibrium film of adsorbed water being considered as part of the weight of the container. Although dry glassware initially does pick up water readily, an equilibrium film of moisture is reached only slowly; thus, it is usually more convenient to approach equilibrium from a condition in which there is too much water on the glass surface. Therefore, in preparing a glass object for weighing, it is customary to wipe it with a slightly dampened cloth so that the surface is fully saturated. The vessel is then wiped gently with a dry cloth to remove any gross excess of water, and the final approach to an equilibrium film of water is accomplished by allowing the object to stand in the balance room for one-half hour before weighing. This half-hour period is also desirable to bring about temperature equilibrium between the object and the balance and its surroundings. The air-dry condition of glass vessels is more critical in microanalytical work than in ordinary analytical work, since the weighings must be more exact. Air conditioning is virtually essential for the balance room in microanalytical laboratories.

Drying and Ignition of Precipitates. In a quantitative determination by a gravimetric precipitation procedure, the desired constituent is separated from other components of the sample by precipitation, washing, and filtration. However, the separation is not complete until the precipitate is dried to remove moisture left by the last portions of wash liquid. Room temperature drying is seldom adequate, but many precipitates can be dried successfully when placed in an oven at 110°C for from one-half hour to two hours. However, a higher temperature is often required for one or more of the following reasons: (a) some substances retain water up to temperatures much higher than 110°C, (b) some precipitates must be transformed to other substances of more definite chemical composition for weighing, and (c) charring and destruction of filter paper requires heating well above 110°C.

Drying ovens, electric furnaces, and the several types of high-temperature burners are all useful in the drying and ignition of precipitates. Special considerations involving the ignition of filter paper and other filter media will be discussed later in this chapter.

WEIGHING

Principles of the Analytical Balance

The analytical balance is basically a first-class lever. The lever is called the **beam** and is represented in Figure 2-4 as the line AB. The beam is supported on a knife edge, its fulcrum, at point O. Weights or other objects may be attached to both ends of the beam by suspension or by any other means of attachment. Distances L and R are the two lever arms, equaling the distances $\overline{AO}$ and $\overline{BO}$, respectively. Some means must be provided to observe the horizontal positioning of the beam, such as the pointer, OP, attached rigidly at right angles to the beam at its fulcrum.

A weight W_L applied at A results in a force, $W_L \times L$, tending to cause a counterclockwise rotation of the beam. Similarly, a weight W_R applied at B results in a force, $W_R \times R$, tending to cause a clockwise rotation of the beam. The beam is in a stationary horizontal position, or at least is oscillating back and forth about such an equilibrium position, when the forces causing clockwise and counterclockwise rotation equal each other. This condition may be represented mathematically as

$$W_L \times L = W_R \times R$$

The weight of the beam is of some significance, as will be described subsequently, but for the present discussion the weight will be considered to be concentrated at point O so that it contributes neither to clockwise nor to counterclockwise rotation. If the beam is initially in a stable position, as represented by this equation, and if an object of weight W_0 is added to W_L, the tendency toward counterclockwise rotation is increased, and the beam departs from its initial position. This behavior leads us to a consideration of the two main methods of making weighings on analytical balances— **substitution** and **direct comparison.**

Weighing by Substitution. In weighing by substitution, the increased tendency toward counterclockwise rotation caused by adding the object to the left side of the beam is offset by removing a corresponding portion of W_L so that the initially stable or equilibrium condition of the beam is restored. No change is made on the right side of the beam, so the initial and final weights at A must equal each other. The weight of the object is equal to that portion of W_L which had to be *removed* to restore the initial equilibrium condition of the beam. Objects of known weight are

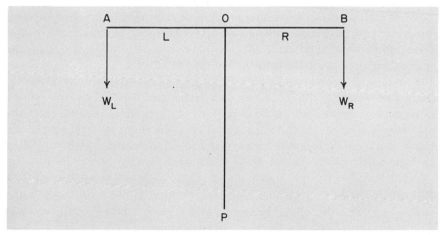

FIGURE 2-4. Diagram to illustrate the principle of the analytical balance. (See text for discussion.)

used for the removable portions of W_L, making it possible to determine the weights of unknown objects by this method.

Weighing by Direct Comparison.   The increased tendency toward counterclockwise rotation caused by adding the object, the weight of which is W_o, to the left side of the beam can be opposed by the *addition* of a corresponding amount of weight to the right side so that the initially stable or equilibrium condition of the beam is again restored. Letting W_w represent the amount of weight on the right which is found to correspond to W_o on the left, one may represent the initial and final states of the beam mathematically as follows. The initial state is given by the equation

$$W_L \times L = W_R \times R$$

and the final state is governed by the relation

$$(W_L + W_o) \times L = (W_R + W_w) \times R$$

The two expressions may be combined to yield the equation

$$W_o \times L = W_w \times R$$

If L and R are equal to each other (as is quite accurately the case with analytical balances designed to be used for weighings by the direct comparison method),

$$W_o = W_w$$

Objects of known weight are used to comprise W_w, so that the weight of an unknown object may be determined directly.

Sensitivity of the Analytical Balance.   Consider now the addition of a *small* weight, w, to the left end of the beam in Figure 2-4. Unless there is a change in the tendency toward clockwise rotation, the counterclockwise rotation produced by w will cause the beam to seek a vertical equilibrium position with point A at the bottom. However, for most analytical balances the beam and its attachments are so constructed that the center of mass is *below* the plane of the line AOB, but still symmetrically distributed to the left and right of point O. In other words, the effective center of gravity of the beam is at some point G on OP, rather than at the fulcrum (point O) itself. The weight of the beam and its attachments, denoted by W_b, will be of no consequence when the beam is perfectly horizontal because the lever arm length is zero. On the other hand, even the slightest deflection of the beam in a counterclockwise direction to some new position A'B', as shown in Figure 2-5, causes in the beam a tendency toward clockwise rotation equal to $W_b \times \overline{GD}$. For purposes of clarity, the extent of deflection in Figure 2-5 has been grossly exaggerated. A new equilibrium condition is established when the beam reaches a position such that the additive clockwise and counterclockwise forces equal each other:

$$(W_L + w) \times \overline{CO} = W_b \times \overline{GD} + W_R \times \overline{EO}$$

Note in Figure 2-5 that the respective lever distances through which the initial forces, W_L and W_R, act are $\overline{AO}$ and $\overline{BO}$ for the original beam position (AB), and are only $\overline{CO}$ and $\overline{EO}$, respectively, for the final beam position (A'B'). However, both arm lengths are reduced by the same relative amount, so the counterclockwise and clockwise forces caused by W_L and W_R equal each other in either situation. It should also be noted that, in practice, the angle of deflection (α) is generally so small that $\overline{CO}$ and $\overline{EO}$ are not much different from $\overline{AO}$ and $\overline{BO}$, respectively. Accordingly, since

$$W_L \times \overline{CO} = W_R \times \overline{EO}$$

the preceding relation can be simplified to

$$w \times \overline{CO} = W_b \times \overline{GD}$$

The term **sensitivity** is used to express quantitatively the magnitude of deflection produced by one unit of weight. This deflection distance may be determined by any one of several techniques, such as by means of a stationary graduated scale placed behind the tip (P) of the pointer. Balance sensitivity is typically stated as scale divisions (or millimeters) per milligram. The reciprocal quantity, weight units per scale division, is also convenient to use for some purposes. It is, however, not even necessary to have a pointer physically attached to the beam. For example, the deflection of the beam

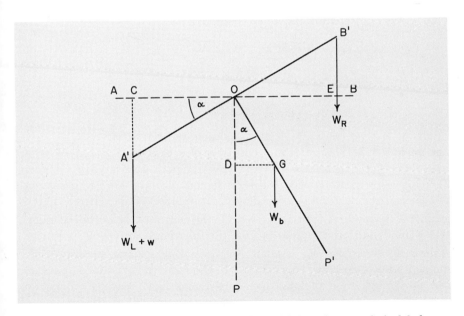

FIGURE 2-5. Diagram to illustrate the sensitivity of an analytical balance. (See text for discussion.)

itself from its initial position, AB, to its new position, A′B′, may be read by an optical method in which a beam of light is reflected off one end of the beam onto a viewing screen, with a graduated scale on the beam or on the viewing screen.

A fundamental relationship can be derived from Figure 2-5 to describe how the design of a balance affects the sensitivity. Two angles having their sides mutually perpendicular are equal, so

$$\text{angle AOA}' = \text{angle POP}' = \alpha$$

In addition, we may write the following trigonometric relationships:

$$\cos \alpha = \frac{\overline{\text{CO}}}{\overline{\text{A}'\text{O}}}$$

and

$$\sin \alpha = \frac{\overline{\text{GD}}}{\overline{\text{OG}}}$$

Using the expression shown earlier, that

$$w \times \overline{\text{CO}} = W_b \times \overline{\text{GD}}$$

we can combine the three preceding equations to obtain

$$w \times \overline{\text{A}'\text{O}} \times \cos \alpha = W_b \times \overline{\text{OG}} \times \sin \alpha$$

Finally, rearrangement of the latter relation gives

$$\frac{\sin \alpha}{\cos \alpha} = \frac{w \times \overline{\text{A}'\text{O}}}{W_b \times \overline{\text{OG}}}$$

or

$$\tan \alpha = \frac{w \times \overline{\text{A}'\text{O}}}{W_b \times \overline{\text{OG}}}$$

The angle α is a measure of the sensitivity of a balance. For a given w, a large value for α signifies a greater sensitivity than does a small α value. Therefore, this equation reveals several factors of importance in designing a balance of high sensitivity. Accordingly, the sensitivity is increased if (1) the balance arm length, $\overline{\text{A}'\text{O}}$ or L, is long, (2) the weight of the beam assembly, W_b, is small, and (3) the distance from the fulcrum to the center of gravity of the beam assembly, $\overline{\text{OG}}$, is small. All three of these factors are somewhat competitive. For example, long arm length and light weight are incompatible, and the combination of long arm length and light weight renders the requirements of mechanical strength and rigidity difficult to achieve.

It is now of interest to apply the last equation to weighings by the two methods, direct comparison and substitution. The quantity W_b includes the weight of the beam and all of its attachments, that is, all of the load which is supported at the fulcrum O. The object being weighed is a part of that load. In the direct comparison method of weighing, the weight of the object (W_o) and the corresponding weights (W_w) serve to increase W_b. By lowering the center of gravity, they also increase $\overline{OG}$. Therefore, in a weighing by direct comparison, the sensitivity of a balance *decreases* as the load is increased. However, in a weighing by substitution, the weight of the object (W_o) is offset by removal of a corresponding amount of W_L, so W_b is constant regardless of the weight of the object. Therefore, in weighing by substitution, the load and the sensitivity are *constant* for all weighings.

Construction of the Analytical Balance

With the exception of a few specialized types, all analytical balances are based upon the principles of the preceding section and are of two types. One is the single-pan balance designed for weighing by the substitution method (Fig. 2-6). The beam is typically mounted from front to back in the case, with the pan suspended from the front end of the beam. The balance functions in all weighings with constant, maximum load on the beam; and the sensitivity is used as an integral part of the weighing operation. The other type is the double-pan balance designed for weighing by the direct

FIGURE 2-6. Side-view section through a single-pan, substitution type balance. When a load is placed on the pan (1), weights (2) are removed until the load on the sapphire plane of the beam (3) is restored to its initial value. A fixed weight remains on the right of the beam—equivalent, for example, to 200 gm on the pan.

FIGURE 2-7. Drawing of a double-pan balance, showing the beam, central knife edge, two pans, pointer, and scale.

comparison method (Fig. 2-7). The beam is mounted from left to right in the case. The beam functions with maximum load only when weighing objects of maximum weight for which the balance is rated. The sensitivity is not necessarily used as an integral part of the weighing operation, although it may be if the variation of sensitivity with load is considered.

Because both types of balances are based upon the same principles, many features of construction are common for both. Stability and sturdiness, along with a sufficiently high degree of sensitivity, are obvious requirements. The beam, as already described, must possess maximum rigidity for minimum weight. The beam can last almost indefinitely in ordinary use, but it may become seriously and permanently warped if the balance is overloaded. The beam in a single-pan, substitution type balance must support its maximum load during every weighing, whereas the beam in the usual double-pan balance generally supports far less than its maximum rated load.

The most critical parts of an analytical balance are the knife edges on which the parts pivot, one as the fulcrum at the center of the beam and one where each pan is suspended from the beam. These pivots must be nearly frictionless, tough enough to withstand ordinary day-to-day wear, and hard enough to resist long-term wear. Each pivot consists of two pieces, a wedge-shaped piece in contact with a flat plate. Agate serves well as the material of which both pieces are made; it is hard enough to withstand years of normal usage but is brittle enough to suffer irreparable damage if subjected to sudden or violent stress. Synthetic sapphire and synthetic ruby are also good materials of construction for the knife edges.

The construction and operation of the balance are planned with an eye to sparing the knife edges from all unnecessary strain. Mechanisms to check the oscillations of the beam and to support the beam and the pan or pans away from the knife edges when the balance is not in use are provided. These supports are actuated from outside the case and should be released only during the brief moments when observations of the beam position or deflection are being made. In the supported condition the knife edges bear no loads and, therefore, cannot be injured by sudden shocks when, for example, objects are added to or removed from a pan.

As already discussed, the position of the center of gravity of the beam system influences the sensitivity of the balance. Slight adjustment of a double-pan balance is possible by moving a small weight on the pointer rod up or down. This is a critical and delicate adjustment and should be made only by persons thoroughly familiar with balance design, construction, and calibration.

Upon initial installation the balance case should be accurately leveled by adjusting the legs on which it rests until the spirit levels indicate that it is level. The door of the case should be kept shut during a weighing operation to avoid the disturbing effects of air currents set up by the room ventilation system or the respiration of the operator. The door of the case should always be kept closed when the balance is not in use to provide maximum protection against laboratory dust and corrosive fumes.

Satisfactory performance of analytical balances requires that they be properly placed. Balances should be located in well lighted, draft-free rooms of reasonably uniform temperature. They should be placed on solidly constructed tables to minimize vibration, and enough tabletop space should be available around the balances for placement of laboratory notebooks.

Many analytical balances are equipped with damping devices. Without such a device the oscillations of the beam assembly back and forth about its rest point make it more time-consuming to perform weighings. One type of **magnetic damping** device is shown in Figure 2-8. The oscillations are damped by eddy currents induced in thin sheet aluminum extensions of the beam by strong permanent magnets fastened to the balance case. Another common damping system is called **air damping.** In one form of it, light pistons are attached to the movable beam assembly in such a way that they move inside close-fitting stationary cylinders with closed ends. In either magnetic or air damping, the effect is to reduce the oscillations to a single, rather slow swing in which the beam travels directly to its rest position.

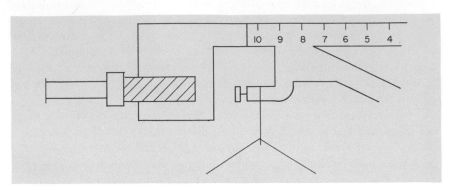

FIGURE 2-8. Drawing of a magnetic damping device mounted around one end of the beam of an analytical balance.

There is no significant loss of sensitivity because the resistance to the movement of the moving beam assembly of the balance drops to zero as it comes to rest. Excessive damping should be avoided. If the system is not allowed to make one or two oscillations before stabilizing, a false rest point may result from nonuniform frictional effects, such as those caused by the inevitable dust particles on the knife edges.

Every analytical balance must be equipped with a reading device by which the position and deflections of the beam assembly may be observed. The simplest, and still very accurate and convenient, method is that shown in Figure 2-7. A pointer is attached at right angles to the beam in line with the fulcrum, and a stationary scale is mounted behind the tip of the pointer.

Several types of reading devices employ optical enlargement of the scale and are called **projection reading devices.**

In one type, designed for use in conjunction with a pointer, light from a lamp outside the balance case is focused through a transparent micro scale attached to the pointer. A magnified image of this scale is projected onto a frosted glass screen which has a sharply defined vertical line in the center, the position of which is adjustable to coincide with the zero on the micro scale under the true rest-point conditions. When the beam is set in motion by releasing the beam and pan supports and when the oscillations are damped, the screen gives a direct indication of how far the new rest point is displaced from the true rest point. In other projection reading devices, there is no pointer at all; instead, a reflecting micro scale is attached directly to one end of the beam. In any event, the scale may be marked off either in empirical units or, if the sensitivity is constant as it is in a balance designed for substitution weighing, directly in weight units. Some projection reading devices employ vernier scales. Some, through ingenious arrangements of scale markings and windows through which the scales are viewed, provide direct digital readout.

Analytical Weights

Construction. The weights used in a single-pan balance designed for weighings by the substitution method are built into the balance and are removed from and added to the load on the beam by controls from outside the case. Physically, the weights may be in any of several shapes and forms, depending on the particular balance design and manufacture. Some are in the form of rings, others as cylinders, and still others as stiff, shaped wire—all with shapes and mechanisms for quick and foolproof manipulation. The weights are typically stainless steel, although other materials are also used. They must be chemically as well as physically stable in order to retain adequate constancy of weight over extended periods of time.

For weighings on a balance designed for the direct comparison method, the weights are individually placed on and removed from the balance pan by the operator. Weights of 1 gm and larger are usually made of bronze, brass, or stainless steel; a thin coating of lacquer protects the weights from atmospheric corrosion. The weights of less than 1 gm are usually made of heavy aluminum foil or thin platinum foil and should require no special protection from atmospheric corrosion. The weights should be handled only with ivory tipped forceps, never directly with the fingers; and these forceps should be used for no other purpose.

It is difficult to handle individual weights of less than about 10 mg, and it is inconvenient to handle even larger individual weights. If the sensitivity of the balance is constant and known, it is not necessary to use weights any smaller than the weight corresponding to the entire range of the scale or the projection reading device. As already noted, these devices are often calibrated directly in weight units. The term "optical range" refers to the range of weight corresponding to the limits of the scale of the optical projection reading device. Thus, in a balance with an optical range of 0.1 gm, no individual weights smaller than 0.1 gm need be used.

In some double-pan balances, the upper edge of the beam is precisely graduated as shown in Figure 2-7, and a small weight called the **rider** may be placed on it at any desired point. The position of the rider is controlled from outside the balance case. The effective weight of the rider is determined by its distance from the fulcrum. For example, a rider placed halfway between the center and right-hand knife edge in Figure 2-7 exerts only half the force it would exert if placed immediately above the right-hand knife edge. The weight corresponding to each graduation on the beam varies with the design of the balance and the actual weight of the rider. In a typical analytical balance, the major divisions correspond to 1 mg with subdivisions for tenths of a milligram.

A fine-linked chain replaces the smaller weights in some balances. As illustrated in Figure 2-9, one end of the chain is attached to the right end of the beam and the other end to a scale with graduations and a vernier, usually reading from 0.1 to 100.0 mg. The scale may be vertical, as shown,

FIGURE 2-9.   Drawing of a chain device attached to the beam of an analytical balance.

or circular. In either case it may be manipulated from outside the balance case. At the zero reading, a fixed fraction (frequently one half) of the chain weight is supported by the beam. As the control is rotated, the effective chain weight supported by the beam is increased, and this weight may be read directly from the scale with the aid of the vernier. A chain is typically used to make readings up to 100.0 mg to the nearest tenth of a milligram, thus obviating the need of any other weights within this range.

Accuracy.   Regardless of the physical form of the analytical weights, there are several quality classifications, as established and designated by the National Bureau of Standards. Class M weights are the highest precision scientific standards and are used almost entirely as reference standards and even then only in the most exacting work. Class S weights are also used for reference and calibration purposes as well as for precision analytical weigh-ings. Class S-1 weights are used for some calibration work and particularly for many routine analytical weighings. Class P weights (formerly designated Class S-2) are also used for much routine laboratory work. There are additional classifications of weights for less precise general laboratory work, for technical weighings, and for industrial and commercial uses.

The tolerances prescribed by the National Bureau of Standards are of two categories: *acceptance tolerances*, which are for new or newly adjusted weights, and *maintenance tolerances*, which are for weights which have been in use. This distinction is made in recognition of the fact that weights of

TABLE 2-2. ACCEPTANCE TOLERANCES FOR
ANALYTICAL WEIGHTS

Denomination	Class M		Class S		Class S-1	Class P
	Ind.	Group	Ind.	Group	Ind.	Ind.
100 gm	0.50 mg		0.25 mg		1.0 mg	2.0 mg
50	0.25		0.12		0.60	1.2
30	0.15		0.074 ⎱		0.45	0.90
20	0.10		0.074 ⎰ 0.154		0.35	0.70
10	0.050		0.074 ⎰		0.25	0.50
5	0.034 ⎱		0.054 ⎱		0.18	0.36
3	0.034 ⎰		0.054 ⎰		0.15	0.30
2	0.034 ⎰ 0.065		0.054 ⎰ 0.105		0.13	0.26
1	0.034 ⎰		0.054 ⎰		0.10	0.20
500 mg	0.0054 ⎱		0.025 ⎱		0.080	0.16
300	0.0054 ⎰		0.025 ⎰		0.070	0.14
200	0.0054 ⎰ 0.0105		0.025 ⎰ 0.055		0.060	0.12
100	0.0054 ⎰		0.025 ⎰		0.050	0.10
50	0.0054 ⎱		0.014 ⎱		0.042	0.085
30	0.0054 ⎰		0.014 ⎰		0.038	0.075
20	0.0054 ⎰ 0.0105		0.014 ⎰ 0.034		0.035	0.070
10	0.0054 ⎰		0.014 ⎰		0.030	0.060
5	0.0054 ⎱		0.014 ⎱		0.028	0.055
3	0.0054 ⎰		0.014 ⎰		0.026	0.052
2	0.0054 ⎰ 0.0105		0.014 ⎰ 0.034		0.025	0.050
1	0.0054 ⎰		0.014 ⎰		0.025	0.050

certain denominations and classes can and should be adjusted initially to very close tolerances so that they will remain within useful tolerances for a reasonable period of time. Within each tolerance category, there are individual tolerances for individual weights and group tolerances for specified groups of weights taken collectively. The acceptance tolerances, both individual and group, are listed in Table 2-2 for the classes of weights which are of most significance in analytical chemistry.

The maintenance tolerances differ from the acceptance tolerances listed in Table 2-2 as follows:

Class M — for weights between 500 and 100 mg, tolerances are 0.0105 mg individual and 0.020 mg group; all others same as acceptance tolerances

Class S — for weights 100 mg and up, tolerances are twice the acceptance tolerances, both individual and group; others are same as acceptance tolerances

Class S-1 — tolerances are same as acceptance tolerances

Class P — tolerances are twice acceptance tolerances

Although there are no detailed group tolerances for Class S-1 and P weights, there is the additional requirement for Class S-1 weights that not more than one third of the weights of a new or newly adjusted set of weights may be in error by more than one half of the prescribed tolerances.

Weights which have been in use for some time and weights for which a higher degree of accuracy is desired must be calibrated directly. There are several possible means of calibration, any one of which can be usefully employed. For example, if another accurately calibrated set of weights is available for comparison, each weight in the balance or set of weights to be calibrated may be weighed against the weight of the corresponding denomination in the standard set. Thus, additive or subtractive corrections are found directly for each weight or combination of weights, and the corrected values should subsequently be used in place of the labeled values. The projection reading device, if it relies upon the sensitivity of the balance, as well as the chain and rider, if any, must be included in the designations of accuracy and in the calibration procedure.

Ratings of Analytical Balances

Many models of analytical balances are commercially available, but not all are equally good for the same purpose. The several types may be rated, first of all, as single-pan balances designed for weighing by the substitution method or as double-pan balances designed for weighing by direct comparison. Double-pan balances have been traditional in analytical chemistry for many years, and it is not unusual to find balances 30 or more years old still providing accurate weighings. Single-pan, substitution type balances have come into widespread use in the last 10 years or so, although the substitution method has been known and occasionally used on double-pan balances for a considerably longer period of time. Single-pan balances are probably now used more widely than the double-pan type. A weighing can be accomplished readily on a modern single-pan balance in a half minute or even less, whereas it takes two or three minutes to do so with a good double-pan balance. An inexperienced person could take longer, of course, with either type. In general, equally accurate weighings can be made with each type.

Single-pan balances invariably include a damping device and a projection reading device. They contain built-in weights, with an external device for removing them from and replacing them on the beam assembly.

They also provide a method for "reading" the weights that have been removed and this corresponds to the weight of the object. Double-pan balances may, but generally do not, have a projection reading device and often, but not necessarily, have a damping device, a chain device, or both. An external set of weights is required.

Ratings or specifications applicable to either type of balance include the maximum capacity of the balance, some statement concerning sensitivity (such as scale divisions per milligram or minimum detectable difference in weight), some form of readability statement (which does not necessarily equal the sensitivity), an optical scale range in weight units, a chain scale range in weight units, and the class of weights. Some balances include a tare device which can be advantageously used to set to zero the apparent weight reading when an empty crucible or sample tube is on the object pan.

The capacity and the sensitivity of an analytical balance are somewhat interrelated. Ratings of 160 or 200 gm capacity with a sensitivity of 0.1 mg (expressed as minimum weight difference that can be detected) are common. If a sensitivity of 0.01 mg is desired, the capacity is generally limited to about 80 gm, whereas a capacity of 20 gm is possible with a sensitivity of about 0.001 mg (1 μg).

Weighing Procedures

The essential steps in weighing an object on an analytical balance of either the single-pan or double-pan type are:
1. Determination of the initial rest point, or setting of the reading device to zero at the initial rest point
2. Placing the object on the appropriate pan
3. Systematic use of weights and comparison of the rest point for each new combination of weights with the initial rest point
4. Summation of the weights

These steps are really of only two types — determination of the rest point and systematic use of weights.

Determination of Rest Point.   The **rest point,** which is the point on the graduated scale at which the pointer comes to rest after its oscillations cease, can be read directly from the scale or other reading device if the balance is equipped with a damping device. Without a damping ·device, the rest point may be calculated from the extreme points reached by the pointer during its oscillations. A whole number of "round trip" swings must be used to avoid an error due to frictional damping. In other words, the first and the last readings from which the rest point is calculated must be on the same side of the midpoint of the swings. Consider, for example, that the successive readings taken as the pointer swings back and forth in front of the scale on a double-pan balance are −3.2, +2.8, −3.0, +2.5, and −2.7.

The readings are tabulated and each set (right and left) is averaged:

	−3.2		+2.8
	−3.0		+2.5
	−2.7		+2.6
average is	−3.0	average is	+2.6

In this example the midpoint between these average extremes is −0.2, and this is the rest point. The scale zero should not be confused with the rest point; they may or may not coincide.

The initial rest point for an unloaded double-pan balance or a fully loaded single-pan balance with no object on the pan should remain quite constant for days and even for weeks. However, it is good practice to check it at the beginning of each weighing session.

Systematic Use of Weights.   The weighing process, on either the single-pan or double-pan balance, requires several trial and error operations until the correct combination of weights is found. It is not necessary to make rest-point observations until one is very close to the correct summation of weights, for a quick glance at the direction in which the pointer deflects will suffice to reveal whether the weights in use are much too heavy or much too light. In fact, some balances are provided with a device for the partial, as well as the full, release of the beam and pan supports. Until the operator is close to the correct total of weights, the partial release position permits him to note rapidly whether his weights are much too heavy or too light. The partial release position also spares the balance arm knife edges from unnecessary wear.

A systematic procedure in making the trials must be followed if accurate weighings are to be accomplished with reasonable speed. The procedure will be described first for use of weights on a double-pan balance in weighing by direct comparison. With the object on the left pan, a weight is selected from the weight box and placed on the right pan. The beam assembly support is released, at least partially, and the direction of deflection of the pointer on the scale is noted. If the pointer deflects to the left of the initial rest point, that weight is too heavy, and it is removed. If the deflection is toward the right, that weight is allowed to remain on the pan. In either event, the next smaller weight is placed on the right pan and the process is repeated. This process is continued systematically, starting with a weight almost certain to be too heavy and progressing through the weight box, using the weights in order of decreasing denomination. Whenever the pointer deflects to the left of the initial rest point, indicating too much weight on the right pan, the most recently added weight is removed. Whenever the pointer deflects to the right, indicating insufficient weight on the right pan, the most recently added weight is kept on the pan. This systematic procedure involves a continual bracketing of the desired weight within narrower and narrower limits. If the analyst were to start out with smaller weights, that is, if he were to proceed on the basis of only lower limits rather than both upper and lower limits, he not only would waste time but would frequently have to remove several smaller weights in favor of one larger one in order to have the proper weights available to complete the weighing.

The procedure is analogous for a single-pan, substitution type balance. The weights are, for example, arranged in decade units with one adjusting knob or control for handling hundreds of grams (0 or 100), another for tens of grams (0, 10, 20, 30, etc.), and another for grams (0, 1, 2, 3, etc.). Starting with the object on the balance pan and all knobs at zero, the operator first adjusts the hundreds, then the tens, then the units, and then the smaller divisions by whatever system the particular balance employs. Each knob or control is set on the highest position which the reading device shows to be lighter than the weight of the object before the next knob or control is adjusted.

Weighing the Sample

Replicate samples are almost invariably required in quantitative work. The number of individual portions which should be carried through the analysis depends upon the desired accuracy, the nature of the method, and the nature of the sample. Generally, triplicate samples are desirable and quadruplicates may be advisable. The number of weighings is held to a minimum if the several samples are weighed out by difference. That is, the container (often a weighing bottle containing the total amount of the sample) is weighed. One portion is removed and the bottle is weighed again. The process is repeated until the desired number of samples has been weighed out. Thus, four weighings suffice for three portions of the sample, and five weighings suffice for four portions.

Solid samples should generally be weighed out in or from weighing bottles. A **weighing bottle** is a thin-walled glass container with a volume of 1 to 100 ml and with a ground glass cover. Powder samples are often weighed in weighing bottles, and liquid samples may also be weighed in such containers. A weighing bottle should be handled with a clean cloth, a piece of chamois skin, or a strip of paper folded around it as in Figure 2-3. Never hold a weighing bottle with the bare fingers. The cover should be in place when the bottle is stored in a desiccator but not when it is dried in an oven. The cover should be dried along with the bottle, however. Powder samples may be inserted or withdrawn by means of a small spatula or a scoop. A useful spoon may be fashioned easily from a strip of aluminum. Some powders may be transferred from a weighing bottle by pouring, which is facilitated by a twisting, rotary motion. A powder funnel, which is a conventional funnel with a short, wide stem, is useful but not necessary.

Small flasks with ground glass stoppers are also useful for weighing out liquid samples. Containers for liquids must be kept stoppered to prevent continual evaporation. In certain cases, liquid samples may be measured by volume rather than by weight.

It is seldom necessary to weigh out any exact, predetermined quantity of sample. It almost always suffices to have portions of individually known weight so that each weighs about the same predetermined value or so that each comes within well spaced, approximate, predetermined limits of maximum and minimum weight. In fact, it is often preferable to have the several replicate samples differing somewhat in weight so that certain types of errors (to be discussed later) can be recognized more readily.

When it is necessary to weigh out a sample of an exact, predetermined weight, it is advisable to use a watch glass instead of a covered weighing bottle. The sample is slowly and carefully poured onto the watch glass until the predetermined weight is obtained and balance is achieved. It is simpler to add the sample slowly until the state of balance is just exceeded and then to withdraw very small portions with a weighing spoon or spatula until the condition of balance is reached exactly.

As an alternative to weighing out replicate samples individually, it is possible to weigh out a single, larger sample and, after its dissolution, to divide it by volume into several replicate portions. For example, a sample weighing 1.0000 gm could be dissolved, the resulting solution diluted quantitatively to 250.00 ml, and 50.00 ml portions taken for each of the replicate samples. The known fractions of the larger quantity of solution are termed **aliquots.** In this example, five separate samples of 0.2000 gm each are obtained by weighing only one sample along with several volume measurements. The major disadvantage of this method of preparing replicate samples is that an error in the one weighing operation results in an error in all five of the sample weights. The method of weighing one large sample followed by the analysis of aliquots and the method of weighing out individual samples for replicate determinations are both widely used.

Errors in Weighing

We have thus far considered the apparatus and the techniques of analytical weighings and will now discuss some of the possible sources of error which have not been mentioned previously.

Balance Arm Inequality.   The method of weighing by direct comparison is subject to error if the distances of the left-hand and right-hand knife edges from the central knife edge are not equal. As shown on page 20, the condition in which the initial rest point is restored may be represented by the equation

$$W_o \times L = W_w \times R$$

Thus, the weight of the object, W_o, equals the summation of the analytical weights, W_w, only if the two arm lengths, L and R, equal each other. The arms of a common analytical balance are typically each 10 cm long and are equal within about 0.0001 cm. Thus, error due to balance arm inequality amounts to about one part in 100,000 (0.0001 cm in 10 cm), which is significant only in the most refined work.

It is of interest to note that even the residual error due to balance arm inequality often corrects for itself in analytical work. Rearrangement of the preceding mathematical equation yields

$$W_o = W_w \times \frac{R}{L}$$

If the weight of one object is to be divided by the weight of another, measured on the same balance (as is done in many practical analytical determinations), the ratio $\frac{R}{L}$ cancels out, so no error results from balance arm inequality. When a single object or sample is to be weighed on the balance and the value of its weight is not to be related by division to another weight, no such self-compensation arises.

In the method of weighing by substitution on a single-pan balance, no error whatever results from balance arm inequality. This is, in fact, one of the advantages of the substitution method compared to the method of direct comparison. Most balances designed specifically for substitution weighing have one arm much longer than the other, with no error resulting from this inequality.

The substitution method may be used in a modified form with a conventional double-pan balance. The object is first placed on the right pan, and some substance (called a **tare**) is placed on the left pan to restore the true rest point. The substance on the left pan may be parts of an old set of weights or copper shot — anything which can be placed on the pan in suitably adjustable quantity. The contents of the left pan are kept intact and the object on the right pan is replaced by calibrated weights to restore the true rest point again. The summation of weights on the right pan required in the second step equals the weight of the object, regardless of any balance arm inequality. To prove this, let W_o, W_w, and W_L equal the weights of the object, the calibrated weights in the second step, and the substance on the left pan, respectively; and let L and R be the balance arm lengths as before. In the first weighing step

$$L \times W_L = R \times W_o$$

whereas in the second step

$$L \times W_L = R \times W_w$$

Therefore,

$$R \times W_o = R \times W_w$$

and

$$W_o = W_w$$

Thus, the weight of the object, W_o, equals the summation of the analytical weights, W_w, regardless of whether the two arm lengths, L and R, equal each other or not.

Air Buoyancy. According to Archimedes' classical principle, the apparent weight of an object immersed in a fluid is less than its true weight in a vacuum by a quantity equal in magnitude to the weight of the fluid displaced by the object. In analytical weighings by direct comparison, the object on one pan is buoyed by the weight of air which it displaces, and the weights on the other pan are buoyed by the weight of air they displace. The two buoyancies cancel each other only if the object and the weights are of the same density so that they displace equal volumes of air. An analogous situation arises with a single-pan balance for substitution weighings. Accordingly, any error resulting from buoyancy effects is made more significant as the difference in density between the object and the weights becomes greater. Brass weights typically have a density of about 8.4 gm/cm³, so the error would be greater, for example, in weighing a solution of density about 1.0 gm/cm³ than it would in weighing a solid precipitate of density closer to that of brass weights.

A mathematical equation has been developed whereby an observed weight can be corrected to the corresponding weight in a vacuum, in which case there would be no buoyancy effects. One form of this equation is

$$W_v = W_a + \left(\frac{W_a}{d_o} - \frac{W_a}{d_w}\right)d_a$$

in which W_v and W_a are the weights of the object in a vacuum and in air, respectively, and d_o, d_w, and d_a are, in order, the densities of the object, of the weights, and of air. It may be noted that $\frac{W_a}{d_o} \times d_a$ equals the weight of air displaced by the object, and $\frac{W_a}{d_w} \times d_a$ is the weight of air displaced by the weights. The value of d_a may be taken as 0.0012 gm/cm³. The correction of weights to vacuum is necessary only in the most refined weighings and in semirefined weighings of water and dilute solutions, the densities of which are much less than that of the weights.

Because this equation does include the density of air and because the density of air is somewhat dependent upon the barometric pressure, fluctuation in barometric pressure will produce variations in the apparent weight of an object. The overall buoyancy error is often insignificant, however, so that any error due to barometric pressure variations would be even less significant.

The use of a double-pan balance permits some self-compensation for the influence of buoyancy during the weighing of bulky glass objects. If a similar piece of glassware is used as a counterweight, the same buoyancy effect (and also the same process of moisture adsorption) occurs on both object and counterweight. This technique for the self-compensation of buoyancy effect is not possible on a single-pan, substitution type of balance.

Temperature Effects. Changes in temperature can cause errors in weighing, and this source of error can be any one of several types. The density of air and, to a much lesser extent, the densities of objects and weights vary with temperature fluctuation, so the temperature also influences the magnitude of the buoyancy error. Again, however, this factor is seldom significant, and allowance is made for it by proper buoyancy corrections.

A more common and more serious temperature effect is encountered whenever the object to be weighed is not at the same temperature as the balance and its surroundings. Without temperature equilibrium between the object and the balance, air convection currents are induced which lead either to false weights or to such erratic balance behavior that no rest point can be observed. These errors can be of appreciable magnitude in analytical work of the accuracy commonly expected in industrial laboratories and in student laboratories as well.

Other Atmospheric Effects.　Another way in which the atmosphere may lead to error in weighing is by adsorption on the object of moisture from the surrounding air. Adsorption of water by the materials being weighed can usually be prevented by weighing them in a closed container, but the possibility of adsorption on the outer surface of the container remains. The extent of this error depends upon both the nature and area of the exposed surfaces and the humidity of the air. A large glass object would probably weigh more on a humid day than on a dry day. In laboratories in which microbalances are used, air conditioning is a necessity. In the more common analytical work, a suitable routine for the drying of specimens and containers must be established.

Other possible interactions between the object and the atmosphere include actual chemical reactions involving atmospheric carbon dioxide or oxygen. The use of tightly closed weighing vessels is valuable in minimizing this type of error. It must be recognized that interaction of the object with atmospheric moisture, carbon dioxide, or oxygen does not signify any shortcomings in the weighing apparatus but rather means that the material being weighed is not entirely the material one desires to weigh.

Electrification of Containers.　Another possibility of serious error arises from electrification of the containers used in weighing. Glass containers tend to acquire a static charge when wiped with a dry cloth or chamois skin. This charge is partially transferred from the object to the balance, causing the latter to swing erratically. Furthermore, the charged pan on which the object rests is attracted to the uncharged floor of the balance so that the apparent weight is too great. The error is more pronounced when the surrounding humidity is low. Some analysts attempt to drain off any such static charges by placing a small amount of radioactive substance in the balance case; presumably enough of the air molecules are ionized to drain off any static charges which may otherwise remain. It is also possible to prevent the formation of the charge in the first place. If the object must be wiped, it should be wiped with a very slightly dampened cloth or chamois skin. In this way no static charge should be developed, and any resulting film of water on the glass surface will evaporate if the object is allowed to stand in the balance room for a few minutes before weighing.

Summary of Precautions. It is generally advantageous to avoid errors, if at all possible, rather than to attempt to correct for them once they have occurred. As an aid in avoiding errors, the following tabulation of precautions in using the balance should be of value:

1. The balance room should be kept as clean and neat as possible. Every movement within the room should be made with due regard for the dangers involved in jarring the balances when they are in operation.

2. The moving parts of the balance should never be touched with the fingers. The weights should be handled with built-in controls or with ivory-tipped forceps which are used for no other purpose. The objects weighed should preferably be handled with forceps or tongs of suitable design, lint-free cloth, or glazed paper.

3. An accumulation of dust on a balance pan and on the weights if they are not built into the balance case (unlikely occurrences if the balance and the weight box are kept shut when not in use) may be removed by gently brushing them with a small camel's hair brush.

4. Only glass or metal objects should be placed directly on the pans. Powdery materials of any sort, wet objects, and chemicals should never rest directly on the pans but should be weighed in suitable containers.

5. Care should be taken that objects placed on the pan carry no detachable material. The bottoms of crucibles should be inspected for soot and, particularly important, for sulfuric acid if this material is used as a desiccant. Any indication of foreign material on the pans should be called to the instructor's attention at once.

6. The initial rest point of the balance should be checked frequently for highest accuracy, preferably before and after each weighing.

7. The balance should never be loaded beyond its capacity rating.

8. Every analysis should preferably be completed on the same pan of the same balance and with the same weights with which it was begun.

9. If large objects of low density (glass vessels) must be weighed, all weighings should be completed within as short a time as possible. All objects weighed must be in complete temperature equilibrium with the balance, and vessels with tightly fitting stoppers should be opened momentarily just before the weighing.

10. The use of the beam and pan arrests is critical in the careful operation of the balance. The prescribed operating procedure should be followed rigidly. The beam support must be manipulated gently and smoothly to avoid chipping either the knife edge or the flat plate in contact with it. Both the beam and the pans should be supported by their arrests when any adjustments in weights are made.

11. The object (also the weights in a double-pan balance) should be centered on the pan so that the pan support hangs vertically. In using weights, one should follow a systematic procedure, always working down from weights that have been shown to be too large. When the final rest point is determined, the door of the balance case must always be shut.

12. After completion of a weighing, no object of any kind should be left on the pans. Both the beam and pan arrests must be in place, and the balance case should be shut as a protection against fumes.

DISSOLVING THE SAMPLE

With few exceptions the weighed sample must be put into solution before separation and measurement of the desired constituent. Whenever possible, the sample is dissolved in water. Organic solvents are suitable for many organic materials. Many different methods are used to modify the solvent properties of water or to change the sample to make it water soluble, and each particular type of sample presents its own problems. The two most general methods are acid treatment and fusion with a flux.

Acid Treatment.   Acids may be classified as nonoxidizing acids, such as hydrochloric, sulfuric, and dilute perchloric, and oxidizing acids, such as nitric and hot, concentrated perchloric. In general, any metal above hydrogen in the electromotive series of the metals will displace hydrogen ion from acid solution and thus be dissolved, although some of the reactions are slow. Metals below hydrogen in the electromotive series generally require use of an oxidizing acid for dissolution.

Strong acids, such as hydrochloric, can dissolve salts of which the anions form weak acid molecules. For example, calcium carbonate dissolves in hydrochloric acid because of the chemical reaction

$$CaCO_3 + 2\ H^+ \longrightarrow Ca^{++} + H_2CO_3$$

An acid solution may serve not only as an acid but also as a complexing or a precipitating agent. Chloride ion, for example, can form soluble complexes with many metal ions, thus increasing the solubility of salts of these metal ions. Sulfate ion is a relatively poor complexing agent.

The practical use of the more common acids in dissolving metals and salts may be summarized as follows:

1. Hydrochloric acid dissolves all common metals except antimony, bismuth, arsenic, copper, mercury, and silver. The dissolution reaction is very slow with lead, cobalt, nickel, cadmium, and a few other metals above hydrogen in the electromotive series. Salts of weak acids and most oxides are soluble. Iron oxide ores are generally soluble by digestion with hydrochloric acid. A residue of siliceous material may remain after dissolution of the ore sample in the acid. Its presence may not interfere in subsequent steps, but it can be removed by filtration or dissolved by a fusion method if desired.

2. Dilute sulfuric acid dissolves all common metals except lead, antimony, bismuth, arsenic, copper, mercury, and silver.

3. Hot, concentrated sulfuric acid dissolves all common metals. An anion of a less volatile acid may be displaced from solution by boiling and evaporation with sulfuric acid.

4. Nitric acid attacks most metals, although the thin oxide films formed on aluminum and chromium surfaces retard further solvent action. Tin dissolves, but immediately forms insoluble metastannic acid. Nitric acid also attacks insoluble salts of oxidizable anions, such as metal sulfides.

5. Hot, concentrated perchloric acid dissolves all common metals, but it should be used with extreme caution since easily oxidizable substances, including some organic substances, react with explosive violence. If there is any doubt whatever, a milder oxidizing agent should be used first, and only approved procedures should be followed in each case. Dilute perchloric acid at room temperature behaves much differently and may be used routinely as a strong acid solution.

6. Aqua regia, composed of three parts hydrochloric acid and one part nitric acid, attacks all metals. This combination provides hydrochloric acid in an oxidizing medium. The complexing characteristics of the chloride ion are particularly significant in the dissolution of gold and platinum.

Some other combinations of two acids or of one acid plus a complexing, oxidizing, or reducing agent are useful as solvents in specific cases.

The use of strong acids to dissolve samples introduces the possibility of loss by volatilization of one or more components of the sample, particularly if a hot medium is employed. Volatile weak acids may be lost, and many other substances which are nominally nonvolatile may be lost to an extent significant in highly accurate work.

If only one constituent of a sample remains undissolved after acid treatment, it may be possible to filter, wash, and weigh that residue to provide a determination for that constituent. Thus, the unit operations of dissolving the sample and of separating the desired constituent are accomplished simultaneously. For example, nitric acid dissolves all of the components of brass except tin, which remains as a residue of metastannic acid. Metastannic acid is converted to tin oxide (SnO_2) upon high temperature ignition, so the amount of tin in the brass sample can be calculated from the weight of the residue after its ignition.

Fusion.   When acid treatment fails to bring a sample into solution, fusion of the sample with a flux may render it water soluble. Fusions are especially useful with silicate and carbonate rocks and ores which are not attacked by hydrochloric acid, but they are also useful with many other samples. The flux is usually alkaline in order to minimize the loss by volatilization of "acid gases," such as hydrogen sulfide and sulfur dioxide.

One of the most commonly used fluxes is sodium carbonate, which converts acidic oxides, such as silicon dioxide, into soluble sodium salts. The reaction may be illustrated by the equation for the fusion of an aluminum silicate, $Al_2(SiO_3)_3$ or $Al_2O_3 \cdot 3 SiO_2$, with sodium carbonate:

$$Al_2(SiO_3)_3 + 4 Na_2CO_3 \longrightarrow 3 Na_2SiO_3 + 2 NaAlO_2 + 4 CO_2$$

Metal ions other than aluminum may end up as carbonates or as oxides which are soluble in acid if not in water. A mixture of sodium and potassium carbonates melts at a lower temperature than just sodium carbonate — a desirable result with some samples but not with others.

In practice about 5 gm of sodium carbonate is used for each gram of the sample. The flux is placed in a platinum crucible that is sufficiently large so that it will not be over half full. The weighed sample is inserted and stirred with the flux. The mixture is heated gradually until it becomes molten, at which temperature it is maintained until the original sample appears to be completely destroyed. A half hour is often sufficient. The melt is then allowed to cool and the solid mass which forms is treated with hot water. The resultant solution is strongly alkaline but is ready for subsequent unit operations of separation and measurement.

Potassium pyrosulfate is also commonly used as an acid flux for oxides that are difficult to dissolve. Upon being heated the pyrosulfate liberates sulfur trioxide, which, in turn, reacts with the oxide to form a soluble sulfate, as illustrated by the following equations for ferric oxide:

$$K_2S_2O_7 \longrightarrow K_2SO_4 + SO_3$$

$$Fe_2O_3 + 3\,SO_3 \longrightarrow Fe_2(SO_4)_3$$

If the heating occurs too rapidly, sulfur trioxide liberated in the first reaction may escape to the surrounding air before entering into the second reaction. Typically, 20 gm or more of potassium pyrosulfate is used for each gram of the sample, and the temperature is held just above the melting point, about 300°C. It is raised to "red heat" only briefly at the end of the reaction time. Platinum or silica crucibles are satisfactory for pyrosulfate fusions.

Other useful fluxes include sodium peroxide and mixtures of either potassium chlorate or potassium nitrate with sodium carbonate. Each of these provides a powerful oxidizing action in an alkaline medium. Iron or nickel crucibles are generally used. Even these materials are attacked by the alkaline melt, but they are relatively inexpensive and the metal introduced into the sample need not be a serious interference.

A mild oxidation can be introduced into sodium carbonate fusions by the use of magnesium oxide along with the carbonate. The magnesium oxide remains solid throughout the fusion in such a form that it provides porosity with resultant free access to air throughout the reaction medium. This flux is known as **Eschka's mixture.**

SEPARATION BY PRECIPITATION

Formation of the Precipitate

Precipitations are generally performed in lipped beakers. Each beaker should be large enough so that it will be no more than about two-thirds full at the end of the precipitation. A different stirring rod with fire-polished ends should be used for each beaker in which a precipitation is made, or a mechanical stirrer should be employed. There are three main types of mechanical stirrers. In one, a motor merely replaces the operator in manipulating the stirring rod; the lower end of the stirring rod may be flattened or bent to provide improved agitation. In another, air pressure operates the stirrer. The third type is a magnetic stirrer; a piece of magnetic metal encased in glass or plastic is inserted into the precipitation vessel and caused to rotate when the beaker is placed over the motor. This type is advantageous in that the space over the beaker is not cluttered with the stirring assembly. In any of the types, only glass (or plastic) should come into contact with the solution. Even though mechanical stirrers are very useful, simple hand mixing with a stirring rod is usually sufficient unless the stirring must be continued for an extended period of time.

The solution of the precipitating agent should usually be quite dilute and should be added slowly, although there are exceptions to these generalizations. Burets, pipets, and medicine droppers are useful for the slow addition of one solution to another.

The amount of reagent solution needed should be calculated in advance from an approximate knowledge of the sample composition. This is important not only to ensure that the separation by precipitation is complete but also because many reagents are expensive and should not be wasted. In addition, the solubility of certain precipitates actually increases if a very large excess of precipitant is added. The amount of reagent used must at least be enough to react with all of the unknown constituent. A 10 to 100 per cent excess is generally desirable. Since the analyst has, at best, only semiquantitative data from which to calculate the necessary amount of reagent, a test for completeness of precipitation is always advisable before one proceeds to or beyond the filtration operation. A test for completeness of precipitation involves adding a little more of the precipitating agent, either to the clear supernatant liquid after the precipitate has settled or to the first bit of filtrate in the filtration operation. In either case, the appearance of any additional precipitate means that more precipitating agent is required before proceeding further.

The ease of subsequent handling is usually, but not always, fulfilled best by precipitation from hot solution. Accordingly, if solubility and other factors permit, the sample solution or the precipitating agent solution should be hot at the time of mixing. It is advisable to keep a hot solution just below, rather than at, its boiling point to prevent possible loss by spattering.

Digestion

A separation by precipitation is not physically complete until the precipitate is removed from its mother liquid, and a precipitate is seldom ready for filtration immediately after formation. In some instances the particles are so small that the filter medium is unable to retain them, and in others an unnecessarily large amount of impurity is retained if filtration is performed at once. To minimize these possible sources of error, the precipitate must be allowed to stand for a period of time in contact with the liquid from which it was precipitated. This process is known as **digestion.** The process is often carried out at elevated temperatures, although room temperature digestion is also useful, particularly when extended periods of time are required.

The particle size of a precipitate may be increased during digestion through one or both of two distinct mechanisms: small particles coagulate to form aggregates; small crystals dissolve and reprecipitate on larger ones so that the average individual crystal size increases. The larger, more readily filterable particles that remain at the end of the digestion period may thus consist of tight aggregates of smaller particles, of larger but fewer single crystals, or of both.

One prominent mechanism whereby impurities are retained by a precipitate involves adsorption of the impurity upon the surfaces of crystals of the precipitate. For a given mass of precipitate, there is less surface if the individual particles are large than if they are small. The increase in particle size during digestion not only aids the filterability of a precipitate but also may improve its purity.

The required duration of the digestion period varies widely from one situation to another. Generally, nothing is gained by allowing digestion of a gelatinous precipitate for any longer than a few minutes. Precipitates which are unstable in water are best not digested at all, but such situations are quite rare. Digestion periods of an hour or so are common, and periods as long as overnight or even a day or two are not rare. Room temperature digestions were continued for several weeks in the extremely accurate work with silver chloride in the historically important analyses from which accurate atomic weights were determined.

Whenever the digestion period extends more than a few minutes, the beaker containing the precipitate and mother liquid should be covered with a watch glass to prevent the entrance of dust or other foreign material. Free access to air should, however, be maintained. The lip on the beaker usually provides enough opening for room temperature digestions. For higher temperature digestions, the watch glass should be supported on three glass hooks set over the top edge of the beaker. This type of covering is preferable when a solution is to be concentrated or evaporated to dryness.

Filtration

At the end of the digestion period, the precipitate should contain essentially all of the unknown constituent or some constituent quantitatively related to it. It should be adequately pure and should be in a physical form ready for filtration. There are several types of filter media. The nature of a precipitate and the temperature at which it must subsequently be dried or ignited frequently dictate which filter medium must be used. If more than one type is usable, convenience is the determining factor.

Filter Paper.   Filter paper is very useful in quantitative work, but it is essential that the proper grade of paper be used for a given precipitate. If the precipitate is subsequently to be weighed, the paper must be removed from the precipitate by burning before the precipitate can be weighed; therefore, the paper used must be of an ashless variety. Filter paper is made ash free during manufacture by treatment with hydrochloric and hydro-fluoric acids; all components of the paper which will not be volatile upon subsequent ignition are effectively removed by this treatment. A small sheet of a good grade of quantitative filter paper will, upon ignition, leave less than 0.1 mg of residue. The carbon of the paper presents a strongly reducing atmosphere during ignition, so filter paper is useful as the filtering medium only with precipitates which are not readily reducible. Ash-free paper is not necessary if the precipitate is subsequently to be subjected, for example, to redissolution rather than to weighing.

Filter papers are available in a variety of porosities. Once the filtration is underway, the mat of precipitate on the paper generally limits the effective pore size. However, the porosity of the paper itself is very important, particularly in the early stages of the filtering operation.

The following points are important in folding and placing the paper into a 60 degree funnel for filtration: The paper should be folded twice. The first fold should be along the diameter of the paper (Fig. 2-10A); the second fold should be such that the edges do not quite match (Fig. 2-10B). Then, a corner of the slightly smaller section should be torn off (Fig. 2-10C) and the paper opened on the slightly larger section. This provides a cone with three thicknesses (two with the torn corner) halfway around, one thickness the other halfway around, and an apex angle very slightly greater than 60 degrees. The paper may then be inserted into a 60 degree funnel, moistened

FIGURE 2-10.   Method of folding filter paper. *A*, First fold is along the diameter of the paper. *B*, Second fold is such that the edges do not quite match. *C*, Corner is torn for tighter fit in the funnel.

with a light stream of water from a wash bottle, and firmly pressed down. Above all, the paper should fit tightly all around its upper circumference. The torn corner prevents an air column from existing between the glass funnel and paper. The filtering operation could be very time-consuming if it were not for the aid of a gentle suction as liquid passes through and down the stem. This suction cannot develop unless the paper fits tightly all the way around its upper circumference.

Some funnels have a constriction in the stem near the apex of the conical portion and others are fluted. This aids in developing the gentle suction action to facilitate the filtration procedure. If the filter is to function properly, the stem should remain continuously full of liquid as long as there is liquid in the conical portion. Actually, a properly fitted filter paper should be able to hold the column of water or solution in the stem of the funnel even when the cone itself is empty. If the filter cannot hold the water column or if spurts of air come along with the liquid, the paper is not fitting properly and much time can be wasted. The stem of the funnel should be several inches long so that it can extend a few centimeters down into the receiving beaker, and the tip should touch the side of the beaker. In this way the filtrate is able to run down the side of the beaker without splashing. A completed filter assembly with a paper filter is illustrated in Figure 2-11.

The filter paper should be large enough so that it is one-fourth to one-half full of precipitate at the end of the filtration. The funnel should, in turn, be large enough for its rim to extend 1 or 2 cm above the top circumference of the paper.

Gooch Crucible.   A Gooch crucible is made of porcelain with a perforated bottom which is covered by a filtering mat of asbestos fibers. It is useful for the filtration of precipitates which must be ignited, particularly those precipitates which would be reduced during ignition in the presence of filter paper. In addition, the Gooch crucible is preferable to papers for filtering solutions, such as potassium permanganate, which attack paper.

The asbestos mat must be freshly prepared for each filtration, and the following procedure is satisfactory: The Gooch crucible is placed in a suction filtering apparatus and, without suction, a well shaken aqueous suspension of asbestos fibers is poured into it. The proper amount of asbestos suspension to be used must be found by experiment — it should fill the crucible about two-thirds full and should contain enough asbestos to result in a mat about 1 mm thick. The suspension is allowed to stand for two or three minutes so that the larger fibers may settle to the bottom. Then gentle suction is applied to draw the water through the base of the crucible leaving an even layer of asbestos. The mat must be washed by passing up to 100 ml of water through it with the aid of suction. The mat is of proper thickness if the perforations in the base are just barely discernible when the crucible is held up to the light. After use, the mat is easily removed and discarded. Once the asbestos mat is prepared, nothing should be poured through a Gooch crucible unless suction is being applied; otherwise, the mat tends to rupture. Sometimes, to

FIGURE 2-11. A filter assembly, with a liquid being decanted into it.

prevent disruption of the asbestos mat, a small perforated porcelain plate is placed over the asbestos mat and a second layer of asbestos is applied.

Porous Base Filtering Crucibles.   There are three types of porous base filtering crucibles: sintered glass, sintered porcelain, and Munroe (platinum). A sintered glass crucible is a glass-walled crucible with a porous glass disk sealed into the bottom. This type of filtering crucible is commercially available with several grades of porosity, the nature of the precipitate determining the desired grade. The actual pore sizes are typically from 3 to 15 microns (1 micron $= 1 \times 10^{-4}$ cm) for "fine" filters, 15 to 40 microns for "medium" filters, and 40 to 70 microns for "coarse" filters. The effective pore size may be somewhat less and is often set, once a filtration has been started, not by the filter medium itself but rather by the tight packing of the particles of precipitate lying on that medium. The sintered glass crucible is very convenient to use because no preparation is needed as with the Gooch crucible and no removal of the filtering medium is required before weighing the precipitate as with filter paper. It does have to be cleaned after use, however, by shaking out loose particles of the precipitate and by soaking or rinsing the crucible in a suitable solvent. The glass cannot withstand high temperatures, so the sintered glass crucible is used primarily with precipitates that can be dried effectively at temperatures not much over 100°C.

The sintered porcelain crucible is similar to the sintered glass variety except for the different material of construction. It possesses the advantages of the sintered glass crucible with the additional fact that it can withstand higher temperatures of ignition.

A Munroe crucible is made of platinum with the base consisting of a permanent layer of spongy platinum. It has an advantage over glass and porcelain filtering crucibles in that it can tolerate a very high temperature. However, platinum is expensive, so this type of crucible is seldom used. A general disadvantage of all the porous base filtering crucibles, compared to filter paper and the Gooch crucible, is the often difficult task of cleaning out a precipitate after use.

Membrane Filters.   Membrane filters are made of cellulose esters, principally of cellulose nitrates. Tiny, uniform holes occupy as much as 80 per cent of the filter volume, and the effective pore sizes of commercially available membrane filters range from several microns to 0.010 microns. This type of filter provides a fast, convenient method for separating particles larger than the pore size from liquids and gases. The particles are retained on the surface of the filter medium. To prevent rupture of a membrane filter during use, it is generally supported on a sintered glass base, the effective pore size of which is significantly larger than that of the membrane.

Transferring the Precipitate to the Filter Assembly.   Special precautions are necessary in transferring a precipitate to the filter assembly. This process is tied in with the washing operation, as most of the washing can be done in the beaker in which the precipitate was formed. All the washings must, of course, be passed through the filter to ensure that no

FIGURE 2-12. Transferring
a precipitate from a beaker to a
filter assembly with the aid of a
stream of liquid from a polyethylene wash bottle.

particles of the precipitate are lost. Liquid should be poured down a glass
rod into the filter assembly to ensure that no splashing occurs. The paper
cone in the funnel or the filtering crucible or holder should never be over
about three-fourths full of liquid plus precipitate.

The bulk of the precipitate is transferred to the filter along with a portion
of wash liquid. The remainder of the precipitate is transferred with the aid
of a fine stream of water from the wash bottle directed around the edges to
push the precipitate out, as illustrated in Figure 2-12. A rubber policeman,
which consists of a small gum-rubber tip over the end of a stirring rod, is
useful in removing final bits of precipitate from the beaker to the filter
assembly. If filter paper is used, a small piece of the same grade of paper may
be used to wipe final traces of the precipitate from the beaker, this paper
then being inserted into the filter.

Suction Filtering.   The passage of liquid through a filter often proceeds extremely slowly unless suction is applied. Suction filtering could be
used with any type of filter medium, but it is most necessary with Gooch and
sintered base filter crucibles and with the finer-pored membrane filters. With
paper-in-funnel filtering, a gentle suction action is developed without any
outside source as long as the paper is fitted properly. If additional suction is
applied in filtration through paper, a hardened filter paper must be used,
or a small perforated cone (generally platinum) must be inserted between
the paper and the funnel to prevent rupture.

The filtering crucible fits into a rubber ring at the top of a regular
suction flask, and the side arm is connected to a water aspirator as the source

of suction. Preferably, a safety bottle should be inserted between the filter flask and the water aspirator to prevent any backup of water from the aspirator into the filtrate. Once the suction is applied, it should never be stopped until the filter flask assembly is disconnected from the aspirator. A pinch clamp on the tube to the aspirator regulates the flow through the filter. Suction filtration is generally beneficial only with crystalline precipitates.

The filtrate should always be received in a clean vessel as a precautionary measure in case a filter paper rupture necessitates a repeat filtration. Frequently, the filtrate must be retained for subsequent determination of another constituent.

Washing

The precipitate frequently must be washed to complete its separation from the mother liquid prior to drying or ignition. Distilled water can serve as the wash liquid in some instances. More often the wash liquid must contain an ion in common with the precipitate to minimize solubility losses or an electrolyte to prevent the aggregates of tinier particles from breaking apart and passing through the filter. The electrolyte must, of course, be one which will not leave an appreciable residue if the precipitate, moist with wash liquid, is subsequently to be dried. Solubility losses are also minimized by using a reasonably small volume of wash liquid, but enough must be used to ensure adequate washing. As in separations by extraction, discussed in Chapter 7, it is much more efficient to use several small portions of wash liquid than to use one large portion. Most washings require eight or 10 portions. Hot liquids generally have lower viscosities than cold ones and therefore run through the filter more rapidly. Remember, however, that solubility losses may be greater in a hot liquid.

Efficient washing and rapid filtration are facilitated by performing most of the washings in the beaker in which the precipitate was formed rather than in the filter assembly. The supernatant liquid is decanted into the filter, a portion of wash liquid is inserted into the beaker, the beaker and its contents are gently swirled, and the supernatant liquid is again poured off through the filter. This process is repeated several times before the bulk of the precipitate is transferred to the filter in the manner already described. For two reasons this technique of washing by **decantation** is distinctly advantageous over the alternate procedure of transferring the precipitate earlier to the filter assembly and washing it there. First, washing is made much more effective by swirling the suspension of precipitate in the beaker with each batch of wash liquid; second, the wash liquid runs through the filter much more readily before the pores are clogged or covered by particles of the precipitate. One can test whether washing is complete by withdrawing a small portion of the filtrate and conducting a qualitative test for some ion known to be present in the original mother liquid.

Gelatinous precipitates are difficult to wash thoroughly because they tend to clog the filtering medium. They can be kept somewhat dispersed by shaking a little filter paper pulp with the suspension prior to filtration. The paper pulp must, of course, be ash free and must be removed in subsequent ignition. A precipitate should not be allowed to dry until it is completely washed. A dried precipitate tends to cake and to crack so that further washing is difficult or impossible.

Ignition of the Precipitate

The general operations of drying and ignition were described earlier in this chapter. It is now of interest to consider more specifically the ignition of a precipitate following its filtration and washing, with particular reference to preparing this precipitate for subsequent weighing.

When paper is used for the filtration, it is folded around the precipitate and inserted into a porcelain, silica, or platinum crucible. The ignition must be carried out in two steps: (1) charring or smoking off the paper at a relatively low temperature and (2) ignition of the precipitate itself at the final desired temperature. If the first step is not completed before the second is begun, the precipitate may be reduced excessively and flames may throw some of the precipitate out of the crucible. The first step is most frequently performed over a burner, even though some other source of heat may be used for the rest of the ignition. The crucible is mounted in a clay, silica, nichrome, or platinum triangle held over a burner (Fig. 2-13). If the paper should accidentally burst into flame, the fire should be smothered immediately by replacing the cover completely with crucible tongs. Ideally, the paper should never burst into flame.

After the paper has been removed completely, the temperature of the flame may be increased up to the full desired ignition temperature, or the crucible and contents may be placed in a muffle furnace at the proper temperature. The bottom of the crucible should be in contact with the blue oxidizing flame; tightly adhering soot may be deposited on the crucible if it is in contact with the center cone or the yellow flame. When the ignition period is ended, the crucible is allowed to cool for a few minutes in air and is then placed in the desiccator for at least half an hour before weighing. The ignition, cooling, and weighing steps should be repeated until successive weighings are in substantial agreement.

A Gooch, Munroe, or sintered porcelain crucible should be inserted into another crucible during ignition so that the burner gases will not come into direct contact with the precipitate. Since the weight of the precipitate is to be obtained from the difference in weights between the empty crucible and the crucible plus precipitate, the empty weight of the crucible must be obtained. This weight should be determined before the precipitate is inserted, and the empty crucible must undergo the same ignition procedure (as will

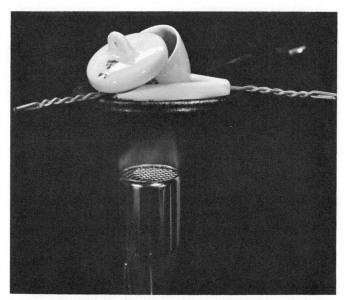

FIGURE 2-13.   Ignition of a precipitate with access of air.

subsequently be used when the precipitate is present) before it is weighed. Each crucible should be alternately ignited and weighed until two successive weighings give reasonably constant results, say to within 0.2 mg. Repetitive ignitions can be of shorter duration than the first one, both with the empty crucible and with a crucible containing the precipitate.

MEASUREMENT OF VOLUME AND THE PERFORMANCE OF TITRATIONS

Volumetric Glassware

There are three principal types of volumetric glassware: flasks, pipets, and burets. Typical items of each type are shown in Figures 2-14 and 2-16.

A volumetric flask is made of thin glass, has a flat bottom, and is calibrated to contain a definite volume of liquid. Occasionally, a second calibration mark is provided to indicate that the flask will deliver a specified volume of liquid. The latter calibration mark provides for the inclusion of a slightly larger volume than does the former, because a thin film of liquid adheres to the inner walls upon emptying.

Pipets are used primarily to deliver aliquot portions of solutions and are of two types. A transfer pipet consists of a long delivery tube, an enlarged bulb of the desired capacity in the center, and a narrow neck or stem on which is a single calibration mark. The delivery tube is long enough to reach

FIGURE 2-14.   Typical volumetric glassware: *A*, a graduated measuring pipet; *B*, a transfer pipet; *C*, a buret.

the bottom of a volumetric flask. A measuring pipet has a straight, uniform bore which is graduated along its length. It is used for the delivery of measured, variable volumes of solution. Measuring pipets are useful primarily for the controlled delivery of volumes of 10 ml and less. Burets are generally more convenient for larger volumes but may be used for smaller volumes as well. Transfer pipets are most widely used in delivering aliquots of fixed size from 1 to 100 ml.

A buret consists of a cylindrical glass tube with graduations along its side and with provision for withdrawing liquid through a small opening at the end. It is usually used in performing titrations. The cross sectional area of a buret is a compromise between two factors: it must be small enough to provide adequate accuracy in the volume measurements and large enough to minimize error from the drainage effects encountered whenever the drainage surface area per unit volume becomes excessive. Delivery of liquid from the buret is accomplished through the capillary tip. The rate of delivery may be controlled by a glass stopcock or Teflon valve assembly just above the tip, or it may be controlled by pinching a rubber tube inside of which is placed a small glass bead in such a manner as to form an opening around one side of the bead for the liquid to pass. The latter method is employed in the Mohr buret and is especially valuable for prolonged use with alkaline solutions, which would cement glass stopcocks in place. Burets with glass stopcocks and those with Teflon valve assemblies are more commonly used.

Any possible error from drainage effects is completely avoided in the weight buret. This type is made much more compact by increasing its cross section, and it is fitted with a glass-stoppered top. No direct readings of volume are made. Instead, the entire buret is weighed on an analytical balance before and after solution is withdrawn. Not only does this technique eliminate drainage errors, but it also increases the sensitivity of measurement. Weighings may be made to the nearest 0.1 mg on an ordinary analytical balance, which corresponds to 0.0001 ml of water. Weight burets have received relatively little use in the past because of the inconvenience and tediousness of weighing, but this situation is changing now that the single-pan type of balance has come into widespread use. Small polyethylene "wash bottles" have been found to function well as weight burets.

Cleaning of Volumetric Glassware.   All items of volumetric glassware must be carefully cleaned prior to use. This is necessary not only to remove possible contaminants but also to assure accurate use. The film of water which adheres to the inner glass walls as a container is emptied of an aqueous solution must be uniform. Even slight traces of grease cause the liquid to adhere in drops rather than as a uniform film. Uneven wetting of the surfaces causes irregularities in the shape of the meniscus, thereby causing further random error in reading the liquid level within the buret, pipet, or volumetric flask.

Perhaps the one most important rule to follow in cleaning volumetric glassware is to empty and clean each item immediately after use. Two or three rinsings with tap water, a moderate amount of agitation with a dilute detergent solution, several rinsings with tap water and, finally, two or three rinsings with small volumes of distilled water are generally sufficient if the glassware is emptied and cleaned immediately after use. If, however, a solution is permitted to evaporate to dryness within a container, the residue may require more drastic treatment. Concentrated detergent solutions should be avoided; a 2 per cent solution is generally adequate. No glassware should be permitted to soak in any detergent solution longer than about 20 minutes.

Direct heat from a flame should never be applied to volumetric glassware, although drying in an oven at about 105°C is permissible. However, adequate drying is usually accomplished by permitting the glassware to stand in air at room temperature or by flushing it with clean, dry air.

Prior to lubricating a glass stopcock, one should wipe the plug and the barrel thoroughly with a clean towel. Any contaminant within the hole through the plug can be pushed out with a piece of wire. A small amount of stopcock grease should be applied near each end of the plug, not directly in line with the hole. The plug is then inserted into the barrel and rotated several times to spread the grease uniformly over the ground-glass surfaces. A properly lubricated stopcock should be seated firmly but should rotate freely. An overlubricated stopcock tends to slide too easily and the hole may soon become clogged with stopcock grease. An underlubricated plug rotates stiffly and unevenly and tends to leak. A stopcock that is properly lubricated can be used for a long period of time without further attention.

Hydrocarbon stopcock greases can be dissolved, when necessary for cleaning, with acetone. Silicone greases do not dissolve readily in any common solvent; some recommended procedures call for soaking the stopcock assembly for two hours in Decalin (decahydronaphthalene) or for 30 minutes in

FIGURE 2-15. In reading the meniscus, the observer should keep his eye
horizontal with the meniscus.

concentrated sulfuric acid. The use of stopcock grease is unnecessary with
Teflon stopcocks.

Reading the Meniscus. The bottom of the meniscus should be read
unless this is impossible as, for example, with a highly colored solution. A
"buret reader" is very useful. It need consist of nothing more than a white
index card with a heavy dark line drawn upon it. The card is held behind
the container so that the observer sees the meniscus against a white background, with the top of the dark band a few millimeters below the meniscus.
Light reflected from the surface of the liquid makes the meniscus stand out
very clearly. The observer's eye should be at the same height as the meniscus
(Fig. 2-15). By noting the appearance of the nearest calibration lines which
go all around the container, he can ascertain readily whether his eye is at
the correct level.

Preparation of Solution in Volumetric Flask. The solute should
be weighed out, transferred to the flask directly or through a funnel, and
dissolved in an amount of water considerably less than the capacity of the
flask. After the solute is completely dissolved, more water or other solvent
is added until the liquid surface lies a few millimeters below the calibration
mark. Final adjustment of the solution level to the calibration mark can be
best done with the aid of a long medicine dropper or a pipet.

Alternatively, the desired solute may be weighed and dissolved in a
beaker and then transferred into the volumetric flask through a funnel. The
beaker must be rinsed several times with small volumes of solvent and the
rinsings used in diluting the solution in the flask. In any case, the solute

should be in the flask and completely dissolved before the final dilution is made.

After the level of solution in the flask is finally adjusted to the calibration mark, the glass stopper should be put in place and the contents of the flask thoroughly mixed to ensure a homogeneous solution. It is generally preferable not to store a solution in a volumetric flask for any great length of time because most volumetric flasks are made of soft glass. It is better to transfer the solution to a clean storage bottle which has been either dried or previously rinsed with a portion of the solution to be stored in it.

Pipet Techniques.   Suction is used to draw solution into a pipet, and delivery is controlled by proper admission of air into the neck end of the pipet. Oral suction is satisfactory for nonvolatile solutions which are dilute and are positively known to be safe for handling in this way. Several types of pipetting bulbs are commercially available. They fit on top of the pipet and do not require the use of oral suction. These devices are absolutely necessary for handling some solutions and are highly recommended for all pipetting operations.

Standardized techniques of filling and emptying pipets are necessary in order to minimize the error which would result from irreproducible drainage effects. First of all, a pipet should always be rinsed with two or three small portions of the sample solution so that the entire inner wall of the pipet is wetted with solution before the actual sample is pipetted. Then, in filling a pipet with solution from a beaker, it is recommended that the pipet be held vertically, that liquid be drawn up about 2 cm above the mark, that the outside of the long delivery tube be wiped dry with a piece of clean filter paper or laboratory tissue paper, that the pipet be held vertically over the beaker with the tip touching the lip of the beaker, and that the liquid be permitted to drain slowly until the meniscus is just at the calibration mark.

In delivering liquid from a transfer pipet, one should permit rapid, free delivery until the liquid level is in the lower stem of the pipet. Then the tip should be held against the inner wall of the receptacle, as shown in Figure 2-16, until the flow stops and for an additional count of 10. The pipet should be moved horizontally from the wall of the receptacle and finally withdrawn entirely. The small "slug" of solution remaining in the tip of a fully drained pipet should always remain, since allowance is made for this in the calibration of a pipet. However, some pipets are calibrated for "blow out", in which case the final part of the delivery procedure should be altered to allow the analyst to blow out the last portion of liquid. This type of pipet, which is relatively uncommon, is marked by the manufacturer with a $\frac{1}{8}$ inch wide frosted glass band near the top of the pipet. Unless a pipet is marked in this way, the blow-out technique should never be used in quantitative work.

These procedures for filling and emptying pipets are quite arbitrary, but they are similar to those which have been adopted by the National

FIGURE 2-16.   The proper position of a pipet while draining it.

Bureau of Standards. A long delivery time followed by a very brief drainage time has been found to be more reproducible in the same overall period of time than a short delivery time and a longer drainage period. The National Bureau of Standards recommends, for example, that the tip of a 100 ml pipet be of such a size that delivery requires 60 seconds or slightly less, in which case very reproducible results are obtained with virtually no additional drainage time.

Buret Techniques.   Delivery of solution from a buret should preferably be made with the stopcock wide open and thus be limited only by the size of the opening of its capillary tip until the volume delivered is within about the last 5 per cent of the required volume. The particular circumstances of a titration may make this impossible, but it is usually possible to anticipate approximately what volume will be required even in the titration of an unknown sample. However, the tip should be small enough to make this "free delivery" time quite long. A good 50 ml buret, for example, typically delivers its full calibrated volume in about 75 seconds. Following this delivery, the level of the meniscus changes by not more than 0.01 ml in several minutes — generally sufficient for completing the titration. A faster delivery rate, resulting from a larger opening in the tip, would cause much more pronounced drainage from the walls of the buret extending over a much longer period of time. A slower delivery rate, from a finer tip, would minimize error from drainage even more, but the longer time would tend to become objectionable.

Prior to an actual titration a buret should be rinsed with several small portions of the titrant solution. These portions should be allowed to run out through the tip of the buret. Burets large enough to deliver at least 25 ml of solution can be filled most conveniently with the aid of a transfer pipet, by using a clean beaker to pour solution into the buret, or by pouring solution from a storage bottle into the buret through a funnel. Some burets, especially those with capacities of only a few milliliters of solution, have special reservoirs to facilitate their filling. Care must always be exercised to avoid trapping air bubbles in the buret tip.

The proper method of manipulating a buret stopcock, while simultaneously swirling the titration vessel, is illustrated in Figure 2-17 and is discussed subsequently in this chapter.

Temperature Effect.   An increase in temperature causes expansion of the glass of which a pipet, buret, or volumetric flask is made and also of the solution within it. With regard to the expansion of the glass, a typical flask which holds 1.00000 liter at 20°C holds 1.00025 liters at 30°C. This change is small enough to be insignificant in most quantitative analyses, but it must be recognized in very precise work. Each piece of volumetric glassware is marked by the manufacturer as to the temperature at which its calibration is valid. A temperature of 20°C has been adopted by the National Bureau of Standards as the normal temperature for its calibration of volumetric glassware. Calibrations made at other temperatures may be corrected to 20°C, and

FIGURE 2-17.   In a titration, the fingers of the left hand should reach around the barrel of the buret to manipulate the stopcock. The right hand is free for swirling the titration flask.

vice versa, by the equation

$$V_{20} = V_t[1 + 0.000025(20 - t)]$$

in which V_{20} and V_t are the volumes at 20°C and at t°C, respectively.

The thermal expansion of the solution is generally much more significant than is that of the glass. The expansion of water or of any dilute aqueous solution is about 2 ml in 1 liter for a temperature change of 10°C. Room temperature fluctuations in a non-air-conditioned laboratory often amount to 5°C over an extended period of time, which means that the volume change would be of the order of one part per thousand.

Calibration of Volumetric Glassware. It is often necessary for an analyst to calibrate his own volumetric glassware. The calibration may be accomplished simply by weighing, at a specified temperature, the water that is delivered by or contained within the piece of apparatus. Buoyancy corrections are *always* required in the calibration of volumetric glassware because of the large difference between the density of water and the density of the weights. One piece of calibrated glassware may, of course, serve for subsequent calibration of others, so a direct weighing is not required for every item. The glassware should be thoroughly clean and any stopcocks should be properly lubricated prior to calibration.

An item calibrated for use with aqueous solutions must be recalibrated if it is to be used with some other solvent, because the different drainage characteristics of water and the other liquid would result in appreciable volume errors.

Standard Solutions

A standard solution is a solution containing a known concentration of a particular chemical species. In a titrimetric analysis, a measured portion of a standard solution reacts with the substance being determined. For example, a standard solution of silver nitrate may be used in the determination of an unknown quantity of chloride ion by precipitimetry, and a standard solution of sodium hydroxide is suitable for the determination of an acid by a neutralization process.

Methods of Expressing Concentration of Solutions. The concentration of a standard solution may be expressed in any one of several different ways. Molarity, formality, and titer are particularly useful in analytical chemistry.

The **molarity** of a solution may be defined as the number of gram molecular weights (moles) of solute per liter of *solution* and is designated by the symbol M. For example, the molecular weight of sodium hydroxide is 40.00, so a 0.5000 M solution contains 20.00 gm of sodium hydroxide per liter of solution. The definition of molarity may be stated mathematically as

$$M = \frac{\text{number of moles of solute}}{\text{liters of solution}}$$

The **formality** of a solution, or the **formal** concentration of a solute, is expressed in terms of the number of gram formula weights of solute dissolved in 1 liter of *solution*. It is indicated by the symbol F. For example, the formula weight of acetic acid, represented by the chemical formula CH_3COOH, is 60.05. Accordingly, a solution prepared by dissolving 60.05 gm, or 1.000 gram formula weight, of acetic acid in enough water to provide a final solution volume of exactly 1 liter would be referred to as a 1.000 F solution of acetic acid. Formality can be expressed in terms of the defining relation

$$F = \frac{\text{number of formula weights of solute}}{\text{liters of solution}}$$

There is a subtly important, but very useful, distinction to be made between molar and formal concentration units. If we specify, for example, that the concentration of acetic acid in a particular aqueous solution is 0.001000 M, it is explicitly meant that the concentration of the *molecular species* CH_3COOH is 0.001000 mole per liter of solution. However, acetic acid is a weak electrolyte and undergoes dissociation into hydrogen ions and acetate ions. Therefore, if we do start with 0.001000 mole or formula weight of acetic acid per liter of solution, the true concentration of molecular acetic acid at equilibrium is only 0.000876 M whereas, as a consequence of dissociation, the concentrations of H^+ and CH_3COO^- are each 0.000124 M. On the other hand, the solution under consideration still contains the original 0.001000 formula weight of acetic acid, although both molecular and dissociated acetic acid are present, and can be correctly specified as a 0.001000 F solution of acetic acid.

Thus, the specifying of a *formal* concentration provides definite and useful information about how a solution is originally prepared, but it does not necessarily imply what happens to the particular solute after it dissolves. However, *molarity* refers specifically to concentrations of actual molecules and ions present in solution at equilibrium and might or might not be synonymous with formality. Because of the truly complex nature of aqueous solutions of analytical interest, we prefer to use *formal* rather than *molar* concentrations wherever possible, since it is frequently difficult, if not impossible, to know or identify the actual species present in solution. Consequently, solutions of acids, bases, and salts will be identified and discussed throughout this book in terms of *formal* concentrations. When it is necessary or desirable to refer to specific ions or molecules in chemical equilibrium calculations, for example, we shall employ *molar* concentrations. However, the reader should always be aware of the possibility for the interchangeable use of these two terms.

Molar and formal concentrations both involve the amount of dissolved solute per unit volume of *solution*, not per unit of volume of *solvent*. The latter method of expressing concentrations has relatively little usefulness in analytical work because of the indeterminate volume changes which occur when solvent and solute are mixed. For highly accurate work, it is sometimes advantageous to prepare a standard solution in terms of the number of gram formula weights of solute *per unit weight of solution*. Such an operation involves, for example, weighing an empty, dry flask, introducing an accurately weighed portion of solute, dissolving the solute in the solvent to obtain a solution of the desired concentration level, and reweighing the flask with its contents to determine by difference the exact weight of the solution. Such a standard solution can be dispensed subsequently by weight with the aid of a weight buret, a procedure at least 10 times more sensitive and accurate than ordinary volume measurements.

Thus far we have been considering expressions of concentration of a solution in terms of how much solute it contains per unit volume. It is alternatively possible to designate the concentration of a standard solution in terms of the quantity of a substance with which it will react. **Titer** refers to the concentration of a standard solution, expressed as the weight of some particular substance with which one unit volume of the solution will react. For example, a standard solution of hydrochloric acid may be prepared of such a concentration that 1.00 ml is equivalent to exactly 5.00 mg of sodium carbonate. In this case, the titer of the acid solution would be 5.00 mg of sodium carbonate per milliliter. The titer value refers, of necessity, to a single specific reaction, so the units in which it is expressed should always be stated along with the number.

Primary and Secondary Standards. Standard solutions may be classified as primary and secondary. A **primary standard solution** is prepared by direct measurements of the weight of the solute and the volume of the solution. A **secondary standard solution** is a solution whose concentration cannot be determined directly from the weight of solute and the volume of solution. The concentration of a secondary standard solution must be determined by analysis of a portion of the solution itself.

The term **primary standard** usually refers to the substance itself. A **primary standard substance** is a substance, a standard solution of which may be prepared by direct measurement of the weight of the substance and the volume to which it is diluted. A primary standard substance must be used, either directly or indirectly, in the preparation of every standard solution. The chief requirements which must be fulfilled by a substance in order for it to be a primary standard substance are the following: it must be obtainable in a pure form; it must be stable both in the pure form and in solution; it must be easily dried and nonhygroscopic; it must be soluble in a suitable solvent; it must be capable of entering into stoichiometric reaction with a solution to be standardized or with a substance to be determined. In addition, a primary standard substance should preferably have an adequately high formula weight so that, when a standard solution is prepared, the quantity weighed out is large enough to prevent significant weighing errors.

The preparation of a standard solution involves two processes which may or may not coincide: (1) weighing out the solute and dissolving and diluting it to the desired volume and (2) determination of the concentration of the solution. Solutions of secondary standards require standardization against some primary standard; and the process of standardization should, whenever possible, be carried out in the same manner in which the solution is to be used for analyses in order to minimize systematic errors. For example, a solution of silver nitrate to be used in titration of unknown chloride solutions should preferably be standardized by titration against primary standard sodium chloride rather than by a gravimetric method.

Preserving Standard Solutions.   Special precautions are necessary in storing and preserving standard solutions. The bottle must be kept tightly stoppered to prevent evaporation of solvent which would cause an increase in solute concentration. The bottle should be swirled carefully before withdrawal of any solution to ensure uniform composition of both the withdrawn portion and the remainder left in the bottle. Portions of solution, once withdrawn, should never be returned to the bottle. This precaution is necessary to minimize the danger of contamination of the main body of solution, and it means that any unused portion of a withdrawn portion should be discarded. Care must also be taken to prevent a standard solution from wetting the ground-glass stopper of the storage bottle. Not only may the solution, upon evaporation, cause the stopper to "cement" or "freeze" in place, but crystals of the solute may subsequently fall back into the solution and alter its concentration.

Some standard solutions must be protected from atmospheric gases. For example, sodium hydroxide solutions are effectively diluted by atmospheric carbon dioxide, which dissolves to form carbonic acid which, in turn, reacts with sodium hydroxide.

Some solutions, for example silver nitrate and potassium permanganate, must be stored in dark glass bottles or otherwise be kept in the dark when not in use to prevent light-catalyzed decomposition. Others, such as sodium thiosulfate, must be protected from possible bacteria-induced decomposition.

Titration of Sample Solution with Standard Solution

In a volumetric determination, the volume of a solution of known concentration of a suitable reagent required to react with a solution of the unknown is measured. The results of the determination are calculated from the amount of that reagent solution required to react with the solution being analyzed. The one main experimental operation in every volumetric determination is the **titration,** which may be defined as the carefully measured and controlled addition of one solution to another with which it reacts.

Equivalence Point and End Point.   Since the result of a volumetric determination is calculated from the amount (concentration and volume) of the reagent which is allowed to react with the substance being determined, an excess of the reagent must not be used. Some means must be provided for

ascertaining the point in the titration at which the desired reaction is completed. This point in the titration is designated as the equivalence point.
The **equivalence point** is defined as that point in the titration at which
stoichiometrically equivalent amounts of the main reactants have been
brought together; that is, the point at which there is no excess of either
reactant.

In practice, an analyst seeks to detect the equivalence point by looking
for a sharp change in some property of the solution in which the reaction
takes place. The point during the titration at which the analyst receives a
signal that this sharp change has occurred is called the **experimental end
point.** Some properties that may undergo change and thereby serve as a
basis for the detection of the end point are: (1) color of solution (disappearance or appearance of one or more colored ions), (2) sharp change in the
concentration of some ion that can be readily measured, (3) appearance of
a precipitate (or appearance of a second precipitate that is highly colored),
and (4) change in some electrical property of the solution.

Quite frequently an experimental end point and a theoretical equivalence point do not coincide perfectly. In other words, the indicator signal
may not be perfect. It is a goal in each method of volumetric analysis to make
the equivalence point and the experimental end point coincide as closely as
possible.

Requirements of Reactions.   A chemical reaction must fulfill four
requirements if it is to serve as the basis of a method of volumetric analysis:

   1. It must be one reaction of well-defined stoichiometry.
   2. The reaction must proceed to completion or nearly so.
   3. The reaction must proceed rapidly.
   4. A convenient method of end point detection must be available.

The first two requirements arise because it would be impossible to
measure how much of one substance is present by measuring how much of
another is required to react with it unless the two substances react quantitatively according to one definite reaction. In general, one of the following
requirements must usually be fulfilled by any chemical reaction to permit
it to go to completion: an insoluble substance is formed, a slightly ionized
substance is formed, a complex ion is formed, the charge of an ion is changed
or removed.

The third requirement arises because the analyst must be able to recognize continuously during the titration when the end point has been reached
in order that he may know whether to continue or to terminate the titration
at each point as he proceeds. It is simply not practical to carry out a titration
between substances which do not react quickly. In general, ionic reactions
do proceed rapidly, and most of the useful titrations involve reactions
between ionic solutions. In recent years, however, many useful titrations have
been developed for nonionic solutes and for solvents of low dielectric constant.

The reason for the fourth requirement is obvious: the analyst could
never tell when to terminate a titration unless some type of end point

detection system were available. No suitable indicators are available for many chemical reactions. This factor alone eliminates such reactions from usefulness as the bases of methods of volumetric analysis. The development of new end point detection systems, especially those utilizing modern physicochemical measurement devices, is one of several fruitful fields of research in modern analytical chemistry.

The various types of volumetric reactions arise directly from the criteria which have been listed for the completion of reactions. Precipitation reactions are those in which an insoluble substance is formed. Neutralization processes are those in which a slightly ionized substance, usually water or a weak acid or base, is formed. Some reactions involving the formation of a complex ion are in general analytical use. Oxidation-reduction processes are those in which the charge on an ion is neutralized or changed.

Performance of Titrations.   Titrations with burets may be carried out either by the **direct titration method** or by the **back titration method.** In the former, the titrating reagent, designated the **titrant,** is added from the buret to the sample solution, called the **titrate**, until the experimental end point is reached, at which point the delivery of titrant from the buret must be stopped abruptly. The last portions of the titrant must be added very slowly in order to permit accurate detection of the end point. In the back titration procedure, the titrant is still added rather slowly, but not necessarily drop by drop, until the end point is actually passed. Then a second titrant, one that will react with the slight excess of the original titrating reagent, is added drop by drop from a second buret until the end point is reached. In this latter method, the volumes and the concentrations of both reagents added from the burets enter into the calculations. Generally speaking, the direct titration procedure is to be preferred. However, the possible advantages of the back titration approach are that the end point signal may be sharper and that a slow reaction between the sample constituent and the original titrating reagent may be overcome.

Special care must be exercised in manipulating the stopcock on the buret during the titration, particularly if it is of the glass stopcock variety. As already noted in Figure 2-17, a right-handed person should mount the buret with the stopcock on the right; and he should manipulate the stopcock with his left hand, reaching his fingers around the buret to the handle of the stopcock. In this way he naturally exerts a slight inward pressure on the stopcock, preventing the possibility of pulling it out; and his right hand is free for swirling the titration vessel.

Titrations are most frequently carried out in Erlenmeyer flasks, although beakers can also be used. The contents of the vessel should be swirled continually during the titration to ensure adequate mixing, and the reagent should be added only a drop at a time near the end point. It is even possible to split a drop by permitting a partial drop to form on the tip of the buret, closing the stopcock, and touching an inner wall of the titration vessel to the buret tip to remove the drop. The inner walls of the vessel should be washed down with a stream from a wash bottle just prior to the final end point to make sure that all of the sample solution is able to react with all the titrant solution which has been delivered from the buret.

Experiment 2-1

INTRODUCTION TO THE ANALYTICAL BALANCE

Purpose

Since the analytical balance is a fundamental measuring instrument for all types of quantitative work in analytical chemistry, a thorough knowledge of and familiarity with the construction and design, the theory of operation, and the inherent accuracy of a balance are important. In this experiment, the precision of weighings made with an analytical balance will be investigated and the magnitude of various common errors encountered in weighing will be evaluated.

Procedure

1. Inspect the balance, identifying the various parts described on pages 23 to 26. Familiarize yourself with the balance controls. If the balance is of the single-pan substitution type, your laboratory instructor may wish to remove the cover of the balance and allow you to inspect the beam assembly, the knife edges, the weights, the beam damping arrangement, and the mechanism used to remove weights from the beam assembly.

2. If the balance is a single-pan substitution type, perform the preliminary zero adjustment. If a double-pan balance is used, it is of interest to determine the rest point and the sensitivity for various loads on the pans.

3. Determine the weight of a clean, dry weighing bottle (without its lid) to within ± 0.1 mg.

4. Determine the weight of the weighing bottle lid separately to within ± 0.1 mg.

5. Determine the total weight of the weighing bottle plus the lid to within ± 0.1 mg. Compare this result with the sum of the separate weighings of the bottle and the lid to see how closely the weights agree.

6. Reweigh the weighing bottle without its lid to see how reproducible this weight is.

7. Roll the weighing bottle around in your hand; i.e., handle it and finger it and then reweigh it and compare the weight with the previous

results. Next, wipe the weighing bottle clean with a dry, lint-free cloth or with laboratory tissue, reweigh it, and again compare the result to previous ones.

8. Hold the weighing bottle an inch from your mouth and breathe on it several times. Weigh it again and compare the result with earlier weights.

9. Place the weighing bottle in a drying oven for two or three minutes. Remove the bottle from the oven with tongs and reweigh it immediately while it is still warm. Follow the change in its apparent weight for several minutes, recording the weight every 30 seconds.

10. Weigh the weighing bottle lid. Remove the lid from the balance and write your initials with a pencil on the ground-glass surface. Reweigh the lid and note the difference in weight.

Discussion

1. On the basis of your experimental work, what can you conclude about the reproducibility of weighings made with the balance?

2. List some possible errors in weighing and give an estimate of the size of each error.

3. Account for the results observed in step 9 of the procedure.

Experiment 2–2

CALIBRATION AND USE OF VOLUMETRIC GLASSWARE

Purposes

One of the major purposes of this experiment is to provide experience in the cleaning and handling of volumetric glassware and in the adjusting and reading of the meniscus of a liquid in a buret, pipet, or volumetric flask. In addition, this experiment gives further practice in the weighing of objects and introduces the important concept of buoyancy corrections in weighing.

Preparation

In this experiment, each item of volumetric glassware is calibrated by determining the weight of water delivered from or contained in that piece of glassware and then calculating the corresponding volume from the known density of water. However, since the density of water is a function of temperature, varying two or three parts per thousand over the range of normal laboratory temperatures, it is important that the water used in the calibrations be at a constant and known temperature throughout the duration of the experiment. Therefore, it is advisable to obtain enough distilled water for all calibrations at the beginning of the experiment and to allow this water to reach the equilibrium laboratory temperature while other preliminary operations are being completed.

Another preliminary step involves the cleaning of the various pieces of volumetric glassware and, in the case of burets, the proper lubrication of stopcocks. As mentioned earlier in the text, all items of volumetric glassware must drain so that a uniform film (not individual droplets) of liquid wets the inner wall of the glass container.

Burets can be effectively cleaned with the aid of a long-handled buret brush and a dilute (2 per cent) aqueous solution of a mild detergent. Care should be exercised not to scratch the inner wall of the buret with the brush, and the buret should be thoroughly rinsed, first with tap water and then distilled water, after the cleaning. In the event that the buret still does not drain uniformly after this simple cleaning procedure, a more drastic treatment, usually with "cleaning solution" (approximately 30 gm of sodium dichromate dissolved in 500 ml of concentrated sulfuric acid) or with $6 F$ sodium hydroxide solution, may be necessary. The use of either of the latter two solvents for cleaning a buret demands special care. A 75 to 100 ml portion of the acid-dichromate or sodium hydroxide cleaning solution should be taken in a small beaker. The buret should be *inverted* with its upper end immersed in the cleaning solution, the stopcock opened, and gentle suction applied at the tip of the buret by means of a rubber bulb or by means of a flexible rubber hose connected to a water aspirator-trap assembly. The cleaning solution should be drawn up only past the calibration marks of the buret, not into the stopcock itself. At this point, the stopcock can be closed. The cleaning solution will remain in the buret as long as desired; however, it is not advisable to keep the cleaning solution in the buret longer than about 10 minutes, especially in the case of sodium hydroxide, because the glass surface will be gradually etched. Thorough rinsing of the buret with tap water and distilled water must always follow a cleaning solution treatment.

Pipets and volumetric flasks may be cleaned in a manner similar to burets. If necessary, a small volume of cleaning solution may be swirled around inside the vessel, followed by thorough rinsing with water.

A piece of volumetric glassware, once cleaned, may be protected from dust, grease, and other contaminants if it is carefully rinsed with tap water and distilled water after use and if it is stored *full* of distilled water. This is easily done with volumetric flasks. Clean pipets may be stored full of distilled water if a small cork is inserted into the upper end after filling. A buret, filled with distilled water, may be conveniently stored upright in a buret holder if a suitably sized test tube is placed over its top, or it may be kept in a desk or bench drawer with a cork inserted in its top. Under no circumstances should solutions be stored in volumetric glassware.

Procedure

Buret.   Fill the buret with distilled water at room temperature so that the meniscus is just slightly above the zero mark. Record the temperature of the water and check it once or twice during the calibration procedure. Any bubbles of air trapped in the buret tip may be ejected if one allows water to drain through the buret with the stopcock wide open. In addition, it is a good practice to test the stopcock for leakage by observing the position of the water meniscus over a 10 minute interval.

For reading the position of a meniscus, the following procedure is usually recommended. First, a 50 ml buret that is calibrated in 0.1 ml divisions should be read to the nearest 0.01 ml by visual inspection. Second, when the bottom of the meniscus is tangent to a calibration mark, the volume reading is equal to that calibration point; when the meniscus appears to be flattened by a calibration mark, the reading is usually taken to be 0.01 ml larger than the value of that calibration; and, when the bottom of the meniscus is barely but distinctly below a calibration mark, the buret reading is usually taken to be 0.02 ml larger. Above all, it is important that one be consistent by always using the same technique for reading a buret.

Weigh to the nearest milligram a clean ground glass-stoppered weighing bottle of suitable size (dry, at least on the outside). As a substitute for the weighing bottle, a glass-stoppered 50 ml Erlenmeyer flask or a conical flask covered with a small watch glass may be employed. Always handle these items with tongs or a piece of lint-free paper.

It should be pointed out that a precision of 1 mg in the weighings to be performed in this experiment is probably unnecessary. Most volume measurements in titrimetry are made only to the nearest 0.01 ml, which corresponds to 10 mg of water. Therefore, it would probably suffice to make all weighings to within only 5 mg. Since two weighings are involved in each separate calibration point, the maximum uncertainty of 10 mg (or 0.01 ml) would be tolerable. However, because it is easy to weigh an object to the nearest milligram and because a specified weighing tolerance of 5 mg could lead to undue carelessness in the calibration, the stated 1 mg precision is preferable. Such considerations as these, however, should routinely be made in all kinds of gravimetric and volumetric determinations.

Adjust the position of the meniscus exactly to the zero mark, allow 30 seconds for drainage of the buret, and readjust the meniscus position if necessary. If a water droplet is clinging to the buret tip, remove the droplet by touching the tip to a moist glass surface (a beaker rim, for example); wipe away any water droplets adhering to the side of the tip with a small piece of filter paper or laboratory tissue.

Slowly withdraw water (at the rate of about 10 ml per 30–40 seconds) into the previously weighed receiving vessel until the meniscus is just above the 10 ml calibration mark. Wait 30 seconds for drainage and carefully adjust the position of the meniscus so that it is exactly *tangent* to the 10 ml mark. If a droplet is hanging on the buret tip, touch the *inner* wall of the receiving vessel to the tip to remove the drop. Throughout these operations the tip of the buret should be well down inside the receiving vessel so that water is not lost by spattering. Promptly stopper or cover the receiving vessel to minimize

TABLE 2-3. DENSITY OF WATER AT VARIOUS TEMPERATURES AND 1 atm PRESSURE

Temperature (°C)	Density (gm/ml)	Temperature (°C)	Density (gm/ml)
15	0.99913	25	0.99708
16	0.99897	26	0.99682
17	0.99880	27	0.99655
18	0.99862	28	0.99627
19	0.99843	29	0.99598
20	0.99823	30	0.99568
21	0.99802	31	0.99537
22	0.99780	32	0.99506
23	0.99757	33	0.99473
24	0.99733	34	0.99440

evaporative loss of water. Record the initial and final buret readings and determine the weight of water delivered by reweighing (to the nearest milligram) the receiving vessel containing the water.

Repeat the entire procedure by withdrawing water between the 0 and 20, 0 and 30, 0 and 40, and 0 and 50 ml marks, as described above.

For each set of data, (a) correct the *observed* weight of water for the effect of air buoyancy as discussed on page 36, (b) calculate the volume of water corresponding to the *corrected* weight from the density of water at the specified temperature (Table 2-3), and (c) correct the volume to a temperature of 20°C, if desired, according to the equation on page 59 which accounts for the thermal expansion of volumetric glassware, although this latter correction is insignificant (within the temperature range from 15 to 34°C) even for precise analytical work. The volume correction to be applied to each buret reading is the difference between the actual volume obtained by calibration and the volume read from the buret markings. Duplicate calibrations should agree to within 0.02 ml.

Tabulate the buret calibration data and retain this information in a conspicuous place in your laboratory notebook.

Data are available to facilitate the series of calculations outlined in the second preceding paragraph. Table 2-4 contains a partial compilation of such data. Suppose, for example, that one calibrates the 0 to 20 ml interval of a buret, finding that at

23°C the water delivered weighs 19.973 gm in air against brass weights. The entry in Table 2-4 corresponding to 23°C means that an observed weight of 1 gm of water measured against brass weights in air occupies a *true* volume of 1.0034 ml at 20°C. Thus, the tabulated result already includes the two corrections for air buoyancy and the thermal expansion of glass along with the density factor for water. Therefore, if 1 gm of water occupies 1.0034 ml, 19.973 gm occupies a volume of (1.0034)(19.973) or 20.041 ml at 20°C. It can also be shown that the volume at 23°C is 20.042 ml,

TABLE 2-4. VOLUME AT 20°C OCCUPIED BY 1 gm OF WATER WEIGHED IN AIR AGAINST BRASS WEIGHTS AT VARIOUS TEMPERATURES

Temperature (°C)	Volume (ml)	Temperature (°C)	Volume (ml)
15	1.0021	25	1.0038
16	1.0022	26	1.0041
17	1.0023	27	1.0043
18	1.0025	28	1.0046
19	1.0026	29	1.0048
20	1.0028	30	1.0051
21	1.0030	31	1.0054
22	1.0032	32	1.0056
23	1.0034	33	1.0059
24	1.0036	34	1.0062

which is essentially the same result as at 20°C. For practical purposes, where only one part per thousand accuracy is needed, the factors in Table 2-4 can be used to calculate with good reliability either the corrected volume at 20°C or the corrected volume at any other temperature between 15 and 34°C.

Transfer Pipet. Weigh to the nearest milligram a clean ground-glass-stoppered weighing bottle, an Erlenmeyer flask covered with a watch glass, or a similar vessel. It need not be dry on the inside.

Fill the pipet with distilled water at the known room temperature by drawing up the water until the meniscus is slightly above the calibration mark. Place the forefinger over the upper end of the pipet to hold the water in place, and carefully remove any droplets of water adhering to the outside of the pipet by wiping them away with filter paper or laboratory tissue.

Hold the pipet vertically over a sink or other receptacle and by manipulating the forefinger adjust the level of the meniscus until it coincides with the calibration mark, discarding the water emptied during this adjustment. While carefully maintaining the column of water in the vertical position, touch the tip of the pipet to a glass surface to remove any droplet of water adhering to the tip itself.

These latter operations do require care since, once the meniscus has been adjusted, any quick movement of the pipet may result in loss of some water. Such a loss is usually quite evident because the water withdraws a fraction of a centimeter or so into the tip, leaving a small void. If this happens, the entire filling operation must be repeated.

While holding the pipet vertically with its tip well inside the receiving vessel to prevent loss of water by spattering, release the forefinger and permit the pipet to drain freely. About 10 seconds after free flow of water from the pipet has stopped, touch the tip of the pipet to the inner wall of the vessel to remove any droplet of water; then withdraw the pipet. Do not blow out the small portion of water remaining in the tip of the pipet, since this has been taken into account in the original calibration of the pipet.

Stopper or cover and reweigh the receiving vessel and its contents to determine the weight of water delivered by the pipet, apply a buoyancy correction to obtain the true weight of water, calculate the volume of water from the data in Table 2-3, and compare the actual volume of water delivered from the pipet with the nominal volume.

The calibration procedure should be repeated, and replicate results should agree to within one or two parts per thousand.

Volumetric Flask. Clean and dry the volumetric flask to be calibrated. If time permits, the flask may be rinsed with distilled water and allowed to air dry. Alternatively, the flask may be rinsed with very pure acetone or ethanol and then dried by passing filtered dry air or nitrogen through it. Volumetric glassware should not be dried over a flame or in an oven, since glass expands on heating but is somewhat slow to recover its original volume on cooling.

The remainder of this procedure applies specifically to the calibration of large volumetric flasks, i.e., those with volumes greater than 250 ml. The accurate weighing of large volumes of water is usually accomplished on large double-pan balances and requires special care because the rest point and sensitivity of such a balance vary considerably with large changes in the loads on the balance pans and because high-capacity balances used to perform the necessary weighings frequently suffer from balance arm inequality. Therefore, the method of weighing by substitution is always employed. On the other hand, for the calibration of flasks of small volume, either the direct comparison or the substitution weighing technique is acceptable.

Place the dry, stoppered flask on the right pan of a balance of suitable capacity and add an accurately known weight in grams (W) equal to the volume of the flask in milliliters. For example, add 500 gm if a 500 ml flask is being calibrated. Add tare weights, which may be parts of an old weight set, to the left pan until balance equilibrium is established, and determine the rest point. Remove the weights (W) from the right pan, but leave the tare weights untouched on the left pan.

Remove the flask from the balance and insert into it a clean, dry glass funnel such that the funnel stem extends below the calibration mark. Fill the flask with water at the known room temperature until the water level is just below the mark. Carefully remove the funnel and fill the flask with the aid of a pipet or dropper so that the bottom of the meniscus is exactly at the calibration line. At this point no droplets of water should be adhering to the inner wall of the flask above the calibration mark; however, a long strip of filter paper may be used to remove them.

Stopper the filled flask and place it back on the right pan of the balance. Add small weights or adjust the balance rider until the first rest point is again obtained. If the small weight added in this case is w, the observed weight of the water contained by the flask is equal to the difference between W and w. Correct the observed weight of water for buoyancy effects, compute the volume of water from the data in Table 2-3, and compare the true volume of the flask with the nominal value at the desired temperature.

A possible alternative approach to the calibration of a volumetric flask involves pouring or transferring into the flask a known volume of water from some other previously calibrated container. Then a new calibration mark (if one is needed) can be placed on the volumetric flask, for example, by affixing to the neck of the flask a gummed label which can be made waterproof by painting it with paraffin or varnish.

Another variation of the preceding method involves calibration of the flask relative to a pipet. For example, a 250 ml volumetric flask can be filled with five portions of water from a 50 ml pipet, and a new calibration mark placed on the neck of the flask. This is a useful calibration method even if the pipet is uncalibrated, because the same pipet may be used subsequently for withdrawal of exactly one-fifth aliquots of the contents of the flask.

QUESTIONS AND PROBLEMS

1. What is the one main requirement of a sampling process?
2. Distinguish critically between absolute dryness and reproducible dryness.
3. In what situations may organic solvents be advantageously used in drying samples and precipitates?
4. Compare platinum crucibles and porcelain crucibles with regard to their usefulness in quantitative analysis.
5. Explain what errors might be involved in interpreting the composition of a sample from the percentage of water if the latter is determined by loss of weight.
6. Name three common desiccants and compare them on the basis of effectiveness, ease of use, and possibility of regeneration.
7. Define or characterize the rest point and the sensitivity of an analytical balance.
8. State concisely the principles involved in making a weighing on an analytical balance by the method of direct comparison and by the method of substitution.
9. Explain clearly how a damping device restricts the movement of the beam yet does not affect the rest point.
10. Is it feasible for a projection reading device to be used on an undamped balance? Explain.
11. Explain how the use of a single-pan balance makes it possible to perform all weighings under constant load conditions.
12. Compare the single-pan and double-pan balances with regard to construction, convenience of use, and accuracy.

13. Indicate the order of magnitude of the error introduced in the use of a common analytical balance by each of the following sources of error: balance arm inequality, air buoyancy, and normal temperature fluctuations.

14. The following pointer readings were obtained for the swings of a balance with equal 10 gm loads on each pan: $+7.6$, -6.4, $+7.0$, -5.8, and $+6.8$. Determine the rest point.

15. When a 1 mg weight was added to the right pan of the balance in the preceding problem, the new set of pointer readings was: $+2.0$, -8.2, $+1.4$, -7.6, and $+0.7$. Calculate the sensitivity of the balance with a 10 gm load on each pan.

16. A crucible was placed on the right pan of a balance and the sum of the weights required to counterbalance it was 19.2624 gm. When the same crucible was transposed to the left pan, its apparent weight was 19.2660 gm. Calculate (a) the balance arm ratio and (b) the correct weight of the crucible.

17. If a bottle made of glass with a density of 2.4 gm/cm^3 weighs 16.1487 gm in air when weighed with brass weights (density of 8.4 gm/cm^3), calculate the weight of the bottle in vacuo.

18. A platinum crucible (density of 21.4 gm/cm^3) was found to weigh 14.8167 gm in air when weighed with brass weights (density of 8.4 gm/cm^3). Calculate the weight of the crucible in vacuo.

19. The volume occupied by 1.0000 g of water weighed in air with brass weights (density of 8.4 gm/cm^3) at 20°C is 1.0028 ml. Calculate the weight in vacuo of 1.0000 ml of water at the same temperature.

20. Calculate the apparent weight, measured in air with brass weights (density of 8.4 gm/cm^3), of 1.0000 ml of mercury if it weighs 13.546 gm in vacuo.

21. If the left arm of a balance is 10.000 cm long and the right arm is 10.010 cm long, what is the apparent weight of a 1.0000 gm object weighed with this object on the left pan?

22. Compare sintered glass crucibles, filter paper, and Gooch crucibles as filtering media on any three significant points.

23. Explain why a hot object should be cooled somewhat in room air before it is placed inside a desiccator. Explain what error may be enhanced at the same time.

24. Define or characterize the following terms: titration, standard solution, primary standard, aliquot, indicator, molarity, formality, normality, equivalent weight, and titer.

25. Give an example of the use of a piece of volumetric glassware calibrated to contain a specified volume of liquid. Give an example of the use of a piece of volumetric glassware calibrated to deliver a specified volume.

26. Contrast an ordinary buret and a weight buret in regard to construction, ease of use, expected accuracy, and significance of drainage effects.

27. Describe and compare three methods of calibrating a volumetric flask.

28. In the calibration of a 25 ml pipet, the contents of the pipet when filled to the calibration mark with water at 25°C were delivered into a weighing bottle and found to weigh 24.92 gm when weighed in air with brass weights (density of 8.4 gm/cm^3). What is the true volume of the pipet?

29. A buret is calibrated by the weight method at 28°C. If 10.00 ml of water, as indicated by the buret, weighed 10.000 gm in air against brass weights (density of 8.4 gm/cm^3), what is the correction to be used for this buret reading?

30. List four requirements that must be fulfilled by a substance to make it suitable for use as a primary standard.

31. Distinguish between equivalence point and end point of a titration.

32. List four requirements which must be met by a chemical reaction to make it suitable as the basis of a method of volumetric analysis.

Chapter Three

Treatment of Analytical Data

Consideration is given in this chapter to some mathematical concepts encountered in all types of quantitative measurements and calculations, to statistically valid methods of handling and interpreting data, and to methods of making stoichiometry calculations in quantitative chemical analysis.

SIGNIFICANT FIGURES

Definition. **Significant figures** are the digits necessary to express the results of a measurement to the precision with which it is made. Consider, for example, the weighing of a crucible first on a rough balance to the nearest tenth of a gram and then on an analytical balance to the nearest tenth of a milligram, the results of the two weighings being 11.2 and 11.2169 gm, respectively. Three digits are used in expressing the result of the first measurement and six for the second. Any fewer digits could not express the results of the measurements to the precision with which they were made, and no more digits could justifiably be used for either value; therefore, the first weight is expressed in three significant figures and the second in six.

Consider next the measurement of an extremely small number, such as the number of moles of hydrogen ion in 1 liter of pure water at room temperature. This quantity can be measured, and the result could be written as 0.0000001 mole. Eight digits, including the zeros, have been used. However, the same number could be written as 1×10^{-7} mole, in which case only one digit has been used exclusive of the exponential factor. Thus, the result of the measurement has only one significant figure no matter which way it is written, because only one digit is *necessary* to express the results of the measurement to the precision with which it was made. The zeros to the left of the 1 in 0.0000001 and the exponential factor of 1×10^{-7} are used merely to locate the decimal point and do not fit into the definition of significant figures. A similar consideration is encountered in measurements of very large numbers. For example, the number of molecules in a mole of any compound can be written as 6.02×10^{23}, and this number contains three significant figures. The exponential factor again serves only to locate the decimal point.

It is important for each person making measurements to express the results of the measurements with the proper number of significant figures. Another person who reads and in any way uses or interprets the results of those measurements can usually tell at a glance how many significant figures are intended. However, there is a possibility of uncertainty and error in recognizing the number of significant figures when reading large numbers. For example, a recorded volume of 2000 ml might involve only one significant figure, meaning that the measured value was closer to 2000 than to 1000 or 3000. Alternatively, it could signify the measured quantity to be closer to 2000 than to 2001 or 1999, in which case four significant figures are indicated. Likewise, the number 2000 might intend only two or three figures to be significant. This possible uncertainty can be avoided very simply if the one who makes the measurement in the first place writes it in an exponential form — 2×10^3, 2.0×10^3, 2.00×10^3, or 2.000×10^3 — clearly showing whether he intends one, two, three, or four figures, respectively, to be significant. It is advisable to express the results of measurements in this exponential form whenever there can possibly be any confusion as to whether zeros to the left of the decimal point are significant or not.

Absolute Uncertainty and Relative Uncertainty.   Uncertainty in measured values may be considered from either of two distinct viewpoints. **Absolute uncertainty** is the uncertainty expressed directly in units of the measurement. A weight expressed as 10.2 gm is presumably valid within a tenth of a gram, so the absolute uncertainty is one tenth of a gram. Similarly, a volume measurement written as 46.26 ml indicates an absolute uncertainty of one hundredth of a milliliter. Absolute uncertainties are expressed in the same units as the quantity being measured — grams, liters, and so forth.

Relative uncertainty is the uncertainty expressed in terms of the magnitude of the quantity being measured. The weight 10.2 gm is valid within one tenth of a gram and the entire quantity represents 102 tenths of a gram, so the relative uncertainty is about one part in 100 parts. The volume written as 46.26 ml is correct to within one hundredth of a milliliter in 4626 hundredths of a milliliter, so the relative uncertainty is one part in 4626 parts, or about 0.2 part in a thousand. It is customary, but by no means necessary to express relative uncertainties as parts per hundred (per cent), as parts per thousand, or as parts per million. Relative uncertainties do not have dimensions of mass, volume, or the like because a relative uncertainty is simply a ratio between two numbers, both of which are in the same dimensional units.

To distinguish further between absolute and relative uncertainty, consider the results of weighings of two different objects on an analytical balance to be 0.0021 gm and 0.5432 gm. As written, the *absolute uncertainty* of each number is one ten-thousandth of a gram, yet the relative uncertainties differ widely — one part in 20 for the first weight and one part in approximately 5000 for the other value.

Significant Figures in Mathematical Operations.　Very seldom is the result of an analytical determination based solely upon one measured value. For example, even the weighing of a single sample normally requires two weight measurements, one before and one after removing a portion of the sample from a weighing bottle. The result of the second weighing must be subtracted from the first to get the sample weight. Frequently, one measured value must be multiplied or divided by another. The analytical chemist is concerned with significant figures not only in dealing with results of single measurements but also in conjunction with numbers computed mathematically from two or more measured quantities. The arithmetical operations of addition and subtraction may be considered together, as may multiplication and division.

Addition and subtraction.　The concept of significant figures in a number obtained by an addition or subtraction operation is illustrated in the following example:

weight of bottle plus sample	11.2169 gm
weight of bottle alone	10.8114 gm
weight of sample	0.4055 gm

Each of the quantities measured directly contains six significant figures, but the weight of the sample has only four. The zero to the left of the decimal point is in good form, because it emphasizes the location of the decimal point, but it is not a significant figure. Now, assume that one weighing was made less precisely, so that the data are as follows:

weight of bottle plus sample	11.2169 gm
weight of bottle alone	10.81　 gm

The correct weight of the sample is not 0.4069 gm but rather 0.41 gm. With the decimal points aligned vertically, the computed result has no more significant figures to the right of the decimal point than the individual number with the fewest decimal places. Note that, with absolute uncertainties of 0.0001 and 0.01 gm for the two numbers to be subtracted, the absolute uncertainty of the difference is 0.01 gm. The rule for handling significant figures in addition and subtraction may be stated thus: the computed result has an *absolute uncertainty* equal to the largest absolute uncertainty of any individual number.

Multiplication and division. The concept of significant figures in the operations of multiplying and dividing must be based upon *relative uncertainties*. A product or quotient should be expressed with sufficient significant figures to indicate a relative uncertainty comparable to that of the factor with the greatest relative uncertainty. Consider the problem $9.678234 \times 0.12 = 1.2$. Expressing this result as, for example, 1.1613 would be totally unjustifiable in view of the fact that the relative uncertainty of the second factor is one part in 12.

The rule that the relative error of a product or quotient is dependent upon the relative error of the least accurately known factor suggests the important generalization that, in measuring quantities which must be multiplied or divided to get a final result, it is advantageous to make all the measurements with approximately the same relative error. It is a waste of time to measure one quantity to one part in a hundred thousand if it must subsequently be multiplied by a number which cannot be measured any better than to within one part in a hundred. Similarly, it is advisable to measure quantities which are to be combined by addition or subtraction to about the same absolute uncertainty. It would be foolish to take pains to measure one weight to a tenth of a milligram if it is to be added to a weight which for some reason cannot be measured any closer than to, say, 10 mg.

Atomic and molecular weights often appear as multiplication and division factors in calculations of analytical results. The computed result can have no less relative uncertainty than that of the atomic or molecular weights; yet these values are known so accurately that they seldom limit the accuracy of a computed result.

PRECISION AND ACCURACY

The terms *precision* and *accuracy* have been used without definition in the preceding discussion. A more detailed look at the meaning of these two terms is now appropriate.

Precision refers to the variability among replicate measurements of the same quantity. Consider three determinations of the percentage of lead in a brass sample by one analyst to be 2.63, 2.62, and 2.62 per cent and three results obtained for the same sample by a second analyst to be 2.60, 2.75, and 2.81 per cent. The results of the first analyst exhibit much less variation among themselves than do those of the second, so the precision of the first set of results is better than that of the second.

Accuracy refers to the difference between a measured value and the true value for a quantity to be measured. Strictly speaking, the true values are never known except in counting discrete objects ("there are exactly 12 students in this class") and in defined quantities ("the atomic weight of a certain isotope of carbon is exactly 12.0000"). All other types of measurements, including mass, length, volume, and so forth, are actually comparisons to standards, and these comparisons must consist of measurements. So the term *accuracy* refers to the difference between a measured value and the value which is accepted as the true or correct value for the quantity measured.

The distinction between precision and accuracy may be likened to the result of shooting a series of arrows at an archery target — *precision* refers to how close together the several arrows hit and *accuracy* refers to how close to the bull's-eye each lands. It is possible for a replicate series of measurements or determinations to be very precise and yet highly inaccurate. It is, however, quite meaningless to consider the accuracy of a series of values unless their precision is reasonably good. The analytical chemist desires to achieve acceptable precision and accuracy in all of his work and to assess how accurate and precise his work and methods are. The terms *accuracy* and *precision* will be treated more quantitatively later in this chapter.

ERRORS

The analytical chemist, in common with other workers in science, is continually interested in the cause and the magnitude of errors in his measurements. He examines the quantitative data he obtains not with the question as to whether error is present but rather with the question as to how much error and uncertainty exist. He recognizes that error is always present and that he will not completely eliminate error even though he does continually strive to recognize, to minimize, and to evaluate the errors which enter into his measurements.

Errors may be arbitrarily divided into two categories, *systematic* and *random*. This classification was mentioned briefly in Chapter 2 with reference to errors in sampling and will now be considered within a more general context.

Systematic Errors. Systematic errors are those one-sided errors which can be traced to a specific source, either in the strategic scheme of the experiment or in the apparatus used to perform it. Such errors can often be minimized by a modified plan of attack. Even when the errors cannot be completely suppressed in this way, an understanding of their origins often makes it possible to deduce a correction factor that can be applied to the final result, or at least to estimate the probable residual error in that result.

When one or more large errors appear to be present, it is frequently possible to discover their origins by a series of carefully controlled experiments in which the experimental conditions and quantities are varied widely in a systematic way. The resultant error must follow one of three courses: (1) the error may remain relatively constant and independent of the experimental conditions, (2) the magnitude of the error may vary systematically with one or more of the experimental conditions, or (3) the error may persist as a random error.

If the error in a precipitation process proves to be constant in magnitude, such possibilities as reagent contamination must be considered. If a systematic variation of the error is evident, the parameter linked to this variation frequently indicates the cause. For example, in a gravimetric determination a negative deviation which increases with the volume of the wash liquid and decreases when the sample size is increased indicates the possibility of a solubility loss. The loss may be reduced, or even entirely suppressed, by employing a different precipitating form or by altering the conditions of precipitation. If this is not possible, a correction factor deduced from the measured solubility of the precipitate involved might be employed advantageously. Similarly, a positive variation linked to the sample size in a gravimetric procedure could indicate that the desired precipitate is retaining some other component and thus is not pure.

When an apparently random error is encountered it may be a systematic error linked to some experimental condition not yet investigated or controlled. For example, an apparently random error could ultimately prove to be associated with variations in atmospheric humidity, perhaps indicating that the sample is adsorbing water during the weighing process.

Systematic errors tend to make the observed or calculated values consistently too high or too low. This means that systematic errors can make results highly inaccurate without affecting the precision of replicate results. Good precision does not necessarily mean good accuracy. The danger of retaining one-sided errors without recognizing their presence can be minimized by varying at least some experimental factors in replicate experiments. When three or four portions of the same sample are to be analyzed, they should vary to a modest but appreciable extent in weight. In critical analyses, duplicate sets of samples should be analyzed by entirely different methods since it is unlikely that the same systematic errors would appear to the same extent in entirely different analytical procedures.

Random Errors. The cause of a random error may or may not be known. Some personal judgment is required in all measurements, such as in reading instrument dials or meters, noting just when a container is filled to a predetermined calibration mark, and so forth; and random inaccuracies are bound to occur. Some random errors arise within the method itself, such as impurity of a supposedly pure precipitate, variations with stirring and with speed of mixing reagents, and so on. Random variations in room temperature and other environmental factors may introduce random error into analytical results.

The analytical chemist can and should minimize random errors insofar as is feasible by careful work, by choice of schemes of analysis which have been or can be proven to be valid, and by keeping environmental factors as constant as possible. However, residual random errors remain even when all reasonable efforts are made to ensure careful and accurate work.

A mathematical analysis of this type of error provides two criteria for the recognition of random errors: (1) small deviations from the correct value

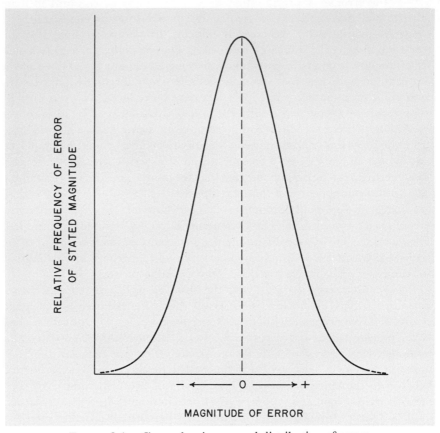

FIGURE 3-1.   Curve showing normal distribution of errors.

are much more frequent than large ones; (2) positive and negative deviations of equal magnitude occur with about the same frequency. These two criteria are expressed graphically in Figure 3-1, which shows the normal distribution of the errors in a large number of runs of a determination which is ideally perfect except for random errors. The characteristic distribution of errors, particularly as expressed in criterion 2, suggests that if a large number of determinations is made of the same quantity and if the measurement is affected only by random errors, the average of all the values should indicate directly the correct value. Even when relatively few measurements are made, the average provides a more reliable estimate of the correct value than does any one of the individual determinations, assuming that only random errors are present. The quantitative treatment of averages and of measures of precision and accuracy will be discussed in the next section of this chapter with further reference to the normal distribution curve of Figure 3-1.

STATISTICAL TREATMENT OF DATA

Every student of quantitative analysis must develop a working familiarity with a few fundamental statistical concepts. In order to recognize errors and to minimize their effects upon the final result, the analyst must run each determination more than once, usually in triplicate or quadruplicate. Then he must combine the results of these replicate experiments to yield his answer for the determination. Statistical methods are employed in combining and in interpreting these replicate measurements.

Average.   The average is defined as a measure of central tendency. There are several methods of expressing the central tendency. However, one method is the simplest and at the same time about the best from a theoretical standpoint. This is the **arithmetic mean,** commonly called by the more general term **average.** It is obtained by adding the replicate results and dividing by the number of those results. Consider the following four results of the determination of chloride in a simple salt mixture:

$$22.64\% \text{ Cl}$$
$$22.54\% \text{ Cl}$$
$$22.61\% \text{ Cl}$$
$$22.53\% \text{ Cl}$$
$$\text{the sum is } \overline{90.32\% \text{ Cl}}$$

The arithmetic mean, or average, is $\dfrac{90.32\% \text{ Cl}}{4}$ or 22.58 per cent Cl.

Deviation.   The average, as the measure of central tendency, is very important, but it does not in itself indicate all the information which can be derived from a series of numerical results. The extent of the variations from this average is also of considerable interest. The variation of a single value from the average may be expressed simply as the difference between the two, and this difference is designated the **deviation.** Thus, if X_1, X_2, and X_3 represent the several numerical values and $\overline{X}$ represents the arithmetic mean calculated as described in the preceding paragraph, the several deviations $(d_1, d_2, \text{ and } d_3)$ are

$$d_1 = X_1 - \overline{X}$$
$$d_2 = X_2 - \overline{X}$$
$$d_3 = X_3 - \overline{X}$$

It is conventional to subtract the arithmetic mean from the specific value, as indicated, and not vice versa. Thus, the deviation is positive if the one experimental value is greater than the arithmetic mean and negative if the arithmetic mean is greater. The algebraic sum of all the deviations in a set must equal zero, at least within the close limits set by rounding off numbers — a consequence of the definition of the arithmetic mean. The individual deviations may be expressed either in absolute units or in relative units. For example, the deviation of the weight 11 gm from the weight 10 gm is one in absolute units of grams, and it is one part in 10 in relative units. The latter may also be expressed as 10 per cent or as 100 parts per thousand.

Average deviation and standard deviation. The chemist is interested not just in averages and individual deviation values. He also needs a single number whereby he can represent the overall deviation within a series of replicate results. This overall deviation is actually the precision. There are several methods of expressing precision numerically, but only two will be mentioned here — the average deviation and the standard deviation.

The **average deviation,** $\bar{d}$, of an individual result is the arithmetic mean of the individual deviations, disregarding the + and − signs on each individual deviation. The **standard deviation,** s, of an individual result is the square root of the arithmetic mean of the squares of the individual deviations. These two definitions may be expressed mathematically as

$$\bar{d} = \frac{d_1 + d_2 + d_3 + \cdots}{n}$$

$$s = \sqrt{\frac{d_1{}^2 + d_2{}^2 + d_3{}^2 + \cdots}{n - 1}}$$

in which d_1, d_2, and d_3 are the individual deviations and n is the number of individual deviations. Consider the following illustrative data:

% Cl	d	d^2
22.64	+0.06	0.0036
22.54	−0.04	0.0016
22.61	+0.03	0.0009
22.53	−0.05	0.0025
90.32	0.18	0.0086

$$\text{average} = \frac{90.32}{4} \qquad \bar{d} = \frac{0.18}{4} \qquad s = \sqrt{\frac{0.0086}{4 - 1}}$$

$$\text{average} = 22.58 \qquad \bar{d} = 0.04 \qquad s = \quad 0.05$$

Obviously, it is easier to calculate the average deviation, $\bar{d}$, than to calculate the standard deviation, s. Nevertheless, there are valid theoretical reasons why the standard deviation is a better measure of the overall deviation, so it is much more widely used.

Confidence Limits.   In order for us to recognize more fully the true significance of the arithmetic mean and the standard deviation, we must refer again to the curve of Figure 3-1. This curve, which may be derived mathematically, represents the normal distribution of the errors or deviations in a large number of runs of a determination which is ideally perfect except for random errors. It has already been pointed out that small deviations are much more frequent than large ones. This latter statement may be made quantitative with the use of the standard deviation. The mathematical treatment from which the curve is derived reveals, for example, that 68 per cent of the individual deviations are less than the standard deviation, that 95 per cent are less than twice the standard deviation, and that 99 per cent are less than 2.5 times the standard deviation. In other words, 68 per cent of the X values fall within the range of $\overline{X} \pm s$, 95 per cent within the range $\overline{X} \pm 2s$, and 99 per cent within the range $\overline{X} \pm 2.5s$.

Data which can be interpreted strictly in terms of the normal distribution curve or on its mathematical origins do not generally arise in most analytical situations. There are two reasons for this fact: the derivation specifies random errors only, whereas many analytical data are influenced by one-sided, systematic errors as well; the derivation specifies a large number of runs (actually an infinite number) whereas only relatively small numbers of runs are feasible in practical situations. Because of the first reason, one-sided, systematic errors must be eliminated before the concept of confidence limits (to be described shortly) can become applicable. As a consequence of the second reason, the analyst can never know with absolute certainty whether his arithmetic mean is the absolutely correct value unless he does run an extremely large number of determinations. Even with a few determinations, however, he can specify a range of values centered upon his arithmetic mean and then state that there is a 50-50 chance, 95 chances out of 100, 99 chances out of 100, or any other desired probability that the true value does lie within that range. That is, he can know and specify the probability that the true answer lies within a given range, and he can indicate that range in terms of the arithmetic mean and the standard deviation. That range is designated as the **confidence limit,** and the likelihood that the true value lies within that range is designated the **probability.** The probability is conveniently expressed in percentage units.

Statistical data are listed in Table 3-1 from which the confidence limits may be ascertained for practical analytical situations. The number of replicate determinations is represented by n, and f_{50}, f_{95}, and f_{99} are the factors by which the standard deviation of an individual result must be multiplied to yield the confidence limits for 50, 95, and 99 per cent probability, respectively, in the form $\overline{X} \pm fs$. Thus, the analyst may conclude that the true value lies within the range $\overline{X} \pm f_{50}s$ and he has a 50-50 chance of being correct, or he may state the true value lies within the range $\overline{X} \pm f_{95}s$ and be 95 per cent certain of being correct.

The use of Table 3-1 may be illustrated by continuing the example used earlier in this chapter. Four results of a chloride determination yielded an arithmetic mean (X) of 22.58 per cent Cl with a standard deviation (s) of 0.05 units. From Table 3-1, for n = 4, f_{50} is 0.38; so there is a 50-50 likelihood that the true value lies within the range 22.58 $\pm$ (0.38 $\times$ 0.05) per cent Cl, or 22.58 $\pm$ 0.02 per cent Cl. Similarly, there is a 95 per cent probability

TABLE 3-1. FACTORS FOR CALCULATING
CONFIDENCE LIMITS

n	f_{50}	f_{95}	f_{99}
2	0.72	9.0	45.
3	0.47	2.5	5.7
4	0.38	1.6	2.9
5	0.33	1.2	2.1
6	0.30	1.0	1.6
10	0.22	0.72	1.0
20	0.15	0.47	0.64

With n individual values for calculating the average, $\overline{X}$, the true value may be expected to lie within the range $\overline{X} \pm f s$ with a % probability as indicated by the f subscript.

that the true value lies within the range 22.58 $\pm$ 0.08 per cent Cl, and a 99 per cent probability that it is 22.58 $\pm$ 0.14 per cent Cl. It is clear from this example, and from the table, that the limits must be widened as the required probability of being correct is increased. It is also evident from the table that the importance of each additional trial beyond three or four diminishes as the total number n increases. These factors are in keeping with common sense — statistical concepts should be considered as a means of putting common sense on a quantitative foundation, but not as a substitute for common sense itself.

The probability value used in expressing the results of an analytical determination is quite arbitrary. In any case, the probability chosen should be stated or otherwise indicated. Probabilities of 95 and 99 per cent are most commonly employed in analytical work, whereas a 50 per cent probability is also useful in student work. Therefore, 50, 95, and 99 per cent data are included in Table 3-1, although other probabilities could be used and occasionally are. In view of these concepts, it is not good practice for a student to report his results for a particular determination as, say, 22.58 per cent Cl; it is much better form to report it as, say, "22.58 $\pm$ 0.02 per cent Cl, with a 50 per cent probability level." Consult your professor for instructions as to what probability form is to be used in reporting results from your laboratory work.

Rejection of an Observation.   Every student of quantitative analysis is occasionally confronted with a series of results of replicate determinations, one of which appears to be far out of line with the others. Even experienced analytical chemists encounter the same situation. Consider the series of results:

22.64 % Cl
22.54 % Cl
22.22 % Cl
22.69 % Cl

The third value appears to be out of line. If this third determination were subject to an obvious large one-sided error, such as the spilling of some precipitate prior to weighing it, the result could immediately be rejected prior to computing the arithmetic mean and confidence limits. However, in a small series of data such as this, all four values *could* be valid for ascertaining the arithmetic mean. The beginning student is perhaps too greatly inclined to discard a datum which does not seem to agree with the body of his measurements, so it is apparent that some standard criterion for such rejection is necessary.

First, any value may be rejected if a particular reason for its inaccuracy is known. If it is known that part of a precipitate was spilled or that a volumetric container leaked, that result may be discarded at once. Sometimes such a determination need not even be completed. Other times, the analyst may suspect that a specific error may have arisen in one sample in a determination but he may not be certain at the time. If such is the case, he

TABLE 3-2. FACTORS FOR RETENTION OR REJECTION OF EXTREME VALUES

n	Critical Values of R_1/R_2	
	At 95% Probability Level	**At 99% Probability Level**
3	16.9	83.3
4	4.3	9.0
5	2.8	4.6
6	2.3	3.3
8	1.9	2.4
10	1.7	2.1

should complete that sample and then discard the result if it appears particularly erroneous in the proper direction. Second, if no experimental reason for rejection is known but a value still appears out of line, some statistical test must be employed before deciding whether to reject an observation. A simple and statistically valid test is based upon the differences between the highest and lowest values as calculated both with and without the suspicious value. Let R_1 be the difference between the highest and lowest values with all values included, and let R_2 be the difference between the highest and lowest values excluding the suspicious one. If the ratio R_1/R_2 *exceeds* the critical value listed for the appropriate n number in Table 3-2, the suspected observation should be rejected; otherwise, it should be retained. For each n value, there are two critical R_1/R_2 ratios listed in Table 3-2: one for the 95 per cent probability level and one for the 99 per cent probability level. When the 95 per cent column is used, the chance of an extreme value being rejected when it should have been retained is 5 per cent, whereas there is only a 1 per cent chance that a value rejected on the basis of the 99 per cent column should really have been retained. Consider again these four values: 22.64 per cent Cl, 22.54 per cent Cl, 22.22 per cent Cl, and 22.69 per cent Cl. R_1 is (22.69 − 22.22) or 0.47 and R_2 is (22.69 − 22.54) or 0.15. The ratio R_1/R_2

is 0.47/0.15 or 3.1. The critical values from Table 3-2 are greater than 3.1, so the value should be retained. Consider next these four values: 22.64, 22.69, 22.65, and 22.22. Here, R_1 is 0.47 and R_2 is 0.05, excluding the 22.22 value; R_1/R_2 is 9.4, which is even greater than the 99 per cent factor in Table 3-2, so the 22.22 result can be rejected with less than a 1 per cent chance of one's making a mistake in doing so.

It is suggested that the 99 per cent probability column of Table 3-2 be employed in student work in deciding whether to reject an observation, unless your professor instructs you differently. In any case, you should recognize, even quantitatively, what the residual chances are that a rejected value should have been retained.

If more than one value is doubtful, this test can be repeated after the most extreme value has been rejected. This is not ordinarily recommended, however. If two values are doubtful in a series of only four or so, it would be much better to repeat the whole experiment to obtain more values. It should be noted that the effect upon the arithmetic mean of one or even two discordant values is relatively less significant when there are many values than when there are only a few.

Comparison of Averages. The student in quantitative analysis is called upon to employ in his laboratory work the statistical concepts described thus far in this chapter. He is not usually called upon to compare averages; yet this operation is of considerable importance in the final interpretation and use of the data obtained in the analytical laboratory. Consider the example of some determinations of the density of nitrogen which were performed in the laboratory of Lord Rayleigh in 1894. Batches of nitrogen were prepared by various means from the chemical compounds NO, N_2O, and NH_4NO_2 and also from dry, carbon dioxide-free air by several methods of removing oxygen. Measurements of the mass of nitrogen required to fill a certain flask under specified conditions revealed for 10 batches of "chemical nitrogen" an arithmetic mean of 2.29971 gm, and for nine batches of "atmospheric nitrogen" an arithmetic mean of 2.31022 gm. The overall standard deviation within each group can be considered to be about 0.00030. A question arose: Was there a significant difference between the two averages? That is, was the density of the "chemical nitrogen" the same as that of the "atmospheric nitrogen" or, more basically, was nitrogen from both sources the same?

We can answer this question on the basis of the **t test** for comparing averages. This test will be presented empirically here along with recognition of its statistical validity. The quantity t is defined as

$$t = \frac{\bar{x} - \bar{y}}{s} \sqrt{\frac{nm}{n + m}}$$

in which $\bar{x}$ and $\bar{y}$ are the two averages, m and n are the number of individual values averaged to obtain $\bar{x}$ and $\bar{y}$, respectively, and s is the overall standard deviation. The larger average is conventionally taken as $\bar{x}$ and the smaller average as $\bar{y}$. Critical t values at 95 and 99 per cent probability levels are listed in Table 3-3. The phrase *degrees of freedom* is a common statistical term which is simply n + m − 2 in this application. If an observed or calculated t *exceeds* the indicated critical t value, the chances are 95 out of 100 or 99 out of 100 (depending upon which critical t value of Table 3-3 is used) that the averages are significantly different.

TABLE 3-3. CRITICAL t VALUES FOR COMPARISON OF AVERAGES

D.F.	Critical t Value at	
	95% Probability Level	99% Probability Level
1	12.7	63.7
2	4.3	9.9
3	3.2	5.8
4	2.8	4.6
5	2.6	4.0
6	2.5	3.7
8	2.3	3.4
10	2.3	3.2
15	2.1	2.9
20	2.1	2.8

(D. F., degrees of freedom, is n + m − 2.)

The t value for the nitrogen data may be calculated as follows:

$$t = \frac{\bar{x} - \bar{y}}{s} \sqrt{\frac{nm}{n + m}}$$

$$t = \frac{2.31022 - 2.29971}{0.00030} \sqrt{\frac{10 \times 9}{10 + 9}}$$

$$t = 76$$

From Table 3-3, the limiting values of t with D.F. = 17 (n + m − 2) arc far less than 76, even at the 99 per cent probability level. (No critical values are listed for D.F. = 17, but they would logically lie between those for D.F. = 15 and 20.) So the "chemical nitrogen" and the "atmospheric nitrogen" are almost certainly different. Lord Rayleigh, employing a somewhat different but comparable statistical test, recognized this difference; and this fact led directly to the discovery shortly thereafter of the so-called inert gases in the atmosphere!

A further example should be in order. Consider four gravimetric determinations of chloride in a particular sample yielding the arithmetic mean, 20.44% Cl, and four volumetric determinations of chloride in the same sample yielding the arithmetic mean 20.54 per cent Cl, both with standard deviations of about 0.08. Are the results of the gravimetric and volumetric methods significantly different? The t test provides the answer.

$$t = \frac{\bar{x} - \bar{y}}{s} \sqrt{\frac{nm}{n+m}}$$

$$t = \frac{20.54 - 20.44}{0.08} \sqrt{\frac{4 \times 4}{4+4}}$$

$$t = 1.77$$

The critical t values for D.F. = 6 (n + m − 2) are 2.5 and 3.7 at the two listed probability levels, so there is no statistical justification for concluding that the two averages are significantly different.

It has been assumed in both examples that the standard deviations are about the same for both averaged sets of data. If the standard deviations differ by more than a factor of two or so, the s value in the equation for t must be a properly weighted combination of the two standard deviations, in which case the t test is more complex. No further consideration will be given to this point in this book. If the t test leads to inconclusive results as, for example, if an observed t value lies between the 95 and 99 per cent critical t values, additional data are required to resolve the question of whether the two averages are significantly different. The t test is particularly useful in comparing two different analytical procedures for the same constituent (although here the standard deviations of the two may differ widely), in comparing test results by two different analysts or in two different laboratories or on two different days, and in establishing the identity of two samples.

STOICHIOMETRY CALCULATIONS

A stoichiometry calculation involves a relationship between the quantities of two substances: "How much of substance A reacts with, is formed by, or is chemically equivalent to a stated amount of substance B?" Most students using this book have already encountered stoichiometry calculations in previous courses. Therefore, this book does not include extensive discussions of problem solving in the chapters describing the various types of analytical methods. However, a brief review and discussion of methods of solving stoichiometry problems, together with several examples, are presented in this section.

The following four-step procedure may be used in making any stoichiometry calculation in quantitative chemical analysis.

STEP 1.   *Write the chemical equation or equations which relate the substances of interest.* Every stoichiometry problem is based upon one or more chemical reactions or chemical equivalencies, so the first step is to write the chemical equation or equations. It is not always necessary that the equations be complete, but the stoichiometric relationship between the particular substances of interest must be specified exactly.

STEP 2. *Write a mathematical equation expressing, in terms of moles, the relationship between the substances of interest.* From the chemical equation, one may directly write an arithmetical equation relating, in moles, the amounts of the substances of interest. In every case, the arithmetical equation takes the general form

$$\text{moles of substance A} = \text{moles of substance B} \times \text{mole ratio}$$

where the mole ratio is derived directly from the balanced chemical equation which relates substances A and B.

STEP 3. *Insert appropriate dimensional units for each mole quantity.* The term **mole** is a shortened form of the longer term **gram molecular weight.** However, it is entirely proper to use the term not only for substances which exist as molecules but also for substances which appear in reaction equations as ions, ionic compounds, and even as parts of ions or molecules. Hence, in defining and using the mole we prefer to employ the more general concept of formula weight rather than molecular weight.

When one of the substances involved in a stoichiometry calculation is either known or sought in weight units, the number of moles of that substance in the equation of step 2 may be expressed in units of *grams per formula weight.*

$$\text{moles} = \frac{\text{grams}}{\text{formula weight}}$$

Frequently, a substance of interest is present as an ion or molecule in solution, so the quantity of that substance is more conveniently given in volume units. The number of moles may be calculated from the relation

$$\text{moles} = M \times V$$

where M and V are, respectively, the molarity of the solution and its volume in liters. This equation is really only a mathematical definition of molarity, which is the number of moles of solute per liter of solution. Again, with certain reservations as indicated in the preceding chapter, it is usually possible to substitute formality in place of molarity as the unit of concentration.

These two arithmetical expressions for the number of moles of a particular substance, one in weight units and the other in volume units, suffice for most stoichiometry calculations in analytical chemistry. Occasionally it is also desirable to express moles in other dimensional units, such as quantity of electricity (coulombs).

STEP 4. *Substitute known numerical data and solve for the desired quantity.* The final step in a stoichiometry calculation is to substitute into the arithmetical equation resulting from step 3 all relevant numerical data which are available. This operation should result in one equation with only one unknown. Particular care must be exercised at this point in using proper units, making necessary conversions from milligrams to grams, from milliliters to liters, and so forth. Whenever a problem calls for a result in terms of percentage, it is usually assumed to be percentage by weight unless specified otherwise.

There are situations in which a single substance, A, reacts quantitatively with two other substances, B and C. Step 1 must include chemical equations for both reactions. The arithmetical equation obtained in step 2 is then of the general form

$$\text{moles A} = \text{moles B} \times (\text{mole ratio})_{AB} + \text{moles C} \times (\text{mole ratio})_{AC}$$

A number of stoichiometry problems, for which this four-step method is useful, are given at the end of this chapter.

Indirect Analysis

When determinations of two constituents of a sample are desired, a separate determination is generally performed for each. However, it is often possible to determine the percentage of each constituent by an indirect procedure in which two distinct determinations are made of the sum of the two constituents rather than one separate determination of each of them. There must be a different stoichiometry equation pertinent to each of the determinations, and the resultant mathematical equations must then be solved as simultaneous equations.

Consider for example the determinations of sodium ion and potassium ion in a mixture. It is quite difficult to accomplish a quantitative separation of these two species in order to determine each one separately. It is possible, however, to precipitate and weigh them together as sodium chloride and potassium chloride and, subsequently, to determine the total chloride content of the precipitate by titration with standard silver nitrate solution.

Example.   A precipitate known to contain only sodium chloride and potassium chloride was found to weigh 0.6542 gm. The solid was dissolved and titrated with $0.4494\,F$ silver nitrate solution, 20.02 ml being required. Calculate the weights of NaCl and KCl in the original precipitate.

From the weight information, we can write:

$$\text{grams NaCl} = 0.6542 - \text{grams KCl}$$

From the titration result, it follows that

$$\text{moles NaCl} + \text{moles KCl} = \text{moles AgNO}_3$$

$$\frac{\text{grams NaCl}}{\text{NaCl}} + \frac{\text{grams KCl}}{\text{KCl}} = F \times V$$

$$\frac{0.6542 - \text{grams KCl}}{58.44} + \frac{\text{grams KCl}}{74.56} = 0.4494 \times 0.02002$$

Solving this equation, we obtain

$$\text{grams KCl} = 0.5730$$
$$\text{grams NaCl} = 0.6542 - 0.5730 = 0.0812$$

It should be noted that, whether the complete analysis is performed by quantitative separation and direct determination of each component or by indirect analysis, there must be as many determinations as there are components to be determined. Furthermore, it can be shown by making the calculations for indirect analyses that much of the relative accuracy achieved in the measurements is often lost in the mathematical operations involved in the calculations. Therefore, indirect analysis is generally advisable only when quantitative separation and direct analysis are not feasible.

QUESTIONS AND PROBLEMS

1. Define and illustrate each of the following terms: significant figures, precision, accuracy, systematic error, random error, average, deviation, standard deviation, confidence limits, absolute uncertainty, relative uncertainty, t test, indirect analysis.
2. What is meant by the expressions "50 per cent probability" and "100 per cent probability"?
3. The following results were obtained for replicate determinations of the percentage of chloride in a solid chloride sample: 59.83, 60.04, 60.45, 59.88, 60.33, 60.24, 60.28, 59.77. Calculate (a) the arithmetic mean, (b) the standard deviation, and (c) the standard deviation in relative (per cent) units.
4. Assuming that the sample of problem 3 was pure sodium chloride, calculate the absolute and relative errors of the arithmetic mean.
5. The following determinations were made of the atomic weight of carbon: 12.0080, 12.0095, 12.0097, 12.0101, 12.0102, 12.0106, 12.0111, 12.0113, 12.0118, 12.0120. Calculate (a) the arithmetic mean and (b) the standard deviation, and (c) express the atomic weight of carbon on the basis of 99 per cent probability confidence limits.
6. A student found values of 39.17, 39.99, 39.21, and 37.72 per cent for the iron (Fe) content of an ore sample. (a) Should any result be rejected on statistical grounds? (b) What is the range of these results for 50 per cent probability confidence limits? If the correct percentage of iron is 39.33, what are the (c) absolute error and the (d) relative error in parts per thousand?
7. A laboratory technician obtained 0.0971, 0.0968, 0.0976, and 0.0984 in repeated measurements of the molarity of a solution. (a) Should any result be rejected on statistical grounds? (b) What is his range for 50 per cent confidence limits? (c) What is his range for 95 per cent confidence limits?
8. An iron determination by a gravimetric procedure yielded an average of 46.20 per cent iron (Fe) for six trials; and four trials according to a volumetric procedure gave an average of 46.02 per cent iron, the standard deviation being 0.08 per cent iron in each case. Is there a significant difference in the results obtained from the two methods?
9. The mass of a crucible was determined to be 18.2463 gm with a standard deviation of 0.0003 gm when weighed by 11 different students in one class, whereas eight students in another class obtained an average of 18.2466 gm with the same

standard deviation. Is there a significant difference in the results found by the two groups of students?

10. How many grams of calcium oxide are obtained when 2.469 gm of calcium carbonate is heated to remove carbon dioxide?

11. A hydrobromic acid solution is known to contain 49.8 per cent HBr and to have a density of 1.515 gm/ml. How many grams of silver nitrate are required to precipitate all the bromide in 250 ml of the hydrobromic acid solution?

12. A hydrochloric acid solution was purchased on the supposition that it contained 450 gm of HCl per liter. In order to check the specifications, a chemist diluted 10.00 ml of the original solution to 1.000 liter and subsequently determined that the resulting solution formed 0.1785 gm of silver chloride per 10.00 ml. By how many milligrams per milliliter was the original hydrochloric acid solution in error?

13. What volume of silver nitrate solution, containing 0.1000 mole of solid $AgNO_3$ per liter, is required to precipitate the bromide from 0.7700 gm of barium bromide $(BaBr_2)$?

14. Calculate the percentage of zinc (Zn) in an ore, 1.0762 gm of which yielded 0.7540 gm of zinc pyrophosphate $(Zn_2P_2O_7)$.

15. A commercial iron sample weighed 2.0019 gm. From this sample were obtained 0.1123 gm of silicon dioxide (SiO_2) and 0.0141 gm of barium sulfate $(BaSO_4)$. Calculate the percentages of sulfur (S) and silicon (Si) in the sample.

16. If a sample of commercial iron weighing 5.644 gm gave 0.0737 gm of magnesium pyrophosphate $(Mg_2P_2O_7)$, what is the percentage of phosphorus (P) in the sample?

17. A 0.9464 gm sample of a brass yielded 0.0837 gm of tin oxide (SnO_2) and 0.8064 gm of metallic copper. What are the percentages of tin (Sn) and copper (Cu) in this brass?

18. An organic compound is known to be $C_3H_5Cl_3$, $C_3H_6Cl_2$, or C_3H_7Cl. A 0.1582 gm sample of the compound was decomposed, and the chloride gave a silver chloride precipitate weighing 0.4016 gm. What is the percentage of chloride and which compound is it?

19. A mixture of potassium iodide and sodium chloride was converted to the potassium and sodium sulfates. The combined sulfate precipitate was found to weigh the same as the original mixture. Calculate the percentage of potassium iodide in the original mixture.

20. A mixture of only calcium carbonate and magnesium carbonate lost 48.00 per cent of its weight when converted to calcium and magnesium oxides. Calculate the percentage of each oxide in the ignited oxide residue.

21. In what proportion should calcium carbonate and barium carbonate be mixed so that the mixture will have the same percentage of carbon dioxide as pure strontium carbonate?

22. A mixture was known to contain only calcium carbonate, strontium carbonate, and barium carbonate. Carbon dioxide, evolved from the sample by heating, weighed 0.2875 gm. The calcium from the same sample was determined as anhydrous calcium oxalate which weighed 0.4357 gm. Finally, the barium from the same sample was precipitated as barium chromate which weighed 0.3853 gm. What were the weights of the three components in the mixture?

23. A sample contains sodium chloride, sodium bromide, sodium iodide, and possibly some inert impurities. A 5.000 gm sample is taken for analysis, dissolved, and the solution volume adjusted to exactly 500.0 ml. One 100 ml portion of the solution gave a precipitate of palladium iodide (PdI_2) weighing 0.2006 gm. A second 100 ml portion gave a precipitate weighing 1.9955 gm when treated with excess silver nitrate solution. When the latter precipitate was heated in a stream of chlorine gas to convert the silver halides into pure silver chloride, the resulting silver chloride weighed 1.6809 gm. Calculate the percentages of each sodium halide salt in the original sample.

24. How many milliliters of a $0.1000\,F$ hydrogen sulfide solution will react with 35.00 ml of $0.02800\,F$ potassium permanganate solution, according to the following reaction?

$$2\,MnO_4^- + 5\,H_2S + 6\,H^+ \rightarrow 2\,Mn^{++} + 5\,S + 8\,H_2O$$

25. To determine lead in an ore, the lead from a 0.6848 gm sample was first precipitated as lead chromate ($PbCrO_4$). The lead chromate precipitate was dissolved in an acid medium, and an excess of iodide was added. The mixture was then titrated with a sodium thiosulfate solution. The titration required 79.62 ml of a solution containing 17.98 gm of $Na_2S_2O_3\cdot5\,H_2O$ per liter. Calculate the percentage of lead in the ore sample.

26. A 1.000 gm sample of a pure oxide of an element (atomic weight of 50.94), containing 51.05 per cent of the element, was dissolved and reduced. The resulting solution required 20.42 ml of a $0.01667\,F$ potassium dichromate titrant to oxidize the element to its $+5$ state, the chromium being reduced to the $+3$ state in the process. Identify the oxidation state of the element in its reduced form prior to the titration.

27. The manganese in a 10.000 gm sample of steel was oxidized to permanganate and treated with 40.00 ml of $0.1000\,F$ ferrous sulfate solution in an acidic medium. Then 10.66 ml of a $0.006000\,F$ potassium permanganate solution was required to titrate the excess iron(II), according to the reaction

$$MnO_4^- + 5\,Fe^{++} + 8\,H^+ \rightarrow Mn^{++} + 5\,Fe^{+++} + 4\,H_2O$$

Calculate the percentage of manganese in the steel sample.

28. A sample of a mixture of oxalic acid dihydrate ($H_2C_2O_4\cdot2\,H_2O$) and anhydrous sodium oxalate ($Na_2C_2O_4$) was dissolved in 1.000 liter of water. A 25.00 ml aliquot of this solution required 25.37 ml of $0.1064\,F$ sodium hydroxide to titrate both protons of the oxalic acid. Another 25.00 ml aliquot, after being acidified, was titrated with 37.43 ml of $0.02746\,F$ potassium permanganate solution. Calculate the weights of oxalic acid dihydrate and sodium oxalate in the original sample.

SUGGESTIONS FOR ADDITIONAL READING

Books

1. E. L. Bauer: *A Statistical Manual for Chemists*, Academic Press, New York, 1960.
2. C. A. Bennett and N. L. Franklin: *Statistical Analysis in Chemistry and the Chemical Industry*, John Wiley & Sons, Inc., New York, 1954.
3. W. J. Dixon and F. J. Massey: *Introduction to Statistical Analysis*, second edition, McGraw-Hill Book Company, New York, 1957.
4. H. A. Laitinen: *Chemical Analysis*, McGraw-Hill Book Company, New York, 1960.
5. E. B. Wilson, Jr.: *An Introduction to Scientific Research*, McGraw-Hill Book Company, New York, 1952.
6. W. J. Youden: *Statistical Methods for Chemists*, John Wiley & Sons, Inc., New York, 1951.

Papers

1. W. J. Blaedel, V. W. Meloche, and J. A. Ramsay: A comparison of criteria for the rejection of measurements. J. Chem. Ed., *28*, 643 (1951).
2. R. B. Dean and W. J. Dixon: Simplified statistics for small numbers of observations. Anal. Chem., *23*, 636 (1951).
3. R. A. Johnson: Indeterminate error estimates from small groups of replicates. J. Chem. Ed., *31*, 465 (1954).

Chapter Four

Chemical Equilibrium

A majority, but definitely not all, of the reactions encountered in the separation and determination of chemical species are alike in at least one respect. This common characteristic is that the chemical interactions which are important to the success of each technique usually proceed or can be made to proceed rapidly compared to the time scale of the experimental operations themselves. There are two significant reasons why fast chemical reactions are highly desirable for separations and measurements in analytical chemistry.

First is the matter of convenience and practicality. Although the interactions between acids and bases, reactions leading to the formation of precipitates or complex ions, and redox processes are all typically fast, the occurrence of a slow reaction in a proposed method of separation or analysis may limit the number of determinations which can be accomplished in a given amount of time or may prevent the use of that method of separation or analysis altogether. In addition, a slow reaction may seriously affect the accuracy and precision of a given determination. For example, the separation of a substance through its selective extraction into a water-immiscible solvent could be impractical if the rate of transfer of this species from an aqueous phase into the nonaqueous phase is slow. Similarly, the performance of repetitive extractions for such a separation would be most unattractive. As a second example, consider the titration of an acid with a standard sodium hydroxide solution. The feasibility of this titrimetric method of analysis depends upon how rapidly the acid and base react with each other. If the acid and base happen to react very slowly, the required waiting time between successive additions of titrant may be discouragingly long. Furthermore, it would be difficult, if not impossible, to locate the equivalence point of the titration, so the accuracy and precision of the determination would suffer.

The second reason why fast reactions are so desirable for separations and measurements in analytical chemistry is the major subject of this chapter. Rapid reactions lead to the almost instantaneous attainment of a state of chemical equilibrium. The virtue of an equilibrium state is that rigorous equations govern the concentrations (activities) of all reactant and product species involved in a chemical system. Therefore, it is possible to calculate and predict with considerable reliability, first, what these equilibrium concentrations should be for any given set of initial conditions and, second, whether these equilibrium concentrations will permit one to achieve the separation or measurement of the desired substance. Parenthetically, it should be emphasized that it is much more difficult to establish the rate of a chemical reaction than it is to calculate the concentrations of species when a state of equilibrium prevails. Throughout much of this chapter, we shall consider chemical equilibria and the concepts of concentration, activity, and activity coefficient pertaining to solubility, acid-base, and complex-formation reactions in analytical chemistry.

KINETIC AND THERMODYNAMIC CONCEPTS OF EQUILIBRIUM

Before we place chemical equilibrium on a firm mathematical foundation, it is worthwhile to examine qualitatively some of the characteristics of chemical systems in order to see what an equilibrium state is and how to recognize that a system has reached such a state of equilibrium.

Let us consider the reaction between iron(III) and iodide ion,

$$2\ Fe^{+++} + 3\ I^- \rightleftharpoons 2\ Fe^{++} + I_3^-$$

to form iron(II) and triiodide. This reaction is a much used example in discussions of chemical equilibrium, perhaps because the equilibrium constant has a value such that significant concentrations of all four species — iron(III), iodide, iron(II), and triiodide — can coexist in the same solution. Suppose that a reaction mixture containing 0.200 M iron(III) and 0.300 M iodide ion is prepared and that we wish to determine *when* and *if* chemical equilibrium is established. As the reaction proceeds in the forward direction, the concentrations of iron(III) and iodide will diminish and, simultaneously, the concentrations of iron(II) and triiodide will build up. If we follow the increase in the triiodide concentration as a function of time, by observing, for example, the intensity of the characteristic yellow-orange color of this species, the concentration of triiodide reaches a maximum value of 0.0866 M and any further net formation of triiodide ceases within a fraction of a second

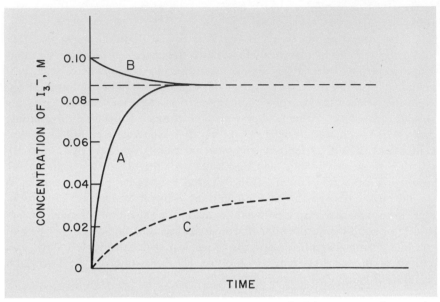

FIGURE 4-1.   Hypothetical rate of change of triiodide concentration as the reaction

$$2\ Fe^{+++} + 3\ I^- \rightleftharpoons 2\ Fe^{++} + I_3^-$$

approaches a state of equilibrium. Curve A: approach to equilibrium in the *forward* direction, the initial concentrations of iron(III) and iodide being 0.200 and 0.300 M, respectively, and no iron(II) or triiodide being initially present. Curve B: approach to equilibrium in the *backward* direction, the initial concentrations of iron(II) and triiodide being 0.200 and 0.100 M, respectively, and no iron(III) or iodide being present originally. The horizontal, dashed line indicates the equilibrium triiodide concentration of 0.0866 M. Curve C: approach to equilibrium in the *forward* direction, showing that, if the rate of reaction is slow, one may conclude erroneously that equilibrium has been reached long before the true state of equilibrium is attained. (See text for discussion.)

(curve A of Fig. 4-1). Therefore, on the basis of the observation that no detectable change in the triiodide concentration occurs after this time, one is tempted to conclude that equilibrium has been established.

However, such a conclusion is invalid unless the same final concentration of triiodide ion is approached when reaction occurs in the reverse direction, that is, when only iron(II) and triiodide are initially present. Accordingly, we must prepare a solution of 0.200 M iron(II) and 0.100 M triiodide, being certain that the *total* amounts of iron and iodine are identical to those in the preceding experiment, and study the changes in the concentrations of the four species. If, as before, the intensity of the yellow-orange color of triiodide is monitored to indicate the progress of the reaction, the triiodide concentration is found to decrease rapidly, although exponentially, to a value of 0.0866 M, as shown in curve B of Figure 4-1. Since there is no decrease in the triiodide concentration below this value and since the final state of the system appears to be independent of the direction of reaction, we can now assert that chemical equilibrium has been definitely attained. To point out the fact that the rate of approach to equilibrium from the two opposite directions is usually different, curves A and B in Figure 4-1 have been purposely drawn so that equilibrium is reached somewhat more rapidly from the forward direction than from the backward direction. However, depending upon the initial concentrations of the various species, equilibrium could be attained more quickly from the backward direction.

It is important to stress that the absence of a detectable change in the concentrations of reactants and products does not constitute by itself a criterion for the state of chemical equilibrium. Some familiar reactions proceed toward equilibrium at such an infinitesimally slow rate that no variations in the concentrations occur even after long periods of time. For example, a two-to-one mixture of hydrogen and oxygen gases should combine to form water,

$$2\ H_2 + O_2 \rightleftharpoons 2\ H_2O$$

the position of equilibrium lying so far to the right that virtually no unreacted hydrogen or oxygen should remain. Nevertheless, in the absence of a catalyst such as spongy platinum, the reaction does not proceed at any measurable rate; yet the mixture of gases cannot be regarded as the true equilibrium state of the system. Therefore, one should always verify the existence of true chemical equilibrium by showing that the same equilibrium state is reached from two directions. Such a procedure is mandatory whenever a chemical system is being investigated for the first time, but proof that this procedure is worthwhile for the iron(III)-iodide reaction can be seen from the following arguments. If the rate of the forward reaction had been relatively slow, the triiodide concentration might have increased only gradually as shown by curve C in Figure 4-1. Furthermore, if the rate of the forward reaction was sufficiently slow — and the technique employed to observe changes in the triiodide concentration was not too sensitive — one might decide that the triiodide concentration was not changing after a certain time and, thus, conclude erroneously that equilibrium had been attained at some point along curve C long before the triiodide concentration ever reached 0.0866 M. Fortunately, this error need not arise when equilibrium is approached from opposite directions, since any difference in the apparent equilibrium states attained from the forward and backward directions would be recognized immediately.

Sometimes, when the forward and backward reactions are so slow that it is inconvenient to wait for true equilibrium to be established, one may attempt to extrapolate a set of experimental results to obtain the equilibrium state. Notice that curves A and B in Figure 4-1 both approach asymptotically a triiodide concentration of 0.0866 M. If one makes measurements of the triiodide concentration as a function of time for the forward and backward reactions and then plots the experimental data as in Figure 4-1, it may be feasible to extrapolate each curve to the equilibrium triiodide concentration, even though true equilibrium is never reached. In order for the extrapolation procedure to be meaningful, however, one must obtain data reasonably close to the equilibrium state so that the limiting slopes of the experimental curves can be accurately defined. Obviously, it would be useless to extrapolate two curves such as B and C in an effort to find the equilibrium triiodide concentration.

Experimental techniques employed to follow the progress of a chemical reaction toward equilibrium are extremely varied, but they do rely on the specific nature of the reactants and products as well as on the environment in which the reaction occurs. Above all, it is essential to select for observation or measurement a property of the chemical system which has a value at equilibrium distinctly different from that for any other state of the system. For the iron(III)-iodide equilibrium just discussed, the spectrophotometric measurement of the concentration of yellow-orange triiodide ion is especially suitable. In addition, iron(III) and iron(II) both exhibit characteristic absorption bands in the visible and ultraviolet regions of the electromagnetic spectrum which might serve as a means of following the iron(III)-iodide reaction. An alternate approach might involve measurement of the potential of a platinum indicator electrode versus a stable reference electrode, both electrodes being immersed into the reaction mixture. Theoretically, the value of this potential is governed by either the iron(III)-iron(II) concentration ratio or the triiodide-iodide concentration ratio. As the iron(III)-iodide reaction proceeded in the *forward* direction, the potential of the platinum indicator electrode would decrease with time until equilibrium was reached. Finally, measurements of the conductance of the solution as a function of time might show when equilibrium was attained, for the conductance of the solution would continue to change until equilibrium was established. Unfortunately, neither conductance nor potential happens to be a highly specific property of a system. Cations which accompany iodide and triiodide and anions which accompany iron(III) and iron(II) in the preparation of the original reaction mixture will contribute to the total conductance of the solution and possibly obscure the relatively small variation in conductance as the reaction proceeded towards equilibrium. The potential exhibited by a platinum indicator electrode is influenced by the presence of dissolved oxygen and other species, so it is all too likely that such a measurement might not provide an unambiguous indication of the attainment of equilibrium.

We shall now turn our attention from an essentially qualitative picture to a more formal mathematical representation of chemical equilibrium. Two theoretical approaches may be employed to derive a fundamental relation pertaining to the state of equilibrium. The first of these methods involves a consideration of reaction kinetics, and the second approach is based upon the concepts of thermodynamics.

Kinetic Approach to Equilibrium

Fundamentally, the rate of a chemical reaction depends on only two factors — the total number of collisions per unit time between the reacting species and the fraction of these collisions which is fruitful in accomplishing reaction. The fraction of collisions which is successful in promoting reaction is, in turn, dependent upon the temperature of the system as well as the presence of catalysts, but when such conditions are held constant, a reaction rate is simply a function of the total number of collisions per unit time between the reactants. If the number of these collisions doubles, the rate of the reaction is likewise doubled.

Consider the general reaction

$$A + B \longrightarrow C + D$$

in which a single species A collides with B to form one particle each of substances C and D. If the concentration of A is suddenly doubled, that is, if the number of A particles in a fixed volume is doubled, it is reasonable to expect that the number of collisions per unit time between A and B will momentarily double and that the rate of reaction will be doubled accordingly. Similarly, if the concentration of A is maintained constant and the concentration of B is doubled, the reaction rate will be doubled. Now, if the concentrations of both A and B are doubled, the number of collisions per unit time between A and B particles is quadrupled, so the rate of reaction is quadrupled. These considerations suggest that the rate or the velocity of the forward reaction, v_f, may be expressed by the equation

$$v_f = k_f[A][B]$$

where k_f is the rate constant and the molar concentrations of A and B are represented by [A] and [B], respectively.*

This treatment may be extended to an even more general process,

$$aA + bB \longrightarrow cC + dD$$

where a, b, c, and d signify the stoichiometric numbers of particles of A, B, C, and D, respectively, which are involved in the completely balanced reaction. Reasoning similar to that of the preceding paragraph leads to the conclusion that the rate of the forward reaction can be written

$$v_f = k_f[A]^a[B]^b$$

In addition, this rate equation is a mathematical expression of the very important and widely applicable **law of mass action,** which states that the velocity or rate of a chemical reaction is proportional to the product of

---

* Although the true reaction mechanism may differ radically from the simple bimolecular process proposed here, equilibrium properties of a system do not depend on the pathway by which equilibrium is reached.

the concentrations of the reacting species, each concentration raised to a power equal to the number of molecules, atoms, or ions of each reactant which appears in the balanced equation for the reaction.

Most reactions of analytical interest are reversible — at least to a slight extent. Consequently, it is more correct to formulate the previous general reaction as

$$a\text{A} + b\text{B} \rightleftharpoons c\text{C} + d\text{D}$$

to indicate that the backward reaction between C and D has definite significance. Accordingly, the law of mass action is applicable to this backward reaction as well as to the forward process. The rates of the forward and backward reactions are expressible by the relations

$$v_f = k_f[\text{A}]^a[\text{B}]^b$$

and

$$v_b = k_b[\text{C}]^c[\text{D}]^d$$

where the subscripts f and b refer to the forward and backward processes, respectively. When A and B are first mixed with no C or D present, the reaction will proceed toward the right at a finite rate. As this forward reaction continues, the concentrations of A and B diminish, and the rate of the forward reaction, v_f, decreases. Initially, the rate of the backward reaction, v_b, is zero since neither C nor D is present. However, as the forward reaction proceeds, the concentrations of C and D build up, so the rate of the backward reaction begins to increase. Thus, v_f starts at its maximum value and continues to diminish, whereas, during the same time, v_b is initially zero but exhibits a steady increase. Sooner or later, however, the two rates become identical and the system is said to be in a **state of equilibrium.** Thereafter, the individual concentrations of A, B, C, and D remain constant. It must be emphasized that the forward and backward reactions do not stop but rather continue at equal rates. This means that the system is in a *dynamic* state of equilibrium, not a static one. The dynamic nature of equilibrium could be demonstrated, in principle, for any chemical system, but it is convenient to recall the iron(III)-iodide reaction. Suppose that we know, in advance, just one of the infinite number of sets of iron(III), iodide, iron(II), and triiodide concentrations corresponding to the state of chemical equilibrium, and suppose we mix solutions of the four species together in such a way that equilibrium prevails immediately at the start of the experiment. If we used a solution of radioactive iodide ion for the preparation of the equilibrium mixture, the radioiodine would eventually distribute itself randomly between triiodide and iodide ions, indicating that the forward and backward reactions

$$2\,\text{Fe}^{+++} + 3\,\text{I}^- \rightleftharpoons 2\,\text{Fe}^{++} + \text{I}_3{}^-$$

occur at equal rates, even though a state of chemical equilibrium was preserved throughout the experiment. On the other hand, if chemical equilibrium were a stationary state, all of the radioiodine would remain in the form of iodide ion.

By equating the rates of the forward and backward reactions, we may represent the equilibrium state mathematically as follows:

$$k_f[A]^a[B]^b = k_b[C]^c[D]^d$$

However, since the individual rate constants k_f and k_b are difficult to evaluate accurately, it is customary to rearrange this equation to obtain the familiar equilibrium-constant expression:

$$\frac{[C]^c[D]^d}{[A]^a[B]^b} = \frac{k_f}{k_b} = K$$

where K is called the **equilibrium constant** for the reaction of interest. Although the concentrations of the various species in the earlier generalized rate equations may assume any values, it is essential to note that the concentrations of A, B, C, and D appearing in the equilibrium-constant expression are the values which exist only at equilibrium. In addition, attention should be directed to the convention — originally chosen quite arbitrarily, but now a matter of international agreement — that the value of an equilibrium constant refers to the ratio in which the concentrations of the products of a reaction appear in the numerator and the concentrations of the reactants are in the denominator. With this convention in mind, one can frequently tell by glancing at the numerical magnitude of the equilibrium constant whether a reaction has a tendency to proceed far toward the right or whether it goes only slightly to the right before reaching equilibrium. Thus, for a reaction having a large K, equilibrium is usually attained only after the reaction has proceeded far to the right. Conversely, when K is small, equilibrium is reached before the reaction has gone very far toward the right.

Some words of caution should be interjected at this point. Although it is true that the magnitude of an equilibrium constant is a criterion by which to judge whether a chemical reaction has a pronounced or only a slight tendency to proceed from left to right as written, the initial concentrations of the reactants and products provide a second and equally important criterion for deciding the direction toward which a reaction will actually go. For example, it is definitely possible to write a chemical reaction which has a *very large* equilibrium constant, but which proceeds from *right to left* as written because the initial concentrations of species on the right-hand side of the balanced chemical equation happen to be much greater than the concentrations of substances on the left-hand side of the chemical equation. A chemical system we have already discussed, namely the iron(III)-iodide reaction,

$$2\ Fe^{+++} + 3\ I^- \rightleftharpoons 2\ Fe^{++} + I_3^-$$

illustrates these factors. The position of equilibrium for this reaction lies toward the right because the equilibrium constant is moderately large, so the formation of iron(II) and triiodide ion is favored. Nevertheless, curve B of Figure 4-1 clearly confirms that, if the original concentrations of iron(II) and triiodide are very large compared to the initial concentrations of iron(III) and iodide, reaction actually proceeds from *right to left*.

In conclusion of this section, it should be reëmphasized that the law of chemical equilibrium tells us absolutely nothing about either the rate or, once the state of equilibrium has been reached, the direction from which it was approached. It is highly significant that the characteristics of the state of equilibrium do not depend in any way on the detailed mechanism of the process whereby equilibrium is attained. No matter how complicated the mechanism of the reactions leading to equilibrium are, however, the equilibrium-constant expression can always be written after an inspection of the balanced chemical equation.

Thermodynamic Concept of Equilibrium

One of the fundamental laws of nature is that a physical or chemical system always tends to undergo a spontaneous and irreversible change from some initial, nonequilibrium state to a final equilibrium state. Furthermore, once a physical or chemical system reaches a state of equilibrium, no additional change will occur unless some new stress is placed upon the system.

In describing chemical equilibrium in thermodynamic terms, one must define a property of the chemical system which can be related to the concentrations of the various species involved in an equilibrium state. The thermodynamic parameter which is most useful in this respect is G, the **Gibbs free energy.** A chemical system which is initially in a nonequilibrium state will have a tendency to change spontaneously until the free energy for the system becomes minimal and the system itself is at equilibrium. It is strictly correct to speak only of a *tendency* for change to occur, since thermodynamics offers no information at all about the rate of a particular process. The driving force which causes a system to pass from an initial state to some final state is measured by the *free-energy change* for that process. In turn, the free-energy change is symbolized by dG when a system undergoes an infinitesimal change of state (or by ΔG when a system undergoes a larger or finite change of state) and is defined as the difference between the free energies of the final and initial states:

$$dG = G_{\text{final}} - G_{\text{initial}}$$

For most calculations, the differential form of the free-energy change, dG, is preferred. Sometimes the free-energy change is referred to as the *maximum amount of useful work or energy other than pressure-volume work* which can be obtained from a physical or chemical process. This latter definition is especially appropriate for the discussion in Chapter 12 concerning the behavior of batteries and other galvanic cells. However, our immediate concern is how to calculate the free-energy change for a particular reaction and how to relate free-energy change to chemical equilibrium.

According to the second law of thermodynamics, the free-energy change for a process in which the chemical composition of the system remains constant can be expressed by the differential equation

$$dG = -S\,dT + V\,dp$$

where dG represents the infinitesimal change in free energy, dT and dp denote small variations in temperature and pressure, respectively, S is the entropy, and V is the volume of the system.

If we intend to treat systems with changing composition, so that chemical reactions may be considered, additional terms are needed in the preceding equation. The thermodynamic relation which takes account of changes in the composition of a system due to chemical reaction is

$$dG = -S\,dT + V\,dp + \sum_i \left(\frac{\partial G_i}{\partial n_i}\right)_{T,p,n_j} \cdot dn_i$$

The last term on the right-hand side of this expression deserves a special explanation. Actually, it represents a *sum* of terms — one for each of the species involved in a reaction. The parameter inside the parentheses, $(\partial G_i/\partial n_i)_{T,p,n_j}$, gives, in effect, the change in free energy per mole of substance i added to or removed from the system when the temperature (T), the pressure (p), and the number of moles of *all* other species (n_j) are assumed to be constant. If $(\partial G_i/\partial n_i)_{T,p,n_j}$ is multiplied by dn_i, which is the number of moles of substance i added to or removed from the system, we then have the total change in free energy resulting from this addition or removal of i. Note that the sign of dn_i is positive if substance i is added to the system and negative if substance i is removed from the system. If we add dn_Y moles of substance Y and dn_Z moles of substance Z to a chemical system, a sum of terms which shows the change in free energy due to each substance must be written, i.e.,

$$\left[\left(\frac{\partial G_Y}{\partial n_Y}\right)_{T,p,n_Z} \cdot dn_Y + \left(\frac{\partial G_Z}{\partial n_Z}\right)_{T,p,n_Y} \cdot dn_Z\right]$$

Similarly, if one introduced five substances all at once into a given system, he would have to write the sum of five free-energy terms.

The chemical reactions in which we will be interested occur under conditions of constant temperature and pressure. Therefore, dT and dp are both zero, so we may conclude that

$$dG = \sum_i \left(\frac{\partial G_i}{\partial n_i}\right)_{T,p,n_j} \cdot dn_1$$

Furthermore, the term $(\partial G_i/\partial n_i)_{T,p,n_j}$ is usually called the **chemical potential** of species i and is designated by the symbol μ_i. Accordingly, for chemical equilibrium at constant temperature and pressure, the most useful form of the free-energy equation is

$$dG = \sum_i \mu_i \, dn_i$$

Suppose we have a solution in which the general reaction

$$aA + bB \rightleftharpoons cC + dD$$

has reached a state of chemical equilibrium, and suppose we assume this to be the *initial state* of the system. To a known volume of the solution, let us add infinitesimal amounts $a\epsilon$ and $b\epsilon$, respectively, of substances A and B. It is important to note that stoichiometric quantities, a and b, of these two species are added and that ϵ is an arbitrarily small number. Since the initial state of equilibrium is slightly disturbed, A and B will react with each other until chemical equilibrium is reëstablished. This new position of equilibrium may be regarded as the *final state* of the system, and the free-energy change for the process can be computed from the previous equation to be

$$dG = \mu_A \cdot a\epsilon + \mu_B \cdot b\epsilon$$

Imagine that, in a second experiment, we add $c\epsilon$ moles of substance C and $d\epsilon$ moles of substance D to a volume of the original solution identical to that employed in the first experiment. Again, after the initial state of chemical equilibrium is upset, a new equilibrium state will be established by the reaction between C and D. The free-energy change corresponding to this process is

$$dG = \mu_C \cdot c\epsilon + \mu_D \cdot d\epsilon$$

It is essential to recognize that the final state in each of these experiments is the same. The reason for this is that the amounts of A and B and of C and D added in the two hypothetical experiments were chosen to be stoichiometrically related to each other. Indeed, these two experiments bear a resemblance to those portrayed in Figure 4-1, except that in the present situation the system was at equilibrium in both the initial and final states. One of the properties of the Gibbs free energy is that the magnitude of the free-energy change for any process is completely independent of the path leading from the initial state to the final state. Therefore, we can equate the free-energy change for the two processes,

$$\mu_A \cdot a\epsilon + \mu_B \cdot b\epsilon = \mu_C \cdot c\epsilon + \mu_D \cdot d\epsilon$$

and cancel ϵ in each of the four terms in the expression to obtain

$$a\mu_A + b\mu_B = c\mu_C + d\mu_D$$

We can relate the chemical potential, μ_i, of an atomic, ionic, or molecular species to the **activity** or "effective" concentration, a_i, of that substance through the equation

$$\mu_i = \mu_i{}^\circ + RT \ln \frac{a_i}{a_i{}^\circ}$$

in which $\mu_i{}^\circ$ and $a_i{}^\circ$ represent the chemical potential and the activity, respectively, of substance i in its standard state, R is 1.987 calories mole^{-1} degree^{-1}, and T is the absolute temperature. In general, the activity, a_i, of a substance differs from its molar concentration. The activity of ionic solutes is affected by the presence of other ions in solution as well as by the dielectric constant of the solution, whereas concentration is independent of such factors. For example, in a solution containing a 0.1 M concentration of chloride ion, the activity or "effective" concentration of chloride may be less than, equal to, or greater than 0.1 M, depending on the nature of the solution itself. However, activity is often a more useful parameter than concentration, because the former takes into consideration all of the environmental factors which influence the true behavior of a substance. The symbols used to distinguish activity from molar concentration should be mentioned: The molar concentration of iodide ion is designated with square brackets, [I$^-$], whereas the activity of iodide may be written with parentheses, (I$^-$), or may be expressed as a_{I^-}.

The choice of **standard state** for a substance depends on whether it is a gaseous, liquid, solid, or solute species; however, all standard states pertain to a temperature of 298°K or 25°C. A gaseous substance, if ideal, exists in its standard state when present at a pressure of exactly 1 atm, whereas the standard state for a liquid or solid is taken to be the pure liquid or the pure solid, respectively, at a pressure of 1 atm. Dissolved or solute species, including electrolytes, nonelectrolytes, and individual ions, are in their standard states if their activities or "effective" concentrations are unity at a pressure of 1 atm. In fact, any gaseous, liquid, solid, or solute species is defined to have *unit activity* $(a_i{}^\circ = 1)$ in its standard state. Therefore, we can rewrite the last equation as

$$\mu_i = \mu_i{}^\circ + RT \ln a_i$$

If we substitute this relation into the expression,

$$a\mu_A + b\mu_B = c\mu_C + d\mu_D$$

we get

$$a\mu_A{}^\circ + aRT \ln a_A + b\mu_B{}^\circ + bRT \ln a_B$$
$$= c\mu_C{}^\circ + cRT \ln a_C + d\mu_D{}^\circ + dRT \ln a_D$$

When this equation is rearranged and the logarithmic terms are collected together, the result is

$$c\mu_C{}^\circ + d\mu_D{}^\circ - a\mu_A{}^\circ - b\mu_B{}^\circ = -RT \ln \frac{(a_C)^c (a_D)^d}{(a_A)^a (a_B)^b}$$

For the general chemical reaction

$$a\text{A} + b\text{B} \rightleftharpoons c\text{C} + d\text{D}$$

it is customary to define a **standard free-energy change,** $\Delta G°$, by means of the expression

$$\Delta G° = c\mu_C° + d\mu_D° - a\mu_A° - b\mu_B°$$

so we can write

$$\Delta G° = -RT \ln \frac{(a_C)^c(a_D)^d}{(a_A)^a(a_B)^b}$$

Finally, recognizing that the ratio of factors in the logarithmic term contains the *equilibrium* activities of all reactants and products involved in the preceding general chemical reaction, we may identify this ratio as a **thermodynamic equilibrium constant,** $\mathscr{K}$. Thus,

$$\frac{(a_C)^c(a_D)^d}{(a_A)^a(a_B)^b} = \mathscr{K}$$

and

$$\Delta G° = -RT \ln \mathscr{K}$$

The equilibrium constant K which we derived from a consideration of kinetics may appear to be different from the thermodynamic equilibrium constant $\mathscr{K}$. However, it should be pointed out that activities rather than molar concentrations could have been employed in the law of mass action and in the derivation of K, in which case the results of the kinetic and thermodynamic derivations would have been identical.

Thermodynamic Criterion for Chemical Reaction

In the preceding section of this chapter, we only considered chemical systems at equilibrium, that is, systems which were at equilibrium in both their initial and final states. Unfortunately, such a treatment is somewhat restrictive, because in analytical chemistry we almost invariably mix reagents together in such a way that the system is not initially at equilibrium. Of course, we anticipate for most reactions involved in chemical analysis that a final state of chemical equilibrium is rapidly reached. We shall now pose the following fundamental question: If arbitrary quantities of substances A, B, C, and D are brought together and if these species interact according to the reversible reaction

$$aA + bB \rightleftharpoons cC + dD$$

how may we correlate the free-energy change for this reaction with the direction, *forward* or *backward*, in which the reaction will actually proceed? The answer to this question can be obtained in several different ways, but only one approach will be used in the present discussion.

Let us begin by obtaining information about the quotient:

$$\left[\frac{(a_C)^c(a_D)^d}{(a_A)^a(a_B)^b}\right]_{actual}$$

Although this quantity resembles the expression for the thermodynamic equilibrium constant, it represents the *actual* ratio of the activities of the reactants and products, raised to appropriate powers, for any initial, non-equilibrium state. By using the fundamental relation

$$\mu_i = \mu_i{}^\circ + RT \ln a_i$$

or

$$RT \ln a_i = \mu_i - \mu_i{}^\circ$$

and applying it to each of the four species — A, B, C, and D — we can arrive in several steps at the result

$$RT \ln \left[\frac{(a_C)^c(a_D)^d}{(a_A)^a(a_B)^b}\right]_{actual} = (c\mu_C + d\mu_D - a\mu_A - b\mu_B)$$
$$- (c\mu_C{}^\circ + d\mu_D{}^\circ - a\mu_A{}^\circ - b\mu_B{}^\circ)$$

If it is recalled that

$$\Delta G^\circ = c\mu_C{}^\circ + d\mu_D{}^\circ - a\mu_A{}^\circ - b\mu_B{}^\circ$$

it follows that a more general relationship is

$$\Delta G = c\mu_C + d\mu_D - a\mu_A - b\mu_B$$

Substitution of the latter two equations into the preceding equation yields

$$RT \ln \left[\frac{(a_C)^c(a_D)^d}{(a_A)^a(a_B)^b}\right]_{actual} = \Delta G - \Delta G^\circ$$

This relation can be rearranged to the more familiar form

$$\Delta G = \Delta G^\circ + RT \ln \left[\frac{(a_C)^c(a_D)^d}{(a_A)^a(a_B)^b}\right]_{actual}$$

Frequently, this expression is written as

$$\Delta G = \Delta G^\circ + RT \ln \frac{(C)^c(D)^d}{(A)^a(B)^b}$$

which will be employed for the derivation of the Nernst equation in Chapter 12. Finally, since

$$\Delta G^\circ = -RT \ln \mathscr{K} = -RT \ln \left[\frac{(a_C)^c(a_D)^d}{(a_A)^a(a_B)^b}\right]_{equil}$$

we may write

$$\Delta G = -RT \ln \left[\frac{(a_C)^c(a_D)^d}{(a_A)^a(a_B)^b}\right]_{equil} + RT \ln \left[\frac{(a_C)^c(a_D)^d}{(a_A)^a(a_B)^b}\right]_{actual}$$

When we examine the significance of this relation with respect to the hypothetical reaction

$$aA + bB \rightleftharpoons cC + dD$$

three important conclusions can be drawn:

First, if

$$\left[\frac{(a_C)^c(a_D)^d}{(a_A)^a(a_B)^b}\right]_{actual} < \left[\frac{(a_C)^c(a_D)^d}{(a_A)^a(a_B)^b}\right]_{equil}$$

the reaction will proceed in the forward direction, A and B reacting to form C and D until equilibrium is established. The thermodynamic criterion for a reaction to occur from left to right, or in the forward direction, is that $\Delta G < 0$.

Second, if

$$\left[\frac{(a_C)^c(a_D)^d}{(a_A)^a(a_B)^b}\right]_{\text{actual}} > \left[\frac{(a_C)^c(a_D)^d}{(a_A)^a(a_B)^b}\right]_{\text{equil}}$$

the reaction will proceed in the backward direction, C and D reacting to form A and B until equilibrium is established. The thermodynamic criterion for a reaction to occur from right to left, or in the backward direction, is that $\Delta G > 0$.

Third, if

$$\left[\frac{(a_C)^c(a_D)^d}{(a_A)^a(a_B)^b}\right]_{\text{actual}} = \left[\frac{(a_C)^c(a_D)^d}{(a_A)^a(a_B)^b}\right]_{\text{equil}}$$

the system is already at equilibrium and no net reaction will occur. The thermodynamic criterion for a system to be at chemical equilibrium is that $\Delta G = 0$.

FACTORS WHICH INFLUENCE CHEMICAL EQUILIBRIUM

We assumed in the thermodynamic treatment of chemical equilibrium that reactions of analytical interest can be made to occur under conditions of constant pressure and temperature. Nevertheless, it is possible to calculate rigorously by the methods of thermodynamics what numerical change in an equilibrium constant results from variations in either of these parameters. However, useful qualitative and even semiquantitative predictions can frequently be made if one refers to tabulated equilibrium-constant data and if one knows how changes in temperature and pressure affect the position of chemical equilibrium. Rather than performing detailed thermodynamic calculations, we shall focus our attention on the latter aspect of equilibrium.

The principle of Le Châtelier enables the chemist to make qualitative predictions of the effects of specific variations upon a system at equilibrium, whereas the equilibrium constant itself provides a basis for quantitative considerations. **Le Châtelier's principle** may be stated in the general form: when a stress is applied to a system at equilibrium, the position of equilibrium tends to shift in such a direction as to diminish or relieve that stress.

Effect of Temperature.   Variations in temperature can produce substantial changes in the numerical values of equilibrium constants. Increasing the temperature of a system at equilibrium, in effect, supplies heat or thermal energy. The Le Châtelier principle predicts that the position of equilibrium will shift in such a way as to consume at least part of this extra thermal energy. That is, when the temperature is raised, an *endothermic* process (one which absorbs heat) is favored over an *exothermic* reaction (one in which heat is liberated). Therefore, if the forward reaction involved in the chemical equilibrium

$$aA + bB \rightleftharpoons cC + dD$$

is exothermic, a rise in temperature will favor the backward reaction and make the numerical value of the equilibrium constant smaller. Conversely, a drop in temperature favors the forward reaction and increases the value of the equilibrium constant. However, if the forward reaction is an endothermic process, the value of the equilibrium constant increases with a rise of temperature and decreases if the temperature drops.

Aside from its influence on the position of a chemical equilibrium, temperature has a pronounced effect on the rates of the forward and backward reactions involved in that equilibrium. Many reactions increase in rate by a factor of approximately two or three for every 10 degree rise in temperature. This increase in the rate of a chemical process arises because the number as well as the energy of collisions between reacting species is enhanced at elevated temperatures. However, it should be evident from the preceding paragraph that an increase in temperature does not affect the rates of the forward and backward reactions to the same extent. For example, we noted that a temperature increase will cause the equilibrium constant to become smaller if the forward reaction is exothermic. This means that a temperature rise must cause the rate constant, k_b, for the backward reaction to increase more rapidly than the rate constant, k_f, for the forward reaction, even though the magnitudes of both rate constants become larger.

Effect of Pressure. Changes in pressure may exert a considerable effect on the position of a chemical equilibrium — or almost none at all. For example, a rise in the pressure of a system in which the gas phase equilibrium

$$2 SO_2(g) + O_2(g) \rightleftharpoons 2 SO_3(g)$$

prevails would be expected to cause a marked increase in the corresponding equilibrium constant. Such a result is explicable on the basis of Le Châtelier's principle, interpreted for the present situation to state that *any increase in pressure favors a shift in the equilibrium position which tends to reduce the volume of the system.* Notice that 3 moles of reactants — 2 moles of sulfur dioxide and 1 mole of oxygen — combine to form 2 moles of sulfur trioxide. Whenever the pressure of a gas mixture increases, it is natural for the volume of the gas to decrease. Provided all three gases behave in a reasonably ideal manner, SO_3 will take up essentially two thirds of the volume occupied by the mixture of SO_2 and O_2 from which the SO_3 is produced at a given temperature and pressure. Consequently, any pressure rise will favor the formation of a higher percentage of sulfur trioxide because the system can most easily relieve this stress through a decrease in volume.

For a gas phase equilibrium such as

$$2 HI(g) \rightleftharpoons H_2(g) + I_2(g)$$

in which the *same* total number of molecules appears in both the reactant and product side of the chemical equation, no change in volume accompanies the decomposition of hydrogen iodide at a specified temperature and pressure. Therefore, the position of equilibrium as well as the equilibrium constant is not influenced by variations in the total pressure of the system.

Equilibria occurring in condensed phases, such as aqueous solutions, are usually not greatly altered by variations in pressure because liquids are so much less compressible than gaseous systems. However, slight changes in the position of an equilibrium which do occur follow the principle of Le Châtelier; that is, a system always responds to an increase in pressure by undergoing a decrease in volume. The *autoprotolysis* or self-ionization of water, for example,

$$H_2O + H_2O \rightleftharpoons H_3O^+ + OH^-$$

takes place with a very small *decrease* in volume because the orientation of other water molecules around the ionic species, H_3O^+ and OH^-, leads to a more compact structure than exists hypothetically before any ionization occurs. Consequently, if the pressure upon a sample of water is raised from 1 atm to several thousand atmospheres, the extent of ionization of water increases by a factor of two or three. By way of contrast, a one thousandfold change in the pressure of a system involving the sulfur dioxide-oxygen-sulfur trioxide reaction would change the equilibrium constant by a factor of 1000.

Effect of Concentration. Le Châtelier's principle provides a qualitative guide to the way in which an equilibrium is shifted by changes in the concentrations of the various chemical species and serves to complement the thermodynamic criterion for the direction of reaction mentioned in the previous section of this chapter. The stress in this case is a change in concentration, so it may be predicted that the position of equilibrium will shift in such a way as to minimize this change. Thus, if one of the components in an equilibrium mixture is diminished in concentration — for example, by removing part of it from the system — the system will reach a new position of equilibrium by moving in such a direction as to restore in part the concentration of the component which was withdrawn. Similarly, when an additional quantity of one of the components is introduced to a system at equilibrium, the system shifts toward a new position of equilibrium in such a direction as to consume part of the added material.

Effect of Catalysts. The presence of a catalyst may hasten the approach of a chemical system to a state of equilibrium as mentioned earlier, but catalysis always affects both the forward and backward reaction rates in dynamic equilibrium to the same extent. Therefore, although a catalyst may diminish the time required to establish a state of equilibrium, it never, under any circumstances, alters the value of the equilibrium constant for a given reaction.

Completeness of Reaction. An equilibrium-constant expression is truly valid only if the reaction to which it pertains is reversible. Fortunately, most reactions encountered in chemical analysis are reversible, so equilibrium calculations are applicable and meaningful. It is important, however, that reactions used for quantitative determinations in analytical chemistry go substantially to completion. For example, when chloride is determined by the precipitation and weighing of silver chloride, essentially all of the chloride present in the unknown sample must be converted to silver chloride:

$$Cl^- + Ag^+ \rightleftharpoons AgCl(s)$$

The precipitation of an indeterminate fraction of the chloride as silver chloride would clearly be worthless. In this example, the precipitation reaction may be considered as quantitatively complete when the amount of material remaining unprecipitated is a negligible fraction of the total weight of silver chloride. Thus, if the precipitate is to be weighed on an analytical balance with a sensitivity limit of 0.0001 gm, any amount of material left in solution which weighs less than this is of no consequence.

It is worthwhile to consider under what conditions reversible reactions will go to practical completion. Le Châtelier's principle suggests that the position of a chemical equilibrium will be shifted to the right if one or more of the reaction products is removed from the system. Under such conditions, the desired reaction may proceed far to the right in an effort to reform the component as fast as it is withdrawn. Even a reaction with a relatively small equilibrium constant goes to practical completion if the removal of one or more reaction products is continuous and successful. Three important ways in which a reaction product may be effectively removed from a system are (1) by allowing a gaseous product to escape, (2) by precipitating the product in a relatively insoluble form, and (3) by complexing one of the products as a stable ion in solution. If one or more of these mechanisms is operative, the reaction should proceed to completion — the degree of completeness depending on the effectiveness with which the reaction product is removed.

ACTIVITY AND ACTIVITY COEFFICIENTS

In analytical chemistry, it is convenient to specify the *molar concentration* or the *formal concentration* of a particular substance in solution because such information tells the quantity of solute dissolved in a certain volume of that solution. In the study of chemical equilibrium, however, we are interested in knowing how completely or effectively a given species participates in a reaction. Therefore, we have to be concerned not only about how much of a substance is present but about the effect of environment on the behavior of this substance. For a hydrochloric acid solution, one must recognize that a hydrogen ion and a chloride ion have mutual attraction for each other, that two chloride ions repel one another, and that hydrogen ion and chloride ion both undergo ion-dipole interactions with the water in which they are dissolved. In addition, if other cations and anions are present, these species will interact with the hydrogen ions and chloride ions. If a solution containing 0.1 M hydrogen ion and 0.1 M chloride ion, and possibly other species, behaved in a perfectly ideal manner, we would expect each of these ions to act as if its concentration were 0.1 M. On the other hand, if a certain fraction of the hydrogen ions is attracted to anionic species, including chloride, the solution will exhibit the properties of one in which the concentration of hydrogen ion is less than 0.1 M — in spite of the fact that a *titration* with standard sodium hydroxide reveals the presence of exactly 0.1 M hydrogen ion. Depending on the relative importance of factors such as ion-ion attractions and repulsions, hydrogen ion or chloride ion in a solution containing 0.1 M hydrochloric acid may behave in chemical reactions as if its concentration were less than, equal to, or greater than 0.1 M.

To distinguish between the molar concentration or analytical concentration of a substance, which can be determined titrimetrically or gravimetrically, and the effective concentration of a substance, which accounts for its nonideal behavior, the latter is defined as the **activity** of the species. However, it is customary to relate the activity of a species to its analytical concentration through the simple expression

$$a_i = f_i C_i$$

in which a_i is the activity of substance i, f_i is the **activity coefficient** of substance i, and C_i is the analytical concentration of substance i. Recalling the symbols mentioned for activity and concentration in the thermodynamic treatment of equilibrium, we may write the activity of hydrogen ion as

$$a_{H^+} = f_{H^+}[H^+] \quad \text{or} \quad (H^+) = f_{H^+}[H^+]$$

and that for chloride ion as

$$a_{Cl^-} = f_{Cl^-}[Cl^-] \quad \text{or} \quad (Cl^-) = f_{Cl^-}[Cl^-]$$

Activity and concentration are always expressed in such a way that both terms have identical units, usually moles per liter, so the activity coefficient is a dimensionless parameter.

It should be apparent from the trend of the discussion that we shall focus our attention on the behavior of ionic species in aqueous solutions. If any doubt exists that interionic attractions and repulsions or ion-dipole interactions can cause marked differences between activity and analytical concentration, the data in Table 4-1 are especially impressive. This table lists various analytical concentrations of hydrochloric acid and, for each concentration, the corresponding activity or "effective" concentration of hydrochloric acid in that solution. Obviously, the activity of hydrochloric acid solutions does differ from the concentration of such solutions, especially at the highest concentrations. Serious discrepancies may arise if one attempts to make predictions based on analytical concentrations instead of activities.

TABLE 4-1. ANALYTICAL CONCENTRATION
AND ACTIVITY OF HYDROCHLORIC
ACID SOLUTIONS

Concentration, M	Activity, M
0.00500	0.00464
0.0100	0.00907
0.0500	0.0416
0.100	0.0796
1.00	0.809
2.00	2.02
3.00	3.95
5.00	11.9
6.00	19.3
7.00	30.6
8.00	47.2
9.00	71.5
12.0	207.

The important features of the data in Table 4-1 can be described most readily if the behavior of hydrochloric acid solutions is depicted in graphical form. When we rearrange the expression

$$a_i = f_i C_i$$

to the relation

$$f_i = \frac{a_i}{C_i}$$

we can see that three situations prevail:

(1) If the activity a_i of a substance is exactly equal to its concentration C_i, the activity coefficient f_i is unity and the substance is said to behave in an *ideal* manner. Since the activity of a species reflects all the possible physical and chemical interactions which can occur in a solution and since these interactions become vanishingly small when the concentrations of ionic species approach zero, f_i should be unity only in infinitely dilute solutions of electrolytes.

(2) If the activity a_i of a substance is smaller than its concentration C_i, the activity coefficient f_i is less than unity and the substance is said to exhibit *negative* deviations from ideal behavior.

(3) If the activity a_i of a substance is larger than its concentration C_i, the activity coefficient f_i is greater than unity and the substance is said to display *positive* deviations from ideal behavior.

From a plot of the activity coefficient f_i of a species as a function of its analytical concentration, we should be able to tell at a glance for a given concentration whether that substance exhibits nearly ideal behavior, negative deviations from ideality, or positive deviations from ideality. Eventually, some concrete explanations will be offered to enable us to understand why

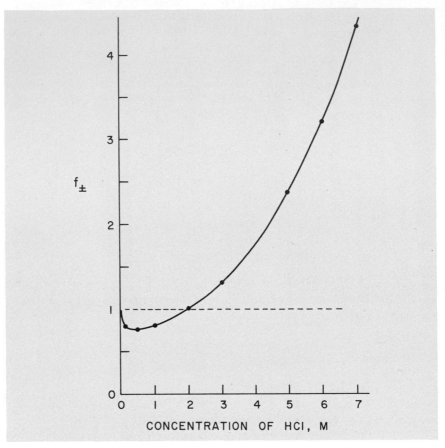

FIGURE 4-2.   Mean activity coefficient $f_{\pm}$ for hydrochloric acid as a function of the analytical concentration of the acid. (See text for discussion.)

positive and negative deviations from ideality do occur. Figure 4-2 shows a plot of the quantity $f_{\pm}$ versus the concentration of hydrochloric acid, the data for the graph having been derived from Table 4-1. Notice that instead of f_i we have plotted on the ordinate of this graph a new parameter, $f_{\pm}$, which is called the *mean activity coefficient*. Although the significance of the mean activity coefficient will become evident later, it suffices to mention here that $f_{\pm}$ is employed because the individual behavior of hydrogen ion and chloride ion in a hydrochloric acid medium cannot be sorted out, since each ion influences the activity of the other species. Nevertheless, the use of $f_{\pm}$ will not alter our interpretation of the behavior of hydrochloric acid solutions, because $f_{\pm}$ is defined in the same way as f_i:

$$f_{\pm} = \frac{a_{\text{HCl}}}{C_{\text{HCl}}} = \frac{a_{\text{H}^+}}{[\text{H}^+]} = \frac{a_{\text{Cl}^-}}{[\text{Cl}^-]}$$

Figure 4-2 confirms that the mean activity coefficient $f_\pm$ for hydrochloric acid is unity at infinite dilution, that is, at a hydrochloric acid concentration of virtually zero. However, as the hydrochloric acid concentration is increased, the activity coefficient decreases, reaching a minimum value of approximately 0.76 at a hydrochloric acid concentration near 0.500 M. If one continues to increase the concentration of hydrochloric acid above 0.500 M, the mean activity coefficient climbs steadily until it attains a value of unity at a concentration slightly less than 2.00 M. For concentrations greater than 2.00 M, the activity coefficient rises very abruptly, indicating that such solutions exhibit large positive deviations from ideality.

One feature of the behavior of hydrochloric acid is especially interesting, namely that the mean activity coefficient is unity for an approximately 2 M hydrochloric acid solution. This observation could be interpreted to mean that the solution behaves ideally. Actually, the activity coefficient is unity only because two opposing phenomena offset each other perfectly. The first factor is that the ion-ion attractions between hydrogen ion and chloride ion cause the activity to be *less* than the concentration of hydrochloric acid and the activity coefficient to be *less* than unity. The second factor is that the solvation of hydrogen ions and chloride ions by water molecules decreases the available quantity of free or unbound solvent, thereby tending to make the activity *greater* than the concentration and the activity coefficient *greater* than unity. These effects just happen to counteract each other in 2 M hydrochloric acid. For hydrochloric acid solutions less concentrated than 2 M, the first factor is of greater importance, whereas the second factor predominates in hydrochloric acid media more concentrated than 2 M. Notice in Figure 4-2, however, that the increase in the activity coefficient in acid solutions more concentrated than 0.5 M indicates that the second effect has begun to overcome the first factor. We shall consider these effects in more detail subsequently.

Another interesting observation is that 12 M hydrochloric acid, which is the commercially available concentrated reagent, behaves as if the hydrochloric acid concentration is really 207 M (see Table 4-1). However, this is by no means extreme behavior. For example, a 20 M solution of lithium bromide in water acts as if the lithium ion and bromide ion concentrations were each approximately 10,000 M, whereas the hydrogen ion activity in a 12 M perchloric acid solution is 6000 M!

It should be emphasized that the behavior shown in Figure 4-2 for hydrochloric acid is typical of all ionic solutes. A plot of activity coefficient versus the concentration of an electrolyte always exhibits a curve which is qualitatively similar to that for hydrochloric acid. Naturally, the absolute values of the activity coefficients, as well as the solute concentration at which the activity coefficient is minimal and at which the activity coefficient rises to unity again, depend on the nature of the solute and particularly on the charges and sizes of the ionic species comprising the solute.

In view of the important difference between activity and analytical concentration for an ionic solute such as hydrochloric acid, it is essential that activities or activity coefficients be used when rigorously correct equilibrium calculations are to be performed. For rough calculations, however, including those made for predictive purposes in analytical chemistry, it may be perfectly satisfactory to use equilibrium-constant expressions involving concentrations rather than activities. Information about the activity of an ionic solute may be obtained in either of two ways — direct experimental measurement or theoretical calculation. First, the activity of a species can be determined experimentally through measurement of the emf of a galvanic cell. One must know the emf of the galvanic cell when all chemical species are present in their standard states at unit activity and then one must measure the actual emf when the concentration of the solute of interest is varied. The difference between these two emf values is related through the Nernst equation to the logarithm of the activity. Second, the activity of an ionic solute may be determined from the simple equation

$$a_i = f_i C_i$$

provided that both the activity coefficient and the analytical concentration of the desired substance are known. The major difficulty in this approach, as we shall soon discover, lies in the fact that activity coefficients themselves can only be calculated reliably for electrolyte solutions up to a concentration level of about 0.1 M. In the concentrated electrolyte solutions normally encountered in analytical chemistry, the theoretical relations from which one can predict activity coefficients are invalid, and one must resort to the potentiometric evaluation of activities mentioned above. However, by examining some of the theoretical equations which have been derived for the calculation of activity coefficients, we can gain considerable insight into the behavior of electrolyte solutions.

Debye-Hückel Limiting Law

One of the most significant contributions to our understanding of the behavior of electrolyte solutions is the Debye-Hückel limiting law, the derivation of which was published in 1923. We shall begin this discussion with a description of the fundamental assumptions underlying the development of the limiting law. Then, by considering how well the predictions of the limiting law agree with experimental observations, we may verify or revise our physical picture of how ionic solutes behave.

A key assumption involved in the derivation of the Debye-Hückel limiting law is that interactions between charged solute species are purely electrostatic in character and can be expressed in terms of Coulomb's law

$$F = \frac{q_1 q_2}{D r^2}$$

where F in dynes is the force of attraction between two oppositely charged ions or the force of repulsion between two similarly charged ions, where q_1 and q_2 are the charges in electrostatic units of the two species, where D is the dielectric constant of the medium in which the ions exist, and where r is the distance in centimeters by which the ions are separated. Electrostatic forces are strictly long-range interactions. All short-range forces, including those due to van der Waals attractions, ion-pair formation, and ion-dipole interactions, are ignored in the formulation of the Debye-Hückel equation.

Second among the assumptions made by Debye and Hückel in their treatment of electrolyte solutions is the applicability of the Boltzmann distribution law. In the context of the behavior of electrolyte solutions, the Boltzmann distribution law is concerned with the fact that the thermal motion of dissolved ions acts to disrupt the orientation of oppositely charged species caused by interionic attractions. The validity of the Boltzmann distribution law essentially means that ions in solution behave randomly, although the long-range electrostatic forces are still operative.

Debye and Hückel simplified their hypothetical model of electrolyte solutions in several other respects by proposing that ionic species cannot be polarized or distorted and, therefore, have spherical charge distribution and that ions can be regarded as point charges. Furthermore, the Debye-Hückel limiting law presumes that the dielectric constant and the viscosity of an electrolyte solution are uniform and independent of the actual concentration of the dissolved solute and that one can simply use the dielectric constant and viscosity of pure water in all calculations. Finally, it must be added that the theoretical model assumes complete dissociation of all electrolytes in the solution or at least dissociation of known fractions of these electrolytes.

No attempt will be made in this text to present the actual derivation of the Debye-Hückel limiting law because, in spite of the numerous simplifications discussed above, the final equation is obtained only after considerable effort. For a single ionic species such as hydrogen ion or chloride ion, the Debye-Hückel limiting law is usually written in the form

$$-\log f_i = A z_i^2 \sqrt{\mu}$$

in which f_i is the activity coefficient and z_i is the charge of the ion of interest. The parameter A, given by the expression

$$A = \frac{1}{2.303} \frac{e^2}{2DkT} \sqrt{\frac{8\pi e^2 N}{1000DkT}}$$

is a collection of constants, including Avogadro's number (N), Boltzmann's constant (k), the charge of an electron (e), the dielectric constant of the solvent (D), and the absolute temperature (T). Note in particular that A is inversely proportional to the three-halves power of the product of dielectric constant and temperature:

$$A \propto \frac{1}{(DT)^{3/2}}$$

The remaining term in the Debye-Hückel limiting law, μ, is *not* the chemical potential of a species but rather is the **ionic strength** of the solution, defined as one-half the sum of the analytical concentration C_i multiplied by the square of the charge z_i for each ionic species in the solution, i.e.,

$$\mu = \tfrac{1}{2} \sum_i C_i z_i{}^2$$

In effect, the ionic strength, μ, measures the total population of ions in a solution.

For water, with a dielectric constant of 78.5 at 25°C, the value of A is very close to 0.512, so the Debye-Hückel limiting law for aqueous solutions at this temperature becomes

$$-\log f_i = 0.512 z_i{}^2 \sqrt{\mu}$$

Although the latter relation may be employed to evaluate the activity coefficient for any single ionic species such as Fe^{++} or I^-, this expression cannot be tested experimentally because it is impossible to prepare a solution containing just one ion. For example, to obtain a solution of Fe^{++} one might use iron(II) chloride, or potassium iodide crystals could be dissolved in water for the preparation of an iodide solution. Obviously, the interaction of chloride ion with Fe^{++} and of potassium ion with iodide will influence the behavior of Fe^{++} and I^-, respectively. Thus, any technique which one utilizes to measure activity coefficients for these systems will yield, in reality, the activity coefficient of Fe^{++} in the presence of twice as much chloride ion or the activity coefficient of I^- in the presence of an equal concentration of potassium ion. Fortunately, by defining a new term, called the **mean activity coefficient** ($f_{\pm}$), we obtain a parameter which can be both experimentally and theoretically evaluated. The mean activity coefficient for a *binary* salt, whose cation M has a charge z_M and whose anion N has a charge z_N, is related to the single-ion activity coefficients f_M and f_N by means of the equation

$$(f_{\pm})^{z_M + z_N} = (f_M)^{z_N} (f_N)^{z_M}$$

If we take the negative logarithm of each side of this expression, the result is

$$-(z_M + z_N) \log f_{\pm} = -z_N \log f_M - z_M \log f_N$$

When the Debye-Hückel limiting law for single ions is substituted into each term on the right-hand side of this relation, one obtains

$$-(z_M + z_N) \log f_{\pm} = 0.512 z_N z_M{}^2 \sqrt{\mu} + 0.512 z_M z_N{}^2 \sqrt{\mu}$$

which upon rearrangement and simplification yields

$$-\log f_{\pm} = 0.512 \sqrt{\mu} \left[\frac{z_N z_M{}^2 + z_M z_N{}^2}{z_M + z_N} \right]$$

and

$$-\log f_{\pm} = 0.512 z_M z_N \sqrt{\mu}$$

It is important to note here that only the *absolute* magnitudes of z_M and z_N are used in this equation.

At this point it is instructive to consider some actual calculations involving the use of the Debye-Hückel limiting law. For example, let us determine the mean activity coefficient for $0.10\,F$ hydrochloric acid. First, we have to evaluate the ionic strength of the solution. Hydrogen ion and chloride ion are the only species present, so it follows that

$$\mu = \tfrac{1}{2} \sum_i C_i z_i^2 = \tfrac{1}{2}[C_{H^+} z_{H^+}^2 + C_{Cl^-} z_{Cl^-}^2]$$

$$\mu = \tfrac{1}{2}[(0.10)(1)^2 + (0.10)(-1)^2] = 0.10$$

Strictly speaking, ionic strength should be expressed in concentration units, such as moles per liter, but in most, if not all, reference books and research publications, ionic strength is reported as a dimensionless number. Next, since the absolute values of the charges on hydrogen ion and chloride ion are unity, the mean activity coefficient may be obtained from the expression

$$-\log f_{\pm} = 0.512 z_M z_N \sqrt{\mu} = 0.512(1)(1)\sqrt{0.10}$$

$$-\log f_{\pm} = 0.512(1)(1)(0.316) = 0.162$$

$$\log f_{\pm} = -0.162 = 0.838 - 1.000$$

$$f_{\pm} = 0.689$$

For purposes of comparison, the mean activity coefficient for $0.10\,F$ hydrochloric acid has been experimentally measured and found to be 0.796.

As a second example, we shall calculate the mean activity coefficient for $0.10\,F$ aluminum chloride solution. The ionic strength is given by the relation

$$\mu = \tfrac{1}{2}[C_{Al^{+++}} z_{Al^{+++}}^2 + C_{Cl^-} z_{Cl^-}^2]$$

$$\mu = \tfrac{1}{2}[(0.10)(3)^2 + (0.30)(-1)^2] = 0.60$$

Notice that the ionic strength is six times greater than the concentration of the aluminum chloride solution. Substitution of the values for ionic strength and for the charges of the ions into the Debye-Hückel limiting law yields

$$-\log f_{\pm} = 0.512(3)(1)\sqrt{0.60} = 1.189$$

$$\log f_{\pm} = -1.189 - 0.811 - 2.000$$

$$f_{\pm} = 0.0647$$

This predicted mean activity coefficient is more than five times smaller than the experimentally determined value of 0.337.

Numerous similar calculations were performed for other concentrations of hydrochloric acid and aluminum chloride, and the results are shown diagrammatically in Figure 4-3. Included in the plot are the actual experimental values of the mean activity coefficients. The two upper curves in Figure 4-3 show the variation of the mean activity coefficient for hydrochloric acid as a function of the square root of ionic strength, the solid line corresponding to the true activity coefficients and the dashed line giving the

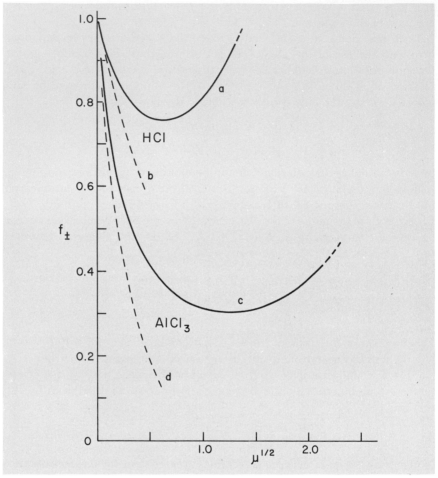

FIGURE 4-3. Comparison of the observed mean activity coefficients for hydrochloric acid (HCl) and aluminum chloride (AlCl$_3$) with the theoretical mean activity
coefficients calculated from the Debye-Hückel limiting law, plotted as a function of
the square root of ionic strength. Curve a: observed mean activity coefficients for
HCl. Curve b: calculated mean activity coefficients for HCl. Curve c: observed mean
activity coefficients for AlCl$_3$. Curve d: calculated mean activity coefficients for
AlCl$_3$. In viewing this graph, note that all curves extrapolate to a mean activity
coefficient of unity at zero ionic strength.

theoretical values. The behavior of aluminum chloride is represented by the
two lower curves in Figure 4-3, the solid and dashed lines again pertaining
to the actual and theoretical activity coefficients, respectively.

The most distinctive feature of Figure 4-3 is that the mean activity
coefficients calculated from the Debye-Hückel limiting law (dashed lines)
become significantly smaller than the true or observed values as ionic strength

increases. Furthermore, the Debye-Hückel limiting law cannot account at all for the upward trend in activity coefficients at relatively high ionic strengths. Nevertheless, it is evident that the theoretical and experimental curves do converge at low ionic strengths and that the Debye-Hückel limiting law accurately describes the behavior of relatively dilute electrolyte solutions. It should be realized that all the curves shown in Figure 4-3 extrapolate to a mean activity coefficient of unity at zero ionic strength. We can conclude that, for small electrolyte concentrations, the assumptions made by Debye and Hückel are valid — particularly the ideas that ions act as point charges in a solution of uniform dielectric constant and that ions undergo simple electrostatic interactions with their neighbors. In general activity coefficients for salts consisting of singly charged species can be evaluated by means of the Debye-Hückel limiting law with an uncertainty not exceeding about 5 per cent for ionic strengths up to 0.05. In other words, for dilute solutions activity coefficients depend only on the charge of the ion and on ionic strength. For salts which consist of doubly charged ions, the Debye-Hückel limiting law gives results reliable to within several per cent up to ionic strengths of perhaps 0.01, whereas, for triply charged species like Al^{+++}, the limiting law fails above ionic strengths of approximately 0.005. However, these limits concerning the applicability of the Debye-Hückel limiting law must be regarded only as rough guidelines, because the specific nature of the ions in question has a great influence on the behavior of an electrolyte.

In discovering the limited usefulness of the Debye-Hückel limiting law, we are faced with the challenge of understanding why the limiting law is inadequate and how the theoretical model could be modified so that a more accurate equation can be formulated. Let us reëxamine the assumptions used by Debye and Hückel in their derivation.

It will be recalled that the limiting law is based on the assumption that ionic species are affected only by long-range electrostatic forces. In a dilute solution, where one may envisage a given ion to be insulated from other ions by a sheath of water molecules, this assumption appears to be valid. In more concentrated solutions, ions are close to each other, so a number of highly specific interactions such as ion-pair formation may occur. In the case of multiply charged species, the formation of ion pairs, triplets, and other aggregates is especially important, owing to the much stronger Coulombic forces which prevail. The Boltzmann distribution law which essentially asserts that ions behave independently of each other should become less and less valid as the ionic strength of the solution increases.

In addition, Debye and Hückel assumed that the dielectric constant of an electrolyte solution is equal to that of pure water and, furthermore, that the dielectric constant is uniform throughout the solution. However, the dielectric constant of a solution is known to vary drastically in the vicinity of an ion. The unusually high dielectric constant of water, 78.5 at 25°C, arises in the first place because hydrogen-bonding between adjacent water molecules promotes the formation of aggregates in which the individual molecular dipole moments reinforce each other. In the presence of an ion, strong ion-dipole interactions occur and the hydrogen-bonded water structure is broken down. Accordingly, the dielectric constant of the water may be only 4 to 10 within a radius of a few angstroms around an ionic species. It is difficult to assess the overall effect of this phenomenon on activity coefficients. As pointed out earlier, the parameter A in the Debye-Hückel limiting law is inversely proportional to the three-halves power of the dielectric constant. Therefore, a decrease in the dielectric constant should cause the mean activity coefficient for a solute to decrease. However, any decrease in the dielectric constant will lead to more extensive ion-pair formation because the Coulombic force of attraction between species of opposite charge is increased.

It is possible to explain why activity coefficients become larger than unity in concentrated electrolyte solutions by considering the interactions between ions and water molecules. For example, we discovered that a 12 M hydrochloric acid solution behaves as if the acid concentration is 207 M, indicating that the mean activity coefficient exceeds 17. Consider the following crude picture: If we have 1 liter of 12 M hydrochloric acid, the solution will contain 12 moles of the acid and, to a first approximation, 55.6 moles of water. If the hydrochloric acid is completely dissociated, 12 moles each of hydrogen ion and chloride ion will be present, and these ions will be solvated by water. Then, if we assume arbitrarily that each ion is solvated on the average by 2.2 water molecules, the total quantity of bound water will be $(24)(2.2)$ or 52.8 moles, leaving only 2.8 moles of water not bound to the ions. It must be emphasized that the water coordinated to these ions is part of the solute and definitely not solvent. Now, if 55.6 moles of water occupies 1 liter, 2.8 moles would occupy a volume of about 50 ml. Imagine that one dissolved 12 moles of hydrochloric acid in only 50 ml of water — the acid concentration would be 240 M, which compares favorably with 207 M. Despite the fact that this picture is terribly oversimplified, it should be evident that very high activity coefficients in concentrated solutions do arise because most of the solvent is actually bound to the ionic species.

It is difficult to incorporate the phenomena which we have been discussing into the general theory of electrolyte solutions. All of these effects tend to be highly specific; they vary considerably depending on the geometry, charge, and electronic configuration of an ion, as well as on the other species which may be present. Therefore, one must rely solely upon experimental measurements of activity coefficients in the concentrated solutions of analytical interest.

One of the other assumptions originally used by Debye and Hückel was that ions are point charges. However, if we consider the fact that ions have finite sizes and that every ion has its own characteristic radius, it should be apparent that the electrostatic fields around an ion of finite size and a point charge will be different. Furthermore, two ions cannot approach each other any closer than the sum of their radii, so the Coulombic force between them is smaller than if they were point charges.

Extended Debye-Hückel Equation

A significant addition to the Debye-Hückel limiting law involves the effect of finite ion size on activity coefficients. In their original paper Debye and Hückel recognized the importance of considering the sizes of ions. The following relation, commonly known as the extended Debye-Hückel equation, may be obtained from the theory developed by these workers:

$$-\log f_{\pm} = 0.512 z_M z_N \left[\frac{\sqrt{\mu}}{1 + Ba\sqrt{\mu}} \right]$$

This expression resembles the limiting law in all respects except for the denominator of the term in brackets. The parameter B is a function of the absolute temperature and the dielectric constant of the solution,

$$B = \frac{50.3}{\sqrt{DT}}$$

If we take the absolute temperature to be 298°K and if we assume the dielectric constant to be the value for pure water (78.5), B is 0.328. The term a in the denominator of the extended Debye-Hückel equation is an *adjustable* number, expressed in units of angstroms, which corresponds to the effective radius of a solvated (hydrated) ion.

If the radius of a typical ion in an aqueous medium has the very reasonable value of 3 Å, the product Ba is essentially unity and the extended Debye-Hückel equation may be written in the convenient form

$$-\log f_{\pm} = 0.512 z_M z_N \left[\frac{\sqrt{\mu}}{1 + \sqrt{\mu}} \right]$$

However, it is unrealistic to propose that all solvated ions have the same radius. In fact, experimental studies and theoretical calculations have indicated that 3 Å is probably the smallest radius an ion will have in an aqueous medium and that some common inorganic species have ionic radii as large as 11 Å. Information concerning the effective radii of a number of solvated inorganic species is presented in Table 4-2. In addition, the last five columns of this table list single-ion activity coefficients for each species at ionic strengths of 0.001, 0.005, 0.01, 0.05, and 0.1. It should be noted that the correct form of the extended Debye-Hückel equation for calculation of the activity coefficients for single ions is

$$-\log f_i = 0.512 z_i^2 \left[\frac{\sqrt{\mu}}{1 + Ba\sqrt{\mu}} \right]$$

The reader may wish to verify some of the entries in Table 4-2 through the use of the latter relation.

TABLE 4-2. SINGLE-ION ACTIVITY COEFFICIENTS BASED ON THE EXTENDED DEBYE-HÜCKEL EQUATION*

Ion	Ion Size a, Å	Ionic Strength				
		0.001	0.005	0.01	0.05	0.10
H^+	9	0.967	0.933	0.914	0.86	0.83
Li^+	6	0.965	0.930	0.909	0.845	0.81
Na^+, IO_3^-, HCO_3^-,	4	0.964	0.927	0.901	0.815	0.77
HSO_3^-, $H_2PO_4^-$, $H_2AsO_4^-$						
K^+, Rb^+, Cs^+, Tl^+,	3	0.964	0.925	0.899	0.805	0.755
Ag^+, NH_4^+, OH^-, F^-,						
SCN^-, HS^-, ClO_3^-,						
ClO_4^-, BrO_3^-, IO_4^-,						
MnO_4^-, Cl^-, Br^-, I^-,						
CN^-, NO_3^-						
Mg^{++}, Be^{++}	8	0.872	0.755	0.69	0.52	0.45
Ca^{++}, Cu^{++}, Zn^{++}, Sn^{++},	6	0.870	0.749	0.675	0.485	0.405
Mn^{++}, Fe^{++}, Ni^{++}, Co^{++}						
Sr^{++}, Ba^{++}, Ra^{++}, Cd^{++},	5	0.868	0.744	0.67	0.465	0.38
Pb^{++}, Hg^{++}, $S^=$, $CO_3^=$, $SO_3^=$						
Hg_2^{++}, $SO_4^=$, $S_2O_3^=$,	4	0.867	0.740	0.660	0.445	0.355
$CrO_4^=$, $HPO_4^=$						
Al^{+3}, Fe^{+3}, Cr^{+3}, Ce^{+3}, La^{+3}	9	0.738	0.54	0.445	0.245	0.18
PO_4^{-3}, $Fe(CN)_6^{-3}$	4	0.725	0.505	0.395	0.16	0.095
Th^{+4}, Zr^{+4}, Ce^{+4}, Sn^{+4}	11	0.588	0.35	0.255	0.10	0.065
$Fe(CN)_6^{-4}$	5	0.57	0.31	0.20	0.048	0.021

* Taken from the paper by J. Kielland, J. Am. Chem. Soc., *59*, 1675 (1937).

Let us return briefly to the subject of the behavior of hydrochloric acid solutions. In particular, we shall employ the extended Debye-Hückel equation to predict the mean activity coefficient for 0.1 F hydrochloric acid. An inspection of Table 4-2 reveals that the ion sizes for hydrogen ion and chloride ion are 9 and 3 Å, respectively; we shall assume, for purposes of our calculation, that the average of these two values, namely 6 Å, may be used. Accordingly, the mean activity coefficient for 0.1 F hydrochloric acid is given by the relation

$$-\log f_\pm = 0.512(1)(1)\left[\frac{\sqrt{0.1}}{1+(0.328)(6)\sqrt{0.1}}\right]$$

which yields when solved

$$-\log f_\pm = 0.512\left[\frac{0.316}{1+0.623}\right] = 0.0998$$

$$\log f_\pm = -0.0998 = 0.900 - 1.000$$

$$f_\pm = 0.794$$

The excellent agreement of this result with the experimentally observed value of 0.796 lends strong support to the conclusion that the effect of ion size on activity coefficients must always be considered in any theoretical treatment of electrolyte solutions. In order to determine how well the predictions of the extended Debye-Hückel equation do follow the true behavior of hydrochloric acid, we constructed the graph shown in Figure 4-4, which repeats some of the information given in Figure 4-3. It is evident that the extended Debye-Hückel equation provides much better agreement between theory and experiment than does the limiting law. However, as suggested earlier, neither the Debye-Hückel limiting law nor any of its extensions predicts an increase in the mean activity coefficient at high ionic strengths, because the theoretical model does not include the solvation of ions by water molecules.

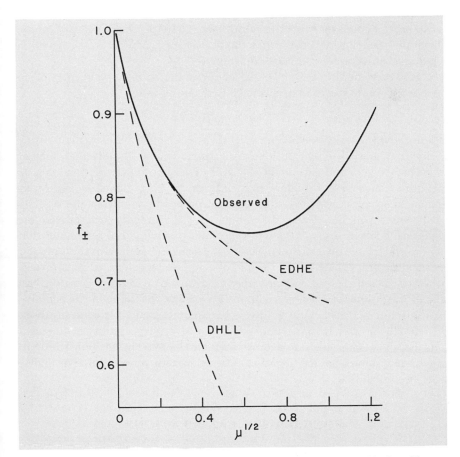

FIGURE 4-4. Comparison of mean activity coefficients for hydrochloric acid computed from Debye-Hückel limiting law (DHLL) and the extended Debye-Hückel equation (EDHE) with observed mean activity coefficients. The results based on the extended Debye-Hückel equation correspond to $a = 6$ Å.

It is worth mentioning that several additional modifications of the basic Debye-Hückel equations have been proposed. In every instance, however, these modifications take the form of empirical correction terms which are added to or subtracted from the extended Debye-Hückel equation in order to improve the agreement between observed and calculated activity coefficients. Unfortunately, it is difficult, if not impossible, to assign any physical significance to these correction terms. Therefore, we shall not discuss these relationships further in this text.

Activity Coefficients of Neutral Molecules

If one considers the behavior of neutral molecules or nonelectrolytes in the light of the Debye-Hückel theory, the conclusion is reached that such substances, being uncharged, should have activity coefficients of unity. Generally speaking, in pure water the activity of a neutral solute is within 1 per cent of its analytical concentration.

However, in the presence of electrolytes the activity coefficient of an uncharged solute varies in accordance with the equation

$$\log f = k\mu$$

where f is the activity coefficient, μ is the ionic strength, and k, the "salting coefficient," may be either positive or negative. For small molecules, such as nitrogen, oxygen, and carbon dioxide, k is usually positive with a value near 0.1, but for sugars and proteins k may be larger. If k is positive, $\log f$ is always greater than zero provided that an electrolyte is present, so the activity coefficient f will be greater than unity and the activity will exceed the analytical concentration of the neutral solute. It is helpful to remember that solutes which have dielectric constants less than water behave in this manner.

Hydrogen cyanide is an example of a substance which exhibits reverse behavior. The dielectric constant of hydrocyanic acid is much greater than that of water, the former being 111 at 25°C. Thus, the value of k is negative for this solute and its activity is always less than its analytical concentration.

Finally, it may be noted that, if k is positive, the solubility of a neutral solute in an aqueous medium decreases with an increase in the ionic strength. Conversely, solutes having negative k values become more soluble at higher ionic strengths.

EQUILIBRIUM CALCULATIONS

This section of the chapter is designed to illustrate a variety of typical equilibrium calculations involving solubility, acid dissociation, and the formation of complex ions. However, since the two following chapters deal with the properties of precipitates and with selected gravimetric methods of analysis, our major attention will be focused upon equilibrium problems related to the solubility of inorganic compounds.

Solubility and Solubility Products

We shall begin our discussion of solubility with a consideration of the dissolution of silver chloride, AgCl, in pure water. In most treatments of the solubility of silver chloride, it is stated that the simple equilibrium

$$AgCl(s) \rightleftharpoons Ag^+ + Cl^-$$

prevails after an aqueous suspension of the solid has been thoroughly shaken. However, one of the interesting features of the behavior of silver chloride is that silver ion and chloride ion may combine to form an aqueous, undissociated silver chloride molecule:

$$Ag^+ + Cl^- \rightleftharpoons AgCl(aq)$$

Alternatively, this latter species may be regarded as an ion pair, but ion-pair formation in water, which is a solvent of high dielectric constant, does not occur to an appreciable extent. The aqueous, undissociated molecule will be in equilibrium with solid silver chloride, according to the reaction

$$AgCl(s) \rightleftharpoons AgCl(aq)$$

Furthermore, the aqueous, undissociated molecule can react with a chloride ion, originating from silver chloride, to form an anionic complex:

$$AgCl(aq) + Cl^- \rightleftharpoons AgCl_2^-$$

If the chloride ion concentration were high enough, other complexes such as $AgCl_3^=$ or $AgCl_4^=$ could form. Thus, the solubility behavior of even a simple compound can be extremely complicated. Only through a careful investigation can one identify all the reactions which occur. Fortunately, in pure water the concentration of chloride ion is so small that the amounts of the anion complexes are negligible. However, the solubility of silver chloride should still be considered as the sum of the concentrations of Ag^+ and $AgCl(aq)$.

If we omit the anionic complexes just mentioned, the solubility behavior of silver chloride may be represented in the following way:

$$AgCl(s) \rightleftharpoons AgCl(aq) \rightleftharpoons Ag^+ + Cl^-$$

According to this picture, we consider that solid silver chloride dissolves to form the aqueous, undissociated molecule which, in turn, dissociates into silver and chloride ions. It is important to emphasize that all of the various equilibria are interrelated. The equilibrium-constant expressions corresponding to this sequence of reactions must be written in terms of activities rather than analytical concentrations, since we are interested in describing the solubility in a completely rigorous manner.

Activity and Intrinsic Solubility of a Solid.   The first step of the solubility reactions is governed by the equilibrium-constant expression

$$\frac{(AgCl(aq))}{(AgCl(s))} = S^\circ$$

where the chemical symbols in parentheses denote activities of the solid and aqueous forms of silver chloride and where S° is called the **intrinsic solubility** of silver chloride. Let us examine the significance of the terms in this equation. Since the standard state of silver chloride is defined to be the pure solid at 25°C, we may conclude that

$$(AgCl(s)) = 1$$

if the silver chloride is not contaminated in any way with impurities and if the temperature is 25°C. Solids which do contain extraneous substances have activities *less* than unity. From information contained in Chapter 5, it is evident that the preparation of an absolutely pure solid may be extremely difficult. Solid silver chloride in a high state of purity can be prepared if one mixes solutions containing stoichiometric amounts of reagent-grade sodium chloride and silver nitrate and washes the resulting precipitate thoroughly to aid the removal of excess sodium and nitrate ions. Experimental studies have indicated that the activity of exceedingly small particles of a solid compound is actually *greater* than unity. However, a detailed discussion of this subject would be extremely lengthy and is beyond the scope of the present treatment of solubility. Suffice it to say that particles greater than approximately 2 microns in diameter exhibit unit activity.

Throughout the remainder of this section of the chapter, the activities of solid phases will always be assumed to be unity, so that for the silver chloride system we may write

$$(AgCl(aq)) = S^\circ$$

This relation states that the activity of the soluble molecular form of silver chloride is a constant whenever one has an excess of solid AgCl in equilibrium with pure water or any other aqueous solution. Regardless of what other competing reactions occur, the activity of AgCl(aq) remains unchanged, which is why S° is termed the intrinsic solubility of silver chloride. In a manner of speaking, this situation is similar to ordinary solvent extraction in which the partitioning of a substance between two immiscible liquids is studied. Here the molecular form of silver chloride is distributed between a solid phase and a solution phase.

The numerical value of S° is exceedingly difficult to measure experimentally because the quantity of AgCl(aq) is almost always small compared to the concentrations of other dissolved silver species. Values for S° reported in the chemical literature vary from 1.0×10^{-7} to 6.2×10^{-7} M. The intrinsic solubility may be determined according to the following typical procedure: One performs careful studies of the total solubility of solid silver chloride in hydrochloric acid media, taking into consideration all of the possible equilibria mentioned earlier. Invariably, the solubility data can be adequately explained only if the existence of a soluble molecular form of silver chloride is proposed. Through a mathematical analysis of the experimental data, one computes the value of $S°$ which is consistent with these results. Unfortunately, the contribution of $AgCl(aq)$ to the total solubility of silver chloride is so small that even slight errors in the solubility data cause large variations in the calculated value of $S°$.

It seems reasonable to conclude that a small concentration of the aqueous, undissociated molecular form of a compound always exists in equilibrium with the solid phase. For $AgCl$, $AgBr$, AgI, $AgSCN$, and $AgIO_3$, the concentration of the molecular species is approximately 0.1 to 1 per cent of the solubility of the parent compound in water. The dissolution of all metallic hydroxides and sulfides, including $Ni(OH)_2$, $Fe(OH)_3$, $Zn(OH)_2$, HgS, CdS, and CuS, is known to yield a small concentration of the corresponding aqueous molecule.

Activity Product. The second step of the solubility reactions of silver chloride may be considered as the dissociation of the aqueous silver chloride molecule into silver ion and chloride ion:

$$AgCl(aq) \rightleftharpoons Ag^+ + Cl^-$$

As the molecular species is consumed in this reaction, additional solid silver chloride dissolves. The thermodynamic equilibrium-constant expression for the dissociation of $AgCl(aq)$ is

$$\frac{(Ag^+)(Cl^-)}{(AgCl(aq))} = \frac{1}{K_1}$$

The unusual representation of the equilibrium constant requires a brief explanation. Frequently, in tables of equilibrium constants, one finds the preceding reaction written as

$$Ag^+ + Cl^- \rightleftharpoons AgCl(aq)$$

and the state of equilibrium represented by the expression

$$\frac{(AgCl(aq))}{(Ag^+)(Cl^-)} = K_1$$

The equilibrium constant K_1 is called the *first stepwise formation constant* for the silver chloride system because it pertains to the reaction in which silver ion combines with the *first* of at least several chloride ions. We shall describe the stepwise formation of metal ion complexes more fully in Chapter 11. Above all, this discussion illustrates the important point that, when we reverse the direction in which a chemical equilibrium is written, the *reciprocal* of the equilibrium constant for the original reaction must be employed.

The first stepwise formation constant (K_1) is approximately 1.3×10^3, and its reciprocal is about 8×10^{-4}. However, since the equilibrium-constant expression corresponding to K_1 contains, as one term, the activity of AgCl(aq), the value of this equilibrium constant is subject to the same uncertainty as the intrinsic solubility, $S°$.

If we now combine the two equilibria,

$$AgCl(s) \rightleftharpoons AgCl(aq)$$

and

$$AgCl(aq) \rightleftharpoons Ag^+ + Cl^-$$

the result is

$$AgCl(s) \rightleftharpoons Ag^+ + Cl^-$$

When two reactions are added together to obtain a third reaction, the equilibrium constants for these two reactions are *multiplied* together to obtain the equilibrium constant for the third reaction. Therefore,

$$(Ag^+)(Cl^-) = \frac{S°}{K_1}$$

because the activity of solid silver chloride is still assumed to be unity. Although the individual values of $S°$ and K_1 are not accurately known, the *ratio* of these two quantities can be obtained precisely since the product of the activities of silver ion and chloride ion is accessible to direct experimental measurement. The product of the activities of silver ion and chloride ion is defined as the **thermodynamic activity product, K_{ap}**:

$$(Ag^+)(Cl^-) = K_{ap}$$

This relation is a statement of the fundamental principle that, in a solution saturated with solid silver chloride, the product of the activities of silver ion and chloride ion is always constant.

The determination of the thermodynamic activity product can be accomplished in several ways, but the most direct method involves the measurement of the activities of Ag^+ and Cl^-. Recalling that the activity of an ion is given by the equation

$$a_i = f_i C_i$$

we can formulate the thermodynamic activity-product expression as

$$f_{Ag^+}[Ag^+]f_{Cl^-}[Cl^-] = K_{ap}$$

whereas if mean activity coefficients are used, we obtain

$$f_{\pm}^2[Ag^+][Cl^-] = K_{ap}$$

Suppose that solid silver chloride is shaken with pure water until solubility equilibrium is attained. After the excess solid is separated from its saturated solution, one can determine titrimetrically the analytical concentrations of silver ion and chloride ion. Then, because the solubility of silver chloride is small, one may confidently employ the Debye-Hückel limiting law to evaluate the mean activity coefficient of silver chloride. Finally, the mean activity coefficient and the analytical data are combined to calculate the thermodynamic activity product. Numerous measurements of the solubility of silver chloride have been performed, and the results are consistent with the conclusion that

$$(Ag^+)(Cl^-) = K_{ap} = 1.78 \times 10^{-10}$$

It should be noted that a correction must be made for the presence of AgCl(aq) when one wishes to determine the analytical concentration of just silver ion, because each of these species behaves identically during a titration or similar procedure.

Solubility Product. In analytical chemistry, we are usually concerned with the concentration of a species instead of its activity, since the former provides information about the quantity of material present in a particular phase or system. For example, it may be of interest to know the analytical concentration of silver ion in a certain solution. In addition, as discussed earlier, activity coefficients for ions cannot be reliably calculated for concentrated electrolyte solutions encountered by analytical chemists. Moreover, it should be remembered that one generally performs equilibrium calculations in order to predict the feasibility of a method of separation or analysis. For these reasons, we shall be satisfied to omit the use of activity coefficients throughout most of this book and to write relations involving only analytical concentrations, such as

$$[Ag^+][Cl^-] = K_{sp}$$

The latter equation is the familiar **solubility-product expression** for silver chloride, and the equilibrium constant is called the **solubility product** or the **solubility-product constant.** For virtually all equilibrium calculations concerned with the solubility of precipitates, we shall use analytical concentrations and we will assume that the activity product K_{ap} and the solubility product K_{sp} are synonymous. Appendix 1 contains a compilation of solubility products.

Let us consider two especially simple examples of solubility-product calculations. Suppose that the solubility of nickel hydroxide is known to be 0.000109 gm per liter of water and that we wish to calculate the solubility product of this compound. The simplest possible representation of the solubility reaction is

$$Ni(OH)_2(s) \rightleftharpoons Ni^{++} + 2\,OH^-$$

and the solubility-product expression is

$$[Ni^{++}][OH^-]^2 = K_{sp}$$

The molar solubility of nickel hydroxide is obtained if we divide the weight solubility by the formula weight or molecular weight of $Ni(OH)_2$, the latter being 92.7. Thus, the molar solubility, S, is given by

$$S = \frac{0.000109 \text{ gm}}{1 \text{ liter}} \frac{1 \text{ mole}}{92.7 \text{ gm}} = 1.10 \times 10^{-6}\,M$$

Since one nickel ion is formed for each nickel hydroxide molecule which dissolves,

$$[Ni^{++}] = 1.18 \times 10^{-6}\,M$$

whereas the hydroxide concentration is twice that of nickel:

$$[OH^-] = 2.36 \times 10^{-6}\ M$$

It follows that the solubility product is given by

$$(1.18 \times 10^{-6})(2.36 \times 10^{-6})^2 = K_{sp}$$
$$6.57 \times 10^{-18} = K_{sp}$$

It should be mentioned that the solubility behavior of nickel hydroxide is much more complicated than this sample calculation suggests, as may be seen in Problem 24 at the end of this chapter.

Starting with the solubility-product expression for a compound, we can calculate the molar solubility. For example, the solubility-product expression for iron(III) hydroxide is

$$[Fe^{+++}][OH^-]^3 = 4 \times 10^{-38}$$

corresponding to the equilibrium

$$Fe(OH)_3(s) \rightleftharpoons Fe^{+++} + 3\ OH^-$$

Since we obtain one Fe^{+++} ion for each iron(III) hydroxide molecule which dissolves, the solubility of $Fe(OH)_3$ should be equal to the concentration of Fe^{+++}:

$$S = [Fe^{+++}]$$

On the other hand, the concentration of the hydroxide ion will be three times the molar solubility S, so

$$3S = [OH^-]$$

Substituting these results into the solubility-product expression, we obtain

$$(S)(3S)^3 = 4 \times 10^{-38}$$
$$27S^4 = 4 \times 10^{-38}$$
$$S = 2 \times 10^{-10}\ M$$

Diverse Ion Effect

Although it is convenient and simple to discuss the solubility of a substance in pure water, the formation and dissolution of a precipitate in analytical procedures invariably occur in the presence of relatively large concentrations of foreign electrolytes. For example, when one prepares pure silver chloride by mixing stoichiometric quantities of solutions containing sodium chloride and silver nitrate, the precipitate will be dispersed in a medium containing dissolved sodium nitrate. Therefore, we must be concerned about the solubility behavior of a precipitate in the presence of a foreign electrolyte. However, we shall restrict this discussion to chemical systems wherein the desired compound is in equilibrium with a solution which contains no ions common to the precipitate — that is, no ions of which the solid is composed, except for those produced when the precipitate itself dissolves.

Before attempting to predict quantitatively how the solubility of a precipitate such as silver chloride depends on the concentration of foreign
electrolyte, we might consider a qualitative picture of the interaction between
silver ion and chloride ion. Let us contrast the behavior of silver ion and
chloride ion in two different environments — pure water and 0.1 F nitric
acid. In the nitric acid medium, the positively charged silver ion will exhibit
a strong attraction for nitrate anions, whereas chloride ions attract hydrogen
ions. Obviously, silver ion and chloride ion have a mutual attraction for each
other. However, the concentrations of silver ion and chloride ion should be
quite small compared to the quantities of hydrogen ion and nitrate ion, so
the ion atmosphere of a silver ion contains nitrate as well as water and the
ion atmosphere of chloride consists predominantly of hydrogen ions and
water. The effect of the ion atmospheres is to neutralize partially the charge
of a silver ion and of a chloride ion and to decrease their force of attraction
for each other. If the force of attraction between Ag^+ and Cl^- is less in nitric
acid than in pure water, it follows that the solubility of silver chloride should
be larger in the former solvent. This conclusion is correct; such a simple
picture affords a valuable way to predict the effects of foreign electrolytes on
chemical equilibria.

Quantitative predictions of the effect of a foreign electrolyte on the
solubility of silver chloride can. be based upon the equation introduced
previously,

$$f_\pm{}^2[Ag^+][Cl^-] = K_{ap}$$

where $f_\pm$ is the mean activity coefficient for silver chloride and $[Ag^+]$ and
$[Cl^-]$ represent the analytical concentrations of silver ion and chloride ion,
respectively. Since the solubility S of silver chloride is measured by the concentration of silver ion (neglecting the presence of aqueous molecular silver
chloride) and since the concentrations of silver and chloride ions are equal,
we may write

$$f_\pm{}^2 S^2 = K_{ap}$$

$$S = \frac{(K_{ap})^{1/2}}{f_\pm}$$

It is evident from the latter equation that the solubility of silver chloride
should increase as the mean activity coefficient decreases; and, of course, the
converse is true. Noting the variation of activity coefficients with ionic
strength in Figures 4-3 and 4-4, we can conclude that a plot of solubility
versus ionic strength will exhibit an initial rise followed by a decrease. It
should be recalled (see Table 4-2) that activity coefficients for ions with
multiple charges are much more sensitive to variations in ionic strength than
those for singly charged species. Consequently, the solubility of precipitates
consisting of multicharged ions will change much more drastically with ionic
strength than, say, the solubility of silver chloride.

Let us compare the solubility of silver chloride in water and in $0.05\ F$ nitric acid. For water, the ionic strength μ is nearly zero because the concentrations of dissolved silver ion and chloride ion are very small. Thus, we shall assume that the mean activity coefficient is essentially unity. Therefore, the solubility S of silver chloride is given by the simple relation

$$S = (K_{ap})^{1/2} = (1.78 \times 10^{-10})^{1/2}$$
$$S = 1.33 \times 10^{-5}\ M$$

However, a calculation of the solubility of silver chloride in $0.05\ F$ nitric acid requires that we determine the ionic strength of the solution and the mean activity coefficient of silver chloride. Although the ionic strength of a solution does depend on the concentrations of all ionic species, the contribution to the ionic strength by dissolved silver chloride is negligible, so

$$\mu = \tfrac{1}{2}[C_{H^+}z_{H^+}{}^2 + C_{NO_3^-}z_{NO_3^-}^2]$$
$$\mu = \tfrac{1}{2}[(0.05)(1)^2 + (0.05)(-1)^2]$$
$$\mu = 0.05$$

We shall use the Debye-Hückel limiting law to obtain the mean activity coefficient, even though the ionic strength is sufficiently high that the limiting law is somewhat inaccurate.

$$-\log f_{\pm} = 0.512 z_M z_N \sqrt{\mu}$$
$$-\log f_{\pm} = (0.512)(1)(1)\sqrt{0.05}$$
$$-\log f_{\pm} = 0.114$$
$$f_{\pm} = 0.77$$

If we now combine this result with the equation for the solubility of silver chloride, the value of S can be calculated:

$$S = \frac{(K_{ap})^{1/2}}{f_{\pm}} = \frac{(1.78 \times 10^{-10})^{1/2}}{0.77}$$
$$S = 1.73 \times 10^{-5}\ M$$

Therefore, the solubility of silver chloride is about 30 per cent higher in $0.05\ F$ nitric acid than in water. We suggest that the reader perform a similar calculation using the extended Debye-Hückel equation.

Common Ion Effect

The influence of an excess of one of the ions comprising a precipitate upon the solubility of that compound is called the **common ion effect.** An application of Le Châtelier's principle to the chemical equation representing the state of equilibrium between dissolved and undissolved solute reveals that the excess of common ion represses the solubility of the substance.

In general, solubility-product considerations permit us to make predictions about the magnitude of the common ion effect.

In the classic gravimetric determination of silver ion, one usually adds an excess of chloride ion to precipitate silver chloride quantitatively. If we examine the simple solubility-product expression for silver chloride,

$$[Ag^+][Cl^-] = K_{sp} = 1.78 \times 10^{-10}$$

it appears that any desired completeness of precipitation could be achieved through a suitable adjustment of the chloride concentration. For example, if the chloride ion concentration were $1 \times 10^{-3} M$, the concentration of silver ion should be $1.78 \times 10^{-7} M$, whereas the concentration of silver ion ought to be only $1.78 \times 10^{-9} M$ when the chloride concentration is $0.1 M$. Although it is important to recognize the usefulness of the common ion effect in the prediction of experimental conditions for a desired gravimetric determination, it is equally important to realize that serious errors can result if one places too much confidence in such calculations. It was previously shown that a certain concentration, approximately $2 \times 10^{-7} M$, of aqueous molecular silver chloride exists in equilibrium with the solid and that this concentration is unaffected by the occurrence of other chemical reactions. Therefore, the concentration of AgCl(aq) represents the minimum concentration of dissolved silver chloride that is attainable in an aqueous solution — in spite of the predictions reached on the basis of the common ion effect.

The following example, in which we will calculate the solubility of lead iodate, $Pb(IO_3)_2$, in pure water and in $0.03 F$ potassium iodate solution, illustrates the principle of the common ion effect. The solubility and solubility-product constant for lead iodate may be represented as

$$Pb(IO_3)_2(s) \rightleftharpoons Pb^{++} + 2 IO_3^-; \qquad K_{sp} = 2.6 \times 10^{-13}$$

In water, each dissolved lead iodate molecule yields one lead ion and two iodate ions. If we represent the solubility of lead iodate by the symbol S, we can write

$$[Pb^{++}] = S \quad \text{and} \quad [IO_3^-] = 2S$$

If these mathematical statements are substituted into the solubility-product expression, we obtain

$$[Pb^{++}][IO_3^-]^2 = (S)(2S)^2 = 2.6 \times 10^{-13}$$
$$4S^3 = 2.6 \times 10^{-13}$$
$$S = 4.0 \times 10^{-5} M$$

for the solubility of lead iodate in water.

In the $0.03 F$ potassium iodate medium, the calculation is slightly more complicated, for there are two sources of iodate ion. At equilibrium the concentration of iodate will be the sum of the contributions from potassium iodate and lead iodate — $0.03 M$ from potassium iodate and $2S$ from lead iodate. As before, the equilibrium concentration of lead ion can be called S. The appropriate solubility-product expression is

$$(S)(2S + 0.03)^2 = 2.6 \times 10^{-13}$$

This relation could be solved in a completely rigorous manner, but the manipulations would involve a third-order equation. Therefore, it is worthwhile to consider the feasibility of a suitable simplifying assumption. Since the solubility of lead iodate in water is only $4.0 \times 10^{-5} M$ and since the presence of potassium iodate should repress the solubility of lead iodate, we will neglect the $2S$ term in the preceding expression:

$$(S)(0.03)^2 = 2.6 \times 10^{-13}$$

This equation may be readily solved.

$$S = \frac{2.6 \times 10^{-13}}{9 \times 10^{-4}} = 2.9 \times 10^{-10} M$$

Certainly our neglect of the $2S$ term in comparison to $0.03\ M$ was justified, since the solubility of lead iodate is substantially decreased through the addition of potassium iodate.

Complexation by Excess Common Ion

At the beginning of this section, the solubility of silver chloride in water was discussed and it was suggested that a complete description of the solubility of silver chloride requires detailed knowledge concerning several interrelated equilibria. In particular, it was indicated that certain anionic complexes such as $AgCl_2^-$ and $AgCl_3^=$ may exist to a significant extent when the chloride concentration is relatively large. Accordingly, it is of considerable interest to examine the solubility behavior of silver chloride in the presence of excess chloride ion. In general, we can express the solubility S of silver chloride as a sum of concentrations of all pertinent species:

$$S = [Ag^+] + [AgCl(aq)] + [AgCl_2^-] + [AgCl_3^=] + [AgCl_4^\equiv]$$

The five silver-containing species in the preceding relation account well for the overall solubility behavior of silver chloride over a wide range of chloride concentrations.

The concentrations of these five species are related to each other through a family of equilibria. First, we can write the solubility-product expression

$$AgCl(s) \rightleftharpoons Ag^+ + Cl^-; \qquad K_{sp} = [Ag^+][Cl^-]$$

and the intrinsic solubility relationship

$$AgCl(s) \rightleftharpoons AgCl(aq); \qquad S^\circ = [AgCl(aq)]$$

Then, we may formulate the expressions for the stepwise formation of the $AgCl(aq)$, $AgCl_2^-$, $AgCl_3^=$, and $AgCl_4^=$ species.

$$Ag^+ + Cl^- \rightleftharpoons AgCl(aq); \qquad K_1 = \frac{[AgCl(aq)]}{[Ag^+][Cl^-]}$$

$$AgCl(aq) + Cl^- \rightleftharpoons AgCl_2^-; \qquad K_2 = \frac{[AgCl_2^-]}{[AgCl(aq)][Cl^-]}$$

$$AgCl_2^- + Cl^- \rightleftharpoons AgCl_3^=; \qquad K_3 = \frac{[AgCl_3^=]}{[AgCl_2^-][Cl^-]}$$

$$AgCl_3^= + Cl^- \rightleftharpoons AgCl_4^=; \qquad K_4 = \frac{[AgCl_4^=]}{[AgCl_3^=][Cl^-]}$$

Since we are mainly interested in the solubility of silver chloride as a function of the chloride ion concentration, it is necessary to express the concentration of each of the individual silver-containing species in terms of the chloride concentration and the various equilibrium constants. When these manipulations are completed, the following results are obtained:

$$[Ag^+] = \frac{K_{sp}}{[Cl^-]}$$
$$[AgCl(aq)] = S^\circ = K_1 K_{sp}$$
$$[AgCl_2^-] = K_1 K_2 K_{sp}[Cl^-]$$
$$[AgCl_3^=] = K_1 K_2 K_3 K_{sp}[Cl^-]^2$$
$$[AgCl_4^=] = K_1 K_2 K_3 K_4 K_{sp}[Cl^-]^3$$

Thus the solubility of silver chloride may be written as

$$S = \frac{K_{sp}}{[Cl^-]} + S^\circ + K_1 K_2 K_{sp}[Cl^-] + K_1 K_2 K_3 K_{sp}[Cl^-]^2 + K_1 K_2 K_3 K_4 K_{sp}[Cl^-]^3$$

The previous equation is inherently difficult to handle, owing to its complicated form. However, it is possible to portray the silver chloride system in a graphical manner which permits one to conclude immediately for any chosen chloride concentration what the solubility of silver chloride is and what the predominant silver-containing species are.

If the expression for the concentration of each silver-containing species is rewritten in logarithmic form, one finds that

$$\log [Ag^+] = \log K_{sp} - \log [Cl^-]$$
$$\log [AgCl(aq)] = \log S^\circ = \log K_1 K_{sp}$$
$$\log [AgCl_2^-] = \log K_1 K_2 K_{sp} + \log [Cl^-]$$
$$\log [AgCl_3^=] = \log K_1 K_2 K_3 K_{sp} + 2 \log [Cl^-]$$
$$\log [AgCl_4^=] = \log K_1 K_2 K_3 K_4 K_{sp} + 3 \log [Cl^-]$$

Using these latter relations, we have constructed Figure 4-5, in which the logarithm of the concentration of each silver species is plotted against the logarithm of the chloride concentration. The important and useful feature of

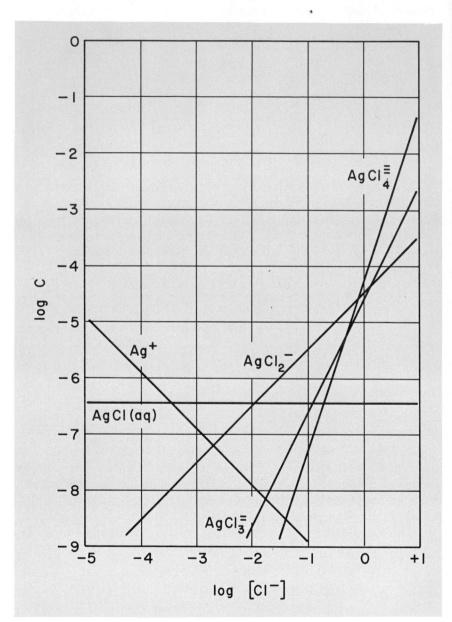

FIGURE 4-5.   Logarithm of the concentration of various silver species in equilibrium with solid silver chloride as a function of the logarithm of the chloride concentration at 25°C. (See text for discussion.)

this graph is that straight-line relationships always exist between the logarithm of the concentration of a given species and the logarithm of the chloride concentration. In addition, there is an interesting correlation between the slope of each straight line and the charge of the species to which that straight line corresponds. For example, if we differentiate the expression

$$\log [Ag^+] = \log K_{sp} - \log [Cl^-]$$

with respect to $\log [Cl^-]$, the result is

$$\frac{d \log [Ag^+]}{d \log [Cl^-]} = -1$$

which confirms that the slope of the straight line denoting Ag^+ is -1, as shown in Figure 4-5. However, notice that the charge on the silver ion is $+1$. In fact, the slope of the straight line for each species is always *equal* in magnitude but *opposite* in sign to the charge of that species, as may be demonstrated for the other four species in the silver chloride system.

With the aid of Figure 4-5, one can evaluate no less than eleven different equilibrium constants pertaining to the silver chloride system. It should be stressed, however, that in order to construct this figure, one must know the equilibrium constants in advance, since these latter parameters actually fix the positions of the straight lines. To illustrate how one determines an equilibrium constant from this graph, let us consider the reaction

$$AgCl(aq) + 2\ Cl^- \rightleftharpoons AgCl_3^=$$

First, we find the point of intersection for the two lines corresponding to $AgCl(aq)$ and $AgCl_3^=$. At the point of intersection the concentration of each species is the same, so we may write

$$\frac{[AgCl_3^=]}{[AgCl(aq)][Cl^-]^2} = K_2 K_3$$

and

$$\frac{1}{[Cl^-]^2} = K_2 K_3$$

Second, we find the logarithm of the chloride concentration corresponding to this point of intersection, which in the present example is -0.9. Thus, since

$$\log [Cl^-] = -0.9 = 0.1 - 1.0$$

it follows that

$$[Cl^-] = 0.126\ M$$

Third, we substitute the chloride concentration into the desired equilibrium expression to obtain the equilibrium constant:

$$\frac{1}{(0.126)^2} = K_2 K_3 = 63$$

A problem dealing with Figure 4-5 is presented at the end of this chapter. In addition, Figure 4-6 shows an analogous, but somewhat more complicated,

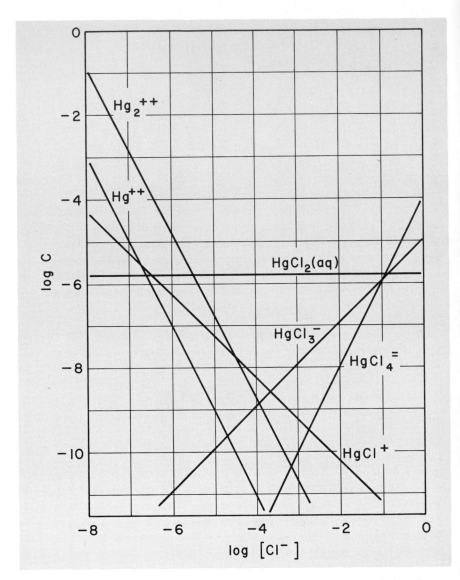

FIGURE 4-6.   Logarithm of the concentration of various mercury(II) and mercury(I) species in equilibrium with Hg_2Cl_2 and Hg as a function of the logarithm of the chloride concentration at 25°C.

logarithmic diagram for the system involving mercury(I) chloride and elemental mercury.

Complexation of Cation with Foreign Ligand

In the preceding paragraphs, we considered the solubility of a precipitate in the presence of excess common ion. In addition, the solubility of a
compound can be markedly enhanced if a foreign complexing agent or
ligand is available which can react with the cation of a precipitate. As an
example of the latter kind of system, we may cite the increase in the solubility
of the silver halides, AgCl, AgBr, and AgI, in ammonia solutions.

If we consider the solubility of silver bromide in aqueous ammonia
solutions, it should be evident that the position of equilibrium for the
reaction

$$AgBr(s) \rightleftharpoons Ag^+ + Br^-; \qquad K_{sp} = 5.25 \times 10^{-13}$$

will be shifted toward the right because of the formation of stable silver-
ammine complexes. Silver ion reacts with ammonia in a stepwise manner,
according to the equilibria

$$Ag^+ + NH_3 \rightleftharpoons AgNH_3^+; \qquad K_1 = 2.5 \times 10^3$$

and

$$AgNH_3^+ + NH_3 \rightleftharpoons Ag(NH_3)_2^+; \qquad K_2 = 1.0 \times 10^4$$

Suppose it is desired to calculate the solubility of silver bromide in a
$0.1\ F$ ammonia solution. On the basis of the preceding reactions, we can
conclude that each silver bromide molecule which dissolves will yield one
bromide ion and either one Ag^+, one $AgNH_3^+$, or one $Ag(NH_3)_2^+$. Therefore,
the solubility S of silver bromide is measured by the concentration of bromide
ion or, alternatively, by the sum of the concentrations of all soluble silver
species, i.e.,

$$S = [Ag^+] + [AgNH_3^+] + [Ag(NH_3)_2^+] = [Br^-]$$

This relation may be transformed into one equation with a single unknown
if we introduce the equilibrium constant expressions for the silver-ammine
species. For the concentration of the silver-monoammine complex, it can be
shown that

$$[AgNH_3^+] = K_1[Ag^+][NH_3]$$

The concentration of the silver-diammine complex may be written as

$$[Ag(NH_3)_2^+] = K_2[AgNH_3^+][NH_3]$$

or

$$[Ag(NH_3)_2^+] = K_1K_2[Ag^+][NH_3]^2$$

If we substitute the relations for the concentrations of the two silver-ammine
complexes into the solubility equation, the result is

$$S = [Ag^+] + K_1[Ag^+][NH_3] + K_1K_2[Ag^+][NH_3]^2 = [Br^-]$$

Next, we should note that, in a solution saturated with silver bromide, the solubility-product expression must be obeyed; that is,

$$[Ag^+] = \frac{K_{sp}}{[Br^-]}$$

so it follows that

$$S = \frac{K_{sp}}{[Br^-]} + \frac{K_1 K_{sp}[NH_3]}{[Br^-]} + \frac{K_1 K_2 K_{sp}[NH_3]^2}{[Br^-]} = [Br^-]$$

However, since $[Br^-] = S$, we can write

$$S = \frac{K_{sp}}{S} + \frac{K_1 K_{sp}[NH_3]}{S} + \frac{K_1 K_2 K_{sp}[NH_3]^2}{S}$$

Finally, solving for the solubility S, we obtain

$$S^2 = K_{sp} + K_1 K_{sp}[NH_3] + K_1 K_2 K_{sp}[NH_3]^2$$
$$S = (K_{sp})^{1/2}(1 + K_1[NH_3] + K_1 K_2[NH_3]^2)^{1/2}$$

Before we insert values for the ammonia concentration and the various constants into the latter equation, it is interesting to note that this relation is a general one for the solubility of *any* sparingly soluble silver salt in an ammonia solution. For the solubility of silver bromide in a 0.1 F ammonia solution, we have

$$S = (5.25 \times 10^{-13})^{1/2}$$
$$\times [1 + (2.5 \times 10^3)(0.1) + (2.5 \times 10^3)(1.0 \times 10^4)(0.1)^2]^{1/2}$$
$$S = 3.6 \times 10^{-4} \ M$$

In addition, we can calculate the concentration of each soluble silver species. For Ag^+:

$$[Ag^+] = \frac{K_{sp}}{[Br^-]} = \frac{5.25 \times 10^{-13}}{3.6 \times 10^{-4}} = 1.46 \times 10^{-9} \ M$$

For $AgNH_3^+$:

$$[AgNH_3^+] = K_1[Ag^+][NH_3] = (2.5 \times 10^3)(1.46 \times 10^{-9})(0.1)$$
$$[AgNH_3^+] = 3.6 \times 10^{-7} \ M$$

For $Ag(NH_3)_2^+$:

$$[Ag(NH_3)_2^+] = K_2[AgNH_3^+][NH_3] = (1.0 \times 10^4)(3.6 \times 10^{-7})(0.1)$$
$$[Ag(NH_3)_2^+] = 3.6 \times 10^{-4} \ M$$

Therefore, the only species which contributes significantly to the solubility of silver bromide is the silver-diammine complex. One of the possible complications which we overlooked in solving this problem was the possibility that the formation of silver-ammine complexes might alter the concentration of ammonia. However, it is apparent that the solubility of silver bromide is small enough that neglect of this effect was justified. If the solubility of silver bromide were of comparable magnitude to the ammonia concentration, it would be necessary to consider the change in the concentration of ammonia.

Reaction of Anion with Acid

Up to this point, those chemical reactions leading to an increase in solubility have involved only the cation of a precipitate. In certain instances, the anion of the slightly soluble compound undergoes an interaction with one or more of the constituents of a solution phase. For example, if the solubility of lead sulfate in nitric acid media is investigated, one finds that the solubility is greater than in pure water and that the solubility becomes larger as the concentration of nitric acid increases.

In pure water the solubility of lead sulfate is governed by the equilibrium

$$PbSO_4(s) \rightleftharpoons Pb^{++} + SO_4^=; \quad K_{sp} = 1.6 \times 10^{-8}$$

and, if no other equilibria prevail, the solubility of lead sulfate should essentially be the square root of the solubility product, or approximately $1.3 \times 10^{-4} \ M$.

If nitric acid is added to the system, the solubility of lead sulfate increases because sulfate ion reacts with hydrogen ion to form the hydrogen sulfate anion:

$$H^+ + SO_4^= \rightleftharpoons HSO_4^-$$

However, the addition of another proton to the hydrogen sulfate ion,

$$H^+ + HSO_4^- \rightleftharpoons H_2SO_4$$

does not occur to any appreciable extent because sulfuric acid is a very strong acid. Therefore, when a lead sulfate molecule dissolves in nitric acid, one lead ion is formed, but the sulfate ion from the precipitate may be present as either $SO_4^=$ or HSO_4^-. Accordingly, we can express the solubility S of lead sulfate in nitric acid by means of the equation

$$S = [Pb^{++}] = [SO_4^=] + [HSO_4^-]$$

A relationship between the concentrations of sulfate ion and hydrogen sulfate ion can be based on the equilibrium expression for the *second* ionization of sulfuric acid, namely,

$$HSO_4^- \rightleftharpoons H^+ + SO_4^=; \quad K_2 = 1.2 \times 10^{-2}$$

By substituting the latter information into the solubility equation, we obtain

$$S = [Pb^{++}] = [SO_4^=] + \frac{[H^+][SO_4^=]}{K_2}$$

and, by utilizing the solubility-product expression for lead sulfate, we can write

$$S = [Pb^{++}] = \frac{K_{sp}}{[Pb^{++}]} + \frac{K_{sp}[H^+]}{K_2[Pb^{++}]}$$

$$[Pb^{++}]^2 = K_{sp} + \frac{K_{sp}[H^+]}{K_2}$$

$$[Pb^{++}] = \left(K_{sp} + \frac{K_{sp}[H^+]}{K_2}\right)^{1/2}$$

Provided that the hydrogen ion concentration is known, we can calculate from the latter relation the concentration of lead ion in equilibrium with solid lead sulfate and, therefore, the solubility of lead sulfate itself.

Suppose that we wish to predict the solubility of lead sulfate in $0.10\,F$ nitric acid. One of the questions that must be answered concerns whether the formation of the hydrogen sulfate anion, through the reaction of $SO_4^=$ with H^+, will consume enough hydrogen ion to change significantly the concentration of the latter. We can either assume that the change will be important — in which case the computations are relatively difficult — or that this change may be neglected as a first approximation. If the second alternative is chosen, it will be necessary to justify the validity of the original assumption after the calculations are completed. Let us assume that the concentration of hydrogen ion remains essentially constant at $0.1\,M$. Thus, the lead ion concentration is given by the equation

$$[Pb^{++}] = \left(1.6 \times 10^{-8} + \frac{(1.6 \times 10^{-8})(0.1)}{(1.2 \times 10^{-2})}\right)^{1/2}$$

which, when solved, yields

$$[Pb^{++}] = 3.9 \times 10^{-4}\,M$$

Even if all the sulfate derived from the dissolution of lead sulfate were converted to hydrogen sulfate anion, the change in the hydrogen ion concentration would be negligibly small. Therefore, by making a simplifying assumption and later justifying its validity, we obtain the desired result in a straightforward way. If, on the other hand, the lead ion concentration is shown to be comparable to the original concentration of nitric acid, we should immediately suspect that our assumption was false and return to a more rigorous solution to the problem. It should be stressed that the primary reason for making the assumption was the smallness of the solubility product of lead sulfate compared to the initial nitric acid concentration. It is essential to be aware of such situations in equilibrium calculations.

The results of this equilibrium calculation have much broader significance. Note that the solubility of lead sulfate in an acid medium was increased because of the reaction between the anion of the precipitate and the hydrogen ion furnished by the acid. In general, any precipitate whose anion happens to be the anion (conjugate base) of a weak acid will exhibit behavior similar to lead sulfate. Included among such species are acetate, fluoride, oxalate, carbonate, phosphate, arsenate, and sulfide — all of which react with hydrogen ion.

QUESTIONS AND PROBLEMS

1. The reaction

$$2\ Fe^{+++} + 3\ I^- \rightleftharpoons 2\ Fe^{++} + I_3^-$$

was discussed in an early section of this chapter. If, as stated in the text, one starts with $0.200\ M$ iron(III) and $0.300\ M$ iodide and if the equilibrium concentration of triiodide ion is $0.0866\ M$, calculate the equilibrium concentrations of Fe^{+++}, Fe^{++}, and I^- and evaluate the equilibrium constant for the reaction. Neglect activity effects and assume that Fe^{+++} and Fe^{++} are the only forms of iron(III) and iron(II) present.

2. Assume that one prepared a solution corresponding to the equilibrium state of the preceding problem by mixing solutions of Fe^{+++}, Fe^{++}, I^-, and I_3^- to give the appropriate equilibrium concentrations. If all the iodide ion is initially radioactive, what is the final concentration of radioactive iodide ion after a true state of dynamic equilibrium is established?

3. Suppose the equilibrium-constant expression for the reaction

$$2\ A + B \rightleftharpoons C + 2\ D$$

is to be formulated according to the law of mass action. Assume that the overall process occurs according to the following series of steps:

$$\text{(a)} \quad A + B \rightleftharpoons Z + D$$
$$\text{(b)} \quad A + Z \rightleftharpoons C + D$$

Using appropriate symbols for the forward and backward rate constants for each step, writing the expressions for the rates of the forward and backward reactions for each step, and proposing the rates of the forward and backward reactions to be equal at equilibrium, show that the resulting equilibrium-constant expression obtained from the two-step reaction mechanism is identical to that which one can write by simple inspection of the overall reaction.

4. A decision regarding the identity or formula of the gold(I) ion in aqueous solutions can be reached by equilibrium calculations. When *solid metallic gold* is shaken (equilibrated) with an acidic solution of gold(III) ion, which exists as the (hydrated) species Au^{+++}, gold(I) ions are formed. Two possible equilibrium reactions can occur:

$$\text{(a)} \quad 2\ Au(s) + Au^{+++} \rightleftharpoons 3\ Au^+$$

if Au^+ is the species of gold(I) present, or

$$\text{(b)} \quad 4\ Au(s) + 2\ Au^{+++} \rightleftharpoons 3\ Au_2^{++}$$

if the dimeric species Au_2^{++} is present. When two such equilibration experiments (shaking solid gold metal with Au^{+++} solutions) were performed and the solutions were finally analyzed for Au^{+++} and for gold(I) species, the following results were obtained: Experiment I, $[Au^{+++}] = 1.50 \times 10^{-3}\ M$ and the *total* analytical concentration of gold(I) $= 1.02 \times 10^{-4}\ M$; Experiment II, $[Au^{+++}] = 4.50 \times 10^{-3}\ M$ and the *total* analytical concentration of gold(I) $= 1.47 \times 10^{-4}\ M$. Write the equilibrium-constant expressions for the two proposed reactions. Designate the equilibrium constant for reaction (a) as K_1 and that for reaction (b) as K_2. On the basis of the equilibrium data given, what conclusion do you draw regarding the formula for the gold(I) ion?

5. (a) In 1 liter of a $1.0\,F$ hydrochloric acid solution, 1.3×10^{-3} formula weight of lead sulfate dissolves. Calculate the solubility of lead sulfate in pure water.

    (b) Let the solubility of lead sulfate (formula weights per liter) in pure water be S_0. Suppose that solid sodium nitrate is dissolved in a saturated lead sulfate solution in equilibrium with excess solid lead sulfate in such a way that the ionic strength μ of the solution is increased until it becomes saturated with sodium nitrate. Construct a qualitative plot to show how the solubility of lead sulfate varies with ionic strength. How do you interpret this plot?

6. (a) Predict qualitatively and explain briefly how an *increase* in ionic strength μ affects the following:

    (i) The *solubility* of silver chloride, according to the equilibrium

    $$AgCl(s) \rightleftharpoons Ag^+ + Cl^-$$

    (ii) The *association* of hydrogen ion and acetate ion to form acetic acid, according to the equilibrium

    $$H^+ + CH_3COO^- \rightleftharpoons CH_3COOH$$

    (iii) The *dissociation* of $AgCl_2^-$, according to the equilibrium

    $$AgCl_2^- \rightleftharpoons AgCl(aq) + Cl^-$$

    (iv) The *dissociation* of $AgCl_2^-$, according to the equilibrium

    $$AgCl_2^- \rightleftharpoons Ag^+ + 2\,Cl^-$$

    (b) Changes in ionic strength μ have a greater effect on the solubility of barium sulfate than on the solubility of silver chloride. Explain briefly.

7. Calculate the solubility product of silver chromate given the following thermodynamic data at $25°C$:

    $$Ag^+(aq): \mu° = +18.4 \text{ kcal/mole}$$
    $$Ag_2CrO_4(s): \mu° = -154.7 \text{ kcal/mole}$$
    $$CrO_4^=(aq): \mu° = -176.1 \text{ kcal/mole}$$
    $$R = 1.99 \text{ cal/mole-deg}$$

8. Calculate the solubility of silver iodide (AgI) in a solution containing $0.01\,F$ sodium thiosulfate ($Na_2S_2O_3$) and $0.01\,F$ potassium iodide (KI).

    $$AgI(s) \rightleftharpoons Ag^+ + I^-; \qquad K_{sp} = 8.3 \times 10^{-17}$$
    $$AgI(s) \rightleftharpoons AgI(aq); \qquad S° = 6.0 \times 10^{-9}$$
    $$Ag^+ + S_2O_3^= \rightleftharpoons AgS_2O_3^-; \qquad K_1 = 6.6 \times 10^8$$
    $$AgS_2O_3^- + S_2O_3^= \rightleftharpoons Ag(S_2O_3)_2^{-3}; \qquad K_2 = 4.4 \times 10^4$$
    $$Ag(S_2O_3)_2^{-3} + S_2O_3^= \rightleftharpoons Ag(S_2O_3)_3^{-5}; \qquad K_3 = 4.9$$

9. The solubility of barium sulfate ($BaSO_4$) in pure water is $0.96 \times 10^{-5}\,M$ at $25°C$. Using the Debye-Hückel limiting law, calculate the solubility of barium sulfate in a $0.030\,F$ potassium nitrate (KNO_3) solution.

10. A solution is saturated with respect to a compound of the general formula AB_2C_3:

    $$AB_2C_3(s) \rightleftharpoons A^+ + 2\,B^+ + 3\,C^-$$

    If this solution is found to contain ion C^- at a concentration of $0.003\,M$, calculate the solubility product of the compound AB_2C_3.

11. The solubility product of calcium sulfate, $CaSO_4$, is 1.9×10^{-4}. What is its solubility in water neglecting activity coefficients? What is its solubility in water

assuming that the activity coefficients are those calculated according to the Debye-Hückel limiting law?

12. Calculate the solubility of barium chromate in an acetic acid-sodium acetate buffer of pH 4.26.

$$BaCrO_4(s) \rightleftharpoons Ba^{++} + CrO_4^=; \qquad K_{sp} = 2.4 \times 10^{-10}$$
$$HCrO_4^- \rightleftharpoons H^+ + CrO_4^=; \qquad K_2 = 3.3 \times 10^{-6}$$
$$2\ HCrO_4^- \rightleftharpoons Cr_2O_7^= + H_2O; \qquad K = 43$$

13. Excess solid barium sulfate was shaken with 3.6 F hydrochloric acid until equilibrium was attained. Calculate the equilibrium solubility of barium sulfate and the concentrations of $SO_4^=$ and HSO_4^-.

$$BaSO_4(s) \rightleftharpoons Ba^{++} + SO_4^=; \qquad K_{sp} = 1.1 \times 10^{-10}$$
$$H_2SO_4 \rightleftharpoons H^+ + HSO_4^-; \qquad K_1 \gg 1$$
$$HSO_4^- \rightleftharpoons H^+ + SO_4^=; \qquad K_2 = 1.2 \times 10^{-2}$$

14. Calcium is frequently determined through its precipitation as $CaC_2O_4 \cdot H_2O$, the dissolution of the precipitate in an acid medium, and the subsequent determination of oxalate by titration with standard potassium permanganate. Suppose that 80 mg of calcium is to be determined by this procedure and that for the precipitation of $CaC_2O_4 \cdot H_2O$ the following conditions are to be established:
(a) Volume of solution is 100 ml.
(b) Maximal weight of dissolved calcium in solution at equilibrium is 0.80 μgm.
(c) The pH of the solution is controlled with an acetic acid-sodium acetate buffer at pH 4.70.
In order to meet the desired conditions for this precipitation (so that the maximal amount of dissolved calcium is not exceeded), what must be the *total concentration* of *all* oxalate species in the solution?

$$CaC_2O_4(s) \rightleftharpoons Ca^{++} + C_2O_4^=; \qquad K_{sp} = 2.6 \times 10^{-9}$$
$$CH_3COOH \rightleftharpoons H^+ + CH_3COO^-; \qquad K = 1.8 \times 10^{-5}$$
$$H_2C_2O_4 \rightleftharpoons H^+ + HC_2O_4^-; \qquad K_1 = 6.5 \times 10^{-2}$$
$$HC_2O_4^- \rightleftharpoons H^+ + C_2O_4^=; \qquad K_2 = 6.1 \times 10^{-5}$$

15. Calculate the solubility of cuprous iodide in a 0.35 F ammonia solution.

$$CuI(s) \rightleftharpoons Cu^+ + I^-; \qquad K_{sp} = 5.1 \times 10^{-12}$$
$$Cu^+ + NH_3 \rightleftharpoons CuNH_3^+; \qquad K_1 = 8.0 \times 10^5$$
$$CuNH_3^+ + NH_3 \rightleftharpoons Cu(NH_3)_2^+; \qquad K_2 = 8.0 \times 10^4$$

16. The various equilibria between mercuric ion, Hg^{++}, and iodide ion, I^-, are given by the following data:

$$Hg^{++} + I^- \rightleftharpoons HgI^+; \qquad pK_1 = -12.87$$
$$HgI^+ + I^- \rightleftharpoons HgI_2(aq); \qquad pK_2 = -10.95$$
$$HgI_2(aq) + I^- \rightleftharpoons HgI_3^-; \qquad pK_3 = -3.78$$
$$HgI_3^- + I^- \rightleftharpoons HgI_4^=; \qquad pK_4 = -2.23$$
$$HgI_2(s) \rightleftharpoons HgI_2(aq); \qquad pS^\circ = 4.10$$

Calculate the solubility (moles per liter) of mercuric iodide in water.

17. If the concentration of rubidium ion, Rb^+, is decreased by a factor of 111 when 3.00 moles of lithium perchlorate, $LiClO_4$, are added to 1 liter of a saturated rubidium perchlorate solution, what is the solubility product of $RbClO_4$?

18. If 1 liter of a saturated solution of $AgIO_3$ (no solid present) is equilibrated with 3.5×10^{-5} mole of $Pb(IO_3)_2$, what will be the equilibrium concentrations of silver, lead, and iodate ions; and how many milligrams of $AgIO_3$, if any, will precipitate?

$$AgIO_3(s) \rightleftharpoons Ag^+ + IO_3^-; \qquad K_{sp} = 3.0 \times 10^{-8}$$
$$Pb(IO_3)_2(s) \rightleftharpoons Pb^{++} + 2\,IO_3^-; \qquad K_{sp} = 2.6 \times 10^{-13}$$

19. Calculate the solubility of zinc hydroxide, $Zn(OH)_2(s)$, in a 0.1 F sodium hydroxide solution, given the following equilibria:

$$Zn(OH)_2(s) \rightleftharpoons Zn^{++} + 2\,OH^-; \qquad K_{sp} = 1.2 \times 10^{-17}$$
$$Zn(OH)_2(s) \rightleftharpoons Zn(OH)_2(aq); \qquad S^\circ = 10^{-6}$$
$$Zn(OH)_2(s) \rightleftharpoons ZnOH^+ + OH^-; \qquad K = 2.4 \times 10^{-13}$$
$$Zn(OH)_2(s) + OH^- \rightleftharpoons Zn(OH)_3^-; \qquad K' = 2.4 \times 10^{-3}$$
$$Zn(OH)_2(s) + 2\,OH^- \rightleftharpoons Zn(OH)_4^=; \qquad K'' = 2.4 \times 10^{-2}$$

20. The equilibria involving the solubilities of lead sulfate and strontium sulfate and the ionization of sulfuric acid are as follows:

$$PbSO_4(s) \rightleftharpoons Pb^{++} + SO_4^=; \qquad K_{sp} = 1.6 \times 10^{-8}$$
$$SrSO_4(s) \rightleftharpoons Sr^{++} + SO_4^=; \qquad K_{sp} = 3.8 \times 10^{-7}$$
$$H_2SO_4 \rightleftharpoons H^+ + HSO_4^-; \qquad K_1 \gg 1$$
$$HSO_4^- \rightleftharpoons H^+ + SO_4^=; \qquad K_2 = 1.2 \times 10^{-2}$$

If an excess of both lead sulfate and strontium sulfate is shaken with a 0.60 F nitric acid solution until equilibrium is attained, what will be the concentrations of Pb^{++}, Sr^{++}, HSO_4^-, and $SO_4^=$?

21. Excess barium sulfate was shaken with 0.25 F sulfuric acid until equilibrium was attained. What was the concentration of barium ion in the solution?

$$BaSO_4(s) \rightleftharpoons Ba^{++} + SO_4^=; \qquad K_{sp} = 1.1 \times 10^{-10}$$
$$H_2SO_4 \rightleftharpoons H^+ + HSO_4^-; \qquad K_1 \gg 1$$
$$HSO_4^- \rightleftharpoons H^+ + SO_4^=; \qquad K_2 = 1.2 \times 10^{-2}$$

22. The following questions pertain to the solubility of $AgCl(s)$ and can and should be answered *only* with the aid of Figure 4-5.

(a) Evaluate the equilibrium constants for the following reactions:

$$AgCl_2^- + Cl^- \rightleftharpoons AgCl_3^=$$
$$AgCl_2^- \rightleftharpoons Ag^+ + 2\,Cl^-$$
$$Ag^+ + 3\,Cl^- \rightleftharpoons AgCl_3^=$$
$$AgCl(s) \rightleftharpoons Ag^+ + Cl^-$$

(b) What is the minimal solubility of silver chloride? At what value of the chloride concentration does this minimal solubility occur? What is the silver ion concentration at this point? What is the predominant silver species in this solution?

23. Using information obtainable from Figure 4-6, answer the following:

(a) Calculate the solubility product of $Hg_2Cl_2(s)$.

(b) Calculate the value of the chloride concentration for which the solubility of $HgCl_2(s)$ is minimal.

(c) Evaluate the equilibrium constant for the reaction

$$Hg^{++} + Cl^- \rightleftharpoons HgCl^+$$

24. The pertinent equilibria for the nickel(II)-hydroxide system are as follows:

$$Ni^{++} + OH^- \rightleftharpoons NiOH^+; \qquad K_1 = 2.0 \times 10^3$$
$$NiOH^+ + OH^- \rightleftharpoons Ni(OH)_2(aq); \qquad K_2 = 6.3 \times 10^8$$
$$Ni(OH)_2(aq) + OH^- \rightleftharpoons Ni(OH)_3^-; \qquad K_3 = 6.3 \times 10^2$$
$$Ni(OH)_2(s) \rightleftharpoons Ni^{++} + 2\ OH^-; \qquad K_{sp} = 6.5 \times 10^{-18}$$

(a) Calculate the *intrinsic solubility* $S°$ of $Ni(OH)_2(s)$.
(b) Calculate the *total* solubility of $Ni(OH)_2(s)$, if excess solid nickel hydroxide is shaken with a well buffered solution of pH 10.00. You may assume activity coefficients of unity and that the buffering agent does not undergo any chemical reactions with $Ni(OH)_2(s)$.
(c) What is the predominant nickel(II) species in the solution in (b)?
(d) Explain why the calculation of the solubility of solid nickel hydroxide in pure water would be more difficult than the problem in (b).

25. The equilibria involving the solubilities of strontium fluoride and calcium fluoride and the ionization of hydrofluoric acid are as follows:

$$SrF_2(s) \rightleftharpoons Sr^{++} + 2\ F^-; \qquad K_{sp} = 2.8 \times 10^{-9}$$
$$CaF_2(s) \rightleftharpoons Ca^{++} + 2\ F^-; \qquad K_{sp} = 4.0 \times 10^{-11}$$
$$HF \rightleftharpoons H^+ + F^-; \qquad K = 6.7 \times 10^{-4}$$

(a) If an excess of both strontium fluoride and calcium fluoride is shaken with an innocuous buffer of pH 3.00 until equilibrium is attained, what will be the concentrations of Sr^{++} and Ca^{++}?
(b) Let the solubility of calcium fluoride (formula weights per liter) in pure water be S_0. Suppose that solid potassium nitrate is dissolved in a saturated calcium fluoride solution in equilibrium with excess solid calcium fluoride in such a way that the ionic strength μ of the solution is slowly increased. Construct a qualitative plot to show how the solubility of calcium fluoride varies with ionic strength. How do you interpret this plot? Be sure to discuss how changes in μ affect the K_{sp} for calcium fluoride and the K for hydrofluoric acid.

26. A saturated solution of magnesium ammonium phosphate ($MgNH_4PO_4$) in pure water has a pH of 9.70, and the concentration of magnesium ion in the solution is $5.60 \times 10^{-4}\ M$. Evaluate the solubility product of $MgNH_4PO_4$.

$$H_3PO_4 \rightleftharpoons H^+ + H_2PO_4^-; \qquad K_1 = 7.5 \times 10^{-3}$$
$$H_2PO_4^- \rightleftharpoons H^+ + HPO_4^=; \qquad K_2 = 6.2 \times 10^{-8}$$
$$HPO_4^= \rightleftharpoons H^+ + PO_4^\equiv; \qquad K_3 = 4.8 \times 10^{-13}$$
$$NH_3 + H_2O \rightleftharpoons NH_4^+ + OH^-; \qquad K_b = 1.80 \times 10^{-5}$$
$$H_2O \rightleftharpoons H^+ + OH^-; \qquad K_w = 1.00 \times 10^{-14}$$

27. The solubility-product data for cupric iodate ($Cu(IO_3)_2$), lanthanum iodate ($La(IO_3)_3$), and silver iodate ($AgIO_3$) may be given as follows:

$$Cu(IO_3)_2(s) \rightleftharpoons Cu^{++} + 2\ IO_3^-; \qquad K_{sp} = 7.4 \times 10^{-8}$$
$$La(IO_3)_3(s) \rightleftharpoons La^{+++} + 3\ IO_3^-; \qquad K_{sp} = 6.0 \times 10^{-10}$$
$$AgIO_3(s) \rightleftharpoons Ag^+ + IO_3^-; \qquad K_{sp} = 3.0 \times 10^{-6}$$

Suppose that you prepare a separate saturated solution of each salt in pure water. Calculate the equilibrium concentration of iodate ion, IO_3^-, in each of these three solutions. Neglect activity effects.

28. Solubility-product data for silver chloride (AgCl) and silver chromate (Ag_2CrO_4) are as follows:

$$AgCl(s) \rightleftharpoons Ag^+ + Cl^-; \qquad K_{sp} = 1.78 \times 10^{-10}$$
$$Ag_2CrO_4(s) \rightleftharpoons 2\,Ag^+ + CrO_4^=; \qquad K_{sp} = 2.45 \times 10^{-12}$$

(a) Suppose you have an aqueous solution containing $0.0020\ M\ CrO_4^=$ and $0.000010\ M\ Cl^-$. If *concentrated* silver nitrate solution (so that volume changes may be neglected) is added gradually with good stirring to this solution, which precipitate (Ag_2CrO_4 or AgCl) will form first? Justify your conclusion with a calculation.

(b) Eventually, the silver ion concentration should increase enough to cause precipitation of the second ion. What will be the concentration of the *first* ion when the second ion just begins to precipitate?

(c) What *percentage* of the *first* ion is already precipitated when the second ion just begins to precipitate?

29. If 1 liter of a saturated solution (*no* excess solid present) of barium iodate, $Ba(IO_3)_2$, is equilibrated with 3.5×10^{-5} mole of pure solid lead iodate, $Pb(IO_3)_2$, what will be the equilibrium concentrations of Ba^{++}, Pb^{++}, and IO_3^-?

$$Ba(IO_3)_2(s) \rightleftharpoons Ba^{++} + 2\,IO_3^-; \qquad K_{sp} = 1.5 \times 10^{-9}$$
$$Pb(IO_3)_2(s) \rightleftharpoons Pb^{++} + 2\,IO_3^-; \qquad K_{sp} = 2.6 \times 10^{-13}$$

30. The solubility equilibrium and the solubility-product constant for barium oxalate are as follows:

$$BaC_2O_4(s) \rightleftharpoons Ba^{++} + C_2O_4^=; \qquad K_{sp} = 2.3 \times 10^{-8}$$

In addition, oxalic acid is a moderately weak diprotic acid which dissociates according to the following equilibria:

$$H_2C_2O_4 \rightleftharpoons H^+ + HC_2O_4^-; \qquad K_1 = 6.5 \times 10^{-2}$$
$$HC_2O_4^- \rightleftharpoons H^+ + C_2O_4^=; \qquad K_2 = 6.1 \times 10^{-5}$$

Calculate the *solubility* of barium oxalate in an aqueous solution whose pH is maintained constant at exactly 2.00 by means of an innocuous buffer.

31. If the solubility of silver carbonate, Ag_2CO_3, in a buffer solution of pH 9.00, containing $0.05\ M\ NH_3$ and $0.09\ M\ NH_4^+$, is 0.51 mole per liter, what is the solubility product of silver carbonate?

$$Ag^+ + 2\,NH_3 \rightleftharpoons Ag(NH_3)_2^+; \qquad \beta_2 = 2.5 \times 10^7$$
$$HCO_3^- \rightleftharpoons H^+ + CO_3^=; \qquad K_2 = 4.68 \times 10^{-11}$$
$$NH_3 + H_2O \rightleftharpoons NH_4^+ + OH^-; \qquad K_b = 1.80 \times 10^{-5}$$
$$H_2O \rightleftharpoons H^+ + OH^-; \qquad K_w = 1.00 \times 10^{-14}$$

32. The solubility-product data for lead hydroxide, $Pb(OH)_2$, and chromium hydroxide, $Cr(OH)_3$, are as follows:

$$Pb(OH)_2(s) \rightleftharpoons Pb^{++} + 2\,OH^-; \qquad K_{sp} = 1.2 \times 10^{-15}$$
$$Cr(OH)_3(s) \rightleftharpoons Cr^{+++} + 3\,OH^-; \qquad K_{sp} = 6.0 \times 10^{-31}$$

(a) Suppose you have an aqueous solution of pH 2 containing $0.030\ M\ Pb^{++}$ and $0.020\ M\ Cr^{+++}$. If the pH of this solution is gradually increased by the addition of a concentrated NaOH solution (so that volume changes may be neglected), which precipitate, $Pb(OH)_2$ or $Cr(OH)_3$, will form *first*? (A guess is unacceptable; justify your answer by calculations.)

(b) Calculate the pH values at which $Pb(OH)_2$ and $Cr(OH)_3$ will start to precipitate.

(c) If it is desired to *separate* the first ion to precipitate from the second ion to precipitate by pH control and if it is desired to have no more than 0.1 per cent of the first ion remaining *unprecipitated* when the second ion begins to precipitate, calculate what *range* of pH values is necessary to accomplish this separation.

33. An excess of pure solid calcium sulfate ($CaSO_4$) was shaken with an aqueous solution whose pH was maintained constant at exactly 2 by means of an innocuous buffer. The solubility of calcium sulfate in the pH 2 solution was determined by measurement of the calcium ion concentration. On the basis of the information:

$$[Ca^{++}] = 1.0 \times 10^{-2} \, M$$

$$[H^+] = 1.0 \times 10^{-2} \, M$$

$$HSO_4^- \rightleftharpoons H^+ + SO_4^=; \qquad K_2 = 1.0 \times 10^{-2}$$

(a) Calculate the solubility-product constant, K_{sp}, of $CaSO_4$ in water.
(b) Calculate the solubility S (moles/liter) of calcium sulfate in pure water.

34. What is the ionic strength of a $0.0030 \, F$ lanthanum chloride ($LaCl_3$) solution?

35. The solubility equilibrium and the solubility-product constant for zinc arsenate are as follows:

$$Zn_3(AsO_4)_2(s) \rightleftharpoons 3 \, Zn^{++} + 2 \, AsO_4^\equiv; \qquad K_{sp} = 1.3 \times 10^{-28}$$

Calculate the final concentration of $AsO_4^\equiv$ ion required to precipitate all but 0.1 per cent of the Zn^{++} in 250 ml of a solution that originally contains 0.2 gm of $Zn(NO_3)_2$. Zinc nitrate is very soluble in water.

36. The solubility of cerium iodate, $Ce(IO_3)_3$, in pure water is 124 mg per 100 ml of water.

(a) Calculate the solubility-product constant for cerium iodate, which dissolves according to the reaction

$$Ce(IO_3)_3(s) \rightleftharpoons Ce^{+++} + 3 \, IO_3^-$$

(b) Calculate the solubility (moles/liter) of cerium iodate in a $0.050 \, F$ potassium iodate (KIO_3) solution.

37. The solubility of solid barium iodate, $Ba(IO_3)_2$, in a $0.000540 \, F$ potassium iodate (KIO_3) solution is 0.000540 mole/liter. What is the solubility-product constant for $Ba(IO_3)_2$?

38. The solubility product for silver chloride ($AgCl$) is given by

$$AgCl(s) \rightleftharpoons Ag^+ + Cl^-; \qquad K_{sp} = 1.8 \times 10^{-10}$$

and the dissociation constant for the silver-ammine complex, $Ag(NH_3)_2^+$, is given by

$$Ag(NH_3)_2^+ \rightleftharpoons Ag^+ + 2 \, NH_3; \qquad K = 4.0 \times 10^{-8}$$

Suppose that you wish to dissolve completely 0.0035 mole of solid AgCl in 200 ml of an aqueous ammonia (NH_3) solution. What must be the final concentration of NH_3 to accomplish this?

39. What is the ionic strength of a solution containing $0.005 \, F$ sodium sulfate (Na_2SO_4) and $0.003 \, F$ lanthanum nitrate ($La(NO_3)_3$)?

40. The solubility of silver azide, AgN_3, in water is 5.4×10^{-5} mole/liter and the solubility reaction may be written

$$AgN_3(s) \rightleftharpoons Ag^+ + N_3^-$$

Hydrazoic acid is a weak acid as indicated by the equilibrium

$$HN_3 \rightleftharpoons H^+ + N_3^-; \qquad K_a = 1.9 \times 10^{-5}$$

If excess solid silver azide is added to 1 liter of 3 F nitric acid (HNO_3), what will be the final equilibrium concentration of Ag^+?

SUGGESTIONS FOR ADDITIONAL READING

1. A. J. Bard: *Chemical Equilibrium*, Harper & Row, New York, 1966.
2. J. N. Butler: *Ionic Equilibrium*, Addison-Wesley Publishing Company Inc., Reading, Massachusetts, 1964.
3. G. M. Fleck: *Equilibria in Solution*, Holt, Rinehart, and Winston, New York, 1966.
4. H. Freiser and Q. Fernando: *Ionic Equilibria in Analytical Chemistry*, John Wiley & Sons, Inc., New York, 1963, pp. 9–34.
5. H. A. Laitinen: *Chemical Analysis*, McGraw-Hill Book Company, New York, 1960, pp. 5–21; 107–122.
6. T. S. Lee: Chemical equilibrium and the thermodynamics of reactions. *In* I. M. Kolthoff and P. J. Elving, eds.: *Treatise on Analytical Chemistry*, Part I, Volume 1, Wiley-Interscience, New York, 1959, pp. 185–275.
7. O. Robbins, Jr.: *Ionic Reactions and Equilibria*, The Macmillan Company, New York, 1967.
8. L. G. Sillén: Graphic presentation of equilibrium data. *In* I. M. Kolthoff and P. J. Elving, eds.: *Treatise on Analytical Chemistry*, Part I, Volume 1, Wiley-Interscience, New York, 1959, pp. 277–317.

Chapter Five

Separation by Precipitation

Gravimetric, volumetric, radiant energy, and electrical methods comprise the four major classifications of quantitative analytical techniques. In starting a systematic discussion of these different yet interrelated techniques, we shall first focus attention on gravimetric methods of analysis. As the name implies, gravimetric determinations are characterized by measurements of mass or weight. Typically, a gravimetric analysis involves two weight determinations, the first being the original sample weight and the second being the final weight of a pure precipitate which contains the desired sample constituent. In every gravimetric determination, except those of the volatilization or electrodeposition types, the precipitate of interest is formed by mixing together solutions of two or more chemical reagents. Consequently, great importance must be placed on understanding the nature of the reaction between the dissolved species which produces the precipitate as well as the subsequent interactions between the precipitate and solution phases. The principles and mechanisms underlying precipitation processes are described in the present chapter, and in Chapter 6 these principles are illustrated and applied in descriptions of several specific gravimetric procedures. However, at the outset of this discussion, it should be recognized that the technique of precipitation is fundamentally a separation method, like liquid-liquid extraction and chromatography, and that separation by precipitation is useful not only in the gravimetric work described in Chapter 6 but in other analytical methods as well.

FUNDAMENTAL REQUIREMENTS

The three requirements which must be fulfilled by any quantitative separation process were introduced very briefly in Chapter 1. These requirements may be restated and expanded with particular reference to separation by precipitation.

1. *The desired constituent must be precipitated quantitatively.* In other words, the quantity of the desired constituent left in solution must be a negligible fraction of the original total amount of that constituent.

2. *The precipitate must be pure or, at least by the time of the final measurement, it must be of known purity.* The precipitate at the time of its formation must not include significant quantities of any other substance unless these substances are readily removable in the washing and drying steps of the procedure.

3. *The precipitate must be in a physical form suitable for subsequent handling.* It is not enough that the precipitate have the correct chemical composition; it must also, for example, consist of particles which are large enough to be retained by the medium used for filtration.

The entire precipitation process must be designed and conducted to meet these three requirements. Decisions concerning such diverse factors as the choice of compound to be precipitated, selection of the precipitating agent, volume and concentrations of reagent solutions, presence and concentration ranges of other constituents, choice of solvent, temperature, pH, rate of addition of precipitating reagent, and time and method of digestion and washing must all be based upon the fulfilling of the three requirements. These requirements are closely interrelated, and a condition which may be desirable from the standpoint of one requirement may adversely affect fulfillment of another requirement. Therefore, the procedure ultimately adopted for any precipitation process is necessarily the result of a series of compromises arrived at in an effort to optimize the extent to which all three requirements are met.

NUCLEATION AND CRYSTAL GROWTH

The formation of a precipitate is a physical phenomenon as well as a chemical one, for it involves both a physical process and a chemical process. The physical reaction generally consists of two processes, **nucleation** and **crystal growth.** Nucleation proceeds through the formation within a supersaturated solution of the smallest particles of a precipitate capable of spontaneous growth. Crystal growth consists of the deposition of ions from the solution upon the surfaces of solid particles which have already been nucleated. The number of particles and, therefore, the particle size of a given mass of precipitate are determined by the number of nuclei formed in the nucleation step.

The number of nuclei which form is generally believed to be influenced by the interaction between two factors — first, the extent of supersaturation in the immediate environment where nucleation occurs and, second, the number and effectiveness of sites upon which nuclei may form.

Significance of Supersaturation in Nucleation. Supersaturation is a condition in which a solution phase contains more of the dissolved precipitate than can be in equilibrium with the solid phase. It is generally a transient condition, particularly when some crystals of the solid phase are present, although some solutions may remain in the supersaturated state for considerable lengths of time under certain conditions.

The influence of the extent of supersaturation upon the rate of precipitation may be expressed mathematically by the equation

$$\text{rate} = \frac{Q - S}{S}$$

in which Q is the *actual* concentration of solute at the instant precipitation begins and S is the *equilibrium* concentration of solute in a saturated solution. This relation was first stated for the overall precipitation process by von Weimarn. It has since been found to be particularly applicable to the nucleation step, however, which means that the number of nuclei that form is directly proportional to the extent of supersaturation, $(Q - S)/S$, existing at the time of nucleation.

Consider the precipitation of barium sulfate when 100 ml of $1 \times 10^{-2} M$ barium chloride solution and 1 ml of $1\ M$ sodium sulfate solution are mixed. If the two solutions were to be completely mixed together before any precipitation occurs, the concentrations of barium ion and of sulfate ion would each be very close to $1 \times 10^{-2} M$. Since the equilibrium solubility S of barium sulfate is approximately $1 \times 10^{-5} M$, the $(Q - S)/S$ ratio would be 1000. However, at the spot where the 1 ml of sodium sulfate solution first comes into contact with the barium chloride solution, the momentary concentration of sulfate ion would be much higher than $1 \times 10^{-2} M$, even close to $1\ M$, so the momentary Q (calculated as $\sqrt{[Ba^{++}][SO_4^{=}]}$) could approach $1 \times 10^{-1} M$, and the corresponding $(Q - S)/S$ ratio would be 10,000. Even though each reactant solution is quickly diluted by the other upon mixing, the transient condition of supersaturation existing immediately after the solutions are brought together is considerably more intense than the condition existing a short time thereafter. The momentary condition of supersaturation is relieved by precipitation as well as by mixing. Nevertheless, the particle size of the final precipitate is markedly influenced by this transient condition. In general, the *larger* the extent of supersaturation, the *smaller* will be the size of the individual particles of the precipitate. For this reason, it is generally important to have the solutions quite dilute at the time of mixing, particularly if the precipitate is an extremely insoluble one, in order to promote the formation of large crystals. Furthermore, it is desirable to form a precipitate under conditions for which it is not so extremely insoluble. For example, the solubility of barium sulfate is greater in an acid medium than in a neutral medium, so the momentary $(Q - S)/S$ value is lower if precipitation occurs from an acid medium; later, when precipitation is nearly complete, the mother liquid can, if necessary, be partially neutralized prior to filtration to minimize the solubility loss.

Spontaneous and Induced Nucleation. Theoretically, it is possible for a sufficiently large cluster of ions to join together in a supersaturated solution to form a nucleus by the process known as **spontaneous nucleation.** In practical situations, however, it is highly probable that purely spontaneous nucleation is far less frequent than **induced nucleation,** in which the initial clustering of ions is aided by the presence in the solution of some sites which can attract and hold ions. Introduction of particles of a precipitate into a solution supersaturated with that solid can initiate further precipitation. Other solid particles or surfaces can also serve as nucleation sites. The surfaces of the container in which the reaction occurs provide many sites, as is indicated by the fact that the particle size of a precipitate may be strongly influenced by the type of container, how scratch-free it is, and how it was cleaned prior to use. Insoluble impurities in the reagents and in the solvent used to prepare solutions also provide nucleation sites. Even common chemicals of reagent grade purity typically contain 0.005 to 0.010 per cent insoluble components which, when dispersed throughout a solution as tiny particles, can provide extremely large numbers of sites for nucleation. The presence of any colloidal particles in the solution can exert a considerable influence upon the number of nuclei which form and persist as discrete particles throughout a precipitation reaction.

The forces of attraction whereby ions are held on these nucleating sites may be largely electrical in nature, but the more specific forces of adsorption (to be discussed later in this chapter) are likewise significant. Consider a solution which is slightly supersaturated with respect to barium sulfate and which contains barium, chloride, sodium, and sulfate ions. Any negatively charged surface in contact with this solution will attract positive ions. The double charge on the barium ion would tend to give it preference over the sodium ion, although their relative concentrations would also be of importance. A group of adsorbed positive ions would, in turn, attract a group of negative ions, with the double charge favoring sulfate over chloride. However, another factor of specificity appears — barium ion has a very specific and very pronounced attraction for sulfate ions so, inasmuch as the first group of adsorbed species consisted of barium ions, the second group would be predominantly sulfate ions. The resultant cluster of barium and sulfate ions comprises a nucleus for a crystal of barium sulfate. An analogous situation prevails if the initial nucleation site is positively charged. It is apparent from this illustration that the effectiveness of any particular site in initiating a nucleus is determined by the specificity of its attraction for one of the ions to be precipitated and that this specificity is influenced by the entire ionic composition of the solution.

Some supersaturation is necessary for any precipitation to occur. It seems reasonable that a relatively effective site would require a smaller degree of supersaturation than would a less effective one. The most effective site would be on the surface of a crystal of the substance to be precipitated; in effect, the process of nucleation would be by-passed. A site of no effectiveness at all would be one which could not attract any ions from the solution. It is doubtful, however, that any solid surface can be completely devoid of effectiveness because virtually all surfaces, including glass, which are in contact with an ionic solution exhibit some electrical effects.

As mentioned above, the number of nuclei which form in a precipitation process is a complex function of two factors. First is the number and the distribution with respect to effectiveness of the sites available to induce nucleation. This factor is influenced by the material and surface features of the container, the area of contact between container and solution, the purity of all reagents, the length of time a reagent solution or the water used as its solvent has been exposed to the atmosphere, and the freshness of the solutions at the time of use. All of these conditions and others equally diverse have been found to influence the number of particles obtained in precipitation processes. Second is the extent of supersaturation existing at the time precipitation is initiated, because, for a given supersaturation, only certain sites are able to initiate nucleation.

Changes in Number of Particles During Growth. The number of nuclei initially formed is indicative of the final number of precipitate particles, although these two numbers are not necessarily identical for several reasons. First, the solubility of small particles is generally greater than that of large particles, the latter being greater in diameter than about 10^{-4} cm in typical cases. During growth and particularly during subsequent digestion, smaller particles tend to dissolve at the expense of larger ones, thus *decreasing* the total number of particles. Second, two or more individual crystals may coagulate to form a tight cluster which behaves through subsequent handling as a single particle, thus *decreasing* the effective number of particles. The mechanism of coagulation will be considered later in this chapter. Third, a crystal which grows irregularly may break apart into two or more particles, particularly upon vigorous stirring, thereby *increasing* the number of particles. Fourth, a nucleation site may become separated from a growing crystal and serve to nucleate another crystal, thus *increasing* the number of particles. These several factors are all closely interrelated with one another.

Processes of Crystal Growth. Crystal growth, once a nucleus has been formed, consists of two steps — the *diffusion* of ions to the surface of the growing crystal and the *deposition* of these ions on the surface. Either process can be the rate-limiting factor. The diffusion rate is influenced by the specific nature of the ions and their concentrations, by the rate of stirring, and by the temperature of the solution. The rate of deposition of ions is affected by concentrations, by impurities on the surface, and by the growth characteristics of the particular crystal. Crystals of overall perfect geometrical shape are rarely formed in analytical precipitation processes because crystal growth generally does not occur uniformly on all faces of a crystal. Preferential growth on certain faces may result, for example, in flat plates or in sticks or rods, whereas preferential growth on corners may result in irregular, branched crystals called **dendrites.** The presence of foreign ions can markedly influence the shape of precipitated particles, probably because by being adsorbed they can inhibit or encourage growth on certain faces.

The subjects of nucleation and crystal growth have been studied in numerous laboratories for many years. Although much knowledge has been obtained, these processes are so complex that much additional basic research is required for complete comprehension of the mechanisms involved.

Significance of Nucleation and Crystal Growth. The physical processes of nucleation and crystal growth bear direct relationship to the fulfillment of all three requirements of precipitation as a means of accomplishing quantitative separation of chemical species. The most obvious relationship is to the third requirement, that of suitable physical form. However, relationships also exist between the physical form (as determined by nucleation and crystal growth) and both the purity and the solubility of a precipitated phase. Each of these relationships will be encountered further in this chapter.

COMPLETENESS OF PRECIPITATION

The completeness of precipitation of the desired species is generally determined by the equilibrium solubility of that substance under the conditions existing at the time of its filtration and washing. It is possible, however, for the state of supersaturation to persist until the time of filtration, resulting in a less complete separation or recovery of the desired substance than would be obtained in the absence of supersaturation. For moderately soluble substances, such as magnesium ammonium phosphate, appreciable solubility loss would occur through supersaturation if the precipitate were filtered immediately after formation, but this source of error is negligible after a reasonable digestion period. It has already been stated that the presence of some of the solid phase tends to relieve supersaturation. Stirring and even the presence of fine scratches on the inner walls of the container also tend to relieve the supersaturated condition, so supersaturation seldom persists until the time of filtration in analytical procedures.

The equilibrium solubility of a precipitate is widely influenced by numerous experimental conditions. One of the most significant factors is the *common ion effect.* In a quantitative separation by precipitation, a reasonable excess of the precipitating agent is invariably added to the sample solution in order to ensure that enough of the reagent is available to react with the unknown substance. Thus, the solubility of the precipitate is decreased by the presence of excess common ion. Solubility product considerations, as discussed in Chapter 4, permit direct calculation of the extent of this common ion effect. It may readily be shown, for example, that the solubility of barium sulfate is approximately 1×10^{-5} mole per liter in pure water, but only one hundredth as great, about 1×10^{-7} mole per liter, in the presence of a barium ion concentration of 1×10^{-3} M. It should be noted, however, that cases exist in which the presence of an unusually high concentration of a common ion causes a substantial increase in solubility because of the formation of complexes. For example, the solubility of silver chloride becomes significantly large in solutions containing a high chloride concentration, such as 1.0 M or above, owing to the formation of $AgCl_2^-$ and $AgCl_3^=$ species.

Unfortunately, the benefit of the common ion effect in repressing the solubility of a precipitate is generally lost in the process of washing a precip-

TABLE 5-1. SOLUBILITY PRODUCT OF SILVER CHLORIDE AS A FUNCTION OF TEMPERATURE

Temperature, °C	Solubility Product, K_{sp}
5	0.21×10^{-10}
10	0.37×10^{-10}
25	1.78×10^{-10}
50	13.2×10^{-10}
100	21.5×10^{-10}

itate. Generally speaking, the wash liquid must not contain any electrolyte which would not be volatile in the subsequent operation of drying or ignition. This requirement usually precludes the presence in the wash liquid of an ion in common with the precipitate. It is fortunate, however, that the wash liquid does not have to remain in contact with the precipitate long enough to become saturated. This *undersaturation* of the wash liquid with the precipitate causes, of course, a smaller loss through dissolution than if the liquid were to become saturated.

Another factor influencing the equilibrium solubility of a precipitate is the *diverse ion effect*. As discussed in Chapter 4, the solubility product rigorously deals with ion activities, not mere ion concentrations, and within certain limits activity coefficients decrease below unity as the overall ion content of a solution increases. Thus, the presence of any ions not in common with the precipitate tends to increase its equilibrium solubility.

Temperature influences the equilibrium solubility of a precipitate. The dissolution of most solutes in water is an endothermic process, so the solubility product constant increases as the temperature is increased. The data of Table 5-1 for silver chloride illustrate this point. The solubility product is about one hundredfold greater at 100°C than at 5°C. For barium sulfate the solubility product increases as the temperature is raised, but much less drastically.

Still another factor influencing the equilibrium solubility of a precipitate is the *nature of the solvent*. Most inorganic precipitates are ionic solids, so they are more soluble in a polar solvent, such as water, than in a nonpolar solvent, such as carbon tetrachloride. Nonpolar solvents are, however, much better solvents for nonionic and nonpolar organic substances than is water. Ethyl alcohol is interesting and versatile as a solvent. It possesses both polar and nonpolar structural characteristics and is, therefore, a moderately good solvent for a variety of substances.

It should be noted that if water is replaced by another solvent to repress the solubility of a desired substance, the solubilities of various impurities may likewise be diminished. Thus, the precipitate could be rendered less pure at the same time that it is rendered less soluble.

PURITY OF A PRECIPITATE

The desired, precipitated substance may be contaminated with one or more other substances because those other substances are themselves insufficiently soluble in the mother liquid. It is not feasible, for example, to separate chloride from bromide by precipitation with silver nitrate because the equilibrium solubilities of the two silver halides are not sufficiently different from each other. Such situations can be avoided in analytical chemistry if one simply resorts to some other means of separation. It is also possible — in fact, almost inevitable — that a precipitated phase can become contaminated with substances from its mother liquid even when the equilibrium solubilities of those other substances are not exceeded. To understand the reason for this latter phenomenon, we must briefly review some properties of the colloidal state.

Colloidal State

Definition and Significance. The term **colloidal state** refers to a dispersion of one phase within a second phase. The dispersed phase may be a solid, a liquid, or a gas; and the other phase may likewise be solid, liquid, or gas. However, the colloids of most interest in gravimetric analysis are dispersions of solid particles in a solution phase, usually of a precipitated substance in its mother liquid. The particles of a colloidal precipitate range in size from approximately 1×10^{-7} to 2×10^{-5} cm in diameter.

A colloidal dispersion is not a true solution. In a true solution the dispersed particles are of ionic or molecular dimensions, whereas they are larger in a colloidal dispersion. A colloidal dispersion is a mixture and a suspension, yet the properties of colloids differ so markedly from simple mixtures and suspensions that it is meaningful to consider colloidal dispersions as a separate subject.

It is distinctly undesirable for a precipitate to be in the colloidal state at the time of its filtration. The most obvious problem is that colloidal particles, although they constitute a distinct phase, are so fine that they pass directly through ordinary filtering media. In addition, two structural features of colloids — the localized electrical character of their surfaces and their tremendously large surface area per unit mass — control and influence the purity of the precipitate. These two factors will now be discussed in turn.

Electrical Charges on Surfaces. Most inorganic substances of analytical interest are ionic solids; that is, they consist of cations and anions arranged according to a specific structural pattern. The regular arrangement of ions in a solid is called a **crystal lattice.** Solid silver chloride consists of silver ions and chloride ions, and barium sulfate consists of barium ions and sulfate ions. A portion of a cubic crystal of silver chloride is depicted by the model in Figure 5-1, in which the dark balls represent silver ions and the light balls represent chloride ions. This model is intended to permit observation of ions both on the surface and within the interior of the crystal; a more perfect but less instructive model would show the silver and chloride ions to be of different sizes, and the distances between these ions would be very small relative to the ionic radii. Each chloride ion in the *interior* of the crystal is surrounded by six silver ions which are its closest neighbors, and each silver ion is similarly surrounded by six chloride ions. Therefore, each interior ion is fixed quite rigidly in its position. However, each chloride ion on the *face* of a crystal is associated with but five silver ions, and each silver ion with only five chloride ions. Under such circumstances, the chloride and silver ions on the faces of a crystal should be expected to possess some residual charges — negative and positive, respectively. An ion on an *edge* is surrounded by only four oppositely charged neighbors, and a *corner* ion has only three such neighbors. So the residual charge centers are even more pronounced for ions on

FIGURE 5-1. Model of a portion of the cubic crystal lattice of silver chloride.

the edges and at the corners of a crystal. Thus, the surface of a crystal is literally covered with localized centers of positive and negative charge. The overall surface may be electrically neutral, with equal numbers of positive and negative centers, but the localized charges are real.

Ratio of Surface to Mass. Perhaps the most unique characteristic of the colloidal state of matter is the enormous ratio of surface to mass which it exhibits. For example, a 1 cm cube of a substance has a total surface area of 6 sq cm. If the same mass of the same material is subdivided into 1×10^{-6} cm cubes, there are about a million million million (10^{18}) cubes, and they expose a total surface area of about 6,000,000 sq cm. In the 1 cm cube, less than one in 10,000,000 ions is on the surface, whereas in the 1×10^{-6} cm cube, about one in every 12 ions is a surface ion (assuming 2×10^{-8} cm per ionic diameter). Colloidal particles are characterized by very large surface to mass ratios, so surface effects are very important in colloid chemistry. Any surface factors, such as the localized positive and negative charge centers, are very pronounced when the particles are in the colloidal state. Colloid chemistry is often defined as surface chemistry because the distinctive characteristics of colloidal particles generally are surface characteristics.

Stability of Colloids. Colloidal dispersions can be exceedingly stable, even though the gravitational force should tend to make colloidal particles settle to the bottom of a container. Some colloids of gold particles in water prepared by Michael Faraday over one hundred years ago are still stable. One reason for the stability of colloids is the fact that the particles are in a state of constant motion. The particles continually collide with and rebound from each other as well as the walls of the container. The colloidal particles are doubtless being hit continually by the smaller molecules of the suspending medium and by any ions contained therein. The continual motion of colloidal particles is called **Brownian movement** and tends to overcome the settling influence of gravity.

A second reason for the stability of colloids is even more significant in analytical chemistry than is Brownian movement. Ions from the mother liquid which are adsorbed at the localized negative or positive charge centers on the surface of colloidal particles impart an electrical charge to those surfaces. If either cations or anions are adsorbed preferentially, all of the surfaces will assume the same overall charge, and the particles will tend to repel each other.

The drawing of Figure 5-2 represents one surface of a silver chloride particle with its localized charge centers. The negative centers will tend to attract and adsorb cations from the mother liquid. The positive centers attract and adsorb anions. This adsorption is highly selective in that a given precipitate will attract certain kinds of ions more readily than others. Generally, one particular type of ion in the mother liquid will be attracted more strongly than other species, so this ion will be preferentially adsorbed and will impart its charge, either positive or negative, to all of the surfaces.

The ions which are adsorbed are held from one direction only, are not as tightly bound as are ions within the interior of the crystal, and are generally hydrated, at least to some extent. If the ion adsorbed most readily is a cation, there is not enough space left for any anions to be adsorbed directly onto the crystal surface. If a cation is most readily adsorbed, all of the colloidal particles become positively charged, whereas all surfaces of the particles become negatively charged if some anion is most readily adsorbed. In either case, the adsorbed ion layer imparts stability to the colloidal dispersion. This adsorbed ion layer is called the **primary adsorbed ion layer,** because it forms directly on the surface of the solid particles.

   Selectivity of Ion Adsorption.   The adsorption of ions upon the surface of solid particles in contact with the mother liquid is based upon an electrical attraction. However, it is not entirely that, or the adsorption would not be so selective. The tendency of a colloid to adsorb one type of ion in preference to another rests upon a combination of four factors.

   Paneth-Fajans-Hahn law.   When two or more types of ions are available for adsorption and when other factors are equal, that ion which forms a compound with the lowest solubility with one of the lattice ions will be adsorbed preferentially. For example, silver chloride adsorbs silver ions in preference to sodium ions because silver chloride is less soluble than sodium chloride. Silver chloride also adsorbs silver ion, a cation, in preference to nitrate ion, an anion, because silver ion forms a less soluble compound with the lattice anion than nitrate does with the lattice cation. As a practical outworking of the law, if either lattice ion is present in excess in the mother liquid, it will be adsorbed preferentially. The law is also applicable when neither lattice ion is available for adsorption. As an illustration, silver iodide adsorbs acetate ion in preference to nitrate ion because silver acetate is less soluble than silver nitrate, even though both compounds are relatively soluble.

   Concentration effect.   Other factors being equal, the ion which is present in greater concentration will be adsorbed preferentially. Furthermore,

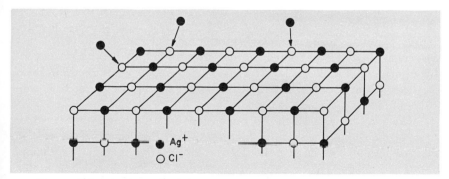

Figure 5-2.   Surface adsorption of silver ions on a silver chloride crystal.

the quantity of any ion which is adsorbed varies directly with its concentration.

Ionic charge effect.   Other factors being equal, a multicharged ion will be adsorbed more readily than a singly charged ion. This effect is entirely reasonable because the strength of adsorption is governed in part by the electrostatic attraction between the ion and the oppositely charged centers on the crystal surface.

Size of ion.   Other factors being equal, the ion which is more nearly the same size as the lattice ion which it replaces will be adsorbed preferentially. Consider again the difference in the environments of interior and surface ions — an interior ion in Figure 5-1 has six equidistant, oppositely charged neighbors, whereas a surface ion is missing one of the six. The adsorbed ion may be considered to take the place of that missing one. Therefore, if an ion in the mother liquid is of the same size as the one whose place it is to take, it should be adsorbed quite readily. For example, radium ion is adsorbed tightly onto barium sulfate but not onto calcium sulfate; the radium ion is close to the size of a barium ion but is considerably larger than a calcium ion.

These four factors are in simultaneous operation in each particular situation. The first factor is very often the dominant one, but any of the four may predominate under certain conditions.

Coagulation and Peptization.   The process whereby colloidal particles agglomerate to form larger particles which can settle to the bottom of the container is called **coagulation.** In order for the colloidal particles to coagulate, the electrical charge imparted to their surfaces by the primary adsorbed ion layer must be either removed or neutralized. The removal of this charge is very unlikely, because the forces of attraction between the surface and the primary adsorbed ion layer are quite intense. However, the overall charge on the particles can be modified by an adsorbed layer of water and by a second layer of adsorbed ions.

The lower portion of Figure 5-3 shows a row of alternating silver and chloride ions on the surface of a particle of silver chloride. If an excess of silver ions is present in the mother liquid, the primary adsorbed layer will consist of silver ions as shown, and the surface will acquire a net positive charge. Water molecules are polar, so water molecules may be adsorbed onto the primary layer on the particle surface. In addition, there is a tendency for the adsorption of a second layer of ions. The secondary adsorbed ion layer is called the **counter ion layer,** which in Figure 5-3 is illustrated as consisting of nitrate ions.

The tightness with which the counter ions are held in and with the water layer, or the completeness with which they cover the primary adsorbed ion layer, determines in large part the stability of the colloidal dispersion. If this secondary layer is sufficient to neutralize the charge due to the primary adsorbed ion layer, the particles coagulate rather than repel each other.

We must now consider what factors influence the tightness and completeness of the counter ion layer. The adsorption of the counter ion layer is much less selective than is adsorption of the primary layer. The Paneth-Fajans-Hahn factor and the ionic size factor are of much less significance because the counter ion layer is more remote from the body of the crystal lattice and because of the presence of the adsorbed water molecules. The concentration factor is generally the most significant factor in determining both the selectivity and the overall extent of counter ion adsorption — the greater the ionic content of the mother liquid, the more completely will the secondary layer neutralize the charge imparted to the surface of the particles by the primary layer. It must further be recognized that each counter ion is attracted and held in a much less rigid position than is a primary adsorbed ion. For these reasons the counter ions are not expected to provide as tight or as complete a coverage as the primary ions. However, the counter ion layer can be sufficient to neutralize the charge imparted to the colloidal surfaces by the primary layer and to cause the particles to coagulate. The tendency toward this condition is a function of the concentration of ions in the mother liquid.

The coagulation of colloidal particles through counter ion adsorption is a reversible process. The process whereby coagulated particles pass back into the colloidal state is designated **peptization.** Special precaution must be taken during the washing of a coagulated precipitate to prevent the agglomerates from peptizing and passing through the filter. When coagulation is accomplished through charge neutralization, as it is in the silver chloride precipitation, peptization would occur if the precipitate were washed with pure water. Instead the wash liquid must contain an electrolyte, such as nitric acid. This electrolyte must be one which will be volatile upon subsequent drying or ignition of the precipitate, lest it contribute to lack of purity of the precipitate at the time of weighing.

Coprecipitation

Coprecipitation is the precipitation of an otherwise soluble substance along with an insoluble precipitate. The two substances may precipitate

FIGURE 5-3. Schematic representation of adsorption of nitrate counter ions onto a primary adsorbed layer of silver ions at the surface of a silver chloride crystal.

simultaneously or one may follow the other. On the basis of solubility considerations alone, it is frequently possible to precipitate one component under such conditions that all other components would be predicted to remain completely in solution. However, coprecipitation always occurs to some extent. The coprecipitation of impurities may be insignificant, even in highly accurate work, as with a properly prepared precipitate of silver chloride, or it may be of considerable significance, as with hydrous ferric oxide.

There are several mechanisms whereby coprecipitation can occur. The classification of these mechanisms used here is a generally useful one and divides coprecipitation phenomena into four types: surface adsorption, occlusion, post-precipitation, and isomorphous replacement.

Surface Adsorption. As already described, ions are adsorbed from the mother liquid onto the surfaces of precipitated particles. This adsorption involves a primary adsorbed ion layer, which is held very tightly, and a counter ion layer, which is held more or less loosely. These ions are carried down with the precipitate, so they cause the precipitate to be impure. In the example illustrated by Figure 5-3, silver nitrate is coprecipitated along with silver chloride. Coprecipitation by surface adsorption is especially significant when the particles are of colloidal dimensions because of the tremendous surface area which even a small mass of colloidal material can present to the mother liquid.

Impurities coprecipitated by surface adsorption contribute to error in a gravimetric determination only if they are present during the final weighing of a precipitate. It is possible to volatilize the impurity during the drying or ignition step if the impurity is a volatile one. During washing it is sometimes possible to replace the initially adsorbed ions with ions which will be subsequently volatile. Yet the wash liquid cannot always get at all the surfaces, particularly if the agglomerates are tightly packed and nonporous. Steps should be taken at the time of precipitation to minimize surface adsorption, except insofar as it is needed to cause the precipitate to coagulate. Steps which may be taken to minimize surface adsorption include the following:

1. Ensure that the solution from which precipitation is made is dilute with respect to all foreign ions.

2. Form the precipitate in such a manner that large crystals are obtained. Aids in accomplishing this often include slow precipitation, stirring during the mixing of reagent solutions, and using dilute solutions.

3. Precipitate the substance of interest from a hot solution. This generally increases the solubility of all components, thus decreasing the tendency toward momentary supersaturation and formation of colloidal particles and also decreasing the selective attractive forces upon which the Paneth-Fajans-Hahn law is based.

4. Replace foreign ions, which form relatively insoluble compounds with the ions of the precipitate, by other ions forming more readily soluble compounds prior to precipitation; this consideration is based directly on the **Paneth-Fajans-Hahn concept.**

5. Remove from the solution, or convert to forms of lower charge, highly charged ions of substances which show a tendency to coprecipitate.

6. Choose a precipitate of the desired ion such that no other ions in the solution are of the same size as any lattice ion.

It is, of course, necessary to combine two or more of these steps with each other and with other steps to minimize other forms of coprecipitation, so an appreciable amount of coprecipitation by surface adsorption may occur even though reasonable precautions are taken to minimize it. Digestion serves to minimize surface adsorption if the individual crystals undergo recrystallization to form larger, and fewer, crystals with correspondingly less surface area. However, digestion serves to prevent subsequent removal of adsorbed ions if it causes the individual particles to coagulate to form tightly packed, nonporous aggregates of the tinier particles.

Occlusion. Occlusion is the simple physical enclosure of a small portion of the mother liquid within small hollows or flaws which form during the rapid growth and coalescence of the crystals. These pockets remain filled with the mother liquid after the precipitate has grown to such an extent that they are completely enclosed. In a typical case, 0.1 to 0.2 per cent of a precipitate formed from solution may consist of the mother liquid from which it was separated.

Ordinary washing is of no aid in removing occluded material. When a precipitate is ignited at high temperature, the internal pressure in the pockets may rupture the particles with resultant release of the trapped solvent. However, any nonvolatile solutes present in the trapped mother liquid remain as impurities in the precipitate.

The measures which can be taken to minimize occlusion are sufficient and effective so that in most instances occlusion need not be a major source of error. These procedures include the following:

1. Keep the solution dilute with respect to all components so that the mother liquid which is trapped will not contain much solute.

2. Perform the precipitation under conditions that promote slow growth of crystals, thus minimizing the formation of flaws and voids within the crystals and crystal aggregates.

3. Perform the precipitation under conditions in which the precipitate has appreciable solubility; for example, keep the hydroxide ion concentration just barely great enough to precipitate calcium oxalate. This leads to an effective recrystallization of the precipitate, during which smaller particles dissolve and reprecipitate on larger ones.

Post-precipitation. Another type of precipitate contamination closely associated with surface adsorption is **post-precipitation.** Perhaps it may best be described by an example in which it occurs — in the separation of calcium ion from magnesium ion by precipitation with oxalate. Calcium oxalate is a moderately insoluble compound which may be precipitated quantitatively. Since it exhibits a tendency to precipitate slowly, it is permitted to remain in contact with the mother liquid for some time

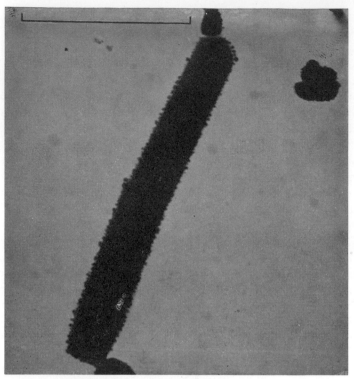

FIGURE 5-4.   Electron photomicrograph showing silver chloride post-precipitated on a crystal of silver thiocyanate.

prior to filtration. Magnesium oxalate is too soluble to precipitate under ordinary conditions. However, if calcium oxalate is precipitated from a solution containing magnesium ions and if the precipitate is allowed to remain in contact with the mother liquid for an excessive time, magnesium oxalate coprecipitates. Three experimental observations may be noted: no magnesium oxalate precipitates in the absence of calcium oxalate; very little magnesium oxalate precipitates simultaneously with calcium oxalate; magnesium oxalate does precipitate as the calcium oxalate stands in contact with the mother liquid. These three facts suggest that the surface of the calcium oxalate must be a major factor in the phenomenon, probably in the following manner: Oxalate ion is present in excess in the solution and, therefore, comprises the primary adsorbed ion layer. This effectively produces a relatively high concentration of oxalate ion localized on the calcium oxalate surface, even to the extent of providing a local state of supersaturation with respect to magnesium oxalate, so that precipitation of some magnesium oxalate ensues.

Figure 5-4 is an electron photomicrograph illustrating the post-precipitation of silver chloride on silver thiocyanate. This crystal was obtained by the slow addition of silver nitrate solution to a solution containing chloride and thiocyanate ions. Silver thiocyanate crystals have a sticklike structure with straight, smooth edges. The surface bumps in this picture show the precipitation of silver chloride upon the surface of the silver thiocyanate crystal. Since silver thiocyanate is less soluble than silver chloride, the silver thiocyanate was first to precipitate; and the general shape of the crystal, except for the surface detail, is that of the silver thiocyanate. This is not an ideal example of post-precipitation since silver chloride is nominally in- soluble, but it is more soluble than the primary precipitate of silver thiocyanate.

The phenomenon of post-precipitation is not uncommon, yet it seldom imparts significant errors to the final results of a gravimetric determination. It may be minimized if one brings the desired precipitate to a filterable condition as soon as possible after its first formation. In certain cases, a water-immiscible liquid may be added as soon as the primary precipitation is complete in order to coat the precipitate particles in such a way that their surfaces are no longer in direct contact with the mother liquid. The organic material must, of course, be volatile upon subsequent ignition of the precipitate.

Isomorphous Replacement. The role of the size of an ion in influencing the selectivity of surface adsorption has already been considered. It is also possible for one ion within a crystal to be replaced right in the crystal lattice by another ion of similar size and shape. This phenomenon is designated **isomorphous replacement.** Through this mechanism, the impurity actually becomes incorporated permanently into the crystal lattice, and it cannot be removed by washing. The only real way to eliminate this type of coprecipitation error is to remove the offending ion prior to precipita- tion of the desired compound or to dissolve the precipitate and reform it under more favorable conditions.

Coprecipitation by isomorphous replacement may be illustrated by the contamination of barium sulfate with the alkali metal ions sodium and potassium. Ionic radii are 0.95×10^{-8} cm for sodium ion, 1.33×10^{-8} cm for potassium ion, and 1.35×10^{-8} cm for barium ion. Experimentally, it is found that potassium ion coprecipitates markedly with barium sulfate, whereas sodium ion does not. This is clearly a case of isomorphous replace- ment of barium ion by potassium ion. It is of further interest to note that replacement of one barium ion by one potassium ion must be accompanied by some other modification of the crystal lattice in order to maintain elec- trical neutrality. Space considerations would certainly not permit two potassium ions to occupy the lattice site of a single barium ion. However, a hydrogen sulfate ion (HSO_4^-) is similar spatially to a sulfate ion, so electrical neutrality is preserved if a hydrogen sulfate anion replaces a sulfate ion every time a potassium ion replaces a barium ion. That this must occur is indicated by the observation that coprecipitation of potassium ion is almost negligible at pH 5, where there are very few hydrogen sulfate ions, but coprecipitation of potassium ions is appreciable at pH 1, where most of the sulfate does exist as HSO_4^-.

Fortunately, coprecipitation by isomorphous replacement is not encountered in very many of the common analytical precipitates. However, it is significant in those cases in which ionic size factors make it possible.

SUITABLE PHYSICAL FORM

The third requirement which a precipitation process must fulfill to make it suitable as the basis of a method of quantitative separation is that the precipitate be in a physical form suitable for subsequent handling. Much has already been said in this chapter about precipitation as a physical reaction, about nucleation and crystal growth, and about the relationship of the physical form to the other requirements which the overall process must fulfill.

Precipitates are often classified as crystalline, curdy, and gelatinous, as illustrated by barium sulfate, silver chloride, and hydrous ferric oxide, respectively. The meaning and significance of each of these terms will be discussed further in Chapter 6.

PRECIPITATION FROM HOMOGENEOUS SOLUTION

It has already been shown that the extent of supersaturation at the time and place of nucleation plays a major role in determining the particle size of a precipitate. Supersaturation should be held to a minimum in order to obtain a precipitate in the analytically desirable form of relatively large individual crystals. The method of **precipitation from homogeneous solution** has been developed to assist in accomplishing this goal. In this method the precipitating agent is not added directly but rather is generated slowly by a homogeneous chemical reaction within the solution at a rate comparable to the rate of crystal growth. Thus, the extent of supersaturation does not reach as high a value as would exist if the two reagent solutions were simply mixed directly.

The homogeneous precipitation technique is applicable to any precipitation process in which the necessary reagent can be generated slowly by some chemical reaction occurring within the solution of the unknown.

Selected Examples of Homogeneous Precipitation Methods

Precipitation by Means of Urea.   Urea is an especially useful reagent for the homogeneous precipitation or separation of any substance whose solubility is affected by pH. It hydrolyzes slowly in hot aqueous solutions according to the reaction

$$(NH_2)_2CO + H_2O \longrightarrow CO_2 + 2\,NH_3$$

The slow generation of ammonia within an initially acidic or neutral solution serves to raise the pH gradually and uniformly. By adjusting the initial concentration of urea and the pH of the sample solution and by controlling the temperature at which the solution is heated, one can obtain any desired final pH value or rate of increase of pH.

One of the more classic gravimetric procedures entails the precipitation of aluminum, chromium, or iron hydrous oxide or hydroxide by the addition of aqueous ammonia to a solution containing one of these species. However, the voluminous and gelatinous character of the resulting precipitate causes numerous complications including difficulty in the filtering and washing steps and serious coprecipitation of other cations and anions. These problems are largely overcome if the homogeneous precipitation technique is employed. Thus the pH of an aluminum ion solution can be adjusted to a value at which hydrous aluminum oxide is soluble, an appropriate quantity of urea added, and the solution heated to hydrolyze the urea and to raise the pH so that the hydrous aluminum oxide will precipitate quantitatively. The physical properties of the precipitate obtained in the homogeneous precipitation procedure can be improved still more if, for example, succinic acid is added to the original aluminum ion solution prior to the precipitation step. Experimentally, it has been discovered that succinate anion is incorporated into the precipitate with the resultant formation of a hydrous basic aluminum succinate rather than a mere hydrous oxide. Such a precipitate possesses more desirable physical characteristics — high density and crystallinity — than a normal oxide. Upon subsequent ignition, the basic succinate salt is converted into aluminum oxide, Al_2O_3, which is an excellent weighing form for the gravimetric determination of aluminum.

Another good example of the advantage of the technique of homogeneous precipitation is seen in the separation and determination of calcium as calcium oxalate. Calcium oxalate is soluble in acidic solutions because the reaction between oxalate and hydrogen ions to form $HC_2O_4^-$ and $H_2C_2O_4$ decreases the concentration of free oxalate anion, $C_2O_4^=$, and thereby prevents the solubility product for calcium oxalate from being exceeded. Normally, one precipitates calcium oxalate by first mixing oxalate and calcium ions in an acidic medium and then raising the pH of the solution through the slow addition of an aqueous ammonia solution. As described earlier in this chapter, this procedure frequently suffers from the almost unavoidable post-precipitation of magnesium oxalate on the original calcium oxalate precipitate. This post-precipitation appears to be due at least in part to the adsorption of an excess of oxalate ions on the calcium oxalate. However, the separation of calcium from magnesium is much sharper if the urea hydrolysis method is employed because the controlled increase in pH minimizes the formation of an excess of oxalate ions.

Homogeneous Generation of Sulfate and Phosphate Ions.   Sulfate ion can be generated homogeneously if one heats a solution containing sulfamic acid:

$$HSO_3NH_2 + H_2O \longrightarrow H^+ + SO_4^= + NH_4^+$$

or if one causes the slow hydrolysis of diethyl or dimethyl sulfate:

$$(C_2H_5)_2SO_4 + 2\ H_2O \longrightarrow 2\ H^+ + SO_4^= + 2\ C_2H_5OH$$

$$(CH_3)_2SO_4 + 2\ H_2O \longrightarrow 2\ H^+ + SO_4^= + 2\ CH_3OH$$

Barium ion, or any other cation which forms an insoluble sulfate, can be precipitated homogeneously by means of these reactions. The use of mixtures of alcohol and water as the solvent along with the homogeneous precipitation technique makes it possible to effect sharper separations of the alkaline earth elements — barium, strontium, and calcium — than is possible by direct addition of a solution containing sulfate ion.

Phosphate ion can be generated homogeneously in solution by the hydrolysis of either triethyl phosphate or trimethyl phosphate. This procedure is valuable in the separation and determination of zirconium and a few other elements.

Precipitation of Sulfides.   Many metal ions form insoluble sulfides, the solubilities of which are very much influenced by pH because hydrogen sulfide is an extremely weak acid. When sulfides are precipitated by the bubbling of hydrogen sulfide gas into a solution, the resulting precipitates have undesirable physical characteristics, not to mention the unpleasant and toxic nature of hydrogen sulfide itself. Metal sulfides can be precipitated homogeneously by the slow acid-or-base-catalyzed hydrolysis of thioacetamide.

$$CH_3CSNH_2 + H_2O \longrightarrow CH_3CONH_2 + H_2S$$

This homogeneous precipitation method yields metal sulfides which are distinctly granular and much easier to handle in subsequent operations of washing and filtering. However, application of this method of generating hydrogen sulfide to analytical procedures is complicated by the fact that some metal ions react directly with thioacetamide to form metal sulfides. In addition to simple hydrolysis, thioacetamide can undergo specific sulfide-producing reactions with substances such as ammonia, carbonate, and hydrazine. Nevertheless, thioacetamide is widely used in the qualitative identification of cations, and several quantitative procedures have been developed. Figure 5-5 shows electron photomicrographs of particles of cadmium sulfide precipitated both by the direct addition of hydrogen sulfide to a cadmium ion solution and by the slow hydrolysis of thioacetamide to yield hydrogen sulfide.

Cation-Release Method.   Each of the preceding examples involves the slow generation of an anion in the presence of the appropriate cation to form a precipitate. Some methods of precipitation from homogeneous solution entail the reverse procedure — that is, the slow "generation" of the cation in the presence of the desired anion. One useful example of such a technique involves the liberation of barium ion, in the presence of sulfate ion, through the reaction between hydrogen peroxide and the one-to-one complex formed by barium ion and ethylenediaminetetraacetic acid. The barium-ethylenediaminetetraacetate complex is soluble and is very stable, but the organic ligand is destructively oxidized by hydrogen peroxide, and the barium ion freed from the complex is then available to react with sulfate. The rate of decomposition of the complex is markedly influenced by temperature. At 80°C a reaction time of an hour or so is usually sufficient to achieve complete precipitation of the quantities or concentrations of barium ion typically encountered in analysis. However, a longer or shorter reaction time may be obtained at lower or higher temperatures, respectively.

In order to ensure that all of the barium ions are complexed before sulfate ion and hydrogen peroxide are added to begin the precipitation reaction, an excess of ethylenediaminetetraacetic acid is required. The excess uncomplexed organic reagent reacts first, and very quickly, with the hydrogen peroxide.

An interesting alternate oxidizing agent for this homogeneous precipitation method is the ammonium salt of peroxydisulfuric acid, $(NH_4)_2S_2O_8$, often called ammonium persulfate. This substance also reacts slowly with the organic portion of the barium complex to liberate barium ion homogeneously throughout the solution. The reduction product of peroxydisulfate ion is sulfate,

$$S_2O_8^= + 2\ e \longrightarrow 2\ SO_4^=$$

FIGURE 5-5. Electron photomicrographs of cadmium sulfide. The precipitate on the left was formed by direct use of hydrogen sulfide gas, whereas that on the right was obtained by the reaction between cadmium ion and the hydrogen sulfide produced homogeneously from the hydrolysis of thioacetamide.

Thus, no separate source of sulfate ion is required, for both the cation and the anion are generated homogeneously for the precipitation of barium sulfate. The precipitate consists of relatively large crystals which may be washed and filtered readily. Unfortunately, however, the results obtained by this latter method for the quantitative determination of barium are subject to a negative error, and the procedure suffers from interferences by strontium and potassium ions. Therefore, the use of hydrogen peroxide as the oxidizing agent is preferred over the use of ammonium peroxydisulfate.

Method of Synthesis of Precipitant. Nickel ion may be precipitated quantitatively as nickel dimethylglyoximate by direct addition of dimethylglyoxime to a solution with a pH between 5 and 9.

The advantages of precipitation from homogeneous solution can be realized if one replaces the direct addition of dimethylglyoxime with the in situ synthesis of this precipitant. The desired synthesis is accomplished by the reaction of biacetyl with hydroxylamine, which proceeds in two steps:

(1) biacetyl   hydroxylamine   dimethylmonoxime

(2)   dimethylglyoxime

The actual mechanism of the precipitation process is more complicated than these reactions indicate. Dimethylmonoxime forms a soluble complex with nickel ion, and this complex can react directly with hydroxylamine to form nickel dimethylglyoximate, providing an alternate route for the precipitation reaction. Nevertheless, the fact remains that dimethylglyoxime is synthesized homogeneously throughout the solution in the presence of nickel ion, and the resulting precipitate does consist of crystals which are appreciably larger and easier to filter than those obtained by the direct addition of the precipitant.

Nucleation in Precipitations from Homogeneous Solution

Ideally, a precipitate formed within a homogeneous solution phase ought to consist of large crystals which can be handled easily in subsequent operations and which possess relatively little surface area for the adsorption of impurities. This often is the case to a considerable extent. However, the particle size sometimes falls short of that which is desired or expected. A possible explanation may be deduced from calculations based upon the rate of the homogeneous reaction used to generate the particular precipitant. These calculations will not be presented in this book, but some conclusions may be stated.

For example, imagine that a $0.1 F$ solution of thioacetamide at a pH of 2.0 is allowed to hydrolyze in order to precipitate cadmium sulfide from a solution originally $0.01 M$ in cadmium ion. Calculations based on the hydrolysis rate of thioacetamide at room temperature, the acid dissociation constants of hydrogen sulfide, and the solubility product of cadmium sulfide reveal that hydrolysis for only 0.17 second provides sufficient sulfide ion to equal the solubility product. It is impossible to use a solution of thioacetamide anywhere near as fresh as this, so the conclusion seems inevitable that the nucleation step occurs during direct mixing of the thioacetamide solution (which contains some sulfide ion) with the cadmium solution and not by any subsequent homogeneous hydrolysis reaction.

Consider next the precipitation of barium sulfate by the hydrolysis of sulfamic acid in a solution in which the initial barium ion concentration is $0.01 M$. Since the solubility product of barium sulfate is 1.08×10^{-10}, a sulfate ion concentration of $1.08 \times 10^{-8} M$ would be sufficient to saturate the solution with respect to barium sulfate. The hydrolysis rate of sulfamic acid at room temperature is not known accurately, but approximate data indicate that only about 1 second of hydrolysis of a 1 per cent sulfamic acid solution would yield enough sulfate ion to start the precipitation. Of even more significance is the fact that reagent grade sulfamic acid may contain up to 0.050 per cent free sulfate ion, which means that the sulfate ion concentration in a 1 per cent solution of sulfamic acid is $5 \times 10^{-5} M$, or 5000 times greater than that required to equal the solubility product without any hydrolysis whatsoever. Again it appears that the initial stage of precipitation, during which all nucleation occurs, is not one of homogeneous precipitation at all but rather one of direct mixing of the barium solution with a solution of sulfamic acid containing sulfate ion. Only the subsequent stages of crystal growth proceed by homogeneous reaction.

The use of reagents other than thioacetamide and sulfamic acid presents different situations, but the conclusions are probably the same for most so-called homogeneous precipitation processes. It must be emphasized that, in spite of these considerations, the concentration of the precipitant at the time precipitation starts is much smaller in the homogeneous type of procedure than in the usual direct mixing procedures. Thus, the use of the homogeneous method does result in less supersaturation at the time of nucleation, and thereby in improved particle size, even though the ideal of a completely homogeneous precipitation process is not attained.

QUESTIONS AND PROBLEMS

1. List the three requirements which a precipitation process must fulfill to make it suitable for a gravimetric determination as well as a method of separation.
2. Distinguish clearly between nucleation and crystal growth, and explain why their mechanisms are not identical to each other.
3. Distinguish between the two processes involved in crystal growth, and state what factors influence the rate of each process.
4. Distinguish between spontaneous and induced nucleation, and state the relation between each and the extent of supersaturation.
5. Under what conditions may the solubility product of a compound be exceeded without formation of a precipitate?
6. Explain why most inorganic substances are more soluble in water than in an organic liquid, such as benzene.
7. Explain why silver chloride is made more soluble by an excess of potassium nitrate in solution but less soluble by an excess of potassium chloride in solution.
8. Why is an indefinitely large excess of a common ion not advisable in a precipitation process?
9. Define or characterize the following terms: colloid, supersaturation, coagulation, peptization, isomorphism, counter ions, coprecipitation, occlusion, Brownian movement.
10. Compare colloids with true solutions and with simple mixtures.
11. To illustrate the importance of surface area in colloids, calculate the surface area of each of the following:
   (a) a cube 1 cm on a side.
   (b) the same cube of (a) cut into eight cubes by slicing it in half in three directions at right angles to each other.
   (c) the same cubes of (b), each sliced further into eight cubes in the same way.
12. Name 10 colloids familiar in everyday life.
13. Explain the role of the counter ion layer in determining the stability of a colloidal dispersion.
14. Why are the forces which hold counter ions less selective than those which hold primary adsorbed ions?
15. State and illustrate with an example the Paneth-Fajans-Hahn law.

16. Distinguish among occlusion, surface adsorption, post-precipitation, and iso-morphous replacement.
17. In terms of the von Weimarn concept of precipitation, discuss the principles of precipitation from homogeneous solution.
18. Describe three distinct types of homogeneous precipitation procedures.

SUGGESTIONS FOR ADDITIONAL READING

Books

1. L. Gordon, M. L. Salutsky, and H. H. Willard: *Precipitation from Homogeneous Solution*, John Wiley & Sons, Inc., New York, 1959.
2. H. A. Laitinen: *Chemical Analysis*, McGraw-Hill Book Company, New York, 1960, pp. 123–182.
3. M. L. Salutsky: Precipitates: their formation, properties, and purity. *In* I. M. Kolthoff and P. J. Elving, eds.: *Treatise on Analytical Chemistry*, Part I, Volume 1, Wiley-Interscience, New York, 1959, pp. 733–766.
4. E. H. Swift and F. C. Anson: The analytical chemistry of thioacetamide. *In* C. N. Reilley, ed.: *Advances in Analytical Chemistry and Instrumentation*, Volume 1, Wiley-Interscience, New York, 1960, pp. 293–345.

Papers

1. F. H. Firsching: Precipitation of metal chelates from homogeneous solution. Talanta,* *10*, 1169 (1963).
2. R. B. Fischer: The origin of nuclei in precipitation reactions. Anal. Chim. Acta, *22*, 501 (1960).
3. R. B. Fischer: Effect of form of reagent on particle sizes of precipitates. Anal. Chim. Acta, *22*, 508 (1960).
4. R. B. Fischer: Nucleation in precipitation reactions from homogeneous solution. Anal. Chem., *32*, 1127 (1960); *33*, 1801 (1961).
5. L. Gordon, P. R. Ellefsen, and G. Wood: Precipitation of nickel and palladium dimethylglyoximates from homogeneous solution. Talanta, *13*, 551 (1966).
6. O. E. Hileman and L. Gordon: The oximation of biacetyl. Talanta, *12*, 451 (1965).
7. D. H. Klein and L. Gordon: Nucleation in analytical chemistry. Talanta, *1*, 334 (1958).
8. D. H. Klein and E. H. Swift: Effect of nucleation on rate of precipitation of metal sulfides by thioacetamide. Talanta, *12*, 363 (1965).
9. E. D. Salesin, E. W. Abrahamson, and L. Gordon: Precipitation of nickel dimethylglyoximate from homogeneous solution. Talanta, *9*, 699 (1962).
10. K. Takiyama and L. Gordon: Electron microscopy studies of nickel dimethyl-glyoximate. Talanta, *10*, 1165 (1963).

---

* It should be noted that the international journal **Talanta**, first published in 1958, contains numerous articles on nucleation, crystal growth, and precipitation from homogeneous solution, only a handful of which have been cited in the above list.

Chapter Six

Selected
Gravimetric Methods

Several specific determinations, in each of which the final quantitative measurement is that of weight, are discussed in this chapter. One involves a quantitative separation by volatilization, and each of the others includes a quantitative precipitation process. The determinations have been selected to encompass a variety of precipitates, procedures, and principles. Each is a practical laboratory method for the determination of the stated constituent.

Considerable emphasis is placed on a description of sources of error, both for pedagogical reasons and for practical reasons. Errors are discussed in terms of the three requirements listed in the preceding chapter, which must be fulfilled by any separation process to make it suitable for quantitative work. To review, as applied to separation by precipitation, these three requirements are that the unknown constituent must be precipitated quantitatively, that the precipitate must be quantitatively pure or of known purity at the time of final measurement, and that the precipitate must be in a physical form suitable for subsequent handling.

DETERMINATION OF WATER IN BARIUM CHLORIDE DIHYDRATE BY VOLATILIZATION

Principle. In a volatilization determination the unknown component or group of components is separated from the rest of the sample by volatilizing it either through application of heat alone or by adding an appropriate reagent. The quantity of volatilized components may be measured *directly* by absorption and weighing of the volatile fraction or *indirectly* from the loss of weight of the sample. Perhaps the most frequent application of a volatilization procedure is the determination of loosely bound water present in compounds which are not themselves volatile. A simple example is the determination of the water of hydration in barium chloride dihydrate, which decomposes upon heating in air at a moderate temperature, according to the following reaction equation:

$$BaCl_2 \cdot 2\ H_2O \longrightarrow BaCl_2 + 2\ H_2O$$

The weight loss of the sample upon heating is due only to the loss of water. Therefore, the procedure for the determination of water in barium chloride dihydrate involves only three steps — weighing the barium chloride dihydrate, heating it to drive off water of hydration, and weighing the anhydrous barium chloride.

The purity of a sample of barium chloride dihydrate may be determined by this process. In fact, the results could be used to calculate the percentage of $BaCl_2 \cdot 2\ H_2O$ present in a mixture, assuming that only water is lost upon heating and that all water comes from the hydrated barium chloride salt. Such a procedure allows for the determination of water in a sample of barium chloride dihydrate which may or may not contain some sodium chloride or other nonvolatile components.

Evaluation of Method.   The first two requirements of a quantitative separation process may be restated for this volatilization procedure to be (1) that the evolution of the water of hydration must be complete and (2) that no other component may be evolved. The third requirement, concerning the physical form of the separated phase, is applicable to the final residue which must be weighed, but no practical difficulty arises in this regard.

Barium chloride dihydrate loses essentially all water of hydration when heated above $113°C$, and the anhydrous salt has melting and boiling points of 962 and $1560°C$, respectively. Accordingly, any temperature over $113°C$ should be adequate for dehydration of the hydrated salt, and a temperature far in excess of this value should be permissible as far as the thermal stability of the anhydrous form is concerned. A temperature of 150 to $200°C$ is usually optimum. The temperature must reach a suitable value throughout the particles of the sample, but the use of finely divided material and a heating time of an hour are adequate. There need be no significant error from incomplete loss of the water of hydration. The anhydrous salt is, however, somewhat hygroscopic in normal room air. It follows that the anhydrous salt should be transferred to a desiccator very soon after completion of the drying operation and that it should be weighed quickly when it is removed from the desiccator.

A source of error arises in this determination from the possible presence in the initial sample of moisture other than the water of hydration. However, this error need not be serious with barium chloride dihydrate if the sample is finely ground in a mortar and exposed for a time to room air prior to its initial weighing. This substance readily reaches a state of equilibrium in air of a wide range of humidity, so that the salt exists stoichiometrically as the dihydrate. The possibility of the adsorption of surface moisture on components other than the barium chloride dihydrate must be considered. The procedure to be described is satisfactory with sodium chloride or other non-volatile and nonhygroscopic substances as possible additional components of the sample.

This determination is a very accurate one, the major possible sources of error being the uptake of moisture by the anhydrous sample prior to or during weighing together with random weighing errors.

Applicability. In principle, the general procedure is applicable to any determination in which one component or group of components can be separated from the rest of the sample by volatilization. Volatilization may be accomplished either by heat or by use of a chemical reagent.

Specific applications in which heat alone is used to volatilize a component include determination of the carbonate content of minerals or rocks by heating them to drive off carbon dioxide, as in the reactions

$$CaCO_3 \longrightarrow CaO + CO_2$$

and

$$MgCO_3 \longrightarrow MgO + CO_2$$

and general determinations of the "weight loss on ignition" of samples, which includes the loss of both moisture and carbon dioxide as well as any volatile organic components. The carbon dioxide content of natural waters can similarly be determined by heat volatilization, but here the evolved gas must be absorbed (water by a desiccant and carbon dioxide by ascarite, which is sodium hydroxide in shredded asbestos) and its quantity measured by the gain in weight of the absorber. Mercury in ores can be determined by heat volatilization and collection of the evolved mercury on a previously weighed piece of silver or gold foil.

Applications in which a component is evolved from the sample by a chemical reagent include the determination of silicon dioxide in rocks. When the rock sample is treated with hydrofluoric acid, the silicon is evolved as SiF_4 during heating:

$$SiO_2 + 4\ HF \longrightarrow SiF_4 + 2\ H_2O$$

The measurement is based upon loss of weight of the sample, although special steps are required to reconvert all other components back to their original forms prior to the final weighing.

Carbon and hydrogen in organic compounds may be determined by burning the sample in a stream of oxygen gas in a closed system. The hydrogen is converted to water, which may be measured by the increase in weight of an absorbing tube containing a desiccant. The carbon is converted to carbon dioxide, which may be measured by the gain in weight of an absorbing tube containing ascarite. These determinations are extremely important, and special pieces of apparatus have been developed to carry out some of the experimental steps semiautomatically.

It may be noted that the simplest and least selective type of volatilization determination consists of volatilizing by heat alone and measuring the evolved materials by loss of weight of the sample. The use of an absorber to collect a certain constituent or the use of a chemical reagent to accomplish the volatilization generally increases the experimental complexity of the method but at the same time increases its possible selectivity.

DETERMINATION OF CHLORIDE

Principle. The chloride content of a sample may be determined by adding an excess of silver nitrate solution to a solution of the unknown and weighing the precipitated silver chloride. The entire determination centers on one chemical reaction:

$$Ag^+ + Cl^- \rightleftharpoons AgCl$$

Silver chloride may be classified as a curdy precipitate. The individual particles are very small and must coagulate into aggregates before they can be filtered. A highly magnified electron photomicrograph of a silver chloride precipitate is shown in Figure 6-1 in which both individual particles and aggregates are clearly seen. The aggregates are often both "chainlike" and "clumplike."

FIGURE 6-1. Electron photo-micrograph of silver chloride, a curdy precipitate.

Evaluation of Method. Again, three requirements must be met by this gravimetric procedure for determination of chloride.

Completeness of precipitation. The solubility of silver chloride in pure water is 0.0014 gm per liter at 20°C and 0.022 gm per liter at 100°C. To avoid appreciable solubility losses, the precipitate should always be washed and filtered at room temperature or below, even if it has been formed at an elevated temperature. Excess silver nitrate, which is regularly present in the mother liquid and in the first washings, represses the solubility loss through the common ion effect. Even if the precipitate is washed with as much as 150 ml of cold, dilute nitric acid, the solubility loss seldom reaches 1 mg because the wash liquid does not ordinarily become saturated with silver chloride. If this loss should be intolerable because of an extremely small amount of precipitate or because of a required high accuracy, a wash liquid containing a little silver nitrate may be employed. Through the common ion effect, 150 ml of water containing 0.01 gm of silver nitrate dissolves somewhat less than 0.00001 gm of silver chloride at room temperature. A very dilute nitric acid medium is desirable to hasten and to maintain flocculation of the tiny particles of the precipitate, but the nitric acid does not markedly alter the solubility of silver chloride. Therefore, the precipitation of silver chloride may readily be made quantitatively complete, and no appreciable error need result from solubility losses.

Chloride ion is an almost omnipresent contaminant, and great care must be exercised to ensure that no undesired chloride is introduced during the determination. In particular, tap water usually contains some chloride ion, which must be removed from all vessels used in the determination with the aid of one or two careful rinsings with distilled water.

Purity of the precipitate. Silver ion forms a large number of sparingly soluble salts. However, the specificity of the precipitating agent for chloride ion is much improved in the presence of a small amount of acid, such as nitric acid. Under these conditions, most of the anions of weak acids which form insoluble silver salts will not produce precipitates. For example, silver phosphate precipitates in an alkaline medium, according to the reaction

$$PO_4^= + 3\ Ag^+ \rightleftharpoons Ag_3PO_4$$

However, in an acid medium, phosphate ion forms $H_2PO_4^-$ and H_3PO_4 by accepting two or three protons, respectively, as indicated by the reaction equations

$$PO_4^= + 2\ H^+ \rightleftharpoons H_2PO_4^-$$

and

$$PO_4^= + 3\ H^+ \rightleftharpoons H_3PO_4$$

Thus, no precipitate forms in the presence of silver nitrate solution. However, even in dilute nitric acid, bromide and iodide ions still yield insoluble precipitates with silver ion, so these ions must be entirely absent or removed before a successful determination of chloride may be undertaken.

A silver chloride precipitate is notable because, when cold-digested, it exists as a porous spongy mass that is readily washed free of practically all common impurities by a very dilute nitric acid washing fluid. This characteristic of the precipitate is discernible from Figure 6-1.

The precipitate must be pure at the time of weighing, so any changes in its composition subsequent to precipitation but prior to weighing are significant. The precipitate may be dried quite adequately by heating it for an hour at 110°C. A few hundredths of 1 per cent of water is held very tightly and can be removed only by fusion of the precipitate at about 450°C, but this is not a recommended procedure for inexperienced chemists. Silver chloride may be extensively decomposed upon fusion by traces of organic matter with which it has become contaminated and, furthermore, the material is slightly volatile at temperatures not much above its melting point. Since silver chloride is readily reduced when strongly heated with organic material, the precipitate should not be collected on filter paper because of the resulting necessity of charring off the paper.

Silver halides are decomposed into their constituent elements on exposure to light. The danger of this type of decomposition is particularly grave during the early stages of the precipitation when the milky suspension presents an enormous surface for photochemical reaction. Therefore, the precipitation should not be conducted in bright light; and the precipitate should, insofar as reasonably possible, be kept out of sunlight, set inside a desk during digestion, and worked on in a shade-darkened room. Silver chloride is almost pure white, but the precipitate is likely to acquire a purplish hue by the time it is weighed. This is due to tiny grains of metallic silver on the surface of the white silver chloride. Even a small amount of photodecomposition results in an appreciable purplish coloration. Therefore, one should not be alarmed at the coloration if he has exercised reasonable caution to prevent excessive decomposition. This photodecomposition may cause either a positive or negative error in the determination. The initial decomposition yields free silver and free chlorine:

$$2\ AgCl \xrightarrow{light} 2\ Ag + Cl_2$$

If excess silver ions are present, as is true prior to the final washing, the liberated chlorine reacts with silver ion to form more silver chloride:

$$5\ Ag^+ + 3\ Cl_2 + 3\ H_2O \longrightarrow 5\ AgCl + ClO_3^- + 6\ H^+$$

Stoichiometrically, then, six molecules of silver chloride which decompose result in the presence in the final precipitate of six atoms of elemental silver plus five molecules of silver chloride. The six silver atoms plus the five silver chloride molecules weigh more than the six silver chloride molecules which should have been present, so the precipitate is too heavy and the result of the determination is high. If no excess silver ions are present, as is the case after washing, the chlorine liberated through photodecomposition of the precipitate is evolved as chlorine molecules into the atmosphere, so the result of the determination is low.

Physical form of the precipitate. As already noted, silver chloride is a curdy precipitate, and the filtered material consists of porous aggregates of tiny particles. The flocculated precipitate is almost ideal for filtration and washing. A coarse filter is adequate, so filtration is quite rapid and there is no tendency for the pores of the filtering membrane to become clogged. The wash liquid can readily come in contact with virtually all of the initially tiny particles because the larger aggregates are quite porous. However, a serious difficulty arises in that the aggregates can conceivably disperse during washing into separate, tinier particles which pass right through the filter membrane. To suppress this phenomenon, known as **peptization,** the precipitate must be washed with a liquid containing some electrolyte. This electrolyte must be volatile upon subsequent drying of the precipitate. Nitric acid serves very well, not only in preventing peptization but in preventing precipitation as silver salts of any other substances which were initially kept in solution by the acid medium at the time of precipitation.

Applicability. Bromide ion may be determined by the same general procedure and with the same order of accuracy. Iodide determinations are also possible, but the procedure is less satisfactory for three reasons: silver iodide tends to peptize more readily than silver chloride; silver iodide adsorbs certain impurities quite tenaciously; silver iodide is extremely photosensitive. Thiocyanate and cyanide ions can also be determined in this fashion.

Several different anions of weak acids can be determined by precipitating their silver salts from a nearly neutral medium. For a successful determination, the sample solution must contain only one kind of anion which can form an insoluble silver salt. For example, phosphate ion may be determined by precipitation and weighing of silver phosphate. In most instances, however, the weak acid anions are more conveniently determined by other procedures.

Several cations may be determined by a reversal of the procedure. Thus, silver may be determined quite accurately by the precipitation and weighing of either silver chloride or silver bromide. Mercury(I) and lead(II) may also be precipitated as their chlorides, but solubility losses are considerable with lead chloride. Thallous ion may likewise be determined by precipitation and weighing of thallous chloride.

DETERMINATION OF SULFATE

Principle. Sulfur is commonly determined by converting all the sulfur-containing material in a weighed sample to sulfate ion, after which barium sulfate is precipitated, washed, filtered, dried, and weighed. The determination centers on the reaction

$$Ba^{++} + SO_4^{=} \rightleftharpoons BaSO_4$$

Barium sulfate is classified as a crystalline precipitate, the individual crystals being large enough so that they can be easily filtered. Some coagulation is desirable prior to filtration; yet the individual crystals are much larger than they are in a curdy precipitate such as silver chloride. A highly magnified electron photomicrograph of barium sulfate crystals is shown in Figure 6-2 along with a photomicrograph of another crystalline precipitate, nickel dimethylglyoximate. The individual crystals obtained in the usual precipitation procedures are not perfect geometrical forms; yet there is a generally characteristic structure of barium sulfate crystals. The apparent gross size and shape of a crystalline precipitate vary with changes in conditions of precipitation; however, the essential difference between a crystalline precipitate and a curdy precipitate is illustrated by a comparison of Figures 6-1 and 6-2.

Evaluation of Method.   We may assess this procedure according to three criteria named earlier.

Completeness of precipitation.   Barium sulfate is soluble in pure water at room temperature only to the extent of about 3 mg per liter. In practice, the solubility is sharply diminished by the presence of excess barium ion in the mother liquid. Barium sulfate is only slightly more soluble at elevated temperatures. This is of particular importance because it permits the use of hot wash water for more effective removal of impurities.

Barium sulfate is markedly more soluble in acid media than in pure water. For example, its solubility in a 1 F hydrochloric acid solution is about 30 times greater than in pure water. This situation arises because sulfuric acid is not a completely strong acid. The first step of ionization,

$$H_2SO_4 \longrightarrow H^+ + HSO_4^-$$

FIGURE 6-2.   Electron photomicrographs of barium sulfate (left) and of nickel dimethylglyoximate (right), both of which are crystalline precipitates.

proceeds toward the right essentially to completion. However, the second step,

$$HSO_4^- \rightleftharpoons H^+ + SO_4^=$$

proceeds only slightly toward the right. The equilibrium expression which represents the second step of the dissociation is

$$\frac{[H^+][SO_4^=]}{[HSO_4^-]} = K_2 = 1.2 \times 10^{-2}$$

Thus, for a solution in which the concentration of hydrogen ions is 1 M, only about 1 per cent of the total sulfate is in the form of $SO_4^=$, about 99 per cent being in the HSO_4^- form. When the precipitation of barium sulfate is attempted in acidic media, both H^+ ions and Ba^{++} ions compete for sulfate ions. The barium ions are more successful competitors because barium sulfate is quite insoluble,

$$BaSO_4 \rightleftharpoons Ba^{++} + SO_4^=; \qquad K_{sp} = 1.08 \times 10^{-10}$$

but some sulfate remains in solution as HSO_4^- ions.

It is interesting and instructive to calculate on the basis of equilibrium considerations how much HSO_4^- is present under the specific conditions of the experimental procedure described later in this chapter. Let us suppose that the weight of sample taken is 0.5 gm and that the sample contains 40 per cent sulfate. This corresponds to 0.2 gm or approximately 2.1 millimoles of sulfate. In the procedure at the end of this section, the sulfate sample is dissolved in water containing 2.0 ml of stock ($12\ F$) hydrochloric acid, and then to this solution is added a 10 per cent excess of barium ions. We shall assume that 2.3 millimoles of Ba^{++} are added and that the final solution volume is about 200 ml. Now let us calculate the concentrations of $SO_4^=$ and HSO_4^- remaining unprecipitated.

Since barium sulfate is insoluble and since an excess of barium ions is present, it is permissible to conclude that nearly all of the 2.1 millimoles of sulfate is precipitated as $BaSO_4$, leaving essentially 0.2 millimole of barium ion in excess. The concentration of barium ions is given by

$$[Ba^{++}] = \frac{0.2\ \text{millimole}}{200\ \text{milliliters}} = 1.0 \times 10^{-3}\ M$$

From the solubility-product expression for barium sulfate, we can calculate the sulfate ion concentration in equilibrium with the $BaSO_4$ precipitate to be

$$[SO_4^=] = \frac{K_{sp}}{[Ba^{++}]} = \frac{1.08 \times 10^{-10}}{1.0 \times 10^{-3}} = 1.08 \times 10^{-7}\ M$$

This result does not provide us with the true concentration of *unprecipitated* sulfate because, as yet, we have not considered the presence of HSO_4^-. In order to do this, we must first calculate the hydrogen ion concentration by recalling that 2.0 ml of 12 F hydrochloric acid was added to the solution of volume 200 ml. Thus,

$$[H^+] = \frac{24 \text{ millimoles}}{200 \text{ milliliters}} = 0.12 \ M$$

Finally, we can calculate the concentration of HSO_4^- by making use of the expression for the second acid dissociation of sulfuric acid.

$$[HSO_4^-] = \frac{[H^+][SO_4^=]}{K_2} = \frac{(0.12)(1.08 \times 10^{-7})}{(1.2 \times 10^{-2})} = 1.08 \times 10^{-6} M$$

The *total concentration of unprecipitated sulfate*, expressed as the sum of $[SO_4^=]$ and $[HSO_4^-]$, is close to $1.2 \times 10^{-6} \ M$. In 200 ml of solution, this is $(200)(1.2 \times 10^{-6})$ or 2.4×10^{-4} millimole of total sulfate, or approximately 0.024 mg. On the basis of these calculations, the solubility loss caused by the formation of HSO_4^- is insignificant.

For another reason to be encountered shortly, a low pH at the time of precipitation is desirable because the purity of the barium sulfate precipitate is substantially increased.

It is worth mentioning here that the barium sulfate precipitate is finally washed with hot water. If, for predictive purposes, it is assumed that 100 ml of wash water is used and that the solubility of barium sulfate is approximately $10^{-5} \ F$, we estimate that 10^{-3} millimole or 0.1 mg of sulfate would be lost *if solubility equilibrium were attained*. Fortunately, however, solubility equilibrium is undoubtedly not attained, and, besides, there would be a considerable number of barium ions in contact with the $BaSO_4$ during the early stages of washing. Consequently, the true solubility loss on washing should be much less than this estimated value. Nevertheless, this calculation serves to illustrate the danger of indiscriminate washing of a precipitate.

Purity of the precipitate. Barium ion forms insoluble precipitates with a variety of anions other than sulfate; yet most of them are anions of weak acids so that their barium salts are soluble in acid media. In solutions which are rather dilute in acid, only a little of the sulfate is lost as bisulfate ion, but all of the anions of much weaker acids are effectively removed from the scene of action through formation of their undissociated acids. The only anion which remains troublesome under these conditions is fluoride ion. Barium fluoride is quite insoluble in dilute acid solutions, and so fluoride must be removed prior to precipitation of barium sulfate. Such removal may be accomplished readily through volatilization of hydrofluoric acid or through complexation with boric acid.

Of the more common cations other than barium, only lead, calcium, and strontium form nominally insoluble sulfates. Interference from lead may be prevented by complexation of lead ion with acetate. Calcium and strontium must be removed prior to precipitation of barium sulfate.

Precipitated barium sulfate tends to retain many extraneous materials from its mother liquid, and herein lies the chief deterrent to the highly accurate determination of sulfate ion. The process whereby an otherwise soluble substance is precipitated along with an insoluble substance is termed **coprecipitation,** and many substances can and do coprecipitate with barium sulfate. Discussion of the mechanisms of coprecipitation was included in Chapter 5.

The influence of various coprecipitations on the direction, positive or negative, of the error in the results is important because it indicates that individual errors may compensate for each other even when coprecipitation cannot be entirely suppressed. Consider first the coprecipitation of anions, such as chloride and nitrate, in a sulfate determination. The negative charges of coprecipitated anions must be compensated electrically by positive ions, and barium ions are the most abundant cations in the medium in which the precipitate is formed. Thus, this coprecipitation is, in effect, a coprecipitation of $BaCl_2$ or $Ba(NO_3)_2$ along with $BaSO_4$. Since the coprecipitated substances are soluble by themselves, this is definitely a case of coprecipitation. Insofar as the determination of sulfate is concerned, these coprecipitated substances are merely extra precipitates for weighing. Therefore, when foreign anions coprecipitate with barium sulfate in a gravimetric sulfate determination, the results tend to be high.

Consider next the coprecipitation of a cation, such as ferric ion, in a sulfate determination. The positive charge of the cation must be compensated by anions to maintain electrical neutrality and, as the precipitation is normally conducted, this anion is invariably the sulfate ion itself. Thus, the precipitate is partially ferric sulfate, $Fe_2(SO_4)_3$, which is decomposed upon ignition to ferric oxide, Fe_2O_3. Each sulfate ion should account for one barium sulfate "molecule" (formula weight 233.40) in the final precipitate, but since each sulfate ion involved in the coprecipitation of iron accounts for only one third of a ferric oxide "molecule" (formula weight 159.69, one third being only 53.23), the precipitate is too light, and the result for sulfate comes out low. Coprecipitation of other cations leads to a similar conclusion whenever the cation replacing a barium ion in the precipitate weighs less than the barium ion itself, as is usually the case. Generally, coprecipitation of foreign cations leads to results that are too low in the determination of sulfate.

One fortunate aspect of coprecipitation phenomena is now clear — when both foreign cations and foreign anions are coprecipitated, the errors tend to compensate and may yield fairly accurate results. The balancing of the positive and negative errors is never perfect, of course, unless it be by mere chance. Some ions coprecipitate much more readily than others. The extent of coprecipitation of any ion is a function of its concentration in the mother liquid, and various other conditions of precipitation also influence the extent of coprecipitation.

Barium sulfate must be ignited at a temperature of 500°C or above to free it of water. The barium sulfate itself is stable well above this temperature, and so the ignition operation need not cause any undesired decomposition. However, at a high temperature barium sulfate may be reduced by carbon, as from filter paper:

$$BaSO_4 + 4\,C \longrightarrow BaS + 4\,CO$$

This possible source of error is avoided entirely if a sintered porcelain filtering crucible is used. However, good results can be obtained even with filter paper if the paper is charred off at the lowest possible temperature, if the paper does not actually inflame, and if there is free access to air during the ignition. One can reverse any slight decomposition to barium sulfide, if necessary, by cooling the precipitate after ignition, adding a drop of concentrated sulfuric acid to it, and gently heating it to fume off the sulfuric acid not used up in the following reaction

$$BaS + H_2SO_4 \longrightarrow BaSO_4 + H_2S$$

Physical form of the precipitate.   Barium sulfate is a crystalline precipitate, so there is little or no danger of its passing through the filter medium. Barium sulfate often exhibits a tendency to "creep" — that is, the fine clumps of precipitate, supported on a liquid surface and moving over it through the action of surface tension, distribute themselves over the entire wetted surface of the containing vessel, even climbing up and over the walls of the container if these surfaces are wet. Thus, the particles of the precipitate can climb up a wetted filter paper onto the side of the glass funnel, if the latter is wet, and may be lost. This possible source of error can be suppressed if one refrains from filling the filter paper any closer than about 2 cm from the top or if one uses a filtering crucible and keeps the upper part entirely dry.

The crystal size, degree of perfection, rate of coagulation, tendency to creep, and other aspects of the physical form of the precipitate are markedly influenced by the conditions of the precipitation. Figure 6-3 shows highly magnified electron photomicrographs of barium sulfate crystals precipitated from solutions of various sulfate ion concentrations. It is seen that the particles precipitated from a relatively dilute solution are more highly perfected crystals than are those precipitated from concentrated sulfate solutions. There is also a size difference. In the case of some other precipitates, the particle size varies much more markedly with the concentrations of the reacting solutions. Figure 6-4 shows electron photomicrographs of barium sulfate crystals precipitated from sulfate media of various hydrogen ion concentrations. At the higher acidity values (lower pH values), the crystals are smaller but definitely more highly perfected. Figure 6-5 shows electron photomicrographs of barium sulfate crystals precipitated with a fresh solution of barium chloride and with a solution of barium chloride which had been allowed to stand for a time before use. Even such a seemingly insignificant factor as the age of the barium chloride solution can markedly influence the size of the resultant crystals. Some of these phenomena were discussed in the previous chapter, although adequate explanations for some of them are still lacking.

.0026 MOLAR

.006 MOLAR

.010 MOLAR

.016 MOLAR

.021 MOLAR

.026 MOLAR

FIGURE 6-3.   Electron photomicrographs of barium sulfate showing the effect of the concentration of the sulfate solution upon the size and degree of perfection of the precipitated particles.

Applicability.   Barium may be determined by adding an excess of sulfate ion to a solution of the unknown, just the reverse of the sulfate procedure. Coprecipitation errors again may be serious. Reasoning similar to that of the preceding section reveals that, in a barium determination, anion coprecipitation leads to low results and cation coprecipitation to high results — just opposite to the situation in sulfate determinations. Lead may be determined by a similar procedure, but lead sulfate is soluble enough (about 4 mg per 100 ml of water at room temperature) to make solubility losses somewhat more significant than in barium sulfate precipitations. Strontium and calcium sulfates are nominally insoluble also, but their solubilities (15 mg of $SrSO_4$ and 100 mg of $CaSO_4$, respectively, per 100 ml of water) are too great for good quantitative work. These substances are rendered less soluble in a mixed solvent of alcohol and water, but even then the determinations are not entirely satisfactory.

pH 0.5   98°C   pH 1.0   98°C

pH 1.5   98°C   pH 2.0   98°C

pH 3.0   30°C   pH 6.0   30°C

FIGURE 6-4.   Electron photomicrographs of barium sulfate showing the effect of the acidity of the sulfate solution upon the size and degree of perfection of the precipitated crystals.

FIGURE 6-5.   Electron photomicrographs of barium sulfate precipitated with a fresh solution of barium chloride (left) and with a solution of barium chloride which had been allowed to stand for several days prior to use (right).

PRECIPITATION OF HYDROUS FERRIC OXIDE

Ferric ion can be precipitated from weakly acidic, neutral, or slightly alkaline solutions as hydrous ferric oxide:

$$Fe^{+++} + 3\,OH^- + xH_2O \longrightarrow Fe(OH)_3 \cdot xH_2O$$

After precipitation, filtration, and washing, the precipitate can be ignited to anhydrous ferric oxide,

$$2\,Fe(OH)_3 \cdot xH_2O \longrightarrow Fe_2O_3 + (2x+3)H_2O$$

in which form it can be weighed. The complete gravimetric determination of iron as ferric oxide was very popular at one time, but easier and highly accurate titrimetric methods are now more commonly used. However, the separation of iron by precipitation is still employed in conjunction with other determinations and measurements.

A precipitate of hydrous ferric oxide is neither curdy, as silver chloride, nor crystalline, as barium sulfate, but rather is gelatinous. A gelatinous precipitate is one which contains as an intimate part of itself an appreciable but indefinite amount of water. A highly magnified electron photomicrograph of hydrous ferric oxide is shown in Figure 6-6, which may be compared with Figures 6-1 and 6-2 to show the three classes of precipitates.

Hydrous ferric oxide is extremely insoluble in water. It is difficult to specify quantitatively just what its solubility is, because the solution in equilibrium with a precipitate of hydrous ferric oxide contains a whole family of soluble species, such as $Fe(H_2O)_6^{+++}$, $Fe(H_2O)_5OH^{++}$, $Fe(H_2O)_4(OH)_2^+$, and $Fe_2(OH)_2(H_2O)_8^{++++}$. The concentrations of these species are related to each other through complicated equilibria, and in most cases the pertinent equilibrium constants are unknown and cannot be easily evaluated. Nevertheless, this precipitate is one of the least soluble ones encountered in analytical chemistry.

Ferric ion is complexed by a number of anions, including citrate, tartrate, thiocyanate, ethylenediaminetetraacetate, sulfate, chloride, fluoride, oxalate, cyanide, and phosphate. Therefore, the presence of any of these ions may partially or entirely prevent the precipitation of ferric ion as the hydrous oxide. This possibility of forming a complex ion is a disadvantage in the iron precipitation, but it may be an advantage in other situations. For example, aluminum or chromium hydroxide may be precipitated selectively as a hydroxide in the presence of complexed ferric ion but not in the presence of uncomplexed ferric ion. Similarly, in the separation of nickel from iron by precipitation as nickel dimethylglyoximate from ammonia solution, ferric ion can be complexed by tartrate anions.

The precipitation of iron as hydrous ferric oxide is incomplete if the iron is not entirely in the ferric state at the time of precipitation. Any ferrous ion which is present may be oxidized with bromine water or nitric acid just prior to precipitation. An alternate and especially convenient reagent for oxidation

FIGURE 6-6.   Electron photomicrograph of hydrous ferric oxide, a gelatinous precipitate.

of any ferrous ion in an acidic medium is hydrogen peroxide, because the reduction product of peroxide is only innocuous water and because the excess peroxide can easily be decomposed by boiling the solution briefly.

Nearly every metallic ion other than the alkali metal ions can form a hydroxide, hydrous oxide, or basic salt in alkaline solution, and so all may interfere in the gravimetric determination or separation of iron. Careful control of the hydroxide ion concentration often provides considerable selectivity in the precipitation of the hydroxide or hydrous oxide of one cation in the presence of another metal ion. Weak bases rather than strong bases are useful in limiting the hydroxide ion concentration to a predetermined value. The problem is made more complicated by momentary local excesses of hydroxide ions where the drops of added reagent enter the solution in the precipitation vessel; this particular source of difficulty is eliminated in the method of precipitation from homogeneous solution.

In the particular case of ferric ion, quantitative precipitation and separation of hydrous ferric oxide can be achieved at a pH value as low as between 3 and 4. This relatively low pH prevents or minimizes the precipitation of most oxides and hydroxides of dipositive metal cations, although coprecipitation may still be a problem. The pH of a solution can conveniently be controlled near a value of 4 through the use of an acetic acid–acetate buffer or a pyridine-pyridinium ion buffer. The latter buffer has a further advantage in that pyridine forms stable complexes with many of the dipositive metal ions, a factor which also decreases coprecipitation.

As already noted, hydrous ferric oxide is a gelatinous precipitate and retains within the solid phase an appreciable quantity of the mother liquid. Even though the water retained by the precipitate may be volatilized subsequently during ignition, any nonvolatile components present in the mother liquid will remain through the final weighing operation. Gelatinous precipitates are seldom pure, but rather retain as impurities at least some of any foreign ion present to an appreciable extent in the mother liquid. In some cases it is beneficial to redissolve a gelatinous precipitate after filtration and then to precipitate it again; any impurities present in the mother liquid at the time of the first precipitation are present in much less concentration for the reprecipitation.

An additional source of impurity in the precipitate arises from the fact that alkaline solutions attack glass. A residue of silica is formed if the alkaline solution is permitted to stand for an appreciable period of time prior to filtration. Any silica present at the time of precipitation of the hydrous oxide is carried down with the main body of precipitate.

Gelatinous precipitates are exceedingly difficult to filter and wash. Prolonged digestion of the precipitate prior to filtration does little or no good. The precipitate tends to clog the pores of the filter, even to the extent of preventing the passage of liquid through the filter. A coarse filter paper should be used, and nearly all of the washing operation should be accomplished in the precipitation vessel by decantation prior to transfer of the main body of precipitate to the filter. Liquid tends to form channels through the precipitate on the paper so that the liquid does not even come in contact with all of the precipitate. The use of filter paper pulp, which can be added to the solution and upon which the precipitate gathers, is recommended as one means of effectively increasing the bulkiness and consequently the ease of handling a gelatinous precipitate. Suction should not be used in the filtration of gelatinous precipitates because it enhances the channeling effect.

Experiment 6-1

GRAVIMETRIC DETERMINATION OF CHLORIDE IN A SOLUBLE SALT MIXTURE

Purposes

This experiment is designed not only to serve as an accurate method for the gravimetric determination of chloride but also to demonstrate various manipulative techniques within a sequence of laboratory operations.

Procedure

Three sintered-glass or sintered-porcelain filtering crucibles should be cleaned, rinsed thoroughly with distilled water, and brought to constant weight. To bring a crucible to a known, constant weight, place it in a beaker-and-watch-glass arrangement (Fig. 2-1) and heat it at 120°C for approximately one hour in a drying oven. After the heating step, the crucible should be cooled in air for two to three minutes, transferred with the aid of crucible tongs to a desiccator and cooled approximately 30 minutes, then weighed to the nearest 0.1 mg. The crucible should be put through a second, shorter (perhaps 30 minutes) heating in the oven, cooled in air and in a desiccator, and then reweighed. The crucible may be considered ready for subsequent use if the two weights agree to within 0.2 mg; otherwise, additional heating periods should be employed until constant weight is finally achieved.

In any gravimetric procedure, it is vitally important that a crucible be treated *before* it contains the precipitate exactly as it is to be treated *later* when it does contain the precipitate. Also, it is important that some marking system be employed so that the three crucibles can be distinguished from each other. Sometimes a different number of small file marks can be made on the rim of each crucible, or a special marking pencil may be employed.

A quantity of the original sample, enough for at least three separate weighed portions, should be dried at 120°C for one hour. The sample to be dried should be transferred to a clean, dry weighing bottle, and the weighing bottle itself placed in a beaker-and-watch-glass arrangement for insertion into an oven. After the sample has been dried for an hour, the weighing bottle plus sample should be cooled in air for two to three minutes, and then transferred to a desiccator for cooling and storage prior to the weighing of individual portions.

Weigh accurately (±0.1 mg) three individual 0.4 to 0.7 gm portions of the dried sample, each into a clean 400 ml beaker.

The weight of each portion of the original sample should be of such size that the final weight of silver chloride precipitate will be about 0.5 to 0.7 gm. This is to minimize the effects of weighing errors in the determination (by difference) of the weight of silver chloride. However, the final weight of AgCl should not be too much greater than 0.7 gm, because a large quantity of precipitate is difficult to handle during the washing and filtering steps of the procedure. From the atomic weights of chlorine and silver, one can calculate that 0.7 gm of AgCl contains approximately 0.17 gm of chloride. Therefore, each portion of the original sample should contain, say, 0.17 to 0.20 gm of chloride. The desired weight of each portion can be calculated if the approximate chloride content of the sample is known. For example, if the sample happens to be potassium chloride (which contains about 47 per cent chloride), one might take the weight of each portion to be about 0.4 gm.

Add approximately 100 ml of distilled water to each beaker to dissolve the sample. Then carefully add (with the aid of a glass stirring rod) 1 ml of concentrated ($16 F$) nitric acid to each solution. (Since it is necessary to heat and stir the solution later, a separate stirring rod should be used for each solution and the rod should be kept in that solution for the duration of the experiment.) Heat each solution to about 80°C and add a previously calculated volume of $0.35 F$ silver nitrate solution (5 gm of $AgNO_3$ per 100 ml of water) in eight to 10 portions down the side of each beaker with the aid of a stirring rod. Stir the mixture thoroughly, but carefully, for a minute or two after each addition of silver nitrate solution.

The required volume of silver nitrate solution can be calculated from the approximate quantity of chloride in each portion of the sample. For example, a 0.4 gm portion of potassium chloride, containing 47 per cent chloride, would correspond to 0.19 gm or 5.4 millimoles of chloride ion and would require the addition of 15.5 ml of a $0.35 F$ silver nitrate solution. However, *you should add approximately 10 to 20 per cent more than the stoichiometric volume of silver nitrate solution to ensure quantitative precipitation.* Furthermore, as will be described, a final test for completeness of precipitation should always be made.

At this stage and for the remainder of the experiment, some careful thought must be given as to how each step of the procedure is to be coordinated. Keep the stirring rod over or in the beaker during the addition of silver nitrate. If the stirring rod must be removed from the beaker, rinse off adhering AgCl or solution with a small volume of distilled water. Do not splash or drip solution into the beaker because solid AgCl or solution may be lost. Think about and plan these operations before actually beginning the experiment.

After the addition of silver nitrate solution has been completed, keep the mixture at about 80°C for 30 minutes in order to coagulate the precipitate. Alternatively, the mixture may be allowed to stand overnight at room temperature to cause the precipitate to coagulate. Test the clear supernatant solution for completeness of precipitation at this point by adding two or three drops of silver nitrate solution. If additional precipitate does form, more silver nitrate solution must be added and the test for completeness of precipitation repeated. It is important that the silver chloride precipitate be well coagulated and that the supernatant solution be perfectly clear before the filtering and washing steps are begun.

Avoid exposing the AgCl precipitate to direct light (especially sunlight), if possible, in order to minimize the surface photodecomposition of silver chloride. If it is convenient, the precipitation may be carried out in a partially darkened room; the precipitate may be coagulated by overnight storage of the beaker and silver chloride suspension inside a cabinet. In general, any photodecomposition which does occur is relatively slight under the experimental conditions and should not affect the accuracy of the results.

Assemble a suction flask and trap for filtration according to the directions given by your laboratory instructor. Insert the crucible into a crucible holder on the suction flask and apply a gentle suction to the filter assembly. To begin the filtration and transfer of AgCl, hold the beaker at an angle so that the silver chloride "nestles" at the lower corner of the beaker; then you can pour most of the clear supernatant solution through the filter crucible. Use a glass stirring rod to direct the solution into the crucible. *Never allow the level of liquid in the crucible to reach above the two-thirds-full point because solutions tend to "creep" upward and particles of AgCl may be lost over the side of the crucible.* When almost all of the clear supernatant has been poured through the crucible, wash the AgCl in the beaker with three or four 20 ml portions of a wash solution prepared by adding about 2 ml of concentrated ($16\,F$) nitric acid to 500 ml of distilled water. After adding each portion of wash solution, gently swirl the mixture, let the AgCl settle into the corner of the beaker, and pour the solution with the aid of a stirring rod through the crucible. After this washing by decantation, transfer the silver chloride precipitate to the crucible. This is accomplished by adding small portions (about 10 ml) of wash solution to the beaker and pouring the AgCl suspension (use a stirring rod) into the crucible. In order to transfer the last bits of the precipitate to the crucible, attach a rubber policeman to another glass stirring rod and use it to transfer the precipitate. Wash AgCl from the rubber policeman by holding the rubber policeman over the crucible and using a small volume of the wash solution.

By adding one or two drops of dilute hydrochloric acid to several milliliters of the filtrate, test the last portions of wash liquid coming through the crucible for excess silver nitrate. If no turbidity due to silver chloride is observed, the precipitate has been adequately washed; otherwise, the precipitate should be washed further until a negative test for silver ion is obtained.

Place each crucible and silver chloride precipitate back into the beaker-and-watch-glass arrangement and heat them in an oven at 120°C for one hour. After the heating, allow the crucible and AgCl to cool for two to three minutes in air, then in a desiccator for 30 minutes. Weigh the crucible and its contents to the nearest 0.1 mg. Repeat the heating, cooling, and weighing operations until the weight of the crucible plus precipitate is constant to within 0.2 mg.

On the basis of three separate results, calculate and report the average percentage of chloride in the original sample.

Experiment 6-2

GRAVIMETRIC DETERMINATION OF SULFATE IN A SOLUBLE SALT MIXTURE AND STUDIES OF COPRECIPITATION PHENOMENA

Purposes

This experiment involves the accurate gravimetric determination of sulfate through its precipitation as barium sulfate. In addition, provision is made for a study of some factors which affect coprecipitation and contamination of crystalline precipitates, such as barium sulfate. The data obtained from the coprecipitation studies may be tested statistically to establish if observed differences in the results are significant.

Procedure

Three porcelain crucibles (with solid bottoms) should be cleaned and brought to constant weight. Each crucible, along with a crucible cover, should be supported on a clay triangle and mounted above a high-temperature burner (Fig. 2-13). Heat the crucibles at approximately 600°C or higher for one hour, allow them to cool in air before transferring them with the aid of crucible tongs to a desiccator, and weigh each crucible (without its cover) to the nearest 0.1 mg after a 30 minute cooling period in the desiccator. A shorter, 20 minute heating period, followed by the cooling and weighing operations, should be carried out to ensure that each crucible has attained constant weight to within 0.2 mg and is ready for subsequent use. Some method must be employed to identify each crucible; crucibles ready for use may be stored in a desiccator.

Transfer a portion of the sample to a clean, dry weighing bottle. Place the weighing bottle in a beaker-and-watch-glass arrangement (Fig. 2-1) and dry the sample at 110°C for about one hour. After the weighing bottle and its contents have cooled in air for two to three minutes, place the weighing bottle and sample into a desiccator for at least 30 minutes prior to the weighing of the individual samples for the analysis.

Weigh, to the nearest 0.1 mg, three 0.3 to 0.6 gm samples, each into a clean 400 ml beaker. Dissolve each sample in 150 ml of distilled water and add to the solution, with the aid of a stirring rod, approximately 2 ml of concentrated $(12\,F)$ hydrochloric acid.

Prepare an approximately $0.04\,F$ barium chloride solution by dissolving 10 gm of barium chloride dihydrate $(BaCl_2 \cdot 2\,H_2O)$ in 1 liter of distilled water.

A precipitate of barium sulfate normally consists of very small crystals or aggregates of crystals. In order to promote the formation and growth of large barium sulfate crystals, it is beneficial to precipitate the sulfate with an *aged* solution of barium chloride (Fig. 6-5). If this is desired, the barium chloride solution may be prepared in advance, so that it can age in its container for at least 24 hours prior to the precipitation and determination of sulfate.

Calculate the volume of the barium chloride solution needed to precipitate the sulfate ion present in each sample solution (including a 10 per cent excess to ensure quantitative precipitation of sulfate) and transfer this volume of the barium chloride solution into a separate clean beaker.

If the original solid sample contains 50 per cent sulfate, for example, a 0.5 gm portion of that sample contains 0.25 gm or about 2.6 millimoles of sulfate. Therefore, one should add 2.6 millimoles of barium ion plus a 10 per cent excess, or a *total* of nearly 2.9 millimoles of barium ion. This quantity of barium ion corresponds to 72 ml of the previously prepared $(0.04\,F)$ barium chloride solution.

Heat both the sample solution and the barium chloride precipitant to between 80 and 90°C. Then pour the hot barium chloride solution (with the aid of a stirring rod) quickly, but carefully, into the sample solution. Stir the mixture thoroughly for two or three minutes, keeping the solution hot. Let the barium sulfate precipitate settle for several minutes and test for completeness of precipitation by adding a few drops of barium chloride solution (adding more precipitant if this test indicates that it is needed).

Place the beaker (covered with a watch glass) containing the freshly precipitated barium sulfate on a steam bath for one to two hours to cause digestion of the precipitate. The supernatant solution should be perfectly clear and the precipitate should have settled to the bottom of the beaker before the next step in the procedure is started.

The purpose of the digestion period is to allow the initially tiny crystals of barium sulfate to undergo recrystallization so that larger, more readily filterable crystals of barium sulfate are produced. Unless the precipitate is digested in this way, some of it will invariably get through the filter paper in the subsequent step, and much time will be lost in recovering the precipitate from the filtrate.

Set up a filter assembly, consisting of an ashless filter paper of fine porosity and a clean glass funnel, as shown in Figures 2-10 and 2-11 and discussed on pages 44 to 46. Decant the clear supernatant solution through the filter, using a stirring rod to direct the flow of solution and making sure that the level of liquid in the filter does not rise above the two-thirds-full mark.

This last point is important, because usually small crystals of barium sulfate floating on the surface of the supernatant (as a result of surface tension) are transferred immediately to the filter paper and may be lost through carelessness in pouring the supernatant solution haphazardly onto the filter.

Wash the precipitate in the beaker by decantation, using several portions of distilled water; then, transfer the precipitate to the filter paper with the aid of a stirring rod and small volumes of distilled water. Use a rubber policeman, if necessary, to transfer the last bits of precipitate to the filter. After all the barium sulfate has been transferred onto the filter paper, wash the precipitate and filter paper repeatedly with small portions of warm distilled water, until a few milliliters of the filtrate give a *negative* test for chloride (from the HCl and $BaCl_2$ originally added to the sample solution) when treated with a few drops of a silver nitrate solution.

Carefully fold the filter paper around the precipitate and place it into one of the previously weighed porcelain crucibles. Set the crucible vertically on a clay triangle and position the crucible cover so that it is just slightly displaced, leaving a narrow opening for steam to escape. Heat the crucible slowly at first to evaporate the water trapped in the precipitate and filter paper. Avoid too rapid heating so that the precipitate will not spatter. Increase the heating after a few minutes to char the filter paper; however, keep the cover only slightly displaced so that the paper will not burst into flame.

Several things must be kept in mind during the ignition. The crucible cover should be slightly displaced to allow limited access of air without the risk that the paper will actually inflame. If the paper does inflame, cover the crucible completely and immediately to extinguish the flame; otherwise some precipitate may be thrown out of the crucible. On the other hand, it is inadvisable to keep the crucible completely covered because, in the absence of sufficient oxygen, the filter paper is combusted to carbon, and the formation of a large deposit of carbon on the inner surfaces of the crucible and crucible cover can actually cement them together.

After the paper has been completely charred, with only a small ash residue remaining, the temperature should be increased so that the crucible glows with a dull redness. The crucible should be inclined on the clay triangle and the cover displaced (as shown in Figure 2-13) to allow free access of air. This heating should be continued in order to burn off any carbon residue adhering to the crucible. Rotate the crucible periodically with the aid of crucible tongs so that the part of the crucible with the carbon residue is brought nearest the burner flame. Finally, when all of the carbon has been removed, heat the crucible strongly for about 15 minutes more.

If there is any reason to suspect that some of the barium sulfate has been reduced to barium sulfide by carbon from the filter paper, cool the crucible and its contents nearly to room temperature and treat the precipitate with one or two drops of concentrated sulfuric acid to convert the barium sulfide back to barium sulfate. Ignite the crucible and the precipitate again strongly for 10 to 15 minutes to expel the excess sulfuric acid.

Allow the crucible to cool in air and then place it into a desiccator for at least 30 minutes before weighing it. Determine the weight of the crucible (without cover) plus precipitate to the nearest 0.1 mg. Reheat the crucible and the precipitate strongly for another 10 to 15 minutes. Cool the crucible and determine the weight of the precipitate. The two final weights should agree to within 0.2 mg, otherwise additional 10 minute heating periods should follow until successive weights are in agreement. Calculate and report the percentage of SO_3 in the original sample.

Coprecipitation Studies. The quantitative importance of certain coprecipitation phenomena can be studied profitably by means of variations in the procedure. It may be preferable for the laboratory class to be divided into a number of groups and for each member of a group to perform *triplicate* determinations according to the procedure just described, except for the modifications which follow. All students should, of course, use the same sample which, instead of an unknown, may be pure sodium sulfate or another compound.

Group I: Follow the procedure exactly as described above.

Group II: Follow the usual procedure except that, after dissolving the weighed sample in 150 ml of water and 2 ml of 12 F hydrochloric acid, dissolve 5 gm of sodium chloride (NaCl) in the sample solution prior to precipitation of barium sulfate.

Group III: Follow the usual procedure except that, after dissolving the weighed sample in 150 ml of water and 2 ml of 12 F hydrochloric acid, dissolve 5 gm of potassium chloride (KCl) in the sample solution prior to precipitation of barium sulfate.

Group IV: Follow the usual procedure except that, after dissolving the weighed sample in 150 ml of water, add 2 ml of concentrated HNO_3 instead of HCl and precipitate the barium sulfate with an approximately 0.04 F barium nitrate solution (11 gm of $Ba(NO_3)_2$ per liter of distilled water) instead of barium chloride solution.

Tabulate the results of your particular set of experiments, calculating (a) the *arithmetic mean* or *average* of your three determinations, (b) the *standard deviation* of an individual result, and (c) the *95 per cent confidence limit* of the mean of your results.

Later, when results from all four groups are available, apply a statistical test to determine whether the differences observed between various groups are significant. Compare groups I and II, groups I and III, groups I and IV, and groups II and III. Critically discuss the results of the experiments and the statistical tests.

QUESTIONS AND PROBLEMS

1. Water in a sample is often determined by loss of weight upon heating. How can the analytical chemist be sure that no other component is being lost at the same time as water?

2. Define or characterize and illustrate the following terms: curdy precipitate, crystalline precipitate, gelatinous precipitate.

3. What problems of experimental technique are introduced by the gelatinous type of precipitate?

4. State whether each of the following occurrences would tend to make the results of a determination of water in barium chloride dihydrate by volatilization too high or too low or whether they would be of no effect. Explain each answer.
    (a) The dehydration temperature is too low.
    (b) The dehydration temperature is too high.
    (c) The crucible and anhydrous barium chloride are placed on the balance pan and weighed while they are still hot.
    (d) The anhydrous barium chloride is allowed to stand uncovered in air between the time it is heated and subsequently weighed.
    (e) A bit of plaster unsuspectedly falls from the wall into the crucible before the final weighing of anhydrous barium chloride.

5. Will the results of a determination of chloride by the usual gravimetric procedure be made too high or too low, or will there be no effect, if each of the following occurs? Explain each answer.
    (a) Some carbonate is present in the original sample.
    (b) The water used in preparing the wash liquid contains some chloride ion.
    (c) The precipitate is exposed to bright sunlight while it is suspended in the mother liquid.
    (d) The precipitate is exposed to bright sunlight after it is washed but prior to its weighing.
    (e) The precipitate is washed with pure water rather than with water containing an electrolyte.

6. Will the results of a determination of sulfate by the usual gravimetric procedure be made too high or too low, or will there be no effect, if each of the following occurs? Explain each answer.
    (a) An excessive amount of acid is present in the mother liquid.
    (b) Fluoride ion is present at the time of precipitation of barium sulfate.
    (c) Nitrate ion is coprecipitated.
    (d) Aluminum ion is coprecipitated.
    (e) The ignition temperature becomes too high before the combustion of the filter paper is complete.

7. A 0.8046 gm sample of impure barium chloride dihydrate weighed 0.7082 gm after it was dried at 200°C for two hours. Calculate the percentage of water in the sample.

8. A silver chloride precipitate weighing 0.3221 gm was obtained from 0.4926 gm of a soluble salt mixture. Calculate the percentage of chloride in the sample.

9. The sulfur content of a sample is usually expressed in terms of the percentage of SO_3 in that sample. Calculate the percentage of SO_3 in a 0.3232 gm sample of a soluble salt mixture which yielded a barium sulfate precipitate weighing 0.2982 gm.

10. What is the percentage of iron in a 0.9291 gm sample of an acid-soluble iron ore which yields a ferric oxide (Fe_2O_3) precipitate weighing 0.6216 gm?

11. From a 0.6980 gm sample of an impure, acid-soluble magnesium compound, a precipitate of magnesium pyrophosphate $(Mg_2P_2O_7)$ weighing 0.4961 gm was obtained. Calculate the magnesium content of the sample in terms of the percentage of magnesium oxide (MgO) present in that sample.

12. A 1.0000 gm sample of a mixture of K_2CO_3 and $KHCO_3$ yielded 0.4000 gm of carbon dioxide (CO_2) upon ignition. What weight of each compound was present in the mixture?

13. A 1.1374 gm sample contains only sodium chloride and potassium chloride. Upon dissolution of the sample and precipitation of the chloride as silver chloride, a precipitate weighing 2.3744 gm was obtained. Calculate the percentage of sodium chloride in the sample.

14. A 0.5000 gm sample of a clay was analyzed for sodium and potassium by precipitation of both as chlorides. The combined weight of the sodium and potassium chlorides was found to be 0.0361 gm. The potassium in the chloride precipitate was reprecipitated as K_2PtCl_6, which weighed 0.0356 gm. Calculate the sodium and potassium content of the clay in terms of the percentages of hypothetical Na_2O and K_2O present in the clay.

15. A 0.2000 gm sample of an alloy containing only silver and lead was dissolved in nitric acid. Treatment of the resulting solution with cold hydrochloric acid gave a mixed chloride precipitate $(AgCl$ and $PbCl_2)$ weighing 0.2466 gm. When this mixed chloride precipitate was treated with hot water to dissolve all the lead chloride, 0.2067 gm of silver chloride remained. Calculate the percentage of silver in the alloy and calculate what weight of lead chloride was not precipitated by the addition of cold hydrochloric acid.

SUGGESTIONS FOR ADDITIONAL READING

1. A. A. Benedetti-Pichler: *Essentials of Quantitative Analysis*, The Ronald Press Company, New York, 1956, pp. 458–485.
2. L. Gordon, M. L. Salutsky, and H. H. Willard: *Precipitation from Homogeneous Solution*, John Wiley & Sons, Inc., New York, 1959.
3. W. F. Hillebrand, G. E. F. Lundell, H. A. Bright, and J. I. Hoffman: *Applied Inorganic Analysis*, second edition, John Wiley & Sons, Inc., New York, 1953, pp. 44–46, 711–723, 822–835.
4. I. M. Kolthoff and E. B. Sandell: *Textbook of Quantitative Inorganic Analysis*, third edition, The Macmillan Company, New York, 1952, pp. 296–411.
5. E. H. Swift: *Introductory Quantitative Analysis*, Prentice-Hall, Inc., New York, 1950, pp. 332–373.

Chapter Seven

Separations by Extraction and by Chromatographic Methods

Recent and continuing advances in instrumentation have allowed chemists to perform and to attempt the analyses of compounds and other complex mixtures which were formerly very difficult, if not impossible, to achieve by classic methods. Instrumental methods have enhanced both the accuracy and the sensitivity of analysis of a wide variety of materials, including ultrapure metals used in solid state electronic devices, special high-temperature alloys used in the space research program, and mixtures of fission products encountered in the nuclear energy program, as well as mixtures of amino acids and complex gas mixtures. It is worth noting that the virtue of many instrumental methods lies in the fact that they greatly improve the accuracy and sensitivity of the measurement step in an analysis, and, in certain instances, an instrumental method is applicable to the original sample material without prior separation of the individual component to be determined. At the same time, however, the advent of modern chemical instrumentation has necessitated the development of new, and sometimes highly specific, techniques of separation so that these instrumental techniques can be fully exploited.

In this chapter, some basic principles and analytical applications of several methods for the separation of chemical species are discussed. A separation by any of these methods may be followed by a wide variety of measurement techniques in the quantitative determinations of various inorganic and organic substances.

Extraction and chromatographic methods of separation bear much in common with each other. The extraction of a solute from one liquid phase into another is usually selective, at least to some extent. Even when a single extraction is insufficient to cause a quantitative separation, it is often possible to separate chemical species quantitatively by multistage extraction procedures. In addition, we shall see that chromatographic methods, including column liquid-phase chromatography, gas-phase chromatography, and ion-exchange chromatography, may be considered to be multistage extraction procedures.

EXTRACTION

The extraction of a solute from one liquid phase into another liquid phase is one of the most simple and rapid separation techniques in analytical chemistry. In contrast to separation by precipitation, discussed in Chapter 5, extraction has a significant advantage in that it usually provides separations which are inherently sharper and cleaner than those obtained by means of precipitation. In particular, the problems encountered in separation by precipitation, such as the contamination of a precipitate by post-precipitation, surface adsorption, occlusion, and isomorphous replacement, are not observed in separation by extraction.

Distribution Coefficients

When two immiscible solvents are placed in contact with each other, a substance which is soluble in both of them *distributes*, or *partitions*, itself between the two phases. A dynamic state of equilibrium is eventually established,

$$A_1 \rightleftharpoons A_2$$

in which A_1 and A_2 represent the solute A in solvents 1 and 2, respectively. It is assumed, in the form in which this equation is written, that substance A exists in the same molecular or ionic form in both solvents. In many practical systems, however, the solute undergoes different types or degrees of association or complexation in the two solvents, and its condition with respect to solvation is usually different in the two phases. The equilibrium constant for the partition of solute may be expressed in terms of activities of the appropriate species. A less rigorous, even semiempirical, mathematical representation of the equilibrium condition is

$$K_d = \frac{[A]_2}{[A]_1}$$

in which K_d is the **distribution coefficient** and $[A]_2$ and $[A]_1$ are the total concentrations of solute A in the two solvent phases, regardless of what molecular or ionic forms of A actually exist. The distribution coefficient is not constant over wide ranges of concentration, as is the thermodynamic equilibrium constant. Nevertheless, for many practical systems the distribution coefficient is reasonably constant over significant ranges both of concentration and of other conditions, so it is useful in describing quantitatively the partitioning of a solute between two immiscible solvents.

The general requirements which must be fulfilled by an extraction process to make it suitable as a method of accomplishing the quantitative separation of chemical species are essentially the same as those for all other separation methods. The desired constituent must be separated completely and selectively, and the separated substance must be in a physical and chemical form suitable for whatever subsequent operations or measurements are to be performed upon it. We have already described separations by precipitation in terms of these requirements in Chapters 5 and 6. Let us now examine each of these three requirements as applied to the extraction process.

Completeness of Extraction

Assume that substance A is initially in solvent 1 and is to be extracted into solvent 2, the two solvents being immiscible. Let V_1 and V_2 be the volumes of the two liquid phases, and let x be the mole fraction of A which is in solvent 2 when equilibrium is established. Thus, the quantity $(1 - x)$ is the mole fraction of A remaining in solvent 1, and x is a direct measure of the completeness of the extraction of A from solvent 1 into solvent 2:

$$K_d = \frac{[A]_2}{[A]_1}$$

$$K_d = \frac{\dfrac{x}{V_2}}{\dfrac{1-x}{V_1}}$$

Solving for x, the equilibrium mole fraction of A in solvent 2, one obtains

$$x = \frac{K_d V_2}{V_1 + K_d V_2}$$

We note that x, and therefore the degree of completeness of extraction, is determined by two factors — the distribution coefficient and the relative volumes of the two phases.

For example, if $K_d = 2$ and if $V_1 = V_2$, the value of x is found to be

0.67, so that 67 per cent of solute A is extracted into phase 2 and 33 per cent remains in phase 1. If $K_d = 100$ and $V_1 = V_2$, the numerical value of x is 0.99, so 99 per cent of A, at equilibrium, is in solvent 2 and only 1 per cent in solvent 1. Figure 7-1 shows a plot of x versus K_d, based on the assumption that the volumes of the two phases are equal. Several interesting conclusions may be derived from this figure: (a) no extraction process with a finite distribution coefficient is absolutely complete; (b) the K_d value must be about 100 to achieve a separation complete to within one part per hundred; (c) the K_d value must be about 1000 for the extraction to be complete to within one part per thousand; and (d) any K_d value greater than 1 signifies some degree of preferential extraction of A into phase 2 from phase 1.

The effect of the relative volumes of the two phases upon the completeness of an extraction process may be illustrated by repeating the preceding calculation for a K_d value of 2, but with V_2 taken to be twice as great as V_1. The value of x turns out to be 0.80, so that 80 per cent of solute A is extracted into phase 2, compared to 67 per cent with equal volumes of the two liquid phases. For an even greater volume of solvent 2, relative to solvent 1, we would achieve a higher degree of completeness of the extraction. However, there are frequently practical limitations as to how far we can go in this direction, because of such factors as the ease of handling large volumes of solvents, the cost of the solvents, and the necessity of maintaining a level of

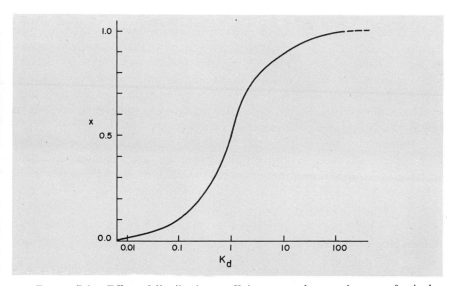

FIGURE 7-1.   Effect of distribution coefficient upon the completeness of a single-extraction process. The fraction x of the solute extracted from an original phase into a new phase is plotted as a function of K_d, the distribution coefficient. It is assumed that the volumes of the two liquid phases are equal.

concentration in phase 2 which is adequate for subsequent recovery or measurement of the extracted substance.

Numerical values of the distribution coefficients for common systems vary widely. In general, the distribution coefficient is directly proportional to the ratio of solubilities of the solute in the two solvents. As mentioned in Chapter 5, one important factor governing solubility is related to the polarities of the molecules of the solute and the solvent. Polar molecules are more soluble in polar solvents than in nonpolar solvents. Therefore, distribution coefficients are generally quite high for extractions of polar solutes into water from organic solvents, and they are very low for the extraction of polar molecules from water into organic solvents. Similarly, the distribution coefficient is high for the extraction of a nonpolar solute from water into an organic solvent. Another factor which markedly influences solubility, and thus the distribution coefficient, is the presence of a complexing agent within a solution. The pH is also of frequent significance, as are the type and extent of solvation within the two phases.

Some distribution coefficients are sufficiently high to permit quantitative extraction of a species in a single operation. The extractions of some metal chelate complexes from aqueous media into organic solvents fall into this category. Other distribution coefficients are far too low to permit quantitative transfer in a single extraction. Even with these systems, however, it is possible to transfer a solute quantitatively from one solvent to another, simply by performing the extraction two or more times with separate batches of the second immiscible solvent. For example, as we have already noted, when $K_d = 2$ and $V_2 = V_1$, a single extraction removes 67 per cent of the solute from solvent 1. A second extraction, with a fresh batch of an equal volume of solvent 2, would remove 67 per cent of what remains from the first extraction, and so forth. This multiple extraction technique is thus very advantageous in making it possible to extract a substance quantitatively from one liquid phase into another. Numerous experimental techniques have been developed for accomplishing multistage extractions, some of which will be discussed in subsequent sections of this chapter.

In summary, the completeness of an extraction can be increased by any or all of the following experimental approaches: any modification of the solvents which results in a higher numerical value of K_d, an increase in V_2 relative to V_1, and the use of the multiple extraction technique with additional fresh batches of solvent 2.

Selectivity of Extraction

When two immiscible solvents, one of which initially contains two solutes, are placed in contact with each other, both solutes distribute themselves between the two phases. The equilibrium distribution of each solute, A and B, is largely independent of the presence of the other unless, of course, there is some chemical interaction involving both A and B. Therefore, the two distribution coefficients, K_{dA} and K_{dB}, are indicative of the completeness with which each solute is extracted from solvent 1 into solvent 2.

Some separation of A from B occurs in the extraction process whenever the two distribution coefficients differ from each other. For example, it may be noted from Figure 7-1 and the associated calculations that, if K_{dA} is 100 and K_{dB} is 0.1 and if the volumes of the two phases are equal to each other, 99 per cent of A and 9 per cent of B are extracted from solvent 1 into solvent 2. Similarly, if K_{dA} is 200 and K_{dB} is 0.01, again with equal volumes of the two phases being present, solvent 2 contains at equilibrium 99.5 per cent of A and 1 per cent of B. It is evident that, in order to achieve a quantitative separation of A from B by extraction of A from one liquid phase into another, the distribution coefficient of A must be high enough to render negligible the amount of A remaining in the initial solution, and the distribution coefficient of B must be so small that the amount of B which is extracted into the second phase is negligible. It is often possible to achieve the desired conditions by judicious selection of complexing agents and of acidity in one or both solvents.

Although an increase of V_2, relative to V_1, enhances the completeness of the extraction of A, this expedient also increases the undesired extraction of B. Furthermore, the multiple extraction technique employing additional batches of solvent 2, which enhances the completeness of the extraction of A, likewise causes more of B to be removed from the initial solution.

If the initial extraction results in the presence in solvent 2 of too much of the undesired solute B, along with the desired solute A, it is possible to remove some B by one or more additional extractions with fresh portions of solvent 1. Consider again that K_{dA} is 100 and K_{dB} is 0.1 and that $V_2 = V_1$. After one extraction, solvent 2 contains 99 per cent of the total amount of A and 9 per cent of the total amount of B. If this solution is then brought in contact with a fresh batch of solvent 1, again of the same volume, all but 9 per cent of the amount of B now present will be removed from solvent 2. The second extraction decreases the amount of B in solvent 2 from 9 per cent to about 1 per cent, both expressed as percentages of the total amount of B initially present. A small amount of solute A is, of course, also removed from solvent 2 in this second extraction.

We have now considered two multiple extraction techniques. One involves fresh portions of solvent 2 and accomplishes a more complete extraction of A at the expense of a greater extraction of B as well. The other involves fresh portions of solvent 1 and results in a solution of A which is more pure but which contains less A than if a single extraction step were used. It is often permissible to sacrifice yield in order to achieve purity, or purity in order to gain yield. There are practical applications of each of the two multiple extraction techniques, both in the research laboratory and in industrial operations. Some special experimental techniques have been developed which combine both types of multiple extraction. Column partition chromatography, which will be discussed later in this chapter, is effectively equivalent to the combined multiple extraction techniques.

Concentration Range and Recoverability
of the Extracted Substance

A separation process is not really useful in analytical chemistry unless the separated substance is in a physical and chemical form suitable for whatever subsequent operations or measurements are to be performed upon it, regardless of how complete and selective the separation itself may be. Of particular significance in conjunction with liquid-liquid extractions are the concentration range of the separated substance and its recoverability from the solvent in which it is dissolved. The concentration of solute in each solution phase is determined by three interacting factors: the total amount of solute; the volumes of the two phases, both absolute and relative to each other; and the distribution coefficient. Suffice it to say that, by judicious choice of the two solvent media and the volume of each phase, it is generally possible to conduct separations and measurements upon analytical samples which vary over extremely wide ranges of gross size and composition.

It may be necessary to recover the extracted substance from its solvent, rather than simply to let it remain in solution for subsequent measurement or for some other desired purpose. Distillation and evaporation of the solvent are useful if the solute is nonvolatile and thermally stable and if the solute and solvent together do not form a mixture of constant boiling point (**azeotrope**). Another interesting and useful technique is to use a third solvent, or to change the conditions appropriately, and to reëxtract the desired component. For example, a metal chelate may be extracted selectively from water at a certain pH into an organic solvent and then reëxtracted from the organic phase into an aqueous solution of a different pH.

Some pairs of solvents, even though immiscible, form emulsions that are quite stable over long periods of time. This means that, if the two phases are shaken vigorously to ensure intimate contact and the attainment of a state of equilibrium distribution of solute between them, the two liquids tend not to separate into distinct layers. Aqueous emulsions, which would otherwise be separable only with difficulty, are occasionally rendered less stable by the presence of a strong electrolyte in the water phase or by the use of an organic phase that is actually a mixture of two self-miscible organic solvents.

Experimental Apparatus

A single-batch type of extraction may be performed readily in a separatory funnel, an example of which is shown in Figure 7-2. The two immiscible liquids are placed in the separatory funnel, the system is shaken vigorously to ensure intimate contact between the phases, the liquids are allowed to separate, and the more dense liquid is withdrawn through the stopcock.

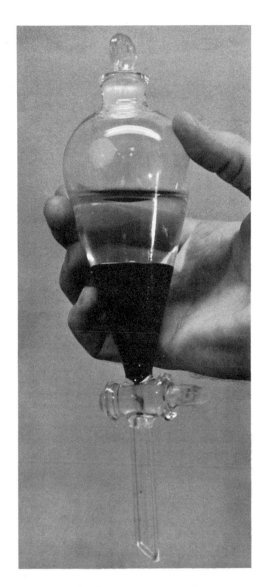

FIGURE 7-2. A separatory funnel, used in single-batch extractions, containing two immiscible liquids that have been shaken together and allowed to separate.

In the **continuous extractor,** shown in Figure 7-3, the initial solution containing the solute is introduced as a single batch, but the second solvent is added, equilibrated, and withdrawn continuously rather than in a single batch. The second solvent, which is the extracting solvent (here assumed to be *less* dense than the initial solvent), is brought into contact with the solution containing the solute to be extracted in the following way: Pure extracting solvent is added to the level of the overflow tube in the extraction vessel, and

FIGURE 7-3. Device for continuous extraction. (See text for discussion.)

Reflux condenser

Boiling flask containing extracting solvent

Extracting solvent

Solution containing solute to be extracted

another portion of the extracting solvent is placed in the boiling flask. Heat is applied to the boiling flask, causing the extracting solvent to be vaporized. The vapors of the pure extracting solvent are converted back to the liquid state in the reflux condenser; this liquid then passes downward through the U-shaped tube and percolates upward through the solution containing the solute to be extracted. Finally, the extracting solvent, now containing solute, overflows back into the boiling flask. If we assume that the solute is non-volatile, only pure extracting solvent is ever vaporized, and eventually all of the desired solute is extracted and caused to accumulate in the boiling flask. A modification of the overflow system can be made to permit the continuous extraction into a second solvent which is *more* dense than the initial one.

The Craig extraction apparatus is perhaps the most sophisticated and efficient system available for the performance of multiple extractions. It consists of a large number of connected glass tubes — frequently as many as several hundred — mounted in a rack so that a whole series of batch extractions can be performed simultaneously. The photograph at the top of Figure 7-4 shows a group of five Craig-type tubes sealed together in a single unit. Any number of these five-tube units can be connected together to provide a complete multistage extraction apparatus. The principle of operation of a Craig extraction device can be most easily understood from an inspection of the drawing in Figure 7-4, which represents a single stage of the apparatus.

Each Craig tube is initially horizontal as indicated. The *first* of the series of Craig tubes is special. To compartment A of the first tube, one adds through opening O a portion of solvent 1 containing *all* of the solute to be partitioned or distributed; the volume of this solution must be carefully measured so that, when the Craig tube is subsequently rotated counterclockwise about 100 degrees, none of this solution will run out through side arm B.

Next, a definite volume of pure extracting solvent 2 is introduced into compartment *A* of the first tube such that, when the Craig tube is rotated counterclockwise, solvent 2 will not pass through side arm *D* (which leads in the *wrong* direction to an adjoining tube). To each of the other Craig tubes in the extraction apparatus, one adds only *pure* solvent 1 of the proper volume so that it cannot run through side arm *B* of that respective tube. Thus, the extraction process begins with solvent 1 containing the solute plus pure solvent 2 in the *first* Craig tube, whereas only pure solvent 1 is in each of the *remaining* Craig tubes.

The actual partitioning process is begun when the Craig apparatus is gently rocked back and forth, as one might do with a separatory funnel, keeping the Craig tubes near the horizontal position so all solvents remain in their respective *A* compartments. When extraction equilibrium is attained, the rack containing the Craig tubes is rotated counterclockwise about 100 degrees or so; this causes solvent 2, now containing some of the solute, to flow through side arm *B* into compartment *C*. Then the Craig apparatus is

FIGURE 7-4. Craig extraction apparatus. The photograph at the top shows a unit consisting of five Craig-type tubes; any number of such units can be coupled together to give an extraction apparatus with several hundred tubes. The diagram illustrates the principle of operation of a Craig tube. (See text for a complete discussion.)

returned to its *original* horizontal position, and solvent 2 with solute flows from compartment C of the first Craig tube, through tube E, into compartment A of the *second* Craig tube. A *fresh* portion of pure solvent 2 is added to compartment A of the first Craig tube, and the apparatus is rocked gently to begin the extraction cycle again. The mixing and transferring steps are repeated over and over, each time with a fresh batch of solvent 2 being added to the first Craig tube. Throughout the extraction procedure, each of the solvent 1 phases remains in the same Craig tube in which it was originally placed. The solvent 2 layers are passed along from one tube to the next in the series. Solute travels along the series by extraction into solvent 2.

When two different solutes are to be separated by this technique, the rate at which each solute travels will depend upon its distribution coefficient, the solute with higher distribution coefficient moving at the greater rate. The degree of separation of two chemical species by this process is a direct function of two factors — the difference in distribution coefficients and the number of extractions and transfers.

The theory for the Craig extraction procedure has been so well developed that it is possible to calculate which Craig tube contains the highest concentration of the desired solute and what fraction of the total amount of solute is present in that tube. If we assume equal volumes of solvents 1 and 2, the number of the tube, n_{max}, containing the maximum concentration of solute can be established from the equation

$$n_{max} = \frac{nK_d}{K_d + 1}$$

where n is the total number of tubes and K_d is the distribution coefficient. The fraction of solute, f, present in this tube is given by the expression

$$f = \frac{K_d + 1}{\sqrt{2\pi n K_d}}$$

The term **countercurrent extraction** signifies a multistage extraction in which solute is partitioned between two immiscible solvents as they flow through each other in opposite directions. The Craig apparatus is a pseudo-countercurrent extractor because only one of the two solvents actually moves. However, in effect the two solvents do move in opposite directions relative to each other.

Several other ingenious devices and experimental procedures have been developed for multiple extractions. Some provide for multiple batches of either one of the two solvents, and some involve a combination of both types of multiple extraction. As already stated, the chromatographic methods which we will discuss later in this chapter may be considered to be special forms of multistage extraction procedures.

Analytical Applications

Many practical applications of liquid-liquid extraction are made in analytical chemistry. It is significant to recognize, however, that most applications have been developed on a rather empirical basis. The underlying principles are quite well understood, but very few distribution coefficients have been measured and tabulated. Some of the practical applications involve the extraction of single species simply for removal purposes, and others involve subsequent measurement of the solute which is extracted. Most, but not all, applications involve organic substances, either as organic molecules or as metallo-organic complexes.

Extraction methods of separation are often applicable to the separation and recovery of microgram quantities of materials, and they are often equally applicable with macro quantities of materials.

The wide applicability of extraction procedures in analytical chemistry may be illustrated by a few examples. Iron(III) can be separated from most monovalent and divalent cations by its extraction from aqueous $6\,F$ hydrochloric acid into diethyl ether. The species $Fe(H_2O)_6^{+++}$ may be regarded as the parent form of iron(III) in aqueous media. However, in the presence of hydrochloric acid, the following equilibria prevail:

$$Fe(H_2O)_6^{+++} + Cl^- \rightleftharpoons FeCl(H_2O)_5^{++} + H_2O$$

$$FeCl(H_2O)_5^{++} + Cl^- \rightleftharpoons FeCl_2(H_2O)_4^+ + H_2O$$

$$FeCl_2(H_2O)_4^+ + Cl^- \rightleftharpoons FeCl_3(H_2O)_3 + H_2O$$

$$FeCl_3(H_2O)_3 + Cl^- \rightleftharpoons FeCl_4(H_2O)_2^- + H_2O$$

When the concentration of hydrochloric acid is high enough, say $4\,F$ or greater, the position of equilibrium lies strongly in favor of $FeCl_4(H_2O)_2^-$, which is usually abbreviated as $FeCl_4^-$. In water, there is only a very slight tendency for $FeCl_4^-$ to combine with a proton to form the neutral molecule $HFeCl_4$. In other words, in an aqueous medium, whose high dielectric constant promotes the separation of charged species, $HFeCl_4$ is essentially completely dissociated. However, diethyl ether is a relatively nonpolar solvent with a low dielectric constant and one in which $HFeCl_4$ is stable and soluble. Actually, the species of iron(III) in the ether phase vary from $(HFeCl_4)_2$ to $(HFeCl_4)_4$, depending on the total concentration of iron present. It should be noted that HCl is extracted into the ether phase and that HCl is probably involved in the mechanism of the extraction process. Nevertheless, iron(III) can be quantitatively (99 per cent) extracted into diethyl ether in a single extraction from aqueous $6\,F$ hydrochloric acid. The success of the extraction depends critically on the concentration of hydrochloric acid, for there must be enough chloride to convert the iron(III) in the aqueous phase to $FeCl_4^-$ and enough acid to permit the formation of

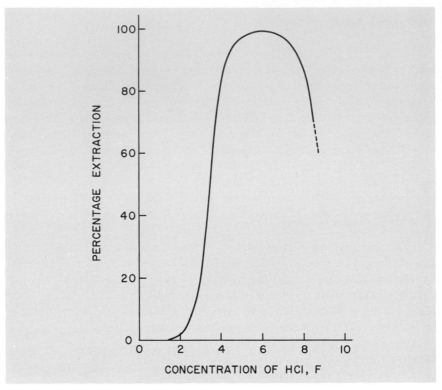

FIGURE 7-5. A plot of the percentage extraction of iron(III) from aqueous hydrochloric acid solutions of various concentrations into diethyl ether. The data pertain to equal volumes of the two phases.

$(HFeCl_4)_n$ in the nonaqueous phase. A plot of the percentage of extraction of iron(III) into diethyl ether for various concentrations of hydrochloric acid is shown in Figure 7-5. Diisopropyl ether and β,β'-dichlorodiethyl ether are also very useful for the extraction of iron(III). Among the other elements which can be separated from aqueous hydrochloric acid solutions by extraction into diethyl ether are antimony(V), arsenic(III), gallium(III), germanium(IV), gold(III), molybdenum(VI), platinum(II), and thallium(III).

Uranium, after being oxidized to UO_2^{++}, can be separated from its fission products by extraction of $UO_2(NO_3)_2$ from an aqueous solution containing nitric acid and calcium nitrate into methyl isobutyl ketone or diethyl ether.

The most important type of analytical application of extraction involves metal chelates, which are readily soluble in organic solvents but only sparingly soluble in water. A chelate compound results from the chemical reaction between a metal ion and a ligand which possesses two or more donor sites. Generally speaking, the bonding in metal chelates is largely covalent in character, which accounts for the low solubility of these compounds in a polar solvent such as water and for their higher solubility in organic liquids. Nickel dimethylglyoximate, previously mentioned in Chapter 5, is an excellent example of a chelate compound. Nickel(II) has a coordination number of four in this compound, each dimethylglyoximate ligand occupying two of the four available coordination positions.

nickel dimethylglyoximate

Nickel dimethylglyoximate can be quantitatively extracted into chloroform if dimethylglyoxime is added to an aqueous nickel(II) solution with a pH between approximately 5 and 12. The factors which affect the extraction of nickel dimethylglyoximate are common to most metal chelate systems. First, dimethylglyoxime may be considered to be a relatively weak monoprotic acid in water. Consequently, the pH of the solution from which the nickel chelate is to be extracted will govern the concentration of dimethylglyoximate according to the equilibrium

$$HL \rightleftharpoons H^+ + L^-$$

where HL is an abbreviation for the parent acid (dimethylglyoxime) and L^- represents the dimethylglyoximate ligand. At pH values less than 4, little free dimethylglyoximate ion exists because the acid-base equilibrium favors the undissociated parent acid; therefore, the formation of the nickel dimethylglyoximate chelate is incomplete and the extraction of the nickel chelate into chloroform is nonquantitative. It should be noted that the parent acid, dimethylglyoxime (HL), is extracted into chloroform, so at low aqueous pH values, where HL is predominant, the formation of the nickel chelate is even less favorable.

Second, the magnitude of the formation constant (designated by β_2) for the nickel dimethylglyoximate in the aqueous phase will affect the completeness of the extraction:

$$Ni^{++} + 2\ L^- \rightleftharpoons NiL_2$$

For the present system, the chelate has a high stability. Furthermore, as the chelate is extracted into chloroform according to the equilibrium

$$NiL_2 \text{ (aqueous phase)} \rightleftharpoons NiL_2 \text{ (chloroform phase)}$$

the formation of the chelate in the aqueous phase is enhanced. Thus, both the formation constant (β_2) for nickel dimethylglyoximate in water and the distribution coefficient (K_d) for its extraction from the aqueous phase into chloroform are important.

A third consideration involves the possible effects of foreign ligands which may be added to the original aqueous solution to eliminate or minimize interferences by other cations. For example, when nickel dimethylglyoximate is extracted from alkaline media, it is common practice to add citrate or tartrate ion to prevent the precipitation of the oxides or hydroxides of such elements as iron(III) or chromium(III). Although dimethylglyoximate forms a very stable chelate compound with nickel(II), the citrate and tartrate ions do form soluble complexes with nickel(II) which will influence to a slight extent the concentration of free nickel ion and thus the completeness of formation and extraction of nickel dimethylglyoximate.

In summary, the stability of the chelate compound, the aqueous acid strength of the chelating reagent, the pH of the aqueous medium, the presence of other complexing agents, and the distribution coefficients of the chelate compound and the chelating reagent all influence the quantitativeness of the extraction process.

Metal oxinates comprise another important class of chelate compounds which are extractable into chloroform. Oxine is the common name for 8-hydroxyquinoline or 8-quinolinol, whose molecular structure is

8–quinolinol (oxine)

Notice that this compound is formulated as a dipolar ion or **zwitterion,** since x-ray studies have indicated the existence of this form of oxine even in the pure solid. Furthermore, the zwitterion predominates in aqueous solutions of oxine because of the high dielectric constant of water. In chloroform, however, the uncharged molecule is the important species because the dielectric constant of this solvent is very low.

Oxine forms chelate compounds with more than 40 metal ions. Trivalent metal cations, including aluminum, bismuth, cerium, iron, scandium, and thallium, react with three oxine ligands according to the equilibrium

$$M^{+++} + 3 \quad \rightleftharpoons \quad M \left(\quad \right)_3 + 3\ H^+$$

whereas dipositive cations, such as cadmium, copper, magnesium, nickel, lead, strontium, and zinc, combine with oxine in a one-to-two metal-to-oxine ratio. Oxine is actually **amphiprotic** in aqueous media because it can either gain or lose a proton, as shown by the following equilibria:

$$\quad + H^+ \rightleftharpoons \quad$$

$$\quad \rightleftharpoons H^+ + \quad$$

Therefore, depending on the stability of the desired metal oxinate, one can adjust the pH of the aqueous phase to achieve a certain degree of selectivity in the extraction. However, the selectivity of separations by extraction with 8-quinolinol can be increased considerably through the use of so-called **masking agents.** These masking agents are other complexing species (e.g., cyanide or EDTA) which are added to a sample solution and which prevent the reaction between oxine and interfering metal ions.

The references cited at the end of this chapter contain descriptions of many other chelate extraction systems.

GENERAL PRINCIPLES OF CHROMATOGRAPHY

The term **chromatography** refers to any separation technique in which the components of a test sample are caused to pass through a column at different rates of speed. In every chromatographic separation, there is a **stationary phase,** which consists of the packing within the column, and a **mobile phase,** which is caused to travel through the column. The test sample is introduced at one end of the column. As the mobile phase passes through the column, each component of the test sample is continuously partitioned, or distributed, between the phases. The process is similar in principle to a multistage extraction process with a large number of stages.

Chromatographic processes may be classified on the basis of the physical states of the two phases. The stationary phase may be either liquid or solid and the mobile phase either gas or liquid. Thus the processes may be classified, naming the physical state of the mobile phase first, as **liquid-liquid chromatography, liquid-solid chromatography, gas-liquid chromatography,** and **gas-solid chromatography.** It is also common to refer to the first two types as **liquid-phase chromatography** and to the last two types as **gas-phase chromatography,** or simply **gas chromatography.**

Chromatographic processes may alternatively be classified on the basis of the mechanism whereby the components of the test sample are distributed between the two phases, regardless of whether the mobile phase is a liquid or a gas. On this basis, there are three major classes of chromatographic separations: **adsorption chromatography,** in which the stationary phase is able to adsorb solutes reversibly from the mobile phase; **partition chromatography,** in which the solute is partitioned between the two phases much as in a liquid-liquid extraction process; and **ion exchange chromatography,** in which charged ions are literally traded back and forth between the two phases.

The experimental apparatus and procedures vary widely. For liquid-solid chromatography, the column may be an ordinary buret, packed with granulated solid particles or beads which comprise the stationary phase. The precise graduation marks on the buret are not necessary, and a tube slightly larger in diameter is generally preferable. For liquid-liquid chromatography, the column is similar except that the solid particles are coated with the liquid that is to serve as the stationary phase before the mobile phase is passed into the column; the solid particles serve merely as a support for the stationary liquid. In gas chromatography, the column is typically much longer and smaller in diameter than in the apparatus for liquid-phase chromatography. Again, the column generally is initially packed with solid particles, which serve either directly as the stationary phase in gas-solid chromatography or as a support for a stationary liquid phase in gas-liquid chromatography.

It must be emphasized that chromatography is a method of separation and that any separation must be followed by some measurement if a qualitative identification or quantitative determination is to be made. In considering further the general principles of chromatography, let us assume that some sort of measurement is continuously made at the exit end of the column. The measurement of almost any physicochemical property of a solute-solvent system, including thermal and electrical conductivity, radioactivity, color, and other spectral characteristics, can be made the basis of a detection device for monitoring the progress of a separation. Let us further assume that the measuring device or detector responds to every component or solute of the test sample, but not to the solvent (whether liquid or gas), which is the mobile phase. Thus, the output of the measuring device is zero whenever pure solvent is emerging from the column and greater than zero whenever a component of the test sample is emerging. The sample is inserted into the entrance end of the column at what we will call time zero $(t = 0)$. It is quickly held, through adsorption, through partition, or through ion exchange, by the first portion of the stationary phase. Figure 7-6A represents this condition, assuming that the test sample contains two solutes and that even a small fraction of the stationary phase has sufficient capacity to retain virtually all of the sample components. From this time on, the liquid or gas which serves as the mobile phase is caused to flow through the column; this liquid or gas may be the same as the solvent for the test sample or it may be a different one. As the flow continues, the two components tend to separate into distinct bands (Fig. 7-6B). Each band migrates through the column and eventually is discharged from the column. The typical response of the measuring device at the exit end of the column is represented in Figure 7-7.

The process of causing the components of the test sample to move through the column, by the continuous flow of the mobile phase, is called **elution.** The solvent gas or liquid chosen for the mobile phase is the **eluent.**

FIGURE 7-6.   Diagrammatic representation of the retention and elution of a two-component mixture on a chromatographic column. (See text for discussion.)

Stationary phase

Component 1

Component 2

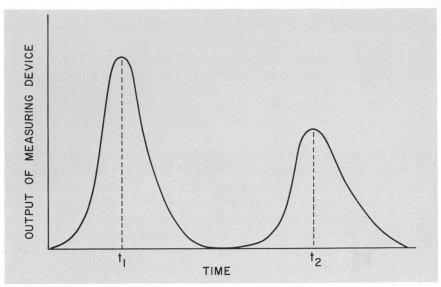

FIGURE 7-7.   Graphical representation of output of the measuring device (or detector) during a chromatographic separation. The retention time for the first component is t_1, and for the second component it is t_2.

The **eluate** is whatever emerges from the column, that is, the eluate is the eluent plus whatever component of the test sample it contains at any particular time.

The **retention time** for each component is the time required for it to pass through the column, measured from the time of injection or introduction of the test sample to the time of its peak response on the measuring device (Fig. 7-7). The **retention volume** for each component is the volume of mobile phase which must flow to cause that component to pass through the column. If the flow rate is constant, the retention volume is the product of the retention time multiplied by the flow rate.

The numerical values of the retention volume and retention time vary from one component to another, which is really the reason why substances may be separated by chromatography. However, these quantities are also influenced by the particular experimental apparatus (column length and diameter, for example) and by the experimental conditions (such as flow rate and temperature). Therefore, the **relative retention volumes** and the **relative retention times** for two or more components within a test sample are more meaningful in describing a chromatographic separation than are the absolute values. The separations often are as distinct and complete as is indicated in Figures 7-6 and 7-7. In many cases, however, there is some overlapping when two or more components are present. Ideally, the solute bands on a chromatographic column should be relatively narrow and should have leading and trailing edges which are perpendicular to the length of the column, as in Figure 7-6B. However, a problem of tremendous practical significance to the analytical chemist is **band broadening.** Band broadening may occur in at least two distinct ways. First, it is virtually impossible to pack a column in a perfectly uniform manner; therefore, there is usually a variable flow rate in the column due to this irregular packing, and the solute bands tend to become uneven and to spread out. Second, any solute in a given solvent has a natural tendency to diffuse under the influence of a concentration gradient; since diffusion is a time-dependent phenomenon, the longer a given solute remains in a chromatographic column before it is eluted, the wider and more uneven will be the corresponding solute band. As a consequence of these effects, much experimental work has been directed toward minimizing band broadening and improving the sharpness of separations in chromatography.

The name **chromatography** is derived from two Greek words meaning "color" and "to write." The earliest applications of this general method of separation did involve colored substances, in which cases it is often possible to see the colored bands on the column as in Figure 7-6B. However, color is only incidental to the separation process, and most chromatographic separations are of colorless materials.

In the remaining sections of this chapter, we will consider in more detail the distinctive principles and analytical applications of adsorption and ion-exchange chromatography in which the mobile phases are liquid, and also the principles and applications of gas chromatography. Other types of chromatographic separations will be mentioned briefly.

ADSORPTION CHROMATOGRAPHY

Separation by Adsorption

When a solid adsorbent substance is brought into contact with a solution containing one solute, A, the solute becomes distributed in a state of dynamic equilibrium between the adsorbent and the solution:

$$A_{solution} \rightleftharpoons A_{adsorbed}$$

The mathematical expression of an equilibrium constant for this system must, of course, take cognizance of the form in which A exists in each phase (whether it is monomolecular or bimolecular, for example). It is generally found, however, that the equilibrium quantities of A in the two phases are related to each other by the equation

$$K = \frac{m}{C^{1/n}} \quad \text{or} \quad m = KC^{1/n}$$

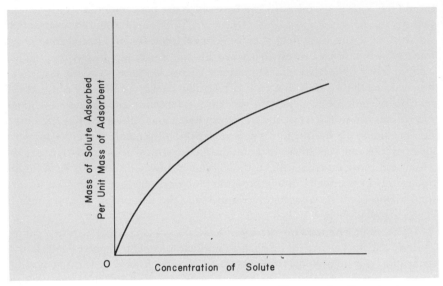

FIGURE 7-8. A typical adsorption isotherm. (See text for discussion.)

in which m is the mass of the substance adsorbed per unit mass of adsorbent, C is the concentration of the substance in the solution phase, K is the adsorption constant, and n is another constant which typically ranges from 1 to 2. The derivation of this relation requires the assumption that only a monolayer of adsorbed material exists at most. It should be noted that the adsorption constant K, which deals with adsorption from a liquid onto a solid surface, is analogous to the distribution coefficient discussed earlier in this chapter for liquid-liquid extractions. A graphical representation of the preceding equation is called an **adsorption isotherm** (Fig. 7-8). The numerical magnitude of K is a designation of the strength of adsorption, that is, of the "tightness" with which the solute species is held by the adsorbent. If adsorption from the solution were absolutely complete, C would be zero and K would be infinity. If there were no adsorption at all, m would be zero and K would also be zero. Every practical situation in which an adsorbent is in contact with a solution falls well within these two extremes.

Let us consider now the possibility of separating one solute, A, from another one, B, by a single batch adsorption process. For the separation to be quantitative, it is necessary that (1) the solid medium adsorb all but a negligible portion of A and that (2) the solid medium adsorb no more than a negligible amount of B. The first requirement is met if the adsorption constant of A is sufficiently large, and the second requirement is satisfied if the corresponding constant for B is sufficiently low. These requirements are occasionally fulfilled in practical situations. More frequently, however, quantitative separation is not accomplished in a single batch adsorption process. Two approaches can be taken to improve the separation. First, the desired adsorption of A from the solution can be increased if one removes the equilibrium solution from contact with the initial batch of adsorbent and places it in contact with a fresh batch of adsorbent. Second, the amount of B on the initial batch of adsorbent can be decreased if one removes this adsorbent from contact with the sample solution and places it in a fresh batch of solvent. These two steps are precisely what column chromatography actually accomplishes, over and over again, during the elution process, so the operation of the column is equivalent to that of a multistage batch type of operation.

The solvent, as well as its solutes, is subject to adsorption. Consequently, there is competition among all species within the mobile phase for occupancy of the adsorption sites, and the equilibrium at each stage is a dynamic one involving all solutes, solvents, and adsorbent. The net result is the separation and elution of the solutes from the chromatographic column.

Adsorbents. The substance which is used as the adsorbent must not enter into any reaction with the test solution or the solvent other than by the desired adsorption mechanisms. In particular, the adsorbent must be extremely insoluble, and it must be chemically inert in the environment in which it is to be used. Among the numerous common adsorbents are cellulose, starch, calcium carbonate, calcium sulfate, magnesium carbonate, calcium oxide, silicic acid, charcoal, magnesium oxide, and aluminum oxide. These substances differ considerably from one another in their adsorption characteristics and in their chemical reactivity, and none is usable for all applications. For example, alkaline adsorbents such as magnesium oxide and calcium carbonate are not useful in acidic media, and some adsorbents exercise catalytic properties in the presence of certain organic substances. It has also been found that two different batches of a supposedly identical substance may exhibit different adsorption characteristics, thus adding to the empirical character of this method of separation.

Some adsorption processes are not reversible. Consequently, the adsorbed substance is not removable from the adsorbent, not even by passage through the column of a large volume of the same solvent in which the substance was initially dissolved. In these cases the adsorbent cannot be used over and over again, and the cost can become prohibitive.

The particles of an adsorbent should typically be within the size range of 100 to 300 mesh. If the particles are larger, relatively little surface is available to the solute unless an unduly large amount of adsorbent is used. With smaller particles, the column may become so tightly packed that the flow rate is unreasonably slow.

Test Solution and Solvents. It is frequently impossible to predict accurately the relative degrees to which various solutes will be adsorbed, or to explain the observed adsorption characteristics of a solute in terms of molecular structure. It is generally found, however, that highly polar molecules are adsorbed more readily than less polar ones. For example, aldehydes and ketones are less strongly adsorbed than are acids and bases, but more so than saturated hydrocarbons. The molecular size of a solute is another significant factor which determines selectivity of adsorption.

Among the common solvents, listed in order of decreasing adsorption onto typical adsorbents, are organic acids, water, alcohols, chloroform, benzene, diethyl ether, carbon disulfide, carbon tetrachloride, and petroleum ether. Unless the solvent is adsorbed quite strongly itself, it is unable to displace an adsorbed solute and cannot elute that solute through the column. Thus, water and low-molecular-weight alcohols are generally better eluting agents than are the less polar organic solvents.

Analytical Applicability.   The dimensions of the column, as well as the dimensions and design of the solvent reservoir above the column and the receiving vessel below the column, may vary widely, depending on such factors as the concentration range of the solution, the differences in relative retention volumes of the solutes to be separated, and the quantities of solution which are to be processed. It is possible to increase the flow rate through a given column by increasing the pressure exerted by the solvent reservoir or by forming a partial vacuum in the receiving vessel.

Many practical applications of adsorption chromatography have been developed. Most involve organic and biochemical substances, but some useful applications have been developed in inorganic chemistry as well.

A classic example of the unique ability of chromatography to resolve two solutes is the separation of α-carotene from β-carotene, two compounds with the same formula, $C_{40}H_{56}$, differing only in the position of one carbon-carbon double bond. If a mixture of α-carotene and β-carotene in a hydrocarbon solvent is passed through a column packed with calcium carbonate,

α-carotene

β-carotene

β-carotene is adsorbed, whereas α-carotene flows through the column. Mixtures of hydrocarbons are particularly susceptible to separation by adsorption chromatography. Chromatographic techniques are often applied in the separation and analysis of complex natural and commercial products, including foods, drugs, and inks.

In qualitative analysis, chromatography not only provides some direct methods of identification through the measurement of relative retention volumes for known and unknown substances, but it also provides a very useful method for concentrating an extremely dilute solution prior to some other means of identification. Chromatography provides a simple and often effective means of checking the purity of a substance.

Partition Chromatography

Partition chromatography is similar to conventional adsorption chromatography except that the adsorbent is coated with a liquid which is immiscible with the liquid phase which is to be passed through the column. The exchange between the two phases is thus one of a continuous liquid-liquid distribution, partition, and redistribution along the length of the column rather than one of adsorption directly onto the solid phase. The adsorbent serves merely as a support for the stationary, nonmobile liquid phase.

Some of the combinations of solid supporting substance and stationary liquid phase, and an example of the analytical application of each, are as follows: silica gel and aniline, for the separation of paraffins and cycloparaffins dissolved in isopropyl alcohol and benzene; silica gel and water, for the separation of amino acids dissolved in butanol and chloroform; cellulose and water, for the separation of inorganic substances dissolved in an organic solvent; silica and methanolic sodium hydroxide, for the separation of aliphatic acids dissolved in isooctane.

Paper Chromatography

The principles underlying paper chromatography are essentially the same as in column adsorption chromatography. The differences in these two techniques lie in the physical form and arrangement of the solid adsorbent. A strip of filter paper serves as the solid adsorbent in paper chromatography. The test solution, generally just one or two drops, is placed near the end of the paper strip. That end is then immersed in a solvent, but not deeply enough for the liquid level to touch the spot at which the test sample was applied. Capillary action causes the solvent to flow in either an upward, horizontal, or downward direction along the length of the paper strip. As the solvent flows, it carries along the components of the test solution, each at its own characteristic rate. The separate components may be collected as the solvent drips off the opposite end of the strip; however, more frequently the elution process is stopped while the components lie in different positions along the paper strip. It is thus possible to conclude the separation process simply by cutting the strip at the proper places with a pair of scissors!

There are many experimental variations which are useful in paper chromatography, and many applications have been developed in inorganic chemistry as well as in organic chemistry and biochemistry. The techniques are particularly useful in qualitative detections; numerous applications have been developed in conjunction with colorimetric and other types of measurements for quantitative determinations.

Thin-Layer Chromatography

In thin-layer chromatography, the stationary phase forms a coating on a glass plate. The mobile phase is caused to flow through the fixed phase much the same as in paper chromatography.

The components of the test sample are, most frequently, retarded as they flow through the stationary phase by adsorption. However, thin-layer chromatographic separations can alternately be accomplished by liquid-liquid partitioning between the stationary and mobile phases or by ion exchange.

ION EXCHANGE

Certain minerals and resins in contact with an aqueous solution exhibit the property of exchanging ions with that solution. To the extent that one type of ion in solution is exchanged in preference to another type, the phenomenon of ion exchange provides a basis for the separation of ionic species.

Ion exchange was first recognized and studied over a hundred years ago, when it was found that certain clay minerals in soil can remove potassium and ammonium salts from water with the release of an equivalent amount of the corresponding calcium salt. Since that time many naturally occurring ion-exchanger substances have been identified and studied, most of them being inorganic substances. Numerous practical applications have been developed. One example is the softening of water by zeolites, which are aluminum silicates with chemical formulas such as $Na_2Al_2Si_4O_{12}$.

In more recent years, primary attention has been shifted from the naturally occurring, inorganic ion exchangers to synthetic organic ion-exchange resins. Compared to the inorganic exchangers, these resins are far superior in regard to mechanical strength, chemical stability, exchange capacity, and rate of ion exchange. Furthermore, ion-exchange resins have been synthesized with a wide variety of desirable exchange characteristics and specificities. Most applications of ion exchangers in analytical chemistry now involve the use of the synthetic organic resins rather than the naturally occurring types of ion-exchange substances.

Ion exchangers may be classified as being of two principal types, cationic and anionic. **Cation exchangers** possess acidic functional groups, such as the sulfonic acid group ($-SO_3H$), the replaceable hydrogen ions of which are exchanged for other cations in the sample solution. A straightforward example of a cation-exchange reaction may be represented by the equation

$$R-SO_3^-H^+ + Na^+ \rightleftharpoons R-SO_3^-Na^+ + H^+$$

in which R signifies all of the ion-exchange resin molecule, except for the sulfonic acid group, and Na^+ represents the cation which is removed from the solution phase. As the exchange reaction proceeds in the forward direction, the solution acquires hydrogen ions in place of other cations. **Anion exchangers** are resins having basic functional groups, one common example being the $-NH_3^+OH^-$ group. The hydroxide ion, which is on the surface of the resin particle, can enter into an exchange reaction with another anion in the sample solution, as typified by the equilibrium

$$R-NH_3^+OH^- + Cl^- \rightleftharpoons R-NH_3^+Cl^- + OH^-$$

In the latter reaction, the liberation of hydroxide ions causes the pH of the original solution phase to increase.

Preparation and Types of Ion-Exchange Resins

Cation Exchangers. One of the most widely used ion-exchange resins consists of a cross-linked sulfonated polystyrene polymer. The synthesis of this resin begins with the catalyzed polymerization of a mixture of styrene

styrene   divinylbenzene

and divinylbenzene. This reaction yields spherically shaped beads of cross-linked polystyrene. Next, the polymer beads are sulfonated to produce a substance of the following general structure:

When this resin is brought into contact with an aqueous solution, the sulfonic acid groups ionize to provide the hydrogen ions which enter into exchange reactions with other cations in the solution.

Various cation-exchange resins differ structurally from each other in their hydrocarbon skeletons or acidic functional groups. The same cross-linked polystyrene polymer can be used with a variety of functional groups in addition to the sulfonic acid group itself. Among the other functional groups employed in cation exchangers are the following:

Carboxylic acid	—COOH
Phosphonic acid	—PO_3H^- or —PO_3H_2
Phosphinic acid	—HPO_2H^- or —HPO_2H_2
Phenolic	—OH
Arsonic acid	—AsO_3H^- or —AsO_3H_2
Selenonic acid	—SeO_3H

The acid strengths of the acidic groups on the organic matrix differ considerably from each other — a factor greatly influencing the selectivity of the exchange reactions.

Anion Exchangers.   One of the most useful of the anion-exchange resins incorporates the same organic matrix as does the sulfonic acid cation exchanger, but it has as its functional groups the quaternary amine group, —$CH_2N(CH_3)_3^+Cl^-$, here being represented with chloride as a counter ion. This functional group is a relatively strong base. Weak base anion-exchange resins frequently contain tertiary or secondary nitrogen atoms rather than quaternary ones, as in the functional groups —$CH_2NH(CH_3)_2^+$ and —$CH_2NH_2(CH_3)^+$, respectively. Basic groups involving phosphorus or sulfur atoms in place of nitrogen atoms are occasionally used, but the amine group is much more frequently employed.

Bifunctional Exchangers.   Some synthetic ion-exchange resins contain two different types of functional groups. One practical form of bifunctional exchanger is amphoteric; that is, one of its functional groups is acidic and the other is basic, as illustrated by the structural formula

$$-CH-CH_2-CH-CH_2-$$

$$N(CH_3)_3^+OH^-$$

$$SO_3^-H^+$$

Cation exchange can occur at the sulfonic acid group and anion exchange at the quaternary amine group.

Other bifunctional exchangers contain two acidic groups, and still others contain two groups of basic character. For example, both sulfonic acid and phosphonic acid groups can be attached to the same hydrocarbon skeleton. The selectivity of ion exchange and the influence of pH upon both the selectivity and completeness of exchange are markedly influenced by what these groups are.

Liquid Ion Exchangers. A quite different form of ion exchanger consists of two components: an organic solvent which is immiscible with water, such as kerosene, xylene, or chloroform; and a compound which contains an ion-exchange group and which is soluble in the organic liquid but not in water. When these two components are shaken together with an aqueous solution, the organic liquid disperses as small droplets throughout the aqueous phase. The exchanger molecules are in solution within the organic droplets, with the functional groups sticking out into the region of the interface with the aqueous solution. Thus, ions in the aqueous phase can enter into exchange reactions with the exchangeable ions of these functional groups.

The exchanger compound may possess either acidic or basic groups and so may be useful for either cation or anion exchange reactions. The so-called fatty acids and dialkylphosphates are commonly used for liquid cation exchangers and long-chain alkyl amines for the anion exchangers.

Liquid ion exchangers possess some interesting features which are often advantageous in comparison to the synthetic resin exchangers. The liquid exchangers are relatively easy to prepare, and the concentration of functional groups may be selected at will over a wide range. The rate of exchange can be made very high simply by means of efficiently dispersing the organic phase throughout the aqueous phase. However, the liquid exchangers possess two drawbacks which are particularly serious in connection with separations in analytical chemistry. First, it is difficult to separate the phases after exchange has occurred as is necessary in order to recover the separated ions. Second, virtually all of the exchanger compounds which have been developed are of finite solubility in water, which decreases the effective completeness of distribution or partition of ions between the two phases.

Characterization of Ion-Exchange Resins

An ion-exchange resin may be characterized by its capacity and by its acid strength. The **maximal capacity** of an ion-exchange resin is the number of ionogenic groups (that is, acidic or basic functional groups) per specified amount of resin. On the other hand, the **effective capacity** is the number of such groups which actually undergo exchange per specified amount of resin. The maximal and effective capacities of a resin are typically expressed in terms of equivalents or milliequivalents (mEq) per gram of resin.

The effective capacity is always lower than the maximal capacity, and the extent by which one differs from the other is dependent upon the structure and composition of the resin and also upon the composition of the aqueous solution. Consider the exchange reaction

$$R—SO_3^-H^+ + Na^+ \rightleftharpoons R—SO_3^-Na^+ + H^+$$

and assume that initially the resin is entirely in its hydrogen form and that the sodium ion is entirely in the solution. The extent to which exchange occurs is, thus, the extent to which the reaction proceeds from left to right before equilibrium is established. The effective capacity would, in an extreme case, equal the maximal capacity if the reaction did proceed quantitatively to the right. However, the position of equilibrium or the extent to which exchange actually occurs is governed jointly by the concentration of sodium ions in the solution, by the pH of the solution, and by the acid strength of the resin. It is clear that any designation of the effective capacity of an ion-exchange resin is meaningful only if a detailed description of the experimental conditions is also reported.

The effective capacities of commercially available ion-exchange resins encompass the range from 1 to 10 mEq per gm of resin.

The acid strength of an ion-exchange resin can conveniently be expressed by its pK value, that is, by the negative logarithm of its acid ionization constant. This can be measured for any resin by titration with a standard acid or base solution. The resin remains insoluble throughout the titration, but it can come into equilibrium with the solution after each addition of titrant. A detailed discussion of acid-base titrations in aqueous media is presented in Chapter 8. It is sufficient to point out here that the titration curve reveals both the capacity and the pK value of the resin.

In Table 7-1 are listed some approximate pK values for several different types of ionogenic groups.

TABLE 7-1. APPROXIMATE pK VALUES OF SOME IONOGENIC GROUPS IN RESINS*

Cation Exchangers		Anion Exchangers	
Ionogenic Group	**Approximate pK**	**Ionogenic Group**	**Approximate pK**
—SO$_3$H	<1	—N(CH$_3$)$_3$OH	>13
—PO$_3$H$_2$	pK_1 2–3	—N(C$_2$H$_4$OH)(CH$_3$)$_2$OH	>13
	pK_2 7–8	—NH$_2$	7–9
—COOH	4–6	$>$NH	7–9
⬡—OH	9–10	⬡—NH$_2$	5–6

* From *Ion Exchange* by F. Helfferich. Copyright 1962, McGraw-Hill Book Company. Used by permission of McGraw-Hill Book Company.

Ion-Exchange Equilibria

Let us consider the exchange of two monovalent cations, A^+ and B^+, between a resin phase (r) and a solution phase (s):

$$A_s{}^+ + B_r{}^+ \rightleftharpoons A_r{}^+ + B_s{}^+$$

We can write the usual concentration equilibrium constant, $K_B{}^A$,

$$K_B{}^A = \frac{[A^+]_r[B^+]_s}{[A^+]_s[B^+]_r}$$

This constant, $K_B{}^A$, is defined as the **molar selectivity coefficient.** A more fundamental approach is to express the equilibrium condition mathematically in terms of a thermodynamic activity constant $\mathscr{K}_B{}^A$, which may be written in terms of concentrations and activity coefficients as

$$\mathscr{K}_B{}^A = \frac{[A^+]_r[B^+]_s}{[A^+]_s[B^+]_r} \cdot \frac{f_{A_r{}^+}}{f_{B_r{}^+}} \cdot \frac{f_{B_s{}^+}}{f_{A_s{}^+}}$$

The molar selectivity coefficient is constant, therefore, only if the activity-coefficient ratios in the resin and in the solution are constant. The activity-coefficient ratio in the solution phase generally is constant for dilute aqueous solutions. However, the activity-coefficient ratio in the resin phase apparently does vary considerably, depending upon the composition of the resin. Unfortunately, there is no simple method for the measurement or calculation of the activities in the resin phase. The consequence is that ion exchange equilibria are most commonly described in terms of molar selectivity coefficients, even though their numerical values are not constant over wide ranges of experimental conditions.

The molar selectivity coefficients for the uptake of cations by a cation exchange resin are such that the relative affinities of the resin for a number of cations are in the following order:

$Pu^{++++} \gg$
$La^{+++} > Ce^{+++} > Pr^{+++} > Eu^{+++} > Y^{+++} > Sc^{+++} > Al^{+++} \gg$
$Ba^{++} > Pb^{++} > Sr^{++} > Ca^{++} > Ni^{++} > Cd^{++} > Cu^{++} >$
$Co^{++} > Zn^{++} > Mg^{++} > UO_2{}^{++} \gg$
$Tl^+ > Ag^+ > Rb^+ > K^+ > NH_4{}^+ > Na^+ > H^+ > Li^+$

An exchange reaction occurs between an aqueous solution and a resin if the cation initially in the solution *precedes*, in this listing, the cation initially in the resin.

Factors other than the molar selectivity coefficient influence the direction and extent of an exchange reaction. In general, the resin exhibits a preference for (1) the ion of higher charge, (2) the ion with the smaller solvated equivalent volume, (3) the ion which has greater polarizability, and (4) the ion which participates least in complex formation with any other ion in the aqueous phase. It should be noted that this situation is closely analogous to the selectivity in the adsorption of ions from solution onto the surface of a colloidal particle, as described in Chapter 5.

Separations by Ion-Exchange Chromatography

The separation of two ionic species present at low concentrations, when another species is present in large excess, is of particular importance in the analytical use of ion-exchange resins. Let us consider a solution containing trace concentrations of cations B and C and a high concentration of cation A, all three ions being capable of undergoing exchange reactions with a resin phase. For purposes of simplicity, we shall assume that each of the ions possesses the same charge, $+n$, although they need not be monovalent cations. In addition, we shall assume that the resin initially has all its exchange sites occupied by A.

When the sample solution, containing A, B, and C, is introduced onto an ion-exchange column, the exchange equilibria involving A and B as well as A and C may be formulated as follows:

$$B_s^{+n} + A_r^{+n} \rightleftharpoons B_r^{+n} + A_s^{+n}$$
$$C_s^{+n} + A_r^{+n} \rightleftharpoons C_r^{+n} + A_s^{+n}$$

where the subscripts r and s denote the resin and solution phases, respectively. For each exchange reaction, we can write a corresponding molar selectivity coefficient,

$$K_A^{\ B} = \frac{[B^{+n}]_r}{[B^{+n}]_s} \cdot \frac{[A^{+n}]_s}{[A^{+n}]_r} \quad \text{and} \quad K_A^{\ C} = \frac{[C^{+n}]_r}{[C^{+n}]_s} \cdot \frac{[A^{+n}]_s}{[A^{+n}]_r}$$

Furthermore, we can describe the distribution of each trace cation, B and C, between the resin phase and the solution phase by means of a distribution coefficient, as in the earlier discussion of liquid-liquid extraction processes. Accordingly, the pertinent distribution coefficients, K_{dB} and K_{dC}, may be defined as

$$K_{dB} = \frac{[B^{+n}]_r}{[B^{+n}]_s} \quad \text{and} \quad K_{dC} = \frac{[C^{+n}]_r}{[C^{+n}]_s}$$

The equations for the molar selectivity coefficient and for the distribution coefficient may now be combined to yield

$$K_{dB} = K_A^{\ B} \frac{[A^{+n}]_r}{[A^{+n}]_s} \quad \text{and} \quad K_{dC} = K_A^{\ C} \frac{[A^{+n}]_r}{[A^{+n}]_s}$$

However, since A is present in large excess and only trace concentrations of B and C exist, the amount of A in the resin phase remains virtually constant, so the two preceding equations reduce to the much simpler expressions

$$K_{dB} = (\text{constant})_A^{\ B} \frac{1}{[A^{+n}]_s} \quad \text{and} \quad K_{dC} = (\text{constant})_A^{\ C} \frac{1}{[A^{+n}]_s}$$

The latter two relations reveal that the distribution coefficient for each ion, B and C, is independent of the respective solution concentration of that trace cation, assuming that activity effects may be neglected. Therefore, the uptake of each trace ion by the resin is directly proportional to its solution concentration. However, the distribution coefficients are *inversely* proportional to the solution concentration of A, which is to be expected since A competes with B and C for exchange sites in the resin phase. It is important to note that the interaction between ions at trace concentration levels can be ignored; thus, the individual distribution coefficient of B or C in a mixture of these two cations can be considered equal to the distribution coefficient of B or C in a solution by itself.

In order to accomplish any separation of B from C, it is necessary that one of these cations be taken up by the resin in distinct preference to the other. In other words, the distribution coefficients for B and C must differ appreciably from each other. This requirement is strictly analogous to that encountered in separations by liquid-liquid extraction and by adsorption. Let us now define the ratio of distribution coefficients for cations B and C as the separation factor, S_C^B.

$$S_C^B = \frac{K_{dB}}{K_{dC}}$$

Inserting mathematical statements of the distribution coefficients, one may show that

$$S_C^B = \frac{K_A^B}{K_A^C}$$

or

$$S_C^B = K_C^B$$

Thus, it is possible by means of ion-exchange techniques to separate one trace component B from another trace component C, even in the presence of a large excess of an adsorbable cation A and regardless of what the concentration of A is, as long as the molar selectivity coefficient K_C^B involving the two trace components is adequately large. It is likewise significant that the molar selectivity coefficient, K_C^B, for two trace cations of equal charge is completely independent (in the ideal situation) of the concentration of A. Consequently, if the molar selectivity coefficient, K_C^B, is unfavorable for the separation of B from C, any variations of the concentration of A will fail to improve the completeness of separation. Put in practical terms, if one desires to separate B from C by eluting an ion-exchange column with a solution of A, the sharpness of the separation will depend only on K_C^B and not on the concentration of A.

The situation is entirely different if B and C have dissimilar charges, $+b$ and $+c$, because it can be demonstrated mathematically that the separation factor, S_C^B, does depend on the concentration of A.

Situations frequently arise in which the separation factor, S_C^B, is so near unity that apparently little or no separation could be accomplished by ion-exchange techniques. In such situations, it is often possible to achieve the separation through the addition of some reagent which will complex one or both trace ions in the aqueous solution. Since the equilibrium constants for the formation of complexes of similar ions, even those of identical charge, may differ significantly, one can alter the relative concentrations of the two adsorbable cations in the solution and the relative affinities of each ion for the resin phase.

A classic example of the application of this approach is the successful separation of the rare-earth (lanthanide) ions. Prior to the time that these elements were first separated by ion-exchange chromatography, the only feasible method for the isolation and purification of the rare earths involved tens or even hundreds of tedious fractional precipitations. Although this precipitation technique presumably did provide pure rare-earth compounds, careful reexamination of these preparations through the application of modern physical-analytical procedures has often revealed that these supposedly pure compounds are relatively impure. If a solution containing rare-earth ions, such as La^{+++}, Ce^{+++}, Eu^{+++}, Gd^{+++}, Tb^{+++}, Er^{+++}, Tm^{+++}, Yb^{+++}, or Lu^{+++}, is introduced into a cation-exchange column, all of these ions will initially be adsorbed on the resin phase. The molar selectivity coefficients for the rare-earth cations are very similar in magnitude because each of these ions has a $+3$ charge and nearly the same ionic (solvated) radius. For reasons discussed previously, it is impossible to separate these cations by elution of the column with a solution of a simple salt such as sodium chloride or ammonium chloride. On the other hand, if citrate is added to the eluent, a remarkably sharp separation of the rare-earth ions is achieved; citrate forms a complex of sufficiently different stability with each cation so that, one at a time, the rare earths can be eluted from the column and collected separately in receiving flasks. The separation is still so difficult, however, that the complete elution of the rare-earth ions may require a period of over 100 hours.

Figure 7-9 presents an ion-exchange elution curve for the separation of six actinide elements. In this situation, a radioactive solution containing fermium(III), einsteinium(III), californium(III), berkelium(III), curium(III), and americium(III) was placed on a cation-exchange column. The column was subsequently eluted with an aqueous solution of ammonium lactate. Notice that the progress of the separation was monitored through the measurement of the α activity of the eluate. The experimental conditions necessary to achieve this separation were particularly critical — a column only 2 inches high and $\frac{5}{32}$ inch in diameter, a $0.4\,F$ ammonium lactate eluent at pH 4.2 ± 0.2 and $87°C$, and an eluent flow rate of approximately 18 μl per minute. However, by stringent control of experimental conditions, it was possible to collect individual drops of the eluate containing just one of these actinide elements.

Analytical Applications

Single-batch ion-exchange separations find only limited application in analytical chemistry. The resin and the test solution are simply mixed together in a beaker or other suitable container until equilibrium is attained, and the two phases are separated by filtration or decantation. Most applications, however, involve the use of ion-exchange chromatography, in which the operation is equivalent to a large number of consecutive batch equilibrations.

A large number of ion-exchange separations have been developed for practical usefulness in analytical chemistry. Some are indicated or implied in the foregoing discussions. Let us now mention a few more selected applications.

The technique of ion exchange is a very efficient method for the removal of cations which interfere in the determination of an anion. In the gravimetric determination of sulfur as barium sulfate, we have seen that many

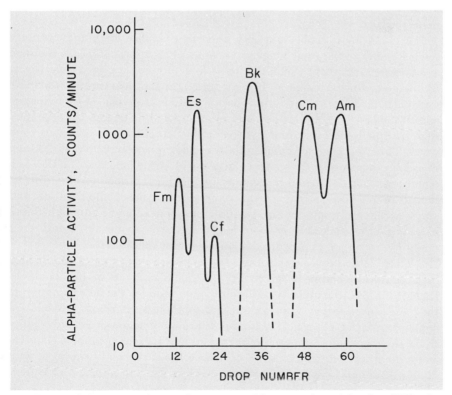

FIGURE 7-9. Ion-exchange chromatographic separation of fermium(III), einsteinium(III), californium(III), berkelium(III), curium(III), and americium(III). [Redrawn, with permission, from the paper by S. G. Thompson, B. G. Harvey, G. R. Choppin, and G. T. Seaborg: J. Am. Chem. Soc., 76, 6229 (1954).]

cations, such as iron(III), sodium, and ammonium, are extensively coprecipitated and cause large negative errors. However, if one passes the sulfate
sample solution through an ion-exchange column containing a sulfonated
resin in its hydrogen form, it is possible to replace all cations with equivalent
amounts of hydrogen ion and then to form the desired barium sulfate precipitate in the absence of the interfering ions.

In much the same way, undesired anions may be separated from cations.
For example, iron(III) can be separated from aluminum if one adds to the
sample solution a large excess of thiocyanate ion, SCN^-, and passes the
resulting solution through an anion-exchange column. In the presence of
excess thiocyanate ion, iron(III) forms anion complexes such as $Fe(SCN)_6^=$,
whereas aluminum remains as a weakly complexed cation.

Still another use of ion-exchange resins is to increase the concentration
of ions initially present at low concentrations. In the determination of calcium
and magnesium in river or lake water, a specified volume of the water is
passed through a properly prepared column at the site of the river or lake,
the column is taken to the laboratory, the desired constituents are eluted with
a minimal volume of a properly chosen eluent, and the analyses are then
performed.

A somewhat different, but very important, application of ion-exchange
resins is in the preparation of deionized water. This is generally accomplished
as a two-step process in which the water to be purified is passed successively
through a cation exchanger in its hydrogen form and then through an anion
exchanger in its hydroxide form. Foreign cations are replaced by hydrogen
ions in the first step, and extraneous anions by hydroxide ions in the second
step. The hydrogen ions and hydroxide ions combine, of course, to form
water. This process is used commercially in many places instead of distillation
to prepare pure water. It is particularly useful in the laboratory, either as a
replacement for distillation or as an additional purification step after distillation to prepare water that is even more highly purified. Both cation and
anion exchangers may be mixed within the same column, although this is
not advisable if there is any intention of regenerating the resins into their
initial hydrogen ion and hydroxide ion forms for repeated use.

Three other applications of ion-exchange procedures are demonstrated
in laboratory experiments given in subsequent chapters of this book. In
Experiment 8-3, the use of a cation-exchange resin for the determination of
the total concentration of metal ions in a solution is described. If a solution
containing one or more cations is passed through a cation-exchange column
in the hydrogen ion form, each of the metal ions is exchanged for an equivalent amount of hydrogen ions. By collecting the eluate and titrating it with
standard sodium hydroxide, one can establish the concentration of cations
in the original sample solution.

The preparation of special titrants with the aid of an anion-exchange
procedure is shown in Experiment 9-1. Although the titrant base, tetrabutylammonium hydroxide, $(C_4H_9)_4N^+OH^-$, is not commercially available, it

can be easily prepared if a solution of $(C_4H_9)_4N^+I^-$ in a suitable nonaqueous solvent is passed through a strong base anion-exchange column in the hydroxide form to exchange iodide ions for hydroxide ions.

Finally, in Experiment 11-4 a simple example of ion-exchange chromatography is provided. If an aqueous solution containing Zn^{++} and Ni^{++} is treated with hydrochloric acid, zinc(II) forms anionic complexes such as $ZnCl_3^-$ and $ZnCl_4^=$, and nickel(II) remains as a cation or neutral species. Consequently, when a hydrochloric acid solution of zinc(II) and nickel(II) is passed through an anion-exchange column, the $ZnCl_3^-$ and $ZnCl_4^=$ ions will be adsorbed and the nickel(II) species can be washed through the column and collected in a receiving vessel. Later, the zinc species can be removed from the column if they are converted back to cations, the latter being most easily accomplished by the use of aqueous ammonia as an eluent to produce the positively charged zinc-ammine complexes.

GAS CHROMATOGRAPHY

Gas chromatography is analogous to liquid-liquid and liquid-solid chromatography except that the mobile phase is a gas rather than a liquid. The stationary phase in gas chromatography may consist either of solid particles or of a solid coated with a liquid film, corresponding to liquid-solid adsorption chromatography and to liquid-liquid partition chromatography, respectively.

The entire column is often enclosed within an oven at a controlled, elevated temperature. This makes possible the separation and analysis of many samples which ordinarily exist as liquids or solids at room temperature. In general, it is possible to use gas chromatography with any sample which exhibits a vapor pressure of at least 10 mm of mercury at the temperature at which the column is operated. The upper limit of temperature which may be used is set by one or more of the following factors: volatility of the stationary phase, chemical stability of the test sample, the materials of which the column and associated apparatus are constructed, and the nature of the detecting system used to identify and measure the gases which emerge from the column.

The mechanisms whereby the components of the test sample are distributed back and forth between the mobile and stationary phases resemble those encountered when the mobile phase is liquid. Distribution equilibrium is generally achieved more quickly in gas chromatography than in liquid chromatography, which makes it feasible to use high flow rates, and thus to make separations very quickly. Furthermore, the low viscosity of gases compared to liquids makes it practical to use much longer columns, and thus to achieve high efficiency of separation.

Practical applications have been made for many years of the adsorption of gases upon charcoal and other solids. Nevertheless, the use of gaseous mobile phases in the separation of chemical species by the chromatographic technique is relatively recent. The year 1952 marked the beginning of the development of gas chromatography, which is now among the most widely used techniques in all of analytical chemistry.

Experimental Apparatus

Many types and models of apparatus are commercially available for gas chromatography. Most instruments include provision not only for the separation of the components of a mixture but also for detecting and measuring the components as they are eluted from the column. As indicated in the block diagram of Figure 7-10, a complete instrument consists basically of a pressure-regulated source of **carrier gas** which serves as the mobile phase, a sample injector, the column, and the detector, along with a recorder and a regulated oven to enclose the column.

Column.   The column is the real heart of the instrument. It usually consists of tubing fabricated from stainless steel, copper, a copper-nickel alloy, or glass. The tubing is typically about 4 mm in diameter, and the total column length is usually at least 1 meter but may be many times longer. The column is coiled or bent in such a way that it need not occupy much space, even though the gas path through the column may be very long.

Numerous different packings have been developed for use as the stationary phase within the column. Each type of column packing exhibits its own characteristic specificities. Diatomaceous earth, silica gel, alumina, and charcoal are among the common adsorbents for gas-solid chromatography. Another type of adsorbent is the **molecular sieve,** a synthetic or naturally occurring substance, characterized by the presence of "cavities" or "holes" within its molecular structure, which may be penetrated only by gas phase

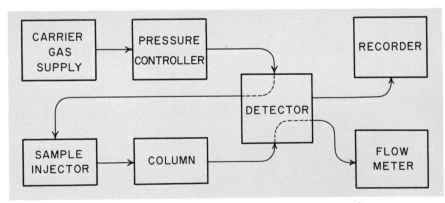

FIGURE 7-10.   Block diagram of a gas chromatograph.

molecules small enough to enter into these cavities. Larger molecules are unretarded by the molecular sieves.

Some of the same solids just mentioned are suitable as the supporting medium for the liquid phase in gas-liquid partition chromatography. A wide choice of liquid phases is available, with varying degrees of selectivity and stability. The liquid must exhibit suitable retention properties for the gas samples with which it is to be used, and it must also be chemically and physically stable over the desired temperature range. Among the common liquids are paraffin oil, silicone oil, and Apiezon grease. The amount of liquid on the solid support ranges from 1 to 40 per cent by weight.

The particle size of the solid phase is typically 0.01 to 0.1 cm in diameter. The smaller sizes result generally in better resolution but higher pressure drop.

Another type of column for gas-liquid chromatography is the Golay capillary column, the inside diameter of which is only 0.25 to 0.5 mm and the overall length of which may be as great as 300 meters. Again, the column is coiled or bent in such a way that it need not occupy much space. The inner walls of the column serve directly as the solid support and are coated with the liquid which serves as the stationary phase. Because of its tremendous length, this type of column can be extremely effective in separating components which are not adequately resolved with other types of columns.

Carrier Gas. Helium is the most widely used carrier gas. It is not appreciably retarded by most stationary phases, and it does not interfere with the response of most detectors to other substances. Among the other gases which are occasionally used as carriers in gas chromatography are hydrogen, nitrogen, argon, carbon dioxide, and air. No one gas is ideal for all applications. For example, the viscosity of helium is greater than that of nitrogen or air; this results in a greater pressure drop in passage through the column and is undesirable with extremely long or tightly packed columns. Also, safety considerations frequently preclude the use of hydrogen, and air causes the oxidation of some samples at high temperatures.

Sample Injector. The sample is most frequently injected into the stream of carrier gas as it enters the column by means of a hypodermic syringe, through a self-sealing rubber septum. Glass or metal sampling valves are occasionally employed. If the sample is injected as a liquid, as is frequently done, provision must be included for it to be vaporized almost instantaneously as it enters the system.

The size of sample is determined by the capacity of the column. Best separation is accomplished if the entire sample is initially adsorbed, or otherwise retarded, just as it enters the column. With columns of the sizes typically used in analytical instruments, liquid samples are generally within the range of 1 to 10 μl and gaseous samples up to 2 or 3 ml in volume. With large capacity columns, larger samples can be tolerated with good separation, whereas capillary columns necessitate the use of smaller samples.

Detector.   The detector is intended to respond to the presence in the column effluent of any component other than the carrier gas. High sensitivity is one important requirement of the detector, because of the small sample sizes and the frequent desire to detect and to measure trace components of the sample. It is generally desirable that the detector respond to every component other than the carrier gas, although highly selective response to a single component may be desirable in some applications. The detector must be stable chemically in the presence of the environment in which it operates. It must also be stable electrically. It is desirable that the quantitative response of the detector be linear over a wide range of concentration. Thermal conductivity cells, which are the most widely used detectors, respond to the presence of any gaseous component which exhibits a thermal conductivity different from that of the carrier gas. Other common detectors make use of other properties of gases, such as gas density, ionization potential, and ionization within a flame.

The detector output is generally recorded automatically, with the data appearing in the form of a graph of detector response versus time, as in Figure 7-11. The retention time for each component, which is useful for

FIGURE 7-11.   Gas chromatogram showing the separation of the 2,4-dinitro-fluorobenzene derivatives of *t*-butylamine, *sec*-butylamine, isobutylamine, and *n*-butylamine. The parent amine compound corresponding to each peak of the chromatogram is indicated on the curve. [Redrawn, with permission, from the paper by E. W. Day, Jr., T. Golab, and J. R. Koons: Anal. Chem., *38*, 1053 (1966).]

qualitative identification, may be read directly from the graph. Quantitative determinations generally require the measurement of the area under the peak on the graph for the desired component. Area measurements may be made on the graph by means of a planimeter. Some commercially available instruments provide for measuring these areas electronically; others provide direct digital readout of the data.

The block diagram of Figure 7-10 shows both the pure carrier gas and the column effluent passing through the detector block. It is common to include two separate detecting units in this block, one for each of the gas streams, and to measure or record the *difference* between the two signals. Thus, any contribution of the carrier gas to the detector response is nullified, and variations due to random fluctuations of temperature or of other experimental conditions are minimized.

Heating Ovens. The temperature of the column must be uniform and, in order to handle samples which are not gases at room temperature, provision must be included to maintain the column at an elevated temperature. Furthermore, the retention time for a given gaseous component is markedly dependent upon the column temperature. Many instruments are designed to change the temperature during a separation, in accordance with a predetermined "program," in order to optimize the separation and retention time for each component of interest.

We have already noted that liquid samples must be vaporized almost instantaneously upon insertion in the instrument. A separate oven is often provided for this purpose; it is always maintained at a temperature as high as, or higher than, the column temperature. It is also necessary that the detector be maintained at the column temperature. If it were to fall lower, the sample components could condense within it rather than flowing through it.

Analytical Applicability

The applications of gas chromatography in analytical chemistry have become so numerous and so important that it is virtually impossible even to attempt to summarize them. Many thousands of distinctly useful separations have been reported in the literature, and it is safe to state that gas chromatography has become one of the most widely used methods of chemical analysis. In principle, any chemical species that can be maintained in a gaseous or vapor state, inorganic or organic, can be separated and analyzed by the methods of gas chromatography.

One important area of application involves hydrocarbons. As many as 50 and more components of a single sample have been identified and determined in one analysis. Many of the applications involve trace constituents for which other methods of analysis are not available.

An example of the kind of analysis which can be accomplished with the aid of gas chromatography is illustrated by Figure 7-11. The direct gas chromatographic determination of simple amines is difficult. However, it is possible to react an amine, such as n-butylamine, with 2,4-dinitrofluorobenzene to prepare a nitrogen-substituted 2,4-dinitroaniline, which in the

$$C_4H_9NH_2 \; + \qquad \longrightarrow \qquad + \; HF$$

present case would be N-n-butyl-2,4-dinitroaniline. If the 2,4-dinitrofluorobenzene reagent is added to a mixture of amines, a benzene solution of the corresponding nitrogen-substituted 2,4-dinitroanilines can be injected into a gas chromatograph. Results obtained for a mixture of n-butylamine, isobutylamine, sec-butylamine, and t-butylamine are shown in Figure 7-11.

The bibliography following this chapter lists several reference works which describe other general and specific applications of gas chromatography.

QUESTIONS AND PROBLEMS

1. Identify or define the following terms: distribution coefficient, countercurrent extraction, metal chelate, stationary phase, mobile phase, masking agent, eluent, eluate, retention time, retention volume, band broadening, adsorption isotherm, cation exchanger, anion exchanger, bifunctional exchanger, liquid ion exchanger; capacity of a resin, molar selectivity coefficient, separation factor, molecular sieve, carrier gas.
2. Explain in detail how you would determine the capacity of an ion-exchange resin.
3. Calculate the fraction of a solute A extracted from 100 ml of an aqueous phase into 50 ml of an originally pure immiscible organic solvent, if the distribution coefficient of the solute, K_d, is 80 and if A exists as a monomeric species in each phase.
4. The multiple-extraction procedure provides one method by which a solute A may be quantitatively extracted from an aqueous phase into an immiscible organic phase. The aqueous phase, originally containing the solute, is shaken with an equal volume of the pure organic liquid, the organic layer is separated, and a fresh batch of the pure organic liquid is added. Eventually, after repeated extractions, the solute can be quantitatively removed from the original aqueous phase, even in unfavorable situations. Derive a relation for x, the fraction of solute A which remains in the aqueous phase, after n successive extractions involving equal volumes (V) of the aqueous and organic phases, and assuming that the distribution coefficient of solute A is K_d.
5. Rederive the equation for the situation described in problem 4, except that the volumes of the aqueous phase, V_{aq}, and the organic phase, V_{org}, are unequal.
6. Using the relationship derived in problem 5, as well as the equation presented earlier in this chapter for the fraction x of solute extracted in a one-step process,

compare the percentages of solute A extracted according to the following procedures, assuming that the distribution coefficient, K_d, is only 2.0.

(a) An aqueous phase of volume 100 ml, containing solute A, is extracted with a single 100 ml portion of a pure organic solvent.

(b) An aqueous phase of volume 100 ml, containing solute A, is extracted with 10 successive 10 ml portions of a pure organic solvent.

7. Suppose that you desire to extract a given solute from one solvent into a second, immiscible solvent, the distribution coefficient for the solute being only 3.50. If the volume of the first phase, initially containing all of the solute, is 10 ml, calculate the number of successive extractions with fresh 10 ml portions of the second solvent necessary to extract a minimum of 99 per cent of the solute from the original solvent.

8. Estimate, from Figure 7-5, the distribution coefficient for the extraction of iron-(III) into diethyl ether from $4 F$ hydrochloric acid. How many successive extractions of the aqueous phase with equal volumes of pure diethyl ether would be required for 99 per cent extraction of iron(III) at a $4 F$ hydrochloric acid concentration level?

9. Suggest an explanation for the observation that, in Figure 7-5, the percentage of extraction of iron(III) from hydrochloric acid into diethyl ether decreases at hydrochloric acid concentrations above approximately $7 F$.

10. List and explain the factors which influence the extraction of metal chelates.

11. If a Craig countercurrent extraction apparatus is employed to separate two solutes, A and B, with distribution coefficients $K_{dA} = 30$ and $K_{dB} = 15$, respectively, calculate the total number of tubes needed such that the tube containing the maximum concentration of A is 10 tubes removed from the tube containing the maximum concentration of B. Calculate the number of the tube in which A is at its maximum concentration. What is the fraction of A present in that tube? Calculate the number of the tube in which B is at its maximum concentration. What is the fraction of B present in that tube?

12. The technique of solvent extraction is a powerful method for the evaluation of equilibrium constants. The equilibrium constant for the reaction

$$I_2 + I^- \rightleftharpoons I_3^-$$

can be determined in this manner.

(a) The distribution coefficient for the partition of molecular iodine between water and carbon tetrachloride was established by measurement of the equilibrium concentrations of I_2 in the two phases. Calculate the distribution coefficient obtained in a typical experiment, if the titration of 100.0 ml of the aqueous phase required 13.72 ml of $0.01239 F$ sodium thiosulfate and if the titration of 2.000 ml of the carbon tetrachloride layer required 23.87 ml of the same sodium thiosulfate solution.

(b) Next, molecular iodine was partitioned between carbon tetrachloride and an aqueous $0.1000 F$ potassium iodide solution. The titration of a 2.000 ml portion of the carbon tetrachloride phase with a $0.01239 F$ sodium thiosulfate solution required 17.28 ml of the titrant, whereas the titration of a 5.000 ml aliquot of the aqueous phase required 25.93 ml of the sodium thiosulfate solution. Calculate the equilibrium constant for the formation of triiodide ion.

(c) Why is molecular iodine so much more soluble in carbon tetrachloride than in water? Why is triiodide ion not extracted into carbon tetrachloride?

13. Suggest some methods by which band broadening in chromatographic separations may be minimized or eliminated.

14. List and explain the factors which influence the affinity of a given cation for a resin phase.
15. In our discussion of ion-exchange chromatography, we restricted ourselves to the separation of trace cations, B and C, having the same charges, and we discovered that the concentration of eluent A has no effect on the separation of B and C. In the event, however, that all three ions—A, B, and C—have different charges, $+a$, $+b$, and $+c$, respectively, the ion-exchange equilibria may be written as follows:

$$aB_s^{+b} + bA_r^{+a} \rightleftharpoons aB_r^{+b} + bA_s^{+a}$$

and

$$aC_s^{+c} + cA_r^{+a} \rightleftharpoons aC_r^{+c} + cA_s^{+a}$$

(a) Write the molar selectivity coefficients, $K_A{}^B$ and $K_A{}^C$, corresponding to each of these equilibria.
(b) Express the distribution coefficients, K_{dB} and K_{dC}, for each trace cation in terms of the appropriate molar selectivity coefficients.
(c) Write simplified expressions for each distribution coefficient, assuming that the quantity of A in the resin phase remains essentially constant.
(d) Using the distribution-coefficient expressions derived in (c), plot the logarithm of K_{dB} versus the logarithm of the concentration of A, assuming that B has a charge of $+2$ and that A has a charge of $+1$. Construct a similar plot of $\log K_{dC}$ versus $\log [A]$, based on the assumption that C has a charge of $+3$ and A a charge of $+1$.
(e) Superimpose the two plots obtained in (d) such that the ion-exchange adsorption isotherms for species B and C intersect. What information can be obtained from this graph in terms of the separation of B and C by ion-exchange chromatography? In particular, what happens to the separation factor, $S_C{}^B$, as the concentration of A is varied?
16. List some specific chemical and physical properties of the eluate from a chromatographic column which may be measured or observed in order to follow the progress of a separation. Include actual examples of chemical systems which exhibit these properties.

SUGGESTIONS FOR ADDITIONAL READING

1. E. W. Berg: *Physical and Chemical Methods of Separation*, McGraw-Hill Book Company, New York, 1963.
2. L. C. Craig and D. Craig: Laboratory extraction and countercurrent distribution. *In* A. Weissberger: *Technique of Organic Chemistry*, second edition, Volume 3, Wiley-Interscience, New York, 1956, pp. 149–332.
3. S. Dal Nogare and R. S. Juvet: *Gas-Liquid Chromatography*, Wiley-Interscience, New York, 1962.
4. E. Heftmann: *Chromatography*, Reinhold Publishing Corporation, New York, 1961.
5. F. Helfferich: *Ion Exchange*, McGraw-Hill Book Company, New York, 1962.
6. P. G. Jeffery and P. J. Kipping: *Gas Analysis by Gas Chromatography*, The Macmillan Company, New York, 1964.
7. A. I. M. Keulemans: *Gas Chromatography*, second edition, Reinhold Publishing Corporation, New York, 1959.
8. I. M. Kolthoff and P. J. Elving, eds.; *Treatise on Analytical Chemistry*, Part I, Volumes 2 and 3, Wiley-Interscience, New York, 1959, pp. 917–1723.
9. E. Lederer and M. Lederer: *Chromatography*, second edition, D. Van Nostrand Co., Inc., New York, 1957.

10. C. J. O. R. Morris and P. Morris: *Separation Methods in Biochemistry*, Wiley-Interscience, New York, 1964.
11. G. H. Morrison and H. Freiser: *Solvent Extraction in Analytical Chemistry*, John Wiley & Sons, Inc., New York, 1957.
12. R. L. Pecsok, ed.: *Principles and Practice of Gas Chromatography*, John Wiley & Sons, Inc., New York, 1959.
13. H. Purnell: *Gas Chromatography*, John Wiley & Sons, Inc., New York, 1962.
14. O. Samuelson: *Ion Exchange Separations in Analytical Chemistry*, John Wiley & Sons, Inc., New York, 1963.

Chapter Eight

Aqueous Acid-Base Titrations

An acid-base titration, or a volumetric neutralization method of analysis, is based upon the chemical reaction between an acid and a base. In the present chapter, we shall consider the practical aspects as well as the underlying theory of acid-base titrimetry in aqueous solutions. Then, in the following chapter, some of the broad concepts of acid-base titrations in nonaqueous solvents will be discussed.

FUNDAMENTAL CONCEPTS OF ACIDITY AND BASICITY

Definitions of Acids and Bases. From the point of view of chemical analysis, the most useful definition of acids and bases is the one suggested independently in 1923 by Brönsted and by Lowry. An acid is defined as a species having a tendency to lose or donate a proton; a base is a substance having the tendency to accept or gain a proton. An important consequence of these definitions is that the loss of a proton by a Brönsted-Lowry acid gives rise to the formation of a corresponding Brönsted-Lowry base, which is generally called the **conjugate base** of the parent acid. Similarly, the addition of a proton to any Brönsted-Lowry base causes the formation of the **conjugate acid** of the original base. This fundamental interrelationship may be indicated most simply by the chemical equilibrium

$$\text{acid} \rightleftharpoons \text{base} + \text{proton}$$

Four typical examples of conjugate acid-base pairs are the following:

$$(1) \qquad \qquad H_2O \rightleftharpoons OH^- + H^+$$

$$(2) \qquad \qquad H_3O^+ \rightleftharpoons H_2O + H^+$$

(3) $NH_4^+ \rightleftharpoons NH_3 + H^+$

(4) $HCO_3^- \rightleftharpoons CO_3^= + H^+$

Notice that H_2O is the conjugate acid of the Brönsted-Lowry base OH^- in reaction 1 as well as the conjugate base of the Brönsted-Lowry acid H_3O^+ in reaction 2.

The Brönsted-Lowry concept of acids and bases was expanded by Lewis to include substances whose reactions do not involve the loss or gain of a proton. The basis of the Lewis definition of acids and bases lies in the grouping of electrons in the outer shells of atoms. An acid is a substance that can accept an electron pair from a base in the formation of a covalent chemical bond, and a base is a substance that can donate a pair of electrons to an acid to form a covalent bond. Thus, a Lewis acid has an incomplete outer electron shell, so that it can accept an electron pair from a Lewis base to complete that electron shell. Acids and bases in the Brönsted-Lowry classification are acids and bases in the Lewis sense as well. For example, when the hydroxide ion OH^- reacts with a proton H^+, the hydroxide ion is donating a pair of electrons to a proton to form a covalent bond. On the other hand, there are substances whose reactions involve no protons which do fit into the Lewis classification of acids and bases but not into the Brönsted-Lowry system of nomenclature. Thus, the reaction between silver ion Ag^+ and chloride ion Cl^- to precipitate silver chloride is an example of a Lewis acid-base reaction simply because chloride ion donates a pair of electrons to silver ion to form the largely covalent silver-chloride bond.

Strengths of Acids and Bases.   A proton cannot exist in solution by itself, that is, independently of its surrounding environment. In aqueous media the hydrogen ion is combined with one or more molecules of water to form the so-called **hydronium ion.** Although the hydronium ion is usually designated as H_3O^+, it should be recognized that the existence of more highly hydrated states of the proton is almost certain. Furthermore, all other ionic as well as molecular species are hydrated in an aqueous medium.

One of the consequences of the nonexistence of bare protons is that acid-base reactions occur by the transfer of a proton from an acid (proton donor) to a base (proton acceptor). Thus, we should consider the direct proton-transfer reaction between a Brönsted-Lowry acid and base to form the conjugate base of the acid and the conjugate acid of the base, according to the general equation

$$\text{acid } 1 + \text{base } 2 \rightleftharpoons \text{base } 1 + \text{acid } 2$$

Typical acid-base reactions are represented by the following equations:

(1) $HCl + H_2O \rightleftharpoons Cl^- + H_3O^+$

(2) $H_2O + NH_3 \rightleftharpoons OH^- + NH_4^+$

(3) $H_3O^+ + OH^- \rightleftharpoons H_2O + H_2O$

(4) $H_3O^+ + CO_3^= \rightleftharpoons H_2O + HCO_3^-$

The extent to which each of these reactions proceeds left to right, or its quantitativeness, is governed by the ease of transferring a proton from acid 1 to base 2 relative to the readiness of proton transfer from acid 2 to base 1. Consider, for example, the titration of sodium hydroxide with hydrochloric acid in an aqueous solution, as represented by equation 3. This reaction proceeds virtually completely to the right because hydroxide ions (base 2) have a much greater affinity for protons than do water molecules (base 1). Similarly, the reaction shown by equation 4 goes very far toward the right because the carbonate ion is a stronger base than water. However, reaction 4 does not proceed as far as reaction 3 because in water the carbonate ion is a weaker base than the hydroxide ion.

This brief discussion brings up a very important point. It would be advantageous to be able to compare the strengths of various Brönsted-Lowry acids strictly in terms of their intrinsic or absolute tendencies to lose protons. Unfortunately, an acid must be dissolved in some specified solvent, and this solvent almost always acts as a Brönsted-Lowry base to give the typical kind of acid-base reaction which has just been described. The intrinsic tendency of the acid to lose its proton is inextricably related to the affinity of the solvent for a proton, and, therefore, we find that the solvent is extremely important in determining the apparent strength of an acid. For example, hydrochloric acid in water is a strong acid, so the reaction expressed by equation 1 in the preceding list goes far to the right because water (acting as a Brönsted-Lowry base) has a much stronger affinity for a proton than does chloride ion. However, hydrochloric acid is a weaker acid in methanol (CH_3OH) because methanol molecules do not accept protons as readily as do water molecules. This means that if methanol were substituted for water in equation 1, i.e.,

$$HCl + CH_3OH \rightleftharpoons Cl^- + CH_3OH_2^+$$

the reaction would not proceed so far to the right. An aqueous solution of ammonia is a weak base because the reaction given by equation 2 does not go far to the right. This is so because the tendency for ammonia to accept a proton from water is significantly, but not tremendously, greater than the tendency for hydroxide ion to accept a proton from the ammonium ion.

The strength of an acid or base solution should not be confused with its concentration. A strong acid or base solution is one in which the solute acid or base reacts virtually completely with the solvent. A weak acid or base solution is one in which only partial, or perhaps insignificant, reaction with the solvent occurs. Generally speaking, we correlate the strength of an acid or base solution with its extent of ionization. Thus, hydrochloric acid is a strong acid in water because it is almost completely ionized, whereas acetic acid is a weak acid in water because it is only slightly ionized. A concentrated solution, on the other hand, is one containing a relatively large amount of solute per unit volume, regardless of whether that solute is highly ionized or not. For example, a 10 M solution is very concentrated, whether it be of a strong acid or base or a weak one. On the other hand, a 0.001 M solution is considered dilute. There is, however, no sharp dividing line between concentrated and dilute solutions, just as there is no clear boundary between strong and weak acids and bases.

The Autoprotolysis of Water. Pure water is slightly ionized, because of the fact that a water molecule is capable of accepting a proton from a second water molecule:

$$H_2O + H_2O \rightleftharpoons H_3O^+ + OH^-$$

The phenomenon represented by this equilibrium is called **autoprotolysis.** The equilibrium expression, written in terms of activities or "effective" concentrations, is

$$K = \frac{(H_3O^+)(OH^-)}{(H_2O)^2}$$

This equation can be considerably simplified, however, when we utilize the thermodynamic convention that a pure liquid (such as water) is defined as having unit activity and when this definition is assumed to be valid also for relatively dilute aqueous solutions. Furthermore, if we assume that the activity coefficients for the hydronium and hydroxide ions are essentially unity in the relatively dilute solutions of analytical interest, we can replace the activities of H_3O^+ and OH^- by their respective concentrations. Finally, it is convenient to write H^+ instead of H_3O^+ (or a more highly hydrated proton) in equations dealing with stoichiometry and equilibrium calculations. Making these changes as required, we arrive at the very familiar ion-product-constant expression for water:

$$K_w = [H^+][OH^-]$$

The ion-product constant, which is also known as the autoprotolysis constant, is particularly temperature dependent, ranging from 1.14×10^{-15} at 0°C through 1.01×10^{-14} at 25°C and 5.47×10^{-14} at 50°C to approximately 5.4×10^{-13} at 100°C. However, unless otherwise specified, it may be assumed in all of the numerical calculations in this chapter that the solution temperature is 25°C and that the ion-product constant K_w is taken to be 1.00×10^{-14}.

Definition of pH. In simplest terms the pH of an aqueous solution may be defined as the negative base-ten or decimal logarithm of the hydrogen ion concentration. That is,

$$pH = -\log [H^+]$$

This definition will be employed exclusively throughout the present discussion because its use is quite satisfactory for practical purposes such as the calculation and construction of acid-base titration curves, the selection of end point indicators, and decisions concerning the feasibility of proposed titration methods. The situation regarding the explicit definition of pH is much more complicated. In the final analysis, the pH of a solution is probably more accurately measured by the negative base-ten or decimal logarithm of the hydrogen ion *activity* a_H^+. However, two fundamental problems preclude the establishment of a theoretically rigorous pH scale. These are the existence of the so-called liquid junction potential in a galvanic cell used to determine pH values and the fact that the activity coefficient for a single ionic species, such as the hydronium ion, cannot truly be defined. In modern analytical chemistry laboratories, pH measurements made with an electronic pH meter are based upon the prior calibration of the particular instrument's electrode system with certain standard buffer solutions. The nominal pH values for these standard buffers are specified by the National Bureau of Standards in order to be as close as possible (within the limitations just mentioned) to the relationship pH $= -\log a_H^+$.

If we return to the ion-product-constant expression for water,

$$K_w = [H^+][OH^-] = 1.00 \times 10^{-14}$$

and take the negative logarithm of each member of this equation, the result is

$$-\log K_w = -\log [H^+] - \log [OH^-] = 14.00$$

or

$$pK_w = pH + pOH = 14.00$$

This equation provides a simple way to calculate the pOH of a solution if the pH is determined and, conversely, the pH can be obtained if the pOH is known. We shall make use of this relationship between pH and pOH in the discussions to follow.

EQUILIBRIUM CALCULATIONS FOR SOLUTIONS OF ACIDS AND BASES

The purposes of this section of the chapter are to establish and to illustrate methods for calculating the pH of aqueous solutions containing an acid, a base, a salt, or a mixture of two or more of these components. As stated earlier, it is assumed in all of the calculations that the solution temperature is 25°C and that the ion-product constant of water is taken as 1.00×10^{-14} for convenience. In addition, it is assumed that molar concentrations of dissolved species may be used in all equilibrium calculations when, in fact, the activities or "effective" concentrations should be employed. Corrections for the nonideality of solutions based on the Debye-Hückel limiting law or its modifications have already been discussed.

Solutions of Strong Acids or Bases and Their Salts

In simple terms, a strong acid or base is one which is fully ionized in aqueous solution. In addition, with few exceptions dissolved salts ionize completely in solution. If the salt is composed of the anion of a strong acid and the cation of a strong base, such as sodium chloride, its ions remain as such in the solution. On the other hand, if the salt is a salt of a weak acid or weak base (or both), as are sodium acetate and ammonium chloride, one or both of its ions will react to some extent with any hydrogen or hydroxide ions which may be present. Let us consider first only solutions of strong acids, strong bases, and salts of strong acids and bases.

Strong Acid Solutions.   For a solution containing a strong mono-protic acid which is fully ionized, the hydrogen ion concentration is equal to the original molar concentration of the acid. Among the familiar strong acids are hydrochloric acid, nitric acid, perchloric acid, and sulfuric acid. For example, a solution prepared by dissolving 0.1 mole of hydrogen chloride in 1 liter of water is $0.1\ M$ in hydrogen (hydronium) ions and $0.1\ M$ in chloride ions.

Example 1.   Calculate the pH of each of the following solutions: (a) $0.00150\ F$ HCl and (b) 1.000 liter of solution containing 0.1000 gm of HCl.

(a) $[H^+] = 1.50 \times 10^{-3}\ M$

$$pH = -\log [H^+] = 2.82$$

(b) Number of moles of HCl $= 0.1000\ \text{gm} \times \dfrac{1\ \text{mole}}{36.46\ \text{gm}}$

$$= 0.00277\ \text{mole}$$

$$\text{Concentration of HCl} = 0.00277\ \text{mole/liter}$$

$$[H^+] = 2.77 \times 10^{-3}\ M$$

$$pH = -\log [H^+] = 2.56$$

Strong Base Solutions.   In a strong base solution, the hydroxide ion concentration is directly related to the original concentration of the base in a manner analogous to the situation for a strong acid solution. The pH may be calculated from the hydroxide ion concentration and the ion-product constant for water.

Example 2.   Calculate the pH of a $0.0023\ F$ barium hydroxide solution.

First of all, we should note that two hydroxide ions are formed from the ionization of each molecule of barium hydroxide originally present. Therefore,

$$[OH^-] = 4.6 \times 10^{-3}\ M$$

$$pOH = -\log [OH^-] = 2.34$$

$$pH = 14.00 - pOH = 11.66$$

Solutions of Salts of a Strong Acid and Strong Base.   In con-sidering the acidic or basic behavior of any salt, we must first determine whether the salt contributes any hydrogen ions or hydroxide ions to the solution, and second, we must see if the ions of the salt react with any hydrogen ions or hydroxide ions already present. If the salt in question is a salt of a strong acid and a strong base, the answers to both of these queries are necessarily in the negative. Therefore, a salt of this type does not influence the acidity or basicity of a solution (other than its effect on the activity coefficients of the hydrogen ions and hydroxide ions, an effect being neglected in this discussion). Accordingly, a solution containing no solute other than a salt of a strong acid and a strong base has the same pH as the pure solvent alone, so the pH of such a solution is 7 at room temperature. Moreover, the addition of such a salt to a solution already containing an acid or base does not change the pH of that acid or base solution.

Solutions of Weak Acids or Bases

A weak acid or base is one which is incompletely ionized in aqueous solution. As a result, the hydrogen ion concentration or the hydroxide ion concentration is, respectively, always less than the original concentration of the weak acid or weak base. The mathematical expression for the state of equilibrium between the ionized and un-ionized forms of the solute serves as the basis for calculations of the pH of a weak acid or weak base solution.

The calculation of the pH of any solution falling into the present category may be accomplished by consideration of a few fundamental principles. First, write balanced reactions for the one or more pertinent chemical equilibria involved. These reactions must include all sources of hydrogen ions in the solution, such as water or an acid present as solute, and they must include any equilibria involving bases which consume hydrogen ions. There will frequently be only one important chemical reaction to consider, but two or even more may be involved in other cases. Second, write equilibrium expressions corresponding to each of the separate chemical reactions. Third, the known reference data as well as specifications for the particular solution must be incorporated into the statement of the problem. Fourth, these equations are solved for the desired unknown quantity or quantities.

These four steps are listed not as a prescription for blind calculations but rather as a set of principles to guide a knowledgeable approach to problems involving weak acid or weak base equilibria. Obviously, the scope of possible problems is so wide that no single sequence of rules can suffice for solving all problems. However, these principles do establish a rational way to attack the varied types of problems. These principles may now be considered with reference to aqueous solutions containing weak acids and bases, salts of weak acids or bases, and combinations of these.

Weak Acid Solutions.   In this section we shall treat two familiar weak acids, acetic acid and formic acid, as typical examples to illustrate the application of equilibrium calculations.

Example 3.   Calculate the pH of a 0.100 F acetic acid solution.

The sources of hydrogen ions in this system are the dissociation of acetic acid which may be represented as

$$CH_3COOH \rightleftharpoons H^+ + CH_3COO^-; \qquad K_a = 1.75 \times 10^{-5}$$

and the ionization of water according to the reaction

$$H_2O \rightleftharpoons H^+ + OH^-; \qquad K_w = 1.00 \times 10^{-14}$$

Actually, each of these reactions is an abbreviated form of the true acid-base equilibrium which occurs. Thus, the ionization reaction for acetic acid should show the transfer of a proton from acetic acid to water, whereas the ionization (autoprotolysis) of water proceeds through the transfer of a proton from one water molecule to another. However, as long as we wish to perform equilibrium calculations involving acid-base reactions in the *same* solvent (water), such abbreviated versions of acid-base equilibria as well as the corresponding equilibrium expressions can be employed.

Although it is true that a few hydrogen ions do come from the dissociation of water, acetic acid is such a stronger acid that ionization of water may be regarded as insignificant. Furthermore, the hydrogen ions from acetic acid will repress the dissociation of water through the common ion effect. It should be pointed out that neglect of the ionization of water may not be justified for extremely dilute acetic acid solutions. For practical situations, however, the ionization of acetic acid is the only important equilibrium:

$$\frac{[H^+][CH_3COO^-]}{[CH_3COOH]} = K_a = 1.75 \times 10^{-5}$$

Each molecule of acetic acid which undergoes ionization produces one hydrogen ion and one acetate ion. Therefore,

$$[H^+] = [CH_3COO^-]$$

At equilibrium the concentration of acetic acid is equal to the initial acid concentration $(0.100 \, F)$ minus the amount ionized (which is expressible by either the concentration of hydrogen ion or the concentration of acetate ion).

$$[CH_3COOH] = 0.100 - [H^+]$$

Substitution of the latter two relations into the equilibrium expression for acetic acid yields

$$\frac{[H^+]^2}{0.100 - [H^+]} = 1.75 \times 10^{-5}$$

There are several ways to solve this equation for the hydrogen ion concentration. First of all, since this relation is a quadratic equation, the formula for the solution of a quadratic equation* may be employed, from which the

---

* An equation of the type $aX^2 + bX + c = 0$ may be solved by means of the quadratic formula, which is

$$X = \frac{-b \pm \sqrt{b^2 - 4ac}}{2a}$$

In the present example, the equilibrium equation may be rearranged to $[H^+]^2 + 1.75 \times 10^{-5}[H^+] - 1.75 \times 10^{-6} = 0$. Applying the quadratic formula, we get

$$[H^+] = \frac{-(1.75 \times 10^{-5}) \pm \sqrt{(1.75 \times 10^{-5})^2 - 4(1)(-1.75 \times 10^{-6})}}{2} = 1.32 \times 10^{-3} \, M$$

(The other root is negative, an impossible situation.)

answer is found to be $[H^+] = 1.32 \times 10^{-3}\,M$ or pH = 2.88. There is, however, an alternate and much simpler procedure for solving the previous equation for $[H^+]$.

Let us assume that the equilibrium concentration of acetic acid is 0.100 M. This assumption is, in effect, saying that the numerical value of $[H^+]$ is a negligible quantity in comparison to 0.100 M or, in other words, that very nearly all of the acetic acid remains as undissociated molecules. Since a weak acid is, by definition, one that is only slightly ionized, this assumption should be expected to be a reasonable one. Ultimately, the validity of this assumption in any particular case must be demonstrated as indicated below. On the basis of the approximation that

$$[CH_3COOH] = 0.100\,M,$$

the equilibrium expression for acetic acid takes the form

$$\frac{[H^+]^2}{0.100} = 1.75 \times 10^{-5}$$

which can be solved as follows:

$$[H^+]^2 = 1.75 \times 10^{-6}$$

$$[H^+] = 1.33 \times 10^{-3}\,M; \qquad \text{pH} = 2.88$$

The results obtained by means of the quadratic formula and by the second, simple approach are identical.

The success of this second, simple method for solving the equilibrium equation could have been predicted without any concern for the quadratic formula. Notice that the hydrogen ion concentration $(1.33 \times 10^{-3}\,M)$ is only 1.3 per cent of the original concentration of acetic acid $(0.100\,F)$. Therefore, the actual equilibrium acetic acid concentration would be

$$[CH_3COOH] = 0.100 - 0.00133 = 0.099\,M$$

which is not significantly different from the assumed approximate value of 0.100 M. In general, if the original concentration of weak, monoprotic acid is at least 10,000 times greater than the ionization constant K_a, the approximation will be accurate to within about 1 per cent. Furthermore, if the original acid concentration is only 1000 times larger than K_a, the approximation will still not be in error by much more than 3 per cent, which is a tolerable uncertainty for most practical purposes.

Another assumption made at the very beginning of this problem was that the contribution of the ionization of water to the hydrogen ion concentration is negligible. If the hydrogen ion concentration is taken to be $1.33 \times 10^{-3}\,M$, the value of $[OH^-]$ can be obtained from the relation

$$[OH^-] = \frac{K_w}{[H^+]} = \frac{1.00 \times 10^{-14}}{1.33 \times 10^{-3}} = 7.5 \times 10^{-12}\,M$$

However, since water is the only source of hydroxide ion in this system and since one hydrogen ion and one hydroxide ion are formed for each water molecule ionized, the $[H^+]$ furnished by water is only $7.5 \times 10^{-12}\ M$.

One other technique used to solve equilibrium problems is called the **method of successive approximations.** We shall now use this procedure to consider the ionization of formic acid.

Example 4.   Calculate the pH of a $0.0250\ F$ formic acid solution.

As in the case of acetic acid, the ionization of the weak acid is the only important source of hydrogen ions.

$$HCOOH \rightleftharpoons H^+ + HCOO^-; \qquad K_a = 1.76 \times 10^{-4}$$

Accordingly, we can set the concentrations of hydrogen ion and formate ion equal to each other,

$$[H^+] = [HCOO^-]$$

and the equilibrium concentration of undissociated formic acid is

$$[HCOOH] = 0.0250 - [H^+]$$

The complete equilibrium expression for the ionization of formic acid now takes the form

$$\frac{[H^+][HCOO^-]}{[HCOOH]} = \frac{[H^+]^2}{0.0250 - [H^+]} = 1.76 \times 10^{-4}$$

To solve this equation by the method of successive approximations, we shall first ignore tentatively the $[H^+]$ term in the denominator of the equation (in spite of the fact that the initial formic acid concentration is only about 140 times larger than K_a). Therefore, we obtain

$$\frac{[H^+]^2}{0.0250} = 1.76 \times 10^{-4}$$

$$[H^+]^2 = 4.40 \times 10^{-6}$$

$$[H^+] = 2.10 \times 10^{-3}\ M$$

Obviously, this hydrogen ion concentration is hardly negligible in comparison to the initial formic acid concentration, but, instead of abandoning this approach and resorting to the quadratic formula, we shall continue. A closer approximation to the formic acid concentration would be to subtract the $[H^+]$ from the original concentration of formic acid, i.e.,

$$[HCOOH] = 0.0250 - 0.0021 = 0.0229\ M$$

This new value for the concentration of formic acid is now substituted back into the equilibrium expression and the equation solved once again for $[H^+]$.

$$\frac{[H^+]^2}{0.0229} = 1.76 \times 10^{-4}$$

$$[H^+]^2 = 4.03 \times 10^{-6}$$

$$[H^+] = 2.01 \times 10^{-3}\ M$$

Through this method of successive approximations, the second approximation to the formic acid concentration ($0.0229\ M$) has led to a self-consistent
set of values for the concentrations of hydrogen ion and formic acid. In other
words, if the formic acid concentration is assumed to be $0.0229\ M$ at equilibrium, the calculated $[H^+]$ is correct because, when the hydrogen ion
concentration of $0.00201\ M$ is subtracted from the original formic acid concentration of $0.0250\ M$, the result ($0.0230\ M$) agrees with the *assumed* value
for $[HCOOH]$. Therefore, the value for $[H^+]$ of $2.01 \times 10^{-3}\ M$ may be
accepted as an accurate result, and the pH is 2.70.

Weak Base Solutions.   Equilibrium calculations involving solutions
of weak bases differ little from those we have already considered. Ammonia
is a typical example of a weak base. The equilibrium between ionized and
un-ionized species in an aqueous solution of ammonia may be written as

$$NH_4OH \rightleftharpoons NH_4^+ + OH^-$$

However, there is good evidence that less than 30 per cent of the dissolved
ammonia actually exists as the species NH_4OH. Instead, the predominant
species is NH_3, so that the chemical equilibrium should be written in the
form

$$NH_3 + H_2O \rightleftharpoons NH_4^+ + OH^-$$

In this discussion, we shall not distinguish between NH_3 and NH_4OH but
will use the formula NH_3 to represent the *total* concentration of both species.
Because we do not differentiate NH_3 from NH_4OH and because the activity
(effective concentration) of water is taken to be unity, the equilibrium
expression for each of the two proposed ionization reactions of ammonia is
the same and can be represented by the equation

$$\frac{[NH_4^+][OH^-]}{[NH_3]} = K_b = 1.80 \times 10^{-5}$$

The following problem illustrates the use of this relation.

Example 5.   Calculate the pH of a solution of $0.0100\ F$ ammonia.

Although ammonia may be classed as a weak base, it is still so much
stronger as a base than water that we can consider ammonia as the only
important source of hydroxide ions. Neglecting the ionization of water, we
may equate the concentrations of ammonium ion and hydroxide ion from the
ionization of the ammonia, i.e.,

$$[NH_4^+] = [OH^-]$$

At equilibrium the concentration of ammonia is given by

$$[NH_3] = 0.0100 - [OH^-]$$

Appropriate substitution of these relations into the equilibrium expression
gives the following result:

$$\frac{[OH^-]^2}{0.0100 - [OH^-]} = 1.80 \times 10^{-5}$$

This equation can be conveniently solved by the method of successive approximations. We shall provisionally assume that the equilibrium concentration of ammonia is $0.0100\,F$ and then solve the expression for $[OH^-]$:

$$\frac{[OH^-]^2}{0.0100} = 1.80 \times 10^{-5}$$

$$[OH^-]^2 = 1.80 \times 10^{-7}; \qquad [OH^-] = 4.24 \times 10^{-4}\,M$$

This calculation shows that the hydroxide concentration is $4.24 \times 10^{-4}\,M$ and that the equilibrium concentration of ammonia is closer to

$$[NH_3] = 0.0100 - [OH^-] = 0.0100 - 0.00042 = 0.0096\,F$$

than to $0.0100\,F$. As a second approximation to the equilibrium ammonia concentration, let us substitute the value $0.0096\,F$ into the equilibrium equation and recalculate the hydroxide ion concentration:

$$\frac{[OH^-]^2}{0.0096} = 1.80 \times 10^{-5}$$

$$[OH^-]^2 = 1.73 \times 10^{-7}; \qquad [OH^-] = 4.16 \times 10^{-4}\,M$$

The latter value for the concentration of hydroxide ion does not differ substantially from the former result. However, the equilibrium concentration of ammonia is indeed very close to $0.0096\,F$, so that $[OH^-] = 4.16 \times 10^{-4}\,M$ is preferable. Noting that the original concentration of ammonia $(0.0100\,F)$ was more than 550 times larger than K_b, we might have concluded that it would be acceptable to ignore entirely the correction of the ammonia concentration due to its ionization. It would be acceptable in the present situation, but when doubt exists some mathematical check must be made to ascertain the validity of an assumption.

Since we accept the hydroxide ion concentration as being 4.16×10^{-4} M, the pH of the solution can be obtained as follows:

$$pOH = -\log[OH^-] = 3.38$$
$$pH = 14.00 - pOH = 10.62$$

Buffer Solutions

A buffer solution consists of either a weak acid along with a salt of that acid or a weak base plus a salt of the base. Two familiar examples of buffer solutions are a mixture of acetic acid and sodium acetate and a solution containing both ammonia and ammonium chloride. In the first case, an equilibrium is established in accordance with the chemical equation

$$CH_3COOH \rightleftharpoons H^+ + CH_3COO^-$$

This buffer solution differs importantly from a solution of just acetic acid in that the sodium acetate provides an additional and major source of acetate ions. In fact, the salt itself is essentially completely ionized in aqueous solution, the acetate ions thus formed entering into the equilibrium between acetic acid molecules, hydrogen ions, and acetate ions. Calculations of the pH of a buffer solution are carried out as in the case of a solution of either a weak acid or a weak base by itself, with due consideration being given to the influence of the additional ions from the salt.

Example 6.   Calculate the pH of a solution initially $0.100\,F$ in acetic acid and $0.100\,F$ in sodium acetate.

The starting point for an attack on this problem is the ionization-constant expression for acetic acid:

$$\frac{[H^+][CH_3COO^-]}{[CH_3COOH]} = 1.75 \times 10^{-5}$$

The fact that acetic acid is a much stronger acid than water, as well as the relatively large amount of acetic acid present, allows us to ignore the ionization of water as a source of hydrogen ions. To determine the hydrogen ion concentration, and thus the pH, we must derive expressions for the acetate and acetic acid concentrations. Since we have identified acetic acid as the only significant source of hydrogen ions, the acetic acid concentration at equilibrium is

$$[CH_3COOH] = 0.100 - [H^+]$$

On the other hand, the concentration of acetate ion at equilibrium is the sum of the acetate added in the form of sodium acetate $(0.100\,M)$ and the acetate formed from the ionization of acetic acid (given by the hydrogen ion concentration):

$$[CH_3COO^-] = 0.100 + [H^+]$$

Substitution of these relationships into the equilibrium expression gives the following equation:

$$\frac{[H^+](0.100 + [H^+])}{0.100 - [H^+]} = 1.75 \times 10^{-5}$$

In the present problem, it is reasonable to expect that the extent of ionization of acetic acid (represented by $[H^+]$) is small compared to the original acid concentration because the concentration of acetic acid is much larger than K_a and also because the acetate ion furnished by the sodium acetate represses the ionization of acetic acid. Accordingly, the above equation can be simplified to

$$\frac{[H^+](0.100)}{0.100} = 1.75 \times 10^{-5}$$

from which it is obvious that $[H^+] = 1.75 \times 10^{-5}\,M$. The assumption that $[H^+]$ is small in comparison to $0.100\,M$ is well justified. The pH of the solution is 4.76.

Example 7. Calculate the pH of 100 ml of a solution containing 0.0100 mole of ammonium chloride and 0.0200 mole of ammonia.

Ammonia, which ionizes in an aqueous medium according to the reaction

$$NH_3 + H_2O \rightleftharpoons NH_4^+ + OH^-$$

is a stronger base than water, so the ionization of water does not contribute appreciably to the hydroxide ion concentration. The equilibrium expression

$$\frac{[NH_4^+][OH^-]}{[NH_3]} = 1.80 \times 10^{-5}$$

can be solved for $[OH^-]$ after appropriate substitutions for $[NH_4^+]$ and $[NH_3]$ are made. From the information given in the statement of the problem, the initial concentrations of ammonium ion and ammonia are 0.100 M and 0.200 M, respectively. After equilibrium is established, the ammonium ion concentration is greater than 0.100 M by the amount of NH_4^+ formed by ionization of ammonia (which is measured in this case by $[OH^-]$):

$$[NH_4^+] = 0.100 + [OH^-]$$

The concentration of ammonia at equilibrium is

$$[NH_3] = 0.200 - [OH^-]$$

However, as in the previous example of the acetic acid-sodium acetate buffer, these small corrections to the ammonium ion and ammonia concentrations are insignificant, so the equilibrium expression may be written

$$\frac{(0.100)[OH^-]}{0.200} = 1.80 \times 10^{-5}$$

Therefore, the solution to this problem is as follows:

$$[OH^-] = 3.60 \times 10^{-5} \, M$$
$$pOH = 4.44$$
$$pH = 9.56$$

Some Properties of Buffer Solutions.   So far no mention has been made of the most important property of a buffer solution — a buffer solution resists pH changes when the solution is diluted (or perhaps concentrated) or when various amounts of acid or base are added.

To illustrate the effect of dilution upon the pH of a buffer solution, let us recall the problem discussed in the preceding Example 6, in which the pH of a solution 0.100 F in both acetic acid and sodium acetate was calculated. In a rigorous manner, we represented the acetic acid concentration at equilibrium as

$$[CH_3COOH] = 0.100 - [H^+]$$

and the acetate ion concentration as

$$[CH_3COO^-] = 0.100 + [H^+]$$

but we assumed and later justified that the term $[H^+]$ in each of these relations was negligibly small, being 1.75×10^{-5} M. What would happen if the solution were diluted one-hundred-fold, that is, if the original concentrations of acetic acid and sodium acetate each became 0.00100 F?

At first glance we might conclude that there would be absolutely no change in the pH at all. In this new problem, however, the rigorous expressions for the acetic acid and acetate ion concentrations would be as follows:

$$[CH_3COOH] = 0.00100 - [H^+]$$
$$[CH_3COO^-] = 0.00100 + [H^+]$$

If, indeed, the $[H^+]$ term in each relation were negligible compared to 0.00100 M, we would be correct in the assertion that no pH change would be observed. This statement must be tested. If the hydrogen ion concentration is taken to be 1.75×10^{-5} M, we discover that the latter rigorous relations yield the results

$$[CH_3COOH] = 0.00100 - 0.00002 = 0.00098 \ M$$
$$[CH_3COO^-] = 0.00100 + 0.00002 = 0.00102 \ M$$

provided that we are willing to round off the hydrogen ion concentration to 2×10^{-5} M for these calculations. What we can now do is substitute these new values for $[CH_3COOH]$ and $[CH_3COO^-]$ into the general equilibrium expression

$$\frac{[H^+][CH_3COO^-]}{[CH_3COOH]} = 1.75 \times 10^{-5}$$

and calculate a new value for the hydrogen ion concentration:

$$\frac{[H^+](0.00102)}{(0.00098)} = 1.75 \times 10^{-5}$$
$$[H^+] = 1.68 \times 10^{-5} \ M$$

This result must now be carefully interpreted.

First of all, the calculation is valid because the values of $[CH_3COOH]$ and $[CH_3COO^-]$ are essentially the same (0.00098 and 0.00102 M, respectively) regardless of which hydrogen ion concentration is employed to correct the original concentrations (0.00100 M) of the reagents. However, the difference in the hydrogen ion concentration is significant in two ways. Our calculations have shown that the hydrogen ion concentration in a buffer solution composed of 0.1 M reagents is 1.75×10^{-5} M (pH $= 4.76$) but that dilution by a factor of 100 causes the hydrogen ion concentration to decrease only to 1.68×10^{-5} M (pH $= 4.78$). This result reveals how well a buffer solution does stabilize the pH even upon great dilution. However, the small, but detectable, change in pH does caution against any indiscriminate dilution. The student can probably foresee the great problem which can arise when the constituents of the buffer are so extensively diluted that the concentrations of acetic acid and acetate ion approach the value of K_a.

Next, we shall consider the effects of adding strong acid or strong base to a buffer solution. The present discussion will be restricted to a buffer consisting of a weak acid and a salt of that weak acid, but the general approach that we follow is directly applicable to other types of buffers. The same buffer solution previously discussed (Example 6) will serve as a convenient starting point. Let us assume that we have exactly 100 ml of a buffer solution which is 0.100 F in both acetic acid and sodium acetate. In Example 6, we found that the hydrogen ion concentration was $1.75 \times 10^{-5}\ M$, corresponding to a pH of 4.76.

Example 8. Calculate the pH of the solution which results from the addition of 10.0 ml of 0.100 F HCl to 100 ml of the buffer solution described in Example 6.

First, we note that the position of equilibrium of the ionization reaction

$$CH_3COOH \rightleftharpoons H^+ + CH_3COO^-$$

will be driven toward the left by the addition of the hydrochloric acid. This is the effect desired of a buffer. In this case the large excess of acetate ions can consume the hydrochloric acid through the formation of the much weaker acetic acid. The following calculation will show how effectively the buffer does its job. The relatively large concentrations of reactants with which we are dealing will permit us to ignore the ionization of water.

We will calculate the hydrogen ion concentration from the expression

$$\frac{[H^+][CH_3COO^-]}{[CH_3COOH]} = 1.75 \times 10^{-5}$$

In 100 ml of the buffer solution, there are initially $(100)(0.100)$ or 10.0 millimoles of acetic acid and also 10.0 millimoles of acetate ion. The addition of 10.0 ml of 0.100 F hydrochloric acid is equivalent to 1.00 millimole of strong acid, which we can assume reacts virtually completely with acetate ion to form acetic acid. Therefore, after this reaction, 11.0 millimoles of acetic acid are present and 9.0 millimoles of acetate remain. Accordingly, the concentrations of acetic acid and acetate ion in the solution whose volume is now 110 ml are as follows:

$$[CH_3COOH] = \frac{11.0 \text{ millimoles}}{110 \text{ milliliters}} = 0.100\ M$$

$$[CH_3COO^-] = \frac{9.0 \text{ millimoles}}{110 \text{ milliliters}} = 0.082\ M$$

Substitution of these values into the equilibrium equation yields

$$\frac{[H^+](0.082)}{0.100} = 1.75 \times 10^{-5}$$

from which we calculate that $[H^+] = 2.14 \times 10^{-5}\ M$ and pH $= 4.67$.

Example 9.   Calculate the pH of the solution which results from the addition of 10.0 ml of 0.100 F NaOH to 100 ml of the buffer solution described in Example 6.

In this situation the principal equilibrium

$$CH_3COOH \rightleftharpoons H^+ + CH_3COO^-$$

will be shifted toward the right because the addition of a certain amount of strong base (NaOH) will consume or neutralize some of the acetic acid with the formation of an equivalent quantity of acetate ion.

The addition of 10.0 ml of a 0.100 F sodium hydroxide solution to the 100 ml sample of the buffer introduces 1.00 millimole of strong base which reacts with a stoichiometric quantity of acetic acid. Consequently, at equilibrium only 9.0 millimoles of acetic acid remain, whereas a total of 11.0 millimoles of acetate ion is present. The concentrations of acetic acid and acetate ion are

$$[CH_3COOH] = \frac{9.0 \text{ millimoles}}{110 \text{ milliliters}} = 0.082 \ M$$

$$[CH_3COO^-] = \frac{11.0 \text{ millimoles}}{110 \text{ milliliters}} = 0.100 \ M$$

From the equilibrium equation

$$\frac{[H^+][CH_3COO^-]}{[CH_3COOH]} = \frac{[H^+](0.100)}{0.082} = 1.75 \times 10^{-5}$$

the hydrogen ion concentration may be found to be $1.43 \times 10^{-5} \ M$ and the pH is 4.84.

Again, these calculations demonstrate how well a buffer solution can maintain constancy of pH. The pH of the solution, initially 4.76, changed only to 4.67 and to 4.84 by the addition, respectively, of 10 ml of 0.1 F hydrochloric acid and 10 ml of a 0.1 F sodium hydroxide solution.

There is a definite limit to how much acid or base can be added to a given buffer solution before any appreciable change in pH results, and this quantity is designated the *capacity* of the buffer solution. If we are still considering the acetic acid-sodium acetate buffer of the previous examples, the **buffer capacity** is set by the original amounts of the acid and its salt, since one or the other is consumed by reaction with the added strong acid or strong base. In the preceding problem (Example 9), the original buffer solution contained 10 millimoles of acetic acid, the strong base added reacting with this species. Obviously, the addition of 10 millimoles of strong base would have neutralized all of the acetic acid, and no buffering action would have remained. Calculations similar to those of Examples 8 and 9 reveal that the pH changes at a rate which increases more and more rapidly as the limiting buffer capacity is approached.

Solutions of Salts of Weak Acids and Weak Bases

The preceding sections have dealt with solutions of all major types except for those containing a salt whose anion or cation can form a weak acid or base. Although such salts were considered briefly in the previous discussion of buffers, we shall now treat them in detail.

Salt of a Weak Acid and Strong Base.   Sodium acetate, which is a salt of this type, ionizes completely in an aqueous medium to give sodium and acetate ions. The only source of hydrogen ions in such a solution is the ionization of water. However, acetate ions will react with hydrogen ions produced by the water ionization and with water itself to form acetic acid molecules. Because of the small concentration of hydrogen ion and the predominance of water, the principal chemical equilibrium which is established is

$$CH_3COO^- + H_2O \rightleftharpoons CH_3COOH + OH^-$$

According to the stoichiometry of this reaction, equal amounts of acetic acid and hydroxide ion are produced. However, since acetic acid is very incompletely ionized and hydroxide ion is a strong base, the solution will definitely contain more hydroxide ions than hydrogen ions. Therefore, a solution of the salt of a weak acid and a strong base is distinctly alkaline. The degree of this alkalinity is determined by the weakness of the acid involved. The weaker the acid which is a product, the higher will be the pH of the solution. This phenomenon can be illustrated by means of the following example:

Example 10.   Calculate the pH of a solution which is 0.100 F in sodium acetate.

A useful approach to this problem is to consider what reactions can be written which directly involve hydrogen ions. First, a source of hydrogen ions is the ionization of water:

$$H_2O \rightleftharpoons H^+ + OH^-$$

Next, hydrogen ions can be consumed by reaction with acetate ions to form acetic acid:

$$H^+ \mid CH_3COO^- \rightleftharpoons CH_3COOH$$

From an inspection of these two reactions, we note that one H^+ and one OH^- are formed for each molecule of water which ionizes and that each acetic acid molecule formed results in the consumption of one hydrogen ion. Therefore, the hydrogen ion concentration at equilibrium is given by

$$[H^+] = [OH^-] - [CH_3COOH]$$

Upon rearrangement, this expression becomes

$$[CH_3COOH] = [OH^-] - [H^+]$$

Looking carefully at this last equation, we can conclude that the hydrogen ion concentration is definitely much smaller than $[OH^-]$ because the solution is basic. Hence, we can make the assumption, and later justify it, that the term $[H^+]$ can be neglected. Thus,

$$[CH_3COOH] = [OH^-]$$

Notice that the same conclusion could have been made by considering that the reaction

$$CH_3COO^- + H_2O \rightleftharpoons CH_3COOH + OH^-$$

produces equal quantities of acetic acid and hydroxide ion.

The next step in solving this problem is to formulate the equilibrium-constant equation for the latter main reaction, as follows:

$$\frac{[CH_3COOH][OH^-]}{[CH_3COO^-]} = K_{eq}$$

To evaluate K_{eq}, it is instructive to multiply the numerator and denominator of the left-hand side of this equation by $[H^+]$ so that

$$\frac{[CH_3COOH][OH^-][H^+]}{[CH_3COO^-][H^+]} = K_{eq}$$

It is possible to recognize in this expression the ion-product constant for water

$$[H^+][OH^-] = K_w$$

and the *reciprocal* of the ionization constant for acetic acid

$$\frac{[H^+][CH_3COO^-]}{[CH_3COOH]} = K_a$$

So, we can write the result of this work as follows:

$$\frac{[CH_3COOH][OH^-]}{[CH_3COO^-]} = K_{eq} = \frac{K_w}{K_a} = \frac{1.00 \times 10^{-14}}{1.75 \times 10^{-5}} = 5.71 \times 10^{-10}$$

We have already established that, to a good approximation,

$$[CH_3COOH] = [OH^-]$$

The equilibrium concentration of acetate ion is equal to the original acetate concentration $(0.100\ M)$ minus that which is converted to acetic acid (expressed by $[OH^-]$):

$$[CH_3COO^-] = 0.100 - [OH^-]$$

However, because the equilibrium constant (K_{eq}) is so small and the initial acetate concentration relatively large, it is permissible to assume that the equilibrium concentration of acetate ion is just $0.100\ M$. Therefore, the equilibrium expression takes the simple form

$$\frac{[OH^-]^2}{0.100} = 5.71 \times 10^{-10}$$

which can be readily solved to give the following results:

$$[OH^-]^2 = 5.71 \times 10^{-11}$$
$$[OH^-] = 7.56 \times 10^{-6} M$$
$$pOH = 5.12 \quad \text{and} \quad pH = 8.88$$

Before leaving this problem, we may note the validity of the important assumptions made in solving this problem: (a) that the hydrogen ion concentration is negligible compared to $[OH^-]$ and (b) that the hydroxide ion concentration is small in comparison to the equilibrium acetate ion concentration. The validity of similar assumptions made for other problems must be carefully assessed. In general, the ability to make meaningful simplifying assumptions depends on one's having a genuine feeling for the chemistry of a particular system.

Salt of a Strong Acid and a Weak Base.   Equilibrium calculations involving an aqueous solution of the salt of a strong acid and a weak base are analogous to those described in the preceding problem. In fact, the only difference is that the roles played by hydrogen ion and hydroxide ion are reversed. For the present example, we shall consider a solution of ammonium chloride. In such a system, there are two sources of hydrogen ions. One is the ionization of water, which may be represented by the reaction

$$H_2O \rightleftharpoons H^+ + OH^-$$

The second, and more significant, source of hydrogen ions is the acid ionization of the ammonium ion

$$NH_4^+ + H_2O \rightleftharpoons NH_3 + H_3O^+$$

The latter reaction may be written in abbreviated form as follows:

$$NH_4^+ \rightleftharpoons NH_3 + H^+$$

The dissociation of water liberates equal quantities of the strong acid H^+ and the strong base OH^-, and the ionization of ammonia produces hydrogen ions and ammonia in the same abundance. However, the relatively weak base ammonia in the presence of the strong acid causes the solution to display definite acidic properties. We must now attack this problem quantitatively.

Example II.   Calculate the pH of a $0.100 F$ ammonium chloride solution.

It has already been suggested that there are two possible sources of hydrogen ions. A quantity of hydrogen ions equivalent to the quantity of hydroxide ions is formed from water, and the ionization of the ammonium ion produces stoichiometrically equal concentrations of H^+ and NH_3. Therefore, the total concentration of hydrogen ion is

$$[H^+] = [OH^-] + [NH_3]$$

This relation can be rearranged to the more useful form,

$$[NH_3] = [H^+] - [OH^-]$$

and, if we are willing to accept the fact that an ammonium chloride solution is acidic, the $[OH^-]$ can be neglected in comparison to $[H^+]$. In effect, what we are saying is that the ionization of the ammonium ion is the only important source of hydrogen ions, so that

$$[NH_3] = [H^+]$$

The acid strength of the ammonium ion should be determined by a calculation of the equilibrium constant for the following expression:

$$\frac{[H^+][NH_3]}{[NH_4^+]} = K_a$$

If the numerator and denominator of the left-hand side of this equation are multiplied by the term $[OH^-]$, the expression becomes

$$\frac{[H^+][NH_3][OH^-]}{[NH_4^+][OH^-]} = K_a$$

and it may be recognized that the numerator now contains the ion-product expression for water and the denominator contains the *basic* dissociation constant for ammonia. These two subsidiary equilibria are as follows:

$$[H^+][OH^-] = K_w = 1.00 \times 10^{-14}$$
$$\frac{[NH_4^+][OH^-]}{[NH_3]} = K_b = 1.80 \times 10^{-5}$$

Hence, we can arrive at the desired equilibrium expression by proper combination of these two subsidiary reactions:

$$\frac{[NH_3][H^+]}{[NH_4^+]} = K_a = \frac{K_w}{K_b} = \frac{1.00 \times 10^{-14}}{1.80 \times 10^{-5}} = 5.55 \times 10^{-10}$$

We have decided earlier that $[NH_3] = [H^+]$; also, ammonium ion is such a weak acid that we may safely assume that 0.100 M is the equilibrium value for $[NH_4^+]$. On the other hand, the ionization constant for ammonium ion (K_a) is still more than 50,000 times greater than the ion-product constant for water (K_w), so the assumption that the ionization of water does not contribute significantly to the hydrogen ion concentration is a valid one.

To calculate the concentration of hydrogen ion, and then the pH, it is only necessary to substitute the various relations deduced from the previous arguments into the equilibrium expression:

$$\frac{[NH_3][H^+]}{[NH_4^+]} = \frac{[H^+]^2}{0.100} = 5.55 \times 10^{-10}$$

The solution of this equation gives the results:

$$[H^+]^2 = 5.55 \times 10^{-11}$$
$$[H^+] = 7.45 \times 10^{-6}\ M$$
$$pH = 5.13$$

Salt of a Weak Acid and a Weak Base.   As the final example of this section, it is of interest to consider the behavior in an aqueous solution of a salt whose cation is a weak acid and whose anion is a weak base. Ammonium formate is a salt which displays such behavior. It ionizes completely to ammonium ions and formate ions. There are several conceivable acid-base reactions which may occur in this relatively complex system.

The ammonium ion, NH_4^+, can donate a proton to water,

$$NH_4^+ + H_2O \rightleftharpoons NH_3 + H_3O^+$$

or it can donate a proton to the formate ion to form a formic acid molecule:

$$NH_4^+ + HCOO^- \rightleftharpoons NH_3 + HCOOH$$

In addition, the formate ion, acting as a base, can accept a proton from water,

$$HCOO^- + H_2O \rightleftharpoons HCOOH + OH^-$$

and we have already written the reaction in which formate ion accepts the proton from the ammonium ion.

By evaluation of the equilibrium constants for these reactions, some insight into the relative importance of each equilibrium can be obtained.

From Example 11, the equilibrium constant for the *first* reaction was found to be:

$$K_a = \frac{[NH_3][H_3O^+]}{[NH_4^+]} = \frac{[NH_3][H^+]}{[NH_4^+]} = 5.55 \times 10^{-10}$$

By analogy to Example 10, the equilibrium constant for the *third* reaction can be obtained as follows:

$$\frac{[HCOOH][OH^-]}{[HCOO^-]} = \frac{K_w}{K_a} = \frac{1.00 \times 10^{-14}}{1.76 \times 10^{-4}} = 5.68 \times 10^{-11}$$

The *second* reaction, between NH_4^+ and $HCOO^-$, can be treated as follows:

$$\frac{[NH_3][HCOOH]}{[NH_4^+][HCOO^-]} = K_{eq}$$

The equilibrium constant K_{eq} can be readily evaluated if we multiply the numerator and denominator of the left-hand side of this equation by the term $[H^+]$:

$$\frac{[H^+][NH_3][HCOOH]}{[H^+][NH_4^+][HCOO^-]} = K_{eq}$$

Careful inspection of the terms reveals that K_{eq} is composed of the equilibrium constant for the acid ionization of ammonium ion,

$$NH_4^+ \rightleftharpoons NH_3 + H^+; \qquad K_a = 5.55 \times 10^{-10}$$

multiplied by the *reciprocal* of the equilibrium constant for the acid ionization of formic acid,

$$HCOOH \rightleftharpoons H^+ + HCOO^-; \qquad K_a = 1.76 \times 10^{-4}$$

Thus, we obtain

$$\frac{[\text{NH}_3][\text{HCOOH}]}{[\text{NH}_4^+][\text{HCOO}^-]} = \frac{5.55 \times 10^{-10}}{1.76 \times 10^{-4}} = 3.15 \times 10^{-6}$$

The reaction between NH_4^+ and HCOO^- is far more important than the other two proposed reactions because its equilibrium constant is on the order of 10,000 to 100,000 times greater than the corresponding equilibrium constants for these reactions.

It is now reasonable to focus full attention on the reaction between NH_4^+ and HCOO^-. Since the salt solution is originally composed of equal molar quantities of NH_4^+ and HCOO^- and since equal molar amounts of NH_3 and HCOOH must necessarily be formed in the reaction, we can state these relationships at equilibrium:

$$[\text{NH}_4^+] = [\text{HCOO}^-] \quad \text{and} \quad [\text{NH}_3] = [\text{HCOOH}]$$

For the purpose of lending some generality to our discussion, we shall rewrite the equilibrium expression as follows:

$$\frac{[\text{NH}_3][\text{HCOOH}]}{[\text{NH}_4^+][\text{HCOO}^-]} = \frac{K_w}{K_a K_b} = 3.15 \times 10^{-6}$$

where K_w is the ion-product constant for water, K_a is the acid dissociation constant for formic acid, and K_b is the base constant for ammonia. Substitution of the equalities $[\text{NH}_4^+] = [\text{HCOO}^-]$ and $[\text{NH}_3] = [\text{HCOOH}]$ gives us

$$\frac{[\text{HCOOH}]^2}{[\text{HCOO}^-]^2} = \frac{K_w}{K_a K_b}$$

However, from the dissociation constant for formic acid, we can write

$$\frac{[\text{HCOO}^-]^2}{[\text{HCOOH}]^2} = \frac{K_a^2}{[\text{H}^+]^2} \quad \text{or} \quad \frac{[\text{HCOOH}]^2}{[\text{HCOO}^-]^2} = \frac{[\text{H}^+]^2}{K_a^2}$$

Therefore, further substitution leads to the relations:

$$\frac{[\text{H}^+]^2}{K_a^2} = \frac{K_w}{K_a K_b}$$

$$[\text{H}^+]^2 = \frac{K_w K_a}{K_b}$$

$$[\text{H}^+] = \sqrt{\frac{K_w K_a}{K_b}}$$

This remarkable result shows that the pH of a solution of ammonium formate, and similar salts, is independent of the salt concentration. The independence of $[\text{H}^+]$ on the concentration of the salt may fail, however, when the salt concentration is small enough to be of the magnitude of K_a

or K_b. Yet, if K_a and K_b are exactly equal, the hydrogen ion concentration is *always* independent of the salt concentration (excepting ionic effects on activity coefficients) and is numerically 7.00. In other words, if K_a and K_b happen to be equal, the tendency of the weak acid to lose a proton is exactly balanced by the affinity of the weak base for a proton, and the salt solution is perfectly neutral. It follows also that the salt solution will be acidic if K_b is less than K_a, and the solution is basic when K_a is less than K_b.

Example 12. Calculate the pH of a $0.0100\,F$ ammonium formate solution.

This problem can be solved immediately by application of the preceding equation:

$$[H^+] = \sqrt{\frac{K_w K_a}{K_b}}$$

$$[H^+] = \sqrt{\frac{(1.00 \times 10^{-14})(1.76 \times 10^{-4})}{1.80 \times 10^{-5}}}$$

$$[H^+] = 3.13 \times 10^{-7}\,M$$

$$pH = 6.50$$

Solutions of Polyprotic Acids and Their Salts

Thus far in this chapter we have considered only those acids, bases, and salts which are capable of single proton-transfer reactions. However, there is a broad and important class of acids, called **polyprotic acids,** which have two or more ionizable hydrogen ions. Included in the list of polyprotic acids are phosphoric acid (H_3PO_4), sulfuric acid (H_2SO_4), oxalic acid ($H_2C_2O_4$), and carbonic acid (H_2CO_3). Similarly, salts of these polyprotic acids exist which are capable of acting as bases and accepting two or more protons. Thus, sodium carbonate can react with two protons, and sodium phosphate can accept three hydrogen ions in forming phosphoric acid.

In this section, we shall focus our attention on three aspects of equilibria involving phosphoric acid and its salts. Phosphoric acid is a triprotic acid which can undergo three stepwise ionizations as indicated by the following equilibria:

$$H_3PO_4 \rightleftharpoons H^+ + H_2PO_4^-; \qquad K_1 = 7.5 \times 10^{-3}$$

$$H_2PO_4^- \rightleftharpoons H^+ + HPO_4^=; \qquad K_2 = 6.2 \times 10^{-8}$$

$$HPO_4^= \rightleftharpoons H^+ + PO_4^{\equiv}; \qquad K_3 = 4.8 \times 10^{-13}$$

From these equilibria, we can see that phosphoric acid itself is a fairly strong acid, being much stronger than acetic or formic acids but not so strong as hydrochloric acid. Dihydrogen phosphate and monohydrogen phosphate ions are increasingly weak acids because the removal of a positively charged proton from a singly and then a doubly negative species is more and more difficult.

Example 13.   Calculate the pH of a 0.1000 *F* phosphoric acid solution.

As usual, we must consider the important sources of hydrogen ions in this system. In principle, phosphoric acid can furnish protons from each of its three ionizations, and water is also a potential source of hydrogen ions. However, in view of the comparatively large value of the first dissociation constant of phosphoric acid, it is reasonable to neglect at this point the second and third ionizations as well as the ionization of water. Therefore, this problem is very similar to Examples 3 and 4, which involve weak monoprotic acids. The equilibrium-constant expression for the first ionization of phosphoric acid is

$$\frac{[H^+][H_2PO_4^-]}{[H_3PO_4]} = K_1 = 7.5 \times 10^{-3}$$

At equilibrium, we shall write for this situation

$$[H^+] = [H_2PO_4^-]$$

and

$$[H_3PO_4] = 0.1000 - [H^+]$$

The ionization of phosphoric acid is too extensive for us to neglect the $[H^+]$ term in the preceding relation, so the expression to be solved for $[H^+]$ is:

$$\frac{[H^+]^2}{0.1000 - [H^+]} = 7.5 \times 10^{-3}$$

This last equation is best solved by means of the quadratic formula, and the result is $[H^+] = 2.39 \times 10^{-2} \, M$; so pH = 1.62.

The next most likely source of hydrogen ions is the ionization of $H_2PO_4^-$. We can show that it and, hence, the other sources of protons, can indeed be neglected. If we provisionally take $[H^+] = 2.39 \times 10^{-2} \, M$ and $[H_2PO_4^-] = 2.39 \times 10^{-2} \, M$, the concentration of $HPO_4^=$ can be calculated from a rearranged form of the second dissociation-constant expression for phosphoric acid. Thus,

$$[HPO_4^=] = K_2 \frac{[H_2PO_4^-]}{[H^+]} = 6.2 \times 10^{-8} \frac{(0.0239)}{(0.0239)} = 6.2 \times 10^{-8} \, M$$

Since the equilibrium concentration of $HPO_4^=$ is so small, it is apparent that an insignificant quantity of $H_2PO_4^-$ has ionized under these conditions. Consequently, our original assumption that the only important source of protons is phosphoric acid is valid, so the pH is 1.62 as calculated.

Example 14.   Calculate the individual concentrations of all phosphate species in 1.00 liter of solution at pH 8.00 and containing 0.100 mole of phosphate species.

In a solution containing several acidic or basic ions, it is useful to determine the *ratios* of concentrations of the various species. The three ionizations of phosphoric acid allow us to write the following equations:

$$\frac{[H_2PO_4^-]}{[H_3PO_4]} = \frac{K_1}{[H^+]}$$

$$\frac{[HPO_4^=]}{[H_2PO_4^-]} = \frac{K_2}{[H^+]}$$

$$\frac{[PO_4^\equiv]}{[HPO_4^=]} = \frac{K_3}{[H^+]}$$

If we now substitute $[H^+] = 1.00 \times 10^{-8}\ M$ and the appropriate values for K_1, K_2, and K_3, the concentration ratios become

$$\frac{[H_2PO_4^-]}{[H_3PO_4]} = \frac{7.5 \times 10^{-3}}{1.00 \times 10^{-8}} = 750{,}000$$

$$\frac{[HPO_4^=]}{[H_2PO_4^-]} = \frac{6.2 \times 10^{-8}}{1.00 \times 10^{-8}} = 6.20$$

$$\frac{[PO_4^\equiv]}{[HPO_4^=]} = \frac{4.8 \times 10^{-13}}{1.00 \times 10^{-8}} = 0.0000480$$

These ratios show that the concentrations of $HPO_4^=$ and $H_2PO_4^-$ are similar in magnitude but that the concentrations of H_3PO_4 and $PO_4^\equiv$ are extremely small in comparison. To a very good approximation, therefore, the sum of the $HPO_4^=$ and $H_2PO_4^-$ concentrations represents virtually all of the total concentration ($0.100\ M$) of phosphate species, i.e.,

$$[H_2PO_4^-] + [HPO_4^=] = 0.100\ M$$

From the ratio relationships above, we have the result

$$[HPO_4^=] = 6.20[H_2PO_4^-]$$

These last two equations, containing two unknowns, may be solved as follows:

$$[H_2PO_4^-] + 6.20[H_2PO_4^-] = 7.20[H_2PO_4^-] = 0.100\ M;$$
$$[H_2PO_4^-] = 0.0139\ M;$$
$$[HPO_4^=] = 0.0861\ M.$$

We can now go back again to the ratio relationships to calculate the concentrations of H_3PO_4 and $PO_4^\equiv$.

$$[H_3PO_4] = \frac{[H_2PO_4^-]}{750{,}000} = \frac{1.39 \times 10^{-2}}{7.50 \times 10^5} = 1.85 \times 10^{-8}\ M$$

$$[PO_4^\equiv] = 4.8 \times 10^{-5}[HPO_4^=] = 4.8 \times 10^{-5}(0.0861) = 4.14 \times 10^{-6}\ M$$

Our assumption that the $HPO_4^=$ and $H_2PO_4^-$ represent essentially all the dissolved phosphate species is correct.

Example 15. Calculate the pH of the solution obtained by mixing 500 ml of 0.200 F phosphoric acid with 500 ml of a 0.0800 F trisodium phosphate (Na_3PO_4) solution.

This problem may be solved if we remember that phosphoric acid, a fairly strong acid, can donate a proton to $PO_4^=$, which has a marked tendency to accept a hydrogen ion and to form $HPO_4^=$:

$$H_3PO_4 + PO_4^= \rightleftharpoons H_2PO_4^- + HPO_4^=$$

The equilibrium constant for the preceding reaction is K_1/K_3 or 1.56×10^{10}. Since we start with 100 millimoles of H_3PO_4 and 40 millimoles of $PO_4^=$, we will have after this reaction is concluded 40 millimoles of $HPO_4^=$, 40 millimoles of $H_2PO_4^-$, and 60 millimoles of *unreacted* H_3PO_4.

Now, we must ask whether the strongest acid present (H_3PO_4) can react with the strongest base available ($HPO_4^=$). The answer is *yes*, because the equilibrium constant for the reaction

$$H_3PO_4 + HPO_4^= \rightleftharpoons 2\ H_2PO_4^-$$

is K_1/K_2 or 1.21×10^5. The reaction of 60 millimoles of H_3PO_4 with 40 millimoles of $HPO_4^=$ produces 80 millimoles of $H_2PO_4^-$ to go with the 40 millimoles of $H_2PO_4^-$ formed in the first reaction, and 20 millimoles of H_3PO_4 still remains. As a result of these two reactions, the solution contains 20 millimoles of H_3PO_4 and 120 millimoles of $H_2PO_4^-$ at equilibrium. There can be no further reaction between H_3PO_4 and $H_2PO_4^-$.

The pH of the solution can be calculated simply as if we are dealing with a buffer solution. The hydrogen ion concentration is governed by the equation

$$[H^+] = K_1 \frac{[H_3PO_4]}{[H_2PO_4^-]} = 7.5 \times 10^{-3} \frac{(0.020)}{(0.120)} = 1.25 \times 10^{-3}\ M$$

$$pH = 2.90$$

These problems are representative of the types encountered for polyprotic acid systems. It is important to recognize that, for the most part, these problems really consist of the elements of the simpler calculations considered for monoprotic acids and their salts.

We are now in the position to investigate acid-base titrations and to apply equilibrium calculations in predicting and assessing the feasibility of proposed titration methods.

STRONG ACID-STRONG BASE TITRATIONS

The analysis of solutions containing acidic and basic constituents by means of acid-base titrimetry requires the availability of standard titrants. Not all acids and bases are equally suitable for the preparation of standard solutions, so it is necessary to consider which acids and bases are preferable as standard reagents.

Of the common acids, only hydrochloric acid, nitric acid, perchloric acid, and sulfuric acid are highly ionized, strong acids. Sulfuric acid is commercially available as high purity, concentrated reagent and is selected occasionally for titrations. It is not suitable for titrations in solutions containing a cation that forms an insoluble sulfate precipitate because the end point may be obscured. Furthermore, it must be remembered that the second step of the ionization of sulfuric acid is not complete; that is, sulfuric acid is not entirely a strong acid, although it is much stronger than acetic acid and formic acid, for example. Nitric acid is never used as a concentrated titrant because such a solution is exceedingly unstable to light and heat. Concentrated nitric acid also suffers the disadvantage of entering into oxidation-reduction reactions. On the other hand, dilute nitric acid solutions at and below the $0.1\,F$ concentration level are stable for long periods of time and make excellent standard acid solutions. Perchloric acid solutions as concentrated as $1.0\,F$ are also good titrants for acid-base reactions. However, boiling, concentrated perchloric acid $(12\,F)$ is a powerful oxidizing agent and can react with explosive violence in the presence of organic matter. Dilute perchloric acid titrants have a singular disadvantage if the sample contains potassium ions, for potassium perchlorate $(KClO_4)$ is a dense, white, and insoluble compound. Without the slightest doubt, hydrochloric acid is the most universally preferred titrant. This favoritism probably stems from the purity of concentrated, commercially available hydrochloric acid and from the long shelf life of dilute solutions. In addition, numerous highly precise methods for the accurate standardization of hydrochloric acid titrants are available.

A weak acid, such as acetic acid, is not suitable as a general-purpose standard titrant in aqueous solutions because the pH change which occurs near the equivalence point of the titration is too small to provide a sharp end point. However, in a solvent such as liquid ammonia, which is more basic than water, acetic acid would act as a strong acid and would be suitable for acid-base titrimetry.

Standard base solutions for general applications are usually prepared from sodium hydroxide. Two less important, but occasionally used, reagents for the preparation of standard base solutions are potassium hydroxide and barium hydroxide. From the chemical standpoint potassium hydroxide is as good as sodium hydroxide. However, the former is more expensive than the latter, so sodium hydroxide is usually chosen. Solutions of barium hydroxide tend to absorb carbon dioxide from the atmosphere with the resultant precipitation of insoluble barium carbonate and the simultaneous decrease in the concentration of hydroxide ions. The reactions which occur are as follows:

$$CO_2 + 2\,OH^- \rightleftharpoons CO_3^- + H_2O$$
$$Ba^{++} + CO_3^= \rightleftharpoons BaCO_3$$

Sodium and potassium hydroxide solutions also absorb atmospheric carbon dioxide, so the problem is a general one which must be counteracted in the preparation, standardization, and storage of titrant base solutions. This problem will be discussed further in the next section.

Weak bases, like weak acids, are generally unsatisfactory for titrations in aqueous solutions — again because sharp end points are not obtained in many cases. In order to cause a weak base, such as ammonia, to behave as a much stronger base, it could be employed as a solution in a solvent which is more acidic than water.

Preparation and Standardization of Solutions of Strong Acids

Solutions of any of the strong acids mentioned previously are most conveniently prepared by dilution of the concentrated, commercially available acids. For example, the concentrated, analytical-reagent-grade hydrochloric acid found in most laboratories is approximately $12\,F$, but its concentration is not accurately known nor sufficiently constant from one batch to another to permit its use directly as a standard acid solution. Therefore, a solution of hydrochloric acid of approximately the desired concentration must be prepared by dilution of the concentrated $(12\,F)$ acid with distilled water, and then the solution must be standardized by one of the methods to be described. The preparation of solutions of nitric acid, perchloric acid, or sulfuric acid is similarly accomplished, that is, by dilution of the concentrated reagents.

Any one of several primary standard bases may be used for the standardization of a hydrochloric acid solution. Pure sodium carbonate is a frequent choice. Reagent-grade sodium carbonate is commercially available in very high purity for standardization purposes. Preferably it should be obtained in small bottles and insofar as possible should not be exposed to the atmosphere; the sodium carbonate should be dried to remove surface moisture prior to use. Carbonate ion can be titrated with hydrochloric acid to form the bicarbonate or hydrogen carbonate ion (HCO_3^-). Further addition of acid leads to the formation of carbonic acid. The individual reactions may be written as follows:

$$CO_3^= + H^+ \rightleftharpoons HCO_3^-$$

$$HCO_3^- + H^+ \rightleftharpoons H_2CO_3$$

The end point corresponding to the addition of a single hydrogen ion to carbonate is indistinct. In contrast, the end point for the addition of a second proton to carbonate, i.e., for the overall reaction

$$CO_3^= + 2\,H^+ \rightleftharpoons H_2CO_3$$

is easily determined by the aid of an acid-base indicator. This latter reaction is the basis of a method for the standardization of hydrochloric acid. The titration reaction is driven farther to completion, and hence the end point becomes sharper, if most of the carbonic acid formed by the titration reaction is removed from the reaction medium. Carbonic acid is in equilibrium with carbon dioxide and water,

$$H_2CO_3 \rightleftharpoons CO_2 + H_2O$$

so by boiling the solution to expel carbon dioxide, just before the final end point is reached, one can accomplish the removal of carbonic acid and the end point is more sharply defined.

The organic base tris(hydroxymethyl)aminomethane, sometimes abbreviated THAM and also known as "tris," is an excellent primary standard reagent. It reacts with hydrochloric acid, much the same as does ammonia, according to the equation

$$H^+ + (CH_2OH)_3CNH_2 \rightleftharpoons (CH_2OH)_3CNH_3^+$$

This substance is available in analytical-reagent-grade purity and presents no particular problems with regard to either drying or weighing. The same end point indicators which are employed in the standardization of hydrochloric acid against sodium carbonate may be used for the hydrochloric acid-tris(hydroxymethyl)aminomethane titration. There is, of course, no need to boil the solution to remove carbon dioxide near the end point of this titration unless the solvent itself contains considerable dissolved carbon dioxide.

Other primary standards which may be used for the standardization of hydrochloric acid solutions include calcium carbonate in the form of clear calcite crystals and borax ($Na_2B_4O_7 \cdot 10\ H_2O$). Alternatively, a hydrochloric acid solution may be standardized gravimetrically by precipitating and weighing the chloride as silver chloride, although it is preferable to standardize an acid directly on the basis of its acidity. It is possible, but certainly not desirable, to standardize a sulfuric acid solution by determining the sulfate gravimetrically as barium sulfate.

One final method of obtaining a standard hydrochloric acid solution involves its preparation from constant-boiling hydrochloric acid. When a solution of this acid is boiled, hydrogen chloride and water molecules are distilled away until eventually the remaining solution approaches a definite, precisely known composition which is fixed by the prevailing barometric pressure. Thereafter this constant-boiling mixture continues to distill off, and it can be collected and stored for future use. The concentration of the constant-boiling solution is close to 6.1 F, greater than that required in most analytical work, but quantitative dilution with distilled water suffices to bring it to a suitable concentration. This procedure is relatively laborious, but excellent results can be achieved. A standard solution of sulfuric acid can be similarly prepared from constant-boiling sulfuric acid.

Preparation and Standardization of Solutions of Strong Bases

Solid sodium hydroxide, from which titrant base solutions are usually prepared, is not available in a pure form. Commercial material is always contaminated by moisture and by small amounts (up to 2 per cent) of sodium carbonate. Sodium chloride may also be present in trace amounts as an impurity. Consequently, a solution of sodium hydroxide must be prepared of approximately the required concentration and then standardized.

As mentioned previously, carbon dioxide from the atmosphere is readily absorbed by alkaline solutions, as in the reaction

$$CO_2 + 2\ OH^- \rightleftharpoons CO_3^= + H_2O$$

Although carbonate ion immediately precipitates as insoluble barium carbonate in a barium hydroxide titrant, the carbonate remains soluble in both sodium and potassium hydroxide solutions. The absorbed atmospheric carbon dioxide does not necessarily cause a change in the effective concentration of the strong base solution, because a carbonate ion can react with two protons just as the two hydroxide ions which are neutralized when the carbon dioxide molecule is originally absorbed. However, sometimes an end point indicator is employed which is perfectly satisfactory for a strong acid-strong base titration, but which changes color at a pH corresponding only to the titration of carbonate to bicarbonate ion:

$$CO_3^= + H^+ \rightleftharpoons HCO_3^-$$

Under such conditions, carbonate *cannot* react with two hydrogen ions, and the effective concentration of the base solution is smaller than expected. This difficulty can be remedied, however, if one is careful to select an end point indicator which does change color at a pH corresponding to the addition of *two* hydrogen ions to the carbonate ion. For similar reasons, the presence of sodium carbonate as an impurity in solid sodium hydroxide may cause anomalous results if the particular titrant base solution is used in titrations with several different end point indicators.

Quite clearly, it is highly desirable to remove carbonate ion from the sodium hydroxide solution prior to its standardization, and the standard solution should subsequently be stored away from atmospheric carbon dioxide. The initial removal of carbonate may be accomplished, for example, by its precipitation as barium carbonate, although excess barium ions may be objectionable because barium forms precipitates with a number of anions. A preferable method to remove carbonate takes advantage of the insolubility of sodium carbonate in very concentrated sodium hydroxide solutions. If a 50 per cent sodium hydroxide solution is prepared, the sodium carbonate impurity is virtually insoluble and will settle to the bottom of the container within a day or so. The clear, carbonate-free sodium hydroxide syrup may be carefully decanted and then diluted appropriately with freshly boiled and cooled distilled water. This procedure allows a carbonate-free standard solution to be prepared. Sodium hydroxide solutions should not be stored in glass containers; screw-cap polyethylene bottles are especially serviceable for the short-term storage and use of these solutions. An apparatus suitable for storing and using the solution away from atmospheric gases is shown in Figure 8-1.

There are several primary standard acids, any one of which may be used to standardize a solution of sodium, potassium, or barium hydroxide. Potassium acid phthalate ($KHC_8H_4O_4$) has the advantages of high equivalent weight and purity, stability on drying, and ready availability. On the other hand, it has the disadvantage of being a weak acid so that it is generally suitable for standardization of carbonate-free base solutions only. Sulfamic acid (NH_2SO_3H) is a very good primary standard, being readily available in a pure form, rather inexpensive, and a strong acid. Oxalic acid dihydrate ($H_2C_2O_4 \cdot 2\ H_2O$) and benzoic acid (C_6H_5COOH) are also occasionally used as primary standard acids.

It should be emphasized that it is unnecessary to standardize both a hydrochloric acid and a sodium hydroxide solution against a primary

FIGURE 8-1.   Storage bottle and buret assembly for volumetric reagent solutions that must be protected from the atmosphere.

standard. The concentration of either one may be established by titration against the other. Consequently, only a hydrochloric acid solution or a sodium hydroxide solution, but not both, need be standardized against a primary standard.

Titration Curve for a Strong Acid-Strong Base Titration

A titration curve for an acid-base reaction consists of a plot of pH versus the volume of titrant added. Such a curve may be constructed by a consideration of the pertinent acid-base equilibria according to the methods developed earlier in this chapter. Theoretical titration curves are of special importance because they provide information concerning the feasibility and possible accuracy of a titration, and they are extremely useful for purposes of choosing what end point indicator should be employed.

If the acid is in the titration vessel and the base is added from a buret, the solution initially contains only strong acid. At all points during the titration prior to the equivalence point, the solution will contain strong acid plus the salt of a strong acid and strong base. The solution contains merely the salt at the equivalence point, whereas beyond the equivalence point the solution consists of an excess of strong base and the aforementioned salt.

Let us construct the titration curve for the neutralization of 50.00 ml of $0.1000\,F$ hydrochloric acid with a $0.1000\,F$ sodium hydroxide solution. Prior to the equivalence point of the titration, there are, in principle, two sources of hydrogen ions. These are the hydrochloric acid itself and the ionization of water. In general, the hydrogen ion concentration furnished by the hydrochloric acid is the number of millimoles of acid *remaining untitrated* divided by the solution volume in milliliters. Now, when water ionizes, one hydrogen ion and one hydroxide ion are formed. Since the ionization of water is the *only* source of hydroxide ions, this hydroxide concentration is a direct measure of the hydrogen ion concentration from water ionization. Therefore, the total concentration of hydrogen ion is the sum of the contributions from hydrochloric acid and from water, i.e.,

$$[H^+] = [H^+]_{\text{from acid}} + [H^+]_{\text{from water}}$$

or

$$[H^+] = \frac{\text{millimoles of acid untitrated}}{\text{solution volume in milliliters}} + [OH^-]$$

or

$$[H^+] = \frac{\text{millimoles of acid untitrated}}{\text{solution volume in milliliters}} + \frac{K_w}{[H^+]}$$

Prior to the addition of any sodium hydroxide titrant, the hydrogen ion concentration contributed by hydrochloric acid is $0.1000\,M$. The contribution from water can be ascertained as follows: If we assume that the *total* hydrogen ion concentration is essentially 0.1000 M, the hydrogen ion contributed from water is exactly equal to the hydroxide ion concentration and is given by

$$[H^+]_{\text{from water}} = [OH^-] = \frac{K_w}{[H^+]} = \frac{1.00 \times 10^{-14}}{0.1000} = 1.00 \times 10^{-13} \, M$$

Quite obviously, the concentration of hydrogen ions from the ionization of water is very unimportant, so it will be temporarily unnecessary to calculate this effect explicitly. Therefore, at the start of the titration, before any sodium hydroxide titrant has been added, the hydrogen ion concentration is 0.1000 M and the pH is 1.00.

After the addition of 10.00 ml of 0.1000 F sodium hydroxide (1.000 millimole of base), 4.000 millimoles of acid remain untitrated in 60.00 ml of solution, so

$$[H^+] = \frac{4.000 \text{ millimoles}}{60.00 \text{ milliliters}} = 6.67 \times 10^{-2} \, M; \qquad \text{pH} = 1.18$$

The hydrogen ion concentration from water is approximately 1.50×10^{-13} M, and hence negligible.

After the addition of 20.00 ml of sodium hydroxide, 3.000 millimoles of acid remain untitrated in 70.00 ml of solution; thus

$$[H^+] = \frac{3.000 \text{ millimoles}}{70.00 \text{ milliliters}} = 4.29 \times 10^{-2} \, M; \qquad \text{pH} = 1.37$$

After the addition of 30.00 ml of sodium hydroxide,

$$[H^+] = \frac{2.000 \text{ millimoles}}{80.00 \text{ milliliters}} = 2.50 \times 10^{-2} \, M; \qquad \text{pH} = 1.60$$

After the addition of 40.00 ml of sodium hydroxide,

$$[H^+] = \frac{1.000 \text{ millimole}}{90.00 \text{ milliliters}} = 1.11 \times 10^{-2} \, M; \qquad \text{pH} = 1.95$$

After the addition of 49.00 ml of sodium hydroxide,

$$[H^+] = \frac{0.1000 \text{ millimole}}{99.00 \text{ milliliters}} = 1.01 \times 10^{-3} \, M; \qquad \text{pH} = 2.99$$

The hydrogen ion concentration from water is only $9.90 \times 10^{-12} \, M$. After the addition of 49.90 ml of sodium hydroxide,

$$[H^+] = \frac{0.01000 \text{ millimole}}{99.90 \text{ milliliters}} = 1.00 \times 10^{-4} \, M; \qquad \text{pH} = 4.00$$

After the addition of 49.99 ml of sodium hydroxide,

$$[H^+] = \frac{0.001000 \text{ millimole}}{99.99 \text{ milliliters}} = 1.00 \times 10^{-5} \, M; \qquad \text{pH} = 5.00$$

After the addition of 49.999 ml of sodium hydroxide,

$$[H^+] = \frac{0.0001000 \text{ millimole}}{99.999 \text{ milliliters}} = 1.00 \times 10^{-6} \ M; \qquad pH = 6.00$$

Notice that the hydrogen ion concentration from water is now 1.00×10^{-8} M. This is still negligible, but any calculations involving points on the titration curve closer to the equivalence point must take account of the ionization of water.

After the addition of 49.9999 ml of sodium hydroxide, 1.000×10^{-5} millimole of acid remains untitrated in essentially 100.0 ml of solution, so the concentration of hydrochloric acid is 1.000×10^{-7} M. The *total* hydrogen ion concentration is:

$$[H^+] = 1.000 \times 10^{-7} + \frac{K_w}{[H^+]}$$

$$[H^+] = 1.000 \times 10^{-7} + \frac{1.00 \times 10^{-14}}{[H^+]}$$

The solution of this equation, as obtained by means of the quadratic formula. is $[H^+] = 1.62 \times 10^{-7} \ M$; so pH $= 6.79$.

After the addition of 50.00 ml of sodium hydroxide, which corresponds to the *equivalence point* of the titration, the hydrogen ion concentration is $1.00 \times 10^{-7} \ M$, water now being the only source of hydrogen ions, and the pH $= 7.00$.

Beyond the equivalence point of the titration, we are simply adding excess sodium hydroxide to a solution of sodium chloride. The two sources of hydroxide ions are the added sodium hydroxide solution and the ionization of water. The *total* hydroxide ion concentration is given by any of the following equations:

$$[OH^-] = [OH^-]_{\text{from base}} + [OH^-]_{\text{from water}}$$

$$[OH^-] = \frac{\text{millimoles of excess base}}{\text{solution volume in milliliters}} + [H^+]$$

$$[OH^-] = \frac{\text{millimoles of excess base}}{\text{solution volume in milliliters}} + \frac{K_w}{[OH^-]}$$

For the remaining calculations of this example, we shall choose points on the titration curve for which the ionization of water is negligible.

After the addition of 51.00 ml of $0.1000 \ F$ sodium hydroxide, there is 0.1000 millimole excess base in a solution volume of 101.0 ml; thus

$$[OH^-] = \frac{0.1000 \text{ millimole}}{101.0 \text{ milliliters}} = 9.90 \times 10^{-4} \ M;$$

$$pOH = 3.04; \qquad pH = 10.96$$

The complete titration curve constructed on the basis of these calculations is shown in Figure 8-2.

Acid-Base Indicators for End Point Detection

The **equivalence point** of a titration is defined theoretically as that point at which the quantity of titrant added is stoichiometrically equivalent to the substance being determined. On the other hand, the **end point** is an experimental phenomenon, such as the color change of an indicator, which signals that the equivalence point has been reached. It is rare for the end point to coincide perfectly with the theoretical equivalence point, although to minimize the titration error the difference between these two points must be as small as possible.

The end point for an acid-base titration may be determined in at least two ways. First, the course of the titration can be followed with a glass electrode pH meter, and the complete titration curve can be recorded as in Figure 8-2. Then, by visual inspection or by various graphical procedures, the inflection point or point of maximal slope of the titration curve may be located and accepted as the end point.

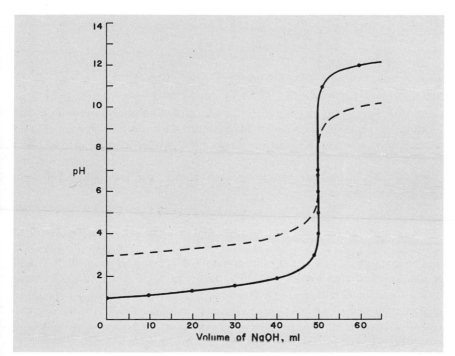

FIGURE 8-2. Titration curves for strong acid-strong base reactions. The solid line represents the titration of 50.00 ml of 0.1000 F hydrochloric acid with a 0.1000 F sodium hydroxide solution. The dashed line is the titration curve for the titration of 50.00 ml of 0.001000 F hydrochloric acid with 0.001000 F sodium hydroxide.

The second method of end point detection makes use of so-called acid-base indicators, which in reality are nothing more than organic dye molecules. An acid-base indicator derives the ability to act as a pH indicator from the fact that it exists in two forms; the acid form possesses one color which, by loss of a proton, is converted to a different colored base form. The pertinent chemical equilibrium is

$$In_A \rightleftharpoons H^+ + In_B$$
$$\text{(color A)} \qquad \text{(color B)}$$

where In_A is the acid form of the indicator with color A and In_B is the base form of the same indicator with a different color, B.

Indicator Constants.   The equilibrium expression for the acid-base indicator, as represented by the preceding reaction, is

$$K_{In} = \frac{[H^+][In_B]}{[In_A]}$$

where K_{In} is called the **indicator constant.** It is quite analogous to the ionization constant for a weak monoprotic acid.

This equation may be rearranged to give

$$\frac{[H^+]}{K_{In}} = \frac{[In_A]}{[In_B]}$$

The substance In_A is of color A and, ideally at least, the intensity of color A should be directly proportional to the concentration of In_A in solution (the relationship between the intensity of color and the concentration of a colored substance is discussed in detail in Chapter 15). Likewise, substance In_B is of color B and, ideally, the intensity of color B will be a direct measure of the concentration of In_B present in solution. Hence, the preceding expression may be rewritten as

$$\frac{[H^+]}{K_{In}} = \frac{\text{(intensity of color A)}}{\text{(intensity of color B)}}$$

To the average human eye, a solution containing two colored species, A and B, will appear to have color A if the intensity of color A is 10 times as great as that of color B. On the other hand, if the intensity of color B is 10 times greater than that of color A, the solution will be of color B. Substituting these two alternative conditions into the latter equation, we can draw the following conclusions:

If $[H^+] = 10\,K_{In}$ or more, the solution will have color A.

If $[H^+] = 0.1\,K_{In}$ or less, the solution will have color B.

These results may be conveniently expressed in terms of pK_{In} and pH as follows:

If $pH = pK_{In} - 1$, or less, the solution will have color A.

If $pH = pK_{In} + 1$, or more, the solution will have color B.

At intermediate ratios of color intensities, there is an intermediate and often indistinguishable color.

TABLE 8-1. SELECTED ACID-BASE INDICATORS

Indicator	Color Change		pH Transition Range	
	Acid Form	Base Form	Acid Form Pre-dominant at pH	Base Form Pre-dominant at pH
Picric acid	colorless	yellow	0.1	0.8
Paramethyl red	red	yellow	1.0	3.0
2,6-Dinitrophenol	colorless	yellow	2.0	4.0
Bromphenol blue	yellow	blue	3.0	4.6
Congo red	blue	red	3.0	5.0
Methyl orange	red	yellow	3.1	4.4
Ethyl orange	red	yellow	3.4	4.5
Alizarin red S	yellow	purple	3.7	5.0
Bromcresol green	yellow	blue	3.8	5.4
Methyl red	red	yellow	4.2	6.2
Propyl red	red	yellow	4.6	6.6
Methyl purple	purple	green	4.8	5.4
Chlorophenol red	yellow	red	4.8	6.4
Paranitrophenol	colorless	yellow	5.0	7.0
Bromcresol purple	yellow	purple	5.2	6.8
Bromthymol blue	yellow	blue	6.0	7.6
Brilliant yellow	yellow	orange	6.6	8.0
Neutral red	red	amber	6.7	8.0
Phenol red	yellow	red	6.7	8.4
Metanitrophenol	colorless	yellow	6.7	8.6
Phenolphthalein	colorless	pink	8.0	9.6
Thymolphthalein	colorless	blue	9.3	10.6
2,4,6-Trinitrotoluene	colorless	orange	12.0	14.0

The validity and usefulness of the previous discussion can now be demonstrated with respect to a specific acid-base indicator. A list of typical indicators is presented in Table 8-1, along with the colors of the acid and base forms of each indicator and the pH value at which one or the other form is sufficiently predominant to impart its color to the solution.

Methyl red is an excellent example of the behavior typical of an acid-base indicator. According to Table 8-1, the red-colored acid form predominates at pH 4.2 and below, whereas the yellow base form is predominant at and above pH 6.2. The structures of the two forms of methyl red, and the fundamental acid-base equilibrium, are given by:

H_3C

N——◯——$N=N$——◯——$COOH$ ⇌

H_3C

(red)

H_3C

N——◯——$N=N$——◯——$COO^- + H^+$

H_3C

(yellow)

The equilibrium expression may be written as

$$\frac{[H^+]}{K_{In}} = \frac{[In_A]}{[In_B]}$$

where $[In_A]$ is the concentration of the red acid form and $[In_B]$ is the concentration of the yellow base form. The value of K_{In} is 7.9×10^{-6} (corresponding to a pK_{In} of 5.1). The ratio $[In_A]/[In_B]$ at pH 4.2 and at pH 6.2 can be calculated as follows:

At pH 4.2, $[H^+] = 6.3 \times 10^{-5}\ M$ and

$$\frac{[In_A]}{[In_B]} = \frac{6.3 \times 10^{-5}}{7.9 \times 10^{-6}} = 8.0$$

At pH 6.2, $[H^+] = 6.3 \times 10^{-7}\ M$ and

$$\frac{[In_A]}{[In_B]} = \frac{6.3 \times 10^{-7}}{7.9 \times 10^{-6}} = 0.080 = \frac{1}{12.5}$$

Thus, in the case of methyl red, we see the red color of the indicator when there is 8.0 times more acid form than base form present. However, in order for us to see the indicator in its yellow form, there must be present 12.5 times more base form than acid form. In other words at pH 4.2 (and below) the human eye recognizes that methyl red is present as the red acid form and that it exists as the yellow base form if the pH becomes 6.2 (and above). This range of pH values over which the acid base indicator is seen to change color is usually called the **pH transition interval** or the **pH transition range.** It should be noted that the pH transition range for the indicators listed in Table 8-1 is often about two pH units, although it may be smaller than this for some indicators. The reason for this is that the human eye responds more readily to some colors than to others and because some indicators are naturally more intensely colored than others, even at identical concentrations.

Effect of Concentration of Indicator.   The majority of the indicators listed in Table 8-1 are two-color indicators because their acidic and basic forms are both colored. However, several of the acid-base indicators included in the list possess acid forms which are colorless; these are the so-called one-color indicators.

If the total concentration of a two-color indicator is increased, the individual concentrations of the acidic and basic forms will increase proportionally, and the pH transition range should remain unchanged, even though the color intensities are increased. Hence, for a two-color indicator such as methyl red, the human eye will always recognize that methyl red indicator has become yellow colored at pH 6.2, although the yellow may be more or less intense depending on the total concentration of the indicator.

The behavior of a one-color indicator is different and more complicated. Phenolphthalein is the most familiar example of such an indicator. It has a colorless, acidic form and a pink-colored basic form in equilibrium with each other as follows:

Phenolphthalein is widely employed as an end point indicator for the titration of strong acids with strong bases. Thus, the end point is signaled by the first permanent appearance of a faint pink color throughout the solution (assuming, quite realistically, that the solution is perfectly colorless prior to the end point). The intensity of the pink color which is discernible to the eye is very small and quite reproducible regardless of the total concentration of phenolphthalein present or the concentrations of the acids and bases involved in the titration. Let us call this "minimum detectable concentration" of the pink form $[In_B]$. The indicator-constant equilibrium expression may be written as

$$K_{In} = \frac{[H^+][In_B]}{[In_A]}$$

or as

$$[H^+] = \frac{K_{In}}{[In_B]} \cdot [In_A]$$

where K_{In} is the indicator constant and $[In_B]$ is the "minimum detectable concentration" of the pink form, which we may assume to be constant. We see from the last equation that the hydrogen ion concentration at which the pink end point color appears will depend on $[In_A]$, the concentration of phenolphthalein in its acidic form. If more indicator is present, the $[H^+]$ at the end point will be higher and the pH lower. Conversely, if less indicator is present, the end point pH will shift toward higher values.

There is one further point in regard to the concentration of the indicator. The change of an indicator from one form to another actually uses up or liberates some hydrogen ions. The quantity of hydrogen ions thus consumed or provided must be negligible in comparison to the amount of acid or base involved in the main titration reaction; otherwise, a significant error is introduced. Obviously, the magnitude of this "indicator error" increases as the concentration of indicator is increased. Therefore, the indicator concentration should not be any larger than required to render the end point color change visible. This "indicator error" is often of slight but measurable magnitude, and it is one reason why experimental end points and theoretical equivalence points may not coincide perfectly. A correction for the "indicator error" can be achieved by means of a **blank titration.** A solution of the same composition as the real sample, containing the indicator but not the acid or base being determined, is titrated to the same end point as in the real titration, and the small volume of titrant is subsequently subtracted from the total volume used in the real titration.

Mixed Indicators.   A mixed indicator, which generally consists of a conventional acid-base indicator with an added organic dye, is sometimes used to increase the sharpness of the visible end point. The added dye may be another indicator, but more commonly it is a substance not affected by pH. A properly selected substance of the latter type serves to block out or mask certain wavelengths of light common to both colors of the acid-base indicator; essentially, only the components of color A and of color B which differ from each other are observed by the analyst. For example, consider an indicator of which color A is blue-green and color B is yellow-green, with an added dye which absorbs green light. This mixed indicator would exhibit a color change from blue to yellow, which would be more distinct than the change from blue-green to yellow-green obtained without the added dye.

Mixed indicators may involve even more complex color relationships. Methyl orange and xylene cyanole FF comprise a common mixed indicator.

Methyl orange appears yellow in alkaline solution. Xylene cyanole absorbs yellow and orange light very strongly, so this mixed indicator appears green in alkaline solutions. In an acid medium, methyl orange absorbs light in the green region, xylene cyanole still absorbs in the yellow-orange region, and the color of the mixed indicator is blue-red. In the intermediate region, which is at approximately pH 4, the solution is nearly colorless because of the transmission of complementary colors.

Another mixed indicator, methyl purple, is of tremendous value. Methyl purple consists of methyl red (red below pH 4.2 and yellow above pH 6.2) mixed with an inert blue dyestuff. This mixed indicator not only has a very pronounced color change, but the color change occurs over a very narrow range of pH values. Methyl purple is purple below pH 4.8, green above pH 5.4, and passes through an intermediate light gray color between pH 4.8 and 5.4.

Selection of Indicators and Feasibility of Titrations

In attempting to make decisions concerning the proper selection of end point indicators, we should bear in mind several general principles. First, an end point is ordinarily signaled by an abrupt change in some property, such as color, of a solution. It is far simpler to titrate to the occurrence of a dramatic color change than to the appearance of some specific color or shade of color. Second, in order for the indicator color change to be very sharply defined, the pH versus volume curve for the proposed titration must exhibit a steeply rising portion in the vicinity of the equivalence point. Furthermore, this steep section of the titration curve must encompass an interval of pH values at least as large as the pH transition range of an indicator. Finally, the pH transition range of the proposed end point indicator must coincide with the steep portion of the titration curve.

The direction in which a titration is performed also influences the choice of an end point indicator. In the titration of a strong acid *with* a strong base, the indicator is initially present in its acidic form, so the end point is signaled by the sudden appearance of the color of the *basic* form of the indicator. Consider the reverse titration, that is, the titration of a strong base *with* a strong acid. Since the indicator starts out in its basic form, this time the end point will be identified when the *acidic* color of the indicator appears. For example, if methyl red indicator were employed in such a pair of titrations, the end point for the first titration would occur at pH 6.2, the point at which the yellow color of the basic form is recognized. However, the reverse titration would have an end point pH of 4.2, because this is the pH at which the red-colored acid form of methyl red is predominant. As we shall see below, certain substances serve very well as end point indicators for the titration of an acid with a base, but are most inadequate for the reverse titration of a base with an acid.

Let us decide which indicators listed in Table 8-1 would be suitable to detect the end point of the titration of 50.00 ml of 0.1000 F hydrochloric acid with 0.1000 F sodium hydroxide. Suppose that we desire to perform this titration so that the titration error does not exceed ± 0.1 per cent. Accordingly, the maximum permissible range of volumes of sodium hydroxide is from 49.95 to 50.05 ml. After the addition of 49.95 ml of base, the number of millimoles of hydrochloric acid untitrated would be 5.00×10^{-3}. In a volume of solution which is very close to 100 ml, the hydrogen ion concentration would be $5.00 \times 10^{-5} M$ and the pH would be 4.30. The addition of 50.05 ml of 0.1000 F sodium hydroxide provides an excess of 5.00×10^{-3} millimole of hydroxide ion in a volume of 100 ml. This corresponds to $[OH^-] = 5.00 \times 10^{-5} M$, pOH = 4.30, and pH = 9.70. On the basis of these simple calculations, one can safely select for the proposed titration any acid-base indicator in Table 8-1 whose pH transition interval has an *upper* extreme within the pH range 4.3 to 9.7. As expected from the nature of our calculations, the steep portion of the titration curve shown in Figure 8-2 coincides with this pH range. A total of 18 indicators listed in Table 8-1, beginning with bromphenol blue and ending with phenolphthalein, would guarantee the desired titration accuracy. However, it should be emphasized that four of these indicators, bromphenol blue, congo red, methyl orange, and ethyl orange, would have a tendency to exhibit a gradual color change because their pH transition ranges begin near pH 3.0, which is somewhat ahead of the steepest portion of the titration curve shown in Figure 8-2. In addition, indicators such as phenolphthalein which give end points on the basic side of the neutral point are less preferred for this titration because traces of carbon dioxide dissolved in the hydrochloric acid sample would be partially titrated to the bicarbonate ion.

Let us now consider briefly the reverse titration, namely, the titration of 50.00 ml of 0.1000 F sodium hydroxide with 0.1000 F hydrochloric acid. Calculations similar to those done in the perceding paragraph indicate that, in order not to incur a titration error larger than ± 0.1 per cent, an end point indicator must be used which changes to its *acidic* color between pH 9.7 and pH 4.3. These are the same pH values obtained above. According to the data in Table 8-1, there are 13 indicators whose acidic form becomes predominant between these pH values. Of these 13, thymolphthalein could pose a problem because its acidic form is colorless, so the end point color change consists of a gradual fading of the blue color of the basic form. This behavior might cause the acceptance of a premature end point. Two indicators not included in the select list of 13 are bromcresol green and methyl orange. Both of these indicators are widely used for the proposed titration, but their use requires that "indicator error" corrections be made. However, these corrections are not excessively large, and generally satisfactory results are obtained with both of these indicators.

Figure 8-2 also presents a titration curve for the titration of 50.00 ml of 0.001000 F hydrochloric acid with a 0.001000 F sodium hydroxide solution.

Although the change in pH in the region of the equivalence point is considerably smaller than for reagents which are one-hundred-fold more concentrated, the titration curve is well defined nevertheless, so it should be possible to perform such a titration with high accuracy. We shall assume again that it is desirable to restrict the magnitude of the titration error to ± 0.1 per cent. As before, this limit of error will define a pH range within which an acid-base indicator must change color abruptly to be useful for end point detection. Therefore, we have to calculate the pH of the solution after the additions, respectively, of 49.95 and 50.05 ml of the titrant base.

After the addition of 49.95 ml of 0.001000 F sodium hydroxide, 5.00×10^{-5} millimole of hydrochloric acid remains untitrated in a solution volume of essentially 100 ml. This corresponds to a hydrochloric acid concentration of 5.00×10^{-7} M, so the contribution to the total hydrogen ion concentration by the ionization of water is significant. Accordingly, we shall fall back to the exact expression used in the construction of the titration curve for 0.1000 F reagents. Thus,

$$[H^+] = 5.00 \times 10^{-7} + \frac{K_w}{[H^+]}$$

$$[H^+] = 5.00 \times 10^{-7} + \frac{1.00 \times 10^{-14}}{[H^+]}$$

Solving this equation by the quadratic formula or by the method of successive approximations yields $[H^+] = 5.19 \times 10^{-7}$ M and pH = 6.29.

After the addition of 50.05 ml of sodium hydroxide titrant, an excess of 5.00×10^{-5} millimole of hydroxide ion is present in 100 ml of solution. This hydroxide ion and that which comes from the ionization of water are the two sources of hydroxide ion in the system. The total concentration of hydroxide ions is given by the relations

$$[OH^-] = 5.00 \times 10^{-7} + \frac{K_w}{[OH^-]}$$

and

$$[OH^-] = 5.00 \times 10^{-7} + \frac{1.00 \times 10^{-14}}{[OH^-]}$$

and the solution of this equation is $[OH^-] = 5.19 \times 10^{-7}$ M. Therefore, the pOH and pH are, respectively, 6.29 and 7.71.

The results of these two calculations show that a suitable end point indicator must change color within the rather narrow range between pH 6.29 and 7.71. Since we are titrating an acid with a base, indicators must be chosen from Table 8-1 which have pH transition intervals with *upper* limits between pH 6.29 and 7.71. Preferable indicators are propyl red, paranitrophenol, bromcresol purple, and bromthymol blue. Several other indicators, including methyl red, chlorophenol red, brilliant yellow, and neutral red, would probably be acceptable if indicator blank titrations were made to correct for small "indicator errors."

The performance of the reverse titration of 50.00 ml of 0.001000 F sodium hydroxide with 0.001000 F hydrochloric acid would require an end point indicator which changes abruptly to its *acidic* form between pH 6.29 and 7.71. Brilliant yellow, neutral red, phenol red, and metanitrophenol would be appropriate indicators, and very likely bromthymol blue could be pressed into service. The interesting and significant conclusion is that certain indicators serve well for the forward titration, but poorly or not at all for the reverse titration.

We should not leave this discussion without making a vital final point. The difficulty in finding suitable indicators for the acid-base titration involving 0.001 F reactants does not stem from the fundamental inaccuracy of the titration. Rather it is caused by the fact that the pH transition range for most indicators is approximately two pH units and that, as a consequence, a large change in hydrogen ion concentration must occur in order for an indicator to change color.

The titrations of 0.001 M acids and bases can be quite successfully accomplished by means of electrometric and electroanalytical procedures, such as those discussed in Chapters 17 and 18. If precautions are taken to exclude carbon dioxide from the solutions, it is possible to titrate with electrogenerated hydroxide ions, the titration error being well below 1 per cent.

TITRATIONS OF WEAK ACIDS WITH STRONG BASES

The titration of a weak acid with a strong base presents some additional complications over the analogous titration of a strong acid. In this section of the chapter, we shall direct our attention to the construction of the titration curve for a weak acid-strong base reaction and to the problems of end point detection and titration errors caused by inappropriate selection and use of indicators.

Construction of Titration Curve for Titration of Acetic Acid with Sodium Hydroxide

We shall consider as a typical example of a weak acid-strong base titration the reaction of acetic acid with sodium hydroxide. Accordingly, the sample solution will consist initially of dilute acetic acid, so that the pH of the solution may be calculated by means of the procedure developed for the analogous problem earlier in this chapter (Example 3). The addition of sodium hydroxide neutralizes some of the acetic acid; therefore, at points on the titration curve prior to the equivalence point, the solution contains acetic acid and sodium acetate in varying amounts and the pH is essentially that of an acetic acid-sodium acetate buffer (Example 6). At the equivalence point, the solution consists only of sodium acetate, the salt of a weak acid;

and the resulting pH is calculated as for Example 10. Beyond the equivalence point, the solution contains sodium acetate and excess sodium hydroxide. Because hydroxide ion is a much stronger base than is acetate anion, the assumption may be made that the effect of acetate ion on the pH is negligible and the pH of such a solution may be evaluated as was done in Example 2.

We will now proceed to construct the theoretical titration curve for the titration of 25.00 ml of 0.1000 F acetic acid with 0.1000 F sodium hydroxide titrant.

The *initial* pH of a 0.1000 F acetic acid solution was determined in Example 3 to be 2.88.

The addition of sodium hydroxide solution neutralizes acetic acid, producing acetate ions according to the following overall titration reaction:

$$CH_3COOH + OH^- \rightleftharpoons CH_3COO^- + H_2O$$

The equilibrium constant for this titration reaction is the reciprocal of the equilibrium constant calculated in Example 10 earlier in this chapter and is 1.75×10^9. Thus, this titration reaction has a large driving force and proceeds far to the right, although less so than a strong acid-strong base reaction with an equilibrium constant of 1.00×10^{14} (the reciprocal of the ion-product constant for water). Each volume increment of sodium hydroxide solution added will react virtually completely to consume and to produce, respectively, stoichiometrically equivalent amounts of acetic acid and acetate. The concentration of hydrogen ions is determined by the ratio of the acetic acid and acetate ion concentrations from the expression

$$[H^+] = K_a \frac{[CH_3COOH]}{[CH_3COO^-]}$$

as shown in Example 6. Notice that, since we have the *ratio* of two concentrations in this last equation, it suffices to substitute just the numbers of millimoles of acetic acid and acetate ion present.

After the addition of 5.00 ml of a 0.1000 F sodium hydroxide solution, 2.000 millimoles of acetic acid remain untitrated and 0.500 millimole of acetate ion is formed. Hence,

$$[H^+] = K_a \frac{[CH_3COOH]}{[CH_3COO^-]} = 1.75 \times 10^{-5} \frac{(2.000)}{(0.500)} = 7.00 \times 10^{-5} M;$$

$$pH = 4.15$$

After the addition of 10.00 ml of sodium hydroxide, 1.500 millimoles of acetic acid and 1.000 millimole of acetate ion is present:

$$[H^+] = 1.75 \times 10^{-5} \frac{(1.500)}{(1.000)} = 2.63 \times 10^{-5} M; \qquad pH = 4.58$$

After the addition of 15.00 ml of sodium hydroxide, pH = 4.93; after the addition of 20.00 ml of sodium hydroxide, pH = 5.36; after the addition

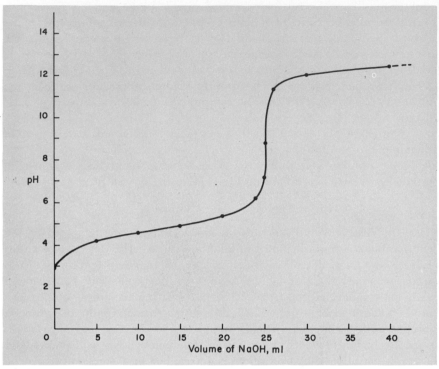

FIGURE 8-3.   Titration curve for the titration of 25.00 ml of 0.1000 F acetic acid with a 0.1000 F sodium hydroxide solution.

of 24.00 ml of sodium hydroxide, pH $= 6.14$; after the addition of 24.90 ml of sodium hydroxide, pH $= 7.15$.

These calculations of the pH prior to the equivalence point are somewhat approximate in nature. We have assumed that the ionization of water may be neglected because the concentrations of the reactants are relatively large. Also, we have avoided any calculations involving points on the titration curve exceedingly close to the equivalence point, where the concentration of acetic acid becomes so small that we would have to take account of the decrease in $[CH_3COOH]$ and the increase in $[CH_3COO^-]$ due to the ionization of acetic acid.

The pH of the solution at the equivalence point may be calculated as in Example 10. After the addition of 25.00 ml of sodium hydroxide, the solution is identical to one which could be prepared by dissolving 0.002500 mole of sodium acetate in 50.00 ml of water. The pH of a 0.05000 F sodium acetate solution is 8.73.

After the addition of 26.00 ml of 0.1000 F sodium hydroxide, there is an excess of 0.1000 millimole of strong base in a total volume of 51.00 ml. Therefore, $[OH^-] = 1.96 \times 10^{-3} M$, pOH $= 2.71$, and pH $= 11.29$.

After the addition of 30.00 ml of sodium hydroxide, the following conditions prevail: $[OH^-] = 9.09 \times 10^{-3} M$, pOH = 2.04, and pH = 11.96.

Finally, after the addition of 40.00 ml of sodium hydroxide, we find that $[OH^-] = 2.31 \times 10^{-2} M$, pOH = 1.64, and pH = 12.36.

The titration curve is plotted in Figure 8-3. This titration curve has two characteristics which distinguish it from the strong acid-strong base titration curve of Figure 8-2. Prior to the equivalence point, the titration curve for a weak acid is displaced toward higher pH values (lower hydrogen ion concentrations) because only a small fraction of the weak acid ionizes to furnish hydrogen ions. In addition, the pH at the equivalence point is on the basic side of pH 7.

Selection of Indicators

A simple visual inspection of the titration curve shown in Figure 8-3 reveals that the steep portion of the curve covers a much smaller pH range than the analogous titration curve of Figure 8-2. It is of interest to consider which indicators listed in Table 8-1 could be employed with assurance that their use would not cause a titration error greater than one part per thousand (± 0.1 per cent). Hence, we shall be interested once again in calculating the pH of the solution 0.1 per cent before and after the theoretical equivalence point.

One-tenth per cent *before* the equivalence point, 99.9 per cent of the original acetic acid has been converted to acetate ion, and 0.1 per cent remains as acetic acid molecules. Thus, the ratio of acetic acid to acetate ion is 1/999, or approximately 1/1000. Recalling that the hydrogen ion concentration prior to the equivalence point is given by

$$[H^+] = K_a \frac{[CH_3COOH]}{[CH_3COO^-]}$$

we can write

$$[H^+] = K_a \frac{1}{1000} = 1.75 \times 10^{-5} \cdot \frac{1}{1000} = 1.75 \times 10^{-8} M; \qquad pH = 7.76$$

One-tenth per cent *after* the equivalence point, there is an excess of 0.025 ml of 0.1000 F sodium hydroxide in a solution whose volume is essentially 50.00 ml. We can neglect the influence of sodium acetate on the pH. The hydroxide concentration is 0.00250 millimole per 50.00 ml or $5.00 \times 10^{-5} M$, which corresponds to a pOH of 4.30 or a pH of 9.70. Notice that this pH is the same value calculated earlier for the strong acid-strong base titration because, beyond the equivalence point of a weak acid-strong base titration, the two systems behave identically.

A suitable acid-base indicator must change abruptly from its acidic color to its basic color within the pH range from 7.76 to 9.70, according to our calculations. Among the indicators listed in Table 8-1, the best choices appear to be brilliant yellow, neutral red, phenol red, metanitrophenol, and phenolphthalein. Phenolphthalein is the almost universal choice for this titration, because the other four indicators have a tendency to undergo gradual color changes slightly ahead of the true equivalence point.

We may employ equilibrium calculations to evaluate the magnitude of the titration error which occurs from the use of an improper indicator. For example, suppose that chlorophenol red indicator were employed to detect the end point of an acetic acid-sodium hydroxide titration. We see from Table 8-1 that chlorophenol red changes from *yellow* to *red* at pH 6.4. Our question must be: What titration error results if we accept the end point as being at pH 6.4? First of all, it is clear that the experimental end point is well ahead of the theoretical equivalence point, so some acetic acid will definitely remain untitrated. Given the pH of any solution containing acidic or basic species, one should always seek to determine the relative concentrations of these species. Therefore, let us calculate the ratio of the acetate ion to acetic acid concentration from the following relationship:

$$\frac{[CH_3COO^-]}{[CH_3COOH]} = \frac{K_a}{[H^+]}$$

A pH of 6.4 corresponds to $[H^+] = 3.98 \times 10^{-7} \, M$, and we already know that the ionization constant K_a for acetic acid is 1.75×10^{-5}. Hence,

$$\frac{[CH_3COO^-]}{[CH_3COOH]} = \frac{1.75 \times 10^{-5}}{3.98 \times 10^{-7}} = 44.0$$

Thus, the acetate ion concentration is 44 times larger than the acetic acid concentration. In other words, $\frac{44}{45}$ of the acetic acid has been titrated, but $\frac{1}{45}$ of it remains untitrated, so the titration error is given by:

$$\text{Titration error} = -\tfrac{1}{45} \times 100\% = -2.2\%$$

Actually, when we say that $\frac{1}{45}$ of the acetic acid remains untitrated, we are implying that *all* of the acetic acid is titrated if the pH of the solution has its theoretical equivalence point value. However, no reaction can ever be 100 per cent complete, so it is useful to determine how much acetic acid remains *untitrated* at the equivalence point. To do this, we can calculate the ratio of the acetate ion concentration to the acetic acid concentration at pH 8.73 (the equivalence point pH). Accordingly, since $[H^+] = 1.87 \times 10^{-9} \, M$, we have

$$\frac{[CH_3COO^-]}{[CH_3COOH]} = \frac{1.75 \times 10^{-5}}{1.87 \times 10^{-9}} = 9360$$

This latter calculation shows that only $\frac{1}{9361}$ of the original acetic acid remains untitrated at the equivalence point. The assumption that essentially all of the acetic acid is titrated at pH 8.73 is an exceedingly good one.

Another improper choice of indicator would be thymolphthalein, which changes color (colorless to blue) at pH 10.6. This value is considerably past the equivalence point pH of 8.73. The titration error in this case is measured directly by the volume of sodium hydroxide titrant required to increase the pH from 8.73 at the equivalence point to 10.6 at the observed end point. Let us calculate the hydroxide ion concentration at pH 10.6. The pOH is 3.4 and $[OH^-] = 3.98 \times 10^{-4} M$. On the other hand, the hydroxide ion concentration corresponding to pH 8.73 is $5.35 \times 10^{-6} M$ and is negligibly small compared to $3.98 \times 10^{-4} M$. The next question to be answered is: What volume of $0.1000 F$ sodium hydroxide titrant must be added to 50.00 ml of solution (the equivalence point volume) to make $[OH^-] = 3.98 \times 10^{-4} M$?

(a) Let v be the volume of sodium hydroxide to be added in milliliters.
(b) Number of millimoles of sodium hydroxide added $= (0.1000)(v)$
(c) Total solution volume in milliliters $= 50.00 + v$

(d) Concentration of hydroxide ion $= 3.98 \times 10^{-4} = \dfrac{(0.1000)(v)}{50.00 + v}$

(e) Volume of sodium hydroxide $= 0.20$ ml

This result reveals that an excess of 0.20 ml of titrant, or a total of 25.20 ml, would be required to reach the thymolphthalein end point. Since the theoretical volume of titrant needed for the titration of acetic acid is 25.00 ml, the titration error is given as follows:

$$\text{Titration error} = \frac{0.20}{25.00} \times 100\% = +0.8\%$$

Feasibility of Titrations

Figure 8-4 shows the effect of varying the acid ionization constant of the weak acid being titrated. As the ionization constant decreases, the size and sharpness of the pH break in the vicinity of the equivalence point diminish greatly. The fact that most acid-base indicators change color over a two-pH-unit interval generally limits the weakest acid which can be successfully titrated to one whose K_a is about 10^{-6} or 10^{-7}. Naturally, the concentrations of the weak acid and the titrant base also influence the sharpness of the pH break.

The accuracy of titrations of weak acids can be much improved if the following procedure is utilized: Suppose, for example, that it is desired to titrate carbonic acid (H_2CO_3) to bicarbonate ion with a standard sodium hydroxide solution, according to the reaction

$$H_2CO_3 + OH^- \rightleftharpoons HCO_3^- + H_2O$$

Carbonic acid is a very weak acid with a dissociation constant $(K_1)^*$ of

---

* Additional information concerning the acid strength and behavior of carbonic acid is given on page 302.

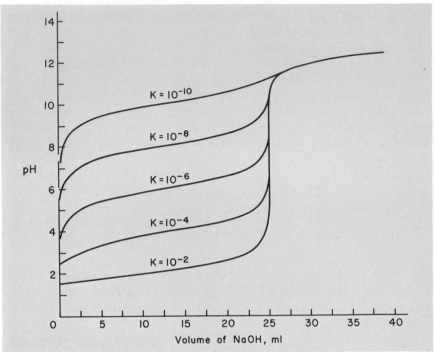

FIGURE 8-4. Family of titration curves for weak acid-strong base titrations, showing the effect of the value of the weak acid ionization constant on the shape and position of the curve. For each titration curve, 25.00 ml of 0.1000 F weak acid is titrated with 0.1000 F sodium hydroxide.

4.47×10^{-7}. At the end point of the titration, the solution is indistinguishable from one prepared by dissolving sodium bicarbonate in water. Phenolphthalein is the usual choice for end point indicator. The very first titration provides a reasonably accurate value for the concentration of carbonic acid present, and from this titration it is possible to calculate the concentration of sodium bicarbonate present at the end point. Now, in a separate titration flask, we reproduce artificially, but as accurately as possible, the conditions at the true end point by adding the proper amounts of water, sodium bicarbonate, and phenolphthalein indicator. What we have, then, is a comparison solution in which the end point pH is correct and in which a definite concentration of phenolphthalein is present in its pink base-form. Therefore, in subsequent titrations of the unknown carbonic acid solution with sodium hydroxide, the titrant is carefully added until the intensities of the end point colors in the real and comparison titration flasks are matched as closely as possible. This expedient can give analytical results accurate to within two or three parts per thousand.

TITRATIONS OF WEAK BASES WITH STRONG ACIDS

The titration of a weak base with a strong acid differs little, if at all, from a weak acid-strong base titration except that the roles of the acid and base are reversed. The analysis of ammonia solutions by titration with standard hydrochloric acid is a classic example of a weak base-strong acid reaction. The titration curve for the titration of 25.00 ml of 0.1000 F ammonia with 0.1000 F hydrochloric acid is depicted in Figure 8-5. Detailed calculations and a discussion of end point indicators and titration errors will be reserved for a problem at the end of this chapter.

SIMULTANEOUS OR SUCCESSIVE TITRATION OF TWO ACIDS OR BASES

It is not unusual in practical situations for two or more acidic or basic species to be present in the same solution. Of particular interest from the

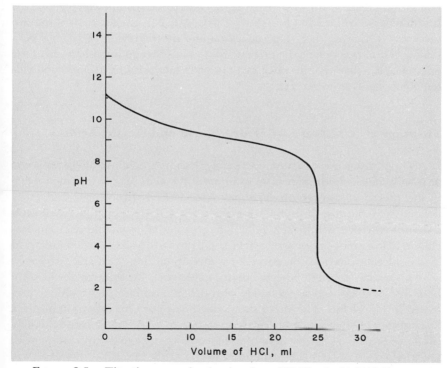

FIGURE 8-5. Titration curve for the titration of 25.00 ml of 0.1000 F ammonia with 0.1000 F hydrochloric acid.

point of view of being able to determine the individual components in a mixture of acids is the difference in the apparent acid strengths of these constituents. Consider a mixture of two acids which is to be titrated with a strong base. If both acids are strong, such as a mixture of hydrochloric acid and perchloric acid, the titration curve would have a shape similar to that in Figure 8-2. Therefore, it is impossible to distinguish between these two strong acids in aqueous media because both acids are completely ionized and act identically as sources of hydrogen ions. We shall see in the next chapter how a change from water to a nonaqueous solvent does allow perchloric and hydrochloric acids to be nicely separated in terms of their acid strengths. A second possibility is that we have a mixture of two weak acids with identical ionization constants. Here, too, the two weak acids would behave quite similarly as hydrogen ion sources. The resulting titration curve would possess the general characteristics of the curve shown in Figure 8-3, with an equivalence point pH above 7, and it would not be possible to analyze the mixture for its individual components.

If, however, the mixture contains one strong acid and one weak acid, or two weak acids of unequal strengths, the stronger of the two acidic species will tend to be titrated first. The extent to which the reaction of the stronger acid is completed before the second one begins to react is determined by the relative strengths of the two acids. If this difference is sufficiently great, the titration curve will exhibit two distinct pH "breaks," one for each of the two successive titrations. We shall now examine the behavior of systems containing more than one acidic or basic species in order to learn how great the difference in acid strengths must be to provide successful titrations of individual components in mixtures.

Titration of a Mixture of Hydrochloric and Acetic Acids

The titration of a solution containing both hydrochloric acid and acetic acid with sodium hydroxide is an example of the kind of situation mentioned in the preceding paragraph. We may expect the hydrochloric acid to be titrated first because it is the stronger acid, followed by the reaction of sodium hydroxide with acetic acid. The question of how completely hydrochloric acid reacts before acetic acid begins to be titrated can be answered by considering the titration curve for a mixture of these two acids.

A titration curve for the titration of 50.00 ml of a solution $0.1000\,F$ in both hydrochloric and acetic acids with $0.2000\,F$ sodium hydroxide is presented in Figure 8-6. The curve shows one break with an inflection at pH 3 and a second, better defined break with a point of inflection at approximately pH 9. The first part of the curve represents the titration of hydrochloric acid, and the second part is the reaction of acetic acid. The titration curve was constructed by considering the presence of only hydrochloric acid during the first part of the titration. This approximation is valid because hydrochloric acid effectively represses the ionization of acetic acid up to within a few per cent of the first equivalence point. The pH at the first equivalence point may be calculated from the equilibrium-constant expression for acetic acid, for at this stage of the titration the solution consists, by definition, of acetic acid only. Beyond the first equivalence point, the titration curve is simply that of a weak acid-strong base reaction and is analogous to Figure 8-3.

The poor quality of the pH "break" at the first equivalence point is rather alarming in terms of being able to determine successfully and accurately the individual concentrations of the two components. The poorly defined first equivalence point stems from the fact that acetic acid has already begun to react slightly before the equivalence point. The combination of 0.1 F hydrochloric acid and 0.1 F weak acid of $K_a = 10^{-5}$ represents a rough limit for a strong acid-weak acid mixture that can be successfully analyzed. The titration curve for a mixture of 1.0 F strong acid and 1.0 F weak acid with a K_a of 10^{-4} would be qualitatively similar to Figure 8-6, as would that for a solution containing 0.01 F strong acid and 0.01 F weak acid of $K_a = 10^{-6}$.

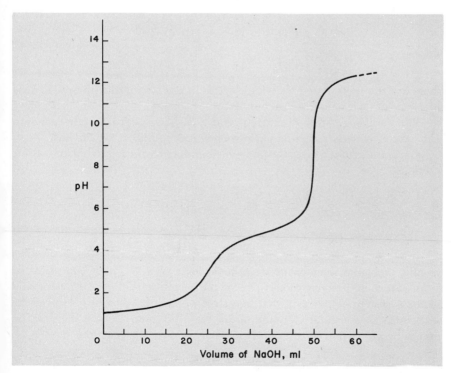

FIGURE 8-6.   Titration curve for the titration of 50.00 ml of a mixture of 0.1000 F hydrochloric acid and 0.1000 F acetic acid with 0.2000 F sodium hydroxide. The first step of the titration curve corresponds to the neutralization of the hydrochloric acid and the second step to the neutralization of acetic acid.

To return to the titration curve of Figure 8-6, the location of the first equivalence point could be best accomplished from a complete plot of the curve as obtained with a glass electrode pH meter. Alternatively, an acid-base indicator which changes to its basic color at pH 3 might be employed. In this case, it would be advisable to prepare a color comparison solution containing the appropriate concentrations of acetic acid and indicator in order to approximate the equivalence point conditions as closely as possible. The location of the second equivalence point could be done with the aid of phenolphthalein in the usual manner.

Titration of a Sodium Carbonate Solution with Hydrochloric Acid

Another common example of the successive titration of two components is that of a sodium carbonate solution with standard hydrochloric acid. In this case, however, the second component to be titrated, HCO_3^-, is the *product* of the reaction between the first component, $CO_3^=$, and hydrochloric acid. The two successive acid-base reactions are represented by the equilibria

$$CO_3^= + H^+ \rightleftharpoons HCO_3^-$$

and

$$HCO_3^- + H^+ \rightleftharpoons H_2CO_3$$

These are the same reactions which occur in the standardization of hydrochloric acid against sodium carbonate.

We shall begin this discussion of the carbonate-bicarbonate-carbonic acid system by examining the various chemical equilibria which exist.

Carbonic acid is a diprotic acid which undergoes the following ionization reactions:

$$H_2CO_3 \rightleftharpoons H^+ + HCO_3^-; \qquad K_1 = \frac{[H^+][HCO_3^-]}{[H_2CO_3]} = 1.72 \times 10^{-4}$$

$$HCO_3^- \rightleftharpoons H^+ + CO_3^=; \qquad K_2 = \frac{[H^+][CO_3^=]}{[HCO_3^-]} = 4.68 \times 10^{-11}$$

Usually, the value given in most textbooks for K_1 is 4.47×10^{-7}, but the use of this latter constant overlooks one of the most interesting features of this chemical system — the fact that most of the carbon dioxide dissolved in water exists as molecular CO_2 and not H_2CO_3. We can represent the equilibrium between carbon dioxide and carbonic acid by the reaction

$$CO_2(aq) + H_2O \rightleftharpoons H_2CO_3; \qquad K_3 = \frac{[H_2CO_3]}{[CO_2(aq)]} = 2.6 \times 10^{-3}$$

Thus, only about 0.26 per cent of the *total* amount of dissolved carbon dioxide really exists as H_2CO_3. As a result, the often quoted value for K_1 of

4.47×10^{-7} actually corresponds to the equilibrium expression:

$$\frac{[H^+][HCO_3^-]}{([CO_2(aq)] + [H_2CO_3])} = 4.47 \times 10^{-7}$$

Still another consequence of the very small concentration of H_2CO_3 present in carbonic acid solutions is that H_2CO_3 is approximately a five-hundred-fold stronger acid than usually assumed. With a K_1 of 1.72×10^{-4}, carbonic acid is almost exactly as strong as formic acid $(K_a = 1.76 \times 10^{-4})$.

For equilibrium calculations and the construction of titration curves, it is immaterial which value of K_1 is used, *provided we are careful to specify whether H_2CO_3 or the sum of $CO_2(aq)$ and H_2CO_3 is being considered.* For practical purposes, however, it is simpler to work with the total analytical concentration of carbon dioxide, i.e., $[CO_2(aq)] + [H_2CO_3]$, and to use the K_1 of 4.47×10^{-7}. Furthermore, for simplicity of writing in all subsequent equilibrium calculations, *we will use the designation $[H_2CO_3]$ to represent the total analytical concentration of carbon dioxide.*

There is a very important difference between the chemistry of CO_2 and H_2CO_3. This difference lies in the reactivities of CO_2 and H_2CO_3 toward water. The reaction between H_2CO_3 and water is virtually instantaneous, whereas the reaction between CO_2 and water is relatively slow. Sometimes a fleeting end point is observed in the titration of carbonate to bicarbonate with a strong acid. The reason for this is that local excesses of the acid convert carbonate ion all the way to carbonic acid, some of which goes to carbon dioxide, and that the carbon dioxide is not immediately transformed back to bicarbonate ion.

Construction of Titration Curve. We shall return to our original problem, that of the titration of a sodium carbonate solution with standard hydrochloric acid. As a particular example, let us construct the titration curve for the titration of 50.00 ml of a 0.05000 F sodium carbonate solution with 0.1000 F hydrochloric acid.

The calculation of the pH of a 0.05000 F sodium carbonate solution, before any hydrochloric acid has been added, can be approached exactly as the previous similar calculation (Example 10) for a sodium acetate solution. The principal equilibrium in the present case is

$$CO_3^= + H_2O \rightleftharpoons HCO_3^- + OH^-$$

and the equilibrium expression is

$$\frac{[HCO_3^-][OH^-]}{[CO_3^=]} = K_{eq} = \frac{K_w}{K_2}$$

To a good approximation,

$$[HCO_3^-] = [OH^-] \quad \text{and} \quad [CO_3^=] = 0.0500 - [OH^-]$$

Hence, the equilibrium equation to be solved is

$$\frac{[OH^-]^2}{0.0500 - [OH^-]} = \frac{K_w}{K_2} = \frac{1.00 \times 10^{-14}}{4.68 \times 10^{-11}} = 2.14 \times 10^{-4}$$

When solved by means of the quadratic formula, the equation yields $[OH^-] = 3.16 \times 10^{-3}\,M$, pOH $= 2.50$, and pH $= 11.50$.

During the first stage of the titration, the conversion of carbonate to bicarbonate, the pH of the solution can be most easily obtained through the buffer equation

$$[H^+] = K_2 \frac{[HCO_3^-]}{[CO_3^=]} = 4.68 \times 10^{-11} \frac{[HCO_3^-]}{[CO_3^=]}$$

which is identical in form to our previously considered weak acid-strong base titration.

After the addition of 5.00 ml of 0.1000 F hydrochloric acid, 2.000 millimoles of carbonate remain untitrated and 0.500 millimole of bicarbonate is present. Since we are dealing with the *ratio* of two concentrations, it is not necessary to convert the number of millimoles of a species into a molar concentration. Therefore,

$$[H^+] = 4.68 \times 10^{-11} \frac{[HCO_3^-]}{[CO_3^=]} = 4.68 \times 10^{-11} \frac{(0.500)}{(2.000)} = 1.17 \times 10^{-11}\,M;$$

$$pH = 10.93$$

After the addition of 10.00 ml of hydrochloric acid, 1.500 millimoles of $CO_3^=$ and 1.000 millimole of HCO_3^- are present:

$$[H^+] = 4.68 \times 10^{-11} \frac{(1.000)}{(1.500)} = 3.12 \times 10^{-11}\,M; \qquad pH = 10.51$$

After the addition of 15.00 ml of hydrochloric acid, pH $= 10.15$; after the addition of 20.00 ml of hydrochloric acid, pH $= 9.73$; after the addition of 22.50 ml of hydrochloric acid, pH $= 9.38$.

The calculation of the pH at the first equivalence point (the "bicarbonate point") is a type of problem we have not previously considered. At the first equivalence point, the solution consists only of sodium bicarbonate. However, the bicarbonate anion is both an acid and a base. It can undergo an acid ionization,

$$HCO_3^- \rightleftharpoons H^+ + CO_3^=$$

and it may accept a proton to form a carbonic acid molecule,

$$HCO_3^- + H^+ \rightleftharpoons H_2CO_3$$

A species such as bicarbonate, which is capable of either accepting or donating a proton, is said to be **amphiprotic.** In addition, a second source of hydrogen ions is the ionization of water:

$$H_2O \rightleftharpoons H^+ + OH^-$$

The total hydrogen ion concentration is that *produced* by the ionizations of bicarbonate and water minus that *consumed* in the formation of carbonic acid, and hence we may write

$$[H^+] = [CO_3^=] + [OH^-] - [H_2CO_3]$$

The preceding equation can be rewritten in terms of the hydrogen ion concentration, the bicarbonate concentration, and the various equilibrium constants as follows:

$$[H^+] - \frac{K_2[HCO_3^-]}{[H^+]} + \frac{K_w}{[H^+]} - \frac{[H^+][HCO_3^-]}{K_1}$$

Rewriting,

$$[H^+]^2 = K_2[HCO_3^-] + K_w - \frac{[H^+]^2[HCO_3^-]}{K_1}$$

collecting terms,

$$[H^+]^2 \left\{ 1 + \frac{[HCO_3^-]}{K_1} \right\} = K_2[HCO_3^-] + K_w$$

and solving for the hydrogen ion concentration, we obtain

$$[H^+] = \sqrt{\frac{K_2[HCO_3^-] + K_w}{1 + \frac{[HCO_3^-]}{K_1}}}$$

If we consider the titration of ordinary concentrations of carbonate, e.g., 0.05000 M, the latter equation may be simplified enormously. Almost invariably, $[HCO_3^-]$ is greater than K_1 in the denominator, so the "1" is negligible in comparison to $[HCO_3^-]/K_1$. The numerator of the square root term can also be simplified. Let us briefly compare the magnitudes of the two terms $K_2[HCO_3^-]$ and K_w. If $[HCO_3^-] = 1.0\ M$, then $K_2[HCO_3^-]$ is 4680 times greater than K_w. However, if $[HCO_3^-]$ is only 0.010 M, $K_2[HCO_3^-]$ is still 46.8 times greater than K_w. For $[HCO_3^-] = 0.010\ M$, we can neglect the K_w term in the numerator and incur an error of just 1 per cent, which is perfectly acceptable (especially when we intend to convert $[H^+]$ to pH). *In conclusion, under the specific condition that the bicarbonate ion concentration at the first equivalence point is no smaller than* 0.010 M, the complicated expression for $[H^+]$ becomes

$$[H^+] = \sqrt{K_1 K_2}$$

The pH of the solution is given by the expression

$$pH = \tfrac{1}{2}(pK_1 + pK_2)$$

so, at the first equivalence point, the pH is 8.34. It is noteworthy that the pH is independent of the bicarbonate ion concentration, provided of course that this concentration is at least 0.010 M as previously specified. The general usefulness and significance of the simple relationship between pH and one-half the sum of the pK values will be discussed further.

Between the first and second equivalence points, the solution pH is governed by the ratio of the carbonic acid and bicarbonate concentrations through the equilibrium expression

$$[H^+] = K_1 \frac{[H_2CO_3]}{[HCO_3^-]}$$

where K_1 is 4.47×10^{-7} and $[H_2CO_3]$ represents the total analytical concentration of dissolved carbon dioxide in its two forms.

After the addition of 30.00 ml of 0.1000 F hydrochloric acid (remembering that a volume of 25.00 ml is required to reach the first equivalence point and that 2.500 millimoles of HCO_3^- is present at the start of the second half of the titration), 0.500 millimole of H_2CO_3 has been formed and 2.000 millimoles of HCO_3^- remains untitrated. Taking the ratio of the numbers of millimoles, we obtain

$$[H^+] = K_1 \frac{[H_2CO_3]}{[HCO_3^-]} = 4.47 \times 10^{-7} \frac{(0.500)}{(2.000)} = 1.12 \times 10^{-7} \, M;$$

$$pH = 6.95$$

After the addition of 35.00 ml of hydrochloric acid, the pH $= 6.53$; after the addition of 40.00 ml of hydrochloric acid, the pH $= 6.17$; after the addition of 45.00 ml of hydrochloric acid, the pH $= 5.75$; after the addition of 47.50 ml of hydrochloric acid, the pH $= 5.40$.

The addition of 50.00 ml of hydrochloric acid brings us to the second equivalence point. At this point the solution consists essentially of the weak acid H_2CO_3, which may be considered in terms analogous to Example 3 in an early section of this chapter. The concentration of carbonic acid is 0.02500 F, so the fundamental equilibrium equation takes the form:

$$\frac{[H^+][HCO_3^-]}{[H_2CO_3]} = \frac{[H^+]^2}{0.02500 - [H^+]} = 4.47 \times 10^{-7}$$

Since the extent of ionization of H_2CO_3 may be neglected, the solution of the previous relation is simply

$$\frac{[H^+]^2}{0.02500} = 4.47 \times 10^{-7}$$

$$[H^+]^2 = 1.12 \times 10^{-8}$$

$$[H^+] = 1.06 \times 10^{-4} \, M; \qquad pH = 3.97$$

Beyond the second equivalence point, an excess of strong acid is being added to the carbonic acid solution, and the pH is governed entirely by this strong acid. After the addition of a total volume of titrant of 52.50, 55.00, and 60.00 ml, the pH values are 2.61, 2.32, and 2.04, respectively.

The complete titration curve is shown in Figure 8-7.

End Point Detection and Feasibility of Titrations.   The titration curve shown in Figure 8-7 is not especially well defined in terms of displaying sharp pH "breaks." This is especially true for the first equivalence point. Phenolphthalein is sometimes used to indicate the first end point. Since phenolphthalein is a one-color indicator, the pH at which the end point color change occurs is dependent upon the indicator concentration. The phenolphthalein end point does come a bit too soon, and it is not as sharp as would ordinarily be desired, so it is not useful in work of extremely high accuracy. Methyl orange provides a good indication of the second end point, the end point being taken as the first perceptible change from the pure canary-yellow color of the base form of methyl orange to the intermediate orange color of the indicator.

The course of the carbonate-hydrochloric acid titration can be nicely followed with the aid of a glass electrode pH meter. A complete plot of pH versus the volume of titrant can be constructed and the regions of the titration curve near the two equivalence points analyzed by graphical procedures to obtain the precise locations of the two inflection points of the titration curve. It is also possible with the aid of a glass electrode pH meter to titrate exactly to the pH of the first equivalence point.

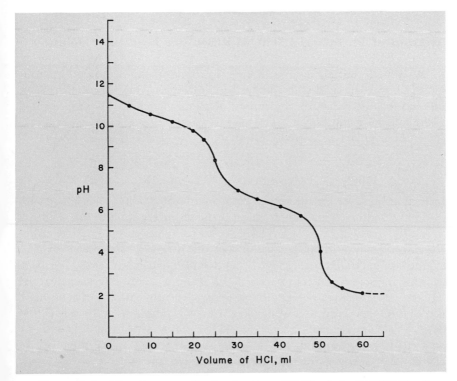

FIGURE 8-7. Titration curve for the titration of 50.00 ml of a 0.05000 F sodium carbonate solution with 0.1000 F hydrochloric acid. The first stage of the titration corresponds to the formation of hydrogen carbonate ion (HCO_3^-), and the second stage pertains to the formation of carbonic acid or carbon dioxide.

Although the titration of carbonate clearly involves the reaction between hydrogen ions and carbonate and bicarbonate ions, which are basic species, the fundamental equilibria which influence the properties of the titration curve are really the ionizations of the two weak acids, H_2CO_3 and HCO_3^-. The fact that the titration curve in Figure 8-7 exhibits two reasonably distinct pH "breaks" is because of the difference in acid strengths of these two weak acids. This difference amounts to four pK units, since K_1 is 4.47×10^{-7} and K_2 is 4.68×10^{-11}. In general, then, it is feasible to titrate successively either two weak acids or the two anions (conjugate bases) of these acids if the pK values of the two acids differ by four or more pK units. Further evidence to substantiate this statement is contained in Figure 8-4. Based on the titration curves shown in Figure 8-4, a mixture of two weak acids having ionization constants of 10^{-4} and 10^{-8} could be successfully titrated. The titration of the weak acid with $K = 10^{-4}$ would be almost complete at just about the pH where the second acid of $K = 10^{-8}$ would begin to react. If the two weak acids in a mixture have pK values which differ by less than four units, the reaction of the weaker acid will be well under way before the titration of the stronger one is complete. In such a case, the titration curve would be very poorly defined.

Titration of Phosphoric Acid with Sodium Hydroxide Solution

As a final example of an acid-base titration, we shall consider the titration of phosphoric acid with standard sodium hydroxide titrant. Earlier in this chapter, the successive ionizations of phosphoric acid were represented by the following equilibria:

$$H_3PO_4 \rightleftharpoons H^+ + H_2PO_4^-; \qquad K_1 = 7.5 \times 10^{-3}$$
$$H_2PO_4^- \rightleftharpoons H^+ + HPO_4^=; \qquad K_2 = 6.2 \times 10^{-8}$$
$$HPO_4^= \rightleftharpoons H^+ + PO_4^=; \qquad K_3 = 4.8 \times 10^{-13}$$

A titration curve for the titration of 25.00 ml of 0.5000 F phosphoric acid with a 0.5000 F sodium hydroxide solution is shown in Figure 8-8. We shall not pursue the detailed calculations required to construct this curve, but rather will emphasize the important features of the titration. The titration curve is quite similar to that expected for the titration of a mixture of three weak acids having ionization constants of K_1, K_2, and K_3. However, only two pH "breaks" are observed, because the titration of the third proton of phosphoric acid does not proceed to any significant extent. The reason for this is that $HPO_4^=$ with an ionization constant (K_3) of 4.8×10^{-13} is an exceedingly weak acid, being only about 48 times stronger than water itself $(K_w = 1.00 \times 10^{-14})$. The two pH "breaks" which do appear correspond to the successive titrations of H_3PO_4 and $H_2PO_4^-$ (which is the product of the neutralization of phosphoric acid). The curves for these two successive titrations are well resolved because the pK values differ by slightly more than five pK units (pK_1 = 2.12 and pK_2 = 7.21). A difference of at least four pK units is usually required to obtain two sharply defined curves for the successive titrations of two weak acids in a mixture.

   The large difference of approximately five units between pK_1 and pK_2 allows us to construct the first step of the titration curve by considering only the ionization of H_3PO_4 and the second step by considering just the ionization of $H_2PO_4^-$. Beyond the *second* equivalence point, it is necessary to consider the ionization of both $HPO_4^=$ and H_2O in order to calculate the pH of the solution. The pH values at the first and second equivalence points deserve special attention. At the *first* equivalence point, corresponding to the removal of one proton from phosphoric acid, the solution consists essentially of NaH_2PO_4. Like the bicarbonate ion, $H_2PO_4^-$ is an amphiprotic species, being capable of acting as either a proton donor or acceptor. Consequently, the calculation of the pH at the first equivalence point is a problem analogous to the calculation of the pH at the so-called "bicarbonate point." Since the concentration of $H_2PO_4^-$ at the first equivalence point (0.2500 M) is significantly greater than the numerical value of K_1, it may be shown that

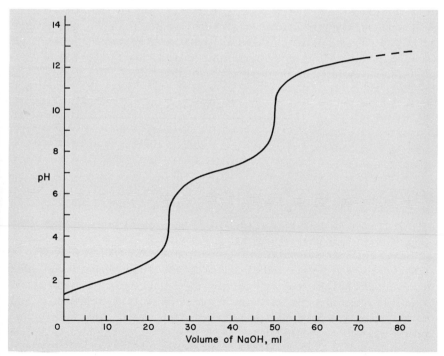

FIGURE 8-8.   Titration curve for the titration of 25.00 ml of 0.5000 F phosphoric acid with a 0.5000 F sodium hydroxide solution. The stepwise titration of H_3PO_4, first to $H_2PO_4^-$ and then to $HPO_4^=$, is evident; however, the titration of the third proton of phosphoric acid cannot be observed because $HPO_4^=$ is too weak an acid in water.

the pH is very accurately given by the following relationships:

$$[H^+] = \sqrt{K_1 K_2}$$
$$pH = \tfrac{1}{2}(pK_1 + pK_2)$$
$$pH = \tfrac{1}{2}(2.12 + 7.21) = 4.67$$

At the *second* equivalence point, the solution is indistinguishable from one containing 0.1667 M $HPO_4^=$. The rigorous equation for the calculation of the hydrogen ion concentration (based on our previous discussion of the sodium carbonate-hydrochloric acid titration) is as follows:

$$[H^+] = \sqrt{\frac{K_3[HPO_4^=] + K_w}{1 + \dfrac{[HPO_4^=]}{K_2}}}$$

In the event that $[HPO_4^=]$ is greater than K_2, and also that the term $K_3[HPO_4^=]$ is greater than K_w by a factor of at least 50, the preceding relation becomes

$$[H^+] = \sqrt{K_2 K_3}$$

Although $[HPO_4^=]$ is indeed very much greater than K_2, the product $K_3[HPO_4^=]$ is $(4.8 \times 10^{-13})(0.1667)$, or 8.0×10^{-14}, which is only eight times larger than K_w. It is of considerable interest, therefore, to compare the pH values computed from these two equations. From the rigorous first equation,

$$[H^+] = \sqrt{\frac{(4.8 \times 10^{-13})(0.1667) + 1.00 \times 10^{-14}}{1 + \dfrac{0.1667}{6.2 \times 10^{-8}}}}$$

$$= 1.83 \times 10^{-10} \, M; \, pH = 9.74$$

and from the approximate relation

$$[H^+] = \sqrt{(6.2 \times 10^{-8})(4.8 \times 10^{-13})} = 1.93 \times 10^{-10} \, M; \qquad pH = 9.78$$

Thus, the approximate equation succeeds remarkably well in providing an accurate value for the pH at the *first* and the *second* equivalence points under the conditions of the present titration.

Many substances of analytical interest fall into the class of amphiprotic species. We have already mentioned the bicarbonate (HCO_3^-) ion and the $H_2PO_4^-$ and $HPO_4^=$ anions. A partial list of amphiprotic species includes hydrogen oxalate ($HC_2O_4^-$), hydrogen sulfite (HSO_3^-), hydrogen sulfide (HS^-), hydrogen phosphite ($H_2PO_3^-$), and hydrogen tartrate ($HOOC(CHOH)_2COO^-$). Aqueous solutions of salts of these amphiprotic ions at reasonably high concentration levels usually have hydrogen ion concentrations and pH values close to those given by the simple approximate equations. It is necessary, of course, to recognize the limitations of these approximate expressions at low concentrations of the amphiprotic substances.

Another important group of compounds which are amphiprotic is the family of amino acids. The amino acids are especially interesting because in aqueous solutions they exist predominantly as **zwitterions** or dipolar ions. A typical example of an amino acid is alanine.

$$CH_3-CH-C\overset{O}{\underset{O^-}{<}}$$
$$\underset{+NH_3}{|}$$

alanine

Alanine, as well as other amino acids, is amphiprotic because the zwitterion may be protonated or deprotonated according to the equilibria

$$CH_3-CH-C\overset{O}{\underset{O^-}{<}} + H^+ \rightleftharpoons CH_3-CH-C\overset{O}{\underset{OH}{<}}$$
$$\underset{+NH_3}{|} \qquad\qquad\qquad \underset{+NH_3}{|}$$

conjugate acid of alanine

$$CH_3-CH-C\overset{O}{\underset{O^-}{<}} \rightleftharpoons H^+ + CH_3-CH-C\overset{O}{\underset{O^-}{<}}$$
$$\underset{+NH_3}{|} \qquad\qquad\qquad \underset{NH_2}{|}$$

conjugate base of alanine

An aqueous solution of alanine is found to have a pH which is given by the expression

$$pH = \tfrac{1}{2}(pK_1 + pK_2)$$
$$pH = \tfrac{1}{2}(2.35 + 9.87) = 6.11$$

where K_1 is the ionization constant for the conjugate acid of alanine and K_2 is the ionization constant for alanine itself. Many other amino acid solutions have pH values in the neighborhood of 5 to 6.

Experiment 8-1

PREPARATION AND STANDARDIZATION OF HYDRO-CHLORIC ACID AND SODIUM HYDROXIDE SOLUTIONS

Purposes

1. To prepare approximately $0.2\,F$ solutions of hydrochloric acid and sodium hydroxide. (More dilute or more concentrated titrants may be prepared by appropriate modification of the procedures.)

2. To determine the *volume ratio* of the hydrochloric acid and sodium hydroxide solutions.

3. To standardize solutions of hydrochloric acid and sodium hydroxide against any one of several primary standard substances.

Procedures

Preparation of Hydrochloric Acid Solution.   Calculate the volume of concentrated $(12\,F)$ reagent hydrochloric acid required for the preparation of 1 liter of a $0.2\,F$ hydrochloric acid solution. Dilute this volume of the concentrated acid to approximately 1 liter with distilled water in a clean, glass-stoppered Pyrex bottle. Mix the solution thoroughly by swirling the bottle and its contents, allow the solution to cool to room temperature, and standardize the solution by one of the methods to be described.

Preparation of Sodium Hydroxide Solution.   Prepare a carbonate-free $0.2\,F$ sodium hydroxide solution by taking the appropriate volume of the supernatant liquid from a 50 per cent sodium hydroxide solution and diluting it to 1 liter in a screw-cap polyethylene bottle with *freshly boiled and cooled* distilled water. Cap the polyethylene bottle tightly after the dilution, mix the solution thoroughly, and open the bottle only during the few times you use the solution.

Sodium carbonate (Na_2CO_3) is very insoluble in 50 per cent sodium hydroxide solutions. Therefore, if a 50 per cent sodium hydroxide solution is prepared from equal weights of water and reagent-grade NaOH, the sodium carbonate impurity in reagent-grade NaOH is insoluble and will settle to the bottom of the container over the course of several days to a week. The correct volume of the clear, syrupy supernatant liquid (which is approximately $19\,F$ in sodium hydroxide) can be carefully withdrawn from the container for the preparation of the carbonate-free titrant. The 50 per cent sodium hydroxide solution must be prepared in advance so that the Na_2CO_3 can settle out, and it is advantageous if enough of this solution is prepared for an entire laboratory class as follows: Dissolve reagent-grade NaOH in an equal weight of distilled water in a Pyrex beaker (use a hood to avoid inhaling sodium hydroxide spray). When the solution has cooled, transfer it to a polyethylene bottle and allow the solution to stand until Na_2CO_3 settles out. The clear supernatant 50 per cent NaOH may be withdrawn directly from the polyethylene container, if care is taken to avoid stirring up the Na_2CO_3. Some provision for mounting the polyethylene container securely in place is desirable.

It should be emphasized that this is only a *temporary expedient* for the preparation and use of a carbonate-free sodium hydroxide solution. Although the sodium hydroxide solution may be initially carbonate-free, it will absorb carbon dioxide each time it is exposed to the atmosphere. However, careful use of this solution provides a substantially carbonate-free titrant over the short duration of the experiments in which it is normally employed and eliminates the need to boil solutions to obtain a sharp end point in titrations.

Volume Ratio of the Acid and Base Solutions. Pipet 25.00 ml of the approximately $0.2\,F$ hydrochloric acid solution into a 250 ml Erlenmeyer flask. Add about 50 to 60 ml of distilled water and three drops of phenolphthalein indicator solution.

The indicator solution is prepared by the dissolution of 0.5 gm of phenolphthalein in 100 ml of 95 per cent ethyl alcohol. Since phenolphthalein is a one-color indicator, it is essential that the same amount of indicator solution be used for each titration if maximum accuracy is to be obtained.

Clean a 50 ml buret and thoroughly rinse it with distilled water. Rinse the buret with two or three 5 to 10 ml portions of the approximately $0.2\,F$ sodium hydroxide solution, allowing the rinsings to run through the buret tip. Then fill the buret with the $0.2\,F$ sodium hydroxide solution. After allowing sufficient time for drainage of the buret, record the initial position of the meniscus (which may be at any convenient point on the calibrated portion of the buret, not necessarily at the zero line).

Procedures for cleaning, handling, and reading burets, as well as other volumetric glassware, are given in Chapter 2 and specifically in Experiment 2-2. It is important that the sodium hydroxide not be permitted to remain in a buret with a glass stopcock any longer than is necessary for the performance of titrations. Sodium hydroxide solution attacks glass, and freezing of the stopcock may occur unless the sodium hydroxide solution is drained out of the buret immediately after the titration and the buret is rinsed thoroughly with tap water and distilled water.

Titrate the aliquot of hydrochloric acid with sodium hydroxide solution from the buret, using the left hand to manipulate the stopcock and the right hand to swirl the flask continuously (see Fig. 2-17), until the first perceptible but permanent appearance of the pink form of phenolphthalein.

If the flask is swirled continuously during the titration, the approach of the end point is signaled by the fact that temporary local excesses of NaOH cause the pink color to spread fleetingly throughout the whole solution before disappearing again. Near the end point, the titrant should be added drop by drop. Add fractions of a drop of titrant by letting a droplet start to form on the tip of the buret, touching the buret tip to the inner wall of the titration flask, and washing down the inner wall of the flask with distilled water from a squeeze-type wash bottle.

The pink end point color gradually fades because of the absorption by the solution of carbon dioxide from the atmosphere.

Allow at least 30 seconds after concluding the titration for drainage of the buret; then record the final position of the meniscus. Titrate at least two more 25.00 ml aliquots of the hydrochloric acid solution in the manner just described. Replicate results should agree to within two or three parts per thousand. Calculate the volume ratio of acid to base by dividing the volume of acid used by the volume of base required in each titration. Compute the average of the results.

Once the volume ratio of the acid to the base is reliably determined, the subsequent standardization of the acid allows the concentration of the base to be calculated, or vice versa.

If the buret or pipet has been previously calibrated, as in Experiment 2-2, appropriate corrections should be applied to the volumes of HCl and NaOH used in the titrations. In addition, a correction should be made for the (very small) volume of NaOH required to transform phenolphthalein from its colorless acid form to its pink base form. This correction may be determined as follows: Add three drops of phenolphthalein indicator solution to a volume of distilled water, contained in a 250 ml Erlenmeyer flask, which is equal to the *final* volume of solution in an actual titration. (Preferably, the distilled water should be freshly boiled and cooled to minimize the amount of dissolved carbon dioxide present.) Titrate the distilled water plus phenolphthalein with *fractions* of a drop of sodium hydroxide solution until the intensity of the pink color matches that obtained in the actual titrations. This small volume of NaOH should be subtracted from the apparent volume of NaOH used in each titration to calculate the true volume of titrant. It should be evident that the validity of the correction depends upon one's reproducing the intensity of the pink color quite closely in each titration.

Standardization of Hydrochloric Acid Solution Against Sodium Carbonate.
Dry a quantity of primary-standard-grade sodium carbonate — enough for several weighed portions — for two hours in an oven at 110°C. Use a beaker-and-watch-glass arrangement (see Fig. 2-1) for drying the sodium carbonate. Cool the sodium carbonate in air for two to three minutes and in a desiccator for at least 30 minutes before weighing the individual samples.

Accurately weigh three 0.25 to 0.30 gm portions of the dried sodium carbonate, each into a clean 500 ml Erlenmeyer flask. Carry each sample completely through the remainder of the procedure before starting on the next sample.

The proper weight of sodium carbonate for the standardization of the hydrochloric acid may be calculated as follows: Assume that 30 ml of hydrochloric acid is a reasonable volume to be used in the titration. This corresponds to 6 millimoles of acid, if $0.2 F$ titrant is employed. Since each millimole of sodium carbonate reacts with 2 millimoles of acid, 3 millimoles of sodium carbonate should be taken. The formula weight of Na_2CO_3 is very close to 106, so about 300 mg or 0.3 gm of sodium carbonate is a reasonable sample size.

Dissolve a sodium carbonate sample in approximately 50 ml of distilled water and add three drops of methyl orange indicator solution.

Prepare the indicator solution, in advance of the standardization, by dissolving 0.1 gm of methyl orange in 100 ml of distilled water.

Titrate the sodium carbonate solution with the hydrochloric acid solution contained in a 50 ml buret. Swirl the flask and its contents continuously during the titration, avoiding too rapid addition of the acid, so that the evolution of carbon dioxide does not result in loss of solution by spattering. Continue the titration until the color of methyl orange first turns from pure canary-yellow toward orange-yellow.

At this first color change, stop the titration and heat and swirl continuously the titration flask over a low Bunsen flame so that the solution boils gently for two to three minutes.

A folded paper towel placed around the neck of the flask serves as a convenient handle while the solution is heated to boiling. The purpose of the heating is to expel the carbon dioxide produced by neutralization of the sodium carbonate. Since carbon dioxide tends to form supersaturated solutions, its presence causes the appearance of a premature end point color change. After the titration solution has been boiled briefly and then cooled, the color of the solution should have reverted back to pure canary-yellow.

Cool the solution to room temperature by running tap water over the outside of the flask. The methyl orange indicator will have changed back to its original canary-yellow color if the end point was not overshot. Wash down the inside wall of the flask with a stream of distilled water from a wash bottle. Continue the titration by adding the hydrochloric acid in drops and then in fractions of drops until the methyl orange undergoes the first perceptible but permanent color change from yellow to orange-yellow. Wait about 30 seconds after reaching the final end point for drainage from the inner wall of the buret, and then record the final buret reading.

If the methyl orange indicator fails to return to its original canary-yellow color, too much acid was added at first. Therefore, a small, known volume (usually 1.00 ml) of sodium hydroxide solution should be pipetted into the titration flask, and the solution should be titrated with hydrochloric acid to the proper end point color change.

A blank titration should be performed to determine the volume of hydrochloric acid required to cause the methyl orange to change color. Into a 500 ml Erlenmeyer flask add a volume of distilled water equal to the solution volume at the end point of an actual titration. Dissolve in the distilled water a weight of solid NaCl approximately equal to the quantity of sodium chloride present at the end point of a titration. Add three drops of methyl orange indicator solution. Titrate the solution with hydrochloric acid, adding fractions of a drop until the indicator changes color as in an actual titration. This small volume of hydrochloric acid should be subtracted from the total volume used in the titration of the sodium carbonate sample.

From the titration data (and the volume ratio of acid to base if any sodium hydroxide solution was used), calculate the concentration of the hydrochloric acid solution. Repeat the standardization procedure with the other two weighed samples of sodium carbonate. The results of the replicate standardizations should agree to within two or three parts per thousand.

Standardization of Sodium Hydroxide Solution Against Sulfamic Acid. (This procedure is similar to that used to determine the volume ratio of acid to base.) Dry a quantity of reagent-grade sulfamic acid

(NH$_2$SO$_3$H) by spreading out the solid on a large watch glass and placing the watch glass and solid in a desiccator for two or three hours. Once dried in this manner, the sulfamic acid may be transferred to a weighing bottle and kept inside a desiccator.

Accurately weigh three samples of dried sulfamic acid, each approximately 0.5 gm in weight, into 250 ml Erlenmeyer flasks. Dissolve each sample in about 50 ml of distilled water (which, preferably, has been boiled to remove carbon dioxide and then cooled), and add three drops of phenolphthalein indicator to each solution.

Titrate each sample solution with sodium hydroxide solution from a 50 ml buret to the first perceptible but permanent appearance of the pink form of phenolphthalein. Allow 30 seconds after finishing the titration for drainage of the buret, and then record the final position of the meniscus. Calculate the average concentration of the sodium hydroxide solution from the results of the three titrations. The individual results should agree to within two or three parts per thousand.

A correction should be made, as described previously for the determination of the volume ratio of acid to base, to allow for the small volume of sodium hydroxide solution required to transform phenolphthalein from its colorless acid form to its pink base form, as in an actual titration.

Standardization of Sodium Hydroxide Solution Against Potassium Acid Phthalate.

Dry approximately 5 gm of primary-standard-grade potassium acid phthalate (KHC$_8$H$_4$O$_4$) in an oven at 110°C for one hour. Place the potassium acid phthalate in a weighing bottle, and then place the weighing bottle in a beaker-and-watch-glass arrangement (see Fig. 2-1) for the drying operation. Cool the weighing bottle plus potassium acid phthalate in air for several minutes and then in a desiccator for at least 30 minutes prior to the weighing of individual samples.

Accurately weigh three 1.2 to 1.5 gm portions of the dried potassium acid phthalate into clean 250 ml Erlenmeyer flasks. Dissolve each weighed sample in approximately 50 ml of distilled water (which has, preferably, been boiled and then cooled to room temperature), and then add three drops of phenolphthalein indicator solution to each flask.

Titrate each sample solution with sodium hydroxide solution from a 50 ml buret to the first perceptible but permanent appearance of the pink form of phenolphthalein. After waiting for drainage of the buret, record the final position of the meniscus. Calculate the average concentration of the sodium hydroxide solution from the results of the three titrations. The results of the three individual titrations should be in agreement to within two or three parts per thousand.

An end point correction should be made for the very small volume of sodium hydroxide solution required to transform phenolphthalein from its colorless acid form to its pink base form. This correction may be determined as follows: Add three drops of phenolphthalein indicator solution to a volume of distilled water, contained in a 250 ml Erlenmeyer flask, which is the same as the final volume of solution in an actual titration. (Preferably, the distilled water should be freshly boiled and cooled to minimize the amount of dissolved carbon dioxide present.) Also dissolve in the solution a weight of pure potassium (or sodium) phthalate which is equivalent to that formed in an actual titration. Titrate this comparison solution with fractions of a drop of sodium hydroxide solution until the intensity of the pink color matches that observed in the titrations of potassium acid phthalate.

Experiment 8-2

VOLUMETRIC ANALYSIS OF A CARBONATE-BICAR-BONATE MIXTURE

Purpose

The volumetric analysis of a carbonate-bicarbonate mixture demonstrates the determination of a pair of substances by titration of a single sample to two successive end points. In addition, this experiment involves the use of a pH meter as a means of following the progress of a titration. Information about the pH transition ranges for two indicators, phenolphthalein and methyl orange, is obtained as well.

Preparation

Mixtures of sodium carbonate and sodium bicarbonate for this experiment may be prepared according to any of several procedures. For a few individual unknown samples, it is straightforward to mix accurately weighed portions of reagent-grade sodium carbonate and sodium bicarbonate (along with sodium chloride if an inert constituent and diluent is desired) just prior to the experiment. Each sample can be used in its entirety as a single unknown for analysis.

In some instances, it is feasible to prepare large quantities of a particular mixture by accurately weighing and thoroughly mixing (with a ball mill or similar device) appropriate sodium or potassium salts. Mixtures of varying compositions can be prepared in this manner, and individual portions of a given mixture serve as samples for analysis. Unfortunately, mixtures of carbonate and bicarbonate salts undergo chemical reactions with moisture and carbon dioxide in the atmosphere during prolonged storage, which alter the relative percentages of carbonate and bicarbonate. Therefore, such mixtures must be periodically analyzed (by, for example, the procedure to be described) to reestablish their compositions.

Solutions containing carbonate and bicarbonate are not suitable as samples because they are not especially stable unless unusual precautions are taken. They absorb carbon dioxide from the atmosphere, and the following reaction occurs to change the relative concentrations of carbonate and bicarbonate:

$$CO_3^= + CO_2 + H_2O \rightleftharpoons 2\ HCO_3^-$$

The most attractive alternative is for each student to prepare his own "unknown" by weight from reagent-grade sodium carbonate and sodium bicarbonate (and sodium chloride) and then to subject his "unknown" to volumetric analysis. In this way, he can obtain a direct check on the applicability and accuracy of the analytical procedure.

Experience has shown that the percentages of sodium carbonate and sodium bicarbonate in a mixture should be comparable and should range between 30 and 50 per cent by weight, with an inert salt, such as sodium chloride, as diluent if desired.

Procedure

A magnetic stirring unit and a pH meter equipped with a glass electrode and a reference electrode should be available and set up in the laboratory prior to the starting of the experiment. Supply your own 50 ml buret and 250 ml beaker. The glass electrode and reference electrode are fragile and quite expensive and should be treated accordingly. BE SURE THAT THE BEAKER AND THE MAGNETIC STIRRING BAR DO NOT STRIKE THE ELECTRODES.

Read and follow the instructions for use of the instrument, then standardize the pH meter with a buffer solution of known pH. Rinse the electrodes prior to use with a stream of distilled water from a wash bottle, carefully wipe them dry with a laboratory tissue, immerse them in the standard buffer, and swirl the buffer solution gently until a steady pH reading is obtained.

A freshly prepared saturated solution of potassium hydrogen tartrate serves as an excellent and convenient pH standard, its pH being 3.57 ± 0.02 at 25°C. Since the pH of an acid salt solution is essentially independent of concentration, the potassium hydrogen tartrate solution need not even be saturated.

It is sufficient to shake a small portion of this salt (which is not very soluble) with distilled water for a few minutes prior to standardization of the pH meter. Potassium hydrogen tartrate solutions have a tendency toward molding, so they should be freshly prepared as needed.

Weigh accurately a 2.0 gm sample of the carbonate-bicarbonate mixture into a small beaker, dissolve the sample completely in a minimal volume of distilled water, transfer the solution quantitatively to a 100 ml volumetric flask, dilute the solution to the calibration mark with distilled water, and thoroughly mix the solution.

As pointed out before, solutions containing carbonate and bicarbonate will undergo a change in composition upon standing, so the sample solution should not be prepared until just before the titrations.

Place a clean 250 ml beaker on the magnetic stirring unit, insert a magnetic stirring bar into the beaker, and mount the glass electrode and reference electrode in position inside the beaker so that they will not be struck by the stirring bar. Pipet a 25.00 ml aliquot of the sample solution into the beaker and add distilled water, as needed, to immerse the tips of the electrodes to a depth of 1 to 2 cm. Adjust the stirring rate so that the solution is stirred thoroughly but not with excessive violence.

This procedure is designed for the analysis of 0.5 gm of the sample (a one-fourth aliquot of the original 2.0 gm sample) by titration with standard 0.2 F hydrochloric acid (without the need for refilling the buret). In addition, it is assumed that the original sample contains 50 per cent each of pure sodium carbonate and sodium bicarbonate. If the experimental conditions differ considerably from these, it may be necessary to change the original sample weight, the volume of the sample solution used in a titration, or the concentration of the hydrochloric acid titrant.

Titrate the sample solution with standard 0.2 F hydrochloric acid from a 50 ml buret. For the first titration, use 2 or 3 ml increments of the acid solution and record the pH after the addition of each increment. At the same time, plot the titration curve (pH versus the volume of standard acid) on graph paper as you measure each point. Continue the titration until the solution pH decreases to less than 3. After concluding the titration, rinse the beaker, the stirring bar, and the electrodes with distilled water in preparation for the next titration.

Titrate a second 25.00 ml aliquot of the sample solution in the manner just described, except that in the immediate vicinity of each equivalence point, add relatively small increments of hydrochloric acid in order to define the titration curve accurately in these regions. Incremental volumes of 0.5 ml for the first equivalence point and 0.2 ml for the second equivalence point should be satisfactory. Again, record the complete titration curve and plot it on graph paper as before.

Another 25.00 ml aliquot of the sample solution should be titrated in the same manner as the second aliquot. For this titration, however, add three drops of phenolphthalein indicator solution at the start of the titration. Observe the pH range of its color change in relation to the first equivalence point as you titrate carefully through this point. After the phenolphthalein has been transformed into its colorless acid form, add three drops of methyl orange indicator solution and similarly note the pH range of its color change in relation to the second equivalence point. Plot the titration curve on graph paper and mark the pH transition ranges for the two indicators.

From the results of the titrations, calculate and report the average weight percentages of sodium carbonate and sodium bicarbonate in the original solid sample. As an aid in locating the equivalence points on the titration curves, plot the first derivative ($\Delta pH/\Delta V$) or the second derivative ($\Delta^2 pH/\Delta V^2$) of your titration data in the vicinity (± 2 ml) of each equivalence point. Such a graphical approach for the location of equivalence points is described in Chapter 17, pages 717 to 721. From your observations of the behavior of the two acid-base indicators, make an estimate of the pK_{In} value for each indicator. In addition, compare the observed pH transition ranges for the indicators with the values listed in Table 8-1. Finally, by analyzing the titration curve, determine values for the two acid dissociation constants K_1 and K_2 for carbonic acid.

When you finish with this experiment, leave the electrodes immersed in distilled water and be sure the pH meter is turned off.

SUGGESTIONS FOR ADDITIONAL LABORATORY WORK

The procedure just described, involving the use of a pH meter to follow the progress of a titration, is generally applicable to numerous other acid-base systems, including phosphate mixtures (such as a solution containing H_3PO_4 and NaH_2PO_4), solid samples of NaH_2PO_4 and Na_2HPO_4, and carbonate-hydroxide mixtures such as solid Na_2CO_3 plus NaOH. It is also instructive simply to titrate a sample of pure sodium carbonate by this procedure.

Experiment 8-3

DETERMINATION OF TOTAL SALT CONCENTRATION BY ION EXCHANGE AND ACID-BASE TITRATION

Purpose

This experiment demonstrates one of the simplest uses of the ion-exchange technique discussed in Chapter 7 — that of exchanging all metal cations in a solution for hydrogen ions. After the exchange process has been accomplished, the liberated hydrogen ion is titrated with standard sodium hydroxide solution as a means of determining the total concentration of cations in a sample solution. This experiment can be used in conjunction with Experiment 11-4.

Procedure

Measure out approximately 50 ml volume of Dowex-50, a sulfonated polystyrene-divinylbenzene cation exchange resin in the hydrogen ion form.

The optimum size of the resin particles is about 50 mesh. Soak the resin overnight in a beaker containing 200 ml of 2 F hydrochloric acid.

One reason for soaking the resin is to ensure that all of the exchange sites are initially occupied by hydrogen ions. In addition, an ion-exchange resin swells or expands somewhat when wet, so it should be equilibrated with an aqueous solution prior to the preparation of the ion-exchange column and should be kept covered with either distilled water or an aqueous solution until the column is finally disassembled.

Pour off the hydrochloric acid solution and wash the resin free of excess acid by repeatedly adding and pouring off portions of distilled water. Continue washing the resin by decantation until the pH of the wash water in contact with the resin is not less than 4, as determined with the aid of pH paper.

Prepare an ion-exchange column free of air bubbles as follows: Use a 50 ml buret as the cation-exchange column. Clean the buret thoroughly and grease the stopcock. Add approximately 5 ml of distilled water to the buret. Insert a one-half-inch plug of glass wool into the buret (to support the resin and keep it from clogging the buret tip), using a glass rod to push the glass wool down against the stopcock. Pour the resin slurry slowly into the buret and allow the resin to settle. For the present experiment, the resin bed should be about 40 cm high. *Maintain the level of liquid at least 1 or 2 cm above the resin bed at all times.*

If the level of liquid falls below the top of the resin bed, air becomes trapped in the resin bed and the air pockets tend to remain even though liquid is subsequently added to the column. The presence of air pockets or air channels reduces the column efficiency by preventing the liquid from contacting all the resin particles.

Test the column for free acid by passing 100 ml of distilled water through the column, collecting the effluent in a clean 250 ml Erlenmeyer flask, and titrating this effluent with sodium hydroxide solution to a phenolphthalein end point. If more than 0.05 ml of a 0.2 F sodium hydroxide solution is required, continue to wash the column by passing distilled water through it until the effluent is acid free.

Adjust the level of distilled water in the column so that it is approximately 1 cm above the top of the resin bed. Place a clean 500 ml Erlenmeyer flask below the column. Transfer exactly 25.00 ml of the sample solution into the column and allow this solution to pass through the column into the flask at a moderate flow rate, i.e., one or two drops per second.

It is assumed for the present procedure that the 25.00 ml of sample solution contains a total of about 6 mEq of cations. If all the cations are univalent, this corresponds to a cation concentration of 0.24 M, whereas if all the cations have a charge of $+2$ (as in Experiment 11-4) the cation concentration would be 0.12 M. If the sample solution differs markedly from these concentration levels, the volume of sample passed through the column should be appropriately changed or the concentration of standard sodium hydroxide subsequently used in the titration of the liberated acid should be varied.

When the liquid level is again 1 cm above the resin, add about 15 ml of distilled water into the column and let this wash solution pass through the column at the somewhat faster rate of two or three drops per second until the liquid level again reaches the top of the resin bed. Repeat the washing of the column, in order to remove the acid liberated by the ion-exchange process, with six more 15 ml portions of distilled water.

Finally, collect a seventh 15 ml washing in a separate 125 ml Erlenmeyer flask, add three drops of phenolphthalein indicator solution, and titrate the solution with standard 0.2 F sodium hydroxide.

The purpose of this separate titration is to obtain a check on the efficiency of the washing procedure. Not more than a single drop of the sodium hydroxide solution should be required to cause the pink form of phenolphthalein to appear. In the unusual event that a significant volume of sodium hydroxide solution is needed, however, a record must be kept of this volume since it indicates the presence of hydrogen ion released by the exchange reaction. Furthermore, the ion-exchange column must be washed with more distilled water to remove quantitatively all of the acid.

Provided that the test for acid in the seventh washing is negative, add three drops of phenolphthalein indicator solution to the 500 ml flask containing the effluent from the cation-exchange column and titrate the solution with standard 0.2 F sodium hydroxide to the first permanent appearance of the pink form of phenolphthalein.

Repeat the ion-exchange procedure with at least two more 25.00 ml aliquots of the sample solution. From the titration data, calculate the milliequivalents of cations per milliliter of the sample solution or, if the charges of all cations in the sample solution are known and are the same, calculate the molar concentration of cations in the sample solution. Replicate results should agree to within two or three parts per thousand.

It is important to keep a record of the number of aliquots of sample solution passed through the column in order to ascertain when the resin must be regenerated. Typical cation-exchange resins have an exchange capacity of approximately 3 mEq/ ml of wet resin, so a rough calculation can be made to determine how many aliquots can be passed through the column. However, it must be remembered that the exchange efficiency of a column gradually decreases from one sample to the next as the exchange sites on the resin are used up. Whether the ion-exchange process has been quantitative can be ascertained if one performs a qualitative spot test for one of the cations in the sample on a small volume of the liquid emerging from the column. If the original sample solution contains one or more colored cations, e.g., nickel(II) or copper(II), the color of the effluent reveals whether the exchange has occurred quantitatively. In addition, if the resin particles are light in color, it is usually possible to see the color of the resin change to the color of the colored cation as it is exchanged. The resin can be regenerated simply by passing 2 F hydrochloric acid through the ion-exchange column.

QUESTIONS AND PROBLEMS

(A comprehensive table of dissociation constants for acids and bases is given in Appendix 2.)

1. Compare the Brönsted-Lowry and the Lewis concepts of acids and bases, noting clearly both the similarities and differences between them.

2. List the factors which influence the strength of an acid and explain how each factor affects the acid strength.
3. Distinguish between concentrated and strong acid and base solutions.
4. Calculate the pH of each of the following solutions, neglecting activity effects;
    (a) 40 ml of $0.100\,F$ hydrochloric acid
    (b) 40 ml of solution containing 1.00 gm of nitric acid, HNO_3
    (c) 40 ml of solution containing 12.0 mg of potassium hydroxide, KOH
    (d) $0.0250\,F$ sodium hydroxide solution
    (e) 40 ml of solution containing 2.0 gm of hydrochloric acid and 1.0 gm of sodium chloride
    (f) $0.0100\,F$ potassium nitrate solution
    (g) $0.0100\,F$ acetic acid solution
    (h) 40 ml of solution containing 0.500 gm of acetic acid
    (i) 40 ml of solution containing 0.500 gm of acetic acid and 1.00 gm of sodium acetate
    (j) 500 ml of a $0.100\,F$ aqueous ammonia solution to which 3.00 gm of solid ammonium chloride has been added
    (k) $0.100\,F$ ammonium chloride solution
    (l) $0.100\,F$ sodium acetate solution
5. Calculate the pH of the solution obtained from the addition of 100 ml of water to 100 ml of a solution originally $0.100\,F$ in hydrochloric acid and $0.100\,F$ in sodium chloride.
6. Calculate the pH of the solution obtained from the addition of 100 ml of water to 100 ml of a solution originally $0.100\,F$ in acetic acid and $0.100\,F$ in sodium acetate.
7. In what ratio must acetic acid and sodium acetate be mixed to provide a solution of pH 6.20?
8. In what ratio must ammonia and ammonium chloride be mixed to provide a solution of pH 8.40?
9. Suppose you wish to prepare 1 liter of a buffer solution, containing sodium carbonate and sodium bicarbonate, having an initial pH of 9.70, and of such composition that, upon the formation of 60 millimoles of hydrogen ion during the course of a chemical reaction, the pH will not decrease below 9.30. What are the minimal original concentrations of sodium carbonate and sodium bicarbonate needed to prepare the desired buffer solution?
10. Calculate the hydrogen ion concentration and the pH of a solution prepared by adding 0.100 ml of $0.0100\,F$ perchloric acid ($HClO_4$) to 10.0 liters of pure water.
11. What is meant by the expression "capacity of a buffer solution"? What limits the capacity of any given buffer solution?
12. Explain with the aid of a generalized equilibrium-constant expression how a buffer solution can maintain a constant pH upon dilution.
13. Consider 100 ml of a $0.100\,F$ acetic acid solution at 25°C.
    (a) Will the addition of 1 gm of pure acetic acid cause the extent (percentage) of ionization of acetic acid to increase, decrease, or remain the same?
    (b) Will the addition of 1 gm of sodium acetate cause the pH of the solution to increase, decrease, or remain the same?
    (c) Will the addition of 1 gm of sodium acetate cause the hydroxide ion concentration to increase, decrease, or remain the same?
14. Consider 50 ml of a $0.100\,F$ aqueous ammonia solution at 25°C.
    (a) Will the solution at the end point of the titration of the ammonia solution with $0.100\,F$ hydrochloric acid have a pH of less than 7, equal to 7, or greater than 7?
    (b) Will the addition of 1 gm of pure acetic acid cause the pH to increase, decrease, or remain the same?

(c) Will the addition of 1 gm of ammonium chloride cause the hydroxide ion concentration to increase, decrease, or remain the same?

15. Why is nitric acid not more commonly used as a standard titrant? Why is acetic acid not suitable for this purpose?

16. Why are aqueous ammonia and potassium hydroxide solutions not more commonly used as standard titrants?

17. List five substances suitable for the standardization of either acid or base solutions and specify whether each substance is used for the standardization of an acid or a base solution.

18. Suppose that reagent-grade sodium hydroxide is used as a primary standard for the standardization of a hydrochloric acid solution. Would the reported concentration of acid be high, low, or correct? Explain.

19. Suppose that a standard solution of sodium hydroxide is permitted to absorb large amounts of carbon dioxide after originally being standardized. Would the original value for the concentration of the sodium hydroxide titrant be high, low, or correct? Explain

20. In the standardization of a hydrochloric acid solution against sodium carbonate, a technician failed to dry the sodium carbonate completely. Did this error cause his reported concentration of hydrochloric acid to be too high, too low, or correct?

21. A 2.500 gm crystal of calcite, $CaCO_3$, was dissolved in excess hydrochloric acid, the carbon dioxide removed by boiling, and the excess acid titrated with a standard base solution. The volume of hydrochloric acid used was 45.56 ml, and only 2.25 ml of the standard base was required to titrate the excess acid. In a separate titration, 43.33 ml of the base solution neutralized 46.46 ml of the hydrochloric acid solution. Calculate the concentrations of the acid and base solutions.

22. If constant-boiling hydrochloric acid, at a pressure of 745 mm of mercury, contains 20.257 per cent HCl by weight, what weight of the constant-boiling solution must be distilled at this pressure for the preparation of exactly 1 liter of 1.000 F hydrochloric acid?

23. If a 4.000 gm sample of potassium acid phthalate is equivalent to 48.37 ml of a sodium hydroxide solution, what is the concentration of the latter?

24. A 1.000 gm sample of pure oxalic acid dihydrate, $H_2C_2O_4 \cdot 2\,H_2O$, required 46.00 ml of a sodium hydroxide solution for its neutralization. Calculate the concentration of the sodium hydroxide solution.

25. A 0.6300 gm sample of a pure organic diprotic acid was titrated with 38.00 ml of a 0.3030 F sodium hydroxide solution, but 4.00 ml of a 0.2250 F hydrochloric acid solution was needed for back titration, at which point the original organic acid was completely neutralized. Calculate the formula weight of the organic acid.

26. A sample of vinegar, weighing 11.40 gm, was titrated with a 0.5000 F sodium hydroxide solution, 18.24 ml being required. Calculate the percentage of acetic acid in the sample.

27. A hydrochloric acid solution was standardized against sodium carbonate. Just 37.66 ml of the acid was required to titrate a 0.3663 gm sample of the sodium carbonate. Later it was discovered that the sodium carbonate was really the hydrated compound, $Na_2CO_3 \cdot 10\,H_2O$, and not the anhydrous compound as expected. What were the reported and the corrected concentrations of the hydrochloric acid solution?

28. What weight of vinegar should be taken for analysis so that the observed buret reading will be exactly 10 times the percentage of acetic acid in the vinegar if a 0.1000 F sodium hydroxide solution is used as the titrant?

29. A 1.500 gm sample of impure calcium oxide (CaO) was dissolved in 40.00 ml of 0.5000 F hydrochloric acid. Exactly 2.50 ml of a sodium hydroxide solution

was required to titrate the excess, unreacted hydrochloric acid. If 1.00 ml of the hydrochloric acid corresponds to 1.25 ml of the sodium hydroxide solution, calculate the percentage of calcium oxide in the sample.

30. The sulfur in a 1.000 gm steel sample was converted to sulfur trioxide, which was, in turn, absorbed in 50.00 ml of a 0.01000 F sodium hydroxide solution. The excess, unreacted sodium hydroxide was titrated with 0.01400 F hydrochloric acid, 22.65 ml being required. Calculate the percentage of sulfur in the steel.

31. Suggest an experimental procedure whereby the ionization constant for an unknown weak monoprotic acid can be determined from the titration curve for that acid, assuming that a pure sample of the unknown acid is available.

32. Construct the titration curve for each of the following titrations:
    (a) 50.00 ml of a 0.5000 F sodium hydroxide solution titrated with 0.5000 F hydrochloric acid
    (b) 50.00 ml of 0.1000 F propionic acid titrated with a 0.1000 F sodium hydroxide solution
    (c) 50.00 ml of a 0.1500 F aqueous ammonia solution titrated with 0.1500 F hydrochloric acid
    (d) 50.00 ml of 0.05000 F acetic acid titrated with a 0.1000 F aqueous ammonia solution
    (e) 50.00 ml of a mixture of 0.1000 F perchloric acid and 0.05000 F propionic acid titrated with a 0.2000 F potassium hydroxide solution
    (f) 50.00 ml of a 0.2000 F disodium hydrogen phosphate solution titrated with 0.5000 F perchloric acid

33. Calculate the pH and the equilibrium concentration of $HPO_4^=$ in a 0.500 F solution of phosphoric acid (H_3PO_4) in water.

34. Calculate the equilibrium concentrations of H^+, NH_4^+, and NH_3 in a solution prepared by dissolving 0.0400 mole of ammonia in a volume of 150 ml of water.

35. Calculate the equilibrium concentrations of NH_4^+ and NH_3 and the pH of the solution obtained from dissolving 0.085 mole of ammonium nitrate and 0.000060 mole of nitric acid in 300 ml of water.

36. Calculate the equilibrium concentrations of H^+, $C_2H_5COO^-$, and C_2H_5COOH in a solution prepared by dissolving 0.0400 mole of propionic acid in 150 ml of distilled water.

37. Calculate the equilibrium concentrations of $C_2H_5COO^-$ and C_2H_5COOH and the pH of the solution obtained by dissolving 0.085 mole of sodium propionate and 0.000050 mole of sodium hydroxide in 250 ml of water.

38. Calculate the pH of a solution prepared by dissolving 0.267 mole of pyridine in 1.00 liter of distilled water.

39. If 0.826 mole of pyridine and 0.492 mole of hydrochloric acid are mixed in 0.500 liter of distilled water, what will be the pH of the resulting solution?

40. Calculate the pH and the equilibrium concentration of $SO_3^=$ in a 0.300 F solution of sulfurous acid in water.

41. Calculate the equilibrium concentrations of H^+, NO_2^-, and HNO_2 in a solution prepared by dissolving 0.100 mole of nitrous acid in 200 ml of distilled water.

42. Calculate the equilibrium concentrations of NO_2^- and HNO_2 and the pH of the solution prepared by dissolving 0.200 mole of potassium nitrite and 0.00030 mole of potassium hydroxide in 2.00 liters of distilled water.

43. Consider the titration of 20.00 ml of 0.01000 F potassium hydroxide with 0.01000 F nitric acid. Calculate the pH of the solution after the addition of the following volumes of titrant: (a) 0 ml, (b) 5.00 ml, (c) 10.00 ml, (d) 15.00 ml, (e) 19.99 ml, (f) 20.00 ml, (g) 25.00 ml.

44. Calculate the equilibrium concentrations of H^+, F^-, and HF in a solution prepared by dissolving 0.100 mole of hydrogen fluoride in 1.00 liter of water.

45. Calculate the equilibrium concentrations of F^- and HF and the pH of the solution prepared by dissolving 0.100 mole of sodium fluoride in 150 ml of distilled water.

46. Consider the titration of 50.00 ml of $1.000 \times 10^{-4} F$ hydrochloric acid with a $1.000 \times 10^{-3} F$ sodium hydroxide solution. Calculate the pH of the solution after the addition of the following volumes of titrant: (a) 0 ml, (b) 1.000 ml, (c) 2.500 ml, (d) 4.900 ml, (e) 4.999 ml, (f) 5.000 ml, (g) 5.555 ml, (h) 6.000 ml.

47. Calculate the equilibrium concentrations of all ionic and molecular species except water, i.e., NH_3, $NH_4{}^+$, H^+, and OH^-, in a solution which initially contains 0.00400 mole of ammonia in 150 ml of distilled water.

48. A 25.00 ml aliquot of a benzoic acid solution was titrated with standard $0.1000 F$ sodium hydroxide, methyl red being used erroneously as the end point indicator. The observed end point occurred at pH 6.20, after the addition of 20.70 ml of the sodium hydroxide titrant.

    (a) Calculate the titration error in per cent with the proper sign.

    (b) Calculate the equivalence point pH for this titration.

    (c) Calculate the concentration of the original benzoic acid solution.

49. The titration curve for the titration of 50.00 ml of a solution containing both sulfuric acid and phosphoric acid with a $1.000 F$ potassium hydroxide solution was followed with a glass electrode pH meter. Among other data, two of the points on the titration curve were:

Volume of KOH added, ml	pH
26.00	7.21
30.00	9.78

Calculate the concentrations of sulfuric and phosphoric acids in the original sample solution.

50. A 1.250 gm sample of a weak monoprotic acid (HZ) was dissolved in 50 ml of water. The volume of a $0.0900 F$ sodium hydroxide solution required to reach the equivalence point was 41.20 ml. During the course of the titration it was observed that, after the addition of 8.24 ml of titrant, the solution pH was 4.30.

    (a) Calculate the formula weight of HZ.

    (b) Calculate the acid dissociation constant of HZ.

    (c) Calculate the theoretical equivalence point pH for the titration.

51. Suppose one desires to determine the concentration C of unknown hydrochloric acid solutions by titration with a standard sodium hydroxide solution of the same C concentration. The titration could be followed with a glass electrode pH meter. If the end point is taken when the pH of the solution exactly reaches the equivalence point pH, if the uncertainty in the pH meter readings is ± 0.02 pH unit, and if one should not want to incur a titration error greater than ± 0.10 per cent, what would be the minimum concentration C of hydrochloric acid which could be titrated by this technique?

52. Calculate and plot the theoretical titration curve for the titration of 25.00 ml of $0.05000 F$ formic acid with $0.1000 F$ sodium hydroxide. Include in your plot the points that correspond to the following volumes in milliliters of sodium hydroxide added: 0, 10.00, 12.45, 12.50, 13.00, and 20.00. What acid-base indicator would you select for this titration? Why? What would be the titration error in per cent with the proper sign if chlorophenol red were used as the indicator? What would be the titration error in per cent with the proper sign if phenolphthalein were used as the indicator?

53. How could the acid dissociation constant for phenol red indicator (which has a pH transition range from 6.7 where the yellow acid form predominates to 8.4 where the red basic form is predominant) be determined experimentally?

54. The equilibria involving the ionization of the tetraprotic substance, ethylene-diaminetetraacetic acid (commonly abbreviated H_4Y), are as follows:

$$H_4Y \rightleftharpoons H_3Y^- + H^+; \qquad pK_1 = 2.00$$
$$H_3Y^- \rightleftharpoons H_2Y^= + H^+; \qquad pK_2 = 2.67$$
$$H_2Y^= \rightleftharpoons HY^{-3} + H^+; \qquad pK_3 = 6.16$$
$$HY^{-3} \rightleftharpoons Y^{-4} + H^+; \qquad pK_4 = 10.26$$

(a) Suppose that you are interested in titrating a solution of the parent acid (H_4Y) with a sodium hydroxide solution and that you follow the progress of the titration with a glass electrode pH meter. How many *distinct* end points would be observed or, in other words, how many "breaks" would the titration curve exhibit?

(b) What would be the pH of the solution corresponding to each of the first two end points?

55. Consider the titration of 100.0 ml of 0.001000 F hydrochloric acid with 0.01000 F barium hydroxide, $Ba(OH)_2$, which is a strong base. Construct the titration curve for this system by calculating and plotting the pH values corresponding to the following volumes of titrant base added: (a) 0 ml, (b) 1.00 ml, (c) 2.00 ml, (d) 4.00 ml, (e) 4.99 ml, (f) 5.00 ml, (g) 6.00 ml.

56. Malonic acid, $HOOC-CH_2-COOH$ (abbreviated H_2M), is a diprotic acid which undergoes the following dissociations:

$$H_2M \rightleftharpoons HM^- + H^+; \qquad pK_1 = 2.86$$
$$HM^- \rightleftharpoons M^= + H^+; \qquad pK_2 = 5.70$$

A 20.00 ml aliquot of a solution containing a mixture of disodium malonate (Na_2M) and sodium hydrogen malonate ($NaHM$) was titrated with 0.01000 F hydrochloric acid. The progress of the titration was followed with a glass electrode pH meter. Two specific points on the titration curve were as follows:

Volume of HCl added, ml	pH
1.00	5.70
10.00	4.28

Calculate the total volume in milliliters of hydrochloric acid required to reach the malonic acid (H_2M) equivalence point.

57. Why is a solution of an acid salt, such as potassium hydrogen tartrate or sodium hydrogen carbonate, a convenient pH standard?

58. A solution was known to contain only sodium carbonate and sodium bicarbonate, and its initial pH was found to be 10.63. When a 25.00 ml aliquot of this solution was titrated with 0.1000 F hydrochloric acid, the pH of the solution after the addition of 21.00 ml of the acid was 6.35. What were the molar concentrations of sodium carbonate and sodium bicarbonate in the original solution? (Note: No distinction is to be made in this problem between $CO_2(aq)$ and H_2CO_3.)

59. Suppose that the following eight acid-base indicators listed in Table 8-1 are available: paramethyl red, methyl orange, bromcresol green, methyl red, chlorophenol red, phenol red, phenolphthalein, and thymolphthalein. Which of these indicators would indicate accurately (within perhaps two or three parts per thousand) the equivalence points of the following titrations? More than one indicator may be suitable, and all suitable ones should be cited.

(a) 0.25 F hydrochloric acid titrated with 0.25 F sodium hydroxide

(b) 0.5 F phosphoric acid titrated to NaH_2PO_4 with 0.5 F sodium hydroxide

(c) 0.5 F phosphoric acid titrated to Na_2HPO_4 with 0.5 F sodium hydroxide

(d) 0.2 F sodium carbonate solution titrated to $NaHCO_3$ with 0.2 F hydrochloric acid

(e) 0.001 F hydrochloric acid titrated with 0.1 F sodium hydroxide

(f) The first equivalence point in the titration of a mixture of 0.05 F hydrochloric acid and 0.05 F propionic acid with 0.10 F sodium hydroxide

(g) The second equivalence point in the titration of part (f)

60. A solution was known to contain only disodium hydrogen phosphate, Na_2HPO_4, and sodium dihydrogen phosphate, NaH_2PO_4. Its initial pH was found to be 8.15. When a 25.00 ml aliquot of this solution was titrated with 0.1000 F hydrochloric acid, the pH of the solution after the addition of 33.00 ml of the hydrochloric acid was 3.15. What were the molar concentrations of $HPO_4^=$ and $H_2PO_4^-$ in the original solution?

61. Consider the titration of 25.00 ml of a 0.2500 F aqueous ammonia solution with 0.2500 F hydrochloric acid. Calculate and plot the complete titration curve (pH versus the volume of titrant), including the points which correspond to the following volumes (in milliliters) of hydrochloric acid added: 0, 5.00, 10.00, 15.00, 20.00, 25.00, 30.00, and 40.00. What acid-base indicator would you select for this titration? What would be the titration error in per cent with the proper sign if methyl orange were used as the indicator? What would be the titration error in per cent with the proper sign if bromthymol blue were used as the indicator?

SUGGESTIONS FOR ADDITIONAL READING

1. R. G. Bates: Concept and determination of pH. *In* I. M. Kolthoff and P. J. Elving, eds.: *Treatise on Analytical Chemistry*, Part I, Volume 1, Wiley-Interscience, New York, 1959, pp. 361–404.

2. R. G. Bates: *Determination of pH*, John Wiley & Sons, Inc., New York, 1964.

3. S. Bruckenstein and I. M. Kolthoff: Acid-base strength and protolysis curves in water. *In* I. M. Kolthoff and P. J. Elving, eds.: *Treatise on Analytical Chemistry*, Part I, Volume 1, Wiley-Interscience, New York, 1959, pp. 421–474.

4. I. M. Kolthoff: Concepts of acids and bases. *In* I. M. Kolthoff and P. J. Elving, eds.: *Treatise on Analytical Chemistry*, Part I, Volume 1, Wiley-Interscience, New York, 1959, pp. 405–420.

5. I. M. Kolthoff and V. A. Stenger: *Volumetric Analysis*, second edition, Volume 2, Wiley-Interscience, New York, 1947, pp. 49–235.

6. C. A. VanderWerf: *Acids, Bases, and the Chemistry of the Covalent Bond*, Reinhold Publishing Corporation, New York, 1961.

Acid-Base Reactions
in Nonaqueous Solvents

As pointed out in the preceding chapter on acid-base equilibria in water, a hydrogen ion cannot exist as a free proton. The form of the hydrogen ion in aqueous medium is the hydronium ion, which is usually written H_3O^+ even though it is undoubtedly more highly hydrated or solvated. In water, other ions and molecules are extensively hydrated as well. In nonaqueous solvents, such as ethanol or glacial acetic acid, the nature of the hydrogen ion and other solutes is less well characterized. However, it is clear that the proton is solvated to a certain extent. So, by analogy to the hydronium ion in water, we shall represent the hydrogen ion in ethanol and in glacial acetic acid by the formulas $C_2H_5OH_2^+$ and $CH_3COOH_2^+$, respectively.

Let us consider the titration of the weak base ammonia (NH_3) with a strong acid in water and in glacial acetic acid. The two titration reactions may be represented by the following equilibria:

(1) $$H_3O^+ + NH_3 \rightleftharpoons H_2O + NH_4^+$$

(2) $$CH_3COOH_2^+ + NH_3 \rightleftharpoons CH_3COOH + NH_4^+$$

As each of these reactions proceeds toward equilibrium from left to right, NH_3 is accepting a proton, and a solvent molecule (water or acetic acid) is accepting a proton as the reverse reaction occurs. The final positions of equilibrium for reactions 1 and 2 are determined by the relative strengths as Brönsted-Lowry bases of NH_3 and H_2O in reaction 1 and of NH_3 and CH_3COOH in reaction 2. In the present example, we know that glacial

329

acetic acid is a much more acidic solvent than water or, conversely, that water is considerably more basic than acetic acid. Therefore, the equilibrium position of reaction 2 lies much farther to the right than that of reaction 1. In other words, NH_3 appears to be a stronger base (or a better proton acceptor) in glacial acetic acid than it is in water because $CH_3COOH_2^+$ is a much better proton donor than H_3O^+. At this point it is worthwhile to recall a statement made in the preceding chapter concerning aqueous acid-base equilibria; that is, in any acid-base reaction the tendency of an acid to lose a proton is closely tied to the affinity of a base for that proton.

This brief introductory discussion leads us to the useful and important conclusion that many bases which are too weak to be titrated with a strong acid in water can be titrated successfully if glacial acetic acid is chosen as the solvent. In glacial acetic acid, such weak bases appear to be much stronger. Other solvents which, like glacial acetic acid, are less basic or more acidic than water could be similarly employed. In addition, we shall discover that weak acids which cannot be titrated in water with strong bases may be determined if the titrations are performed in solvents more basic than water. A solvent which is more basic than water will enhance the strength of a weak acid because such a solvent has a greater affinity for protons. Finally, another key reason why solvents other than water are of analytical interest is that many organic compounds having acidic or basic functional groups are insoluble in water and can be titrated only if they are dissolved in organic solvents or perhaps in mixtures of water and an organic solvent.

In the present chapter, we shall consider several factors which affect acid-base titrations in nonaqueous solvents. Included among these factors are the acid-base properties of the solvent, the autoprotolysis constant of the solvent, and the dielectric constant of the solvent. In addition, some titrations in three representative solvents — glacial acetic acid, anhydrous ethylenediamine, and methyl isobutyl ketone — will be discussed.

SOME PROPERTIES OF SOLVENTS

The acid-base behavior of any solute dissolved in a given solvent will usually depend on the acid-base properties of the solvent relative to the solute, on the autoprotolysis constant of the solvent, and on the dielectric constant of the solvent.

Classification of Solvents. An **amphiprotic solvent** is one capable of acting as either a Brönsted-Lowry acid or base, and the most familiar example of such a solvent is water itself. The amphiprotic character of water is shown by the reaction between one water molecule (acting as an acid) and a second molecule of water (acting as a base):

$$H_2O + H_2O \rightleftharpoons H_3O^+ + OH^-$$

This reaction is the so-called **autoprotolysis** of water. Most alcohols such as methanol and ethanol, undergo analogous autoprotolysis reactions and have acid-base properties similar to water:

$$CH_3OH + CH_3OH \rightleftharpoons CH_3OH_2^+ + CH_3O^-$$

$$C_2H_5OH + C_2H_5OH \rightleftharpoons C_2H_5OH_2^+ + C_2H_5O^-$$

Glacial acetic acid represents a somewhat different kind of amphiprotic solvent. Although glacial acetic acid does undergo the usual type of auto-protolysis reaction,

$$CH_3COOH + CH_3COOH \rightleftharpoons CH_3COOH_2^+ + CH_3COO^-$$

it is a distinctly more acid solvent than water because all bases appear to be stronger in acetic acid than in water. Other solvents such as liquid ammonia

$$NH_3 + NH_3 \rightleftharpoons NH_4^+ + NH_2^-$$

and ethylenediamine

$$H_2N-CH_2CH_2-NH_2 + H_2N-CH_2CH_2-NH_2 \rightleftharpoons$$

$$H_2N-CH_2CH_2-NH_3^+ + H_2N-CH_2CH_2-NH^-$$

exhibit amphiprotic behavior but, compared to water, these are much more basic since they cause all acids to be stronger.

There is another class of solvents, called **inert** or **aprotic solvents,** which do not show any detectable acid or base properties. Benzene, chloroform, and carbon tetrachloride are typical aprotic solvents, for they have no ionizable protons and they have little or no tendency to accept protons from other substances. In general, it is unrealistic to propose an autoprotolysis reaction for such a solvent.

Still another group of solvents includes those which possess definite base properties but which are without acid properties. Consequently, for these solvents an autoprotolysis reaction cannot be written. Therefore, such solvents are frequently included in the list of aprotic or inert solvents. For example, pyridine (C_5H_5N) can accept a proton from a Brönsted-Lowry acid such as water,

but the acid properties of pyridine are virtually nonexistent. Ethers and ketones are capable of accepting protons from strong Brönsted-Lowry acids such as sulfuric acid, but like pyridine they have no ionizable protons.

The Leveling Effect and Differentiating Ability of a Solvent. In aqueous acid-base chemistry the strongest acids known are the so-called mineral acids — perchloric acid, sulfuric acid, hydrochloric acid, and nitric acid. In water these acids all appear to be equally strong; it is impossible to decide whether any real differences in acid strength exist for these acids. If we study the acid strengths of perchloric acid and hydrochloric acid in water, the following acid-base equilibria are involved:

$$HClO_4 + H_2O \rightleftharpoons ClO_4^- + H_3O^+$$
$$HCl + H_2O \rightleftharpoons Cl^- + H_3O^+$$

Since $HClO_4$ and HCl are both much stronger acids than the hydronium ion, H_3O^+ (or because water is a stronger base than either ClO_4^- or Cl^-), the position of equilibrium in each case lies so far to the right that it is impossible experimentally to distinguish any difference between the two equilibrium positions. Because the strengths of perchloric and hydrochloric acids appear to be identical in water, we speak of water as exerting a **leveling effect** on these two acids.

If the same acids, $HClO_4$ and HCl, are compared in glacial acetic acid as solvent, the pertinent acid-base reactions are

$$HClO_4 + CH_3COOH \rightleftharpoons ClO_4^- + CH_3COOH_2^+$$

and

$$HCl + CH_3COOH \rightleftharpoons Cl^- + CH_3COOH_2^+$$

In the beginning of this chapter, we stated that glacial acetic acid is a much weaker base than water and that the protonated acetic acid molecule ($CH_3COOH_2^+$) is a stronger acid than the hydronium ion (H_3O^+). The relative weakness as a base of CH_3COOH and the strength of $CH_3COOH_2^+$ as an acid both act to decrease the extent of the acid-base reactions in glacial acetic acid compared to water. In fact, neither of these acid-base reactions proceeds so far toward the right in acetic acid as in water. However, the greater acid strength of perchloric acid shows up in the fact that its reaction with the glacial acetic acid solvent attains a greater degree of completion than the reaction of hydrochloric acid with the solvent. In the present example, we find that glacial acetic acid possesses the capability to differentiate the acid strengths of $HClO_4$ and HCl. We call it a **differentiating solvent.**

It is very important to recognize that the *leveling* or *differentiating* effect of a solvent depends to a large extent on the acid-base properties of the solvent relative to the dissolved solutes. Thus, although water is a very poor choice of solvent to differentiate the acid strengths of $HClO_4$ and HCl, it is a good solvent to differentiate a mineral acid such as $HClO_4$ or HCl from the much weaker acetic acid. However, a strongly basic solvent such as liquid ammonia would fail to differentiate a mineral acid from acetic acid because the reactions

$$HClO_4 + NH_3 \rightleftharpoons ClO_4^- + NH_4^+$$

and

$$CH_3COOH + NH_3 \rightleftharpoons CH_3COO^- + NH_4^+$$

would both proceed virtually to completion because of the great base strength of NH_3 and the relative weakness of NH_4^+ as an acid.

   The Autoprotolysis Constant. Another factor which affects the differentiating ability of a given solvent is its *autoprotolysis constant*, which we will designate by K_s. In our discussion of the classification of solvents, we mentioned that an amphiprotic solvent is one that is capable of acting both as an acid and a base. If we represent an amphiprotic solvent as SH, the general form of the autoprotolysis reaction is

$$SH + SH \rightleftharpoons HSH^+ + S^-$$

The equilibrium expression for this reaction has the form

$$\frac{(HSH^+)(S^-)}{(SH)^2} = K_{eq}$$

where the parentheses denote activities or "effective" concentrations. However, by convention the activity of the pure solvent (SH) is taken to be unity. In addition, for the majority of solvents the extent of the autoprotolysis reaction is quite small, so that it is permissible to replace activities of ions, e.g., HSH^+ and S^-, by their analytical concentrations. Thus, the usual simplified form for the autoprotolysis equilibrium expression is

$$[HSH^+][S^-] = K_s$$

in which K_s is the autoprotolysis constant. For water the ion-product constant K_w and the autoprotolysis constant K_s are synonymous.

$$[H_3O^+][OH^-] = [H^+][OH^-] = K_w = K_s = 1.00 \times 10^{-14}$$

Values of pK_s, the negative base-ten logarithm of the autoprotolysis constant, for several different solvents at 25°C are as follows: water, 14.0; ethanol, 19.1; methanol, 16.7; acetic acid, 14.5; formic acid, 6.2; and ethylenediamine, 15.3.

   We must now decide how the magnitude of the autoprotolysis constant is related to the differentiating ability of a solvent. To establish a basis for subsequent discussion, let us consider the familiar case of water, which has an autoprotolysis constant (K_s or K_w) of 1.00×10^{-14} at 25°C. In the preceding chapter on aqueous acid-base titrimetry, it was shown for the titration of $0.1\,F$ strong acid with $0.1\,F$ strong base (or for the reverse titration) that the pH range within which one part per thousand precision and accuracy can be achieved is from about pH 4 to pH 10, i.e., approximately six pH units total or three pH units on each side of the neutral point. This range of pH values is significant in another way, because it represents the so-called useful pH range of the solvent water. Between pH 4 and 10 the relative strengths of acids in water can be differentiated, as suggested by Figure 8-4, for example. Below pH 4 and above pH 10, water exerts a definite leveling effect on acids and bases dissolved in it. It should be noted that these two pH extremes correspond, respectively, to the pH of a $10^{-4} F$ strong acid solution and to the pH of a $10^{-4} F$ strong base solution; this information will be useful later.

Compare these observations for water with the situation for ethanol. Ethanol has an autoprotolysis reaction of the form

$$C_2H_5OH + C_2H_5OH \rightleftharpoons C_2H_5OH_2^+ + C_2H_5O^-$$

and an autoprotolysis-constant expression given by the relation

$$[C_2H_5OH_2^+][C_2H_5O^-] = K_s = 7.9 \times 10^{-20}$$

The $C_2H_5OH_2^+$ ion in ethanol is the counterpart of the hydronium ion in an aqueous medium, and the ethoxide ion $(C_2H_5O^-)$ is the equivalent of the hydroxide ion. Let us assume that pH represents the negative logarithm of the $C_2H_5OH_2^+$ concentration. If 10^{-4} mole of strong acid is dissolved in a liter of ethanol, the predominant proton-containing species will be the $C_2H_5OH_2^+$ ion and, according to the previous arguments, the pH will be 4.0. The best choice of strong base for acid-base titrimetry in ethanol is an alkali metal salt of the solvent, for example, sodium ethoxide $(Na^+C_2H_5O^-)$. If we dissolve 10^{-4} mole of sodium ethoxide in one liter of ethanol, the concentration of $C_2H_5O^-$ will be $10^{-4} M$, and the concentration of $C_2H_5OH_2^+$ and the pH may be calculated as follows:

$$[C_2H_5OH_2^+] = \frac{K_s}{[C_2H_5O^-]} = \frac{7.9 \times 10^{-20}}{1.0 \times 10^{-4}} = 7.9 \times 10^{-16} M$$

$$pC_2H_5OH_2 = pH = 15.1$$

Therefore, in ethanol the pH range encompassed by a $10^{-4} F$ strong acid solution and a $10^{-4} F$ strong base solution is $(15.1 - 4.0)$ or 11.1 pH units, almost twice as great as the useful pH range of six units in water.

It should be emphasized that obvious differences in the chemical and physical properties of the two solvents, water and ethanol, mean that a pH of, say, 7.00 in water is definitely not the same as a pH of 7.00 in ethanol. In general, it is difficult, and in many cases almost impossible, to relate the pH scales for two different solvents to each other in a quantitative way.

The general conclusion to be drawn from these calculations is that the useful pH range for a solvent increases as the autoprotolysis constant decreases. In other words, the smaller the autoprotolysis constant, the greater is the range of acid or base strengths which can exist in a solvent and the greater is the likelihood that it will be a differentiating solvent. It is evident, for example, that formic acid with an autoprotolysis constant of 6.3×10^{-7} ($pK_s = 6.2$) is a poor differentiating solvent because only a very narrow range of acid strengths can exist in it.

The overall differentiating ability of a particular solvent must be carefully assessed in terms of the acid-base properties of the solvent relative to the solutes dissolved in it and in terms of the autoprotolysis constant. Water, with an autoprotolysis constant of 1.00×10^{-14} at $25°C$, cannot differentiate the strong mineral acids because it is a relatively basic solvent.

On the other hand, glacial acetic acid has an autoprotolysis constant of similar magnitude (3.2×10^{-15}), but the mineral acids are differentiated in it because of the acidic character of glacial acetic acid.

Effect of the Dielectric Constant. Another factor to be considered in nonaqueous acid-base titrimetry is that, compared to water, most other solvents have low dielectric constants.

The reaction of an *uncharged* solute acid BH with a solvent SH may be formulated as follows:

$$BH + SH \underset{\text{ionization step}}{\xrightleftharpoons{\qquad\qquad}} \{B^-HSH^+\} \underset{\text{dissociation step}}{\xrightleftharpoons{\qquad\qquad}} B^- + HSH^+$$

The reaction between BH and SH, which is called the *ionization step*, gives rise to the ion-pair B^-HSH^+ in which a proton has been transferred from the solute acid BH to the solvent SH. There is a definite separation of charges in such an ion-pair, although the individual ions B^- and HSH^+ are very close to each other. The second step of the process, termed *dissociation*, occurs when additional solvent molecules attack the ion-pair B^-HSH^+ and separate it completely into the solvated ions B^- and HSH^+. The force of attraction (F) between two charged particles of charges q_1 and q_2, respectively, is given by Coulomb's law,

$$F = \frac{q_1 q_2}{Dr^2}$$

where r is the distance which separates the two charged particles and D is the dielectric constant of the medium (solvent) in which the particles exist.

The dielectric constant of a solvent is a measure of the ease of separation of two oppositely charged ions or the ease of dissociation of an ion-pair in that solvent. For solvents of high dielectric constant such as water ($D = 78.5$ at 25°C), the force of attraction between the ions of an ion-pair is relatively small and the dissociation step will be virtually complete. However, for solvents having low dielectric constants (ethanol, $D = 24.3$; acetic acid, $D = 6.1$; ethylenediamine, $D = 12.5$; methyl isobutyl ketone, $D = 13.1$; acetone, $D = 20.7$; and benzene, $D = 2.3$), there is considerable ion pairing as well as formation of larger ion aggregates.

The effect of dielectric constant on the strength of a solute acid can be illustrated qualitatively if we contrast the behavior of acetic acid in water and in ethanol. Since the ionization and dissociation of acetic acid molecules in a given solvent lead to the formation of protonated solvent molecules (HSH^+) and negatively charged acetate ions (CH_3COO^-), the acid strength of acetic acid would be enhanced in a solvent of high dielectric constant, such as water, which facilitates the separation of charged species. However, in ethanol which has a lower dielectric constant, the formation and separation of ion-pairs of the type $CH_3COO^-{}^+H_2OC_2H_5$ would not be favored, so the strength of acetic acid should be less in ethanol than in water.

It is interesting to note that the acidity of a *positively charged* solute of the type BH^+ should be substantially unaffected by variations in the dielectric constant of the solvent. The reason for this is that the transfer of a proton from BH^+ to SH does not produce an ion-pair:

$$BH^+ + SH \xrightleftharpoons[\text{ionization step}]{} \{B\ HSH^+\} \xrightleftharpoons[\text{dissociation step}]{} B + HSH^+$$

Therefore, in the absence of ion-pairs, neither the ionization step nor the dissociation step involves the separation of charges. This line of reasoning might be expected to apply in the case of species such as ammonium ion $(NH_4{}^+)$ or pyridinium ion $(C_5H_5NH^+)$. The picture is not quite so simple, however, because the $NH_4{}^+$ species, for example, would be added to the solvent in the form of an ammonium salt, the anion of which would undoubtedly form ion-pairs with $NH_4{}^+$ and thereby influence its acid strength.

A low dielectric constant for a given solvent (SH) has a pronounced effect on the autoprotolysis constant K_s of that solvent. The detailed process of autoprotolysis should actually include an ion-pair intermediate as shown by the following reaction scheme:

$$SH + SH \xrightleftharpoons[\text{ionization step}]{} \{S^-HSH^+\} \xrightleftharpoons[\text{dissociation step}]{} S^- + HSH^+$$

The autoprotolysis constant is the product of an *ionization constant* and a *dissociation constant*,

$$K_s = [HSH^+][S^-] = K_{\text{ioniz}}K_{\text{diss}}$$

If the magnitude of the dissociation constant, K_{diss}, is small because the dielectric constant of the solvent is low, the autoprotolysis constant K_s is also likely to be small. This effect seems to be operative for glacial acetic acid which has a surprisingly low dielectric constant of 6.1 and an autoprotolysis constant of 3.5×10^{-15}. In sharp contrast to acetic acid is anhydrous formic acid. Although formic acid is chemically very similar to acetic acid, its autoprotolysis constant is 6.3×10^{-7}. Such a relatively large autoprotolysis constant is partly explicable on the basis of the high dielectric constant of 58.5 for formic acid which promotes the dissociation of ion-pairs of the type $HCOO^-HCOOH_2{}^+$. The unique properties of water as a solvent stem from its unusually high dielectric constant and its relatively small autoprotolysis constant. The ion-product or autoprotolysis constant for water of 1.00×10^{-14} at $25°C$ permits a reasonably wide range of acid strengths to exist in aqueous solutions. The formation of hydrogen bonds between water molecules is responsible for the high dielectric constant of this solvent. In turn, such a large dielectric constant means that the formation of ion-pairs in solutions containing dissolved solutes at ordinary concentration levels, e.g., 0.01 or 0.10 M, does not occur to any significant extent.

TITRATIONS IN BASIC SOLVENTS

The titration of weakly acidic substances in aqueous media is limited in general to those species whose acid dissociation constants or K_a values are not smaller than approximately 10^{-8} to 10^{-7} in water. A significant factor determining the feasibility of such a titration is the strength of the acid relative to the base strength of the solvent water. Acids which possess dissociation constants below about 10^{-7} in water are too weak to provide adequately sharp titration curves for titrations performed in an aqueous medium with the common strong titrant bases such as sodium or potassium hydroxide. On the other hand, the use of solvents which are more basic than water can greatly improve the sharpness of titration curves and the accuracy of the titrations themselves by enhancing the strengths of the solute acids.

Typical Solvents and Titrants. Among the common basic solvents are butylamine, ethylenediamine, dimethylformamide, and liquid ammonia (which can be used only at low temperatures). Methanol-benzene mixtures are sometimes used for nonaqueous acid-base titrations.

The role of a basic solvent in making possible the titration of very weak acids can be seen from the following examples. Solutions of both hydrochloric and acetic acids in butylamine are ionized virtually completely according to the reactions

$$HCl + C_4H_9NH_2 \rightleftharpoons C_4H_9NH_3{}^+Cl^-$$

and

$$CH_3COOH + C_4H_9NH_2 \rightleftharpoons C_4H_9NH_3{}^+{}^-OOCCH_3$$

However, because butylamine (as well as the other basic solvents named) has a low dielectric constant ($D = 5.3$ at $25°C$), these two acids exist almost entirely as undissociated ion-pairs. Acetic acid, which is rather weak in water, is leveled to the strength of a strong acid in butylamine because of the great affinity of this solvent for protons. Other acids, which are much weaker than acetic acid and far too weak to be titrated successfully with a strong base in water, become sufficiently strong in butylamine to make their titrations feasible. For example, phenol (C_6H_5OH) is such a weak acid in water ($K_a = 10^{-10}$) that the reaction

scarcely proceeds at all. However, when phenol is dissolved in butylamine, the transfer of a proton from the solute acid to the solvent base occurs to a large extent,

with the resultant formation of ion-pairs.

The selection of a titrant base for a nonaqueous acid-base titration is as important as the choice of solvent itself. First of all, the base strength of the titrant must be comparable to the base strength of the conjugate base of the solvent for best results. An example from aqueous acid-base titrimetry will illustrate the point. The titration of acetic acid with sodium hydroxide in water yields a sharply defined titration curve with an easily detected end point (Fig. 8-3). Imagine, however, the shape of the titration curve, especially the greatly diminished sharpness of the curve in the region of the equivalence point, if the much weaker base ammonia is used as the titrant instead of sodium hydroxide. The conclusion to be drawn is that, if possible, one should employ a salt of the conjugate base of the solvent as the titrant, since this is the strongest base which is capable of existence in a given solvent. To use a weak titrant base in a strongly basic solvent is to defeat the whole purpose of the nonaqueous titration.

A wide variety of titrant bases has been employed for nonaqueous titrations. When simple alcohols such as methanol or ethanol are used as solvents for the titrimetric determinations of carboxylic acids, the usual titrants are sodium methoxide or sodium ethoxide in the corresponding alcoholic solvent. Such titrants are prepared by the reaction between pure sodium metal and the anhydrous alcohol. Occasionally, it is possible to use alcoholic solutions of sodium or potassium hydroxide as titrants. Ethylenediamine is one of the outstanding basic solvents for use in the titration of weak and very weak acids. However, the sodium salt of the conjugate base of ethylenediamine is not sufficiently soluble in the parent solvent to permit its preparation and use as the titrant. As an alternative, sodium aminoethoxide ($Na^{+-}O—CH_2CH_2—NH_2$) in ethylenediamine-ethanolamine solvent mixtures has been recommended as a suitable titrant. Another class of titrant bases which have gained in popularity in recent years is the tetraalkylammonium hydroxides. For example, tetrabutylammonium hydroxide, which has the formula $(C_4H_9)_4N^+OH^-$, may be prepared in a variety of solvents, including alcohols and benzene-alcohol mixtures, if one passes a solution of tetrabutylammonium iodide through an anion-exchange column in the hydroxide form. Alternatively, the $(C_4H_9)_4N^+I^-$ solution may be treated with silver oxide followed by removal of silver iodide and the excess silver oxide.

A few words should be added concerning the handling and storage of strongly basic solvents and titrant solutions. Even more than aqueous sodium hydroxide solutions, they quickly absorb atmospheric carbon dioxide and other acidic impurities, and so they should be guarded carefully. Furthermore, the absorption of moisture can be equally detrimental to the proper behavior of nonaqueous titrants and solvents because the presence of even a trace of water in these nonaqueous systems can exert a pronounced leveling effect on the strengths of solute acids — and perhaps prevent them from being titrated at all.

End Point Detection.   The problem of end point detection in nonaqueous titrations is by no means a trivial one. For one thing the pH ranges over which colored acid-base indicators change color in nonaqueous solvents are different from water. Furthermore, since most of these solvents have low dielectric constants, the acid-base indicators exist as ion-pairs, and the ion-pair equilibria themselves are complicated because of variations in the charges and charge types (cationic, neutral, and anionic) exhibited by the indicators in their different forms. In addition, the whole concept of a pH scale must be modified for solvent systems other than water. Nevertheless, several of the more familiar acid-base indicators, including methyl violet, methyl red, phenolphthalein, and thymolphthalein, have been found to function satisfactorily in certain nonaqueous titrations. Frequently, the color changes are not the same as in water, probably because of ion-pairing phenomena and other structural (electronic) changes in the indicator molecules caused by the solvent environment.

In practice, the progress of an acid-base titration may be best followed potentiometrically. Details concerning the techniques of potentiometric titrations are described in Chapter 17. Briefly stated, a potentiometric acid-base titration consists of measuring, as a function of the volume of titrant added, the potential or emf developed between a reference electrode and a suitable indicator electrode, the latter being sensitive to the hydrogen ion activity of the solution. The resulting titration curves appear as those shown in Figures 8-2 through 8-8. The end point or equivalence point of a titration can be located by visual inspection of the complete titration curve. For aqueous acid-base titrations, the potential readings in volts or millivolts are usually expressed in terms of pH units. However, because of the fundamental difficulties of relating the aqueous pH scale to pH values in nonaqueous solvents, it is preferable not to attempt a conversion of voltage readings to pH values.

The design and construction of suitable reference and indicator electrodes for nonaqueous potentiometric titrations can pose some difficult problems. The familiar glass electrode used for pH measurements and titrations in aqueous media may not perform properly when it is immersed in strongly basic and nonaqueous solvents. This malfunction is frequently due to the so-called "alkaline" or "sodium-ion" error, in which the response of the electrode to changes in the hydrogen ion activity ceases when the relative concentration of sodium ions (introduced through the addition of titrant bases) is large. In addition, the presence of water molecules within the glass membrane itself is apparently essential to the mechanism of operation of a glass electrode, and this water is "leached" by nonaqueous solvents to which the electrode is exposed. The antimony oxide electrode, the stainless steel electrode, and even several forms of the classic hydrogen gas electrode have been employed instead of the glass electrode. The roster of reference electrodes for nonaqueous titrations includes the aqueous saturated calomel electrode (SCE) as well as several nonaqueous versions of the calomel electrode.

Examples of Substances Titrated.   We have suggested at least two classes of weakly acidic organic compounds which can be titrated in basic solvents. These are carboxylic acids and phenols. Carboxylic acids are sufficiently strong, having pK_a values in water in the neighborhood of 5 or 6, that only modestly basic solvents such as methanol or ethanol are needed to obtain nicely defined titration curves with sharp end points. On the other hand, the determination of phenols, which have pK_a values of approximately 10 in water, requires a much more basic solvent than an alcohol. Anhydrous ethylenediamine is an excellent solvent, provided that care is taken to remove and exclude traces of water from the system.

Several other general types of weak acids that have not been previously mentioned may be titrated in basic solvents; they are sulfonamides, alcohols, and certain salts of amines. Sulfonamides, known more familiarly as the sulfa drugs, possess the —SO_2NH— group whose acidity is considerably enhanced in basic solvents such as butylamine or ethylenediamine. For example, sulfanilamide can be determined by titration with sodium methoxide in butylamine. The addition of sulfanilamide to butylamine results in the following acid-base reaction:

The titration reaction itself can be represented as

Mixtures of sulfonamides can be analyzed by taking advantage of the different acid strengths of these compounds in various solvents.

A wide variety of amine salts can be determined by titration in basic solvents. One representative example of such a titration involves butylamine hydrochloride, $C_4H_9NH_3{}^+Cl^-$. Although the acid strength of $C_4H_9NH_3{}^+$ is indeed slight in a solvent such as water, the addition of ethylenediamine to an aqueous suspension of butylamine hydrochloride not only dissolves the amine salt but increases the apparent acid strength of $C_4H_9NH_3{}^+$ to the point where it can be titrated with sodium methoxide. Thus, the overall titration reaction may be written as

$$C_4H_9NH_3{}^+Cl^- + CH_3O^-Na^+ \rightleftharpoons C_4H_9NH_2 + CH_3OH + Na^+Cl^-$$

One interesting and necessary requirement for the successful titration of amine salts is that the anion of the salt cannot be too strong a base. If it is, it may compete so well with the titrant base in competition for the proton that a poorly defined end point is obtained. Among the other amine salts which have been successfully titrated are methylamine hydrochloride $(CH_3NH_3{}^+Cl^-)$, pyridine perchlorate $(C_5H_5NH^+ClO_4{}^-)$, and quinine sulfate.

QUANTITATIVE TREATMENT OF EQUILIBRIA AND TITRATIONS IN ETHYLENEDIAMINE*

Ethylenediamine $(H_2N—CH_2CH_2—NH_2)$ is a strongly basic solvent with properties that render it particularly applicable to the titrations of numerous weakly acidic substances, including carboxylic acids, phenols, and amino acids. It has a much greater viscosity than water and has a pungent odor resembling that of ammonia. It melts at $11°C$ and boils at $117°C$ and thus is a suitable solvent for use over a relatively wide range of temperatures.

Figures 9-1 and 9-2 compare and contrast curves for the titrations of benzoic acid and phenol with sodium hydroxide in water and for the titrations of these acids with sodium aminoethoxide $(Na^+{}^-O—CH_2CH_2—NH_2)$ as the titrant in ethylenediamine. An inspection of these titration curves suggests the conclusion that benzoic acid behaves as a strong acid in ethylenediamine because its titration curve is extremely well defined, much like that of a strong acid–strong base titration in water. Similarly, the titration curve for phenol in ethylenediamine is as sharply defined as that for the titration of benzoic acid with sodium hydroxide in an aqueous medium. However, although benzoic acid appears to behave as a strong acid in ethylenediamine, it is not completely dissociated as might be expected on the basis of the analogy to a strong acid in water. In fact, there are no completely dissociated electrolytes in ethylenediamine because of its low dielectric constant $(D = 12.5$ at $25°C)$. Even ionic compounds such as sodium bromide or sodium nitrate are only slightly dissociated electrolytes. Consequently it is necessary to consider the effects of ion-pair formation on acid-base titrations in ethylenediamine.

Ion-Pair Formation in Ethylenediamine. We have already pointed out that there is extensive ion-pair formation in any solvent with a

---

* This section of the chapter is intended as supplementary material and may be omitted if desired.

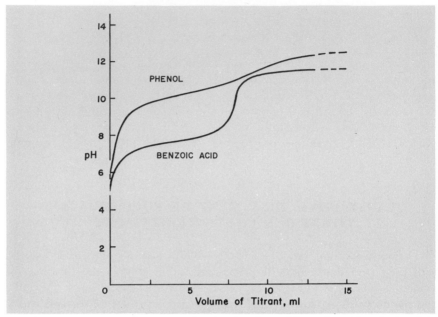

FIGURE 9-1. Titration curves for the titrations of benzoic acid and phenol in water with a 0.5 F sodium hydroxide solution. [Redrawn, with permission, from the paper by M. L. Moss, J. H. Elliott, and R. T. Hall: Anal. Chem., *20*, 784 (1948).]

low dielectric constant. Consider a univalent-univalent salt such as sodium bromide. Sodium bromide dissolved in ethylenediamine exists largely as ion-pairs (Na^+Br^-) with the dissociated sodium and bromide ions being in equilibrium with the ion-pairs according to the reaction

$$Na^+ + Br^- \rightleftharpoons Na^+Br^-$$

The ion-pair formation constant expression may be written in the form

$$K_{NaBr} = \frac{(Na^+Br^-)}{(Na^+)(Br^-)} = 3950$$

where K_{NaBr} is the formation constant for the ion-pair, and the terms in parentheses represent the activities of the species involved in the equilibrium. The evaluation of ion-pair formation constants can be accomplished by conductance measurements. Most salts have ion-pair formation constants ranging from 1000 to 10,000 in ethylenediamine.

The preceding equilibrium expression can be simplified because the activity coefficient for the uncharged ion-pair is essentially unity. In addition, if the total analytical concentration of dissolved sodium bromide is 0.05 F or greater, it is reasonable to neglect the dissociation of ion-pairs and to assume that the Na$^+$Br$^-$ concentration is nearly equal to the original total sodium bromide concentration, C_{NaBr}. Thus the ion-pair formation constant expression becomes

$$K_{NaBr} = \frac{C_{NaBr}}{(Na^+)(Br^-)}$$

For a salt such as sodium bromide, the activities of sodium and bromide ions are taken to be equal, and the individual ion activities are given by the relation

$$(Na^+) = (Br^-) = \left(\frac{C_{NaBr}}{K_{NaBr}}\right)^{1/2}$$

Solutions of Acids in Ethylenediamine. When an acid such as hydrogen bromide is dissolved in ethylenediamine, the following reaction occurs:

$$HBr + H_2N\!-\!CH_2CH_2\!-\!NH_2 \rightleftharpoons H_2N\!-\!CH_2CH_2\!-\!NH_3{}^+Br^-$$

Similarly, if hydrogen bromide is dissolved in water, the reaction

$$HBr + H_2O \rightleftharpoons H_3O^+ + Br^-$$

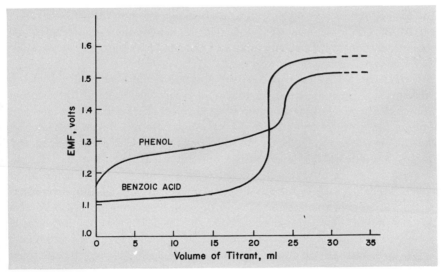

FIGURE 9-2.   Titration curves for the titrations of benzoic acid and phenol in ethylenediamine (a strongly basic solvent). The titrant was 0.2 F sodium aminoethoxide dissolved in a mixture of ethanolamine and ethylenediamine. The use of a much more basic titrant solvent system enhances the acidity of benzoic acid and phenol and makes the titration curves more sharply defined than in Figure 9-1. Although expressed in different units, the size of the vertical scale is the same as in Figure 9-1. [Redrawn, with permission, from the paper by M. L. Moss, J. H. Elliott, and R. T. Hall: Anal. Chem., *20*, 784 (1948).]

proceeds completely from left to right. The species $H_2N—CH_2CH_2—NH_3^+$ in ethylenediamine is the counterpart of the hydronium ion (H_3O^+) in an aqueous medium. A further difference between water and ethylenediamine solutions of hydrogen bromide is that no ion-pairs exist in the former, whereas in the latter solvent the ion-pair $H_2N—CH_2CH_2—NH_3^+Br^-$ is overwhelmingly predominant. If we abbreviate this ion-pair as H^+Br^-, the equilibrium between dissociated and undissociated ion-pairs can be written as follows:

$$H^+ + Br^- \rightleftharpoons H^+Br^-$$

The ion-pair formation constant is

$$K_{HBr} = \frac{(H^+Br^-)}{(H^+)(Br^-)} = 4180$$

Making the same kind of assumptions as for our previous discussion of sodium bromide ion-pairs, we may write

$$K_{HBr} = \frac{C_{HBr}}{(H^+)(Br^-)}$$

and

$$(H^+) = (Br^-) = \left(\frac{C_{HBr}}{K_{HBr}}\right)^{1/2}$$

The last equation reveals the very interesting fact that the hydrogen ion activity of a solution of a *mineral acid* in ethylenediamine depends on the square root of the total concentration of the acid. This result exactly parallels the behavior of *weak acids* in water.

Mixtures of Salts and Acids.   When an acid is neutralized with a base during a titration, a salt of that acid is formed as one of the reaction products. Therefore, it is of interest to determine how the hydrogen ion activity, (H^+) or $(H_2N—CH_2CH_2—NH_3^+)$, is affected by the presence of this salt. As one example, let us consider a mixture of hydrobromic acid and sodium bromide in ethylenediamine and let us assume that the sodium bromide acts as the only significant source of bromide ions. This assumption will certainly be justified if the analytical concentration of sodium bromide is much greater than the amount of acid present. The assumption would also be valid if the ion-pair formation constant for H^+Br^- were considerably larger (more association) than that for Na^+Br^-; however, this is not the case for the present situation. Thus, the bromide ion activity may be obtained solely from the ion-pair formation constant for sodium bromide:

$$(Br^-) = \left(\frac{C_{NaBr}}{K_{NaBr}}\right)^{1/2}$$

where C_{NaBr} is the total analytical concentration of sodium bromide present in the acid-salt mixture.

The general expression for the hydrogen ion activity in any solution of hydrogen bromide in ethylenediamine is

$$(\mathrm{H^+}) = \frac{C_{\mathrm{HBr}}}{K_{\mathrm{HBr}}(\mathrm{Br^-})}$$

but, since the bromide ion activity is governed only by the presence of the large excess of sodium bromide, we may simply combine the two preceding equations to calculate the hydrogen ion activity:

$$(\mathrm{H^+}) = \frac{C_{\mathrm{HBr}}}{K_{\mathrm{HBr}}} \left(\frac{K_{\mathrm{NaBr}}}{C_{\mathrm{NaBr}}} \right)^{1/2}$$

On the basis of this result for a mixture of HBr and NaBr in which the activity of the common anion, $(\mathrm{Br^-})$, is determined by the concentration of NaBr alone, we conclude that the hydrogen ion activity is directly proportional to the analytical concentration (C_{HBr}) of the HBr. This behavior is identical to that expected for a strong acid in water, so we have our first hint as to why an acid which is really only slightly dissociated in ethylenediamine can behave as a strong or completely dissociated acid.

Other acid-salt mixtures can be prepared in which the acid and the salt both make appreciable contributions to the anion activity. For a mixture containing more or less similar concentrations of sodium bromide and hydrobromic acid, the activity of bromide ion may be considered equal to the sum of the sodium and hydrogen ion activities:

$$(\mathrm{Br^-}) = (\mathrm{Na^+}) + (\mathrm{H^+})$$

This relation is simply a statement of the law of electroneutrality. The activities of $\mathrm{Na^+}$ and $\mathrm{H^+}$ may be expressed in terms of the total bromide ion activity, the appropriate ion-pair formation constants, and the analytical concentrations of the salt and acid:

$$(\mathrm{Br^-}) = \frac{C_{\mathrm{NaBr}}}{K_{\mathrm{NaBr}}(\mathrm{Br^-})} + \frac{C_{\mathrm{HBr}}}{K_{\mathrm{HBr}}(\mathrm{Br^-})}$$

The bromide ion activity, $(\mathrm{Br^-})$, can be obtained by solving the preceding equation:

$$(\mathrm{Br^-})^2 = \frac{C_{\mathrm{NaBr}}}{K_{\mathrm{NaBr}}} + \frac{C_{\mathrm{HBr}}}{K_{\mathrm{HBr}}}$$

$$(\mathrm{Br^-}) = \left(\frac{C_{\mathrm{NaBr}}}{K_{\mathrm{NaBr}}} + \frac{C_{\mathrm{HBr}}}{K_{\mathrm{HBr}}} \right)^{1/2}$$

or

$$(\mathrm{Br^-}) = \left(\frac{C_{\mathrm{NaBr}}K_{\mathrm{HBr}} + C_{\mathrm{HBr}}K_{\mathrm{NaBr}}}{K_{\mathrm{NaBr}} \cdot K_{\mathrm{HBr}}} \right)^{1/2}$$

As before, the derivation of these relationships includes the assumption that we may neglect changes in the analytical concentrations of sodium bromide and hydrobromic acid due to the dissociation of the ion-pairs Na^+Br^- and H^+Br^-.

Since the general relation for the hydrogen ion activity was shown to be

$$(H^+) = \frac{C_{HBr}}{K_{HBr}(Br^-)}$$

for any ethylenediamine solution containing hydrogen bromide, the previous equation for (Br^-) may be substituted into this last expression to yield

$$(H^+) = \frac{C_{HBr}}{K_{HBr}} \left(\frac{K_{NaBr} \cdot K_{HBr}}{C_{NaBr}K_{HBr} + C_{HBr}K_{NaBr}} \right)^{1/2}$$

The latter equation is a perfectly general result, applicable to any mixture of salt and acid. However, it is possible to recognize within this expression two limiting cases. If the amount of acid present in the mixture is comparatively large, $C_{HBr} \gg C_{NaBr}$, or if the association of sodium bromide ion pairs is much greater than that of H^+Br^- ion-pairs ($K_{NaBr} \gg K_{HBr}$), the equation may be simplified to

$$(H^+) = \left(\frac{C_{HBr}}{K_{HBr}} \right)^{1/2}$$

On the other hand, when the opposite circumstances prevail, $C_{NaBr} \gg C_{HBr}$ or $K_{HBr} \gg K_{NaBr}$, the complicated equation becomes

$$(H^+) = \frac{C_{HBr}}{K_{HBr}} \left(\frac{K_{NaBr}}{C_{NaBr}} \right)^{1/2}$$

Thus, depending on the relative amounts of the acid and the salt and the magnitudes of the ion-pair formation constants, the hydrogen ion activity may vary in the way expected of either a "strong" or a "weak" acid.

Acid-Base Titrations in Ethylenediamine. The high base strength of ethylenediamine causes almost any monoprotic acid (HX) dissolved in it to exist mainly in the form of $H_2N-CH_2CH_2-NH_3^+X^-$ ion-pairs.

$$HX + H_2N-CH_2CH_2-NH_2 \rightleftharpoons H_2N-CH_2CH_2-NH_3^+X^-$$

As a base for neutralization titrations in ethylenediamine, a logical choice is the sodium salt of the conjugate base of the solvent, i.e.,

$$Na^+-NH-CH_2CH_2-NH_2.$$

This would parallel the use of sodium hydroxide in aqueous acid-base titrations. Unfortunately, the preparation of an ethylenediamine solution of this base is unsuccessful because of the small solubility of this substance, so usually the sodium salt of another related compound is employed as the titrant. Many workers have recommended the use of a titrant solution of sodium aminoethoxide, $Na^+{}^-O$—CH_2CH_2—NH_2, in ethylenediamine. Presumably, any of the other alkali metal salts of aminoethanol would be suitable. Therefore, we will write the titrant base in a general way as $M^+{}^-O$—CH_2CH_2—NH_2. We can formulate the overall titration reaction as

$$H_2N—CH_2CH_2—NH_3{}^+X^- + M^+{}^-O—CH_2CH_2—NH_2 \rightleftharpoons$$

$$M^+X^- + HO—CH_2CH_2—NH_2 + H_2N—CH_2CH_2—NH_2$$

Let us investigate some of the properties of an acid-base titration curve in ethylenediamine. As a relatively simple example, we can consider the titration of an acid HX in the presence initially of a high concentration of the salt MX (which is one product of the neutralization reaction). The specification of a large excess of MX is indeed useful, because we can neglect the change in the MX concentration due to the neutralization of the acid and, in addition, it is permissible to assume that the activity of X^- remains constant throughout the titration, being governed solely by the ion-pair association constant for M^+X^-. One other simplifying assumption we can make is that the volume of the sample solution remain constant during the titration. This assumption is realizable experimentally if the titrant base solution is much more concentrated than the acid sample solution. Thus, we can ignore the effect of dilution on the titration curve.

Hydrogen ion activity before the equivalence point. Prior to the addition of any of the titrant base solution, the activity of hydrogen ions in the presence of a large concentration of the salt can be written according to the relationship presented in the preceding section of this discussion:

$$(H^+) = \frac{C_{HX}{}^\circ}{K_{HX}} \left(\frac{K_{MX}}{C_{MX}} \right)^{1/2}$$

where $C_{HX}{}^\circ$ is the original analytical concentration of the acid to be titrated, K_{HX} is the ion-pair formation constant of the acid, K_{MX} is the ion-pair formation constant of the salt, and C_{MX} is the concentration of the salt MX (which is taken to be constant for the present titration). This equation has general applicability in many actual situations, e.g., an ethylenediamine solution of HBr in the presence of excess NaBr, although the effect of dissociation of H^+X^- and M^+X^- ion-pairs on the analytical concentrations of the acid HX and the salt MX has been neglected.

As the $M^+{}^-O$—CH_2CH_2—NH_2 titrant base is added, an equivalent amount of the acid is neutralized. If a certain fraction F of the total stoichiometric quantity of base required to neutralize all of the acid is introduced into the titration vessel ($F = 1.00$ at the equivalence point), the amount of acid remaining *untitrated* at this stage in the titration is $(1 - F)C_{HX}{}^\circ$. Thus, the hydrogen ion activity at such a point is

$$(H^+) = \frac{(1 - F)C_{HX}{}^\circ}{K_{HX}} \left(\frac{K_{MX}}{C_{MX}} \right)^{1/2}$$

This latter relation has the interesting feature that, prior to the equivalence point, the hydrogen ion activity varies in a way expected of a strong acid-strong base titration in water even though all acids in ethylenediamine are largely ion-paired and are, therefore, very weak electrolytes. This result stems from the fact that the activity of X^- remains virtually constant, being fixed by the comparatively large and unchanging concentration of MX. In other words, throughout the titration up to the equivalence point, a constant fraction of the acid remaining untitrated is dissociated. A tenfold change in $C_{HX}°$ causes a tenfold change in (H^+).

Hydrogen ion activity after the equivalence point. The addition of titrant base beyond the equivalence point amounts in essence to the addition of excess $M^+{}^-O—CH_2CH_2—NH_2$ to an ethylenediamine solution of the neutral salt MX. It should be recalled that in aqueous acid-base titrations we considered the hydroxide ion concentration in conjunction with the ion-product constant (K_w) to calculate the pH after the equivalence point. In the same way, therefore, we can obtain the hydrogen ion activity in an ethylenediamine medium from the autoprotolysis-constant expression and the activity of $H_2N—CH_2CH_2—NH^-$, the conjugate base of the solvent.

The problem of determining the concentration or the activity of $H_2N—CH_2CH_2—NH^-$ in the present titration is a formidable one because of the lack of sufficient information about the relative basicities of the aminoethoxide ion $(^-O—CH_2CH_2—NH_2)$ and the $H_2N—CH_2CH_2—NH^-$ ion. The principal acid-base reaction which can generate the conjugate base of ethylenediamine beyond the equivalence point is

$$M^+{}^-O—CH_2CH_2—NH_2 + H_2N—CH_2CH_2—NH_2 \rightleftharpoons$$

$$HO—CH_2CH_2—NH_2 + M^+{}^-NH—CH_2CH_2—NH_2$$

which shows the alkali metal aminoethoxide (titrant base) accepting a proton from the solvent to form the $M^+{}^-NH—CH_2CH_2—NH_2$ ion-pair and ethanolamine.

A simplifying and very useful assumption is to postulate that ethylenediamine is a much stronger base than aminoethanol. Thus, when excess $M^+{}^-O—CH_2CH_2—NH_2$ is added to the titration vessel, it reacts immediately with ethylenediamine to form $M^+{}^-NH—CH_2CH_2—NH_2$ according to the preceding reaction. This assumption seems to be valid especially at points of the titration just barely beyond the equivalence point where the limited solubility of $M^+{}^-NH—CH_2CH_2—NH_2$ is not exceeded. If we adopt this assumption, we are essentially adopting $M^+{}^-NH—CH_2CH_2—NH_2$ and not $M^+{}^-O—CH_2CH_2—NH_2$ as being the titrant base. Let us pursue the present problem on this basis.

As are all salts in ethylenediamine, $M^+{}^-NH—CH_2CH_2—NH_2$ would be largely associated. Therefore, we can write

$$M^+ + {}^-NH—CH_2CH_2—NH_2 \rightleftharpoons M^+{}^-NH—CH_2CH_2—NH_2$$

or we can abbreviate the base $^-$NH—CH$_2$CH$_2$—NH$_2$ as B$^-$ and rewrite this equilibrium as

$$M^+ + B^- \rightleftharpoons M^+B^-$$

This latter reaction has an ion-pair formation constant of the usual form

$$K_{MB} = \frac{C_{MB}}{(M^+)(B^-)}$$

where C_{MB} represents the analytical concentration of the titrant base at some specified point beyond the equivalence point. It is convenient to relate the analytical concentration of the excess titrant base to the original concentration of the acid being determined. This can be done as follows: Since we are assuming that there is no change in the solution volume during the titration and since a one-to-one stoichiometric relationship exists between the acid and the base, the analytical concentration of base at any point after the equivalence point is

$$C_{MB} = (F - 1)C_{HX}{}^o$$

where F, the fraction of acid titrated, now has values greater than 1.00 and $C_{HX}{}^o$ is the original concentration of acid. Thus, at $F = 2.00$ the concentration of *excess* base is simply identical to the original acid concentration. By substituting the relation for C_{MB} into the ion-pair formation-constant expression for M$^+$B$^-$ and solving for the activity of the base, i.e., (B$^-$), we can obtain

$$(B^-) = \frac{(F - 1)C_{HX}{}^o}{K_{MB}(M^+)}$$

Since we assumed that the relatively large and virtually constant concentration of the salt MX controlled the activity of X$^-$ prior to the equivalence point, it is also safe to assume that the same concentration of MX governs the activity of M$^+$ after the equivalence point by means of the equation

$$(M^+) = \left(\frac{C_{MX}}{K_{MX}}\right)^{1/2}$$

If we now substitute for (M$^+$) in the equation for (B$^-$), the result is

$$(B^-) = \frac{(F - 1)C_{HX}{}^o K_{MX}{}^{1/2}}{K_{MB}C_{MX}{}^{1/2}}$$

The final step in calculating the hydrogen ion activity beyond the equivalence point is to relate it to the activity of the base, (B$^-$). In the same way that we handled the ion-product constant for water in the case of aqueous titrations, we can relate the conjugate acid and conjugate base of ethylenediamine to each other through the autoprotolysis equilibrium.

$$2 \; H_2N\text{—}CH_2CH_2\text{—}NH_2 \rightleftharpoons H_2N\text{—}CH_2CH_2\text{—}NH_3{}^+$$
$$+ \; H_2N\text{—}CH_2CH_2\text{—}NH^-$$

Since the activity of the pure solvent, ethylenediamine, is taken by convention to be unity (and assumed to be unity also in the relatively dilute solutions of analytical interest), the autoprotolysis constant K_s is given by

$$K_s = (H_2N\text{—}CH_2CH_2\text{—}NH_3{}^+)(H_2N\text{—}CH_2CH_2\text{—}NH^-) = (H^+)(B^-)$$

in which (H^+) is the abbreviation for the activity of the protonated solvent, $H_2N\text{—}CH_2CH_2\text{—}NH_3{}^+$, and (B^-) represents the activity of the solvo-anion or conjugate base of the solvent. Using the autoprotolysis relation and the value of (B^-) just determined, we may obtain the hydrogen ion activity as follows:

$$(H^+) = \frac{K_s}{(B^-)} = \frac{K_s K_{MB} C_{MX}{}^{1/2}}{(F-1)C_{HX}{}^{\circ} K_{MX}{}^{1/2}}$$

According to this latter equation, the activity of hydrogen ions beyond the equivalence point varies inversely as the analytical concentration of excess titrant base added, i.e., as $1/(F-1)C_{HX}{}^{\circ}$. This kind of relationship exactly parallels the type of behavior observed when a strong acid is titrated with a strong base in water.

Factors which govern the size of the pH break at the equivalence point. It was shown in the previous chapter that the magnitude of the pH change near the equivalence point of an aqueous acid-base titration is a key factor in setting the precision and accuracy with which the equivalence point can be located experimentally. In general, the larger this pH change or the sharper the titration curve, the greater is the precision and accuracy in locating the equivalence point and in determining the unknown concentration of acid or base. It is of particular importance, therefore, to establish what factors are involved in increasing the size of the pH break for a typical titration in ethylenediamine.

What change in pH will be observed as we proceed in our hypothetical titration from just slightly before to just slightly beyond the equivalence point? This question can be answered if we calculate the pH of the solution corresponding to two specific points on the titration curve, one at a value of F (the fraction of acid titrated) less than 1.00 by a small fraction F' and the other at a value of F greater than 1.00 by the same small fraction F'. For example, we might select the two points to be at $F = 0.99$ and $F = 1.01$. i.e., 1 per cent on each side of the equivalence point, in which case the value of F' is 0.01. In general, in our equations for (H^+) prior to the equivalence point, we have $(1-F) = F'$, whereas after the equivalence point $(F-1) = F'$.

Before the equivalence point, the hydrogen ion activity was found to be

$$(H^+) = \frac{(1-F)C_{HX}{}^\circ K_{MX}{}^{1/2}}{K_{HX}C_{MX}{}^{1/2}}$$

so that substitution of the relation $(1-F) = F'$ gives

$$(H^+) = \frac{F'C_{HX}{}^\circ K_{MX}{}^{1/2}}{K_{HX}C_{MX}{}^{1/2}}$$

Since $pH = -\log(H^+)$, the pH of the solution before the equivalence point is

$$pH_{before} = -\log F'C_{HX}{}^\circ K_{MX}{}^{1/2} + \log K_{HX}C_{MX}{}^{1/2}$$

On the other hand, the hydrogen ion activity after the equivalence point is

$$(H^+) = \frac{K_s K_{MB}C_{MX}{}^{1/2}}{(F-1)C_{HX}{}^\circ K_{MX}{}^{1/2}}$$

However, at a small fraction F' beyond the theoretical equivalence point,

$$(H^+) = \frac{K_s K_{MB}C_{MX}{}^{1/2}}{F'C_{HX}{}^\circ K_{MX}{}^{1/2}}$$

and

$$pH_{after} = -\log K_s K_{MB}C_{MX}{}^{1/2} + \log F'C_{HX}{}^\circ K_{MX}{}^{1/2}$$

The *difference* in the pH values before and after the equivalence point of the titration represents the size of the pH break. Thus we can write

$$\Delta pH = pH_{after} - pH_{before}$$

or

$$\Delta pH = \log \frac{(F')^2(C_{HX}{}^\circ)^2 K_{MX}}{K_s K_{MB} K_{HX} C_{MX}}$$

Correspondence between size of pH break and driving forces for reaction. The result of the derivation of the preceding equation for ΔpH is not truly meaningful unless the various parameters in the expression can be correlated in an intuitive way with the nature of the titration reaction. Although the titration reaction was originally formulated to be

$$H_2N-CH_2CH_2-NH_3{}^+X^- + M^{+-}O-CH_2CH_2-NH_2 \rightleftharpoons$$
$$M^+X^- + HO-CH_2CH_2-NH_2 + H_2N-CH_2CH_2-NH_2$$

it was necessary to assume (in order to permit the calculation of the hydrogen ion activity after the equivalence point) that $M^{+-}NH-CH_2CH_2-NH_2$ and not $M^{+-}O-CH_2CH_2-NH_2$ was the *effective* titrant base. Accordingly, it probably would have been better (but perhaps chemically less correct) to write the titration reaction as

$$H_2N-CH_2CH_2-NH_3{}^+X^- + M^{+-}NH-CH_2CH_2-NH_2 \rightleftharpoons$$
$$M^+X^- + 2\ H_2N-CH_2CH_2-NH$$

or, in terms of our adopted abbreviations, as

$$H^+X^- + M^+B^- \rightleftharpoons M^+X^- + BH$$

Notice that the symbol BH represents the solvent molecule (ethylenediamine) and that only *one* solvent molecule is formed in the abbreviated reaction.

The interesting thing is that this abbreviated reaction can be visualized as consisting of four subsidiary reactions, each of which has its corresponding equilibrium constant. Thus, we have

(1) $$H^+X^- \rightleftharpoons H^+ + X^-; \qquad K_1 = \frac{1}{K_{HX}}$$

(2) $$M^+B^- \rightleftharpoons M^+ + B^-; \qquad K_2 = \frac{1}{K_{MB}}$$

(3) $$M^+ + X^- \rightleftharpoons M^+X^-; \qquad K_3 = K_{MX}$$

(4) $$H^+ + B^- \rightleftharpoons BH; \qquad K_4 = \frac{1}{K_s}$$

When these four subsidiary reactions are added together, the overall abbreviated titration reaction is obtained. Also, whenever two or more chemical reactions are combined to produce just one reaction, *the equilibrium constant for the overall reaction is the product of the separate or individual constants for the subsidiary equilibria*. Therefore, we obtain

$$H^+X^- + M^+B^- \rightleftharpoons M^+X^- + BH; \qquad K_{overall} = K_1K_2K_3K_4 = \frac{K_{MX}}{K_sK_{MB}K_{HX}}$$

The equilibrium constant for the overall titration reaction is a direct measure of the driving force of this reaction. The larger the equilibrium constant, the larger is the driving force or free-energy change for reaction, the sharper will be the titration curve, and the greater will be the pH break at the equivalence point. The four factors which make up the overall equilibrium constant can be identified as follows:

1. The overall equilibrium constant is increased as the ion-pair formation constant for the acid HX *decreases*. In other words, as dissociation of the H^+X^- ion-pairs increases, the reaction is driven toward completion.

2. The overall equilibrium constant is increased as the ion-pair formation constant for the titrant base MB *decreases*. Again, as dissociation of the M^+B^- ion-pairs increases, the reaction is driven toward the right.

3. The overall equilibrium constant is increased as the ion-pair formation constant for the salt MX *increases*. This is to be expected, since greater association of the M^+X^- ion-pairs should "pull" the reaction toward completion.

4. The overall equilibrium constant is increased as the autoprotolysis constant for ethylenediamine *decreases*. This may be anticipated because decreased ionization of the solvent will reduce the concentrations of unreacted H^+ and B^- and "pull" the reaction toward the right.

It should be evident that the four factors which may act to increase the equilibrium constant for the titration reaction also increase the size of the pH break (ΔpH) near the equivalence point. However, there are two terms in the previous equation for ΔpH which do not appear in the expression for the overall equilibrium constant; these are C_{HX}° and C_{MX}. How can the inclusion of these two parameters in the relation for ΔpH be interpreted?

5. An increase in the original concentration (C_{HX}°) of acid being titrated is seen to cause a corresponding increase in the size of the pH break at the equivalence point. Such behavior exactly parallels that observed for the titration of different concentrations of a strong acid in an aqueous medium, as shown in Figure 8-2. As a general rule, any time the concentration of a chemical reactant is increased, the driving force for the forward reaction is likewise increased (Le Châtelier's principle). Therefore, for an acid-base titration, the change in pH at the equivalence point will be larger.

6. On the other hand, when the concentration of the salt MX is increased, the value of ΔpH becomes less. Qualitatively, this is the expected effect, because an increase in the concentration of any reaction product naturally opposes the forward reaction. In this example, an increase in the amount of salt (C_{MX}) has the following effects: (a) the activity of M^+ is increased; (b) the activity of B^- is decreased according to the ion-pair formation constant for M^+B^-; and (c) the pH break is smaller if less free base, B^-, is present.

TITRATIONS IN GLACIAL ACETIC ACID

In attempting to titrate a variety of bases of widely differing strength with standard acid in an aqueous solution, one soon discovers that only those bases which have considerably greater affinity for protons than the solvent (water) can be satisfactorily determined. The fundamental titration reaction requires the transfer of a proton (introduced by the titrant) from the solvent SH to the base B being determined:

$$SH_2^+ + B \rightleftharpoons SH + BH^+$$

If the affinity of the solvent SH for protons happens to be comparable, or even greater, than that of the base B, the titration reaction can never attain any substantial degree of completion and the titration will fail. Therefore, to achieve success in the titration of weak and very weak bases, one must select an acidic solvent with little affinity for protons to enhance as much as possible the meager basicity of the compounds of interest. Note that the solvent requirement is just the opposite of that for the titrimetric determination of weakly acidic substances.

The solvent which has received overwhelming attention as a titration medium is glacial acetic acid. Glacial acetic acid has a low dielectric constant ($D = 6.1$ at 25°C), so ion-pairing phenomena are extremely important in any detailed consideration of acid-base equilibria in this solvent. Its autoprotolysis constant is approximately 3×10^{-15} which means that, as an acidic solvent, glacial acetic acid can differentiate a reasonably wide range of weak bases. On the other hand, glacial acetic acid exerts a leveling effect on all strong bases.

Perchloric acid dissolved in glacial acetic acid is almost universally used as a titrant for weak bases. When the exclusion or removal of water from the titrant or solvent is desirable in order to prevent leveling effects and improve the sharpness of titration curves, the common practice is to add approximately stoichiometric quantities of acetic anhydride, which consumes water to form more acetic acid by the reaction

$$
\begin{array}{c}
\text{CH}_3\text{—C} \overset{\displaystyle O}{\diagdown} \\
\text{O} + \text{H}_2\text{O} \rightarrow 2\ \text{CH}_3\text{COOH} \\
\text{CH}_3\text{—C} \diagup \\
\diagdown \text{O}
\end{array}
$$

End point detection can be accomplished on an empirical basis with the aid of colored acid-base indicators. However, a better approach is to employ the previously mentioned technique of potentiometric titration. In the case of glacial acetic acid, both the glass electrode and the aqueous saturated calomel reference electrode have been found to function very well, and so some of the problems encountered with potentiometric titrations in basic solvents do not appear in glacial acetic acid.

There are three broad classes of weak bases which are frequently titrated in glacial acetic acid — amines, amino acids, and anions of weak acids. Primary, secondary, and tertiary amines can be titrated in anhydrous acetic acid with perchloric acid as titrant. The titration of aniline, a primary amine, can be represented by the following equilibrium:

$$
\langle\!\!\bigcirc\!\!\rangle\text{—NH}_2 + \text{CH}_3\text{COOH}_2{}^+ \rightleftharpoons \langle\!\!\bigcirc\!\!\rangle\text{—NH}_3{}^+ + \text{CH}_3\text{COOH}
$$

where $\text{CH}_3\text{COOH}_2{}^+$ is the solvated proton in glacial acetic acid.

In the preceding chapter on aqueous acid-base reactions, the amphiprotic character of alanine (a typical amino acid) was explained. Alanine may accept or lose a proton as shown by the equilibria

$$
\underset{\underset{\text{NH}_2}{|}}{\text{CH}_3\text{—C—COO}^-} \underset{-\text{H}^+}{\overset{}{\rightleftharpoons}} \underset{\underset{\text{NH}_3{}^+}{|}}{\overset{\text{H}}{\text{CH}_3\text{—C—COO}^-}} \underset{-\text{H}^+}{\overset{+\text{H}^+}{\rightleftharpoons}} \underset{\underset{\text{NH}_3{}^+}{|}}{\overset{\text{H}}{\text{CH}_3\text{—C—COOH}}}
$$

alanine

However, in an acidic solvent such as glacial acetic acid, the carboxylic acid group (—COOH) is rendered completely unreactive, and so the titration of an acetic acid solution of alanine with perchloric acid proceeds according to the reaction

$$
\begin{array}{c}
\text{H} \\
| \\
\text{CH}_3\text{—C—COOH} \\
| \\
\text{NH}_2
\end{array}
+ \text{CH}_3\text{COOH}_2{}^+
\rightleftharpoons
\begin{array}{c}
\text{H} \\
| \\
\text{CH}_3\text{—C—COOH} \\
| \\
\text{NH}_3{}^+
\end{array}
+ \text{CH}_3\text{COOH}
$$

Thus, the titration of amino acids in glacial acetic acid is analogous to the determination of amines. It is interesting to note that alanine exists as a dipolar ion or *zwitterion* in a solvent of high dielectric constant such as water. However, the low dielectric constant of glacial acetic acid does not favor the separation of charge, so the uncharged form of alanine is predominant.

Anions of weak acids are sufficiently basic in glacial acetic acid to be titrated. Just a few of the anions which can be determined by titration with standard perchloric acid are bicarbonate, carbonate, acetate, bisulfite, cyanide, and sulfate.

TITRATIONS IN METHYL ISOBUTYL KETONE

Any one of the different solvents discussed up to this point has certain limitations as to its usefulness in the determination of a broad range of acidic or basic compounds. For example, ethylenediamine is best used in the determination of various weak acids, for it exerts a powerful leveling effect on acids stronger than acetic acid. It is of no use at all in the titration of basic substances. Similarly, although glacial acetic acid is an excellent solvent for the determination of weak bases, strong bases cannot be differentiated and acidic species cannot be determined. There are several inter-related characteristics of these two solvents which impose the limitations on their wide-range usefulness. First of all, we must recognize that the basic and acidic characters of ethylenediamine and acetic acid, respectively, influence acid and base strengths of solutes dissolved in them. Second, each of these solvents is amphiprotic, which means that we can write an appropriate autoprotolysis-constant expression for each solvent. Although the autoprotolysis constant for glacial acetic acid is relatively small (approximately 10^{-15}), it is nevertheless large enough that, coupled with the acidity of the solvent, we can expect a definite limit on the total range of base strength which can be seen in the acetic acid. A similar statement can be made concerning ethylenediamine.

In view of the limitations just mentioned for ethylenediamine and acetic acid, it would be desirable to have available a versatile solvent whose properties would permit the existence in it of a much broader range of acids and bases than the former solvents. Ideally, such a wide-range solvent should not exhibit any acid or base properties of its own; that is, it should be aprotic or inert. An inert or aprotic solvent undergoes no auto-protolysis reaction. It allows dissolved substances to exhibit as nearly as possible their intrinsic acid or base properties. In fact, a truly inert solvent does not participate at all in the transfer of a proton when a dissolved acid reacts with titrant base or vice versa.

Methyl isobutyl ketone is a solvent which seems to possess many of the desired qualities of a wide-range titration medium. However, it should be pointed out that methyl isobutyl ketone is not a true aprotic solvent because the oxygen atom can attract a proton by sharing a lone pair of electrons with H^+. On the other hand, the loss of a proton by methyl isobutyl ketone cannot occur readily, so this solvent does not undergo the usual type of autoprotolysis reaction. As we shall soon see, a remarkably wide variety of acids is differentiable in this solvent. In addition, many types of bases can be titrated in methyl isobutyl ketone. The formula of methyl isobutyl ketone is

$$\begin{array}{c} H_3C \\ \diagdown \\ CH-CH_2-\overset{\displaystyle O}{\overset{\displaystyle \|}{C}}-CH_3 \\ \diagup \\ H_3C \end{array}$$

Although the commercially available solvent is suitable for use without additional purification, it has been recommended that trace acidic impurities be removed by passing the methyl isobutyl ketone through a small column packed with activated alumina (Al_2O_3). A solution of tetrabutylammonium hydroxide in isopropanol is the usual titrant for acids, and perchloric acid dissolved in dioxane may be employed to titrate bases. Titrations can be performed in open vessels without precautions to prevent the absorption of atmospheric moisture and carbon dioxide. However, it is always advisable to use comparatively concentrated titrant solutions in order to avoid the leveling effects which would occur if large volumes of titrant were added. Acid-base titrations in methyl isobutyl ketone are invariably followed by means of the potentiometric technique mentioned earlier in this chapter. A glass indicator electrode and an aqueous calomel reference electrode both function well in methyl isobutyl ketone.

Titrations of Strong Acids.   The ability of an inert solvent to resolve or differentiate the mineral acids is shown strikingly in Figure 9-3. This figure presents plots of the potential (emf) of a glass electrode versus a saturated calomel electrode as a function of titrant volume for four different strong-acid mixtures. Curve A shows clearly the resolution of perchloric and sulfuric acids. In addition, the diprotic character of sulfuric acid is revealed. A mixture of perchloric and nitric acids can be resolved even better, as demonstrated by curve B. Curve C shows a way by which a mixture of sulfuric acid and hydrochloric acid could be successfully analyzed for each component. The first equivalence point corresponds to the sum of the sulfuric acid and hydrochloric acid present. However, the volume of titrant added between the first and second equivalence points is equivalent only to the sulfuric acid, so the quantity of hydrochloric acid in the sample can be calculated by difference. The fourth titration curve in Figure 9-3 establishes that nitric and hydrochloric acids cannot be resolved in methyl isobutyl ketone.

Two interesting conclusions can be drawn from Figure 9-3. First, notice that the initial potential of the glass indicator electrode for the titration of perchloric acid is approximately -700 mv versus the saturated calomel reference electrode, whereas the potential in the presence of excess titrant base is around $+700$ mv versus the reference electrode. The total interval of at least 1400 mv is related to the useful range of acid strengths which can exist in methyl isobutyl ketone. Since 60 mv is equivalent to one pH unit, the overall operating range in this solvent is equivalent to at least 23 pH

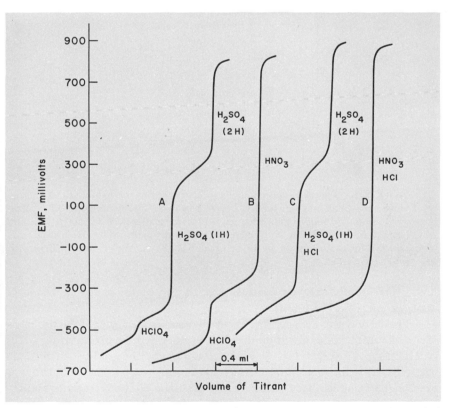

FIGURE 9-3. Titration curves for various mixtures of strong acids in methyl isobutyl ketone with 0.2 F tetrabutylammonium hydroxide (in isopropanol) as the titrant. A glass indicator electrode and an aqueous saturated calomel reference electrode were employed to measure the emf values. [Redrawn, with permission, from the paper by D. B. Bruss and G. E. A. Wyld: Anal. Chem., *29*, 232 (1957).]

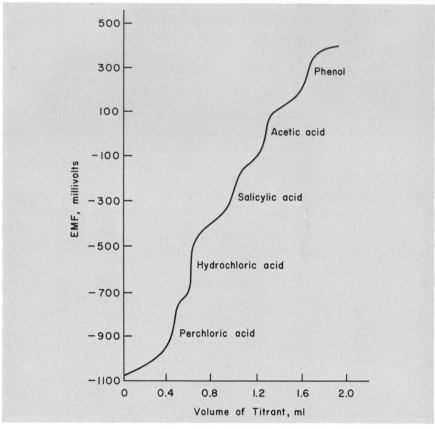

FIGURE 9-4. Titration curve showing the resolution of a mixture of strong, weak, and very weak acids in methyl isobutyl ketone. The titrant was 0.2 F tetra-butylammonium hydroxide in isopropanol. A glass indicator electrode and a platinum wire (sealed into the buret tip) reference electrode were used. [Redrawn, with permission, from the paper by D. B. Bruss and G. E. A. Wyld: Anal. Chem., 29, 232 (1957).]

units! This result may be contrasted with the useful range in water of approximately six pH units.

The second point concerning Figure 9-3 is that the order of the strengths of the mineral acids as based on the positions of the different titration curves is $HClO_4 > H_2SO_4 > HCl > HNO_3$, although the difference in the strengths of hydrochloric and nitric acids in only very slight. This order is exactly the same as that established on the basis of conductance measurements. Thus, the relative strengths of the mineral acids can be determined from titration curves obtained in an inert solvent.

Titration of Complex Acid Mixtures.   A more impressive demonstration of the resolving power of methyl isobutyl ketone is the titration curve shown in Figure 9-4 for a five-component acid mixture. The particular components in this mixture range all the way from the strongest mineral acid, perchloric acid, to the very weak acid phenol (which has an ionization constant in water near 10^{-10} and which cannot be titrated in an aqueous medium). The potential or emf scale in Figure 9-4 varies slightly from Figure 9-3 because of the use of a different reference electrode. The reference electrode used in the recording of the titration curve in Figure 9-4 was a platinum wire sealed directly into the buret tip, and the tip of the buret was kept immersed in the titration vessel (along with the glass indicator electrode) to complete the electrical circuit to the potentiometer.

In the laboratory experiment described at the end of this chapter, a procedure is given for the analysis of both known and unknown acid mixtures similar to the ones used to obtain the titration curve in Figure 9-4. It is helpful to recognize that each component in a mixture gives rise to a "step" in the titration curve occurring at a potential characteristic of that individual component. Actually, it is convenient to define a *midpoint potential* for a given component as being the *potential observed when exactly one half of the*

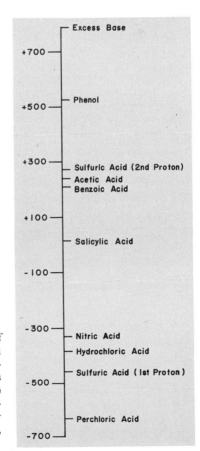

FIGURE 9-5. Midpoint potentials or emf values for the titrations of various acids in methyl isobutyl ketone with tetrabutylammonium hydroxide (in isopropanol). Potentials were measured with a glass electrode versus the aqueous saturated calomel electrode. [Redrawn, with permission, from the paper by D. B. Bruss and G. E. A. Wyld: Anal. Chem., *29*, 232 (1957).]

constituent has been titrated. Then, by comparing the observed midpoint potential for each step in the titration curve for an unknown mixture with a list of known midpoint potentials, one can *qualitatively* identify each unknown component, although some substances have nearly identical midpoint potentials. Next, the volume of standard titrant used in neutralizing each component gives a *quantitative* measure of the amount of each in the unknown. A graphical tabulation of midpoint potentials (measured with a glass electrode versus a saturated calomel reference electrode) for a number of different acids is presented in Figure 9-5.

Experiment 9-1

ACID-BASE TITRATIONS IN A NONAQUEOUS SOLVENT (METHYL ISOBUTYL KETONE)

Purpose

The present experiment is designed to demonstrate the advantages and applications of acid-base titrations in a nonaqueous solvent. In particular, this experiment allows the identification and determination of individual acids in a mixture of acids which cannot be resolved in water. Furthermore, experience is provided in the preparation of a standard titrant solution of tetrabutylammonium hydroxide by means of an ion-exchange technique. The method of potentiometry, in which the potential of a glass electrode versus an aqueous saturated calomel reference electrode (SCE) is measured as a function of titrant volume, is employed to follow the progress of the titration.

Procedure

Preparation of Tetrabutylammonium Hydroxide Titrant. Measure out about 50 ml of Dowex-1 resin (a quaternary ammonium salt, strong base anion exchanger) in the chloride form, transfer the resin to a beaker, and soak the resin overnight in approximately 200 ml of a $2F$ aqueous potassium hydroxide (KOH) solution.

The purpose of these steps is to convert the anion-exchange resin from the chloride to the hydroxide form. If the anion-exchange resin is already in the *hydroxide* form, this part of the procedure may be by-passed. Strong base anion-exchange resins are commercially available in both the chloride and hydroxide forms, but the hydroxide form is more expensive.

Prepare an anion-exchange column (free of air bubbles) by first pouring some of the clear supernatant $2 F$ aqueous KOH solution into a clean 50 ml buret (containing a glass-wool plug at the bottom of the buret to support the resin and prevent it from clogging the buret tip). Then pour the resin slurry slowly into the buret and allow the resin to settle. The height of the resin bed should be approximately 50 cm for the present experiment. *At no time should the level of solution* (either aqueous or nonaqueous) *be allowed to fall below the top of the resin bed*; if this does happen, air channels may form in the resin bed, and these air channels would cause very inefficient ion exchange. Wash the column with a fresh $2 F$ aqueous potassium hydroxide (KOH) solution until the effluent is free of chloride ion (as indicated by no more than a slight turbidity when a sample of the effluent is acidified with nitric acid and tested with several drops of silver nitrate solution). Next wash the column with 100 ml of distilled water, followed by 100 ml of 50 per cent isopropanol (by volume with distilled water) and then 200 ml of reagent-grade *anhydrous* isopropanol.

To wash an ion-exchange column, add a portion of the desired solution carefully into the buret, without disturbing the resin bed unnecessarily, and allow the wash solution to pass through the column at maximal flow rate. However, never let the level of solution fall below the top of the resin bed; in general, leave at least 1 cm of liquid above the resin bed at all times.

If anion-exchange resin in the hydroxide form is available, the preparation of the resin column can be accomplished more easily. Soak the required amount of resin in the hydroxide form overnight in reagent-grade *anhydrous* isopropanol to which has been added a few crystals of solid reagent-grade potassium hydroxide (KOH). Transfer the slurry of the resin to a 50 ml buret (containing a glass-wool plug) to prepare the ion-exchange column as previously described. Wash the column with 200 to 250 ml of reagent-grade *anhydrous* isopropanol.

The preparation of the ion-exchange column is time-consuming, particularly if the resin is originally in the chloride form. Therefore, sufficient time must be set aside, in advance of the experiment itself, for the completion of the various operations. Alternatively, if time is limited, it may be preferable for the ion-exchange column to be prepared beforehand by a laboratory assistant. Several 100 ml portions of titrant base solution can be prepared from a single column before the resin must be discarded or regenerated.

Prepare 100 ml of a $0.2 F$ tetrabutylammonium iodide solution, $(C_4H_9)_4N^+I^-$, in reagent-grade *anhydrous* isopropanol. (This is an approximately saturated solution and might well be prepared in advance.) Pass this solution through the ion-exchange column at the rate of about 1 ml per minute (one drop about every three seconds). Discard the first 20 ml of effluent which comes through the column after the $(C_4H_9)_4N^+I^-$ solution is added. Collect the next 80 ml of effluent in a clean, *dry* screw-cap polyethylene bottle. After all the $(C_4H_9)_4N^+I^-$ solution has been transferred to the column, wash the column with reagent-grade *anhydrous* isopropanol, adding the next 20 ml of effluent to the 80 ml of titrant already collected. Keep the bottle containing the titrant base tightly closed.

Experience has shown that the exchange of I^- in $(C_4H_9)_4N^+I^-$ for OH^- is not complete under the usual conditions of this experiment. If a 0.2 F $(C_4H_9)_4N^+I^-$ solution is employed, the resulting concentration of the $(C_4H_9)_4N^+OH^-$ is normally around 0.15 F, corresponding to a 75 per cent exchange efficiency. The incompleteness of the exchange causes no difficulty, however, because the residual $(C_4H_9)_4N^+I^-$ does not interfere with the subsequent standardization and use of the titrant base.

Standardization of Tetrabutylammonium Hydroxide Titrant. The procedure for the standardization of the titrant base solution is essentially the same as that employed for the standardization of a sodium hydroxide solution against sulfamic acid (Experiment 8-1). Dry reagent-grade sulfamic acid as described in Experiment 8-1. Weigh two portions of dried reagent-grade sulfamic acid, each into a clean 125 ml Erlenmeyer flask.

The desired weight of a sulfamic acid sample should be calculated in advance and should be of such a size that approximately 7 ml of the titrant base will be required for the titration if it is assumed that the concentration of $(C_4H_9)_4N^+OH^-$ is 0.15 F.

Use a 10 ml buret for the titrations, and rinse the buret several times with small portions of the titrant before filling the buret and recording the initial position of the meniscus. Dissolve each sulfamic acid sample in 50 ml of distilled water, add three drops of phenolphthalein indicator solution, and titrate the solution to the first perceptible but permanent appearance of a pink color. From the volume of titrant base required to reach the end point in each titration, calculate the concentration of the $(C_4H_9)_4N^+OH^-$ solution.

Titration of Known and Unknown Acid Mixtures. Consult the laboratory instructor to decide which acids should be included in "known" mixtures to be titrated. Titration curves obtained with known acids should be compared to the titration curves in Figures 9-3 and 9-4 and should be correlated with the graph of midpoint potentials in Figure 9-5.

The following acids have been shown to be especially suitable for the preparation of known and unknown acid mixtures: perchloric acid, sulfuric acid, hydrochloric acid, acetic acid, salicyclic acid, and phenol. Prepare 0.2 F stock solutions of each of these acids in 100 ml volumetric flasks, using concentrated commercially available acids or pure solids and using *anhydrous* methyl isobutyl ketone as solvent. The solutions of perchloric, sulfuric, and hydrochloric acids must be freshly prepared at the beginning of a laboratory period because they decompose upon standing, but the other acid solutions are stable for long periods of time. One milliliter aliquots may be pipetted from each of the desired acid stock solutions and mixed together to prepare a known or unknown acid mixture. If 1 ml aliquots of each acid stock solution are taken, each step in the titration curve should then require about 1 ml of the 0.15 to 0.2 F titrant base (unless two acids are titrated simultaneously). The following acid mixtures are suggested as possible knowns or unknowns: (a) $HClO_4$, H_2SO_4, salicylic acid; (b) $HClO_4$, HCl, salicylic acid, phenol; (c) $HClO_4$, HCl, salicylic acid, acetic acid; (d) $HClO_4$, salicylic acid, acetic acid, phenol; (e) H_2SO_4, salicylic acid, phenol; (f) H_2SO_4, HCl, salicylic acid, phenol; (g) H_2SO_4, salicylic acid, acetic acid, phenol; (h) $HClO_4$, H_2SO_4, salicylic acid, phenol; (i) HCl, salicylic acid, acetic acid, phenol.

Prepare a sample containing a mixture of acids by pipetting 1 ml of each desired acid stock (0.2 F) solution into a clean, *dry* 150 ml beaker. Dilute the sample with about 50 ml of *anhydrous* methyl isobutyl ketone. Insert a clean, *dry* stirring bar into the beaker and position the beaker over a magnetic stirring motor. Rinse a glass electrode and an aqueous saturated calomel electrode with distilled water. Carefully wipe them dry with a laboratory tissue, mount them so that their tips are immersed in the sample solution, and connect the electrodes to a pH meter (calibrated to read millivolts as well as pH). Start the stirrer, making sure that it does not strike the electrodes. Add standard tetrabutylammonium hydroxide titrant from a 10 ml buret, as in the standardization of the base described previously. Record the potential or emf of the glass electrode versus the calomel reference electrode as a function of the volume of titrant added, so that a complete titration curve may be constructed (see Fig. 9-4). The volume increments between successive emf readings should range from 0.1 to 0.25 ml, depending on whether the emf values are rapidly or only slowly changing with added titrant.

Plot the titration curve corresponding to the titration of each known mixture, indicating what acid is reacting at each step of the curve (compare to Figure 9-4). For each mixture titrated, prepare a table listing the identity of each acid in the mixture, the observed midpoint potential for each acid, the volume of base required to titrate that acid, and the number of millimoles of that acid found.

After one or two known mixtures have been successfully titrated, an unknown mixture of acids should be analyzed in the same way.

Details concerning techniques for potentiometric titrations are presented in Chapter 17.

Remember that an observed titration curve may correspond to more than one set of acids. For example, the midpoint potentials for the titrations of the *first* proton of H_2SO_4 and of HCl are nearly the same, as are the midpoint potentials for the titrations of the *second* proton of H_2SO_4 and of CH_3COOH. Therefore, a mixture of 0.2 millimole of HCl and 0.2 millimole of CH_3COOH cannot be distinguished from 0.2 millimole of H_2SO_4 alone. Note also that the titration curve for a mixture containing all three of these acids — H_2SO_4, HCl, and CH_3COOH — is very difficult to interpret.

SUGGESTIONS FOR ADDITIONAL LABORATORY WORK

A number of procedures, highly suitable for laboratory experiments on nonaqueous acid-base titrimetry, may be found in the 47-page booklet by J. S. Fritz, *Acid-Base Titrations in Nonaqueous Solvents*, published in 1952 by the G. F. Smith Chemical Company (867 McKinley Avenue, Columbus, Ohio).

QUESTIONS AND PROBLEMS

1. Define or identify clearly each of the following: amphiprotic solvent, aprotic solvent, leveling effect of a solvent, differentiating ability of a solvent, autoprotolysis constant, dielectric constant, ion-pair.

2. There are at least three factors which can affect or influence the strength of an acid in a given solvent. These are the acid or base properties of the solvent, the autoprotolysis constant for the solvent, and the dielectric constant of the solvent. In three paragraphs, discuss how each of these factors relates to acid strength. Use specific examples to illustrate your conclusions and statements.

3. Which of the following species exhibits amphiprotic character? (a) HCO_3^-, (b) Cl^-, (c) NH_4^+, (d) H_3O^+, and (e) CH_3COO^-.

4. Among the following solvents, which one would succeed best in making acetic acid, benzoic acid, hydrochloric acid, and perchloric acid all appear to have equal acid strengths? (a) pure water, (b) syrupy (85 per cent) phosphoric acid, (c) liquid ammonia, (d) concentrated sulfuric acid, and (e) methyl isobutyl ketone.

5. Explain briefly why the mineral acids, such as HNO_3, HCl, $HClO_4$, HBr, and HI, all appear to have about the same strength in water. Explain how you would proceed to establish *experimentally* the *relative* strengths of these mineral acids. Explain why it is impossible to establish the *true* or *intrinsic* strength of any of the mineral acids.

6. Suppose that a solution containing hydrobromic acid (HBr) and a large excess of sodium bromide (NaBr) in ethylenediamine ($H_2N-CH_2CH_2-NH_2$) as solvent is titrated with an ethylenediamine solution of the sodium salt,

$$Na^+{}^-NH-CH_2CH_2-NH_2.$$

(a) Although hydrobromic acid is a strong electrolyte in water, it exists predominantly as the ion-pair $H_2N-CH_2CH_2-NH_3^+Br^-$ in ethylenediamine. To what factor can such behavior be attributed?

(b) The titration reaction can be written in the following abbreviated form:

$$H^+Br^- + Na^+{}^-NH-CH_2CH_2-NH_2$$
$$\rightleftharpoons Na^+Br^- + H_2N-CH_2CH_2-NH_2$$

List the various factors which influence the size of the pH break at the equivalence point, and state for each factor whether the pH break is increased or decreased.

7. Consider the case of a univalent-univalent salt, MX, dissolved in a solvent of low dielectric constant. Derive an exact equation for the activity of M^+ in which dissociation of ion-pairs is not neglected. Include activity coefficients by letting $f_\pm$ be the mean activity coefficient of the ions M^+ and X^-. Let K_{MX} be the ion-pair formation constant and let C_{MX} represent the total analytical concentration of the salt MX present.

8. Consider the titration of a base with an acid carried out in an acidic solvent of low dielectric constant, such as glacial acetic acid. List all the factors that determine the magnitude of the pH break at the equivalence point of the titration and state the qualitative effect of each on the size of ΔpH.

9. It is known that ion-pair formation must be taken into account in order to explain the shapes of acid-base titration curves in solvents of low dielectric

constant. Consider the titration of a simple acid HX with a base MB, where B⁻ is the conjugate base of the very slightly ionized solvent BH.

$$HX + MB \rightleftharpoons MX + BH$$

Show in a logical order all the steps in the derivation of the following correct expression for (H^+) prior to the equivalence point of such a titration. (Assume that you are the first person to derive this equation and are intending to publish the complete derivation and the reasons for each step in a scientific journal.)

$$(H^+) = (1 - F)\left(\frac{C_{HX}^{\,\circ}}{K_{HX}}\right)^{1/2}\sqrt{\frac{K_{MX}}{K_{MX} + F(K_{HX} - K_{MX})}}$$

In this expression, dissociation of ion-pairs is ignored; that is to say, the slight changes in the analytical concentrations of ion-paired species caused by dissociation is ignored. In addition, F is the fraction of acid titrated, K_{HX} is the ion-pair formation constant for the acid, K_{MX} is the ion-pair formation constant for the salt, and $C_{HX}^{\,\circ}$ is the original concentration of the acid. Dilution may be neglected. (Hint: In this problem, the only salt MX present is that formed by the titration reaction, so you must relate the salt concentration to the original concentration of acid.)

10. Classify each of the following solvents as amphiprotic or aprotic. In addition, indicate (1) if each amphiprotic solvent is predominantly acidic or basic in character and (2) if each aprotic solvent can or cannot accept a proton from a Brönsted-Lowry acid. (a) glacial acetic acid, (b) dioxane, (c) ethylenediamine, (d) methyl isobutyl ketone, (e) benzene, (f) water, (g) diethyl ether, (h) isopropanol, (i) acetone, and (j) butylamine.

11. Describe the practical and theoretical problems which are encountered if one attempts to relate a pH value measured for a nonaqueous solution to the aqueous pH scale.

12. Explain why the strongest base capable of existence in a given amphiprotic solvent is the conjugate base of that solvent and why, similarly, the strongest possible acid is the conjugate acid of the solvent.

13. An inspection of Appendix 2, which tabulates the ionization constants for acids in water, shows that the hydrogen sulfate ion (HSO_4^-) is about 10 times stronger as an acid than salicyclic acid and is significantly stronger than either benzoic acid or acetic acid. However, the graph of midpoint potentials for the titration of various acids in methyl isobutyl ketone (Fig. 9-5) indicates that HSO_4^- is a much weaker acid than salicylic acid and of comparable strength only to benzoic acid and acetic acid. Suggest an explanation for the reversal of behavior in methyl isobutyl ketone.

14. Calculate the activity of sodium ion (Na^+) in a 0.05 F solution of sodium bromide in ethylenediamine, in which the ion-pair formation constant for Na^+Br^- ion-pairs is 3950. How good is the assumption that the concentration of Na^+Br^- ion-pairs is simply equal to the total analytical concentration of sodium bromide? How large must the total analytical concentration of sodium bromide be in order that 99 per cent of the Na^+Br^- ion-pairs remain associated?

15. In a solvent of high dielectric constant such as water, glycine (one of the amino acids) exists almost entirely as the zwitterion $^+NH_3$—CH_2—COO^-, whereas in a solvent of low dielectric constant such as glacial acetic acid the predominant form of glycine is the neutral molecule NH_2—CH_2—$COOH$. Suggest an experimental method, including the types of measurements and calculations needed, which might be used to determine the equilibrium constant for the following reaction in water:

$$^+NH_3\text{—}CH_2\text{—}COO^- \rightleftharpoons NH_2\text{—}CH_2\text{—}COOH$$

SUGGESTIONS FOR ADDITIONAL READING

Books

1. R. G. Bates: *Determination of pH*, John Wiley and Sons, Inc., New York, 1964, pp. 172–229.
2. J. S. Fritz: *Acid-Base Titrations in Nonaqueous Solvents*, G. F. Smith Chemical Company, Columbus, Ohio, 1952.
3. I. M. Kolthoff and S. Bruckenstein: Acid-base equilibria in nonaqueous solutions. *In* I. M. Kolthoff and P. J. Elving, eds.: *Treatise on Analytical Chemistry*, Part I, Volume 1, Wiley-Interscience, New York, 1959, pp. 475–542.
4. H. A. Laitinen: *Chemical Analysis*, McGraw-Hill Book Company, New York, 1960, pp. 57–83, 101–105.
5. H. H. Sisler: *Chemistry in Non-aqueous Solvents*, Reinhold Publishing Corporation, New York, 1961.

Papers

1. D. B. Bruss and G. E. A. Wyld: Methyl isobutyl ketone as wide-range solvent for titration of acid mixtures and nitrogen bases. Anal. Chem., *29*, 232 (1957).
2. J. S. Fritz: Titration of certain salts as acids in nonaqueous solvents. Anal. Chem. *24*, 306 (1952).
3. J. S. Fritz: Acid-base titrations in nonaqueous solvents. Record Chem. Progr., *21*, 95 (1960).
4. J. S. Fritz and R. T. Keen: Determination of sulfa drugs and sulfonamides. Anal. Chem., *24*, 308 (1952).
5. R. E. Griswold: Effect of amine structure on the relative acidity of conjugate acids. J. Chem. Ed., *42*, 483 (1965).
6. I. M. Kolthoff and S. Bruckenstein: Acid-base equilibria in glacial acetic acid. J. Am. Chem. Soc., *79*, 1 (1956).
7. G. W. Latimer, Jr.: The non-aqueous titration of salts of weak acids. J. Chem. Ed., *43*, 215 (1966).
8. P. C. Markunas and J. A. Riddick: Titrimetry in glacial acetic acid. Anal. Chem., *23*, 337 (1951).
9. M. L. Moss, J. H. Elliott, and R. T. Hall: Potentiometric titration of weak acids in anhydrous ethylenediamine. Anal Chem., *20*, 784 (1948).
10. G. F. Nadeau and L. E. Branchen: The quantitative titration of amino acids in glacial acetic acid solution. J. Am. Chem. Soc., *57*, 1363 (1935).
11. C. W. Pifer and E. G. Wollish: Potentiometric titration of salts of organic bases in acetic acid. Anal. Chem., *24*, 300 (1952).
12. C. W. Pifer and E. G. Wollish: Acidimetric titration of inorganic salts in glacial acetic acid. Anal. Chem., *24*, 519 (1952).
13. W. B. Schaap, R. E. Bayer, J. R. Siefker, J. Y. Kim, P. W. Brewster, and F. C. Schmidt: Electrochemistry in anhydrous ethylenediamine. Record Chem. Progr., *22*, 197 (1961).

"Annual Reviews," published as part of the journal *Analytical Chemistry* each April since 1955, contains a section devoted to nonaqueous titrations in all even-numbered years beginning in 1956.

Chapter Ten

Precipitation Titrations

In earlier chapters of this book, a wide variety of gravimetric procedures was discussed. Using classic gravimetric methods of analysis, one can determine a large number of metal ions by the quantitative precipitation, drying, and weighing of a halide, oxide, chromate, sulfate, oxalate, or phosphate. Conversely, each of these anions as well as many more can be determined by the precipitation, drying, and weighing of an appropriate metal salt. Gravimetric methods of analysis invariably require the addition of an excess, even if only a slight one, of the precipitating species in order to achieve the desired completeness of precipitation.

REQUIREMENTS FOR PRECIPITATION TITRATIONS

Suppose that it would be possible to determine what quantity of precipitant added was stoichiometrically equivalent to the substance being precipitated. Then, without ever collecting, drying, and weighing the resulting precipitate, one could calculate from the stoichiometry of the precipitation reaction the quantity of substance in the original sample solution. It is this idea which is the basis of precipitation titrations. To be suitable for a precipitation titration, a chemical reaction involving the formation of a slightly soluble compound must satisfy three important requirements. First, the rate of reaction between the precipitant and the substance to be precipitated must be fast. Second, the reaction should be quantitative and should proceed according to a definite stoichiometric relationship. Third, a reasonably simple and convenient means must be available for locating or identifying the point at which the quantity of precipitant added is stoichiometrically equivalent to the substance being precipitated.

The rate of reaction between a precipitant and the substance to be precipitated, and the attainment of solubility equilibrium between the precipitate and the ions in solution, must be rapid throughout the course of the titration. This requirement is necessary in order to allow the progress of the titration, as reflected by the changes in concentrations, to be followed accurately and closely. Of course, this requirement also satisfies the desire of the analytical chemist to complete a titration in a conveniently short time. In some precipitation titrations, the concentrations of the reacting species become very small as the equivalence point is approached; consequently, the rate of reaction can become slow, although usually not inconveniently slow. However, in the event of a very slow rate of precipitation or attainment of solubility equilibrium, the technique of back-titration can sometimes be employed. In this method, a measured excess of the precipitant is added which reacts at a favorable rate to form the desired precipitate; then, the unreacted precipitant is back-titrated with a standard solution of another reagent.

The second requirement, that the precipitation reaction proceed in an exactly stoichiometric way, probably poses the greatest limitation to the wide application of precipitation titrations in chemical analysis. Few precipitates of analytical interest are formed from a complex aqueous solution with the high purity and definiteness of composition necessary for a successful titration. In gravimetric analysis, an impure or contaminated precipitate can be dissolved and reprecipitated under conditions which favor the formation of a pure compound. This is impractical in titrimetry. Thus, it is mandatory that, when a solution containing chloride is titrated with standard silver nitrate, chloride and silver ions react in an exact one-to-one ratio, i.e., that the reaction follow the stoichiometric equation

$$Ag^+ + Cl^- \rightleftharpoons AgCl(s)$$

In this instance, the reaction stoichiometry is nicely obeyed. Many metallic cations, including zinc, nickel, cobalt, manganese, aluminum, iron, chromium, lead, copper, bismuth, and cadmium, form very insoluble hydroxides and sulfides. It might be expected that these elements could be determined by precipitation titration with standard sodium hydroxide solution. Unfortunately, the precipitations of the hydroxides, and sulfides, of these metals do not proceed according to straightforward stoichiometric relationships. Instead, the hydroxides and sulfides adsorb appreciable hydroxide and sulfide ions as well as extraneous cations, and the amounts of adsorbed substances vary greatly, depending upon the temperature and the concentration and composition of the solution.

If a prospective precipitation reaction satisfies the first two requirements, it is usually possible to devise a suitable means for detection of the equivalence point of the titration. In practice, of course, one actually detects the end point of a titration by a means which makes the theoretical equivalence point and the experimental end point coincide as nearly as possible. A large number of end point detection methods are available. The development of many relatively new instrumental methods of analysis based on the measurement of the physical properties of matter (electrical resistance or conductance, other electrical properties, light scattering, color, magnetic properties, and radiochemistry), plus the availability of classic methods of end point detection, has enhanced the use of this type of analysis. Several of the classic indicator methods of end point detection will be discussed in detail later in this chapter, and some of the newer instrumental methods are described in later chapters.

In summation, it is usually true that the rate of precipitation and attainment of solubility equilibrium and the stoichiometry of the reaction are the important factors in assessing the feasibility of a precipitation titration. By and large, the silver halides, silver thiocyanate, and a few mercury, lead, and zinc salts are the most important compounds involved in precipitation titrations.

TITRATION CURVES

Calculation and Construction of Titration Curves. The construction of the titration curve for a particular precipitation reaction serves to provide a graphical representation of the variation which occurs in the concentration of the substance being determined during the course of the titration. Furthermore, titration curves give valuable information about the precision or reproducibility with which the equivalence point of the titration can be located, and they also provide information which aids in the selection of the method of end point detection. Finally, an understanding of titration curves implies a detailed knowledge of the fundamental chemical equilibrium or equilibria which govern the behavior of a chemical system.

Because knowledge of the change in concentration of the substance being titrated in the region of the equivalence point of the titration is so important to the selection of an end point indicator system, titration curves are constructed in a way which particularly emphasizes what happens near the equivalence point of the titration. This is achieved by plotting the negative logarithm of the concentration of the substance being determined versus the volume of titrant added to cause precipitation to occur. Although a titration curve can be plotted from experimentally measured data, it is far more meaningful to construct a titration curve for some hypothetical, yet reasonable and typical, system. Thus, as an example, the titration curve for the titration of 50.00 ml of a 0.1000 F sodium chloride solution with a 0.1000 F silver nitrate solution will now be considered. Hopefully, the information derived from the resulting titration curve will be useful for the following: (1) knowing the chloride concentration at the equivalence point, (2) determining the rate of change of the chloride concentration near the equivalence point and, hence, how precisely the equivalence point can be located, and (3) deciding what range of chloride concentrations is feasible for precipitation titrations. The titration curve will consist of a plot of the negative logarithm of chloride concentration (pCl) against the volume of silver nitrate solution in milliliters.

Before any silver nitrate solution has been added, the chloride concentration is 0.1000 M, so that pCl is 1.00. However, just as soon as the first increment of silver nitrate solution is added, silver chloride is precipitated according to the following equilibrium:

$$Ag^+ + Cl^- \rightleftharpoons AgCl$$

To calculate pCl prior to the equivalence point, it is necessary to consider the chloride ion remaining untitrated plus the chloride ion resulting from the solubility of solid silver chloride:

$$[Cl^-] = [Cl^-]_{untitrated} + [Cl^-]_{from\ AgCl}$$

The chloride concentration remaining untitrated is given by the total millimoles of chloride originally taken minus the number of millimoles of silver nitrate added, divided by the total volume of the solution in milliliters at the particular point:

$$[Cl^-]_{untitrated} = \frac{\text{millimoles Cl}^-\ \text{taken} - \text{millimoles Ag}^+\ \text{added}}{\text{total solution volume in milliliters}}$$

The chloride concentration which results from the dissolution of the solid silver chloride may be calculated by means of the following consideration. In calculating $[Cl^-]_{untitrated}$ it is assumed that all of the added silver nitrate reacts to precipitate silver chloride. Actually, the precipitation of AgCl is not perfectly complete, and so some silver chloride remains dissolved according to the equilibrium

$$AgCl \rightleftharpoons Ag^+ + Cl^-$$

It follows that for each silver chloride molecule that dissolves, one silver ion and one chloride ion are formed. Therefore, it may be concluded that

$$[Cl^-]_{from\ AgCl} = [Ag^+]$$

However, the silver ion concentration is, in turn, given by the solubility product of silver chloride divided by the *total* concentration of chloride ion in the solution, which is $[Cl^-]$. That is,

$$[Cl^-]_{from\ AgCl} = [Ag^+] = \frac{K_{sp}}{[Cl^-]}$$

The final result of these manipulations is the following general relation for the total chloride concentration for any point, except the initial point, up to and including the theoretical equivalence point:

$$[Cl^-] = \frac{\text{millimoles } Cl^- \text{ taken } - \text{ millimoles } Ag^+ \text{ added}}{\text{total solution volume in milliliters}} + \frac{K_{sp}}{[Cl^-]}$$

On the basis of this equation, the pCl values corresponding to the addition of various volumes of the silver nitrate solution can be calculated. At 10.00 ml of silver nitrate added,

$$[Cl^-] = \frac{5.000 \text{ millimoles } - 1.000 \text{ millimole}}{60.00 \text{ milliliters}} + \frac{1.78 \times 10^{-10}}{[Cl^-]}$$

$$[Cl^-] = \frac{4.000 \text{ millimoles}}{60.00 \text{ milliliters}} + \frac{1.78 \times 10^{-10}}{[Cl^-]}$$

$$[Cl^-] = 0.0667 \, M + \frac{1.78 \times 10^{-10}}{[Cl^-]}$$

This equation can be solved by the quadratic formula.* However, the second term on the right-hand side of the equation can be neglected, as shown by the following reasoning: If the value of $[Cl^-]$ is provisionally taken to be 0.0667 M, this second term has a value of only 2.67×10^{-9} M, which is negligibly small compared to 0.0667 M. In other words, the value 0.0667 M is an excellent approximation for $[Cl^-]$, and so pCl $= 1.18$.

This simplified approach — neglecting the second term (or the contribution to $[Cl^-]$ due to the dissolution of silver chloride) — is valid in the present example until one is very close to the equivalence point. However, if the original chloride concentration is very much smaller than 0.1 M, say 10^{-4} M, then, even at the beginning of the titration, the dissolution of silver chloride must be considered and the equation solved exactly by the quadratic formula or by the method of successive approximations.†

At 20.00 ml of silver nitrate added, $[Cl^-] = 0.0429 \, M$; pCl $= 1.37$. At 30.00 ml of silver nitrate added, $[Cl^-] = 0.0250 \, M$; pCl $= 1.60$. At 40.00 ml of silver nitrate added, $[Cl^-] = 0.0111 \, M$; pCl $= 1.95$. At 49.00 ml of silver nitrate added, $[Cl^-] = 0.00101 \, M$; pCl $= 3.00$. At 49.90 ml of silver nitrate added, $[Cl^-] = 1.00 \times 10^{-4} \, M$; pCl $= 4.00$. Note that up to this point, the dissolution of silver chloride has been neglected.

At 49.99 ml of silver nitrate added, neglect of the dissolution of silver chloride is no longer justifiable, and so the exact equation must be used to calculate $[Cl^-]$:

$$[Cl^-] = \frac{5.000 \text{ millimoles } - 4.999 \text{ millimoles}}{99.99 \text{ milliliters}} + \frac{1.78 \times 10^{-10}}{[Cl^-]}$$

$$[Cl^-] = \frac{0.001 \text{ millimole}}{100.0 \text{ milliliters}} + \frac{1.78 \times 10^{-10}}{[Cl^-]}$$

---

* See page 255.
† See page 257.

From the quadratic formula, one calculates that $[Cl^-] = 1.92 \times 10^{-5}\,M$; $pCl = 4.72$.

At 50.00 ml of silver nitrate added (the theoretical equivalence point), the exact equation simplifies to

$$[Cl^-] = \frac{K_{sp}}{[Cl^-]}$$

so that $[Cl^-]^2 = K_{sp}$; $[Cl^-] = (K_{sp})^{1/2} = 1.33 \times 10^{-5}M$; $pCl = 4.87$.

Beyond the equivalence point, the situation is just reversed. An excess of silver ion is present in the solution, the sources of silver ion being the excess silver nitrate added and the dissolution of the silver chloride precipitate:

$$[Ag^+] = [Ag^+]_{excess} + [Ag^+]_{from\ AgCl}$$

The concentration of silver ion added in excess is just the number o millimoles of silver nitrate added beyond the equivalence point divided by the volume of the solution in milliliters,

$$[Ag^+]_{excess} = \frac{\text{millimoles of AgNO}_3 \text{ added beyond equivalence point}}{\text{total volume of solution in milliliters}}$$

and the silver ion concentration from the dissolution of silver chloride is exactly equal to the chloride ion concentration (since, beyond the equivalence point, dissolved silver chloride is the only source of chloride):

$$[Ag^+]_{from\ AgCl} = [Cl^-]$$

The chloride concentration, which is the quantity desired in this problem, is related to the *total* silver ion concentration through the solubility product:

$$[Ag^+]_{from\ AgCl} = [Cl^-] = \frac{K_{sp}}{[Ag^+]}$$

When these relations are combined, the following equation for the *total* silver ion concentration is obtained

$$[Ag^+] = \frac{\text{millimoles of AgNO}_3 \text{ added beyond equivalence point}}{\text{total volume of solution in milliliters}} + \frac{K_{sp}}{[Ag^+]}$$

Once $[Ag^+]$ is calculated from this relationship, the value of $[Cl^-]$, and hence pCl, can be determined from the solubility-product expression. In addition, except for points very close to the equivalence point or for the titration of very dilute solutions, the second term on the right-hand side of this last equation can be neglected.

At 60.00 ml of silver nitrate added, there is an excess of 1.000 millimole of silver ion in a total volume of 110.0 ml of solution:

$$[Ag^+] = \frac{1.000 \text{ millimole}}{110.0 \text{ milliliters}} = 9.09 \times 10^{-3}\,M$$

$$[Cl^-] = \frac{1.78 \times 10^{-10}}{9.09 \times 10^{-3}} = 1.96 \times 10^{-8}\,M; \ pCl = 7.71$$

Note that the silver ion concentration from the dissolution of silver chloride would be virtually identical to $[Cl^-]$ and, thus, it is negligible compared to $9.09 \times 10^{-3} M$.

At 70.00 ml of silver nitrate added,

$$[Ag^+] = \frac{2.000 \text{ millimoles}}{120.0 \text{ milliliters}} = 0.0167 \ M$$

$$[Cl^-] = \frac{1.78 \times 10^{-10}}{1.67 \times 10^{-2}} = 1.07 \times 10^{-8} M; \ pCl = 7.97$$

The titration curve (pCl versus volume of silver nitrate) constructed on the basis of these calculations is shown in Figure 10-1.

Factors Which Govern the Shapes of Titration Curves. The steepness or sharpness of the titration curve ultimately determines with

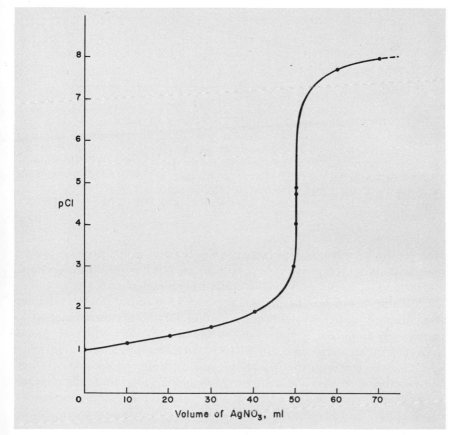

FIGURE 10-1. Calculated titration curve for the titration of 50.00 ml of a $0.1000 \ F$ sodium chloride solution with a $0.1000 \ F$ silver nitrate solution.

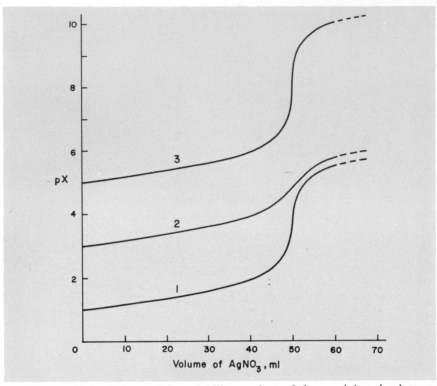

FIGURE 10-2. Effects of the solubility product of the precipitated substance and of the concentrations of the reactants on the sharpness of titration curves. Curve *1*: titration of 50.00 ml of 0.1000 M iodate ion with 0.1000 F silver nitrate (K_{sp} for $AgIO_3$ = 3.02 $\times$ 10^{-8}). Curve *2*: titration of 50.00 ml of 0.001000 M chloride ion with 0.001000 F silver nitrate (K_{sp} for $AgCl$ = 1.78 $\times$ 10^{-10}). Curve *3*: titration of 50.00 ml of 1.000 $\times$ 10^{-5} M iodide ion with 1.000 $\times$ 10^{-5} F silver nitrate (K_{sp} for AgI = 8.31 $\times$ 10^{-17}).

what precision (or sensitivity) the equivalence point of the titration can be located. In turn, there are two important factors which govern the magnitude of the "break" in the pCl-volume curve in the region of the equivalence point. These factors are the original concentration of the chloride solution being titrated and the equilibrium constant for the titration reaction — namely, the reciprocal of the solubility product for silver chloride. For a given precipitation titration, these two quantities provide the "driving force" for the reaction; the higher the concentration of chloride or other substance being titrated and the more insoluble the precipitate, the sharper is the titration curve and the greater is the precision in locating the equivalence point. These conclusions are illustrated by the titration curves shown in Figure 10-2.

In Figure 10-2 the titration curve for the titration of 50.00 ml of 0.1000 M iodate ion with the same concentration of silver nitrate solution is shown (curve *1*). The curve is less sharp than that depicted in Figure 10-1 for 0.1 M chloride because the solubility product of silver iodate (3.02×10^{-8}) is 170 times larger than that for silver chloride. Curve *2* shows a titration curve for $10^{-3} M$ chloride ion titrated with $10^{-3} F$ silver nitrate. Obviously, the curve does not exhibit a very sharp break near the equivalence point, and this concentration of chloride would be close to the lower limit for which the equivalence point could be precisely located. Finally, for a much more insoluble salt, such as silver iodide ($K_{sp} = 8.31 \times 10^{-17}$), the titration curve is still very well defined at a concentration level of $10^{-5} M$ (curve *3*). Thus, the potential success of a precipitation titration must be judged in terms of both the concentration of the substance being titrated and the degree of insolubility of the precipitate. In some cases, the solubility of a precipitate can be markedly decreased by a change in the solvent system. For example, the addition of water-miscible organic solvents, such as acetone or ethanol, to an aqueous solution will significantly decrease the solubilities of most inorganic salts and, therefore, will improve the shapes of titration curves.

END POINT DETECTION

The most important characteristic of a titration curve is the usually very great and abrupt change in the concentration of the substance being titrated in the region of the theoretical equivalence point. The purpose of any method of end point detection is to provide a signal that this point of rapid concentration change has been reached. In addition, the end point signal should occur exactly at the theoretical equivalence point or as close to it as possible. Any difference between the true equivalence point of the titration and the experimentally detected end point constitutes an error in the titration. Much careful consideration has gone into the development of suitable, new end point detection schemes as well as the modification and perfection of those already widely used. In the following discussion, three common end point detection methods which involve the use of so-called "indicators" will be examined in connection with the titration of chloride. Sources of end point errors for these methods will be considered, and ways in which these errors may be minimized or eliminated will be described.

THE MOHR TITRATION

In the Mohr method for the determination of chloride, the chloride ion is precipitated as silver chloride by titration with standard silver nitrate solution in the presence of a small concentration of chromate ion. The end point is signaled by the first detectable and permanent appearance of a precipitate of brick-red-colored silver chromate throughout the solution.

Silver chromate forms upon addition of a slight excess of silver nitrate only after virtually all of the chloride ion has been precipitated as silver chloride.

The equilibria involved in this method are as follows:

$$Ag^+ + Cl^- \rightleftharpoons AgCl(s)$$

$$2\ Ag^+ + CrO_4^= \rightleftharpoons Ag_2CrO_4(s)$$

The solubility-product constants for silver chloride and silver chromate are, respectively, 1.78×10^{-10} and 2.45×10^{-12}. Note that silver chromate, which has a smaller K_{sp}, dissolves to form three ions and is actually more soluble. Thus, for a small concentration of chromate ion in the presence of a relatively large amount of chloride, silver chloride is preferentially precipitated upon addition of silver nitrate, and the free silver ion concentration never becomes high enough to cause the solubility product of silver chromate to be exceeded until chloride ion has been almost completely precipitated.

Ideally, it is desirable for red-colored silver chromate just to begin to precipitate at the equivalence point of the titration of chloride ion with silver nitrate, or when $[Cl^-] = [Ag^+] = (K_{sp})^{1/2} = 1.33 \times 10^{-5}\ M$. The concentration of chromate ion which must be present to cause precipitation of silver chromate when $[Ag^+]$ reaches $1.33 \times 10^{-5}\ M$ can be calculated from the solubility-product relationship for silver chromate:

$$[CrO_4^=] = \frac{K_{sp}}{[Ag^+]^2} = \frac{2.45 \times 10^{-12}}{(1.33 \times 10^{-5})^2} = 0.014\ M$$

Unfortunately, because the chromate ion has a fairly intense canary-yellow color, this relatively large concentration of chromate tends to conceal the appearance of the red-colored silver chromate precipitate. Therefore, in practice it is necessary to use a somewhat lower chromate concentration, and $0.005\ M$ is usually chosen to be the value of the chromate concentration at the end point.

With this lower chromate concentration, a slight excess of silver nitrate must be added beyond the equivalence point in order to exceed the solubility product and to cause precipitation of silver chromate. Also, the equivalence point must be surpassed even more because a certain finite amount of silver chromate must be precipitated before the end point can be seen. It has been determined experimentally that the minimum detectable quantity of silver chromate corresponds to a "concentration" of approximately $1.0 \times 10^{-5}\ M$.

It is instructive to calculate the magnitude of the titration error caused by these experimental problems. Consider the titration of 50.00 ml of $0.1000\ M$ chloride ion with a $0.1000\ F$ silver nitrate solution. The percentage relative titration error is defined as:

$$\left(\frac{\begin{array}{l}(\text{milliliters of AgNO}_3 \text{ required to reach end point}) \\ - (\text{milliliters of AgNO}_3 \text{ required to reach theoretical equiv-} \\ \hspace{6cm}\text{alence point})\end{array}}{\begin{array}{l}(\text{milliliters of AgNO}_3 \text{ required to reach} \\ \hspace{3cm}\text{theoretical equivalence point})\end{array}} \right) \times 100$$

Since an excess of silver nitrate must be added in the present situation, the percentage relative titration error is given by

$$\frac{\text{(milliliters of AgNO}_3 \text{ added in excess)}}{\text{(milliliters of AgNO}_3 \text{ required to reach theoretical equivalence point)}} \times 100$$

The volume of silver nitrate added in excess can be evaluated by considering the difference between the conditions of the equivalence point and the end point.

At the equivalence point, by definition, $[Ag^+] = [Cl^-] = K_{sp}^{1/2} = 1.33 \times 10^{-5} M$. Silver chromate does not enter into a discussion of the theoretical equivalence point.

At the end point, the chromate concentration is taken to be $0.005\ M$. The silver ion concentration at which the solubility product of silver chromate is just exceeded is

$$[Ag^+] = \left(\frac{2.45 \times 10^{-12}}{[CrO_4^=]}\right)^{1/2} = \left(\frac{2.45 \times 10^{-12}}{0.005}\right)^{1/2} = 2.21 \times 10^{-5} M$$

and the value of the chloride concentration at the end point is obtained through the solubility product of silver chloride:

$$[Cl^-] = \frac{1.78 \times 10^{-10}}{[Ag^+]} = \frac{1.78 \times 10^{-10}}{2.21 \times 10^{-5}} = 0.81 \times 10^{-5} M$$

These calculations show that, in going from the equivalence point to the end point, silver nitrate must be added to *increase* $[Ag^+]$ from 1.33×10^{-5} to $2.21 \times 10^{-5} M$. Silver nitrate must also be added to *decrease* $[Cl^-]$ from 1.33×10^{-5} to $0.81 \times 10^{-5} M$, because the only way $[Cl^-]$ can decrease is by the addition of silver nitrate and the precipitation of *more* silver chloride. Another factor is that extra silver nitrate is required to produce the $1.0 \times 10^{-5} M$ silver chromate needed to signal the end point. Note that, because silver chromate contains two silver ions, this is equivalent to $2.0 \times 10^{-5} M$ more silver nitrate.

Exactly 50.00 ml of $0.1000\ F$ silver nitrate is required to reach the equivalence point in the titration of 50.00 ml of $0.1000\ M$ chloride. The solution volume at the equivalence point is 100.0 ml, and the end point volume may be assumed to be very close to 100 ml.

The number of millimoles of silver nitrate added to *increase* $[Ag^+]$ from 1.33×10^{-5} to $2.21 \times 10^{-5} M$ is $(2.21 - 1.33)\ (10^{-5})\ (100)$ or 0.88×10^{-3} millimole. To *decrease* $[Cl^-]$ from 1.33×10^{-5} to $0.81 \times 10^{-5} M$, one must add $(1.33 - 0.81)\ (10^{-5})\ (100)$ or 0.52×10^{-3} millimole excess silver nitrate, and $(2.0 \times 10^{-5})(100)$ or 2.0×10^{-3} millimole of silver nitrate must be added to form the silver chromate precipitate needed to signal the end point. A total of 3.4×10^{-3} millimole excess of silver nitrate titrant is required to go from the equivalence point to the end point. This corresponds to 0.034 ml of 0.1000 F silver nitrate titrant. Therefore, the percentage relative titration error is

$$\frac{0.034 \text{ ml}}{50.00 \text{ ml}} \times 100 = +0.068\%$$

For the titration of 0.01000 M chloride with 0.01000 F silver nitrate, the equivalence point conditions and the end point conditions would be identical to the previous example; therefore, the percentage relative titration error would be +0.68 per cent. These calculations are useful in that they reveal the major source of the titration error as being the amount of silver ion required to precipitate a detectable concentration of silver chromate. Frequently, it is feasible to perform a blank titration with a solution containing no chloride ion but the same concentration of chromate as an actual experiment. The silver chloride precipitate is simulated by a suspension of white-colored calcium carbonate, the mixture is titrated with silver nitrate, and the volume of silver nitrate required to produce the same end point color is measured. This small volume, when subtracted from the total volume of silver nitrate used in an actual titration, provides an end point correction.

The Mohr titration must be carried out in a solution which is neither too acidic nor too basic. The basic or upper pH limit is fixed by the insolubility of silver hydroxide or oxide:

$$Ag^+ + OH^- \rightleftharpoons AgOH$$

$$2\ AgOH \rightleftharpoons Ag_2O + H_2O$$

One form of the solubility-product relationship for silver hydroxide or oxide is given by

$$[Ag^+][OH^-] = 2.6 \times 10^{-8}$$

In an actual titration, the concentration of silver ion at the end point is about $2.2 \times 10^{-5}\ M$. In order that the formation of silver hydroxide does not interfere in the titration, the hydroxide ion concentration cannot exceed the value given by

$$[OH^-] = \frac{2.6 \times 10^{-8}}{[Ag^+]} = \frac{2.6 \times 10^{-8}}{2.2 \times 10^{-5}} = 1.2 \times 10^{-3}\ M$$

This corresponds to a pOH of about 2.9, or a pH of 11.1. However, because of the possibility of the transient formation of AgOH or Ag_2O, the upper pH limit for practical titrations must be somewhat lower, preferably lower than approximately 10.

The lower pH limit is set by the increased solubility of silver chromate in acidic solutions:

$$Ag_2CrO_4 + H^+ \rightleftharpoons 2\ Ag^+ + HCrO_4^-$$

$$2\ Ag_2CrO_4 + 2\ H^+ \rightleftharpoons 4\ Ag^+ + Cr_2O_7^= + H_2O$$

In slightly acidic chromate solutions the important equilibria, along with the appropriate equilibrium constants, are as follows:

$$CrO_4^= + H^+ \rightleftharpoons HCrO_4^-; \quad K = 3.2 \times 10^6$$

$$2\ HCrO_4^- \rightleftharpoons Cr_2O_7^= + H_2O; \quad K' = 33$$

Using these equilibria and the requirement that the total chromium(VI) concentration at the end point be 0.005 M, one can calculate the effect of pH on the concentration of chromate ion.

First of all, the general equation can be written that

$$0.005 = [CrO_4^=] + [HCrO_4^-] + 2[Cr_2O_7^=]$$

and

$$0.005 = [CrO_4^=] + (3.2 \times 10^6)[CrO_4^=][H^+]$$
$$+ (2)(33)(3.2 \times 10^6)^2[CrO_4^=]^2[H^+]^2$$

For a specified hydrogen ion concentration, this latter relation can be solved for $[CrO_4^=]$. At pH 7, $[H^+] = 10^{-7}\ M$, and $[CrO_4^=]$ is found to be $3.7 \times 10^{-3}\ M$. Similarly, at pH 6 and pH 5, respectively, the chromate ion concentration is 1.0×10^{-3} and $1.2 \times 10^{-4}\ M$. Thus, below pH 7 the chromate ion concentration decreases quite rapidly, and the titration error increases correspondingly, because more and more silver nitrate titrant must be added beyond the equivalence point to exceed the solubility product of silver chromate. Therefore, in the Mohr titration of chloride, the solution pH should be no less than approximately 7.

Both bromide and chloride may be determined by the Mohr titration. However, iodide and thiocyanate do not give satisfactory results because precipitates of silver iodide and silver thiocyanate adsorb chromate ions, giving indistinct end point signals.

THE VOLHARD TITRATION

The Volhard titration for the direct determination of silver ion, or for the indirect determination of a number of ions which form insoluble silver salts, is an example of a volumetric precipitation titration in which the equivalence point is detected by the formation of a soluble, colored complex ion.

Advantage is taken of the fact that ferric ion in an acid medium forms an intense blood-red complex with thiocyanate:

$$Fe^{+++} + SCN^- \rightleftharpoons FeSCN^{++}$$

Although the equilibrium constant for this reaction as written is only 138 and even though the FeSCN^{++} ion is not an especially stable one, the use of this complex as an end point signal gains its sensitivity from the fact that, even at very small concentrations, the FeSCN^{++} complex is detectable. It has been established experimentally that $6.4 \times 10^{-6}\ M$ FeSCN^{++} imparts a noticeable color to a solution. Ferric and thiocyanate ions react to form higher complexes, e.g., Fe(SCN)$_2{}^+$, all the way up to Fe(SCN)$_6{}^=$, but this is unimportant in the Volhard titration because the thiocyanate concentration is always quite low.

The requirement that the Volhard titration be performed in an acidic solution is an important one. In aqueous solutions, the pure ferric ion exists as the hexaaquo species, Fe(H$_2$O)$_6{}^{+++}$, which is a completely colorless ion. However, Fe(H$_2$O)$_6{}^{+++}$ is a fairly strong acid and undergoes acid ionizations such as

$$Fe(H_2O)_6{}^{+++} \rightleftharpoons Fe(H_2O)_5(OH)^{++} + H^+$$

and

$$Fe(H_2O)_5(OH)^{++} \rightleftharpoons Fe(H_2O)_4(OH)_2{}^+ + H^+$$

The first acid dissociation constant for Fe(H$_2$O)$_6{}^{+++}$ is comparable to the second ionization constant for sulfuric acid, being about 10^{-2}. The species Fe(H$_2$O)$_5$(OH)$^{++}$ and Fe(H$_2$O)$_4$(OH)$_2{}^+$ are intensely orange and brown, and so their presence would completely mask the first appearance of the red-colored FeSCN^{++}. Therefore, to repress these acid dissociations of Fe(H$_2$O)$_6{}^{+++}$, the acidity of the solution being titrated must be in the neighborhood of 0.1 to 1 M.

Direct Determination of Silver. The Volhard method for the direct determination of silver involves the titration of an acidic solution containing silver ion (and a small concentration of ferric ion as the indicator) with a standard potassium thiocyanate solution. The end point is marked by the appearance of the blood-red-colored FeSCN^{++} complex with the addition of the first slight excess of thiocyanate into the titration vessel.

The titration reaction is

$$Ag^+ + SCN^- \rightleftharpoons AgSCN$$

and the solubility product for silver thiocyanate is 1.00×10^{-12}. The indicator is usually added to the solution prior to the start of the titration in the form of an acidic solution of ferric ammonium sulfate (ferric alum). The concentration of ferric ion must be adjusted so that the first permanent appearance of the FeSCN^{++} ion occurs at the equivalence point of the titration of silver ions with thiocyanate. At the equivalence point of the titration, $[Ag^+] = [SCN^-] = K_{sp}{}^{1/2} = 1.00 \times 10^{-6}\ M$. The required ferric ion concentration can be calculated from the expression

$$[Fe^{+++}] = \frac{[FeSCN^{++}]}{138[SCN^-]}$$

where $[SCN^-]$ is taken to be the equivalence point value $(1.00 \times 10^{-6}\ M)$ and $[FeSCN^{++}]$ is the minimum detectable concentration of the ferric-thiocyanate complex $(6.4 \times 10^{-6}\ M)$. Thus,

$$[Fe^{+++}] = \frac{(6.4 \times 10^{-6})}{(138)(1.0 \times 10^{-6})} = 0.046\ M$$

This concentration of ferric ion is sufficiently large that, in spite of the high acidity of the solution being titrated, the acid ionization of the $Fe(H_2O)_6^{+++}$ ion proceeds far enough to cause a distinct orange-brown color in the solution. Consequently, most practical procedures for the Volhard determination of silver ion call for the use of approximately 0.015 M ferric ion. This compromise does not affect the accuracy of the Volhard titration for silver nearly as much as the similar compromise in the Mohr titration for chloride. Considerations identical to those discussed previously for the Mohr method lead to the conclusion that the error for the Volhard titration of 0.1 M silver ion with 0.1 M thiocyanate is somewhat less than +0.02 per cent. Even with 0.01 M reactants, the percentage relative titration error should not exceed +0.2 per cent.

Indirect Determination of Chloride. The Volhard method has been extensively employed for the determination of chloride and other anions. In the classic Volhard titration, a carefully measured excess of standard silver nitrate is added to the chloride sample solution, the proper amounts of acid and ferric alum indicator having been introduced. An amount of silver nitrate stoichiometrically equivalent to the chloride reacts with chloride, being precipitated as silver chloride; then, the excess of silver nitrate is back-titrated with standard potassium thiocyanate solution to the appearance of the red $FeSCN^{++}$ complex. The quantity of chloride (or other anion) in the sample solution is computed by subtracting the milli-moles of silver ion equivalent to the thiocyanate used in the back-titration from the total number of millimoles of silver nitrate originally added to the sample solution.

A serious difficulty occurs when the excess silver ion is back-titrated with potassium thiocyanate in the presence of the silver chloride precipitate. Because silver chloride is more soluble than silver thiocyanate, the addition of thiocyanate during the back-titration of the excess silver nitrate causes *metathesis* of silver chloride according to the reaction

$$AgCl + SCN^- \rightleftharpoons Cl^- + AgSCN$$

Taking 1.00×10^{-12} for the solubility product of silver thiocyanate and 1.78×10^{-10} for the solubility product of silver chloride, one calculates that the equilibrium constant for this reaction is 178.

$$K = \frac{[Cl^-]}{[SCN^-]} = \frac{[Ag^+][Cl^-]}{[Ag^+][SCN^-]} = \frac{1.78 \times 10^{-10}}{1.00 \times 10^{-12}} = 178$$

In effect, some of the silver nitrate reacts both with chloride and with thiocyanate, and so the resulting titration data are useless. It is worthwhile to consider the importance of this metathesis to the overall titration error as well as various means for the elimination of the metathesis reaction.

As for the Mohr titration, the relative percentage titration error for the Volhard titration can be calculated by determining what concentration differences exist for the equivalence point and end point.

The *equivalence point* condition is governed solely by the equilibria involving silver chloride and silver thiocyanate. At the equivalence point of the back-titration, the number of millimoles of silver ion equals the sum of the millimoles of chloride and the millimoles of thiocyanate; therefore, it follows that

$$[Ag^+] = [Cl^-] + [SCN^-]$$

From the solubility-product expressions

$$[Ag^+][Cl^-] = 1.78 \times 10^{-10}$$

and

$$[Ag^+][SCN^-] = 1.00 \times 10^{-12}$$

$$[Ag^+] = \frac{1.78 \times 10^{-10}}{[Ag^+]} + \frac{1.00 \times 10^{-12}}{[Ag^+]}$$

$$[Ag^+]^2 = 1.79 \times 10^{-10}; \qquad [Ag^+] = 1.33 \times 10^{-5} \, M$$

The concentrations of chloride and thiocyanate ions at the equivalence point can be calculated from the solubility products.

$$[Cl^-] = \frac{1.78 \times 10^{-10}}{1.33 \times 10^{-5}} = 1.33 \times 10^{-5} \, M$$

$$[SCN^-] = \frac{1.00 \times 10^{-12}}{1.33 \times 10^{-5}} = 7.50 \times 10^{-8} \, M$$

The *end point* is marked by the first permanent appearance of the red-colored $FeSCN^{++}$ complex ion; the minimum detectable concentration is $6.4 \times 10^{-6} \, M$. Since the ferric ion concentration at the end point is usually close to $0.015 \, M$, the thiocyanate concentration can be calculated from the relation

$$[SCN^-] = \frac{[FeSCN^{++}]}{138[Fe^{+++}]} = \frac{(6.4 \times 10^{-6})}{(138)(0.015)} = 3.1 \times 10^{-6} \, M$$

This value is over 40 times greater than that at the equivalence point. The concentrations of silver and chloride ions can be calculated from the appropriate solubility-product equations:

$$[Ag^+] = \frac{1.00 \times 10^{-12}}{[SCN^-]} = \frac{1.00 \times 10^{-12}}{3.1 \times 10^{-6}} = 3.2 \times 10^{-7} \, M$$

$$[Cl^-] = \frac{1.78 \times 10^{-10}}{[Ag^+]} = \frac{1.78 \times 10^{-10}}{3.2 \times 10^{-7}} = 5.6 \times 10^{-4} \, M$$

A comparison of the concentrations at the equivalence point and at the end point reveals that the experimental end point appears *beyond* the theoretical equivalence point. First of all, the thiocyanate concentration is larger at the end point. Second, the silver ion concentration is smaller at the end point than at the equivalence point because slightly more thiocyanate has been added and a little more silver thiocyanate has been precipitated. Third, the chloride concentration is significantly larger at the end point because of the metathesis of silver chloride by excess thiocyanate. Each of these three effects can be interpreted in terms of a certain number of millimoles of thiocyanate beyond the equivalence point. In addition, $6.4 \times 10^{-6} M$ thiocyanate must be added in excess in order to form the $FeSCN^{++}$ indicator ion.

If the volume of the solution is taken to be 100 ml at both the equivalence point and end point (the slight difference in volume may be neglected), the number of millimoles of each ion can be calculated. At the *equivalence point*, the number of millimoles of each ion is as follows: SCN^-, $(7.50 \times 10^{-8})(100)$ or 7.5×10^{-6}; Cl^-, $(1.33 \times 10^{-5})(100)$ or 1.33×10^{-3}; and Ag^+, $(1.33 \times 10^{-5})(100)$ or 1.33×10^{-3}. On the other hand, the number of millimoles of each ion at the *end point* is $(3.1 \times 10^{-6})(100)$ or 3.1×10^{-4} for SCN^-, $(5.6 \times 10^{-4})(100)$ or 5.6×10^{-2} for Cl^-, $(3.2 \times 10^{-7})(100)$ or 3.2×10^{-5} for Ag^+, and $(6.4 \times 10^{-6})(100)$ or 6.4×10^{-4} for $FeSCN^{++}$. A careful analysis of the results gives these conclusions: There is essentially 3.1×10^{-4} millimole excess thiocyanate at the end point. The increase of approximately 5.5×10^{-2} millimole of chloride requires that 5.5×10^{-2} millimole of thiocyanate must have been added to metathesize silver chloride. The decrease of about 1.3×10^{-3} millimole of silver is caused by the precipitation of more silver thiocyanate. The formation of a detectable concentration of $FeSCN^{++}$ requires the addition of 6.4×10^{-4} millimole of thiocyanate.

Summing up these conclusions, one discovers that, in going from the equivalence point to the end point, a total of 0.057 millimole excess thiocyanate ion is added and that almost all of this thiocyanate is consumed by the metathesis of silver chloride. Since the number of millimoles of potassium thiocyanate used in the back-titration is subtracted from the total millimoles of silver nitrate originally added to the sample solution in order to calculate the millimoles of chloride present, the quantity of chloride will appear to be *low* by 0.057 millimole. If the original sample was 50 ml of 0.1 M chloride, or 5.0 millimoles, the percentage relative titration error would be

$$-\frac{0.057}{5.0} \times 100 = -1.2\%$$

These calculations show, however, that the only significant source of error is the metathesis of silver chloride by thiocyanate. If this metathesis can be minimized or eliminated, the titration error can be reduced to below -0.1 per cent.

The most obvious way to eliminate metathesis is to remove the silver chloride by filtration after the excess of silver nitrate is added. Care must be taken to wash the silver chloride completely free of the excess silver ions. After removal of the silver chloride, the titration of silver ion with thiocyanate is identical to the direct determination of silver outlined earlier.

A second approach to the problem of metathesis is based on decreasing the rate of the (heterogeneous) reaction between the solid silver chloride and thiocyanate ion. This can be accomplished by decreasing the effective surface area of the silver chloride precipitate. There are two possibilities: boiling the solution to coagulate the silver chloride (followed by cooling the solution, then titrating it with thiocyanate) and coating the silver chloride particles with a water-immiscible substance such as nitrobenzene.

One of the most elegant means to overcome the problem of metathesis was first recognized by Swift and co-workers. If the thiocyanate ion concentration is much smaller at the end point than the value of $3.1 \times 10^{-6} M$, and preferably it should be the theoretical equivalence point concentration of $7.50 \times 10^{-8} M$, it is possible to minimize the metathesis and to reduce the titration error substantially. Experimentally, in order for the first permanent appearance of $FeSCN^{++}$ to occur at a lower thiocyanate concentration, a much higher ferric ion concentration than usual is required. If the thiocyanate concentration is taken to be $7.5 \times 10^{-8} M$ and if $[FeSCN^{++}] = 6.4 \times 10^{-6} M$, then the requisite amount of ferric alum indicator is obtained from the relation

$$[Fe^{+++}] = \frac{[FeSCN^{++}]}{138[SCN^-]} = \frac{(6.4 \times 10^{-6})}{(138)(7.5 \times 10^{-8})} = 0.62 \ M$$

This would be the concentration of ferric ion which, theoretically, would guarantee that there would be no titration error. However, even in a solution containing $1 M$ hydrogen ion, this much ferric ion imparts a distinct color to the solution, owing to the acid ionization of the ferric ion. Therefore, the ferric ion concentration is usually lowered somewhat to $0.2 M$, but the titration error (even with the silver chloride precipitate left in the titration vessel) is no greater than about -0.1 per cent.

Other Applications of the Volhard Titration. In addition to the direct determination of silver, the Volhard titration is also useful for the quantitative determination of mercuric ion, according to the reaction

$$Hg^{++} + 2 \ SCN^- \rightleftharpoons Hg(SCN)_2(aq)$$

In actual fact, the titration of mercuric ion with thiocyanate is not a true precipitation reaction. The species $Hg(SCN)_2$ (aq) is a fairly soluble (approximately $0.0022 F$ at $25°C$) molecule, but it is only very slightly ionized. Thus, it behaves like a stable complex ion rather than an insoluble precipitate. The equation for dissociation of the aqueous $Hg(SCN)_2$ molecule,

$$Hg(SCN)_2(aq) \rightleftharpoons Hg^{++} + 2 \ SCN^-$$

has an equilibrium constant of 3.2×10^{-18}. During the titration of mercuric ion with thiocyanate, no solid mercuric thiocyanate precipitates until the equivalence point is nearly reached because of the relatively high solubility of solid mercuric thiocyanate, its tendency to form supersaturated solutions, and the stability of the $HgSCN^+$ ion. Nevertheless, the stoichiometry of the titration reaction is closely followed and, with ferric alum as the indicator in an acidic medium, the titration is quite successful.

The indirect Volhard determination of other anions can also be accomplished. In particular, for the determinations of bromide and iodide, the metathesis of the silver halide by excess thiocyanate does not occur because silver bromide ($K_{sp} = 5.25 \times 10^{-13}$) and silver iodide ($K_{sp} = 8.31 \times 10^{-17}$) both have smaller solubility products than silver thiocyanate. None of the special precautions used in the determination of chloride has to be employed for bromide or iodide. However, because iodide does react with ferric ions, it is necessary to add the excess of silver nitrate before the ferric alum indicator. The successful determination of anions which form silver salts *more soluble* than silver chloride requires that an excess of silver nitrate be added and that the silver salt be removed by filtration before the back-titration with standard potassium thiocyanate solution.

ADSORPTION INDICATOR METHODS

Certain organic dyes are adsorbed by colloidal precipitates more strongly on one side of the equivalence point than on the other. In certain cases the dye undergoes an abrupt color change in the process of being adsorbed, and it may serve as a sensitive end point indicator in titrations. The analytical applications of these so-called *adsorption indicators* are quite specific and relatively few in number, but they are of considerable importance nevertheless.

One important family of adsorption indicators is derived from fluorescein. The sodium salt of this compound, sodium fluoresceinate, is frequently used as an adsorption indicator for the titration of chloride with silver nitrate in a neutral or very slightly basic solution.

fluorescein   sodium fluoresceinate

Two other adsorption indicators of this family are sodium dichloro-fluoresceinate and sodium eosinate, the latter being the salt of tetrabromo-fluorescein.

sodium dichlorofluoresceinate

sodium eosinate

The behavior of an adsorption indicator may be understood in terms of the properties of colloidally dispersed precipitates in an electrolyte solution. As discussed in Chapter 5, a colloidal particle attracts to its surface a primary adsorbed ion layer consisting preferentially of the lattice ion which is present in excess in the surrounding solution phase. In other words, a precipitate particle most strongly adsorbs the ions of which it is composed. For example, in the titration of chloride with a standard silver nitrate solution, the primary ion layer adsorbed on the silver chloride consists of chloride ions prior to the equivalence point. After the equivalence point, the primary ion layer contains adsorbed silver ions. In addition, a secondary (counter) ion layer is attracted more or less strongly, the sign of the charges of the ions in the counter ion layer being opposite to those of the primary layer.

Consider now the titration of chloride with standard silver nitrate in the presence of a small concentration of sodium fluoresceinate. Sodium fluoresceinate is ionized in solution to form sodium ions and fluoresceinate ions, which will be designated as the indicator anions, Ind⁻. As soon as the titration is begun, some solid silver chloride is formed in the titration vessel. At all points prior to the equivalence point, chloride ion is in excess, and so the primary ion layer consists of adsorbed chloride ions and the secondary ion layer of any available cations, such as sodium or hydrogen ions. Few negatively charged indicator ions, Ind⁻, are adsorbed because chloride displaces them. However, beyond the equivalence point, excess silver nitrate is present, so the primary adsorbed ion layer is composed of silver ions and the secondary ion layer consists of negative ions, an appreciable number of which will be the indicator anions. The indicator imparts a yellow-green color to the solution, but when the indicator anions are adsorbed as counter ions on the precipitate, a dramatic color change occurs and the precipitate particles become bright pink. The cause of the color change is believed to be due to a distortion or bending of the fluoresceinate structure when it is attracted to a precipitate particle by the presence of the positively charged, adsorbed silver ions. In effect, the fluoresceinate anion acts as an indicator for adsorbed silver ions. Thus, the end point is marked by the change from a green solution to a pink precipitate. In practice, the particles of precipitate are kept well dispersed so that the observed color change appears to be one of yellow-green to pink throughout the entire solution. This procedure for determining chloride is commonly called the Fajans method.

The fluoresceinate ion is the anion of the weak acid fluorescein, whose pK_a is approximately 7. Therefore, the titration of chloride with silver nitrate must be performed in neutral or slightly alkaline solutions. Naturally, the pH cannot be so high that silver oxide might be formed. If the titration is attempted below pH 6, the indicator anions are converted to the parent, uncharged acid, fluorescein,

$$Ind^- + H^+ \rightleftharpoons HInd$$

which displays no tendency to be adsorbed.

Since the color on one side of the equivalence point appears on the surface of the precipitate particles, it is desirable to have as large a precipitate surface area as possible. This means that the individual particles should be kept very small and should be well dispersed throughout the solution. Dextrin is used as a protective colloid in the determination of chloride by the adsorption indicator method to help ensure the desired physical character-istics of the precipitate. It should be noted that these characteristics are exactly opposite to those deemed desirable in gravimetric analysis.

Dichlorofluorescein (pK_a about 4) and eosin (pK_a about 2) are stronger acids than fluorescein and serve as adsorption indicators over a wider range of solution pH conditions. Whereas fluorescein is applicable to silver halide precipitations only if the pH is within the approximate limits of 6 to 10, a pH as low as 4 is acceptable with dichlorofluorescein. In practice, the use of dichlorofluorescein rather than fluorescein is preferable for the titration of halides. Eosin is suitable as an indicator for the precipitation titrations of

rhodamine B

bromide, iodide, and thiocyanate (but not chloride) in solutions as acidic as pH 2. Chloride cannot be determined because the eosinate anion is more strongly adsorbed than chloride even at the start of the titration. Thus, the relative strength of adsorption of an indicator anion is another important criterion in the selection of a suitable adsorption indicator. For each of the three indicators mentioned so far, the adsorption of the indicator *anion* is responsible for the color change. Several other dyes, principally rhodamine and related compounds, have been developed as adsorption indicators for use in very acidic solutions. In these cases, it is the protonated (cationic) form of the indicator which is adsorbed on the precipitate.

For example, in the titration of silver ion in a nitric acid medium with a standard chloride solution, the primary adsorbed ion layer consists of silver ions before the equivalence point and chloride ions after the equivalence point. Beyond the equivalence point, the presence of these chloride ions attracts the positively charged indicator cation, e.g., rhodamine B, with the resultant characteristic color change. The uses of adsorption indicators are almost exclusively restricted to precipitation titrations involving silver salts, but a few applications to mercuric and lead precipitates have been suggested.

TITRATION OF HALIDE MIXTURES

If a sample solution contains several ions, each of which forms an insoluble precipitate with a particular titrant solution, and if the solubility products of the resulting precipitates differ enough, then it may be possible to titrate the solution and to obtain an end point corresponding to the successive titration of each component. Such is the case for mixtures of iodide, bromide, and chloride. Since the solubility products of the silver halides are 8.31×10^{-17} for silver iodide, 5.25×10^{-13} for silver bromide, and 1.78×10^{-10} for silver chloride, a solution containing a mixture of halides of not too greatly differing concentrations can be titrated with a standard silver nitrate solution, and the amount of each individual halide can be determined.

Consider the titration of 50.00 ml of a solution which is $0.02000\ M$ each in iodide, bromide, and chloride with a $0.05000\ F$ silver nitrate solution. The titration curve can be constructed by plotting pAg versus the volume of silver nitrate, as shown in Figure 10-3. At the very beginning of the titration, before any silver nitrate has been added, pAg is not really defined. However, when only one drop of titrant is added, silver iodide will precipitate. Since the volume of the solution is essentially 50.00 ml and the iodide concentration is virtually $0.02000\ M$, the silver ion concentration may be readily computed from the silver iodide solubility-product relation,

$$[Ag^+] = \frac{8.31 \times 10^{-17}}{[I^-]} = \frac{8.31 \times 10^{-17}}{0.0200} = 4.16 \times 10^{-15}\ M,$$

and pAg is 14.38. For practical purposes, this pAg may be considered as the value at the beginning of the titration.

At 5.00 ml of silver nitrate added, the solution volume is 55.00 ml and 0.75 millimole of iodide remains untitrated, so the iodide concentration is 0.75 millimole/55.00 ml, or 0.0136 M:

$$[Ag^+] = \frac{8.31 \times 10^{-17}}{0.0136} = 6.10 \times 10^{-15} \, M; \qquad pAg = 14.21$$

Because the halide concentration being titrated is relatively large and because no point on the titration curve very close to the equivalence point (except for the equivalence point itself) will be considered in this series of calculations, the contribution to $[Ag^+]$ because of the dissolution of the silver halide can be neglected throughout this discussion.

At 10.00 ml of silver nitrate added, $[I^-] = 8.34 \times 10^{-3} \, M$; $[Ag^+] = 9.97 \times 10^{-15} \, M$; $pAg = 14.00$. At 15.00 ml of silver nitrate added, $[I^-] = 3.85 \times 10^{-3} \, M$; $[Ag^+] = 2.16 \times 10^{-14} \, M$; $pAg = 13.67$.

Upon the addition of 20.00 ml of silver nitrate, the equivalence point for iodide is reached. If iodide were the only species present, the following

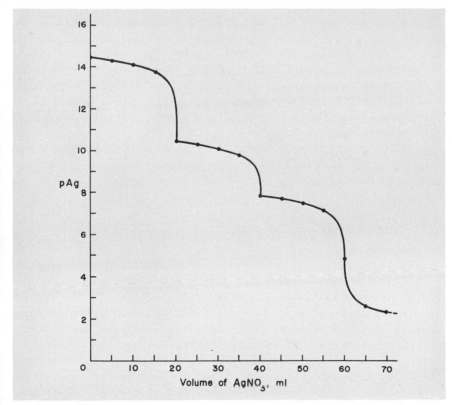

FIGURE 10-3. Titration curve for the titration of 50.00 ml of a solution containing 0.02000 M each of iodide, bromide, and chloride with a 0.05000 F silver nitrate solution.

equivalence point conditions would prevail: $[Ag^+] = [I^-] = K_{sp}^{1/2} = (8.31 \times 10^{-17})^{1/2} = 9.12 \times 10^{-9}\ M$; $pAg = 8.04$. However, both bromide and chloride remain untitrated at this point, each at a concentration of $0.0143\ M$. In particular, silver bromide has just begun to precipitate at this point, and, therefore, the silver ion concentration in equilibrium with silver bromide is

$$[Ag^+] = \frac{5.25 \times 10^{-13}}{[Br^-]} = \frac{5.25 \times 10^{-13}}{0.0143} = 3.68 \times 10^{-11}\ M; \quad pAg = 10.43$$

This calculation shows that, in the presence of the bromide, $[Ag^+]$ cannot reach the value of $9.12 \times 10^{-9}\ M$, which corresponds to the iodide equivalence point. Instead, the silver ion concentration increases only to $3.68 \times 10^{-11}\ M$, the point at which silver bromide just begins to precipitate. The iodide concentration left in solution when silver bromide starts to precipitate is

$$[I^-] = \frac{8.31 \times 10^{-17}}{[Ag^+]} = \frac{8.31 \times 10^{-17}}{3.68 \times 10^{-11}} = 2.26 \times 10^{-6}\ M$$

Thus, in comparison to the original iodide concentration of $0.02\ M$, the precipitation of silver iodide is quantitatively complete when 20.00 ml of silver nitrate has been added. Only $(70.00)(2.26 \times 10^{-6})$ or 0.000158 millimole of iodide remains untitrated. The value of pAg at which iodide is quantitatively precipitated and bromide has just started to precipitate is called the "break point." The "break point" is marked by a discontinuity in the titration curve. The titration curve for a mixture of three halides exhibits two "break points."

The values of pAg at 25.00, 30.00, and 35.00 ml of silver nitrate added can be calculated from the bromide concentration and the solubility-product expression for silver bromide. At 25.00 ml of silver nitrate added, $[Br^-] = 0.0100\ M$ and

$$[Ag^+] = \frac{5.25 \times 10^{-13}}{0.0100} = 5.25 \times 10^{-11}\ M; \quad pAg = 10.28$$

At 30.00 ml of silver nitrate added, $[Br^-] = 6.25 \times 10^{-3}\ M$; $[Ag^+] = 8.40 \times 10^{-11}\ M$; $pAg = 10.08$. At 35.00 ml of silver nitrate added, $[Br^-] = 2.94 \times 10^{-3}\ M$; $[Ag^+] = 1.78 \times 10^{-10}\ M$; $pAg = 9.75$.

The addition of 40.00 ml of the silver nitrate solution presents a situation analogous to that corresponding to the addition of 20.00 ml. The equivalence point for the titration of bromide has been reached, and silver chloride has just barely begun to precipitate. There is 1.00 millimole of chloride in 90.00 ml of solution, so $[Cl^-] = 0.0111\ M$, and the silver ion concentration in equilibrium with the precipitate of silver chloride is given by

$$[Ag^+] = \frac{1.78 \times 10^{-10}}{0.0111} = 1.60 \times 10^{-8}\ M; \quad pAg = 7.80$$

Therefore, although pAg at the equivalence point of the titration of bromide with silver nitrate should be 6.14, in the presence of the chloride ion, pAg reaches only 7.80. It can be shown that the amount of bromide left untitrated is

$$[Br^-] = \frac{5.25 \times 10^{-13}}{1.60 \times 10^{-8}} = 3.28 \times 10^{-5} \, M$$

which, in the solution of volume 90.00 ml, amounts to only 0.00295 millimole of the original 1.000 millimole.

For volumes of silver nitrate greater than 40.00 ml, the titration curve is identical, at least in theory, to that for the titration of 90.00 ml of 0.0111 M chloride with 0.05 F silver nitrate. The construction of the titration curve may be done exactly as in Figure 10-1.

At 45.00 ml of silver nitrate added, $[Cl^-] = 7.90 \times 10^{-3} \, M$ and

$$[Ag^+] = \frac{1.78 \times 10^{-10}}{7.90 \times 10^{-3}} = 2.26 \times 10^{-8} \, M; \qquad pAg = 7.65$$

At 50.00 ml of silver nitrate added, $[Cl^-] = 5.00 \times 10^{-3} \, M$; $[Ag^+] = 3.56 \times 10^{-8} \, M$; $pAg = 7.45$. At 55.00 ml of silver nitrate added, $[Cl^-] = 2.38 \times 10^{-3} \, M$; $[Ag^+] = 7.48 \times 10^{-8} \, M$; $pAg = 7.13$. At 60.00 ml of silver nitrate added, the equivalence point for the titration of chloride, $[Cl^-] = [Ag^+] = (1.78 \times 10^{-10})^{1/2} = 1.33 \times 10^{-5} \, M$; $pAg = 4.87$. At 65.00 ml of silver nitrate added, there is 5.00 ml excess of $0.05000 \, F$ silver nitrate in a solution volume of 115.0 ml: $[Ag^+] = 2.17 \times 10^{-3} \, M$; $pAg = 2.66$. Finally, at 70.00 ml of silver nitrate added, $[Ag^+] = 4.16 \times 10^{-3} \, M$; $pAg = 2.38$.

The idealized titration curve shown in Figure 10-3 for a mixture of halides is not usually followed in practice. The most troublesome problem in the titration of halide mixtures is the contamination of one silver halide by coprecipitation of a second, more-soluble silver halide. This results from the tendency of the silver halides to adsorb other halide ions and to form solid solutions or mixed crystals with each other. Ion adsorption and solid-solution formation are promoted by several factors. First, the charges on halide ions are the same. Second, because the ionic radii of the halides decrease in the order of iodide, bromide, and chloride, an iodide ion can be replaced in a crystal lattice by bromide, and bromide by chloride. Third, because silver bromide and silver chloride have identical (cubic) crystal structures, the formation of solid solutions of these precipitates is especially serious. Silver iodide and silver bromide are less prone to form solid solutions, and silver iodide and silver chloride form almost no mixed crystals at all.

Depending upon the relative concentrations of halides in a mixture, ion adsorption and mixed-crystal formation can frequently cause titration errors on the order of 1 per cent. Thus, for example, in the titration of a bromide-chloride mixture with silver nitrate, the coprecipitation of chloride with silver bromide causes the first end point to occur too late. Consequently, a positive titration error results for the determination of bromide, and a negative error for chloride. Coprecipitation phenomena cause the "break points" in a titration curve for halide mixtures to appear somewhat late in the titration and to be rounded rather than sharp.

The progress of the titration can be followed best by observation of the silver ion concentration (pAg) as a function of the volume of silver nitrate titrant added. In turn, the changing silver ion concentration can be monitored by the measurement of the potential of a silver indicator electrode versus a reference electrode. Thus, a potentiometric titration is usually performed for the determination of halides in a mixture. There is no chemical indicator which could be used for such a titration.

The principles of potentiometric titrations will be discussed in detail in a later chapter. However, a brief practical treatment will be given here. If a clean silver electrode (wire) is dipped into the unknown halide solution and a second, stable reference electrode is immersed in the same solution, the potential E developed across this cell (composed of the solution and the two electrodes) is related to the silver ion concentration by the following relations:

$$E = \text{constant} - 0.059 \log \frac{1}{[Ag^+]}$$

$$E = \text{constant} + 0.059 \log [Ag^+]$$

$$E = \text{constant} - 0.059 \text{ pAg}$$

The value of the constant term in these expressions is influenced by the particular reference electrode used; but, for a given experimental setup, it should not vary. The important thing is that the potential E is a linear function of pAg only. Therefore, instead of a plot of pAg versus volume of titrant, it is easier to construct a graph of E against volume. The shape of the titration curve will be the same in either case. Although it is wholly unnecessary, the observed values of E could be converted to pAg values, if the magnitude of the constant term is known. This constant can be evaluated by measuring E for a known silver ion concentration.

This potentiometric method of following the course of titrations is useful not only for halide mixtures but for individual halides as well. Obviously, this technique completely eliminates the problems associated with chemical end point indicators described earlier.

Experiment 10-1

PREPARATION OF A STANDARD SILVER NITRATE SOLUTION

Purpose

The purpose of this experiment is to prepare 500 ml of a 0.1 F standard silver nitrate solution.

Procedure

Weigh approximately 8.5 gm of analytical-reagent-grade or primary-standard-grade silver nitrate ($AgNO_3$) into a clean, dry weighing bottle.

Since silver nitrate is very expensive, the appropriate weight of $AgNO_3$ needed to prepare the standard solution should be weighed out roughly, so that silver nitrate will not be wasted.

Place the weighing bottle and silver nitrate in a beaker-and-watch-glass arrangement, as shown in Figure 2-1, and dry the $AgNO_3$ in an oven at 110°C for one to two hours. After the heating period, allow the weighing bottle, plus silver nitrate, to cool in air for several minutes and then in a desiccator for at least 30 minutes.

Some samples of silver nitrate acquire a pale pink or brown discoloration during heating. Presumably this is due to traces of organic matter which reduces silver nitrate to silver metal on the surface of each crystal. This very slight decomposition does not cause any difficulty and may be ignored except in highly precise work.

Weigh accurately, to the nearest milligram, the bottle and silver nitrate.

The weight of silver nitrate will be approximately 8.5 gm, and so it is definitely unnecessary to make weighings more precise than ± 1 mg. Since two weighings are ultimately involved in determining the concentration of the silver nitrate solution, an uncertainty of 1 mg in each weight would cause a maximum weighing uncertainty of 2 mg in 8.5 gm, or one part in 4250. It is obvious that a somewhat greater weighing uncertainty can be tolerated. At the same time, however, it is easy to weigh objects to the nearest milligram, so undue carelessness in the preparation of a standard solution is not to be encouraged.

Insert a long-stem glass funnel into a clean 500 ml volumetric flask so that the end of the stem is a few centimeters below the calibration mark. By tilting and rotating the weighing bottle, carefully transfer the silver nitrate from the weighing bottle to the funnel. Do not attempt to remove any small crystals of $AgNO_3$ remaining in the bottle. Close the weighing bottle and return it to the desiccator.

In handling a weighing bottle (which is to be subsequently weighed), one should hold the bottle, not between the fingertips, but by wrapping a piece of lint-free paper (or chamois skin) around it, as in Figure 2-3. In the present situation, the weight of silver nitrate is sufficiently large that the weight of "fingerprints" will not affect the weighings. In most instances, however, sample sizes may be 0.5 gm or less, so maximum weighing accuracy demands that weighing bottles be properly handled to avoid fingerprints and to prevent warming the bottles before weighing them. (See Experiment 2-1.)

Dissolve the silver nitrate in the glass funnel by directing a slow stream of distilled water over it from a wash bottle. After the silver nitrate has been dissolved and passed into the volumetric flask, add more distilled water through the funnel to wash it thoroughly. Remove the funnel just before the liquid level reaches the bottom of the stem. Using a dropper or pipet, carefully add distilled water until the meniscus of the liquid reaches the calibration mark exactly.

It is advantageous if the silver nitrate is dissolved *before* the volume of solution is brought up to the calibration mark. The reason for this is that the volumetric flask can be efficiently swirled to dissolve the silver nitrate in a small amount of distilled water. It is not as easy to dissolve a solid in a volumetric flask *after* the volume of liquid has been adjusted to the calibration mark because the solution cannot be swirled effectively.

When the level of liquid is finally adjusted to the calibration mark, any droplets of water adhering to the inner wall of the flask above the mark should be carefully wiped away with a piece of filter paper.

Stopper the volumetric flask and mix the solution very thoroughly by shaking, swirling, and inverting the flask repeatedly.

One of the most insidious sources of difficulty in volumetric analysis arises from the incomplete mixing of a standard titrant solution.

Rinse a clean ground-glass-stoppered (Pyrex) bottle with two or three small portions of the silver nitrate solution, discard the rinsings, and transfer the remainder of the solution to the bottle for storage.

Note that standard solutions should not be allowed to wet the ground-glass stopper of the storage bottle because the stopper may be cemented in place when the solution dries. Furthermore, the crystals which form around the stopper may fall back into the solution at a later time, thus altering the titrant concentration.

Finally, weigh the empty weighing bottle to determine the weight of silver nitrate, then calculate the concentration of the solution.

Silver nitrate solutions should be protected from light to prevent the very slow photoreduction of silver ion to silver metal.

Experiment 10-2

DETERMINATION OF CHLORIDE BY THE MOHR TITRATION

Purpose

This experiment for the titrimetric determination of chloride with standard silver nitrate solution illustrates a method for end point detection based upon the formation of a colored precipitate.

Procedure

Place a quantity of the chloride-containing sample (adequate for several 0.2 gm portions) in a clean, dry weighing bottle, and employ a beaker-and-watch-glass arrangement (see Fig. 2-1) to dry the sample in an oven for one hour at 110°C. After removing the sample from the oven, allow the weighing bottle plus sample to cool in air for several minutes and then in a desiccator for 30 minutes.

Accurately weigh, to the nearest 0.1 mg, three 0.2 to 0.25 gm portions of the chloride sample, each into a clean 250 ml Erlenmeyer flask.

Each weighed portion should be of such size that between 30 and 40 ml of a 0.1 F silver nitrate solution will be required for the titration. Thus, each portion should contain approximately 3 to 4 millimoles of chloride, or about 105 to 140 mg of chloride. If the sample contains 50 per cent chloride, the weight of each portion should range from 0.20 to 0.28 gm. If the percentage of chloride in the sample is known to differ considerably from 50 per cent, the weight of each portion should be varied appropriately.

Dissolve each weighed portion of chloride sample in approximately 50 ml of distilled water, then add to each flask 2 ml of a 0.25 F potassium chromate (K_2CrO_4) solution.

It is essential that the solution be neutral or barely alkaline at this point. Most common chloride-containing samples are neutral, water-soluble salts such as sodium chloride or potassium chloride. If there is any reason to suspect that the sample solution may contain acidic species or that the distilled water used to dissolve the sample is acidic, add a pinch of analytical-reagent-grade sodium bicarbonate $(NaHCO_3)$ to neutralize the acid. If, upon the addition of $NaHCO_3$, the solution should effervesce, add several more small portions of $NaHCO_3$ until the evolution of CO_2 ceases and the solution is neutral. In any case, it is probably advisable to add at least a small amount of sodium bicarbonate as a routine procedure.

As an aid in recognizing the end point color change, prepare two color comparison solutions as follows: Add about 85 to 90 ml of distilled water (the approximate end point volume in the subsequent titrations) into two 250 ml Erlenmeyer flasks. Then add 2 ml of a 0.25 F K$_2$CrO$_4$ solution to each flask. Next, add 300 mg of powdered, reagent-grade (chloride-free) calcium carbonate (CaCO$_3$) to each flask to simulate the white precipitate of AgCl. Swirl the solutions to suspend the powdery CaCO$_3$. Reserve one of these mixtures as a comparison solution of the color *prior* to the equivalence point. Titrate the other mixture with *fractional* drops of standard 0.1 F silver nitrate solution until the first detectable change in color occurs from canary-yellow to orange-yellow (or brown-yellow). Perform this titration against a white background. Reserve this mixture as a comparison solution of the color just *beyond* the equivalence point. Record the volume of standard silver nitrate solution required for this blank titration for later use as an end point correction; this volume should not exceed 0.05 to 0.07 ml.

Now proceed to titrate each of the chloride sample solutions with standard 0.1 F silver nitrate solution from a 50 ml buret. Use a white background for the titrations and manipulate the buret stopcock and the titration flask as suggested by Figure 2-17. Swirl the solution continuously, but slowly, throughout the titration in order to facilitate the attainment of solubility equilibrium. Continue the titration, adding drops and fractions of drops of titrant, until the canary-yellow color of the solution just changes permanently to orange-yellow or brown-yellow and matches the color of the comparison solution prepared earlier. At the conclusion of each titration, wait 30 seconds for drainage of the buret, then record the volume of titrant used.

The approach of the end point is indicated by the observation that, as the solution is swirled and titrated with AgNO$_3$, the red color of Ag$_2$CrO$_4$ spreads fleetingly throughout the entire solution before it disappears (until finally, at the end point, it persists). The solution must be swirled continuously throughout the titration because one is dealing with a heterogeneous phase equilibrium between solid AgCl and the ions in solution.

From the volume of standard silver nitrate solution used in each titration (with the end point correction subtracted) and from the corresponding weight of each portion of sample and the known concentration of the silver nitrate solution, calculate and report the average percentage of chloride in the sample. Replicate results should agree to within two or three parts per thousand.

Experiment 10-3

PREPARATION AND STANDARDIZATION OF A POTAS-SIUM THIOCYANATE SOLUTION

Purpose

The purpose of this experiment is to prepare an approximately 0.1 F potassium thiocyanate solution and to standardize it against a standard silver nitrate solution.

Procedure

Preparation of Potassium Thiocyanate Solution. Weigh approximately 9.8 gm of analytical-reagent-grade potassium thiocyanate (KSCN) into a clean, 1 liter, ground-glass-stoppered (Pyrex) bottle. Add enough distilled water to dissolve the potassium thiocyanate, then fill the bottle with additional distilled water to give approximately 1 liter of solution. Stopper the bottle and mix the solution thoroughly by shaking, swirling, and inverting the bottle repeatedly. Remove any solution which has wet the ground-glass stopper by carefully wiping the ground-glass surfaces with a piece of lint-free laboratory tissue.

Note that, since the potassium thiocyanate solution is to be subsequently standardized, the weight of KSCN and the total volume of water added to prepare the solution need be measured only approximately.

Standardization of Potassium Thiocyanate Solution. Pipet a 25.00 ml aliquot of standard 0.1 F silver nitrate solution into each of three clean 250 ml Erlenmeyer flasks. Add to each flask 5 ml of 6 F nitric acid (HNO$_3$); 2 ml of saturated ferric alum solution, Fe(NH$_4$)(SO$_4$)$_2$·12H$_2$O; and 20 ml of distilled water.

Prepare the ferric alum indicator solution in advance by saturating a suitable volume of 1 F nitric acid with ferric ammonium sulfate, Fe(NH$_4$)(SO$_4$)$_2$·12 H$_2$O.

Titrate each solution with the potassium thiocyanate solution to be standardized, delivering it from a 50 ml buret. Swirl the solution continuously during the titration, adding the potassium thiocyanate solution until the red color of the FeSCN^{++} indicator complex spreads transiently throughout the solution before fading. Thereafter, add the potassium thiocyanate in drops and then in fractions of drops until the first perceptible but permanent appearance of a faint red-brown color occurs. Allow approximately 30 seconds for drainage from the inner wall of the buret, then record the volume of potassium thiocyanate solution used in the titration. No indicator blank titration is required because of the sensitivity of the end point color change.

Care must be taken not to confuse the very pale yellow-brown color of the original solution, due to the presence of an iron(III) species such as $Fe(H_2O)_5(OH)^{++}$, and the end point color due to $FeSCN^{++}$. If the solution is continuously swirled as the end point is approached, the solution will appear almost milklike because of suspended AgSCN, and the end point may be recognized as the first noticeable *change* to a faint reddish-brown color. If there is any doubt about having reached the end point, record the buret reading and add one more drop of titrant; if one more drop of titrant definitely intensifies the red $FeSCN^{++}$ color, accept the buret reading prior to the addition of the extra drop.

Care must also be taken to ensure that a stable or permanent end point color change has occurred. The end point can be regarded as stable if the pale red-brown color due to $FeSCN^{++}$ persists for several minutes. Silver thiocyanate does have a tendency to adsorb silver ions. These adsorbed silver ions desorb somewhat slowly near the equivalence point, and so the solution should be swirled vigorously at this point to be sure that the reaction between silver and thiocyanate ions is complete.

From the volumes of potassium thiocyanate solution required in the three titrations and from the known volume and concentration of the standard silver nitrate solution used, calculate the average concentration of the potassium thiocyanate solution. Replicate standardizations should agree to within one or two parts per thousand.

Experiment 10-4

INDIRECT DETERMINATION OF CHLORIDE BY THE VOLHARD TITRATION

Purpose

This experiment for the indirect titrimetric determination of chloride employs standard solutions of silver nitrate and potassium thiocyanate, and it emphasizes two approaches which may be taken to overcome the metathesis of silver chloride by thiocyanate ion.

Procedure

Place a quantity of the chloride-containing sample (enough for several 0.3 gm portions) in a clean, dry weighing bottle, and insert the weighing bottle into a beaker-and-watch-glass arrangement (see Fig. 2-1) to dry the sample in an oven for one hour at 110°C. Upon removing the sample from the oven, cool the weighing bottle and chloride sample in air for a few minutes and then in a desiccator for at least 30 minutes prior to weighing out individual portions for the analysis.

Weigh accurately, to the nearest 0.1 mg, three 0.3 gm portions of the dried sample material, each portion into a clean 250 ml Erlenmeyer flask.

Each weighed portion should contain approximately 4 millimoles, or about 140 mg, of chloride ion. If the sample material consists of 50 per cent chloride, the weight of each portion should be about 0.28 gm. If the percentage of chloride in the sample is known to differ from 50 per cent, the weight of each portion should be changed accordingly.

Dissolve each weighed portion of the chloride sample in approximately 20 ml of distilled water, and follow one of the two procedures that follow (although it may be of interest to determine the percentage of chloride by means of both procedures in order to compare the results of each method).

Method I. To the aqueous solution of the chloride sample, add 5 ml of 6 F nitric acid (HNO_3). Pipet into the solution exactly 50.00 ml of standard 0.1 F silver nitrate. Swirl the flask to coagulate the silver chloride precipitate.

An *excess* of silver nitrate must, of course, be added. The present procedure calls for the addition of 5 millimoles of silver ion to a sample solution which, presumably, contains 4 millimoles of chloride. Evidence that silver ion is in excess is also provided by the fact that the AgCl precipitate should coagulate and settle to the bottom of the flask. In addition, if the sample solution is gently swirled as the silver nitrate is delivered slowly from the pipet, a point will be observed at which the AgCl precipitate suddenly coagulates and the solution becomes clear. This "clear point" occurs when an amount of silver ion equivalent to the chloride has been added and thereby serves to indicate if enough silver nitrate solution is being added.

Set up a clean, long-stem glass funnel, fitted properly with a medium porosity filter paper (see Figs. 2-10 and 2-11) and use a clean 500 ml Erlenmeyer flask as the receiving vessel. Using a glass stirring rod, carefully pour the supernatant solution containing the excess silver nitrate onto the filter but retaining, if possible, the bulk of the silver chloride precipitate in the original flask. Wash the silver chloride precipitate thoroughly by decanting it with 10 ml of 1 F nitric acid, then carefully pour the wash liquid through the filter to wash the latter as well. Repeat the washing procedure with five more 10 ml portions of 1 F nitric acid in order to recover quantitatively the excess of silver nitrate originally added to precipitate the silver chloride.

Add, to the combined filtrate and washings in the 500 ml flask, 4 ml of saturated ferric alum indicator solution, and titrate the solution with standard 0.1 F potassium thiocyanate from a 50 ml buret exactly as described for the standardization procedure in Experiment 10-3.

Calculate the percentage of chloride in the original sample from the volumes of standard silver nitrate and potassium thiocyanate used and from the weight of the chloride sample. Repeat the procedure with the other two chloride sample solutions. Compute and report the average percentage of chloride in the sample. Replicate determinations should agree to within two parts per thousand.

   Method II.   To the aqueous solution of the chloride sample, add 20 ml of 6 F nitric acid (HNO_3) and 10 ml of 2 F ferric nitrate, $Fe(NO_3)_3$, solution. Then pipet exactly 1.00 ml of standard 0.01 F potassium thiocyanate solution into the mixture.

   The standard 0.01 F KSCN solution may be conveniently prepared if 10.00 ml of standard 0.1 F potassium thiocyanate is diluted with distilled water to exactly 100.0 ml in a volumetric flask.

   Titrate the solution with standard 0.1 F silver nitrate delivered from a 50 ml buret. Swirl the solution vigorously during the titration. Continue the titration until the red color due to $FeSCN^{++}$ just *disappears*.

   The disappearance of the red-colored iron(III) thiocyanate complex is not as easy to detect as the appearance of the red color in other Volhard titrations. There will always be a slight yellow color at the end point because of the presence of iron(III) species, such as $Fe(H_2O)_5(OH)^{++}$. If any uncertainty exists as the final end point is approached, take a buret reading and then add another drop of titrant to determine if any further color change occurs. It is also helpful to use, for purposes of color comparison, a solution which is similar to the one being titrated but which contains several drops excess of silver nitrate titrant.

   From the volumes of standard 0.1 F silver nitrate and standard 0.01 F potassium thiocyanate solutions used in the procedure and from the weight of the chloride sample, calculate the percentage of chloride in that sample. Repeat the procedure with the other two chloride sample solutions. Then compute and report the average percentage of chloride. Replicate determinations should agree to within two or three parts per thousand.

QUESTIONS AND PROBLEMS

1. Contrast gravimetric and volumetric precipitation methods on several different points.
2. Write chemical equations for the primary and indicator reactions in the Mohr titration and in the Volhard titration of chloride.
3. In a chloride determination by one of the modified Volhard procedures, a chemist failed to coat the precipitated silver chloride completely with nitrobenzene. Was his result high, low, or correct? Explain.
4. Explain why it is unnecessary to remove the precipitated silver iodide before the final titration in an iodide determination by the Volhard procedure.
5. In the Mohr method for the determination of chloride, why must not the solution be acidic? Why must it not be basic?
6. In the determination of chloride by the Mohr procedure, a chemist added the proper amount of potassium chromate indicator, made the solution distinctly acidic, and titrated the solution with silver nitrate. Was the quantity of chloride found by this technique high, low, or correct? Explain.

7. Make sketches of the silver chloride precipitate during a chloride determination according to the Fajans method, showing the relative positions and composition of the primary adsorbed ion layer and the counter ion layer.

8. Contrast the desirability of coagulating the silver chloride precipitate in a Fajans determination of chloride and in a gravimetric determination of chloride.

9. What volume of $0.2000 F$ potassium thiocyanate solution is required to precipitate the silver from a solution containing 0.4623 gm of silver nitrate?

10. If 25.00 ml of a sodium chloride solution was required to precipitate the silver in the solution obtained by dissolving 0.2365 gm of 98.00 per cent pure silver metal, what was the concentration of the sodium chloride solution?

11. Calculate the percentage of potassium iodide (KI) in a 2.145 gm sample of a mixture of potassium iodide and potassium carbonate that, when analyzed according to the Volhard procedure, required 3.32 ml of a $0.1212 F$ potassium thiocyanate solution after the addition of 50.00 ml of a $0.2429 F$ silver nitrate solution.

12. For the analysis of a commercial solution of silver nitrate, a 2.075 gm sample of the solution was weighed out and diluted to 100.0 ml in a volumetric flask. A 50.00 ml aliquot of the solution was then titrated with 35.55 ml of a potassium thiocyanate solution, of which 1.000 ml corresponds to exactly 5.000 mg of silver. Calculate the weight percentage of silver nitrate in the original solution.

13. An analytical chemist analyzed 0.5000 gm of an arsenic-containing sample by oxidizing the arsenic to arsenate, precipitating silver arsenate (Ag_3AsO_4), dissolving the precipitate in acid, and titrating the silver with a $0.1000 F$ potassium thiocyanate solution — 45.45 ml being required. Calculate the percentage of arsenic in the sample.

14. A 25.00 ml portion of a silver nitrate solution was treated with an excess of sodium chloride solution, and the resulting silver chloride precipitate was coagulated, filtered, washed, and found to weigh 0.3520 gm. In a subsequent experiment, 22.00 ml of the same original silver nitrate solution was found to react with 16.25 ml of a potassium thiocyanate solution. Calculate the concentrations of the silver nitrate and potassium thiocyanate solutions.

15. A solid sample is known to contain only sodium hydroxide, sodium chloride, and water. A 6.700 gm sample was dissolved in distilled water and diluted to 250.0 ml in a volumetric flask. A one-tenth aliquot required 22.22 ml of $0.4976 F$ hydrochloric acid for titration to a phenolphthalein end point. When another one-tenth aliquot of the sample solution was titrated according to the Volhard procedure, 35.00 ml of a $0.1117 F$ silver nitrate solution was added and 4.63 ml of $0.0962 F$ potassium thiocyanate solution was required for the back-titration. The water content of the sample was determined by difference. What was the percentage composition of the original sample?

16. Calculate the concentration of silver ion at the experimental end point in the Mohr titration of chloride if the pH of the solution is 4.00. Assume that the total concentration of all chromium(VI) species at the end point is $0.005 M$.

17. Suppose that you desire to determine iodate ion according to the Mohr procedure. Calculate the concentration of chromate ion which must be present so that precipitation of silver chromate just begins at the equivalence point.

18. Construct the titration curve for the titration, with a $0.05000 F$ silver nitrate solution, of 50.00 ml of a solution containing $0.03000 M$ iodide ion, $0.01500 M$ bromide ion, and $0.02500 M$ chloride ion.

19. A method for the determination of low concentrations of chloride ion takes advantage of the common ion effect and the solubility-product principle. The "concentration solubility product" of AgCl(s) in $0.0250 F$ nitric acid at $25°C$ is 2.277×10^{-10}. The concentration of chloride in an unknown was determined as follows: A $0.0250 F$ nitric acid solution containing chloride ion at an unknown

concentration was shaken with excess pure AgCl(s) at 25°C until solubility equilibrium was attained. A 100.0 ml sample of the equilibrated solution was withdrawn by suction through a sintered-glass filter stick in order to remove any solid AgCl which might have been dispersed in the solution. The 100.0 ml sample was then titrated with a standard $1.020 \times 10^{-4} F$ potassium iodide (KI) solution. The end point was reached when 7.441 ml of the standard KI had been added. Calculate the concentration of chloride ion in the original solution to four significant figures. Neglect activity effects, the presence of molecular AgCl(aq), and the possible formation of anionic complexes between silver and chloride ions.

20. To each of three flasks, labeled A, B, and C, was added 50 ml of 0.05 F silver nitrate solution and three drops of a 0.10 per cent aqueous solution of sodium fluoresceinate. The solution in each flask was treated separately as follows:

    Flask A: When 100 mg of dextrin and 1.0 ml of a 1.0 F potassium chloride solution were added, the mixture became bright pink.

    Flask B: When 100 mg of dextrin and 50 ml of a 1.0 F potassium chloride solution were added, white AgCl was observed to be in suspension and the solution was colored a fluorescent yellow-green.

    Flask C: When 100 mg of dextrin and 1.0 ml of a 1.0 F potassium chloride solution were added, the mixture became bright pink. However, upon the addition of 5.0 ml of concentrated nitric acid, white AgCl was observed to be in suspension and the solution was colored a fluorescent yellow-green.

    Explain the phenomena which occurred in each of these three experiments.

21. Construct the titration curve for the titration of 50.00 ml of a 0.01000 F silver nitrate solution with 0.1000 F potassium thiocyanate solution in a 1 F nitric acid medium.

22. Construct the titration curve for the titration of 50.00 ml of a 0.02000 F mercuric nitrate solution with a 0.1000 F potassium thiocyanate solution.

23. For the calculation and construction of the titration curve for the titration of 50.00 ml of 0.1000 F sodium chloride with 0.1000 F silver nitrate discussed in an early part of this chapter, it was necessary to consider the dissolution of solid AgCl in order to calculate the chloride ion concentration and the value of pCl after the addition of 49.99 ml of titrant. What would have been the values of [Cl$^-$] and pCl if the dissolution of AgCl had been ignored? What are the magnitudes of the errors in [Cl$^-$] and pCl when the dissolution of AgCl is ignored?

24. It might be possible to determine Pb^{++} by titration with a standard solution of potassium chromate. For the end point indicator one could conceivably use silver ion, which would form a precipitate of silver chromate. Lead chromate is bright yellow, whereas silver chromate is brick-red.

    (a) Calculate what concentration of silver ion would be required so that silver chromate would just begin to precipitate at the equivalence point of the titration. (This should be a theoretical calculation, uncomplicated by solid-solution formation, activities, adsorption, or the requirement that a finite amount of silver chromate would be needed to see the end point.)

In practice, it seems evident that an unusually large amount of red-colored silver chromate must be formed in order to observe the end point in the presence of yellow-colored lead chromate. Therefore, to compensate for this, one might arrange conditions so that silver chromate would start to precipitate a little *before* the equivalence point, and thus obtain enough silver chromate to see the end point just at the equivalence point. In other words, you would probably want to make the silver ion concentration larger than the theoretical value, so that, when you see the end point, the amount of chromate added in the titration would really equal the amount of lead in the sample. Thus, although some lead remains unprecipitated, this should be exactly compensated by the chromate consumed in the precipitation of silver chromate.

      (b) Suppose that the minimum detectable concentration of silver chromate is $1 \times 10^{-4} M$ in the presence of yellow-colored lead chromate. Calculate what concentration of Ag^+ should be present to make the titration error virtually *zero* for the titration of 50.00 ml of 0.1000 M Pb^{++} with 0.1000 F potassium chromate.

25. An attempt was made to analyze a solution of potassium iodate according to the Volhard method. To a 50.00 ml sample of the potassium iodate solution containing nitric acid, 50.00 ml of 0.1000 F silver nitrate was added to precipitate silver iodate. Then 5.00 ml of a 2.00 F ferric nitrate solution was added, and, without removal of the silver iodate precipitate, the mixture was back-titrated with a 0.1000 F potassium thiocyanate solution. An end point was reached after the addition of 34.80 ml of potassium thiocyanate solution.

      (a) Calculate the concentrations of thiocyanate and iodate ions at the end point.

      (b) Calculate the titration error in per cent with the proper sign.

      (c) Calculate the concentration of the original potassium iodate solution.

SUGGESTIONS FOR ADDITIONAL READING

Books

1. J. F. Coetzee: Equilibria in precipitation reactions. *In* I. M. Kolthoff and P. J. Elving, eds.: *Treatise on Analytical Chemistry*, Part I, Volume 1, Wiley-Interscience, New York, 1959, pp. 767–809.
2. I. M. Kolthoff and V. A. Stenger: *Volumetric Analysis*, second edition, Wiley-Interscience, New York, 1947, pp. 239–344.
3. H. A. Laitinen: *Chemical Analysis*, McGraw-Hill Book Company, New York, 1960, pp. 203–219.
4. J. J. Lingane: *Electroanalytical Chemistry*, second edition, Wiley-Interscience, New York, 1958, pp. 114–128.

Paper

1. E. H. Swift, G. M. Arcand, R. Lutwack, and D. J. Meier: Determination of chloride. Anal. Chem., *22*, 306 (1950).

Chapter Eleven

Complexometric Titrations

The formation of stable metal-complex ions by the titration of a metal ion solution with a suitable standard solution of a complexing agent, or ligand, has gained increasing importance as a method of volumetric analysis. A consideration of the basic requirements for titrations, as applied to complexometric titrations, will serve to demonstrate why complex-formation reactions have only relatively recently become widely used.

For a reaction to be suitable for such a titration, it must fulfill the same requirements as all other volumetric methods of analysis. A complex-formation reaction must be rapid, must proceed according to well-defined stoichiometry, and must possess the desired characteristics for the application of the various end point detection systems.

An interesting example of the formation of a metal complex is the reaction between the hexaaquochromium(III) ion, $Cr(H_2O)_6^{+++}$, and cyanide to form the hexacyanochromate(III) anion:

Although the product species, canary-yellow $Cr(CN)_6^=$, is a very stable complex ion, the rate of reaction between violet $Cr(H_2O)_6^{+++}$ and CN^- to form this complex is very slow under conditions suitable for a titration — namely, at room temperature and for stoichiometric quantities of the reactants. The reaction rate is inconveniently slow because cyanide ions cannot readily displace the water molecules bound to chromium. Therefore, although the formation of the $Cr(CN)_6^=$ ion might be expected to be suitable as a titrimetric method on the basis of its stability, the slow rate of reaction prohibits the straightforward use of this reaction for analytical purposes.

The formation or dissociation of many complex ions is characterized by a slow rate of reaction. Among the metal ions whose complexes frequently display relatively slight reactivity are chromium(III), cobalt(III), and platinum(IV). Such complex ions are called inert or *nonlabile* complexes. Likewise, there is a group of metals which characteristically form reactive or *labile* complex ions, including cobalt(II), copper, lead, bismuth, silver, cadmium, nickel, zinc, mercury, and aluminum. Although most complexes of iron(II) and iron(III) are labile, the cyanide complexes $Fe(CN)_6^{\equiv}$ and $Fe(CN)_6^=$ are familiar examples of nonlabile species.

An equally important problem in complexometric titrations concerns stoichiometry. First, the metal cations of analytical interest have several available orbitals for bond formation with complexing agents; for example, the zinc ion characteristically has four coordination positions. Second, many complexing agents or ligands, including chloride, bromide, iodide, cyanide, thiocyanate, hydroxide, and ammonia, can occupy only one coordination position of a metal ion. Such species are called **monodentate ligands,** the word *dentate* being derived from the Greek word for "tooth." Therefore, a single zinc ion can react with a maximum of four chlorides, four cyanides, four hydroxides, or four ammonia molecules to form $ZnCl_4^=$, $Zn(CN)_4^=$, $Zn(OH)_4^=$, or $Zn(NH_3)_4^{++}$. However, the reaction between zinc ion and ammonia (as well as other monodentate ligands) always proceeds in a stepwise way, according to the following equilibria:

$$Zn(H_2O)_4^{++} + NH_3 \rightleftharpoons Zn(NH_3)(H_2O)_3^{++} + H_2O$$

$$Zn(NH_3)(H_2O)_3^{++} + NH_3 \rightleftharpoons Zn(NH_3)_2(H_2O)_2^{++} + H_2O$$

$$Zn(NH_3)_2(H_2O)_2^{++} + NH_3 \rightleftharpoons Zn(NH_3)_3(H_2O)^{++} + H_2O$$

$$Zn(NH_3)_3(H_2O)^{++} + NH_3 \rightleftharpoons Zn(NH_3)_4^{++} + H_2O$$

These equations represent the stepwise formation of the monoammine, diammine, triammine, and tetraammine complexes of zinc, although, as emphasized below, an aqueous solution of zinc ions and ammonia will usually contain at least several of the zinc ammines in equilibrium with each other. A **stepwise formation constant** is associated with each equilibrium and is designated by K_n, where, in the present example, the subscript n takes an integral value to indicate the addition of the nth ammonia ligand to a complex containing $(n - 1)$ ammonia molecules. Thus, the *first stepwise formation constant*, K_1, for the formation of the $Zn(NH_3)(H_2O)_3^{++}$ complex is 186 at

25°C, and the appropriate equilibrium expression is

$$K_1 = \frac{[\text{Zn(NH}_3)(\text{H}_2\text{O})_3{}^{++}]}{[\text{Zn(H}_2\text{O})_4{}^{++}][\text{NH}_3]}$$

Similarly, the values of K_2, K_3, and K_4 are 219, 251, and 112, respectively; and the equilibrium expression corresponding to the *fourth stepwise formation constant* is

$$K_4 = \frac{[\text{Zn(NH}_3)_4{}^{++}]}{[\text{Zn(NH}_3)_3(\text{H}_2\text{O})^{++}][\text{NH}_3]}$$

Notice that the concentration (activity) of water does not appear in these equilibrium expressions.

Sometimes **overall formation constants** are used to describe the equilibria in complexometric titrations. The equilibria corresponding to overall reactions for the zinc-ammonia system would be as follows:

$$\text{Zn(H}_2\text{O})_4{}^{++} + \text{NH}_3 \rightleftharpoons \text{Zn(NH}_3)(\text{H}_2\text{O})_3{}^{++} + \text{H}_2\text{O}$$
$$\text{Zn(H}_2\text{O})_4{}^{++} + 2\,\text{NH}_3 \rightleftharpoons \text{Zn(NH}_3)_2(\text{H}_2\text{O})_2{}^{++} + 2\,\text{H}_2\text{O}$$
$$\text{Zn(H}_2\text{O})_4{}^{++} + 3\,\text{NH}_3 \rightleftharpoons \text{Zn(NH}_3)_3(\text{H}_2\text{O})^{++} + 3\,\text{H}_2\text{O}$$
$$\text{Zn(H}_2\text{O})_4{}^{++} + 4\,\text{NH}_3 \rightleftharpoons \text{Zn(NH}_3)_4{}^{++} + 4\,\text{H}_2\text{O}$$

Overall formation constants are designated by β_n, where the subscript n gives the total number of ligands added to the original complex ion. For example, the *third overall formation constant*, β_3, refers to the addition of three ammonia ligands to $\text{Zn(H}_2\text{O})_4{}^{++}$ to form $\text{Zn(NH}_3)_3(\text{H}_2\text{O})^{++}$, and the pertinent equilibrium expression is

$$\beta_3 = \frac{[\text{Zn(NH}_3)_3(\text{H}_2\text{O})^{++}]}{[\text{Zn(H}_2\text{O})_4{}^{++}][\text{NH}_3]^3}$$

Again note that the concentration of water is absent from the equilibrium expression.

The relationship between the *stepwise formation constants* and the *overall formation constants* is a simple one:

$$K_1 = \beta_1$$
$$K_1 K_2 = \beta_2$$
$$K_1 K_2 K_3 = \beta_3$$
$$K_1 K_2 K_3 K_4 = \beta_4$$
$$K_1 K_2 K_3 K_4 \cdots K_n = \beta_n$$

For the zinc-ammonia system, the *overall formation constants* have the following values: $\beta_1 = 186$, $\beta_2 = 4.08 \times 10^4$, $\beta_3 = 1.02 \times 10^7$, and $\beta_4 = 1.15 \times 10^9$.

For most metal ions, and the majority of monodentate ligands, the relative stabilities of the various complexes within a family are such that several complexes are present in solution for a given concentration of ligand. Thus, for the zinc-ammonia system, several different complexes will be present in the same solution for a specified concentration of ammonia. Figure 11-1 shows how the mole fractions of the different zinc-ammine complexes vary as the concentration of uncomplexed (free) ammonia changes. The areas bounded by the curved solid lines in Figure 11-1 are determined as follows: Using the overall formation constants for the zinc-ammine complexes, one evaluates the concentration of each zinc-ammine complex in terms of $[Zn^{++}]$ for a given ammonia concentration. Once these values are known, the mole fraction of each zinc species is calculated; then, these mole fractions are plotted. The order of plotting the mole fractions (from zero mole fraction upwards) begins with the highest zinc-ammine complex, $Zn(NH_3)_4^{++}$, followed in succession by the tri-, di-, and monoammine and the tetraaquo complexes. The points which separate each adjacent pair of complex ions, e.g., $Zn(H_2O)_4^{++}$ and $Zn(NH_3)(H_2O)_3^{++}$, over the desired range of ammonia concentrations are connected with a solid line to outline the different areas in Figure 11-1. For example, when the free ammonia concentration is $10^{-2}\ M$, all five possible zinc complexes, $Zn(H_2O)_4^{++}$, $Zn(NH_3)(H_2O)_3^{++}$, $Zn(NH_3)_2(H_2O)_2^{++}$, $Zn(NH_3)_3(H_2O)^{++}$, and $Zn(NH_3)_4^{++}$, are present in significant amounts. A vertical line drawn at $\log[NH_3] = -2$ crosses the regions of Figure 11-1 corresponding to all these species. The length of the line within each region gives the mole per cent of the particular species.

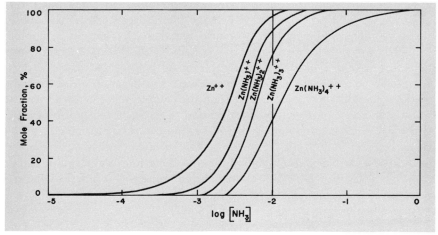

FIGURE 11-1. Distribution diagram showing the percentage mole fractions of the zinc-ammine complexes as a function of the logarithm of the free (uncomplexed) ammonia concentration. To determine the percentage mole fraction of a particular zinc-ammine species, draw a vertical line at the desired free NH_3 concentration and locate the *field* or *area* corresponding to the desired complex. Measure the length of the segment of the vertical line that lies between the curved boundary lines for the given field and compare the length of this segment with the markings on the abscissa. For example, the percentage mole fractions of the zinc-ammine complexes in a solution containing 0.01 F free ammonia are as follows: $Zn(H_2O)_4^{++}$, 3.2 per cent; $Zn(NH_3)(H_2O)_3^{++}$, 6.8 per cent; $Zn(NH_3)_2(H_2O)_2^{++}$, 14.2 per cent; $Zn(NH_3)_3$-$(H_2O)^{++}$, 35.8 per cent; and $Zn(NH_3)_4^{++}$, 40.0 per cent. Note that the water molecules coordinated to zinc have been omitted for simplicity in the distribution diagram.

At log $[NH_3] = -2$, the following mole percentages of complexes are present: 3.2 per cent $Zn(H_2O)_4^{++}$, 6.8 per cent $Zn(NH_3)(H_2O)_3^{++}$, 14.2 per cent $Zn(NH_3)_2(H_2O)_2^{++}$, 35.8 per cent $Zn(NH_3)_3(H_2O)^{++}$, and 40.0 per cent $Zn(NH_3)_4^{++}$.

Complexes involving monodentate ligands are generally unsuitable for complexometric titrations for several reasons. First, unless one of a family of complex ions has unusual stability relative to the other members of the family, the solution will contain a mixture of several complex ions. For a mixture of complexes, no simple stoichiometric ratio of ligand to metal prevails. Second, even when exact stoichiometric quantities of the titrant complexing agent are added, giving apparent ligand-to-metal ratios of 1, 2, 3, or 4, such points during the titration go completely unnoticed because, again, several complexes are really present and the concentration of none of the species changes greatly enough to serve as an end point signal. Third, stabilities of complexes involving monodentate ligands are not characteristically large, and so to obtain a solution containing, say, essentially only $Zn(NH_3)_4^{++}$, it is necessary to have a large excess of uncomplexed (free) ammonia. Obviously, this only happens at points well beyond the equivalence point of such a titration.

A significant advance in this area of analytical chemistry has been the development of a number of multidentate ligands or **chelates** (after the Greek word for "claw"), so called because these species can coordinate at several or all positions around a central metal ion by literally wrapping themselves around the metal cation. With these multidentate ligands, the problem of stepwise formation of complexes no longer exists because only one-to-one metal-ligand complexes are formed. Furthermore, these complex ions are generally much more stable than the complexes formed with monodentate ligands. Consequently, the location of end points is quite precise. Although the use of multidentate ligands minimizes the stoichiometry problem in complexometric titrations, the reactivity of complexes can remain a difficulty. Nevertheless, the availability of a large number of multidentate ligands, which form very stable one-to-one complexes with practically every metal cation in the periodic table, has increased tremendously the application of complexometric titrations in chemical analysis.

THE LIEBIG TITRATION

Direct Determination of Cyanide. The Liebig titration for the determination of cyanide is one of the relatively few satisfactory complexometric titrations involving a monodentate ligand. In the classic Liebig method, a solution containing cyanide ion is titrated with standard silver nitrate. Two cyanide ions react with one silver ion to form a soluble, colorless complex:

$$Ag^+ + 2\ CN^- \rightleftharpoons Ag(CN)_2^-$$

The overall formation constant, β_2, for this reaction is 1.26×10^{21}. Under the conditions of this titration, namely the addition of silver nitrate to a cyanide solution, the precipitation of solid AgCN, or $Ag[Ag(CN)_2]$, does not occur until the formation of $Ag(CN)_2^-$ is virtually complete. Upon the addition of the first slight excess of silver nitrate solution, the following reaction occurs:

$$Ag^+ + Ag(CN)_2^- \rightleftharpoons Ag[Ag(CN)_2](s)$$

A solubility-product expression of the form

$$K_{sp} = [Ag^+][Ag(CN)_2^-]$$

may be written, for which the solubility product, K_{sp}, is 5.0×10^{-12}. The turbidity caused by the precipitation of white AgCN, or $Ag[Ag(CN)_2]$, signals the end point of the titration.

Another factor is that cyanide ion is the anion of a very weak acid, hydrocyanic acid (HCN), which has a pK_a of 9.14. Therefore, throughout the course of the titration, the true cyanide ion concentration is smaller than expected, because of the reaction between cyanide and water:

$$CN^- + H_2O \rightleftharpoons HCN + OH^-$$

The equilibrium constant for this reaction is K_w/K_a or 1.39×10^{-5}. Although the position of chemical equilibrium lies well to the left under ordinary conditions, i.e., for cyanide concentrations greater than 10^{-3} M, the position of equilibrium shifts in the direction favoring hydrogen cyanide at lower total cyanide concentrations. Therefore, near the equivalence point of the titration, when the cyanide concentration becomes very small, much of the unreacted cyanide is in the form of hydrogen cyanide. The effect of this equilibrium on the equivalence point conditions will be discussed.

Construction of the Titration Curve.   On the assumption that the formation of hydrogen cyanide from cyanide ion can be neglected, the titration curve for the determination of cyanide with silver nitrate solution may be constructed. The titration of 50.00 ml of 0.2000 M cyanide with 0.1000 F silver nitrate will be considered, and a plot of pAg as a function of volume of silver nitrate added will be made.

Prior to the addition of any silver ion, pAg is not truly defined (pAg = $-\infty$). However, when the smallest possible increment of silver nitrate has been added, the $Ag(CN)_2^-$ complex is formed, and the concentration of silver ion in equilibrium with the complex can be calculated from the following relationship:

$$[Ag^+] = \frac{[Ag(CN)_2^-]}{1.26 \times 10^{21}[CN^-]^2}$$

Suppose that only 0.001 ml (1 μl) of titrant is added. The volume of solution is almost unchanged, and the concentration of cyanide is still very close to 0.2 M. The great stability of the $Ag(CN)_2^-$ complex, together with the presence of a relatively high cyanide concentration, allows us to say that all of the added silver ion $(1.00 \times 10^{-4}$ millimole$)$ reacts to form the $Ag(CN)_2^-$ complex; so $[Ag(CN)_2^-]$ is 2.00×10^{-6} M. Thus,

$$[Ag^+] = \frac{(2.00 \times 10^{-6})}{(1.26 \times 10^{21})(0.2)^2} = 3.97 \times 10^{-26} \, M; \qquad pAg = 25.40$$

When 1.00 ml of standard silver nitrate solution is added, the total solution volume is 51.00 ml. The cyanide concentration is calculated by dividing the number of millimoles of cyanide remaining untitrated by the volume. Since 0.100 millimole of silver ion added consumes 0.200 millimole of cyanide, 9.800 millimoles of cyanide is left in 51.00 ml, so $[CN^-] = 0.192 \, M$. The concentration of $Ag(CN)_2^-$ is simply $1.96 \times 10^{-3} \, M$. Again, this simplified approach to the problem is valid because the equilibrium constant for the formation of $Ag(CN)_2^-$ is very large, because the concentration of cyanide is relatively large, and because points on the titration curve very close to the equivalence point will not be considered. Therefore, at 1.00 ml of titrant added,

$$[Ag^+] = \frac{(1.96 \times 10^{-3})}{(1.26 \times 10^{21})(0.192)^2} = 4.22 \times 10^{-23} \, M; \qquad pAg = 22.37$$

Other points on the titration curve may be obtained similarly. At 5.00 ml of silver nitrate added, $[Ag^+] = 2.70 \times 10^{-22} \, M$; $pAg = 21.57$. At 10.00 ml of silver nitrate added, $[Ag^+] = 7.44 \times 10^{-22} \, M$; $pAg = 21.13$. At 20.00 ml of silver nitrate added, $[Ag^+] = 3.09 \times 10^{-21} \, M$; $pAg = 20.51$. At 30.00 ml of silver nitrate added, $[Ag^+] = 1.19 \times 10^{-20} \, M$; $pAg = 19.92$. At 40.00 ml of silver nitrate added, $[Ag^+] = 7.15 \times 10^{-20} \, M$; $pAg = 19.15$. At 45.00 ml of silver nitrate added, $[Ag^+] = 3.40 \times 10^{-19} \, M$; $pAg = 18.47$.

Upon the addition of 50.00 ml of the silver nitrate titrant, the equivalence point is reached and the relationship between $[Ag^+]$ and $[CN^-]$ is given by

$$[Ag^+] = \tfrac{1}{2}[CN^-]$$

This expression is based upon the stoichiometry of the titration reaction and upon neglect of the formation of hydrogen cyanide from the cyanide-water reaction. The concentration of $Ag(CN)_2^-$ at the equivalence point is essentially 0.0500 M because the dissociation of the very stable $Ag(CN)_2^-$ complex is negligible. It follows that

$$1.26 \times 10^{21} = \frac{[Ag(CN)_2^-]}{[Ag^+][CN^-]^2} = \frac{(0.0500)}{4[Ag^+]^3}$$

and

$$[Ag^+]^3 = \frac{(0.0500)}{(4)(1.26 \times 10^{21})} = 9.92 \times 10^{-24}; \qquad [Ag^+] = 2.15 \times 10^{-8} \, M;$$
$$pAg = 7.67$$

The true equivalence point pAg value is actually lower than 7.67. The reason for this is that the cyanide concentration is smaller than anticipated because of the formation of HCN. In turn, a lower cyanide concentration means a correspondingly higher silver ion concentration and, thus, a smaller pAg. The correct value of pAg at the equivalence point may be computed, if the silver ion concentration at the equivalence point is equated to one-half the sum of the cyanide and hydrogen cyanide concentrations:

$$[Ag^+] = \tfrac{1}{2}([CN^-] + [HCN])$$

In other words, the silver ion concentration at the equivalence point should be equal to one-half the total analytical concentration of cyanide (which is present as CN^- and HCN). The relation between $[CN^-]$ and [HCN] can be obtained from the following equilibrium:

$$CN^- + H_2O \rightleftharpoons HCN + OH^-$$

Each cyanide which reacts produces one HCN and one OH^-, so that the appropriate equilibrium expression may be written as

$$K_{eq} = 1.39 \times 10^{-5} = \frac{[HCN][OH^-]}{[CN^-]} = \frac{[HCN]^2}{[CN^-]}$$

Therefore, $[HCN] = (1.39 \times 10^{-5}[CN^-])^{1/2}$, and at the equivalence point

$$[Ag^+] = \tfrac{1}{2}\{[CN^-] + (1.39 \times 10^{-5}[CN^-])^{1/2}\}$$

When this latter expression is substituted into the equilibrium relation for $Ag(CN)_2^-$ and the resulting equation is solved for $[Ag^+]$ by the method of successive approximations, the silver ion concentration at the equivalence point turns out to be $2.18 \times 10^{-7} M$ and pAg is 6.66. Hence, the actual silver ion concentration at the equivalence point is almost exactly 10 times larger than the value calculated if the presence of hydrogen cyanide is neglected.

However, long before the silver ion concentration reaches the $10^{-7} M$ level, $Ag[Ag(CN)_2]$ begins to precipitate. If the $Ag(CN)_2^-$ concentration is taken to be $0.0500 M$ near the equivalence point, the value of $[Ag^+]$ at which $Ag[Ag(CN)_2]$ will precipitate can be calculated from the solubility-product expression:

$$[Ag^+] = \frac{5.0 \times 10^{-12}}{[Ag(CN)_2^-]} = \frac{5.0 \times 10^{-12}}{0.0500} = 1.0 \times 10^{-10} M; \qquad pAg = 10.00$$

In view of the fact that the titration curve (see Fig. 11-2) is very steep near the equivalence point, it is evident that the end point (marked by the appearance of $Ag[Ag(CN)_2]$) coincides very well with the equivalence point.

Once $Ag[Ag(CN)_2]$ has started to precipitate, further addition of silver nitrate causes more precipitate to form. In effect, a precipitation titration is carried out according to the reaction

$$Ag^+ + Ag(CN)_2^- \rightleftharpoons Ag[Ag(CN)_2]$$

Points on the titration curve for the titration of 100.0 ml of $0.05000 M$ $Ag(CN)_2^-$ with $0.1000 F$ silver nitrate may be calculated by the procedures employed in the preceding chapter on precipitation titrations. To simplify the calculations here, we shall avoid points on the titration curve very close to the equivalence point.

After the addition of a total of 60.00 ml of silver nitrate (10.00 ml of titrant having been added beyond the first equivalence point), the silver ion concentration may be evaluated from the expression

$$[Ag^+] = \frac{5.0 \times 10^{-12}}{[Ag(CN)_2^-]}$$

The concentration of $Ag(CN)_2^-$ remaining unprecipitated may be obtained from the knowledge that 1.000 millimole of the original 5.000 millimoles of $Ag(CN)_2^-$ has been precipitated. Thus, in a total solution volume of 110.0 ml, the $[Ag(CN)_2^-]$ is 4.000/110.0 or 0.0364 M. Therefore,

$$[Ag^+] = \frac{5.0 \times 10^{-12}}{3.64 \times 10^{-2}} = 1.38 \times 10^{-10}\ M; \qquad pAg = 9.86$$

For a total of 70.00 ml added, $[Ag^+] = 2.00 \times 10^{-10}\ M$; pAg = 9.70. For a total of 80.00 ml added, $[Ag^+] = 3.25 \times 10^{-10}\ M$; pAg = 9.49. For a total of 90.00 ml added, $[Ag^+] = 7.00 \times 10^{-10}\ M$; pAg = 9.16. For a total of 95.00 ml added, $[Ag^+] = 1.45 \times 10^{-9}\ M$; pAg = 8.84. For a total of 99.00 ml added, $[Ag^+] = 7.45 \times 10^{-9}\ M$; pAg = 8.13. For a total of 100.0 ml added, which is the equivalence point for the titration of $Ag(CN)_2^-$, $[Ag^+] = [Ag(CN)_2^-] = (5.0 \times 10^{-12})^{1/2} = 2.24 \times 10^{-6}\ M$; pAg = 5.65. For a total of 101.0 ml added, which is just 1.00 ml beyond the second equivalence point, there is an excess of 0.1000 millimole of silver ion in a volume of 151.0 ml, so $[Ag^+] = 0.1000/151.0 = 6.62 \times 10^{-4}\ M$ and pAg = 3.18. By similar reasoning, it can be shown that, at 105.0 ml added, $[Ag^+] = 3.23 \times 10^{-3}\ M$ and pAg = 2.49. At 110.0 ml added, $[Ag^+] = 6.25 \times 10^{-3}\ M$ and pAg = 2.20; and, at 120.0 ml added, $[Ag^+] = 1.18 \times 10^{-2}\ M$ and pAg = 1.93.

The titration curve constructed on the basis of these calculations is shown in Figure 11-2. In practice, since little is to be gained by continuing the titration beyond the first equivalence point, the titration is usually terminated upon the first permanent appearance of $Ag[Ag(CN)_2]$. Some difficulty may arise in this method from the premature formation of the precipitate. Near the equivalence point of the titration, when the cyanide concentration is relatively small, local excesses of silver nitrate may cause the temporary precipitation of $Ag[Ag(CN)_2]$. Once formed, the rate of dissolution of the precipitate is slow in the presence of small quantities of cyanide, and the true end point is obscured.

Another and better scheme for detection of the end point calls for the titration of cyanide to be done in the presence of ammonia and a small amount of iodide. Ammonia forms a complex with silver ion, $Ag(NH_3)_2^+$, which is less stable than the cyanide complex of silver, yet stable enough to prevent the precipitation of $Ag[Ag(CN)_2]$. Therefore, when a solution containing cyanide, ammonia, and a small amount of iodide is titrated with silver nitrate, $Ag(CN)_2^-$ is formed according to the desired titration reaction, but at the equivalence point a precipitate of canary-yellow silver iodide is formed instead of $Ag[Ag(CN)_2]$.

Other Analytical Applications. Silver ion itself may be determined by means of an extension of the Liebig titration. All that is necessary is to add a known excess of a standard potassium cyanide solution to the silver-containing sample solution and measure the number of millimoles of unreacted cyanide by back-titration with a standard silver nitrate solution. Still another possibility for the determination of silver is to add ammonia and a trace of iodide to the sample solution and titrate it with a standard cyanide solution. The added cyanide reacts first with the silver-ammonia complex:

$$Ag(NH_3)_2^+ + 2\,CN^- \rightleftharpoons Ag(CN)_2^- + 2\,NH_3$$

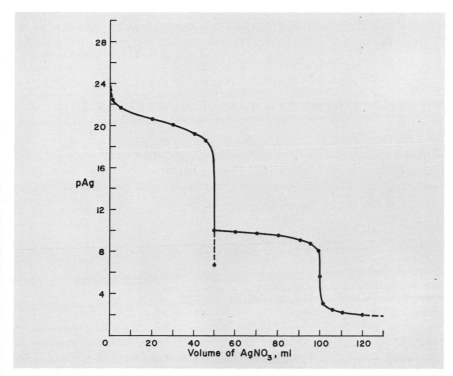

FIGURE 11-2. Titration curve for the titration of 50.00 ml of 0.2000 M cyanide ion with a 0.1000 F silver nitrate solution. The first step of the titration curve corresponds to the formation of $Ag(CN)_2^-$, and the second step to the formation of $Ag[Ag(CN)_2]$. The point at the end of the dashed line (pAg = 6.66) indicates the theoretical equivalence point for the formation of $Ag(CN)_2^-$; however, the experimental end point for the first step is observed at pAg = 10.00, where $Ag[Ag(CN)_2]$ just begins to precipitate.

Finally, just at the equivalence point, cyanide reacts with the silver iodide, which has been in suspension throughout the titration, and the solution loses its yellow turbidity and becomes perfectly clear:

$$AgI(s) + 2\ CN^- \rightleftharpoons Ag(CN)_2^- + I^-$$

A Liebig-type titration may also be used to determine several other metal cations which form stable cyanide complexes. For example, nickel ion in an ammonia solution may be titrated with a standard potassium cyanide solution. A small quantity of silver iodide in suspension serves as an end point indicator. Nickel ion in aqueous ammonia exists as a family of nickel-ammine complexes of the general formula $Ni(NH_3)_n(H_2O)_{6-n}^{++}$, where n is any integer from zero to six. For ammonia concentrations around several-tenths molar, the predominant species is usually $Ni(NH_3)_4(H_2O)_2^{++}$. The nickel-ammine complexes react first with cyanide:

$$Ni(NH_3)_4(H_2O)_2^{++} + 4\ CN^- \rightleftharpoons Ni(CN)_4(H_2O)_2^= + 4\ NH_3$$

Only after all the nickel ion has been complexed with cyanide does the cyanide then react with AgI, causing it to dissolve and the turbidity to disappear. The success of this method rests on the fact that the $Ni(CN)_4(H_2O)_2^=$ complex is more stable than the $Ag(CN)_2^-$ ion.

TITRATIONS WITH ETHYLENEDIAMINETETRAACETIC ACID

Ethylenediaminetetraacetic acid, abbreviated as EDTA, is the most important and well-known member of a group of aminopolycarboxylic acids. The advent of these multidentate ligands has provided the impetus to the wide application of complexometric titrations in chemical analysis. The structural formula of the EDTA molecule is

$$HOOC-CH_2 \qquad\qquad CH_2-COOH$$
$$\ddot{N}-CH_2-CH_2-\ddot{N}$$
$$HOOC-CH_2 \qquad\qquad CH_2-COOH$$

Ethylenediaminetetraacetic acid is a tetraprotic acid. Each of the hydrogen atoms on the carboxyl (—COOH) groups undergoes an acid dissociation. Usually, the parent acid, EDTA, is written as H_4Y in order to show the tetraprotic character of this acid. Thus, the four stepwise or successive acid ionizations and the pertinent dissociation constants may be written as follows:

$$H_4Y \rightleftharpoons H^+ + H_3Y^-; \qquad K_1 = 1.00 \times 10^{-2}$$
$$H_3Y^- \rightleftharpoons H^+ + H_2Y^=; \qquad K_2 = 2.16 \times 10^{-3}$$
$$H_2Y^= \rightleftharpoons H^+ + HY^\equiv; \qquad K_3 = 6.92 \times 10^{-7}$$
$$HY^\equiv \rightleftharpoons H^+ + Y^\equiv; \qquad K_4 = 5.50 \times 10^{-11}$$

The $Y^{\equiv}$ ion represents the ethylenediaminetetraacetate ion. Throughout the remainder of this discussion, the abbreviation EDTA will be used for general purposes, whereas H_4Y (and its acid dissociation products) will be employed in chemical reactions and equilibria and to designate specific EDTA species.

The parent acid (EDTA) is only sparingly soluble in water, and so it is not ordinarily used for complexometric titrations. On the other hand, the disodium salt is relatively soluble, and, being commercially available in the form $Na_2H_2Y \cdot 2\, H_2O$, serves as the starting material for the preparation of the standard EDTA solutions used in titrimetry. Since the predominant species in such a solution is the $H_2Y^{=}$ ion, the pH of the resulting solution is very close to $\frac{1}{2}(pK_2 + pK_3)$ or 4.42.

The partition of EDTA among its completely undissociated form and its four dissociated forms varies considerably with pH. At any particular pH, the distribution of EDTA species may be calculated from the acid ionization constants for H_4Y. For example, let us substitute a value for $[H^+]$ of $1.00 \times 10^{-10}\, M$, corresponding to a pH of 10, into each of the four acid ionization equilibrium expressions:

$$\frac{[H_3Y^-]}{[H_4Y]} = \frac{1.00 \times 10^{-2}}{[H^+]} = \frac{1.00 \times 10^{-2}}{1.00 \times 10^{-10}} = 1.00 \times 10^8$$

$$\frac{[H_2Y^=]}{[H_3Y^-]} = \frac{2.16 \times 10^{-3}}{[H^+]} = \frac{2.16 \times 10^{-3}}{1.00 \times 10^{-10}} = 2.16 \times 10^7$$

$$\frac{[HY^=]}{[H_2Y^=]} = \frac{6.92 \times 10^{-7}}{[H^+]} = \frac{6.92 \times 10^{-7}}{1.00 \times 10^{-10}} = 6.92 \times 10^3$$

$$\frac{[Y^{\equiv}]}{[HY^=]} = \frac{5.50 \times 10^{-11}}{[H^+]} = \frac{5.50 \times 10^{-11}}{1.00 \times 10^{-10}} = 5.50 \times 10^{-1}$$

These ratios reveal the following facts. First, the concentration of H_3Y^- is 100 million times greater than that of H_4Y. It is also apparent that the $H_2Y^=$ species is almost 22 million times more abundant than H_3Y^-, and, in turn, $HY^=$ is approximately 7000 times more abundant than $H_2Y^=$. Finally, we see that the ratio of $Y^{\equiv}$ to $HY^=$ is 55/100. What these calculations prove is that at pH 10 only $Y^{\equiv}$ and $HY^=$ are present in significant concentrations. The concentrations of the other three species, $H_2Y^=$, H_3Y^-, and H_4Y, are negligibly small. Therefore, the fraction of EDTA in the $Y^{\equiv}$ form is 55/155 or 0.355 and in the $HY^=$ form it is 100/155 or 0.645. The fractions of the other species present are much less than 0.001 In Table 11-1 the fraction of EDTA present as each species at pH values from 0 to 14 is listed. The fraction is less than 0.001 if no entry appears in the table. It is seen from Table 11-1 that H_4Y predominates below pH 2, H_3Y^- between pH 2 and 3, H_2Y between pH 3 and 6, $HY^=$ between pH 6 and 10, and $Y^{\equiv}$ above pH 10.

TABLE 11-1.   FRACTION OF EDTA PRESENT AS VARIOUS SPECIES
AS A FUNCTION OF pH*

pH	H_4Y	H_3Y^-	$H_2Y^=$	$HY^{\equiv}$	$Y^{\equiv}$
0	0.990	0.010			
1	0.907	0.091	0.002		
2	0.451	0.451	0.098		
3	0.031	0.307	0.662		
4		0.044	0.949	0.007	
5		0.004	0.931	0.065	
6			0.591	0.409	
7			0.127	0.873	
8			0.014	0.981	0.005
9			0.001	0.947	0.052
10				0.645	0.355
11				0.154	0.846
12				0.018	0.982
13				0.002	0.998
14					1.000

* No entry appears if the fraction of a species present is less than 0.001.

METAL-EDTA COMPLEXES

The ethylenediaminetetraacetate ion, $Y^{\equiv}$, forms very stable, one-to-one complexes with practically every metal ion in the periodic table. This one-to-one nature of metal-EDTA complexes arises from the fact that the $Y^{\equiv}$ ion possesses a total of six functional groups — four carboxyl groups and two amine groups — which can occupy four, five, or six coordination positions around a central metal ion. The cobalt(III)-EDTA complex, CoY^-, is one known example of a six-coordinated species. The structure of this complex is

Because the ethylenediaminetetraacetate ion does coordinate at several positions around a central metal ion, only one-to-one metal to ligand complexes are formed. The problems encountered in the stepwise reactions between metal ions and monodentate ligands are not present. Metal-EDTA complexes gain particular stability from the five-membered chelate rings which are formed. In the cobalt(III)-EDTA complex shown above, there are five such five-membered rings. A five-membered ring is an especially stable configuration because the bond angles allow all five atoms in the ring to lie in a plane. Frequently, only four or five of the six functional groups in the EDTA anion are bound to a metal ion. The remaining positions around the metal may be occupied by monodentate ligands such as water, hydroxide, or ammonia.

The general reaction for the formation of metal-EDTA complexes may be written as:

$$M^{+n} + Y^{\equiv} \rightleftharpoons MY^{n-4}$$

where M^{+n} represents an aquated or hydrated metal cation of charge $+n$. In the simplest case, water molecules are displaced by EDTA during the course of the titration. The equilibrium expression for the formation of metal-EDTA complexes has the general form

$$K_{MY} = \frac{[MY^{n-4}]}{[M^{+n}][Y^{\equiv}]}$$

TABLE 11-2. FORMATION CONSTANTS OF METAL-EDTA COMPLEXES

Element	Cation	log K_{MY}
Aluminum	Al^{+++}	16.13
Barium	Ba^{++}	7.76
Cadmium	Cd^{++}	16.46
Calcium	Ca^{++}	10.70
Cobalt	Co^{++}	16.31
Copper	Cu^{++}	18.80
Gallium	Ga^{+++}	20.27
Indium	In^{+++}	24.95
Iron	Fe^{++}	14.33
	Fe^{+++}	25.1
Lead	Pb^{++}	18.04
Magnesium	Mg^{++}	8.69
Manganese	Mn^{++}	14.04
Mercury	Hg^{++}	21.80
Nickel	Ni^{++}	18.62
Scandium	Sc^{+++}	23.1
Silver	Ag^{+}	7.32
Strontium	Sr^{++}	8.63
Thorium	Th^{++++}	23.2
Titanium	Ti^{+++}	21.3
	TiO^{++}	17.3
Vanadium	V^{++}	12.70
	V^{+++}	25.9
	VO^{++}	18.77
Yttrium	Y^{+++}	18.09
Zinc	Zn^{++}	16.50

where K_{MY} is the formation constant for the MY^{n-4} complex. In Table 11-2 are listed a number of formation constants for metal-EDTA complexes.

Most metal-EDTA titrations are performed in neutral or alkaline solutions. The reason for this is that metal-EDTA complexes, although generally quite stable, can undergo dissociation in the presence of an acid because of protonation of the $Y^{\equiv}$ ion; for example,

$$MY^{n-4} + 2\,H^+ \rightleftharpoons M^{+n} + H_2Y^=$$

By the same token, the predominant EDTA species in neutral or alkaline media are the $H_2Y^=$ and $HY^{\equiv}$ ions, so we may more appropriately visualize the net titration reaction as

$$M^{+n} + H_2Y^= \rightleftharpoons MY^{n-4} + 2\,H^+$$

or

$$M^{+n} + HY^{\equiv} \rightleftharpoons MY^{n-4} + H^+$$

depending on the exact solution pH. The formation of hydrogen ions as a reaction product would cause the pH of the solution to decrease and the desired titration reaction to cease or even reverse itself, unless the solution is buffered against the pH change. Therefore, in practice a large excess of an innocuous buffer system, such as acetic acid-sodium acetate or ammonia-ammonium nitrate, is employed to keep the pH at the desired value for the particular application. In a number of instances, this buffer serves a vital second function. For example, cadmium, copper, nickel, and zinc form insoluble hydroxides near pH 7 or 8. However, these metal ions also form stable ammonia complexes, and so the use of an ammonia-ammonium nitrate buffer in the metal-EDTA titration serves to prevent the undesired precipitation of these hydroxides as well as to maintain the desired pH. It should be pointed out that the ammonia complexes of these elements, being less stable than the corresponding EDTA complexes, do not interfere in the determinations of these metals. A buffer such as ammonia-ammonium nitrate, which performs the special requirements for metal-EDTA titrations just described, is frequently known as the **auxiliary complexing agent.**

In the remaining sections of this chapter, several specific examples of metal-EDTA titrations will be presented with emphasis on the construction of titration curves, influence of solution conditions on titration curves, and end point detection.

DIRECT TITRATION OF CALCIUM WITH EDTA

A simple illustration of the determination of a metal ion by direct titration with a standard EDTA solution (actually Na_2H_2Y) is the titration of calcium in a medium well-buffered at pH 10. At this pH, the predominant EDTA species is $HY^=$, and the net titration reaction may be written as

$$Ca^{++} + HY^= \rightleftharpoons CaY^= + H^+$$

The calcium-EDTA complex is one of the less stable metal-EDTA complexes (see Table 11-2). Thus, in order for a well-defined titration curve to be obtained, the fraction of EDTA in the $Y^{\equiv}$ form, and thus the pH of the solution, must be sufficiently high to guarantee the completeness of the complexation reaction. A pH of 10 is readily achieved and maintained with an ammonia-ammonium ion buffer. A much higher pH would incur the possibility of precipitation of calcium hydroxide. For this particular system, ammonia does not form a stable complex with calcium.

Construction of the Titration Curve. The titration curve consists of a plot of the negative logarithm of the calcium ion concentration (pCa) as a function of the volume of EDTA titrant added and may be constructed by calculations similar to those done for other types of titrations. Prior to the equivalence point of the titration, the pCa may be computed directly from the quantity of unreacted calcium ion. At the equivalence point, the only calcium ions present are those resulting from the incompleteness of the titration reaction. The value of pCa may be calculated from the formation constant for the calcium-EDTA complex. Beyond the equivalence point, the amount of EDTA governs the calcium ion concentration through the equilibrium constant for the calcium-EDTA complex.

Let us consider the titration of 50.00 ml of 0.01000 M calcium ion with a 0.01000 F Na$_2$H$_2$Y solution. We will assume also that the calcium sample solution is buffered at pH 10 with an ammonia-ammonium chloride buffer.

At the beginning of the titration, before any EDTA solution has been added, the calcium ion concentration is 0.01000 M, and pCa is 2.00.

After 1.00 ml of EDTA titrant has been added, the calcium ion concentration will be very closely given by the number of millimoles of calcium remaining untitrated, divided by the solution volume in milliliters. Thus, since 0.4900 millimole of calcium remains untitrated in 51.00 ml, $[Ca^{++}] = 0.00961\ M$. However, since the titration reaction is not 100 per cent complete, the true calcium ion concentration will be larger than 0.00961 M by the amount of dissociation of the calcium-EDTA complex. The contribution to $[Ca^{++}]$ from dissociation of the complex may be determined as follows: For each CaY$^=$ complex ion that dissociates, one calcium ion will be formed and one EDTA-type ion will be formed. The concentration of $Y^{\equiv}$ from dissociation of the complex may be calculated from the equilibrium expression for the formation of the calcium-EDTA complex:

$$K_{CaY} = \frac{[CaY^=]}{[Ca^{++}][Y^{\equiv}]} = 5.01 \times 10^{10}$$

Rearrangement of this equation gives

$$[Y^{\equiv}] = \frac{[CaY^=]}{5.01 \times 10^{10}[Ca^{++}]}$$

Let us assume, provisionally, that $[Ca^{++}] = 0.00961\ M$ and that the concentration of the CaY$^=$ complex is given by the millimoles of EDTA added thus far (0.01000 millimole) divided by the solution volume (51.00 ml). Consequently, $[CaY^=]$ may be taken to be $0.01000/51.00$ or $1.96 \times 10^{-4}\ M$. If these values are substituted into the latter expression, the result is

$$[Y^{\equiv}] = \frac{[CaY^=]}{5.01 \times 10^{10}[Ca^{++}]} = \frac{1.96 \times 10^{-4}}{(5.01 \times 10^{10})(9.61 \times 10^{-3})}$$

$$= 4.07 \times 10^{-13}\ M$$

Table 11-1 shows that at pH 10, the predominant EDTA species are $HY^=$ (64.5 per cent) and $Y^{\equiv}$ (35.5 per cent). If $[Y^{\equiv}] = 4.07 \times 10^{-13}\ M$, $[HY^=]$ will be $(64.5)(4.07 \times 10^{-13}\ M)/(35.5)$ or $7.40 \times 10^{-13}\ M$. The sum of $[HY^=]$ and $[Y^{\equiv}]$ is $1.15 \times 10^{-12}\ M$, and this value is equal to the concentration of calcium ion contributed by dissociation of the complex. In comparison to the concentration of calcium ion remaining *untitrated* $(9.61 \times 10^{-3}\ M)$, this latter figure is negligibly small, and our provisional assumptions regarding $[Ca^{++}]$ and $[CaY^=]$ were quite valid. We can conclude from these considerations that the calcium-EDTA complex is sufficiently stable, and so its dissociation may be neglected. Similar calculations indicate that dissociation of the complex may still be neglected within approximately ± 0.10 per cent of the equivalence point. Thus, the remainder of the titration curve may be treated in a simple manner. After the addition of 1.00 ml of the EDTA solution, $[Ca^{++}] = 9.61 \times 10^{-3}\ M$ and pCa $= 2.02$.

After the addition of 5.00 ml of the titrant, 0.4500 millimole of calcium ion remains untitrated in a solution whose volume is 55.00 ml, so $[Ca^{++}] = 8.18 \times 10^{-3}\ M$ and pCa $= 2.09$. After the addition of 10.00 ml of EDTA, $[Ca^{++}] = 6.67 \times 10^{-3}\ M$ and pCa $= 2.18$. After the addition of 20.00 ml, $[Ca^{++}] = 4.29 \times 10^{-3}\ M$ and pCa $= 2.37$. After the addition of 30.00 ml, $[Ca^{++}] = 2.50 \times 10^{-3}\ M$ and pCa $= 2.60$. After the addition of 40.00 ml, $[Ca^{++}] = 1.11 \times 10^{-3}\ M$ and pCa $= 2.95$. After the addition of 45.00 ml, $[Ca^{++}] = 5.26 \times 10^{-4}\ M$ and pCa $= 3.28$. After the addition of 49.00 ml, $[Ca^{++}] = 1.01 \times 10^{-4}\ M$ and pCa $= 4.00$. After the addition of 49.90 ml, $[Ca^{++}] = 1.00 \times 10^{-5}\ M$ and pCa $= 5.00$. After the addition of exactly 50.00 ml of EDTA titrant, corresponding to the equivalence point of the titration, the calcium ion concentration may be calculated from the equilibrium expression for the formation of the calcium-EDTA complex:

$$K_{CaY} = \frac{[CaY^=]}{[Ca^{++}][Y^{\equiv}]} = 5.01 \times 10^{10}$$

At the equivalence point, equal concentrations of calcium ion and EDTA remain unreacted. However, at pH 10 both $HY^=$ and $Y^{\equiv}$ are present, 35.5 per cent of the total EDTA being $Y^{\equiv}$ (see Table 11-1). Thus, at the equivalence point, $[Y^{\equiv}] = 0.355[Ca^{++}]$. Because of the stability of the $CaY^=$ complex, it may be assumed that there is 0.5000 millimole of $CaY^=$ in a volume of 100.0 ml, and so the calcium-EDTA complex is at a concentration of $0.5000/100.0$ or 5.00×10^{-3} M. If these values are substituted into the preceding equation, the result is

$$0.355[\text{Ca}^{++}]^2 = \frac{[\text{CaY}^=]}{5.01 \times 10^{10}} = \frac{5.00 \times 10^{-3}}{5.01 \times 10^{10}} = 1.00 \times 10^{-13}$$

$$[\text{Ca}^{++}]^2 = \frac{1.00 \times 10^{-13}}{0.355} = 2.82 \times 10^{-13}$$

$$[\text{Ca}^{++}] = 5.31 \times 10^{-7} \ M; \qquad p\text{Ca} = 6.27$$

Beyond the equivalence point, the calcium ion concentration is calculated from the following relation:

$$[\text{Ca}^{++}] = \frac{[\text{CaY}^=]}{5.01 \times 10^{10}[\text{Y}^\equiv]}$$

After the addition of 50.10 ml of EDTA, there is $(0.10)(0.01000)$ or 0.00100 millimole excess EDTA, of which 35.5 per cent or 0.000355 millimole is $\text{Y}^\equiv$.

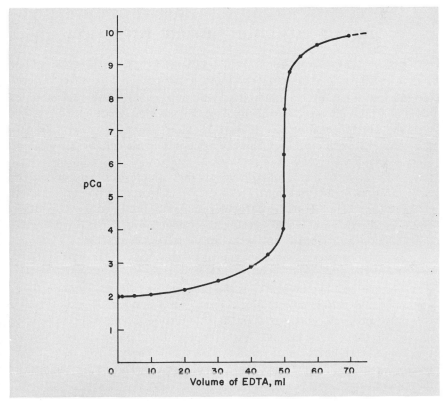

FIGURE 11-3. Titration curve for the titration of 50.00 ml of 0.01000 M calcium ion with 0.01000 F EDTA. The titration solution is buffered at pH 10 with ammonia and ammonium chloride.

The number of millimoles of $CaY^=$ remains 0.5000. Since both $Y^\equiv$ and $CaY^=$ are in the same solution of volume, 100.1 ml, and since the ratio of the concentrations of $CaY^=$ to $Y^\equiv$ appears in the expression for $[Ca^{++}]$, it is unnecessary to calculate $[CaY^=]$ and $[Y^\equiv]$. Only the ratio of the number of millimoles of these two species is required in the calculation of the calcium ion concentration. Therefore, after the addition of 50.10 ml of titrant,

$$[Ca^{++}] = \frac{(0.5000)}{(5.01 \times 10^{10})(3.55 \times 10^{-4})} = 2.81 \times 10^{-8} \, M; \qquad pCa = 7.55.$$

Other points on the titration curve beyond the equivalence point may be similarly calculated, provided it is remembered that only 35.5 per cent of the total millimoles of excess EDTA added is in the form of $Y^\equiv$.

At 51.00 ml of EDTA added, $[Ca^{++}] = 2.81 \times 10^{-9} \, M$; $pCa = 8.55$. At 55.00 ml of EDTA added, $[Ca^{++}] = 5.63 \times 10^{-10} \, M$; $pCa = 9.25$. At 60.00 ml of EDTA added, $[Ca^{++}] = 2.81 \times 10^{-10} \, M$; $pCa = 9.55$. At 70.00 ml of EDTA added, $[Ca^{++}] = 1.40 \times 10^{-10} \, M$; $pCa = 9.85$. Figure 11-3 shows the titration curve determined according to these calculations.

DIRECT TITRATION OF ZINC WITH EDTA

In contrast to the titration of calcium with EDTA, the titration of zinc with a standard solution of Na_2H_2Y, which will now be discussed, is a more complicated situation. An ammonia-ammonium ion buffer of approximately pH 9 or 10 usually serves as the auxiliary complexing agent in order to prevent the precipitation of zinc hydroxide. However, as discussed earlier in this chapter, the zinc cation forms a series of ammonia complexes which are quite stable. The formation of these zinc-ammine complexes means that, in the construction of a plot of pZn versus the volume of titrant added, the concentration of the zinc ion, $Zn(H_2O)_4^{++}$ will depend on the ammonia concentration. The pH of the particular ammonia buffer employed will also influence the titration curve because the fraction of the EDTA present as the $Y^\equiv$ anion is dependent on the hydrogen ion concentration.

For the purposes of the following discussion, we will consider the titration of a 50.00 ml sample of $0.001000 \, F$ zinc nitrate with a $0.1000 \, F \, Na_2H_2Y$ solution. We will assume also that the zinc nitrate solution contains $0.10 \, F$ ammonia and $0.10 \, F$ ammonium nitrate. Note that the EDTA titrant is 100 times more concentrated than the zinc nitrate sample solution in order to avoid dilution of the ammonia-ammonium nitrate buffer. This simplification makes the numerical calculations easier. Since only 0.5000 ml of EDTA titrant is required for the titration, it would be performed with the use of a microburet.

Construction of the Titration Curve Before the Equivalence Point.   The concentration of the zinc ion, $Zn(H_2O)_4^{++}$, and thus the value of pZn, prior to the equivalence point of the titration can be calculated from the quantity of zinc remaining untitrated. Since the zinc-EDTA complex is quite stable (see Table 11-2), one is justified in neglecting dissociation of this complex except very close to the equivalence point of the titration. The presence of ammonia in the sample solution keeps the concentration of $Zn(H_2O)_4^{++}$ exceedingly small. Furthermore, since the ammonia concentration is $0.10\,F$ and the total zinc ion concentration is only $0.001000\,M$, it is reasonable to assume that, to a good approximation, the ammonia concentration remains constant at $0.10\,F$. Figure 11-1 shows that the predominant zinc species at this ammonia concentration are $Zn(NH_3)_4^{++}$ and $Zn(NH_3)_3(H_2O)^{++}$; the second species may be abbreviated $Zn(NH_3)_3^{++}$. Although the concentration of $Zn(H_2O)_4^{++}$ is extremely small, it is important to recognize that *a constant fraction of the zinc remaining untitrated exists as* $Zn(H_2O)_4^{++}$. In other words, for a given ammonia concentration, the amount of zinc present as $Zn(H_2O)_4^{++}$ is a constant, small fraction of the *total* analytical concentration of zinc which is untitrated. The predominant zinc-ammine complexes in the $0.10\,F$ ammonia solution are $Zn(NH_3)_4^{++}$ and $Zn(NH_3)_3^{++}$, and, since we are interested in the concentration of $Zn(H_2O)_4^{++}$, the pertinent equilibria are

$$Zn(H_2O)_4^{++} + 3\,NH_3 \rightleftharpoons Zn(NH_3)_3(H_2O)^{++} + 3\,H_2O$$

and

$$Zn(H_2O)_4^{++} + 4\,NH_3 \rightleftharpoons Zn(NH_3)_4^{++} + 4\,H_2O$$

The equilibrium expressions for these reactions are, respectively,

$$\frac{[Zn(NH_3)_3(H_2O)^{++}]}{[Zn(H_2O)_4^{++}][NH_3]^3} = \beta_3 \quad \text{and} \quad \frac{[Zn(NH_3)_4^{++}]}{[Zn(H_2O)_4^{++}][NH_3]^4} = \beta_4$$

where the overall formation constants, β_3 and β_4, have respective values of 1.02×10^7 and 1.15×10^9. The concentration of water does not appear in these relations.

Now, in order to calculate pZn prior to the equivalence point of our titration, we may take the ammonia concentration to be $0.10\,M$ and the sum of $[Zn(NH_3)_3^{++}]$ and $[Zn(NH_3)_4^{++}]$ to represent the total analytical concentration of zinc remaining untitrated, because these are by far the predominant species not complexed by EDTA. The fraction of untitrated zinc present as $Zn(H_2O)_4^{++}$, which may be abbreviated as Zn^{++}, is given by:

$$\frac{[Zn^{++}]}{[Zn(NH_3)_3^{++}] + [Zn(NH_3)_4^{++}]}$$

From the previous equilibrium expressions, we can write

$$\frac{[Zn^{++}]}{[Zn(NH_3)_3^{++}] + [Zn(NH_3)_4^{++}]} = \frac{[Zn^{++}]}{\beta_3[Zn^{++}][NH_3]^3 + \beta_4[Zn^{++}][NH_3]^4}$$

$$= \frac{1}{(1.02 \times 10^7)(0.10)^3 + (1.15 \times 10^9)(0.10)^4} = \frac{1}{1.25 \times 10^5} = 8.00 \times 10^{-6}$$

On the basis of these calculations, it follows that the *fraction* of untitrated zinc present as $Zn(H_2O)_4^{++}$ is 8.00×10^{-6}.

Before any of the EDTA titrant has been added, the total concentration of zinc, present almost entirely as $Zn(NH_3)_3^{++}$ and $Zn(NH_3)_4^{++}$, is $1.00 \times 10^{-3}\ M$. The concentration of $Zn(H_2O)_4^{++}$, or Zn^{++}, is

$$[Zn^{++}] = (8.00 \times 10^{-6})(1.00 \times 10^{-3}) = 8.00 \times 10^{-9}\ M$$

and pZn is 8.10.

Upon the addition of the EDTA titrant, the zinc-EDTA complex is formed according to the reaction

$$Zn^{++} + HY^{\equiv} \rightleftharpoons ZnY^{=} + H^+$$

where Zn^{++} may be any of the species $Zn(H_2O)_4^{++}$, $Zn(NH_3)(H_2O)_3^{++}$, $Zn(NH_3)_2(H_2O)_2^{++}$, $Zn(NH_3)_3(H_2O)^{++}$, or $Zn(NH_3)_4^{++}$. It is likely that the rate of reaction between $HY^{\equiv}$ and each individual zinc species varies. The protons produced by the titration reaction are consumed by the large excess of ammonia. Since the concentration of the EDTA titrant is 100 times greater than that of the zinc solution being titrated, the solution volume remains almost constant at 50.00 ml and the ammonia concentration stays nearly fixed at 0.10 M. After the addition of 0.0500 ml of $0.1000\ F\ Na_2H_2Y$ (exactly 10 per cent of the stoichiometric quantity of EDTA), the total analytical concentration of zinc remaining untitrated is essentially 0.0009000 M (dilution of the solution and dissociation of the zinc-EDTA complex being neglected). Proceeding as before, we can write:

$$[Zn^{++}] = (8.00 \times 10^{-6})(9.00 \times 10^{-4}) = 7.20 \times 10^{-9}\ M$$

and

$$pZn = 8.14.$$

After the addition of 0.100 ml of EDTA, $[Zn^{++}] = 6.40 \times 10^{-9}\ M$; pZn = 8.19. After the addition of 0.200 ml of EDTA, $[Zn^{++}] = 4.80 \times 10^{-9}\ M$; pZn = 8.32. After the addition of 0.300 ml of EDTA, $[Zn^{++}] = 3.20 \times 10^{-9}\ M$; pZn = 8.50. After the addition of 0.400 ml of EDTA, $[Zn^{++}] = 1.60 \times 10^{-9}\ M$; pZn = 8.80. After the addition of 0.450 ml of EDTA, $[Zn^{++}] = 8.00 \times 10^{-10}\ M$; pZn = 9.10.

After the addition of 0.490 ml of EDTA, $[Zn^{++}] = 1.60 \times 10^{-10}\ M$; pZn = 9.80. Up to this point, dissociation of the zinc-EDTA complex may be neglected. Moreover, consideration of the fact that the solution volume is not 50.00 ml but almost 50.50 ml does not change the conclusions, for $[Zn^{++}]$ turns out to be $1.58 \times 10^{-10}\ M$, and pZn remains 9.80.

Conditions Near and At the Equivalence Point.   The calculation of the zinc ion concentration and the value of pZn near and at the equivalence point requires the use of the formation constant for the zinc-EDTA complex:

$$K_{ZnY} = \frac{[ZnY^{=}]}{[Zn^{++}][Y^{\equiv}]} = 3.16 \times 10^{16}$$

Detailed calculations will be performed only for the equivalence point.

The concentration of the zinc-EDTA complex at the equivalence point is $1.00 \times 10^{-3}\ M$ minus that which has dissociated. The extent of this dissociation is measured by the total analytical concentration of all non-zinc-EDTA species. However, since the only important species are $Zn(NH_3)_4^{++}$ and $Zn(NH_3)_3^{++}$, it is correct to write

$$[ZnY^=] = 1.00 \times 10^{-3} - \{[Zn(NH_3)_3^{++}] + [Zn(NH_3)_4^{++}]\}$$

or

$$[ZnY^=] = 1.00 \times 10^{-3} - 1.25 \times 10^{5}[Zn^{++}]$$

The concentration of $Y^{\equiv}$ at the equivalence point depends on the pH of the solution. The ammonia-ammonium nitrate buffer determines the pH through the following equilibrium:

$$NH_3 + H_2O \rightleftharpoons NH_4^+ + OH^-$$

$$\frac{[NH_4^+][OH^-]}{[NH_3]} = K_b = 1.75 \times 10^{-5}$$

For the present titration, where $[NH_4^+]$ and $[NH_3]$ are both $0.10\ M$, the hydroxide ion concentration, $[OH^-]$, is $1.75 \times 10^{-5}\ M$. The hydrogen ion concentration is $K_w/[OH^-]$, or $5.72 \times 10^{-10}\ M$, and the pH is 9.24. Table 11-1 reveals that at pH 9.24 the only important EDTA species are $HY^{\equiv}$ and $Y^{\equiv}$. Using the expression for the fourth acid ionization of EDTA and substituting into it $[H^+] = 5.72 \times 10^{-10}\ M$, one obtains the following:

$$\frac{[Y^{\equiv}]}{[HY^=]} = \frac{K_4}{[H^+]} = \frac{5.50 \times 10^{-11}}{5.72 \times 10^{-10}} = 0.0962$$

Now, at the equivalence point, by definition, the concentration of unreacted zinc in all its forms is equal to the concentration of unreacted EDTA in all its forms:

$$[Zn(H_2O)_4^{++}] + [Zn(NH_3)(H_2O)_3^{++}] + [Zn(NH_3)_2(H_2O)_2^{++}]$$
$$+ [Zn(NH_3)_3(H_2O)^{++}] + [Zn(NH_3)_4^{++}]$$
$$= [H_4Y] + [H_3Y^-] + [H_2Y^=] + [HY^=] + [Y^{\equiv}]$$

However, since the only species present in significant amounts are $Zn(NH_3)_4^{++}$, $Zn(NH_3)_3^{++}$, $HY^=$, and $Y^{\equiv}$, we can simplify this expression by writing

$$[Zn(NH_3)_3^{++}] + [Zn(NH_3)_4^{++}] = [HY^=] + [Y^{\equiv}]$$

It can now be recalled that the relation between the concentration of $Zn(H_2O)_4^{++}$ (or Zn^{++}) and the sum of the concentrations of $Zn(NH_3)_3^{++}$ and $Zn(NH_3)_4^{++}$ is

$$[Zn^{++}] = 8.00 \times 10^{-6}\{[Zn(NH_3)_3^{++}] + [Zn(NH_3)_4^{++}]\}$$

When the last two equations are combined, the result is

$$[HY^=] + [Y^{\equiv}] = \frac{[Zn^{++}]}{8.00 \times 10^{-6}} = 1.25 \times 10^{5}[Zn^{++}]$$

from which

$$\frac{[Y^\equiv]}{0.0962} + [Y^\equiv] = 1.25 \times 10^5[Zn^{++}]$$

$$11.4[Y^\equiv] = 1.25 \times 10^5[Zn^{++}]$$

$$[Y^\equiv] = 1.10 \times 10^4[Zn^{++}]$$

The final step in this calculation is to substitute the appropriate results into the formation-constant expression for the zinc-EDTA complex:

$$K_{ZnY} = \frac{[ZnY^=]}{[Zn^{++}][Y^\equiv]} = \frac{1.00 \times 10^{-3} - 1.25 \times 10^5[Zn^{++}]}{1.10 \times 10^4[Zn^{++}]^2} = 3.16 \times 10^{16}$$

This equation can be solved easily for $[Zn^{++}]$ if the dissociation of the $ZnY^=$ complex (the negative term in the numerator) is neglected:

$$[Zn^{++}]^2 = \frac{1.00 \times 10^{-3}}{(1.10 \times 10^4)(3.16 \times 10^{16})} = 2.88 \times 10^{-24}$$

$$[Zn^{++}] = 1.70 \times 10^{-12} M; \qquad pZn = 11.77$$

Note that neglect of the dissociation of the complex (negative term) is well justified.

Calculations of pZn either slightly before or slightly after the equivalence point may be carried out in a similar manner, although they are somewhat more involved. Just prior to the equivalence point, the $ZnY^=$ concentration is virtually identical to that computed from the millimoles of EDTA added. The concentration of $Y^\equiv$ is obtained from the knowledge that the extent of dissociation of the $ZnY^=$ complex is measured by the sum of the concentrations of $HY^=$ and $Y^\equiv$. The Zn^{++} concentration is equal to the concentration of zinc remaining untitrated plus the sum of the concentrations of $HY^=$ and $Y^\equiv$, all multiplied by the factor 8.00×10^{-6}. Just beyond the equivalence point, when a slight excess of EDTA is present, the concentration of $ZnY^=$ may be taken to be $1.00 \times 10^{-3} M$. The total concentration of uncomplexed EDTA is equal to that originating from dissociation of the $ZnY^=$ complex plus that in excess of the equivalence point. The total concentration of uncomplexed EDTA ($[HY^=] + [Y^\equiv]$) may be related to $[Y^\equiv]$ alone and then to $[Zn^{++}]$.

Construction of the Titration Curve After the Equivalence Point. Beyond the equivalence point of the titration, the formation-constant expression for the $ZnY^=$ complex can be rearranged to obtain the zinc concentration, that is,

$$[Zn^{++}] = \frac{[ZnY^=]}{K_{ZnY}[Y^\equiv]}$$

Since dilution of the solution beyond the equivalence point will be ignored, the concentration of the zinc-EDTA complex, $[ZnY^=]$, will be close to $1.00 \times 10^{-3} M$. If dissociation of the $ZnY^=$ complex is ignored, the sum of the concentrations of $HY^=$ and $Y^\equiv$ is equal to the concentration of EDTA added in excess beyond the equivalence point. Consider the calculation of pZn after the addition of 0.510 ml of the EDTA titrant. This corresponds to an excess of $(0.010)(0.1000)$ or 1.00×10^{-3} millimole of EDTA in a volume which we shall take to be 50.00 ml. Therefore, the concentration of the EDTA is $2.00 \times 10^{-5}\ M$. As discussed previously, the only important EDTA species are $HY^=$ and $Y^{\equiv}$, and so

$$[HY^=] + [Y^{\equiv}] = 2.00 \times 10^{-5}\ M$$

$$\frac{[Y^{\equiv}]}{0.0962} + [Y^{\equiv}] = 2.00 \times 10^{-5}\ M$$

$$[Y^{\equiv}] = 1.75 \times 10^{-6}\ M$$

Solving the expression for the zinc concentration, we obtain

$$[Zn^{++}] = \frac{[ZnY^=]}{K_{ZnY}[Y^{\equiv}]} = \frac{1.00 \times 10^{-3}}{(3.16 \times 10^{16})(1.75 \times 10^{-6})} = 1.81 \times 10^{-14}\ M$$

and pZn is 13.74. It might be noted that the ratio of the concentrations of $ZnY^=$ and $Y^{\equiv}$ obviates the need for concern over the change in solution volume caused by the addition of the titrant. Other points beyond the equivalence point may be treated similarly.

After the addition of 0.550 ml of EDTA, $[Zn^{++}] = 3.62 \times 10^{-15}\ M$; pZn = 14.44. After the addition of 0.600 ml of EDTA, $[Zn^{++}] = 1.81 \times 10^{-15}\ M$; pZn = 14.74. After the addition of 0.700 ml of EDTA, $[Zn^{++}] = 9.05 \times 10^{-16}\ M$; pZn = 15.04. The titration curve for the proposed titration is shown in Figure 11-4.

EFFECT OF SOLUTION CONDITIONS ON TITRATION CURVES

Before considering the subject of end point indicators for complexometric titrations, we shall discuss the important problem of the influence or effect of solution conditions on the shape of the titration curve, particularly the size of the break in the titration curve near the equivalence point.

Direct Titration of Calcium with EDTA. For the titration of 50.00 ml of $0.01000\ M$ calcium ion with $0.01000\ F\ Na_2H_2Y$ buffered at pH 10 with ammonia and ammonium ions (see Fig. 11-3), we note that the calcium ion concentration changes from $1.00 \times 10^{-5}\ M$ (pCa = 5.00) only 0.2 per cent prior to the equivalence point to $2.81 \times 10^{-8}\ M$ (pCa = 7.55) at 0.2 per cent beyond the equivalence point. This represents an approximately 350-fold decrease in the calcium ion concentration over a narrow range of titrant volumes added (49.90 to 50.10 ml of EDTA). Such a large change in the calcium ion concentration is a highly desirable feature of this titration and means that the equivalence point can be located with considerable precision.

Prior to the equivalence point, the points on the titration curve are determined solely by the concentration of unreacted calcium ions. Thus, the

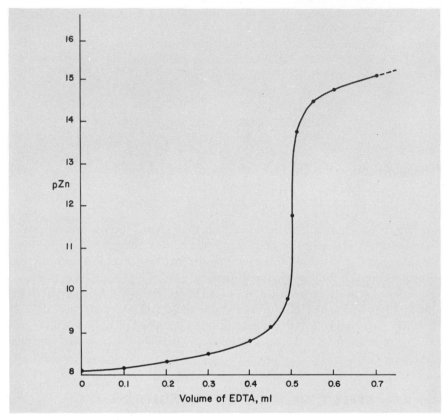

FIGURE 11-4.   Titration curve for the titration of 50.00 ml of 0.001000 M zinc ion with 0.1000 F EDTA. The zinc solution is also 0.1 F in ammonia and 0.1 F in ammonium nitrate.

titration curve before the equivalence point is unaffected by changes in the pH of the solution—except that calcium hydroxide would precipitate at very high pH values. Furthermore, the concentrations of ammonia and ammonium chloride, or any other buffer, have no effect because calcium forms no stable complex ions of importance except for the EDTA-like complexes themselves. Obviously, if the original calcium ion concentration were greater than 0.01 M, the titration curve would be displaced downward to lower pCa values prior to the equivalence point. Conversely, for calcium ion concentrations smaller than 0.01 M, the titration curve would be pushed upward to larger pCa values.

Exactly at the equivalence point, it was necessary to consider the formation-constant expression for the calcium-EDTA complex. In general, the more stable a metal-EDTA complex is, the smaller will be the concentration of the uncomplexed metal ion and the larger will be the size of the break in the titration curve. Also at the equivalence point, we had to consider the effect of pH on the value of pCa; since pH controls the concentration of the $Y^{\equiv}$ ion, pH thereby affects the calcium ion concentration. At pH values greater than 10, a larger fraction of EDTA exists as $Y^{\equiv}$ (see Table 11-1) and, for a higher concentration of $Y^{\equiv}$, the value of $[Ca^{++}]$ is lower and the equivalence point pCa is higher. Naturally, a higher value for pCa at the equivalence point means a sharper break in the titration curve. If the pH of the sample solution is made less than 10, we can conclude by similar reasoning that the quality of the break in the titration curve will be poorer.

For the titration of calcium with EDTA, the titration curve beyond the equivalence point is affected by the values of K_{CaY} and pH the same way as at the equivalence point itself. So, in summary, a well-defined titration curve is favored by large values of the original calcium ion concentration, the pH, and the formation constant for the calcium-EDTA complex. In other words, these are the three factors which provide the driving force for the titration reaction

$$Ca^{++} + HY^{\equiv} \rightleftharpoons CaY^{=} + H^{+}$$

Direct Titration of Zinc with EDTA. For the titration of zinc with EDTA in an ammonia-ammonium ion buffer, the titration curve prior to the equivalence point is influenced by the concentration of ammonia as well as by the total analytical concentration of zinc not complexed by EDTA. As pointed out before, the concentration of ammonia determines what fraction of the total analytical concentration of zinc uncomplexed by EDTA is present as $Zn(H_2O)_4^{++}$. Thus, if the total analytical concentration of zinc is increased or if the ammonia concentration decreased, the value of pZn and the titration curve are both lowered.

From our calculation of pZn at the equivalence point of the titration, it may be seen that three factors are important in determining the zinc ion concentration. First of all, the formation constant for the zinc-EDTA complex affects $[Zn^{++}]$ at the equivalence point. Since the formation constant for the $ZnY^{=}$ complex is larger than that for the $CaY^{=}$ species, the value of $[Zn^{++}]$ at the equivalence point may be expected to be smaller than the corresponding value of $[Ca^{++}]$. However, the presence of ammonia further decreases the Zn^{++} concentration because of formation of stable zinc-ammine complexes. The magnitude of this last effect is exactly the same as it is prior to the equivalence point. Finally, the pH of the solution, as fixed by the ammonia-ammonium ion buffer, determines what fraction of EDTA unreacted at the equivalence point is present as $Y^{\equiv}$. In turn, the concentration of $Y^{\equiv}$ influences the value of pZn. The higher the pH, the more EDTA present as $Y^{\equiv}$ and the smaller will be $[Zn^{++}]$. Therefore, the value of pZn at the equivalence point is increased if any or all of the following are increased: K_{ZnY}, the ammonia concentration, and the pH of the solution. Notice that by suitable adjustment of the concentrations of NH_3 and NH_4^{+} it is possible to raise the pH and lower the ammonia concentration or vice versa.

The concentration of zinc ion beyond the equivalence point is determined by the value of the formation constant for the zinc-EDTA complex and by the concentration of $Y^{\equiv}$ Since the pH of the solution governs the fraction of EDTA present as the $Y^{\equiv}$ ion, K_{ZnY} and the pH are the two quantities which affect the position of the titration curve after the equivalence point. An increase in either or both of these quantities makes the values of pZn beyond the equivalence point larger and thus raises the titration curve.

We can summarize the conclusions regarding the titration curve as follows: Before the equivalence point, an increase in the ammonia concentration raises the titration curve to higher pZn values. At the equivalence point, the value of pZn increases if either the ammonia concentration or the pH is raised; whereas, beyond the equivalence point, the titration curve is raised if the pH is increased. For any particular titration, the formation constant for the metal-EDTA complex, K_{MY}, will have a fixed value, and so it cannot be considered as a titration variable. However, it should be obvious that, for a group of metal ions forming EDTA complexes, the most stable metal-EDTA complex will exhibit the most sharply defined titration curve, all other factors being equal.

It is important to emphasize that the quantitative effects of the different variables on titration curves can be calculated by the procedures just employed. However, it is equally important to be able to visualize and explain how the titration variables affect the titration curves in a qualitative way.

END POINT INDICATORS

The wide applicability of complexometric titrations has done much to stimulate the development of techniques for end point detection. In particular, a very large number of colored indicators have been studied and employed for complexometric titrations. The term **metallochromic indicators** is frequently used to describe these substances, because they form stable, brightly colored complexes with most metal ions of analytical interest.

The chemical equilibria which involve these metallochromic indicators are of special interest. Not only do metallochromic indicators form complexes with metal cations, but they are acid-base indicators as well. It is a combination of these two properties which is utilized to obtain the indicator behavior desired in complexometric titrations. One of the most widely used indicators is Eriochrome Black T, which has the following structural formula:

Eriochrome Black T

Eriochrome Black T is a triprotic acid which may be abbreviated as H_3In. The ionization of the proton from the $-SO_3H$ group, like the first acid dissociation of sulfuric acid, is virtually complete in water. The other two ionizations can be represented by the following equilibria and equilibrium constants:

$$H_2In^- \rightleftharpoons H^+ + HIn^=; \qquad K_2 = 5.00 \times 10^{-7}$$
$$HIn^= \rightleftharpoons H^+ + In^=; \qquad K_3 = 2.82 \times 10^{-12}$$

The species H_2In^-, $HIn^=$, and $In^=$ are red, blue, and orange-yellow colored, respectively. Eriochrome Black T forms stable, one-to-one, wine-red-colored complexes with most of the metal cations listed in Table 11-2. In addition, complexes in which two or three indicator molecules are bound to one metal cation are not uncommon; however, their existence will be neglected for the present discussion. Many EDTA titrations are performed in the presence of a buffer such as ammonia-ammonium ion, or a tartrate or citrate buffer. Therefore, the pH of the solution is in the neighborhood of 8 to 10, and the predominant form of Eriochrome Black T is the bright-blue-colored $HIn^=$ anion.

Direct Titration of Zinc. In the direct titration of zinc with EDTA in an ammonia-ammonium ion buffer containing a small amount of Eriochrome Black T, the solution has a wine red color prior to the equivalence point because of the zinc-Eriochrome Black T complex. Suddenly, when the first slight excess of EDTA titrant is added, the color of the solution becomes bright blue because the formation of the zinc-EDTA complex frees the $HIn^=$ indicator ion according to the following reaction:

$$ZnIn^- + HY^= \rightleftharpoons ZnY^= + HIn^-$$
$$\text{(wine red)} \qquad\qquad\qquad \text{(blue)}$$

In order to verify that the end point color change does indeed occur very close to the theoretical equivalence point for the zinc-EDTA titration, some quantitative calculations should be made.

The formation of the zinc-Eriochrome Black T complex, $ZnIn^-$, may be written as follows:

$$Zn^{++} + In^\equiv \rightleftharpoons ZnIn^-$$

where the formation constant K_{ZnIn} has a value of 7.95×10^{12}. Combination of this equilibrium with the expression for the third acid dissociation of Eriochrome Black T gives the overall reaction

$$Zn^{++} + HIn^= \rightleftharpoons ZnIn^- + H^+$$

which has an equilibrium constant of $K_3 K_{ZnIn}$ or 22.4. Thus,

$$\frac{[ZnIn^-][H^+]}{[Zn^{++}][HIn^=]} = 22.4$$

In the direct titration of zinc with EDTA described earlier, the pH of the solution, as determined by the ammonia-ammonium ion buffer, was 9.24.

This corresponds to a hydrogen ion concentration of 5.72×10^{-10} M. If this value for $[H^+]$ is substituted into the preceding equation, which is then solved for $[Zn^{++}]$, the result is

$$[Zn^{++}] = \frac{[ZnIn^-][H^+]}{22.4[HIn^=]} = \frac{[ZnIn^-](5.72 \times 10^{-10})}{22.4[HIn^=]} = 2.55 \times 10^{-11} \frac{[ZnIn^-]}{[HIn^=]}$$

In the proposed titration of zinc, the color of the solution prior to the end point will be wine red because of the presence of the zinc-Eriochrome Black T complex. Even though the total analytical concentration of Eriochrome Black T in a typical complexometric titration is on the order of 10^{-5} to 10^{-4} M, the color of the $ZnIn^-$ indicator complex is sufficiently intense that a concentration of the $ZnIn^-$ ion (and other metal-indicator ions) as low as 10^{-6} M is visually detectable. The human eye normally recognizes a mixture of two colors (such as wine red and bright blue) as a single color alone if the intensity of one color is about 10 or more times greater than the intensity of the other color. Presumably, for the present discussion, color intensity and concentration can be considered proportional to each other. In the titration of zinc, therefore, the visual end point will not be recognized until the concentration of blue-colored $HIn^=$ is at least 10 times larger than the concentration of wine-red-colored $ZnIn^-$. When such a point is reached, the observer will recognize that a color change from red to blue has taken place.

Let us now calculate at what value of pZn the end point color change occurs. At the end point, the ratio of the concentration of $ZnIn^-$ to the concentration of $HIn^=$ is $1/10$. Thus, we can write

$$[Zn^{++}] = 2.55 \times 10^{-11} \frac{[ZnIn^-]}{[HIn^=]} = \frac{2.55 \times 10^{-11}}{10} = 2.55 \times 10^{-12} \, M$$

and pZn is 11.59 at the end point. Note that this value of pZn is extremely close to the theoretical equivalence point value of 11.77, and so we conclude that Eriochrome Black T is an ideal choice for the end point indicator.

Direct Titration of Calcium.   Considerations similar to those made for the zinc titration can be made for the calcium-EDTA titration. Calcium also forms a wine-red-colored complex with Eriochrome Black T, so that the end point color change is again the transition from a red- to a blue-colored solution. The calcium-Eriochrome Black T complex has a formation constant of 2.51×10^5, so it is much less stable than the analogous $ZnIn^-$ complex.

Let us combine the two equilibria

$$Ca^{++} + In^= \rightleftharpoons CaIn^-; \qquad K_{CaIn} = 2.51 \times 10^5$$

and

$$HIn^= \rightleftharpoons H^+ + In^=; \qquad K_3 = 2.82 \times 10^{-12}$$

to obtain the reaction

$$Ca^{++} + HIn^= \rightleftharpoons CaIn^- + H^+$$

with an equilibrium constant of $K_{CaIn}K_3$ or 7.08×10^{-7}. In our example of the calcium-EDTA titration discussed previously, the solution pH was 10, so we can write

$$[Ca^{++}] = \frac{[CaIn^-][H^+]}{(7.08 \times 10^{-7})[HIn^=]} = \frac{[CaIn^-](1.00 \times 10^{-10})}{(7.08 \times 10^{-7})[HIn^=]}$$

$$= 1.41 \times 10^{-4} \frac{[CaIn^-]}{[HIn^=]}$$

If, as before, the assumption is made that the ratio $[CaIn^-]/[HIn^=]$ is 1/10 at the observed end point, the calcium ion concentration turns out to be

$$[Ca^{++}] = 1.41 \times 10^{-4} \frac{[CaIn^-]}{[HIn^=]} = \frac{1.41 \times 10^{-4}}{10} = 1.41 \times 10^{-5} \, M$$

and pCa at the experimental end point is 4.85. However, the theoretical equivalence point pCa is 6.27, so there is a real question concerning the accuracy of the titration.

A simple, although only approximate, calculation of the titration error can be made. Looking back at the construction of the titration curve for the calcium-EDTA titration, we note that the experimental value of pCa of 4.85 would occur between the addition of 49.00 and 49.90 ml of EDTA titrant. Thus, the total solution volume at the end point can be taken to be 100 ml. Furthermore, for our approximate calculations the calcium ion concentration at the equivalence point $(5.31 \times 10^{-7} \, M)$ can be neglected in comparison to the calcium ion concentration at the end point $(1.41 \times 10^{-5} \, M)$. Consequently, to a first approximation, $(1.41 \times 10^{-5})(100)$ or 1.41×10^{-3} millimole of calcium remains untitrated at the experimental end point. The original sample solution, 50.00 ml of 0.01000 M calcium ion, contained a total of 0.5000 millimole of calcium ion. Therefore, the relative percentage titration error is

$$- \frac{0.00141}{0.5000} \times 100 - -0.28\%$$

Although a theoretical titration error of about -0.3 per cent is not objectionably large, the absolute magnitude of the error could easily increase to as much as 0.5 per cent or even 1.0 per cent in an actual titration.

How might the titration error be reduced? First of all, a very practical way to minimize the titration error is to standardize the Na_2H_2Y titrant solution against a carefully prepared standard calcium ion solution under conditions exactly identical to those used in the analysis of unknown calcium solutions. This expedient goes a long way toward canceling out the systematic sources of error in the titration.

Another approach is to employ a different metallochromic indicator for the calcium-EDTA titration. Eriochrome Blue Black B, which is very similar to Eriochrome Black T, is a good indicator for this titration. Eriochrome

Blue Black B has the following structural formula:

Eriochrome Blue Black B

Like Eriochrome Black T, the dissociation of the sulfonic acid group ($-SO_3H$) is complete in water. The dissociation of the phenol groups ($-OH$) may be represented by the following equilibria:

$$H_2In^- \rightleftharpoons HIn^= + H^+; \qquad K_2 = 6.3 \times 10^{-7}$$
$$HIn^= \rightleftharpoons In^\equiv + H^+; \qquad K_3 = 3.2 \times 10^{-13}$$

The formation and formation constant for the calcium-Eriochrome Blue Black B complex, which has a red color, are given by

$$Ca^{++} + In^\equiv \rightleftharpoons CaIn^-; \qquad K_{CaIn} = 5.0 \times 10^5$$

The titration of calcium with EDTA in the presence of Eriochrome Blue Black B as indicator is usually carried out in an ammonia-ammonium ion buffer of pH 11.5 ($[H^+] = 3.2 \times 10^{-12}\,M$), and the end point is signaled by a change in the color of the solution from the red color of the calcium-Eriochrome Blue Black B complex to the blue color of the $HIn^=$ indicator ion.

The calcium ion concentration at the experimental end point may be computed according to the procedure described previously:

$$[Ca^{++}] = \frac{[CaIn^-][H^+]}{K_3 K_{CaIn}[HIn^=]} = \frac{[CaIn^-][H^+]}{(3.2 \times 10^{-13})(5.0 \times 10^5)[HIn^=]}$$
$$= \frac{[CaIn^-][H^+]}{1.6 \times 10^{-7}[HIn^=]}$$

At a pH of 11.5 and for a ratio $[CaIn^-]/[HIn^=]$ of 1/10, we obtain

$$[Ca^{++}] = \frac{(3.2 \times 10^{-12})}{(1.6 \times 10^{-7})(10)} = 2.0 \times 10^{-6}\,M; \qquad pCa = 5.70$$

The experimental end point value of pCa (5.70) occurs sufficiently close to the equivalence point (pCa = 6.27) that the percentage relative titration error is reduced theoretically to only about -0.03 per cent. In practice, the titration error is more likely to be closer to ± 0.1 per cent, owing to the uncertainties in the calibration of volumetric glassware and in the visual detection of the end point color change.

No discussion of metallochromic indicators is complete without mention of one other compound, Calmagite, which has tended to replace Eriochrome Black T as an end point indicator for complexometric titrations. One of the chief difficulties in using Eriochrome Black T is that solutions of it decompose rather rapidly, and so they must be freshly prepared in order for the proper end point color change to be realized. The reason for this instability appears to stem from the fact that the Eriochrome Black T molecule possesses an oxidizing substituent, the nitro group ($—NO_2$), and two different types of reducing groups, azo ($—N=N—$) and phenolic hydroxyl, which are probably involved in redox reactions leading to the destruction of the indicator molecules.

Calmagite has chemical and physical properties which are remarkably similar to those of Eriochrome Black T, but its structural formula reveals the

Calmagite

absence of a nitro group. Solutions of Calmagite are exceedingly stable, having a shelf life of years. More important, however, is the fact that Calmagite may be used routinely as a substitute for the less stable Eriochrome Black T in all procedures which require the latter indicator, and without any modification of these procedures.

Calmagite is a triprotic acid, although the sulfonic acid group ($—SO_3H$) is almost completely ionized in water. Therefore, only the ionization of the phenol groups has any bearing on the behavior of Calmagite as an indicator. If we abbreviate the parent indicator molecule as H_3In, the second and third ionizations may be represented by the following equilibria and equilibrium constants:

$$H_2In^- \rightleftharpoons H^+ + HIn^=; \qquad K_2 = 7.24 \times 10^{-9}$$
$$HIn^= \rightleftharpoons H^+ + In^=; \qquad K_3 = 4.47 \times 10^{-13}$$

When Calmagite is substituted for Eriochrome Black T in the complexometric titration of zinc with EDTA, for example, the end point color change is the same as described earlier — from the wine red color of the zinc-Calmagite complex ($ZnIn^-$) to the pure blue color of the indicator ($HIn^=$).

OTHER APPLICATIONS AND INDICATORS

Direct Titration of Nickel. Some metal ions form such stable complexes with Eriochrome Black T that EDTA cannot displace the indicator ion from the complex. Therefore, no solution color change occurs at the equivalence point of the titration or, if a color change does occur, it happens only gradually after a large excess of EDTA has been added. Nickel ion behaves in this manner. However, nickel can be determined by direct titration with EDTA if murexide is used as the end point indicator.

The titration is performed in an ammonia-ammonium ion buffer of pH 9 in which nickel forms a series of ammonia complexes all the way up to $Ni(NH_3)_6^{++}$. Usually, the tetraammine complex, $Ni(NH_3)_4(H_2O)_2^{++}$, predominates for the experimental conditions employed. Nickel forms an orange-yellow complex with murexide. The murexide indicator itself has the following structural formula:

murexide

which may be abbreviated H_4In^-. Below about pH 9 the H_4In^- species is predominant; it has a red-violet color. Between pH 9 and 11, another proton is lost, giving the violet-colored $H_3In^=$ species. At pH values above 11 the blue $H_2In^=$ ion is present. The end point color change is therefore from orange-yellow to red-violet or violet.

Quite frequently the original nickel-containing sample solution has a relatively high concentration (such as 2 or $3 F$) of hydrochloric acid in it. The hydrochloric acid may result from the dissolution and decomposition of nickel dimethylglyoxime which is the form in which nickel is generally separated from such interferents as iron, cobalt, and manganese. In order to carry out the nickel-EDTA titration, it is necessary to add aqueous ammonia to the solution until the pH reaches approximately 9. However, if ammonia is simply added to the nickel-hydrochloric acid solution, large amounts of ammonium chloride are formed. High concentrations of ammonium ion cause an indistinct end point color change. This problem is easily remedied if the nickel-hydrochloric acid solution is evaporated to dryness in order to expel the hydrochloric acid. The nickel chloride residue can be dissolved in a small volume of water, the proper amounts of ammonia and murexide indicator added, and the solution titrated with EDTA. A detailed procedure for the determination of nickel is given at the end of this chapter.

Direct Titration of Iron(III).   Salicylic acid is a good indicator for the determination of iron(III) by titration with EDTA in an acetic acid medium of approximately pH 3. Salicylic acid (HIn) undergoes the following ionization.

salicylic acid

One, two, or three salicylate ions can react with iron(III) to form red-brown-colored complexes. The pH of the solution must be sufficiently high to produce enough salicylate ions for the indicator reaction, but not so high that the formation and presence of orange and brown-colored iron(III) hydroxide complexes might decrease the rate of the iron(III)-EDTA reaction or obscure the end point color change. The iron(III)-EDTA complex is very stable (log K_{FeY} = 25.1), so that at pH 3 the titration curve is well defined and a sharp end point color change is obtained. At the end point, the following indicator reaction occurs:

$$FeIn_3 + H_3Y^- \rightleftharpoons FeY^- + 3\ HIn$$
$$\text{(red-brown)} \qquad\qquad \text{(colorless)}$$

Although the solution should become colorless at the end point, it actually retains a pale yellow color, probably because of the existence of small concentrations of mixed hydroxide-EDTA complexes of iron(III), such as $Fe(OH)Y^=$ and $Fe(OH)_2Y^=$. Nevertheless this pale yellow color does not cause any difficulty.

Determination of Calcium by Back-Titration with Magnesium. It was pointed out before that Eriochrome Black T is not a suitable end point indicator for the direct titration of calcium with EDTA. However, it is possible to determine calcium by a back-titration procedure at pH 10 in which a measured excess of standard EDTA solution is added to the calcium sample, a small amount of Eriochrome Black T is added, and the solution is titrated with a standard magnesium ion solution. As revealed in Table 11-2, the calcium-EDTA complex is more stable than the magnesium-EDTA complex, and so the addition of an excess of EDTA reacts with calcium to form the calcium-EDTA complex; this effectively removes calcium from further chemical reaction. The excess unreacted EDTA is then titrated with a standard solution of magnesium ion, Eriochrome Black T serving as the indicator. The end point color change is from blue to red as a consequence of the reaction

$$HIn^= + Mg^{++} \rightleftharpoons MgIn^- + H^+$$
$$\text{(blue)} \qquad\qquad \text{(wine red)}$$

which occurs with the first slight excess of magnesium ion. It is important that the magnesium-EDTA complex not be more stable than the calcium-EDTA complex; if it were, the magnesium would not only react with the excess EDTA but would also displace calcium from its EDTA complex and thereby ruin the determination of calcium. To calculate the number of millimoles of calcium ion present in the sample, it is only necessary to subtract the number of millimoles of magnesium used in the back-titration from the total number of millimoles of EDTA added. Since this is a difference method of analysis, the most accurate results are obtained when the amount of magnesium ion used in the back-titration is small relative to the quantity of calcium ion in the sample solution. This latter desirable situation could be easily achieved as follows: Add four or five drops of Eriochrome Black T indicator solution to the calcium sample solution. Add standard EDTA from a calibrated buret until an end point color change from red to blue is obtained. (Although this is not the desired end point, it gives a reasonably good idea of how much calcium is present.) Then, add approximately 5 to 10 per cent more EDTA solution from the buret. Finally, back-titrate the solution with standard magnesium solution until the solution changes color from blue ($HIn^=$) to wine red ($MgIn^-$) and record the volume of magnesium ion solution used. The accuracy of this determination can also be improved if the magnesium and EDTA solutions are standardized against each other.

Determination of Nickel by Back-Titration with Magnesium. The general technique of back-titration is a common one in complexometric titrations and is especially useful when the reaction between EDTA and the metal ion of interest is slow or when no suitable end point indicator is available.

We pointed out earlier that Eriochrome Black T cannot be employed as an end point indicator for the direct titration of nickel with EDTA. However, Eriochrome Black T can be used in a back-titration procedure. An excess of standard EDTA solution may be added to an ammonia solution of pH 9 or 10 which contains the nickel ion to be determined, and then the EDTA remaining unreacted after the formation of the $NiY^=$ complex is back-titrated with a standard solution of magnesium ion with Eriochrome Black T serving as the end point indicator.

Spectrophotometric End Point Detection.   Metallochromic indicators are almost invariably intensely colored, and they form brightly colored complexes with most metal ions. This fact allows spectrophotometry or colorimetry to be employed as a means for the precise location of titration end points.

For example, the end point of the direct titration of zinc with EDTA can be determined spectrophotometrically. Eriochrome Black T, the usual metallochromic indicator for this titration, forms a wine red complex, $ZnIn^-$, with zinc. The $ZnIn^-$ complex appears to be wine red because it absorbs light of the green and yellow wavelengths of the visible spectrum. The titration of zinc is performed in an ammonia-ammonium ion buffer in which Eriochrome Black T exists as the blue-colored $HIn^=$ ion (because it has an absorption spectrum with a maximum in the orange region of the spectrum). To the human eye, the end point color change is from the wine red of the $ZnIn^-$ complex to the blue of the $HIn^=$ ion. The progress of the titration can be followed spectrophotometrically if the amount of light absorbed in the orange region of the spectrum is observed as a function of the volume of EDTA titrant added. As long as zinc ion remains untitrated, there will be no absorption of light in the orange region of the spectrum because no $HIn^=$ is present. At and beyond the end point, the blue $HIn^=$ ion will be formed and it will absorb light in the orange region of the spectrum in proportion to its concentration. If a plot of the absorbance of light at a suitable

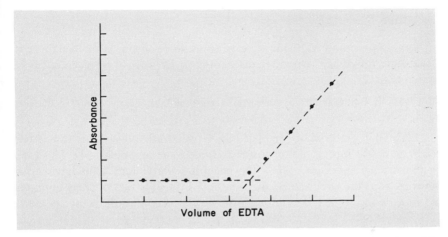

FIGURE 11-5.   Schematic plot of the absorbance of a solution as a function of the volume of EDTA titrant during the complexometric titration of zinc ion in the presence of Eriochrome Black T indicator. The intersection of the two dashed straight lines is the location of the equivalence point. The absorbance does not change prior to the equivalence point because all of the indicator is present as the wine-red-colored $ZnIn^-$ complex. The absorbance increases beyond the equivalence point because EDTA displaces the Eriochrome Black T indicator according to the reaction $ZnIn^- + HY^= \rightleftharpoons HIn^= + ZnY^=$.

wavelength of light in the orange region of the spectrum at various volumes of EDTA is constructed, the result shown in Figure 11-5 is obtained. The intersection of the two straight-line portions of the absorbance versus volume plot may be taken as the end point of the titration. Such *spectrophotometric titrations* have proven very valuable for end point detection in complexometric titrations as well as other titrations.

Experiment 11-1

PREPARATION OF A STANDARD SOLUTION OF EDTA

Purpose

The purpose of this experiment is to prepare by weight 500 ml of standard $0.05\ F$ disodium ethylenediaminetetraacetate solution.

Procedure

Dry approximately 10 gm of reagent-grade disodium ethylenediamine-tetraacetate dihydrate (hereafter designated as EDTA) in an oven at 80°C for two hours.

EDTA is commercially available in a state of high purity (100.0 ± 0.5 per cent).

Place the material to be dried in a weighing bottle and insert the weighing bottle into a beaker-and-watch-glass arrangement (see Fig. 2-1) for the drying operation. After the weighing bottle and solid have been removed from the oven, allow them to cool in air for two or three minutes and in a desiccator for 30 minutes prior to the preparation of the standard EDTA solution.

Accurately weigh, to the nearest milligram, a 9.3 gm portion of dried EDTA salt (formula weight = 372.24) into a clean 400 ml beaker. Insert a clean, long-stem glass funnel into a 500 ml volumetric flask. Add small portions of distilled water to the EDTA in the beaker and pour the aqueous suspension of EDTA through the funnel into the volumetric flask (using a glass stirring rod to guide the flow of solution into the funnel). After all the EDTA has been transferred into the volumetric flask, rinse the beaker and stirring rod with distilled water (adding all rinsings to the volumetric flask through the funnel) and finally rinse the funnel itself. Swirl the flask to dissolve the EDTA.

EDTA does not dissolve rapidly, and so it is inadvisable to transfer the solid EDTA directly to the glass funnel (as is done in the preparation of a standard silver nitrate solution in Experiment 10-1) because the EDTA will probably clog the funnel. The procedure just described is one approach that is satisfactory. Another approach is to weigh the solid EDTA salt and transfer it directly to the volumetric flask. Still another procedure is to dissolve the EDTA salt completely in the 400 ml beaker (possibly with gentle warming at about 50° to 60°C to increase the rate of solution) and transfer the resulting solution through a funnel to the volumetric flask for the final volume adjustment and mixing of the solution.

Add distilled water to bring the volume of solution to exactly 500 ml. Use a dropper or pipet to make the final volume adjustment. With a piece of filter paper, wipe away any droplets of water adhering to the inner wall of the flask *above* the calibration mark.

Stopper the volumetric flask and thoroughly mix the solution by swirling, shaking, and inverting the flask repeatedly. Thoroughly rinse a clean 500 ml polyethylene bottle with two or three small portions of the EDTA solution, and then transfer the remainder of the solution to the bottle for storage.

Solutions of EDTA should preferably be stored in polyethylene containers. When stored in glass bottles, EDTA solutions gradually leach metal ions out of the glass and undergo, in the process, a change in effective concentration. This does not happen with polyethylene containers.

From the weight of EDTA salt and the final volume of solution (500 ml), calculate the concentration of the standard EDTA solution.

Experiment 11-2

DETERMINATION OF ZINC BY DIRECT TITRATION WITH EDTA

Purpose

This experiment demonstrates a typical complexometric titration in which zinc, in an ammonia-ammonium ion buffer solution, is titrated with a standard EDTA solution to an end point determined with the aid of a metallochromic indicator (Eriochrome Black T or Calmagite). This procedure may be used in conjunction with Experiment 11-4.

Procedure

Submit a 100 ml volumetric flask to your instructor, who will add enough aqueous zinc nitrate solution, $Zn(NO_3)_2$, so that when the volume of solution is adjusted to the calibration mark with distilled water, the final zinc ion concentration will be about 0.05 M. Add distilled water to the volumetric flask, if necessary, to bring the solution volume to exactly 100 ml. Stopper the flask and mix the solution thoroughly.

Throughout this experiment, it is essential that all glassware and associated equipment be clean and be rinsed thoroughly with *distilled* water, and preferably *deionized* water. Trace amounts of certain cations found in tap water (such as copper, nickel, and iron) can prevent proper indicator behavior.

Rinse a 25.00 ml pipet with two very small portions of the unknown zinc nitrate solution, and then pipet a 25.00 ml aliquot of the zinc ion solution into each of three 250 ml Erlenmeyer flasks. Add to each flask 10 ml of an ammonia-ammonium chloride buffer solution, and dilute each solution to approximately 100 ml with distilled water.

Prepare this buffer solution in advance by first dissolving 70 gm of solid NH_4Cl in 600 ml of concentrated reagent-grade (15 F) ammonia and then diluting the mixture to 1 liter.

Next add five drops of Eriochrome Black T (or Calmagite) indicator solution to the first of the unknown zinc solutions.

Prepare the indicator *just prior* to the start of the experiment by dissolving about 0.2 gm of solid, reagent-grade Eriochrome Black T in any of the following: 20 ml of formamide, 5 ml of pure ethanol plus 15 ml of triethanolamine, 20 ml of diethanol-amine, or 20 ml of pure ethanol. Alternatively, use a *fresh* bottle of commercially available indicator solution. A Calmagite indicator solution, which is a very stable substitute for Eriochrome Black T, may be prepared by dissolving 0.05 gm of solid Calmagite in 100 ml of distilled water.

Rinse a 50 ml buret with two or three small portions of standard 0.05 F EDTA solution (see Experiment 11-1), allowing the rinsings to run out the buret tip. Fill the buret with the standard EDTA solution, and record the initial position of the meniscus. Titrate the zinc solution with the standard EDTA until the wine red color of the zinc-indicator complex starts to change to the pure blue color of the free indicator. Then add the titrant in drops and in fractions of drops until the color change from wine red to *pure* blue is permanent. Record the final position of the meniscus after waiting 30 seconds for drainage of the buret.

Repeat the titration procedure with the other two unknown zinc solutions, adding five drops of the metallochromic indicator at the start of each titration. From the experimental data, calculate and report the average concentration of the zinc nitrate solution. Replicate results should agree to within a few parts per thousand.

Experiment 11-3

DETERMINATION OF NICKEL BY DIRECT TITRATION WITH EDTA

Purpose

This experiment, another typical application of the technique of complexometric titration, involves the determination of nickel with EDTA in an ammonia-ammonium chloride buffer, the end point being detected with murexide indicator. This procedure may be used in conjunction with Experiment 11-4.

Procedure

Submit a 100 ml volumetric flask to your instructor, who will add enough aqueous nickel nitrate solution, $Ni(NO_3)_2$, so that when the volume of solution is adjusted to the calibration mark with distilled water, the final nickel ion concentration will be approximately 0.05 M. Add distilled water to the volumetric flask, if necessary, to bring the solution volume to exactly 100 ml. Stopper the flask and mix the solution thoroughly.

Throughout this experiment, it is essential that all glassware and associated equipment be clean and be rinsed thoroughly with *distilled* water, although *deionized* water is preferable. Trace amounts of certain cations found in tap water (and sometimes even in distilled water), such as copper, cobalt, and iron, can prevent proper indicator action.

Rinse a 25.00 ml pipet with two small portions of the unknown nickel nitrate solution, and then pipet a 25.00 ml aliquot of this nickel ion solution into each of three clean 250 ml Erlenmeyer flasks. Add to each flask 10 ml of an ammonia-ammonium chloride buffer solution and dilute each nickel solution to approximately 100 ml with distilled or deionized water.

Prepare this buffer solution in advance by first dissolving 70 gm of solid NH_4Cl in 600 ml of concentrated, reagent-grade (15 F) ammonia and then diluting the mixture to 1 liter with distilled water.

Next add 0.2 gm of solid murexide indicator to the first of the unknown nickel solutions.

Prepare the murexide indicator by intimately mixing (perhaps by grinding them in a mortar) 0.2 gm of murexide with 100 gm of reagent-grade sodium chloride. A solid indicator is used because solutions of murexide are unstable.

Rinse a 50 ml buret with two or three small portions of standard 0.05 F EDTA solution (see Experiment 11-1), allowing the rinsings to run out the buret tip. Fill the buret with the standard EDTA solution, and record the initial position of the meniscus. Titrate the nickel solution with standard EDTA until the yellow color of the nickel-murexide complex starts to change to the purple color of the free indicator. Thereafter, add the titrant in drops and in fractions of drops until the color change from yellow to purple is permanent. Wait 30 seconds for drainage from the inner wall of the buret, and then record the final position of the meniscus.

Repeat the titration procedure with the other two unknown nickel solutions, adding a 0.2 gm portion of the indicator at the start of each titration. From the experimental data, calculate and report the average nickel ion concentration in the unknown solution. Replicate results should agree to within a few parts per thousand.

Experiment 11-4

DETERMINATION OF ZINC AND NICKEL IN A MIXTURE BY ION-EXCHANGE SEPARATION AND COMPLEXO-METRIC TITRATION

Purposes

This experiment employs two of the analytical applications of ion-exchange resins discussed in Chapter 7 — first, the determination of the total metal ion content of a solution by titration of exchanged hydrogen ions, and second, the separation of individual metal ions by means of ion-exchange chromatography. The separated metal ions are titrated complexometrically with EDTA, the titration end points being detected with the aid of metallochromic indicators. The individual determinations of the separated metal ions can be compared to the determination of the total metal ion content of the sample solution.

Procedure

Submit a clean 250 ml volumetric flask to your instructor, who will add portions of stock aqueous solutions of zinc nitrate and nickel nitrate so that when the volume of solution is adjusted to the calibration mark with distilled water, the total metal ion concentration will be close to 0.1 M and the individual concentrations of zinc and nickel ions will each range from approximately 0.04 to 0.06 M. Add distilled water to the volumetric flask, if necessary, to bring the volume of solution to exactly 250 ml. Stopper the flask and mix the solution by shaking, swirling, and inverting the flask repeatedly.

Throughout this experiment, it is advisable that all glassware and associated equipment be clean and be rinsed thoroughly with *distilled* water (and preferably specially *deionized* water) before use. Trace quantities of certain cations found in tap water (and even sometimes in distilled water), such as copper and iron, can prevent the metallochromic indicators from functioning properly.

Determination of Total Concentration of Zinc and Nickel. Follow the detailed instructions given in Experiment 8-3 in order to determine the total concentration of zinc nitrate and nickel nitrate in the unknown sample solution.

Separation of Zinc and Nickel by Means of Anion-Exchange Chromatography. Measure out a volume of approximately 40 to 50 ml of Dowex-1, a quaternary ammonium salt strong-base exchange resin, in the chloride ion form. The optimum size of the resin particles is about 50 mesh. Soak the resin overnight in a beaker containing distilled water.

Prepare an ion-exchange column free of air bubbles as follows: Use a 50 ml buret as the anion-exchange column. Add approximately 5 ml of distilled water into the buret. Insert a glass-wool plug into the buret (to support the resin and prevent it from clogging the buret tip), using a glass rod to push the glass wool down against the stopcock. Pour the resin slurry into the buret and allow the resin to settle; the resin bed should have a height of about 30 to 35 cm. Maintain the level of liquid at least 1 or 2 cm above the resin bed at all times in order to keep air channels from forming inside the resin bed itself. Wash the column by passing first 100 ml of distilled water and then 100 ml of $2 F$ hydrochloric acid through the column at maximal flow rate (with the stopcock wide open).

The presence of $2 F$ hydrochloric acid solution in the column prior to the introduction of the sample is important. The separation of nickel and zinc is based upon the fact that nickel forms no negatively charged chloride complexes, even in concentrated hydrochloric acid, whereas zinc ion forms $ZnCl_3^-$ and $ZnCl_4^=$ species even in $1 F$ hydrochloric acid. The anion-exchange process involves the replacement of Cl^-, originally in the resin phase, by $ZnCl_3^-$ and $ZnCl_4^=$ from the solution phase. Therefore, the exchange process results in the zinc being retained by the resin while the nickel species, none of which is negatively charged, pass on through the column. Consequently, if only water (and no hydrochloric acid) is initially in the column, the chloride subsequently added to the sample solution might be temporarily diluted to the extent that the $ZnCl_3^-$ and $ZnCl_4^=$ species are converted back to neutral or cationic species which pass through the column along with nickel.

Pipet a 25.00 ml aliquot of the original zinc-nickel sample solution into a 50 ml beaker, and add to the solution 4 to 5 ml of concentrated, reagent-grade $(12 F)$ hydrochloric acid. Swirl the beaker gently to mix the solution. Transfer this solution quantitatively into the column, using a glass funnel inserted into the buret and a stirring rod to guide the sample solution from the beaker into the funnel. Allow the solution to pass through the column into a 250 ml Erlenmeyer flask as the receiving vessel at a moderate flow rate, i.e., one or two drops per second. Close the stopcock of the buret when the level of the sample solution just reaches the top of the resin bed. Rinse the 50 ml (sample) beaker with two 5 ml portions of $2 F$ hydrochloric acid, transferring each portion, separately and quantitatively, to the column. Allow these washings to pass through the column until the liquid level again reaches the top of the resin bed. Add 10 ml of $2 F$ hydrochloric acid solution into the column, and let this solution pass through the column to elute the nickel ion. Repeat this process with five more 10 ml portions of $2 F$ hydrochloric acid. Place the 250 ml flask containing the eluate on a steam bath, and allow the solution to evaporate to dryness overnight.

The nickel-containing eluate must be evaporated to dryness in order to remove excess hydrochloric acid. The evaporation process may be expedited if the solution is evaporated *almost* to dryness over a burner and then to *complete* dryness on a steam bath. The flask containing a residue of nickel chloride must not be strongly heated, because the readily soluble nickel chloride will be converted to insoluble nickel oxide.

Place a clean 500 ml Erlenmeyer flask beneath the column, and elute the zinc from the column by passing 50 ml of distilled water, in 10 ml portions, through the column at a flow rate of three or four drops per second. Then wash the column with 150 ml of a 1 F ammonia solution, in 25 ml portions, at the same flow rate.

Zinc is displaced from the column by elution with water and aqueous ammonia. In very dilute chloride solutions, or in pure water, the anionic zinc complexes are converted back to neutral and cationic species which are no longer retained by the resin. The ammonia yields positively charged zinc-ammine complexes which are removed from the resin faster. It should be noted that elution with a 0.001 M hydrochloric acid solution would certainly be adequate to remove zinc from the resin. However, distilled water and ammonia are employed to hasten this process because the anion-exchange column is not being utilized under conditions of maximum efficiency with respect to column dimensions and flow rates.

Retain the anion-exchange column since it will be necessary, during the subsequent titration of zinc, to test the column for the complete removal (elution) of the zinc.

Titration of Zinc with EDTA. Add five drops of Eriochrome Black T (or Calmagite) indicator solution to the separated zinc solution, and titrate the mixture, as directed in Experiment 11-2, with standard 0.05 F EDTA solution (see Experiment 11-1) until the wine red color of the zinc indicator complex changes to the *pure* blue color of the free indicator. After reaching the end point, pass 25 ml of distilled water through the anion-exchange column into the titrated solution (as a check on the efficiency of elution of zinc). The reappearance of a wine red color in the solution indicates that zinc remains on the column. If a wine red color does appear, titrate the solution with standard EDTA to the blue color of the free indicator. This procedure should be repeated until no color change occurs upon washing the column. Record the volume of standard EDTA titrant used, and calculate the concentration of zinc nitrate present in the original sample solution.

Titration of Nickel with EDTA. Dissolve the nickel chloride residue in approximately 25 ml of distilled water. Then add to the flask 10 ml of an ammonia-ammonium chloride buffer solution, prepared as described in Experiment 11-3, and dilute the nickel solution to about 100 ml with more distilled water. Add 0.2 gm of murexide indicator, and titrate the solution as described in Experiment 11-3 with standard 0.05 F EDTA. Record the volume of standard EDTA solution used, and calculate the concentration of nickel nitrate in the original sample solution.

Repeat the separation and individual determination of zinc and nickel with two more 25.00 ml aliquots of the original sample solution; however, be sure to wash the anion exchange column with 100 to 150 ml of 2 F hydrochloric acid solution *before proceeding with the next sample* in order to remove residual ammonia from the column and to convert the resin back to the chloride form.

Compute the average individual concentrations of zinc and nickel in the original sample solution, and compare the sum of these results with the total average concentration of metal ions based on the cation-exchange procedure. (Replicate results for the cation-exchange procedure should agree to within two or three parts per thousand, whereas the replicate results for the anion-exchange part of the experiment typically agree to within about 0.5 to 1.0 per cent. The two sets of results should agree to within approximately 1 per cent.)

QUESTIONS AND PROBLEMS

1. Write the chemical equations for the primary titration reaction and the indicator reaction in the Liebig method for the determination of cyanide.
2. In view of the fact that ethylenediaminetetraacetate forms stable complexes with so many cations, discuss two approaches by which reactions between EDTA and metal ions can be made quite selective.
3. Account qualitatively for the general stability of EDTA complexes as compared to other types of complexes with the same cations.
4. Suggest an analytical procedure, involving an EDTA titration, for the direct or indirect determination of sulfate ion.
5. Define or identify each of the following terms: labile complex, nonlabile complex, bidentate ligand, stepwise formation constant, overall formation constant, chelate, ammine complex, auxiliary complexing agent, metallochromic indicator.
6. Estimate from Figure 11-1 the mole fractions of the various zinc-ammine complexes in a solution containing a free ammonia concentration of $0.00316\ F$. If the total concentration of zinc-ammine complexes in such a solution is $0.00100\ M$, calculate the concentration of each individual zinc-ammine complex.
7. Write the equilibrium reaction and the equilibrium expression corresponding to the fourth stepwise formation constant for the $Ni(NH_3)_4(H_2O)_2^{++}$ complex.
8. Write the equilibrium reaction and the equilibrium expression corresponding to the third overall formation constant for the $Cd(NH_3)_3(H_2O)_3^{++}$ complex.
9. What is the percentage purity of an impure sample of sodium cyanide if a $2.000\ gm$ sample requires $25.00\ ml$ of a $0.2500\ F$ silver nitrate solution for titration according to the Liebig procedure?
10. A standard solution of calcium chloride was prepared by dissolving $0.2000\ gm$ of pure calcium carbonate in hydrochloric acid, boiling the solution to remove carbon dioxide, and diluting the solution to $250.0\ ml$ in a volumetric flask. When a $25.00\ ml$ aliquot of the calcium chloride solution was used to standardize an EDTA solution by titration at pH 10, $22.62\ ml$ of the EDTA solution was required. Calculate the concentration of the EDTA solution.
11. What should be the concentration of a standard silver nitrate solution so that each $1.00\ ml$ of titrant will correspond to $1.00\ mg$ of cyanide ion, CN^-, in the Liebig titration?
12. A $1.000\ ml$ aliquot of a nickel(II) solution was diluted with distilled water and an ammonia-ammonium chloride buffer; it was then treated with $15.00\ ml$ of a $0.01000\ F$ EDTA solution. The excess EDTA was back-titrated with a standard $0.01500\ F$ magnesium chloride solution, of which $4.37\ ml$ was required. Calculate the concentration of the original nickel(II) solution.

13. Construct the titration curve for the titration of 50.00 ml of a 0.001000 M copper(II) solution with a 0.1000 F EDTA solution. Assume that the copper(II) sample solution contains 0.400 F ammonia and 0.200 F ammonium nitrate. The successive formation constants for the copper-ammine complexes are given in Appendix 3.

14. Construct the titration curve for the titration of 100.0 ml of a 0.002000 M magnesium ion solution with a 0.1000 F EDTA solution at pH 10.

15. A solution was prepared by adding 500 ml of a solution 0.01000 F in ethylene-diaminetetraacetic acid (H_4Y) to 500 ml of a solution 0.02000 F in tetrasodium ethylenediaminetetraacetate (Na_4Y) and 0.01500 F in sodium hydroxide. Calculate the pH of the resulting solution and the concentrations of all five EDTA species.

16. For a solution in which the *total* analytical concentration of silver ion is 0.00500 M, what must be the concentrations of ammonia and ammonium ion so that the pH of the solution is 9.70 and the average number of ammonia ligands per silver ion is 1.50? The successive formation constants for the silver-ammine complexes are given in Appendix 3.

17. Suppose that the direct EDTA titration of a metal cation M^{++} of initial concentration 0.0100 M is performed using an acetic acid-sodium acetate buffer of pH 5.00 and a metallochromic indicator of formula H_2In. Assume that the following data are available:

$$M^{++} + Y^{\equiv} \rightleftharpoons MY^{=}; \qquad K_{MY} = 1.00 \times 10^{18}$$
$$H_2In \rightleftharpoons H^+ + HIn^-; \qquad K_1 = 1.00 \times 10^{-2}$$
$$HIn^- \rightleftharpoons H^+ + In^{=}; \qquad K_2 = 1.00 \times 10^{-7}$$
$$M^{++} + In^{=} \rightleftharpoons MIn; \qquad K_{MIn} = 1.60 \times 10^{11}$$

Also assume that M^{++} does not form any stable hydroxide or acetate complexes at pH 5.00. If the end point color change is observed when the concentration of the metal-indicator complex (MIn) and the concentration of the free indicator (in all of its forms) are equal, calculate the theoretical titration error in per cent with the proper sign. The original solution volume may be taken to be 50.0 ml, and dilution may be ignored.

SUGGESTIONS FOR ADDITIONAL READING

Books

1. F. Basolo and R. Johnson: *Coordination Chemistry*, W. A. Benjamin, Inc., New York, 1964, pp. 114–140.
2. A. Ringbom: Complexation reactions. *In* I. M. Kolthoff and P. J. Elving, eds.: *Treatise on Analytical Chemistry*, Part I, Volume 1, Wiley-Interscience, New York, 1959, pp. 543–628.
3. G. Schwarzenbach: *Complexometric Titrations*, Methuen, London, 1957.
4. L. G. Sillén: Graphic presentation of equilibrium data. *In* I. M. Kolthoff and P. J. Elving, eds.: *Treatise on Analytical Chemistry*, Part I, Volume 1, Wiley-Interscience, New York, 1959, pp. 277–317.
5. F. J. Welcher: *The Analytical Uses of Ethylenediaminetetraacetic Acid*, D. Van Nostrand Co., Inc., Princeton, New Jersey, 1958.

Paper

1. H. Diehl: Development of metallochromic indicators. Anal. Chem., *39*, 31A (March, 1967).

Chapter Twelve

Principles and Theory of Oxidation-Reduction Methods

Oxidation-reduction methods of analysis, commonly called **redox methods,** probably rank as the most widely used volumetric analytical methods. Additional importance has been given to these techniques by the large amount of research in the field of electroanalytical chemistry. Although acid-base, precipitation, and complexometric titrations have their definite realms of usefulness, many substances cannot be determined satisfactorily by means of these types of titrations. Redox methods are, however, of much broader applicability for the determinations of a wide variety of chemical species. The principles, theory, and definitions underlying redox reactions are considered in this chapter, and some examples of typical analytical applications are described in the two following chapters.

ELECTROCHEMICAL CELLS

A consideration of the behavior and properties of electrochemical cells will serve as a useful introduction to the subject of oxidation-reduction methods of analysis. An **electrochemical cell** consists essentially of two electrodes which are immersed either into the same electrolyte solution or into two different electrolyte solutions in electrolytic contact with one another. One of the most familiar examples of an electrochemical cell is the

SPONGY
Pb

PbO₂

38% H₂SO₄
ELECTROLYTE

Pb-Sb GRIDS

FIGURE 12-1.   A simplified version of the lead storage cell. This galvanic cell consists of two electrodes immersed in 38 per cent sulfuric acid. The anode is a lead-antimony support or grid impregnated with spongy lead. The cathode is a second lead-antimony grid impregnated with solid lead dioxide. A fully charged lead storage cell has an emf close to 2 v.

lead storage cell. A schematic diagram of this cell is shown in Figure 12-1. One electrode comprises a lead-antimony support or grid which is impregnated with spongy lead metal. The other electrode also consists of a lead-antimony alloy grid, but it is impregnated with solid lead dioxide (PbO_2). Both of these electrodes are immersed in a sulfuric acid electrolyte. If we short-circuit this cell, that is, if we connect the two electrodes to each other by a conducting wire, electrolysis occurs. A microscopic examination of each electrode just after electrolysis begins would reveal that the spongy lead is *oxidized* to solid lead sulfate, which adheres to the electrode surface, and that the lead dioxide is *reduced*, also to form lead sulfate.

Oxidation and Reduction.   Oxidation is the loss of electrons, and reduction is the gain of electrons. The substance which is reduced, that is, the substance which causes another chemical species to be oxidized, is the **oxidizing agent** or **oxidant.** Conversely, the substance which causes another species to be reduced, thereby becoming oxidized itself, is a **reducing agent** or **reductant.**

With regard to the lead storage cell, we can represent the oxidation of spongy lead to lead sulfate by the reaction

$$Pb + HSO_4^- \rightleftharpoons PbSO_4 + H^+ + 2\ e$$

and the reduction of lead dioxide can be written as

$$PbO_2 + 3\ H^+ + HSO_4^- + 2\ e \rightleftharpoons PbSO_4 + 2\ H_2O$$

The overall reaction is simply the sum of these two reactions

$$Pb + PbO_2 + 2\ H^+ + 2\ HSO_4^- \rightleftharpoons 2\ PbSO_4 + 2\ H_2O$$

Thus, lead metal is the reductant in this reaction; it reduces PbO_2 to $PbSO_4$ and becomes oxidized in the process. By the same token, lead dioxide is an oxidant, for it oxidizes lead metal to lead sulfate and is itself reduced. Oxidation cannot take place without a corresponding reduction, and no substance can be reduced without some other substance simultaneously being oxidized. It should be mentioned that in the example under discussion there is no direct transfer of electrons between the lead and lead dioxide, although electrons are transferred through the external conducting wire. There is an important advantage in such a situation which will be discussed later. In oxidation-reduction reactions employed for analytical purposes, however, there usually is direct electron transfer from one reactant to another reactant.

In an electrochemical cell the electrode at which oxidation occurs is always called the **anode,** whereas the **cathode** is the electrode at which the reduction process takes place. Therefore, the spongy lead electrode is the *anode* because it undergoes oxidation to lead sulfate, and the lead dioxide electrode functions as the *cathode* because it is reduced to lead sulfate.

Galvanic and Electrolytic Cells.   There are two kinds of electrochemical cells. The first of these is called a galvanic cell. A **galvanic cell** may be defined as an electrochemical cell in which the *spontaneous* occurrence of electrode reactions produces electrical energy which can be converted into useful work. Thus, the "discharge" of a lead storage cell as described earlier is an example of a spontaneous process which, in turn, causes a flow of electrons in an external circuit and makes useful electrical energy available. Three or six lead storage cells in series comprise the familiar 6 v or 12 v lead storage battery used in automobile ignition systems. The **electrolytic cell** is the second type of electrochemical cell. In it, nonspontaneous electrode reactions are forced to proceed when an external voltage is impressed or connected across the two electrodes. In the operation of an electrolytic cell, electrical energy or work must be expended in causing the electrode reactions to occur. The "charging" of a weak lead storage cell is an example of the behavior of an electrolytic cell.

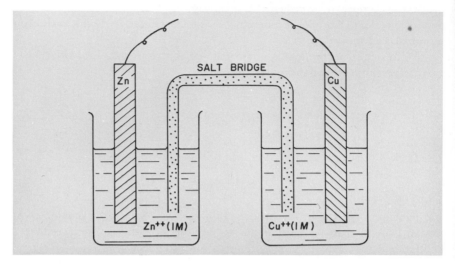

FIGURE 12-2. A simple galvanic cell involving a zinc metal–zinc ion half cell and a cupric ion–copper metal half cell connected by a potassium chloride salt bridge. For this cell the concentration (activity) of each ionic species, Zn^{++} and Cu^{++}, is unity, although in general any values are possible.

As a lead storage cell continues to discharge spontaneously for a time, according to the reaction

$$Pb + PbO_2 + 2\,H^+ + 2\,HSO_4^- \rightleftharpoons 2\,PbSO_4 + 2\,H_2O$$

the reactants — lead, lead dioxide, and sulfuric acid — are gradually exhausted, and the voltage and electrical energy obtainable from the cell decrease. In order to restore the cell to its original condition, it must be "recharged." This recharging is accomplished by placing across the two electrodes an external voltage which both opposes the voltage of the cell itself and is larger than the cell voltage. In this way the reactions occurring within the cell are completely reversed. Lead sulfate is reduced back to spongy lead at one electrode, lead sulfate is oxidized to lead dioxide, more sulfuric acid is produced, and in the ideal situation the net cell reaction is exactly the opposite of the preceding "discharge" process.

As a second example of a galvanic cell, let us consider briefly the cell depicted diagrammatically in Figure 12-2. One beaker contains a solution of some zinc salt into which a metallic zinc electrode is immersed. The other beaker contains a solution of a cupric salt into which an electrode of metallic copper is placed. For the purpose of this discussion, the concentrations of zinc and cupric ions will both be assumed to be 1 M. The function of the **salt bridge,** which connects the two beakers, is to provide a pathway for the migration of ions (flow of current) from one beaker to the other when an electrical circuit is completed, yet prevent gross mixing of the solutions in the two beakers as well as any direct electron-transfer reaction between one electrode and the solution in the opposite beaker. In its simplest form, a salt bridge consists of an inverted U-tube filled with a mixture of potassium chloride solution and gelatin, the latter forming a gel which minimizes the leakage of potassium chloride into the two beakers.

If the two metal electrodes are connected by means of a conducting wire, it can be observed that the zinc electrode dissolves according to the reaction

$$Zn \rightleftharpoons Zn^{++} + 2\ e$$

and that cupric ions are reduced to copper atoms which deposit upon the copper electrode:

$$Cu^{++} + 2\ e \rightleftharpoons Cu$$

Again, the net or overall process occurring in this galvanic cell may be represented as the combination of the two individual electrode reactions; that is,

$$Zn + Cu^{++} \rightleftharpoons Zn^{++} + Cu$$

Electrons produced at the zinc electrode, as zinc atoms are oxidized to zinc ions, flow through the external wire to the copper electrode, where they are available to combine with incoming cupric ions to form more copper metal. Although current flowing in the external wire can be described in terms of the movement of electrons, it is more realistic to view the flow of current in the solutions as the migration of ions. (It is worth mentioning here that recent research points clearly to the existence of solvated or hydrated electrons in aqueous solution. It remains questionable at present, however, whether free electrons are associated in any important way with the passage of current through solutions.) Along with the flow of electrons in the external circuit from the zinc to the copper electrode, negatively charged ions in the solutions migrate from the copper cell through the salt bridge in the direction of the zinc cell. The migration of ions in solution is not all one way, for the production of zinc ions and the consumption of cupric ions cause the migration of cations from the zinc electrode toward the copper electrode.

In keeping with previous definitions, the zinc electrode is the *anode*, because it is the electrode at which oxidation occurs. The copper electrode is the *cathode* since reduction takes place there.

FREE ENERGY AND ELECTROMOTIVE FORCE

In the thermodynamic treatment of chemical equilibrium discussed in Chapter 4, we considered the general chemical reaction

$$aA + bB + \cdots \rightleftharpoons cC + dD + \cdots$$

and found that the free-energy change ΔG for such a chemical process is
given by

$$\Delta G = \Delta G^{\circ} + RT \ln \frac{(C)^{c}(D)^{d}}{(A)^{a}(B)^{b}}$$

where ΔG° is the **standard free-energy change** for the reaction when all
the reactants and products are in their standard states and have unit
activities. The standard free-energy change is, in turn, related to the equilibrium constant K (or $\mathscr{K}$) for the reaction by the equation

$$\Delta G^{\circ} = -RT \ln K$$

Therefore, the measurement of ΔG for any nonequilibrium state of a
reaction can be used to evaluate the equilibrium constant if, and only if,
the nonequilibrium concentrations (activities) of the reactants and products
are also known.

The free-energy change ΔG for any chemical reaction measures the
driving force or tendency for reaction. The quantity ΔG also represents the
maximal amount of useful energy that can be obtained from the process. However,
in order for this maximal energy to be actually realized, the chemical
process must occur infinitely slowly or with thermodynamic reversibility.
A reaction is thermodynamically reversible whenever an infinitesimal force
in opposition to the forward reaction can cause the reaction to reverse and
proceed in the other direction. If a process occurs rapidly, i.e., at a finite or
observable rate, the maximal quantity of useful energy cannot be obtained.

To explore these points further, let us consider the behavior of the lead
storage cell. If a lead storage cell is discharged infinitely slowly, the current
flowing through the external circuit will be infinitesimally small, and the
theoretical, maximal amount of useful energy will be obtained (although the
rate of production of energy would be intolerably slow). However, if we
allow a lead storage cell to discharge rather rapidly, the quantity of useful
energy will be less than before because the flow of a sizable current through
the external circuit dissipates some of the energy as heat. No real process
occurs infinitely slowly, and so the maximal amount of useful energy, ΔG,
can never be obtained. We shall see that a galvanic cell provides a means for
studying chemical reactions under conditions which come remarkably
close to ideality.

Electromotive Force. A quantity which is characteristic of any
galvanic cell is E, the electromotive force or emf expressed in volts. The
free-energy change for a process which occurs or can be made to occur in a
galvanic cell is related to the electromotive force by the equation

$$\Delta G = -nFE$$

where n is the number of faradays of electricity generated by the cell reaction
and F is the Faraday constant (96,487 coulombs or 23,060 calories per
faraday).

By using a galvanic cell and measuring the electromotive force, we can determine the free-energy change ΔG for a given reaction as well as the equilibrium constant K or the standard free-energy change $\Delta G°$. The unique feature of a galvanic cell is that we can obtain all this information when the reaction virtually does not occur at all, i.e., under conditions very close to thermodynamic reversibility. Let us see how this can be done for the reaction

$$Zn + Cu^{++} \rightleftharpoons Zn^{++} + Cu$$

A galvanic cell in which the desired reaction can occur is shown in Figure 12-2. In setting up a galvanic cell for the measurement of electromotive force, one must specify exactly the concentrations of all ionic and molecular species in solution as well as temperature. If gaseous reactants or products are involved, their partial pressures should be stated. In the cell of Figure 12-2, the concentrations of Zn^{++} and Cu^{++} are both 1 M. However, the concentration (activity) of each ion could have any value, and the two concentrations need not be the same.

When the zinc and copper electrodes are connected by a conducting wire, there is a flow of electrons from the zinc to the copper electrode. Simultaneously, the zinc electrode dissolves to form zinc ions in the left-hand solution, and cupric ions in the right-hand solution are reduced and plated upon the copper electrode. At the instant the external wire is first connected between the two electrodes, there will be a certain initial value of the electromotive force E. However, the production of zinc ions in the left cell and the consumption of cupric ions in the right cell will change the original concentrations of these ions, thereby diminishing the electromotive force E and the value of ΔG.

It is well known that the concentrations of the ions immediately adjacent to the surfaces of the electrodes affect the driving force for the reaction, so these surface concentrations must be accurately known. The concentrations of the ions away from the electrodes have no effect on the electromotive force. Unfortunately, it is extremely difficult to determine what the surface concentrations of zinc and cupric ions are because they keep changing as current continues to flow through the cell.

At this point, there is a logical question to ask. Why not prevent the flow of current in order to avoid altering the surface concentrations of zinc and cupric ions? Then, we could be confident that the surface concentrations were invariant and equal to the original values of the concentrations, e.g., 1 M. The answer is that this can be done, and in fact, this is exactly what is done in the measurement of the electromotive force of a galvanic cell.

Potentiometric Measurement of Electromotive Force. A **potentiometer** is an instrument used to determine the electromotive force or emf of a galvanic cell. As a brief introduction to the principles of operation of a potentiometer, let us consider the following simple concepts. Figure 12-3A shows the zinc-copper galvanic cell with an external conducting wire connecting the zinc and copper electrodes. In addition, a current-measuring galvanometer, G, has been inserted into the external circuit.

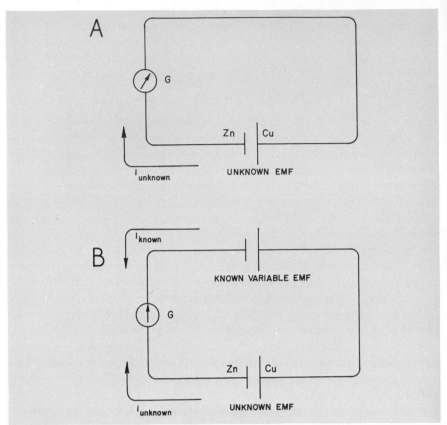

FIGURE 12-3. Diagram to illustrate the principles of the potentiometric measurement of electromotive force. (See text for discussion.)

Suppose we introduce into the external circuit a source of known emf, as shown in Figure 12-3B, in such a way that the direction of current flowing from it will *oppose* the current flowing from the zinc-copper cell. If the known emf is now varied until the current from the source of known emf (i_{known}) becomes just equal to the current from the zinc-copper cell ($i_{unknown}$), the galvanometer will register a net current of zero. When no net current flows in the circuit, it follows that the emf values of the zinc-copper cell and the known source are identical, and hence the emf of the zinc-copper cell is determined. In practice, an actual potentiometric measurement consists of varying the known emf until the galvanometer indicates zero current.

If the known emf is *less* than that of the zinc-copper cell, the latter will discharge spontaneously as a normal *galvanic* cell according to the reaction

$$Zn + Cu^{++} \rightleftharpoons Zn^{++} + Cu$$

at a rate proportional to the difference in the emf values. On the other hand, if the known emf is *greater* than that of the zinc-copper cell, the latter will behave as an *electrolytic* cell and the reverse reaction,

$$Zn^{++} + Cu \rightleftharpoons Zn + Cu^{++}$$

will occur at a rate governed again by the difference in the emf values. However, at the point of potentiometric balance, where virtually no current flows, the unknown and the known emf values are equal and no net reaction occurs in the zinc-copper cell. Therefore, the major advantages of a potentiometric measurement are that we prevent any electrochemical reaction from occurring in the zinc-copper cell, we avoid disturbing or changing the concentrations of ions at the electrode surfaces, and yet we obtain a highly accurate value for the emf of the zinc-copper cell. It may be added here that with the aid of modern electronic measuring devices, one can easily balance the known and unknown emf values to make the net flow of current no greater than about 10^{-12} ampere (one *picoampere*). Depending on the direction of current flow, this would correspond, for example, to either an increase or decrease of 5×10^{-18} mole of zinc ions per second in the zinc cell. This result clearly demonstrates how valid the conclusion is that there is no electrochemical reaction occurring in the zinc-copper cell.

The basic design of a simple potentiometer is illustrated in Figure 12-4. First, there must be a source of *known* and *constant* emf, E_{KC}, which could be, for example, an ordinary dry cell or a standard galvanic cell. This known, constant emf is then impressed across the ends of a uniform, precision resistance or slidewire AB. From this arrangement, a *known*, *variable* emf,

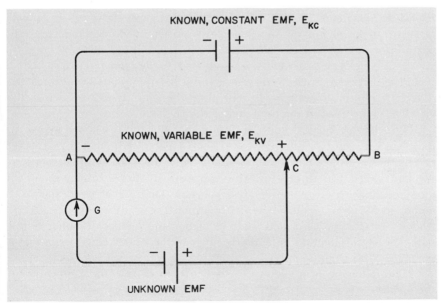

FIGURE 12-4. Diagram showing the operation of a simple potentiometer. (See text for discussion.)

E_{KV}, can be obtained: When the position of the sliding contact C coincides with the left end, A, of the slidewire, E_{KV} is zero; when the contact C is moved to the opposite end, B, the variable emf, E_{KV}, is equal to E_{KC}; and when contact C lies between A and B, intermediate values of E_{KV} are obtained. To measure an unknown emf, one simply moves contact C along the slidewire AB until the galvanometer G indicates that potentiometric balance is attained. The value of the unknown emf can be read directly from the final position of contact C.

Notice that the successful potentiometric measurement of an unknown emf requires that the *negative* electrode of the unknown cell be connected to the *negative* side of the known emf so that the known and unknown currents will *oppose* each other as discussed for Figure 12-3B. Although the correct connections can always be established by trial and error, a simple way to decide whether an electrode in a galvanic cell is negative or positive will be described in the section on sign conventions.

SHORTHAND REPRESENTATION OF CELLS

It is both time-consuming and space-consuming to draw a complete diagram of an electrochemical cell — electrodes, salt bridge, solutions, and containers — each time a cell is discussed. As a result, a system for representing cells in a shorthand fashion has been developed. The following set of rules is in widespread use:

1. Conventional chemical symbols are used to indicate the ions, molecules, elements, gases, and electrode materials involved in a cell. Concentrations of ions or molecules are written in parentheses, and the partial pressure of each gaseous species is enclosed in parentheses.

2. A single vertical line | is employed to designate the fact that a boundary between an electrode phase and a solution phase or between two different solution phases exists and that the emf developed across this interface is included in the total emf of the cell.

3. A double vertical line ‖ indicates that the emf developed across the interface between two different solutions is ignored or that it is minimized or eliminated by placing a suitable salt bridge between the two solutions. An emf called the **liquid-junction potential**, always originates at the interface between two nonidentical solutions because charged species — anions and cations — diffuse across this interface at different rates. A salt bridge containing a saturated solution of potassium chloride almost eliminates the liquid-junction potential because of the nearly equal mobilities of potassium and chloride ions.

The following examples will serve to demonstrate the application of these rules:

Example 1.   The zinc-copper cell depicted in Figure 12-2 may be represented as $$\text{Zn} \mid \text{Zn}^{++} (1\ M) \parallel \text{Cu}^{++} (1\ M) \mid \text{Cu}$$

This shorthand abbreviation indicates that a zinc electrode in contact with a 1 M solution of zinc ions gives rise to an emf and, similarly, that a 1 M cupric ion solution in contact with a copper electrode produces another emf — the sum of these two emf values being the total emf of the galvanic cell. The double vertical line indicates the presence of a salt bridge and reminds us also that any liquid-junction potential is neglected in considering the overall emf of the cell.

Example 2. If, for the zinc-copper cell, we wished to specify 1 F solutions of particular salts, such as $Zn(NO_3)_2$ and $CuSO_4$, and if instead of a salt bridge we allowed the two solutions to contact each other directly through a thin porous membrane (to prevent mixing of the two solutions), the cell would be correctly indicated as

$$Zn \mid Zn(NO_3)_2 \ (1 \ F) \mid CuSO_4 \ (1 \ F) \mid Cu$$

Example 3. Suppose we construct an entirely new galvanic cell. Let one electrode consist of a platinum wire in a mixture of 0.2 M ferric ion and 0.05 M ferrous ion in a 1 F hydrochloric acid medium, and let the other electrode be a second platinum wire immersed in a 2 F hydrochloric acid solution saturated with chlorine gas at a pressure of 0.1 atm. A salt bridge can be used to prevent mixing of the two solutions. The shorthand cell representation would be

$$Pt \mid Fe^{+++} \ (0.2 \ M), \ Fe^{++} \ (0.05 \ M), \ HCl \ (1 \ F) \ \| \ HCl \ (2 \ F) \mid Cl_2 \ (0.1 \ atm), \ Pt$$

This example brings up two other significant points. First, when several soluble species are present in the same solution, no special order of listing these is needed. Second, although electron transfer between chloride ion and chlorine molecules occurs with species dissolved in solution, it is customary to indicate gaseous substances as part of the electrode phase along with the electrode material, e.g., platinum metal.

Mention should be made of one additional point; that is, the relative orientation of any cell on paper can be reversed just as the relative position of the actual physical cell can be changed by turning it around on a table top. Thus, the cell described in Example 2 could have been written

$$Cu \mid CuSO_4(1 \ F) \mid Zn(NO_3)_2(1 \ F) \mid Zn$$

However, once a given shorthand cell representation has been set down, certain conventions must be followed subsequently in making thermodynamic and electrochemical predictions on the basis of this representation.

THERMODYNAMIC AND ELECTROCHEMICAL SIGN CONVENTIONS

It was previously stated in this chapter that determination of the electromotive force of a galvanic cell is a powerful means for the evaluation

FIGURE 12-5. A galvanic cell consisting of a standard or normal hydrogen electrode (NHE) and a silver-silver chloride electrode.

of ΔG, which, in turn, measures the driving force for chemical reaction. We shall now explore some of the relationships between thermodynamics and electrochemistry.

Let us discuss the galvanic cell shown in Figure 12-5. In the left-hand compartment is a platinum electrode dipped into a hydrochloric acid solution of *unit activity* and bathed with hydrogen gas at a pressure of 1 atm. For convenience, the platinum electrode can be sealed into an inverted tube, with an enlarged open bottom to admit the hydrochloric acid solution and with exit ports for the hydrogen gas to escape. Hydrogen gas at 1 atm pressure enters through a side-arm tube. It is important that the hydrogen gas come into intimate contact with the platinum electrode. This require-ment can be fulfilled if the platinum electrode is coated prior to its use with a thin layer of finely divided, spongy platinum metal (so-called **platinum black**). A platinum-black electrode is easily prepared if one cathodically polarizes a shiny platinum electrode in a dilute solution of $PtCl_6^=$. With platinum black on the electrode surface, hydrogen gas permeates and virtually dissolves in the spongy platinum, and electron transfer between hydrogen ions and hydrogen molecules (or atoms) is greatly facilitated. This special combination of a platinum-black electrode, hydrochloric acid of unit activity, and hydrogen gas at 1 atm pressure is called the **standard hydrogen electrode** or the **normal hydrogen electrode** (NHE).

In the right-hand compartment is a silver electrode coated with a layer of silver chloride and placed into a hydrochloric acid solution of unit activity. The hydrochloric acid solution must be saturated with respect to silver chloride and, although excess solid AgCl could simply be added to the compartment, the thin coating of silver chloride on the electrode provides an especially convenient source of AgCl. In addition, the layer of silver chloride serves as a source of silver ions in contact with the metallic silver electrode, and so electron transfer between elemental silver and silver ions can occur readily and reversibly.

It is possible, although not necessary, to insert a porous membrane between the two compartments of the cell as a means of preventing direct mixing of the solutions. However, the liquid-junction potential for this cell is virtually zero because the solutions on each side of the membrane are nearly identical in terms of their ionic compositions; the very slight solubility of silver chloride in hydrochloric acid means that both solutions contain essentially hydrochloric acid at unit activity. Cells of this general type, sometimes called *galvanic cells without liquid-junction potentials*, have been used extensively in the precise determination and definition of the pH scale at the National Bureau of Standards.

The word and picture description of this cell can be portrayed by means of the shorthand cell representation, as described earlier in this chapter:

$$\text{Pt, } H_2 \text{ (1 atm) } | \text{ HCl } (a = 1 \ M), \text{ AgCl(s) } | \text{ Ag}$$

Once the shorthand cell representation has been written, it is useful to consider the overall electrochemical reaction which will occur when the electrodes are connected by an external conducting wire. To write this cell reaction, we must adopt a definite rule or convention which must *always* be obeyed. This rule may be stated as follows:

Looking at the shorthand cell representation, we combine as *reactants* **the reductant (reducing agent) of the left-hand electrode and the oxidant (oxidizing agent) of the right-hand electrode. As** *products* **we obtain the oxidant of the left-hand electrode and the reductant of the right-hand electrode.**

If we now apply this rule, hydrogen gas (reductant of the left-hand electrode) reacts with silver chloride (oxidant of the right-hand electrode) to yield hydrogen ions (oxidant of the left-hand electrode) and elemental silver (reductant of the right-hand electrode). Chloride ions, freed by the reduction of silver chloride, are also formed as a reaction product. The cell reaction is

$$H_2 + 2 \ AgCl \rightleftharpoons 2 \ H^+ + 2 \ Ag + 2 \ Cl^-$$

The value of ΔG, the free-energy change for this process, provides us with information about the tendency for this cell reaction to occur as written. According to thermodynamic conventions, the cell reaction will be spontaneous if ΔG is a negative quantity. However, if ΔG is positive, the reaction is nonspontaneous and, in fact, will proceed in the reverse direction. In the event that ΔG is zero, the system is at equilibrium and no net cell reaction will occur, the rates of the forward and backward reactions being equal. From the relationship between free-energy change ΔG and electromotive force E,

$$\Delta G = -nFE$$

it can be seen that E is positive for spontaneous processes, negative for nonspontaneous reactions, and zero for systems at equilibrium. Therefore, by measuring the electromotive force for a galvanic cell, we can determine the direction of the electrochemical reaction along with the free-energy change or driving force for that reaction.

The electromotive force for the cell must be measured potentiometrically as described in a previous section of this chapter. When this measurement is performed, it is found that the emf of the cell has an absolute magnitude of 0.2222 v. In addition, the cell reaction proceeds from left to right as written; this fact can be demonstrated if we connect the electrodes by a conducting wire and examine their behavior. To indicate that the cell reaction is a spontaneous process and that the driving force for this reaction is 0.2222 v, we can write

$$H_2 + 2\ AgCl \rightleftharpoons 2\ H^+ + 2\ Ag + 2\ Cl^-; \qquad E = +0.2222\ v$$

Let us now focus our attention more closely on the galvanic cell itself. In the potentiometric measurement of a cell emf, no electrochemical reaction occurs because no net current flows through the cell. However, we do measure the tendency for the reaction to proceed when the electrodes are connected by an external wire. Since the cell reaction should proceed spontaneously ($E = +0.2222$ v) from left to right, we can conclude that there is a tendency for hydrogen gas to be oxidized to hydrogen ions and a tendency for silver chloride to be reduced to silver metal. Therefore, the hydrogen gas-hydrogen ion electrode is the *anode*, and the silver-silver chloride electrode functions as the *cathode*. Likewise, there is a tendency for an excess of electrons to accumulate at the left-hand electrode and for a deficiency of electrons to exist at the right-hand electrode. Note that we can speak only of a tendency because, under the conditions of an ideal potentiometric emf measurement, there is no flow of electrons. An excess of electrons at the hydrogen gas-hydrogen ion electrode causes the anode to be the *negative* electrode of the galvanic cell, and a deficiency of electrons at the silver-silver chloride electrode means that the cathode is the *positive* electrode. The signs of the electrodes are often indicated on the shorthand cell representation as follows:

$$-Pt,\ H_2\ (1\ atm)\ |\ HCl\ (a = 1\ M),\ AgCl(s)\ |\ Ag+$$

We come now to one of the most important and fundamental conclusions of this discussion:

There is no direct relationship between the sign of the electromotive force (emf) for a cell reaction and the signs (+ or −) of the electrodes of the cell. The sign of an emf is a *thermodynamic* concept; it may be positive (+) when a process occurs spontaneously or it may be negative (−) when a process is nonspontaneous. On the other hand, the sign of any particular electrode of a galvanic cell is an *electrochemical* concept and is completely invariant.

To illustrate the significance of these statements, the following galvanic cell may be considered:

$$\text{Ag} \mid \text{AgCl(s), HCl } (a = 1\ M) \mid \text{H}_2(1 \text{ atm}), \text{Pt}$$

Notice that this is the same galvanic cell we have been discussing, except for the fact that we are viewing it from the other side of the bench top. According to our rule for writing the electrochemical reaction corresponding to a shorthand cell representation, we combine the reductant of the left-hand electrode and the oxidant of the right-hand electrode to yield the oxidant of the left-hand electrode and the reductant of the right-hand electrode:

$$2\ \text{H}^+ + 2\ \text{Ag} + 2\ \text{Cl}^- \rightleftharpoons \text{H}_2 + 2\ \text{AgCl}$$

This reaction is exactly the reverse of the process we considered earlier, and so it follows that the present reaction is nonspontaneous and that the sign of the electromotive force is negative $(-)$. However, since the galvanic cell is the same as before, the absolute magnitude of the emf is identical to the previous value. To indicate these facts, we may write

$$2\ \text{H}^+ + 2\ \text{Ag} + 2\ \text{Cl}^- \rightleftharpoons \text{H}_2 + 2\ \text{AgCl}; \qquad E = -0.2222 \text{ v}$$

In *thermodynamics*, whenever we reverse the direction of a process, the magnitude of the emf remains the same, whereas the sign of the emf is changed to denote whether the process is spontaneous or nonspontaneous. This rule carries over to all kinds of thermodynamic calculations, such as those involving energies of chemical bonds, heats of formation, and heats of combustion.

The sign of the electromotive force $(E = -0.2222 \text{ v})$ reveals that the reaction is nonspontaneous as written, *that it actually would proceed from right to left if the electrodes were short-circuited.* There is a tendency for hydrogen gas to be oxidized to hydrogen ions and for silver chloride to be reduced to silver metal. Thus, the *electrochemical* conclusions made previously about the galvanic cell,

$$-\text{Pt, H}_2 \text{ (1 atm)} \mid \text{HCl } (a = 1\ M), \text{AgCl(s)} \mid \text{Ag}+$$

are completely valid for the cell

$$+\text{Ag} \mid \text{AgCl(s), HCl } (a = 1\ M) \mid \text{H}_2 \text{ (1 atm), Pt}-$$

The hydrogen gas-hydrogen ion electrode is the *anode* and the *negative* electrode, whereas the silver-silver chloride electrode is the *cathode* and the *positive* electrode.

There is a useful correlation between the sign of the emf of the cell reaction and the sign of the right-hand electrode of the shorthand cell representation — *these signs are identical when the reaction corresponding to a shorthand representation is written in accord with the rule stated earlier.*

STANDARD POTENTIALS AND HALF-REACTIONS

It is convenient and customary to consider every overall cell reaction as being composed of two separate half-reactions. A **half-reaction** is a balanced chemical equation showing the transfer of electrons between two different oxidation states of the same element. We have already written half-reactions in our discussion of the lead storage cell and the zinc-copper cell. Each half-reaction must represent as accurately as possible one of the two individual electrode processes which occur in a galvanic cell. As a familiar example, for the cell

$$-\text{Pt, H}_2 \ (1 \text{ atm}) \mid \text{HCl} \ (a = 1 \ M), \text{AgCl(s)} \mid \text{Ag}+$$

the overall cell reaction is

$$\text{H}_2 + 2 \text{ AgCl} \rightleftharpoons 2 \text{ H}^+ + 2 \text{ Ag} + 2 \text{ Cl}^-$$

and the two half-reactions are

$$\text{H}_2 \rightleftharpoons 2 \text{ H}^+ + 2 \text{ e}$$

and

$$2 \text{ AgCl} + 2 \text{ e} \rightleftharpoons 2 \text{ Ag} + 2 \text{ Cl}^-$$

Notice that each half-reaction contains the same number of electrons, so when these half-reactions are added together the electrons cancel and the overall cell reaction is obtained. It is important to recognize that the overall cell reaction could have been correctly written as

$$\tfrac{1}{2} \text{ H}_2 + \text{AgCl} \rightleftharpoons \text{H}^+ + \text{Ag} + \text{Cl}^-$$

and the half-reactions as

$$\tfrac{1}{2} \text{ H}_2 \rightleftharpoons \text{H}^+ + \text{e}$$

and

$$\text{AgCl} + \text{e} \rightleftharpoons \text{Ag} + \text{Cl}^-$$

The electromotive force for an overall reaction or for an individual half-reaction is *independent* of how much reaction occurs. For example, the emf for the reaction

$$\text{H}_2 + 2 \text{ AgCl} \rightleftharpoons 2 \text{ H}^+ + 2 \text{ Ag} + 2 \text{ Cl}^-$$

has exactly the same sign and magnitude as that for the process

$$\tfrac{1}{2} \text{ H}_2 + \text{AgCl} \rightleftharpoons \text{H}^+ + \text{Ag} + \text{Cl}^-$$

in spite of the fact that the former reaction involves twice as many units of the reactant and product species as the latter. In other words, electromotive force or emf does not depend on the quantity of reaction — electromotive force is a measure of reaction intensity. This fact becomes apparent when we realize that a common 1.5 v dry cell has the same emf regardless of its physical size. Clearly, a large dry cell can supply more electrical energy than a small cell, simply because it contains more chemical ingredients, but the emf values are identical.

Definition and Determination of Standard Potentials. It is logical to expect that the electromotive force for the overall cell reaction

$$H_2 + 2\,AgCl \rightleftharpoons 2\,H^+ + 2\,Ag + 2\,Cl^-$$

or

$$\tfrac{1}{2}\,H_2 + AgCl \rightleftharpoons H^+ + Ag + Cl^-$$

can be regarded as the sum of two emf values, one being associated with the half-reaction occurring at each electrode of the cell. Unfortunately, it is theoretically impossible either to measure or to calculate the *absolute* value for the emf of any single half-reaction because the activity of a single ionic species, such as hydrogen ion or chloride ion, can never be known exactly. In order to make further progress, it is necessary to define arbitrarily the value for the electromotive force of some half-reaction chosen as a reference; then, the emf values for all other half-reactions can be quoted *relative* to this standard.

The hydrogen electrode has been adopted as the standard. This electrode involves the hydrogen ion-hydrogen gas half-reaction with hydrogen ion and hydrogen gas in their standard states of unit activity and 1 atm pressure, respectively. Under these specific conditions, the electromotive force for this half-reaction is assigned the value of *zero* at all temperatures and is called the *standard potential, $E°$, for the hydrogen ion-hydrogen gas couple.*

$$2\,H^+ + 2\,e \rightleftharpoons H_2; \qquad E° = 0.0000\ v$$

The standard potential for any other half-reaction *relative to the standard hydrogen electrode* can be determined if a suitable galvanic cell is constructed in which one electrode is the standard hydrogen electrode and the second electrode involves the unknown half-reaction.

Let us use this approach to determine the standard potential for the silver chloride-silver metal half-reaction. The galvanic cell to be used for this measurement is the same one discussed on the preceding several pages:

$$-Pt,\ H_2\ (1\ atm)\ |\ HCl\ (a = 1\ M),\ AgCl(s)\ |\ Ag+$$

Notice that the hydrogen ion-hydrogen gas electrode actually is the standard hydrogen electrode because all species are present in their standard states. In addition, the substances which comprise the silver chloride-silver metal electrode are in their standard states. Chloride ion is present at unit activity, and silver chloride and silver metal are in their standard states as solids. Although $E°$ for the standard hydrogen electrode is *defined* to be independent of temperature, standard potentials for all other half-reactions do vary with temperature. By convention, standard potentials are always determined at 25°C. The conditions which are necessary for the successful measurement of a standard potential are included in the basic definition of this quantity:

The *standard potential* for any redox couple is the emf or potential (sign and magnitude) of an electrode consisting of that

redox couple under standard-state conditions measured in a galvanic cell against the standard hydrogen electrode at 25°C.

Since the galvanic cell just described fulfills all requirements of the definition of standard potential, we can anticipate that the potentiometric measurement of the emf of this cell will provide us with information about $E°$ for the silver chloride-silver metal electrode.

Let us carefully examine the results of this emf measurement in the light of the previous discussion of thermodynamic and electrochemical sign conventions. First, we discover that the magnitude of the emf of the galvanic cell is 0.2222 v. Second, we find that the silver chloride-silver metal electrode is always the positive electrode regardless of the bench-top orientation of the cell. Therefore, we can conclude correctly that *the standard potential, $E°$, of the silver chloride-silver metal electrode is* $+0.2222$ v (relative to the standard hydrogen electrode).

The standard potential for any other electrode can be determined in an analogous manner if one constructs a galvanic cell which consists of the standard hydrogen electrode and an electrode involving the unknown half reaction under standard-state conditions. Although the hydrogen electrode is the universal standard, it is seldom used in practice because it is cumbersome as well as hazardous. Instead of the hydrogen electrode, secondary standard electrodes (whose standard potentials have been previously measured against the hydrogen electrode) are employed. It is a very simple matter to relate the potential of an unknown electrode, measured against a secondary standard electrode, to the standard hydrogen electrode itself. The saturated calomel electrode and the silver chloride-silver metal electrode are two especially good secondary standards because they are easy to prepare and handle and because they are exceptionally stable and reproducible.

Table of Standard Potentials.   Table 12-1 presents a selected list of standard potentials along with the half-reaction to which each pertains. It should be noted that all the half-reactions are written as *reductions*. This practice follows the recommendation set down by the International Union of Pure and Applied Chemistry (IUPAC) in 1953. The rationale of such a convention may be explained as follows:

1. Although only half-reactions appear in the table, standard potentials are always derived from a galvanic cell which consists of a standard hydrogen electrode and an electrode involving the desired half-reaction under standard-state conditions.

2. Each half-reaction in a table of standard potentials automatically implies an overall cell reaction in which the half-reaction of interest (written as a reduction) is combined with the *hydrogen gas-hydrogen ion* half-reaction,

$$\tfrac{1}{2} H_2 \rightleftharpoons H^+ + e$$

or its equivalent. For example, the half-reaction

$$AgCl + e \rightleftharpoons Ag + Cl^-$$

TABLE 12-1. STANDARD AND FORMAL POTENTIALS

$E°$	Half-reaction
2.87	$F_2 + 2\,e = 2\,F^-$
2.07	$O_3 + 2\,H^+ + 2\,e = O_2 + H_2O$
2.01	$S_2O_8^= + 2\,e = 2\,SO_4^=$
1.927	$Ag^{++} + e = Ag^+ \;(4\,F\;HNO_3)$
1.842	$Co^{+++} + e = Co^{++}$
1.77	$H_2O_2 + 2\,H^+ + 2\,e = 2\,H_2O$
1.70	$Ce^{++++} + e = Ce^{+++} \;(1\,F\;HClO_4)$
1.695	$MnO_4^- + 4\,H^+ + 3\,e = MnO_2 + 2\,H_2O$
1.685	$PbO_2 + SO_4^= + 4\,H^+ + 2\,e = PbSO_4 + 2\,H_2O$
1.68	$NiO_2 + 4\,H^+ + 2\,e = Ni^{++} + 2\,H_2O$
1.61	$Ce^{++++} + e = Ce^{+++} \;(1\,F\;HNO_3)$
1.52	$2\,BrO_3^- + 12\,H^+ + 10\,e = Br_2 + 6\,H_2O$
1.51	$MnO_4^- + 8\,H^+ + 5\,e = Mn^{++} + 4\,H_2O$
1.50	$Au^{+++} + 3\,e = Au$
1.47	$2\,ClO_3^- + 12\,H^+ + 10\,e = Cl_2 + 6\,H_2O$
1.455	$PbO_2 + 4\,H^+ + 2\,e = Pb^{++} + 2\,H_2O$
1.44	$Ce^{++++} + e = Ce^{+++} \;(1\,F\;H_2SO_4)$
1.41	$Au^{+++} + 2\,e = Au^+$
1.3595	$Cl_2 + 2\,e = 2\,Cl^-$
1.33	$Cr_2O_7^= + 14\,H^+ + 6\,e = 2\,Cr^{+++} + 7\,H_2O$
1.288	$PdCl_6^= + 2\,e = PdCl_4^= + 2\,Cl^-$
1.25	$Tl^{+++} + 2\,e = Tl^+$
1.23	$MnO_2 + 4\,H^+ + 2\,e = Mn^{++} + 2\,H_2O$
1.229	$O_2 + 4\,H^+ + 4\,e = 2\,H_2O$
1.20	$2\,IO_3^- + 12\,H^+ + 10\,e = I_2 + 6\,H_2O$
1.15	$ClO_3^- + 2\,H^+ + e = ClO_2 + H_2O$
1.15	$NpO_2^{++} + e = NpO_2^+$
1.15	$PuO_2^+ + 4\,H^+ + e = Pu^{++++} + 2\,H_2O$
1.15	$SeO_4^= + 4\,H^+ + 2\,e = H_2SeO_3 + H_2O$
1.087	$Br_2(aq) + 2\,e = 2\,Br^-$
1.07	$NO_2 + H^+ + e = HNO_2$
1.067	$PuO_2^{++} + 4\,H^+ + 2\,e = Pu^{++++} + 2\,H_2O$
1.065	$Br_2(l) + 2\,e = 2\,Br^-$
1.05	$Br_3^- + 2\,e = 3\,Br^-$
1.03	$NO_2 + 2\,H^+ + 2\,e = NO + H_2O$
1.00	$HNO_2 + H^+ + e = NO + H_2O$
1.000	$VO_2^+ + 2\,H^+ + e = VO^{++} + H_2O$
0.987	$Pd^{++} + 2\,e = Pd$
0.97	$Pu^{++++} + e = Pu^{+++}$
0.96	$NO_3^- + 4\,H^+ + 3\,e = NO + 2\,H_2O$
0.94	$NO_3^- + 3\,H^+ + 2\,e = HNO_2 + H_2O$
0.93	$PuO_2^{++} + e = PuO_2^+$
0.920	$2\,Hg^{++} + 2\,e = Hg_2^{++}$
0.88	$H_2O_2 + 2\,e = 2\,OH^-$
0.86	$Cu^{++} + I^- + e = CuI$
0.854	$Hg^{++} + 2\,e = Hg$
0.85	$OsO_4 + 8\,H^+ + 8\,e = Os + 4\,H_2O$
0.80	$NO_3^- + 2\,H^+ + e = NO_2 + H_2O$
0.7995	$Ag^+ + e = Ag$

TABLE 12-1. STANDARD AND FORMAL POTENTIALS *(contd.)*

$E°$	Half-reaction
0.789	$Hg_2^{++} + 2 e = 2 Hg$
0.771	$Fe^{+++} + e = Fe^{++}$
0.75	$NpO_2^+ + 4 H^+ + e = Np^{++++} + 2 H_2O$
0.740	$H_2SeO_3 + 4 H^+ + 4 e = Se + 3 H_2O$
0.71	$Fe(CN)_6^= + e = Fe(CN)_6^{\equiv}$ (1 F HCl or HClO$_4$)
0.70	$Fe^{+++} + e = Fe^{++}$ (1 F HCl)
0.6994	$C_6H_4O_2 + 2 H^+ + 2 e = C_6H_4(OH)_2$ (quinhydrone electrode)
0.682	$O_2 + 2 H^+ + 2 e = H_2O_2$
0.68	$Fe^{+++} + e = Fe^{++}$ (1 F H$_2$SO$_4$)
0.68	$PtCl_6^= + 2 e = PtCl_4^= + 2 Cl^-$
0.62	$UO_2^+ + 4 H^+ + e = U^{++++} + 2 H_2O$
0.6197	$I_2(aq) + 2 e = 2 I^-$
0.6151	$Hg_2SO_4 + 2 e = 2 Hg + SO_4^=$
0.61	$Fe^{+++} + e = Fe^{++}$ (0.5 F H$_3$PO$_4$-1 F H$_2$SO$_4$)
0.581	$Sb_2O_5 + 6 H^+ + 4 e = 2 SbO^+ + 3 H_2O$
0.564	$MnO_4^- + e = MnO_4^=$
0.559	$H_3AsO_4 + 2 H^+ + 2 e = HAsO_2 + 2 H_2O$
0.5355	$I_3^- + 2 e = 3 I^-$
0.5345	$I_2(s) + 2 e = 2 I^-$
0.53	$Mo^{+6} + e = Mo^{+5}$ (2 F HCl)
0.48	$HgCl_4^= + 2 e = Hg + 4 Cl^-$
0.361	$VO^{++} + 2 H^+ + e = V^{+++} + H_2O$
0.36	$Fe(CN)_6^= + e = Fe(CN)_6^{\equiv}$
0.337	$Cu^{++} + 2 e = Cu$
0.334	$Hg_2Cl_2(s) + 2 e = 2 Hg + 2 Cl^-$ (0.1 F KCl)
0.334	$UO_2^{++} + 4 H^+ + 2 e = U^{++++} + 2 H_2O$
0.280	$Hg_2Cl_2(s) + 2 e = 2 Hg + 2 Cl^-$ (1 F KCl)
0.26	$W^{+6} + e = W^{+5}$ (12 F HCl)
0.2415	$Hg_2Cl_2(s) + 2 K^+ + 2 e = 2 Hg + 2 KCl(s)$ (saturated calomel electrode)
0.2222	$AgCl + e = Ag + Cl^-$
0.17	$SO_4^= + 4 H^+ + 2 e = H_2SO_3 + H_2O$
0.16	$BiCl_4^- + 3 e = Bi + 4 Cl^-$
0.154	$Sn^{++++} + 2 e = Sn^{++}$
0.153	$Cu^{++} + e = Cu^+$
0.147	$Np^{++++} + e = Np^{+++}$
0.141	$S + 2 H^+ + 2 e = H_2S$
0.14	$SnCl_6^= + 2 e = SnCl_4^= + 2 Cl^-$ (1 F HCl)
0.10	$TiO^{++} + 2 H^+ + e = Ti^{+++} + H_2O$
0.08	$S_4O_6^= + 2 e = 2 S_2O_3^=$
0.073	$AgBr + e = Ag + Br^-$
0.05	$UO_2^{++} + e = UO_2^+$
0.0000	$2 H^+ + 2 e = H_2$
−0.126	$Pb^{++} + 2 e = Pb$
−0.136	$Sn^{++} + 2 e = Sn$
−0.151	$AgI + e = Ag + I^-$
−0.23	$N_2 + 5 H^+ + 4 e = N_2H_5^+$
−0.24	$Ni^{++} + 2 e = Ni$
−0.255	$V^{+++} + e = V^{++}$

TABLE 12-1. STANDARD AND FORMAL POTENTIALS *(contd.)*

E°	Half-reaction
-0.277	$Co^{++} + 2\,e = Co$
-0.3363	$Tl^{+} + e = Tl$
-0.3563	$PbSO_4 + 2\,e = Pb + SO_4^{=}$
-0.37	$Ti^{+++} + e = Ti^{++}$
-0.403	$Cd^{++} + 2\,e = Cd$
-0.41	$Cr^{+++} + e = Cr^{++}$
-0.440	$Fe^{++} + 2\,e = Fe$
-0.49	$2\,CO_2 + 2\,H^{+} + 2\,e = H_2C_2O_4$
-0.61	$U^{++++} + e = U^{+++}$
-0.763	$Zn^{++} + 2e = Zn$
-0.828	$2\,H_2O + 2\,e = H_2 + 2\,OH^{-}$
-0.91	$Cr^{++} + 2\,e = Cr$
-0.93	$Sn(OH)_6^{=} + 2\,e = HSnO_2^{-} + H_2O + 3\,OH^{-}$
-1.04	$Zn(NH_3)_4^{++} + 2\,e = Zn + 4\,NH_3$
-1.09	$Cd(CN)_4^{=} + 2\,e = Cd + 4\,CN^{-}$
-1.18	$Mn^{++} + 2\,e = Mn$
-1.18	$V^{++} + 2\,e = V$
-1.66	$Al^{+++} + 3\,e = Al$
-1.85	$Be^{++} + 2\,e = Be$
-2.35	$Al(OH)_4^{-} + 3\,e = Al + 4\,OH^{-}$
-2.37	$Mg^{++} + 2\,e = Mg$
-2.714	$Na^{+} + e = Na$
-2.87	$Ca^{++} + 2\,e = Ca$
-2.89	$Sr^{++} + 2\,e = Sr$
-2.90	$Ba^{++} + 2\,e = Ba$
-2.92	$Cs^{+} + e = Cs$
-2.925	$K^{+} + e = K$
-2.925	$Rb^{+} + e = Rb$
-3.045	$Li^{+} + e = Li$

should be thought of as the overall reaction

$$\tfrac{1}{2}\,H_2 + AgCl \rightleftharpoons H^{+} + Ag + Cl^{-}$$

Similarly, the entry

$$Zn^{++} + 2\,e \rightleftharpoons Zn$$

in the table may be considered as

$$H_2 + Zn^{++} \rightleftharpoons 2\,H^{+} + Zn$$

3. In turn, the first of these overall reactions occurs in a galvanic cell whose shorthand representation is

$$-\ Pt,\ H_2\ (1\ atm)\ |\ HCl\ (a = 1\ M),\ AgCl(s)\ |\ Ag\ +$$

and the second reaction occurs in the galvanic cell

$$+\ Pt,\ H_2\ (1\ atm)\ |\ H^{+}\ (a = 1\ M)\ \|\ Zn^{++}\ (a = 1\ M)\ |\ Zn\ -$$

4. As stated previously, a positive electromotive force or emf for any chemical process (such as a cell reaction or a half-reaction) indicates that this process is a spontaneous one, whereas a negative emf denotes a non-spontaneous process. The electromotive force for the first galvanic cell has an absolute magnitude of 0.2222 v. Furthermore, the cell reaction

$$\tfrac{1}{2} H_2 + AgCl \rightleftharpoons H^+ + Ag + Cl^-$$

is a *spontaneous* process, and so we can write

$$\tfrac{1}{2} H_2 + AgCl \rightleftharpoons H^+ + Ag + Cl^-; \qquad E = +0.2222 \text{ v}$$

On the other hand, the emf for the second galvanic cell has an absolute magnitude of 0.763 v. However, the fact that the process

$$H_2 + Zn^{++} \rightleftharpoons 2 H^+ + Zn$$

is *nonspontaneous* can be indicated by the thermodynamic statement

$$H_2 + Zn^{++} \rightleftharpoons 2 H^+ + Zn; \qquad E = -0.763 \text{ v}$$

5. Notice that the standard potential for the silver chloride-silver metal electrode is $+0.2222$ v and that the standard potential for the zinc ion-zinc metal electrode is -0.763 v. When any half-reaction is written as a reduction (either by itself or combined in an overall reaction with the hydrogen gas-hydrogen ion half-reaction) and when all species involved are present in their standard states, the emf of this half-reaction (or the overall reaction, since the emf for the standard hydrogen electrode is zero) is identical in *sign* and *magnitude* to the standard potential for the half-reaction.

Standard-potential data are utilized for many types of thermodynamic calculations. In cases where reduction processes are involved, one may employ the data exactly as they appear in the table of standard potentials. Thus, for the reduction of dichromate to chromic ion, we obtain from the table

$$Cr_2O_7^= + 14 H^+ + 6 e \rightleftharpoons 2 Cr^{+++} + 7 H_2O; \qquad E^\circ = +1.33 \text{ v}$$

The positive sign for the emf indicates that, relative to the hydrogen ion-hydrogen gas half-reaction, the reduction is spontaneous. However, if we should desire to consider the oxidation of chromic ion to dichromate, both the direction of the half-reaction and the sign of the emf must be reversed; that is,

$$2 Cr^{+++} + 7 H_2O \rightleftharpoons Cr_2O_7^= + 14 H^+ + 6 e; \qquad E^\circ = -1.33 \text{ v}$$

Because emf is a thermodynamic quantity which depends on the direction of a reaction, we shall use subscripts to indicate the direction of the half-reaction to which each emf corresponds whenever we wish to write the emf value separately from the half-reaction. Thus, $E^\circ_{Cr_2O_7^=, Cr^{+++}}$ or, more generally, $E_{Cr_2O_7^=, Cr^{+++}}$ written by itself in some expression (such as the Nernst equation) would denote the electromotive force for the half-reaction

$$Cr_2O_7^= + 14 H^+ + 6 e \rightleftharpoons 2 Cr^{+++} + 7 H_2O$$

$E_{\text{Zn,Zn}^{++}}$ would represent the emf for the half-reaction

$$Zn \rightleftharpoons Zn^{++} + 2\ e$$

and $E_{\text{I}_3^-,\text{I}^-}$ would stand for the emf of the half-reaction

$$I_3^- + 2\ e \rightleftharpoons 3\ I^-$$

Formal Potentials. The use of standard potentials to make chemical and thermodynamic predictions is frequently unjustified and may even lead to serious error. This situation arises because the nature of solutions is so very complicated. One difficulty stems from the fact that aqueous solutions of analytical interest are usually so concentrated that activity coefficients cannot be reliably calculated. In turn, if activity coefficients are unknown, the activities of ions and molecules involved in half-reactions cannot be determined. Another problem is that the simple ionic and molecular species written in half-reactions do not necessarily represent the true state of affairs in aqueous solution. For example, the entry

$$Fe^{+++} + e \rightleftharpoons Fe^{++}; \qquad E^\circ = +0.771\ \text{v}$$

in the table of standard potentials applies to an aqueous solution in which the activities of the species $Fe(H_2O)_6^{+++}$ and $Fe(H_2O)_6^{++}$ are both unity. However, it is virtually impossible to prepare any aqueous solution containing just these species, so the validity of using this standard potential may be questioned. Most cations form complexes with anions present, and some highly charged cations also form polymeric species. In a $1\ F$ hydrochloric acid medium, it is reasonable to expect the species of iron(III) to include $Fe(H_2O)_6^{+++}$, $Fe(H_2O)_5OH^{++}$, $Fe(H_2O)_3Cl_3$, $Fe(H_2O)_2Cl_4^-$, $Fe(H_2O)_4Cl_2^+$, $Fe_2(H_2O)_8(OH)_2^{++++}$, and others, and $Fe(H_2O)_6^{++}$, $Fe(H_2O)_5Cl^+$, and $Fe(H_2O)_4Cl_2$ are likely species of iron(II). Unfortunately, the identities of the various species and the equilibria and equilibrium constants which describe such a system are very difficult to ascertain. The general complexity of the iron(III)-iron(II) system tends to be the rule rather than the exception. Nevertheless, the use of standard potentials to predict chemical reactions is extremely successful.

The use of formal potentials has been suggested as a means to overcome the uncertainties resulting from the variation of activity coefficients, from the formation of complexes, and from other chemical interactions. A **formal potential** is defined as the potential (relative to the standard hydrogen electrode) of an electrode involving the half-reaction of interest in a specified electrolyte solution when the *formal concentrations* of the oxidant and reductant are both unity. In thermodynamic calculations, a formal potential is usually denoted by the symbol $E^{\circ\prime}$. As an example, the formal potential for the iron(III)-iron(II) half-reaction is $+0.70\ \text{v}$ in $1\ F$ hydrochloric acid. This differs significantly from the standard potential of $+0.771\ \text{v}$ for the iron(III)-iron(II) couple. In order to measure the formal potential, we might first prepare a solution by dissolving *1 formula weight* of solid $FeCl_3$ and *1 formula*

weight of solid $FeCl_2$ in enough 1 F hydrochloric acid to give *1 liter of solution.*
The resulting solution would undoubtedly contain some or all of the various
species listed in the preceding paragraph. Although we may not know what
individual species of iron(III) and iron(II) are present or what their
activities are, there is still 1 formula weight of iron(III)-containing species
and 1 formula weight of iron(II)-containing species per liter of the 1 F
hydrochloric acid medium. Thus, if we immersed a platinum electrode into a
portion of this solution and measured its potential versus the standard
hydrogen electrode, the platinum electrode would exhibit a potential of
$+0.70$ v relative to the hydrogen electrode.

Values for some formal potentials are included in Table 12-1. The
specific electrolyte solutions to which these data pertain, e.g., 2 F hydrochloric acid or 0.1 F potassium chloride, are indicated in parentheses
following the half-reactions. When available, a formal potential should be
used for thermodynamic calculations if experimental conditions correspond
closely to those used in the original measurement of the formal potential.
In such a case, a much more reliable result will be obtained with a formal
potential than with a standard potential. However, it is not a valid procedure
to apply a formal potential for one system to an entirely different chemical
situation.

THE NERNST EQUATION

The driving force for a chemical reaction, and thus the electromotive
force, depends on the activities (concentrations) of reactants and products.
We can derive an equation which relates electromotive force to the activities
of the reactants and products by starting with the fundamental expression

$$\Delta G = \Delta G^\circ + RT \ln \frac{(C)^c(D)^d}{(A)^a(B)^b}$$

This equation gives the change in free energy ΔG for any general chemical
process, such as

$$aA + bB + \cdots \rightleftharpoons cC + dD + \cdots$$

in terms of the *standard free-energy change* ΔG° for the same process and the
activities of the reactants and products raised to appropriate powers.

It has already been indicated that the relation between electromotive
force and free-energy change is

$$\Delta G = -nFE$$

and we may write the specific equation

$$\Delta G^\circ = -nFE^\circ$$

If we substitute the two latter expressions into the fundamental relation,
the result is

$$-nFE = -nFE^\circ + RT \ln \frac{(C)^c(D)^d}{(A)^a(B)^b}$$

If we divide each member of this expression by the term $-nF$, the familiar **Nernst equation** is obtained:

$$E = E° - \frac{RT}{nF} \ln \frac{(C)^c(D)^d}{(A)^a(B)^b}$$

For practical purposes, several simplifications of the Nernst equation are usually made. First, it is customary to employ concentrations rather than activities of reactant and product species. Second, base-ten or decimal logarithms are preferred to natural logarithms. Third, the temperature T is conventionally taken to be 298°K (25°C). If these changes are made, if the value used for R is 1.987 calories mole^{-1} degree^{-1}, and if F is taken to be 23,060 calories per faraday, the Nernst equation becomes

$$E = E° - \frac{0.05915}{n} \log \frac{[C]^c[D]^d}{[A]^a[B]^b}$$

For most calculations the numerical constant 0.05915, valid only for 25°C, is shortened to 0.059.

The Nernst equation is strictly a thermodynamic relation in which E is the actual emf for a half-reaction or an overall cell reaction and $E°$ is the emf for the same half-reaction or overall reaction under standard-state conditions. Concentration terms should be expressed in conventional units. Thus, the concentrations of dissolved ionic and molecular species are given in molarities, and pressure in atmospheres is used for gases. The concentration of water molecules is taken to be unity, and concentrations of pure solids are likewise assumed to be unity. One final point should be mentioned. We stated earlier that emf is a thermodynamic quantity whose sign, $+$ or $-$, is dependent on the direction of reaction. Therefore, the practice of adding subscripts to E and $E°$ in the Nernst equation to indicate the direction of the reaction of interest should always be followed. The proper form for writing the Nernst equation will become more evident from the sample problems that follow.

Example 4. Write the Nernst equation corresponding to the half-reaction

$$Cu^{++} + 2\,e \rightleftharpoons Cu$$

The correct expression is

$$E_{Cu^{++},Cu} = E°_{Cu^{++},Cu} - \frac{0.059}{n} \log \frac{1}{[Cu^{++}]} = +0.337 - \frac{0.059}{2} \log \frac{1}{[Cu^{++}]}$$

Several features of this equation should be noted. The arrangement of the subscripts (Cu^{++}, Cu) of E and $E°$ indicates the direction of reaction. The logarithmic term always contains products in the numerator and reactants in the denominator. The value for n of 2 is readily determined by inspection of the half-reaction. The significance of n is that it denotes the number of faradays or equivalents of electricity needed to reduce 1 mole of cupric ions to copper metal.

Example 5. Write Nernst equations for each of the following half-reactions:

(1)
$$2\ H^+ + 2\ e \rightleftharpoons H_2$$

$$E_{H^+,H_2} = E^\circ_{H^+,H_2} - \frac{0.059}{n} \log \frac{p_{H_2}}{[H^+]^2} = 0.0000 - \frac{0.059}{2} \log \frac{p_{H_2}}{[H^+]^2}$$

(2)
$$Cr_2O_7^= + 14\ H^+ + 6\ e \rightleftharpoons 2\ Cr^{+++} + 7\ H_2O$$

$$E_{Cr_2O_7^=,Cr^{+++}} = E^\circ_{Cr_2O_7^=,Cr^{+++}} - \frac{0.059}{n} \log \frac{[Cr^{+++}]^2}{[Cr_2O_7^=][H^+]^{14}}$$

$$= +1.33 - \frac{0.059}{6} \log \frac{[Cr^{+++}]^2}{[Cr_2O_7^=][H^+]^{14}}$$

(3)
$$MnO_4^- + 8\ H^+ + 5\ e \rightleftharpoons Mn^{++} + 4\ H_2O$$

$$E_{MnO_4^-,Mn^{++}} = E^\circ_{MnO_4^-,Mn^{++}} - \frac{0.059}{n} \log \frac{[Mn^{++}]}{[MnO_4^-][H^+]^8}$$

$$= +1.51 - \frac{0.059}{5} \log \frac{[Mn^{++}]}{[MnO_4^-][H^+]^8}$$

Since electromotive force is independent of the quantity of chemical reaction, each of the preceding half-reactions could be multiplied or divided by an integer without altering the value of E obtained from the Nernst equation. For example, the dichromate-chromic ion half-reaction could be written as

$$\tfrac{1}{2}\ Cr_2O_7^= + 7\ H^+ + 3\ e \rightleftharpoons Cr^{+++} + 3\tfrac{1}{2}\ H_2O$$

and the corresponding Nernst equation would be

$$E_{Cr_2O_7^=,Cr^{+++}} = E^\circ_{Cr_2O_7^=,Cr^{+++}} - \frac{0.059}{n} \log \frac{[Cr^{+++}]}{[Cr_2O_7^=]^{1/2}[H^+]^7}$$

$$= +1.33 - \frac{0.059}{3} \log \frac{[Cr^{+++}]}{[Cr_2O_7^=]^{1/2}[H^+]^7}$$

which is mathematically identical to that written above.

Sometimes it is necessary or desirable to write a half-reaction as an oxidation rather than a reduction. The reversal of the direction of reaction necessitates an appropriate change in the Nernst equation. If we are interested in calculating E for the half-reaction

$$Mn^{++} + 4\ H_2O \rightleftharpoons MnO_4^- + 8\ H^+ + 5\ e$$

the proper form for the Nernst equation is

$$E_{Mn^{++},MnO_4^-} = E^\circ_{Mn^{++},MnO_4^-} - \frac{0.059}{n} \log \frac{[MnO_4^-][H^+]^8}{[Mn^{++}]}$$

$$= -1.51 - \frac{0.059}{5} \log \frac{[MnO_4^-][H^+]^8}{[Mn^{++}]}$$

Notice that the order of the subscripts for E and E° has been appropriately reversed to show the direction of the half-reaction being considered. Also, the sign of E° has been changed and the concentration terms in the logarithmic part of the equation have been inverted.

APPLICATIONS OF STANDARD POTENTIALS AND THE NERNST EQUATION

This section of the chapter is concerned with specific examples of the various types of thermodynamic calculations which make use of standard-potential data and the Nernst equation.

Calculation of the Electromotive Force for an Overall Cell Reaction. As pointed out previously, the potentiometric measurement of the emf of a galvanic cell is an ideal means for the determination of the driving force for a chemical process. This is so because the potentiometric method permits us to evaluate the driving force or free-energy change for the reaction under the condition of zero current flow. Thus, no net reaction occurs and the chemical system is undisturbed. However, if we attempt to measure the emf for the reaction while it is actually proceeding toward equilibrium, the value obtained will vary continuously with time because of changes in the concentrations (activities) of reactants and products. It would be extremely difficult to correlate an instantaneous value for the emf with the instantaneous concentrations of the reactant and product species. We shall now see how to calculate the emf for an overall cell reaction.

Example 6. Calculate the emf for the overall reaction occurring in the galvanic cell

$$Cu \mid Cu^{++} \ (a = 1 \ M) \parallel Fe^{++} \ (a = 1 \ M), \ Fe^{+++} \ (a = 1 \ M) \mid Pt$$

First, we should write the overall cell reaction according to the rule established earlier.

$$Cu + 2 \ Fe^{+++} \rightleftharpoons Cu^{++} + 2 \ Fe^{++}$$

This overall reaction can be viewed in terms of its component half-reactions,

$$Cu \rightleftharpoons Cu^{++} + 2 \ e$$

and

$$2 \ Fe^{+++} + 2 \ e \rightleftharpoons 2 \ Fe^{++}$$

Since the activities of all ions in the galvanic cell are unity and the activity of the copper metal electrode is also unity, the value for the emf of each half-reaction may be obtained directly from the table of standard potentials. Thus, we can write

$$E_{Cu, Cu^{++}} = E^\circ_{Cu, Cu^{++}} = -0.337 \ v$$

and

$$E_{Fe^{+++}, Fe^{++}} = E^\circ_{Fe^{+++}, Fe^{++}} = +0.771 \ v$$

Again, notice that, although we are considering two units of the iron(III)-iron(II) half-reaction, we do *not* multiply $E^{\circ}_{Fe^{+++},Fe^{++}}$ by a factor of two — emf is an intensity factor and does not depend on the quantity of reaction. In the present example, the emf for the overall cell reaction is just the sum of the emf values for the two separate half-reactions:

$$E_{overall} = E^{\circ}_{Cu,Cu^{++}} + E^{\circ}_{Fe^{+++},Fe^{++}} = -0.337 + 0.771 = +0.434 \text{ v}$$

In general, it is not permissible to add two intensity factors together as we have just done. For example, if one mixed a sample of a gas at pressure P_1 with a second gas sample at pressure P_2, the final pressure of the mixture would *not*, in general, be $(P_1 + P_2)$. To be correct, one should add together only so-called extensive variables such as ΔG or ΔG°.

We shall now repeat our calculation of the emf for the overall cell reaction starting with free-energy changes. It is *rigorously* true that the free-energy change for the overall reaction is equal to the sum of the free-energy changes for the two individual half-reactions:

$$\Delta G_{overall} = \Delta G_{Cu,Cu^{++}} + \Delta G_{Fe^{+++},Fe^{++}}$$

However, since

$$\Delta G = -nFE$$

we can write

$$-nFE_{overall} = -nFE_{Cu,Cu^{++}} - nFE_{Fe^{+++},Fe^{++}}$$

or

$$-nFE_{overall} = -nFE^{\circ}_{Cu,Cu^{++}} - nFE^{\circ}_{Fe^{+++},Fe^{++}}$$

Inspection of the two half-reactions, which when added give the overall cell reaction, shows that each involves *two electrons*, since the electrons must cancel to produce the net reaction. In addition, the overall cell reaction must itself involve *two electrons*. Accordingly, the value of n is the same for all three terms of the preceding equation. Dividing each term by the common factor $-nF$, we obtain

$$E_{overall} = E^{\circ}_{Cu,Cu^{++}} + E^{\circ}_{Fe^{+++},Fe^{++}}$$

which is the identical answer found by simply adding the emf values together at the start. The present situation is unique, however, because of the fact that n has the same value in both the overall cell reaction and the two half-reactions. The conclusion to be drawn from this discussion can be summarized in the form of a useful rule.

When two and only two half-reactions are combined to give an overall reaction with no net electrons appearing in it, the emf for the overall reaction is the algebraic sum of the emf values for the two appropriately written half-reactions. For all other calculations which do not fall into this category, it is absolutely required that the free-energy-change method be followed.

Example 7.   Calculate the emf for the overall reaction occurring in the galvanic cell

$$\text{Cu} \,|\, \text{Cu}^{++}(0.01 \ M) \,\|\, \text{Fe}^{++} \,(0.1 \ M), \, \text{Fe}^{+++} \,(0.02 \ M) \,|\, \text{Pt}$$

The overall cell reaction and the two half-reactions are the same as for the preceding example:

$$\text{Cu} + 2 \ \text{Fe}^{+++} \rightleftharpoons \text{Cu}^{++} + 2 \ \text{Fe}^{++}$$
$$\text{Cu} \rightleftharpoons \text{Cu}^{++} + 2 \ \text{e}$$
$$2 \ \text{Fe}^{+++} + 2 \ \text{e} \rightleftharpoons 2 \ \text{Fe}^{++}$$

In agreement with the preceding rule, the emf for the overall cell reaction is the sum of the emf values for the half-reactions.

$$E_{\text{overall}} = E_{\text{Cu,Cu}^{++}} + E_{\text{Fe}^{+++},\text{Fe}^{++}}$$

For the present example, the concentrations of the various ions differ from unity, and so it is necessary to use the Nernst equation to calculate the emf for each half-reaction:

$$E_{\text{Cu,Cu}^{++}} = E^{\circ}_{\text{Cu,Cu}^{++}} - \frac{0.059}{n} \log \, [\text{Cu}^{++}] = -0.337 - \frac{0.059}{2} \log \, (0.01)$$

$$= -0.337 - \frac{0.059}{2} \, (-2) = -0.278 \text{ v}$$

$$E_{\text{Fe}^{+++},\text{Fe}^{++}} = E^{\circ}_{\text{Fe}^{+++},\text{Fe}^{++}} - \frac{0.059}{n} \log \frac{[\text{Fe}^{++}]}{[\text{Fe}^{+++}]}$$

$$= +0.771 - \frac{0.059}{1} \log \frac{(0.1)}{(0.02)} = +0.771 - 0.059 \log 5$$

$$= +0.771 - 0.059 \, (0.70) = +0.730 \text{ v}$$

$$E_{\text{overall}} = -0.278 + 0.730 = +0.452 \text{ v}$$

Example 8.   Calculate the emf for the overall reaction occurring in the galvanic cell

$$\text{Pb} \,|\, \text{PbSO}_4(\text{s}), \, \text{SO}_4^{=} \,(0.5 \ M) \,\|\, \text{Ag}^{+} \,(0.003 \ M) \,|\, \text{Ag}$$

The overall cell reaction is

$$\text{Pb} + 2 \ \text{Ag}^{+} + \text{SO}_4^{=} \rightleftharpoons \text{PbSO}_4 + 2 \ \text{Ag}$$

and the individual half-reactions are

$$\text{Pb} + \text{SO}_4^{=} \rightleftharpoons \text{PbSO}_4 + 2 \ \text{e}$$

and

$$2 \ \text{Ag}^{+} + 2 \ \text{e} \rightleftharpoons 2 \ \text{Ag}$$

The electromotive force for the overall reaction is

$$E_{\text{overall}} = E_{\text{Pb,PbSO}_4} + E_{\text{Ag}^{+},\text{Ag}}$$

Again, it is necessary to use the Nernst equation in order to evaluate the emf values for the half-reactions:

$$E_{Pb,PbSO_4} = E^\circ_{Pb,PbSO_4} - \frac{0.059}{n} \log \frac{1}{[SO_4^=]} = +0.356 - \frac{0.059}{2} \log \frac{1}{(0.5)}$$

$$= +0.356 - \frac{0.059}{2} \log 2 = +0.356 - \frac{0.059}{2} (0.30) \quad \bullet$$

$$= +0.356 - 0.009 = +0.347 \text{ v}$$

$$E_{Ag^+,Ag} = E^\circ_{Ag^+,Ag} - \frac{0.059}{n} \log \frac{1}{[Ag^+]} = +0.800 - \frac{0.059}{1} \log \frac{1}{(0.003)}$$

$$= +0.800 - 0.059 \log (3.33 \times 10^2) = +0.800 - 0.059(2.52)$$

$$= +0.800 - 0.149 = +0.651 \text{ v}$$

$$E_{overall} = +0.347 + 0.651 = +0.998 \text{ v}$$

It is not strictly necessary that an overall chemical reaction be related to a galvanic cell in which that reaction will occur. For example, the statement of Example 8 could have been phrased as follows: Calculate the emf for the reaction

$$Pb + 2\,Ag^+ + SO_4^= \rightleftharpoons PbSO_4 + 2\,Ag$$

when the initial concentrations of silver ion and sulfate ion are 0.003 and 0.5 M, respectively. The method of solving the problem as well as the numerical result would be identical to that just presented, but the mention of any galvanic cell is completely forgotten. This discussion will be continued as we consider next the evaluation of equilibrium constants from standard-potential data.

Calculation of Equilibrium Constants. One of the most widespread and useful applications of emf measurements is the evaluation of equilibrium constants for chemical reactions.

An important relation between the equilibrium constant and the emf for an overall reaction can be derived. The standard free-energy change for a reaction is related to the equilibrium constant by the equation

$$\Delta G^\circ = -RT \ln K$$

In addition, the standard free-energy change and the emf for a reaction under standard-state conditions may be equated through the expression

$$\Delta G^\circ = -nFE^\circ$$

By combining these two equations, we obtain

$$RT \ln K = nFE^\circ$$

or

$$\ln K = \frac{nFE^\circ}{RT}$$

If we convert this relation for use with base-ten logarithms and substitute appropriate values for the various physical constants ($F = 23{,}060$ calories per faraday, $R = 1.987$ calories mole^{-1} degree^{-1}, and $T = 298°$K), the following useful result is obtained:

$$\log K = \frac{nE°}{0.059}$$

This equation is valid only for 25°C or 298°K. It should be noted that $E°$ is the emf for the reaction of interest under standard-state conditions; this value can be easily determined by proper combination of the standard-potential data from Table 12-1. Let us apply this equation to the solution of several problems.

Example 9.   Compute the equilibrium constant for the reaction

$$\mathrm{HAsO_2 + I_3^- + 2\,H_2O \rightleftharpoons H_3AsO_4 + 2\,H^+ + 3\,I^-}$$

The equilibrium constant for this reaction may be expressed as

$$K = \frac{[\mathrm{H_3AsO_4}][\mathrm{H^+}]^2[\mathrm{I^-}]^3}{[\mathrm{HAsO_2}][\mathrm{I_3^-}]}$$

The overall reaction is composed of the two half-reactions

$$\mathrm{HAsO_2 + 2\,H_2O \rightleftharpoons H_3AsO_4 + 2\,H^+ + 2\,e}$$

and

$$\mathrm{I_3^- + 2\,e \rightleftharpoons 3\,I^-}$$

both of which appear side by side in the table of standard potentials. In accord with previous sample calculations, we may write

$$E°_{\text{overall}} = E°_{\mathrm{HAsO_2,H_3AsO_4}} + E°_{\mathrm{I_3^-,I^-}}$$

From data in Table 12-1, it follows that

$$E°_{\text{overall}} = -0.559 + 0.536 = -0.023 \text{ v}$$

If this value is substituted into the expression for log K along with $n = 2$, we find that

$$\log K = \frac{nE°}{0.059} = \frac{(2)(-0.023)}{0.059} = -0.780; \quad K = 0.166$$

Example 10.   Calculate the solubility-product constant for silver chloride from standard-potential data.

The equilibrium which expresses the solubility of silver chloride is

$$\mathrm{AgCl \rightleftharpoons Ag^+ + Cl^-}$$

A search of Table 12-1 shows that the two half-reactions

$$\mathrm{Ag \rightleftharpoons Ag^+ + e}$$

and

$$\mathrm{AgCl + e \rightleftharpoons Ag + Cl^-}$$

may be added together to yield the desired overall reaction. We can also write

$$E_{overall}^{\circ} = E_{Ag,Ag^+}^{\circ} + E_{AgCl,Ag}^{\circ} = -0.7995 + 0.2222 = -0.5773 \text{ v}$$

Substituting this latter value for $E_{overall}^{\circ}$ into our equation for $\log K$, we obtain

$$\log K = \frac{nE^{\circ}}{0.059} = \frac{(1)(-0.5773)}{0.059} = -9.78$$

$$K = K_{sp} = 1.66 \times 10^{-10}$$

Using this approach, we can calculate the equilibrium constants for redox reactions, solubility products, formation or dissociation constants for complex ions, and ionization constants for acids and bases. The major requirement is that we be able to represent the desired reaction as the sum of appropriate half-reactions. If standard-potential data are available, the calculation may be performed as in the preceding two examples. However, if the pertinent standard potentials are unknown, it may be possible to set up a galvanic cell suitable for the experimental determination of the equilibrium constant. The following example will illustrate how this latter method can be accomplished.

Example II.   Calculate the dissociation constant for the $Ag(S_2O_3)_2^=$ complex ion, which dissociates according to the equilibrium

$$Ag(S_2O_3)_2^= \rightleftharpoons Ag^+ + 2 \ S_2O_3^=$$

if you are given the information that the emf of the following galvanic cell is 0.903 v:

$$-Ag \ | \ Ag(S_2O_3)_2^= \ (0.001 \ M), \ S_2O_3^= \ (2 \ M) \ \| \ Ag^+ \ (0.05 \ M) \ | \ Ag+$$

The solution comprising the left-hand electrode could be prepared by dissolving 0.001 mole of silver nitrate and 2.002 moles of sodium thiosulfate in water to give 1 liter of solution. The nearly complete reaction between one Ag^+ ion and two $S_2O_3^=$ ions would produce essentially 0.001 M $Ag(S_2O_3)_2^=$ and leave 2.000 M $S_2O_3^=$. It should be pointed out that small concentrations of Ag^+ and $AgS_2O_3^-$ are in equilibrium with the $Ag(S_2O_3)_2^=$ complex in the left-hand compartment of the cell. The small concentration of silver ion is important because Ag^+ is involved in the equilibrium which we are studying. However, the presence of the $AgS_2O_3^-$ complex may be neglected because it is not involved directly in the equilibrium of interest. Note that it is unnecessary to specify the concentration of either Ag^+ or $AgS_2O_3^-$ in the left compartment because these are not independently variable but are governed by the stated concentrations of $Ag(S_2O_3)_2^=$ and $S_2O_3^=$.

We can write the half-reaction occurring in the left-hand compartment as

$$Ag + 2 \ S_2O_3^= \rightleftharpoons Ag(S_2O_3)_2^= + e$$

and at the right-hand electrode we have

$$Ag^+ + e \rightleftharpoons Ag$$

The overall cell reaction is the sum of these two half-reactions:

$$Ag^+ + 2\,S_2O_3^= \rightleftharpoons Ag(S_2O_3)_2^=$$

The signs of the electrodes in the schematic or shorthand representation of the galvanic cell provide very useful information. These signs are automatically obtained as a consequence of the potentiometric measurement of emf. There is a tendency for electrons to accumulate at the left-hand electrode, which explains why it is the negative electrode. At the right-hand electrode, there is a tendency for a deficit of electrons, and so the right-hand electrode is positive. *These facts are true regardless of how the galvanic cell is oriented on the desk top ; the silver-silver thiosulfate complex electrode is always negative and the silver-silver ion electrode is positive.* More important, these facts also indicate that the two half-reactions and the overall reaction written above are spontaneous processes. Therefore, the emf for the overall cell reaction is $+0.903$ v.

The emf for the overall cell reaction is the sum of the emf values for the two separate half-reactions

$$E_{overall} = E_{Ag,Ag(S_2O_3)_2^=} + E_{Ag^+,Ag}$$

The emf for the silver ion-silver metal half-reaction can be computed from the Nernst equation:

$$E_{Ag^+,Ag} = E^\circ_{Ag^+,Ag} - \frac{0.059}{n}\log\frac{1}{[Ag^+]} = +0.800 - \frac{0.059}{1}\log\frac{1}{(0.05)}$$

$$= +0.800 - 0.059\log 20 = +0.800 - 0.059\,(1.30)$$

$$= +0.800 - 0.078 = +0.722\ \text{v}$$

Next, we can calculate the emf for the silver-silver thiosulfate electrode:

$$E_{Ag,Ag(S_2O_3)_2^=} = E_{overall} - E_{Ag^+,Ag} = +0.903 - 0.722 = +0.181\ \text{v}$$

Although $E^\circ_{Ag,Ag(S_2O_3)_2^=}$ is unknown, it can be calculated from the Nernst equation as follows:

$$E_{Ag,Ag(S_2O_3)_2^=} = E^\circ_{Ag,Ag(S_2O_3)_2^=} - \frac{0.059}{n}\log\frac{[Ag(S_2O_3)_2^=]}{[S_2O_3^=]^2}$$

$$E^\circ_{Ag,Ag(S_2O_3)_2^=} = E_{Ag,Ag(S_2O_3)_2^=} + \frac{0.059}{n}\log\frac{[Ag(S_2O_3)_2^=]}{[S_2O_3^=]^2}$$

$$= +0.181 + \frac{0.059}{1}\log\frac{(0.001)}{(2)^2}$$

$$= +0.181 + 0.059\log(2.5 \times 10^{-4})$$

$$= +0.181 + 0.059\,(-3.60) = +0.181 - 0.212$$

$$= -0.031\ \text{v}$$

Even though we have not quite arrived at the dissociation constant for the $Ag(S_2O_3)_2^=$ complex, this problem has already demonstrated how standard potentials are determined from galvanic cells. The standard potential $E°$ for the $Ag(S_2O_3)_2^=$–Ag couple (half-reaction written as a *reduction*) is +0.031 v relative to the standard hydrogen electrode.

The calculation of the dissociation constant for the $Ag(S_2O_3)_2^=$ complex can now proceed as shown in Example 10 for the solubility product of silver chloride. The dissociation reaction

$$Ag(S_2O_3)_2^= \rightleftharpoons Ag^+ + 2\,S_2O_3^=$$

is a combination of the half-reactions

$$Ag(S_2O_3)_2^= + e \rightleftharpoons Ag + 2\,S_2O_3^=$$

and

$$Ag \rightleftharpoons Ag^+ + e$$

The emf for the dissociation equilibrium under standard-state conditions can be written as

$$E°_{overall} = E°_{Ag(S_2O_3)_2^=,Ag} + E°_{Ag,Ag^+} = +0.031 - 0.800 = -0.769\text{ v}$$

When this value is substituted into the equation for $\log K$, the result is

$$\log K = \frac{nE°}{0.059} = \frac{(1)(-0.769)}{0.059} = -13.0$$

$$K = K_{diss} = 1.0 \times 10^{-13}$$

Calculation of the Standard Potential for an Unknown Half-Reaction.   Another application of standard-potential data is the evaluation of standard potentials for half-reactions which do not appear in Table 12-1. The type of calculation involved differs from any considered previously.

Example 12.   Calculate the standard potential which pertains to the half-reaction

$$Cu^+ + e \rightleftharpoons Cu$$

The emf for this reduction half-reaction under standard-state conditions is identical in sign and magnitude to the standard potential for the copper(I)-copper metal electrode. However, the standard potential is not to be found in Table 12-1, and so it must be calculated from other information. Two entries which do appear in the table are

$$Cu^+ \rightleftharpoons Cu^{++} + e$$

and

$$Cu^{++} + 2\,e \rightleftharpoons Cu$$

which, if added together in the manner just written, will yield the desired half-reaction.

The present problem cannot be solved by simple addition of the emf values for the latter two half-reactions because the numbers of electrons involved in the three half-reactions are not identical. The rule stated in our discussion of Example 6 indicates that the method of addition of free-energy changes must be followed here. The fundamental equation

$$\Delta G°_{Cu^+,Cu} = \Delta G°_{Cu^+,Cu^{++}} + \Delta G°_{Cu^{++},Cu}$$

may be expressed in terms of standard free-energy changes because we wish to consider all substances, Cu, Cu^+, and Cu^{++}, in their standard states at unit activity. Each free-energy term can be related to the electromotive force for the appropriate half-reaction. Thus,

$$-nFE^{\circ}_{Cu^+,Cu} = -nFE^{\circ}_{Cu^+,Cu^{++}} - nFE^{\circ}_{Cu^{++},Cu}$$

If we substitute values for n from each half-reaction written above and values for $E^{\circ}_{Cu^+,Cu^{++}}$ and $E^{\circ}_{Cu^{++},Cu}$ from Table 12-1, the equation becomes

$$-1\,FE^{\circ}_{Cu^+,Cu} = -1\,F(-0.153) - 2\,F(+0.337)$$

By dividing each term of this expression by $-F$, we can simplify the relation to

$$E^{\circ}_{Cu^+,Cu} = -0.153 + 0.674 = +0.521\text{ v}$$

Thus, the standard potential for the copper(I)-copper metal electrode is $+0.521$ v versus the standard hydrogen electrode.

Example 13.   Calculate the standard potential for the half-reaction

$$SeO_4^= + 8\,H^+ + 6\,e \rightleftharpoons Se + 4\,H_2O$$

The two half-reactions in Table 12-1 from which the desired standard potential can be computed are as follows:

$$SeO_4^= + 4\,H^+ + 2\,e \rightleftharpoons H_2SeO_3 + H_2O; \qquad E^{\circ} = +1.15\text{ v}$$
$$H_2SeO_3 + 4\,H^+ + 4\,e \rightleftharpoons Se + 3\,H_2O; \qquad E^{\circ} = +0.740\text{ v}$$

The free-energy-change relation is

$$\Delta G^{\circ}_{SeO_4^=,Se} = \Delta G^{\circ}_{SeO_4^=,H_2SeO_3} + \Delta G^{\circ}_{H_2SeO_3,Se}$$

As the next step, we may write

$$-nFE^{\circ}_{SeO_4^=,Se} = -nFE^{\circ}_{SeO_4^=,H_2SeO_3} - nFE^{\circ}_{H_2SeO_3,Se}$$

If we substitute values for n and for emf from the above half-reactions, it follows that

$$-6\,FE^{\circ}_{SeO_4^=,Se} = -2\,F(+1.15) - 4\,F(+0.740)$$

or

$$6\,E^{\circ}_{SeO_4^=,Se} = 2(+1.15) + 4(+0.740)$$

Solution of the preceding expression yields

$$E^{\circ}_{SeO_4^=,Se} = \tfrac{1}{3}(+1.15) + \tfrac{2}{3}(+0.740) = +0.383 + 0.493 = +0.876\text{ v}$$

This result is the standard potential for the selenate-selenium metal electrode relative to the standard hydrogen electrode.

The present section has been concerned primarily with the thermodynamic applications of standard potentials and the Nernst equation. In addition, there are at least several other uses of these concepts which can be more conveniently discussed in connection with titrations involving oxidation-reduction reactions.

THE CERIUM(IV)-IRON(II) TITRATION

One of the classic oxidation-reduction or redox procedures is the determination of iron(II) by titration with a standard solution of cerium(IV). The fundamental titration reaction is

$$Fe^{++} + Ce^{++++} \rightleftharpoons Fe^{+++} + Ce^{+++}$$

This simple representation implies the reaction between $Fe(H_2O)_6^{++}$ and $Ce(H_2O)_6^{++++}$ to form $Fe(H_2O)_6^{+++}$ and $Ce(H_2O)_6^{+++}$. Although the true nature of the reactants and products is complicated and unknown, it is nevertheless clear that these simple aquated ions do not predominate in aqueous media. Cerium(IV) is so strong an acid that reactions such as

$$Ce(H_2O)_6^{++++} + H_2O \rightleftharpoons Ce(H_2O)_5(OH)^{+++} + H_3O^+$$

$$Ce(H_2O)_5(OH)^{+++} + H_2O \rightleftharpoons Ce(H_2O)_4(OH)_2^{++} + H_3O^+$$

and

$$2\,Ce(H_2O)_5(OH)^{+++} + H_2O \rightleftharpoons$$
$$[(OH)(H_2O)_4CeOCe(H_2O)_4(OH)]^{++++} + 2\,H_3O^+$$

occur to a significant extent even in $1\,F$ acid media. The species produced by these reactions, especially dimeric $[(OH)(H_2O)_4CeOCe(H_2O)_4(OH)]^{++++}$ and more complex polymeric forms of cerium(IV), react somewhat slowly with iron(II). Iron(II) is not nearly as acidic as cerium(IV), and reactions of the types just written do not occur until the pH of a solution exceeds 7.

The titration is always carried out in solutions which have a hydrogen ion concentration of 0.5 M or higher. The presence of a large concentration of acid is necessary to repress the reactions of cerium(IV) and to promote the rapid reaction between iron(II) and cerium(IV). Frequently, the titration of iron(II) is performed in a 0.5 to 2 F sulfuric acid medium, with the titrant consisting of a solution of cerium(IV) in $1\,F$ sulfuric acid. In sulfuric acid the chemistry of both cerium(IV) and iron(II) is modified by formation of complexes such as $Ce(H_2O)_5SO_4^{++}$ and $Fe(H_2O)_4(SO_4)_2^{=}$.

In the present discussion, we shall consider the cerium(IV)-iron(II) titration in a $1\,F$ sulfuric acid medium. Therefore, it is appropriate for us to utilize the *formal* potentials for the iron(III)-iron(II) and cerium(IV)-cerium(III) half-reactions in $1\,F$ sulfuric acid. Such data account fully for the combined effects of the acidic characters of the reactants and products, the formation of sulfate complexes, and the ionic strength. The formal potential for the cerium(IV)-cerium(III) couple in $1\,F$ sulfuric acid is listed in Table 12-1,

$$Ce^{++++} + e \rightleftharpoons Ce^{+++}; \qquad E^{\circ\prime} = +1.44\ \text{v}$$

and that for the iron(III)-iron(II) half-reaction is $+0.68$ v versus the standard or normal hydrogen electrode:

$$Fe^{+++} + e \rightleftharpoons Fe^{++}; \qquad E^{\circ\prime} = +0.68 \text{ v}$$

Equilibrium Constant for the Cerium(IV)-Iron(II) Reaction. It is of interest to calculate the equilibrium constant for the titration reaction. The overall titration reaction

$$Fe^{++} + Ce^{++++} \rightleftharpoons Fe^{+++} + Ce^{+++}$$

is composed of the two half-reactions

$$Fe^{++} \rightleftharpoons Fe^{+++} + e$$

and

$$Ce^{++++} + e \rightleftharpoons Ce^{+++}$$

and the emf for the overall reaction is given by

$$E^{\circ\prime}_{overall} = E^{\circ\prime}_{Fe^{++},Fe^{+++}} + E^{\circ\prime}_{Ce^{++++},Ce^{+++}}$$

when all species are at unit formal concentration. If values for the formal potentials are substituted into this expression, we obtain

$$E^{\circ\prime}_{overall} = -0.68 + 1.44 = +0.76 \text{ v}$$

The equilibrium constant may be computed as follows:

$$\log K = \frac{nE^{\circ\prime}}{0.059} = \frac{(1)(+0.76)}{0.059} = +12.9$$

$$K = 7.9 \times 10^{12}$$

The relatively large magnitude for the equilibrium constant indicates that the reaction between iron(II) and cerium(IV) is strongly favored and, therefore, that the quantitative determination of iron(II) should be successful. It must be noted, however, that a thermodynamically favorable reaction may not proceed at a conveniently rapid rate. For some redox reactions, the rate of electron exchange between the reductant and oxidant is so slow that the reaction cannot be usefully employed as a titrimetric method of analysis. We shall mention some features of slow redox reactions in the next chapter. The iron(II)-cerium(IV) reaction is fast, partly because it involves the transfer of only one electron.

Construction of the Titration Curve. As for all types of titrations, the calculation and construction of a complete titration curve provides insight into the probable success of the proposed titration and gives information which aids in the selection of either a colored end point indicator or a physico-chemical method of end point detection. We shall consider the titration of 25.00 ml of 0.1000 M iron(II) with 0.1000 M cerium(IV) in a 1 F sulfuric acid medium.

According to the Nernst equation, the emf for a half-reaction depends on the concentrations (activities) of reducing and oxidizing agents in solution. Therefore, the variation of emf as a function of the volume of added titrant serves to show the progress of a redox titration. A key point of this discussion centers on the technique used to monitor the progress of the titration. In order to observe continuously the variation of emf during the course of the titration, it is necessary to make potentiometric measurements of the emf of a galvanic cell which consists of a reference electrode and an indicator electrode. A **reference electrode** is one whose emf or potential is fixed with respect to the standard hydrogen electrode. In principle, the reference electrode may be the standard hydrogen electrode itself, although the saturated calomel electrode is almost universally employed. The actual value of the emf of the reference electrode need not be known as long as it remains perfectly constant throughout the titration. On the other hand, an **indicator electrode** is one whose emf or potential varies in accord with the Nernst equation as the concentrations of reactant and product change during a titration. For example, a platinum wire dipped into an iron(II)-iron(III) mixture in 1 F sulfuric acid exhibits an emf which depends on the ratio of concentrations (activities) of iron(II) and iron(III). When a reference electrode and indicator electrode are combined to make a galvanic cell, any change in the overall cell emf is due solely to a change in the emf or potential of the indicator electrode, which reflects in turn a variation in the concentrations of oxidized and reduced species. It is convenient for the purposes of calculating, constructing, and discussing the titration curve to take the standard hydrogen electrode (with an emf defined to be zero) as the reference electrode and a platinum wire electrode as the indicator electrode. Then the emf of the complete galvanic cell consisting of these two electrodes will be identical in magnitude to the emf of the indicator electrode alone.

In constructing any titration curve, one always plots a physically real quantity or some mathematical function of that quantity, such as pH, pAg, or pCl, versus the volume of titrant. Thus, the titration curve for a redox reaction consists of a plot of the potential or emf of the platinum indicator electrode, with respect to the reference electrode, as a function of the volume of added titrant. It should be recalled that the *sign* and *magnitude* of the potential of an electrode in a galvanic cell do not vary if the bench-top orientation of a cell is altered. However, the emf of a half-reaction is a thermodynamic quantity and does depend on the direction in which the half-reaction is written. As we proceed through the construction of the titration curve, we shall employ the Nernst equation to calculate the emf for the desired half-reaction and then we will interpret the result of each calculation in terms of the potential of the indicator electrode.

At the start of the titration.   It is not possible to predict exactly by calculation what the potential of the indicator electrode is at the beginning of the titration. This situation arises because the concentration of iron(III) in the original iron(II) sample solution is unknown; thus, the Nernst equation cannot be applied. Although the sample solution is specified to contain only iron(II), a very small amount of iron(III) will inevitably exist. In fact, it is theoretically impossible to obtain or prepare an iron(II) solution entirely free of iron(III). There are at least two reasons why this is so.

First, even if it were possible to conceive of an aqueous sulfuric acid solution initially containing only iron(II), the solution would be unstable. The iron(II) would reduce a small quantity of hydrogen ions, and small amounts of hydrogen gas and iron(III) would be formed:

$$Fe^{++} + H^{+} \rightleftharpoons Fe^{+++} + \tfrac{1}{2} H_2$$

The equilibrium constant for this reaction can be calculated from the emf values for the half-reactions

$$Fe^{++} \rightleftharpoons Fe^{+++} + e$$

and

$$H^{+} + e \rightleftharpoons \tfrac{1}{2} H_2$$

The emf for the overall reaction is given by

$$E^{\circ}_{overall} = E^{\circ}_{Fe^{++},Fe^{+++}} + E^{\circ}_{H^{+},H_2} = -0.68 + 0.00 = -0.68 \text{ v}$$

and the equilibrium constant is

$$\log K = \frac{nE^{\circ}}{0.059} = \frac{(1)(-0.68)}{0.059} = -11.5$$

$$K = 3.2 \times 10^{-12}$$

Although the magnitude of this equilibrium constant indicates that the oxidation of iron(II) by hydrogen ions occurs only to a very slight extent, a small concentration of iron(III) must exist under equilibrium conditions.

A second reason why a small amount of iron(III) may be present in an iron(II) solution is that dissolved atmospheric oxygen can oxidize iron(II) to iron(III). The rate of the reaction between oxygen and iron(II) is very fast in alkaline media, but quite slow in acid solutions. Nevertheless, the formation of a small quantity of iron(III) is almost unavoidable in an acid medium.

In the determination of iron(II) by titration with a standard solution of cerium(IV) or some other oxidant, the original sample may consist either partly or wholly of iron(III). Therefore, prior to the actual titration, the iron(III) must be converted quantitatively to iron(II) with the aid of some reducing agent. Regardless of the strength of this reducing agent, however, a small quantity of unreduced iron(III) will always remain.

There is no doubt that a small concentration of iron(III) is present in any iron(II) sample solution. The fact that this iron(III) concentration is not precisely known prevents us from *predicting* the potential of the indicator electrode, although the potential can be reliably *measured* experimentally.

Above all, under the usual titration conditions, the quantity of iron(III) formed or remaining unreduced is too small to cause a significant error in the determination of iron.

Prior to the equivalence point. As the first definite point on the titration curve, let us calculate the potential of the platinum indicator electrode after the addition of 1.00 ml of 0.1000 M cerium(IV) titrant to the 25.00 ml sample of 0.1000 M iron(II) in 1 F sulfuric acid.

Initially, 2.500 millimoles of iron(II) is present. The addition of 1.00 ml of 0.1000 M cerium(IV), or 0.100 millimole, results in the formation of 0.100 millimole of iron(III) and 0.100 millimole of cerium(III) as reaction products, and 2.400 millimoles of iron(II) remains. These conclusions follow from the simple stoichiometry of the titration reaction because the equilibrium constant is so large $(K = 7.9 \times 10^{12})$ that the reaction between cerium(IV) and iron(II) is essentially complete. As a further consequence of the large equilibrium constant or driving force for the reaction, the quantity of cerium(IV) titrant remaining unreacted is extremely small, but may be computed from the known quantities of cerium(III), iron(II), and iron(III) and the equilibrium constant. It should be emphasized that the potential of the platinum indicator electrode can have only one value which is governed in principle by either the iron(III)-iron(II) concentration ratio or the cerium(IV)-cerium(III) concentration ratio. However, the iron(III)-iron(II) ratio prior to the equivalence point can be easily determined from the reaction stoichiometry, whereas the determination of the cerium(IV)-cerium(III) ratio requires a calculation involving the use of the equilibrium expression. Therefore, it is more straightforward to employ the Nernst equation for the iron(III)-iron(II) half-reaction for all points on the titration curve *prior* to the equivalence point.

The Nernst equation for the iron(III)-iron(II) half-reaction may be written as

$$E_{Fe^{+++},Fe^{++}} = E^{o\prime}_{Fe^{+++},Fe^{++}} - \frac{0.059}{n} \log \frac{[Fe^{++}]}{[Fe^{+++}]}$$

$$= +0.68 - \frac{0.059}{1} \log \frac{[Fe^{++}]}{[Fe^{+++}]}$$

Notice that the logarithmic term involves the ratio of two concentrations, each raised to the first power. Therefore, it is not necessary to convert the quantities of iron(II) and iron(III) expressed in millimoles into concentration units. After the addition of 1.00 ml of cerium(IV) titrant, there is 0.100 millimole of iron(III) and 2.400 millimoles of iron(II) present. Thus,

$$E_{Fe^{+++},Fe^{++}} = +0.68 - 0.059 \log \frac{(2.400)}{(0.100)} = +0.68 - 0.059 \log 24$$

$$= +0.68 - 0.08 = +0.60 \text{ v}$$

This emf of $+0.60$ v pertains to the half-reaction

$$Fe^{+++} + e \rightleftharpoons Fe^{++}$$

If, on the other hand, we had chosen to consider the reverse half-reaction

$$Fe^{++} \rightleftharpoons Fe^{+++} + e$$

the appropriate Nernst equation would have been

$$E_{Fe^{++},Fe^{+++}} = E^{o\prime}_{Fe^{++},Fe^{+++}} - \frac{0.059}{n} \log \frac{[Fe^{+++}]}{[Fe^{++}]}$$

$$= -0.68 - 0.059 \log \frac{(0.100)}{(2.400)} = -0.68 - 0.059 \log 0.0417$$

$$= -0.68 + 0.08 = -0.60 \text{ v}$$

Each of these results is correct from a thermodynamic standpoint, for we expect the magnitude of an emf to remain the same while the sign of the emf changes as the direction of the half-reaction is varied.

However, we are really interested in the potential of the platinum indicator electrode versus the standard hydrogen reference electrode. The potential is obtained when we consider a galvanic cell composed of the platinum indicator electrode and the hydrogen electrode. The shorthand representation of such a cell is

$$\text{Pt, H}_2 \text{ (1 atm)} \mid \text{H}^+ \ (a = 1 \ M) \parallel \text{Fe}^{++}, \text{Fe}^{+++} \mid \text{Pt}$$

and the overall cell reaction is

$$\tfrac{1}{2} \text{H}_2 + \text{Fe}^{+++} \rightleftharpoons \text{H}^+ + \text{Fe}^{++}$$

The two half-reactions which comprise the cell reaction are

$$\tfrac{1}{2} \text{H}_2 \rightleftharpoons \text{H}^+ + e$$

and

$$\text{Fe}^{+++} + e \rightleftharpoons \text{Fe}^{++}$$

Since the emf for the cell reaction is the sum of the emf values for the two half-reactions, we can write

$$E_{\text{overall}} = E_{H_2,H^+} + E_{Fe^{+++},Fe^{++}} = 0.00 + 0.60 = +0.60 \text{ v}$$

This result shows that the overall cell reaction is spontaneous and that iron-(III) has a *tendency* to be reduced to iron(II) at the platinum indicator electrode. Thus, there is a tendency for a deficiency of electrons to exist at the electrode and, as a consequence, the platinum indicator electrode is the *positive* electrode of the cell. We would conclude, therefore, that *the potential of the platinum indicator electrode is +0.60 v versus the standard hydrogen electrode.* The reader should confirm that the same result is obtained if the shorthand cell representation is reversed.

For the purpose of constructing any redox titration curve, an important rule to remember is that *the emf for the half-reaction of interest, when it is written as a reduction process, is always identical in both sign and magnitude to the potential of the indicator electrode versus the standard hydrogen electrode.*

After the addition of 2.00 ml of the cerium(IV) titrant, there is 0.200 millimole of iron(III) and 2.300 millimoles of iron(II), so we have

$$E_{\text{Fe}^{+++},\text{Fe}^{++}} = E^{\circ\prime}_{\text{Fe}^{+++},\text{Fe}^{++}} - \frac{0.059}{n} \log \frac{[\text{Fe}^{++}]}{[\text{Fe}^{+++}]}$$

$$= +0.68 - 0.059 \log \frac{(2.300)}{(0.200)} = +0.68 - 0.059 \log 11.5$$

$$= +0.68 - 0.06 = +0.62 \text{ v}$$

Similarly, after the addition of 5.00 ml of the cerium(IV) titrant, $E_{\text{Fe}^{+++},\text{Fe}^{++}} = +0.64$ v.

After the addition of 10.00 ml of titrant, $E_{\text{Fe}^{+++},\text{Fe}^{++}} = +0.67$ v.

After the addition of 15.00 ml of titrant, $E_{\text{Fe}^{+++},\text{Fe}^{++}} = +0.69$ v.

After the addition of 20.00 ml of titrant, $E_{\text{Fe}^{+++},\text{Fe}^{++}} = +0.72$ v.

After the addition of 24.00 ml of titrant, $E_{\text{Fe}^{+++},\text{Fe}^{++}} = +0.76$ v.

After the addition of 24.50 ml of titrant, $E_{\text{Fe}^{+++},\text{Fe}^{++}} = +0.78$ v.

After the addition of 24.90 ml of titrant, $E_{\text{Fe}^{+++},\text{Fe}^{++}} = +0.82$ v.

After the addition of 24.99 ml of titrant, $E_{\text{Fe}^{+++},\text{Fe}^{++}} = +0.88$ v.

It should be noted that, even at a point on the titration curve this close to the equivalence point, it is valid to determine the quantities of iron(III) and iron(II) from the simple reaction stoichiometry. For points much closer to the equivalence point, it is necessary to use the equilibrium expression for the titration reaction to obtain accurate values for the quantities or concentrations of iron(III) and iron(II).

At the equivalence point. In order to calculate the potential of the platinum indicator electrode at the equivalence point, it is helpful to recall that the potential can be viewed as being determined by either the iron(III)-iron(II) or the cerium(IV)-cerium(III) half-reaction. The potential of the indicator electrode as well as the emf for each half-reaction (written as a reduction) will be designated by the symbol E_{ep} at the equivalence point. Then the Nernst equation for each half-reaction may be written.

$$E_{\text{ep}} = E^{\circ\prime}_{\text{Fe}^{+++},\text{Fe}^{++}} - 0.059 \log \frac{[\text{Fe}^{++}]}{[\text{Fe}^{+++}]}$$

$$E_{\text{ep}} = E^{\circ\prime}_{\text{Ce}^{++++},\text{Ce}^{+++}} - 0.059 \log \frac{[\text{Ce}^{+++}]}{[\text{Ce}^{++++}]}$$

An inspection of the titration reaction

$$\text{Fe}^{++} + \text{Ce}^{++++} \rightleftharpoons \text{Fe}^{+++} + \text{Ce}^{+++}$$

provides us with two useful relations. The *equivalence point* of any titration is defined as the point at which we have added a quantity of titrant stoichiometrically equivalent to the substance being titrated. In the present example, we are determining 2.500 millimoles of iron(II), and so the equivalence point corresponds to the addition of 2.500 millimoles of cerium(IV). No reaction is ever 100 per cent complete, but the iron(II)-cerium(IV) reaction has a large equilibrium constant and does attain a high degree of completion. At the equivalence point, the small concentration of unreacted iron(II) is equal to the small concentration of unreacted cerium(IV):

$$[Fe^{++}] = [Ce^{++++}]$$

Similarly, the concentrations of the products, iron(III) and cerium(III), are equal:

$$[Fe^{+++}] = [Ce^{+++}]$$

If we rewrite the first of the preceding two Nernst equations,

$$E_{ep} = E^{o\prime}_{Fe^{+++},Fe^{++}} - 0.059 \log \frac{[Fe^{++}]}{[Fe^{+++}]}$$

substitute the concentration relationships just derived into the second Nernst equation,

$$E_{ep} = E^{o\prime}_{Ce^{++++},Ce^{+++}} - 0.059 \log \frac{[Fe^{+++}]}{[Fe^{++}]}$$

and add these two equations together, the result is

$$2\,E_{ep} = E^{o\prime}_{Fe^{+++},Fe^{++}} + E^{o\prime}_{Ce^{++++},Ce^{+++}} - 0.059 \log \frac{[Fe^{++}]}{[Fe^{+++}]}$$
$$- 0.059 \log \frac{[Fe^{+++}]}{[Fe^{++}]}$$

However, the last term on the right side of this expression is equivalent to

$$+0.059 \log \frac{[Fe^{++}]}{[Fe^{+++}]}$$

so the two logarithmic terms cancel and we have

$$2\,E_{ep} = E^{o\prime}_{Fe^{+++},Fe^{++}} + E^{o\prime}_{Ce^{+++},Ce^{+++}}$$

or

$$E_{ep} = \frac{E^{o\prime}_{Fe^{+++},Fe^{++}} + E^{o\prime}_{Ce^{++++},Ce^{+++}}}{2}$$

Therefore, at the equivalence point the potential of the platinum indicator electrode with respect to the standard hydrogen electrode is

$$E_{ep} = \frac{0.68 + 1.44}{2} = +1.06 \text{ v}$$

In the present example, the potential at the equivalence point is the simple average of the formal potentials for the two half-reactions. However, in general the equivalence point potential is a *weighted* average of the formal or standard potentials for the two half-reactions involved in the titration. Also, in some situations the potential at the equivalence point may depend on the pH and on the concentrations of one or more of the reactants or products. Several of these special situations are included in the problems at the end of this chapter.

Before ending our consideration of the equivalence point, it is of interest to use the equivalence point potential to calculate the concentration of iron(II) and thereby determine how complete the oxidation of iron(II) to iron(III) is. We can write the Nernst equation

$$E_{ep} = E^{o'}_{Fe^{+++},Fe^{++}} - 0.059 \log \frac{[Fe^{++}]}{[Fe^{+++}]}$$

If we assume that the iron(III) concentration is essentially 0.05 M, which because of dilution is exactly one half of the original concentration of iron(II), and substitute this value along with E_{ep} and $E^{o'}_{Fe^{+++},Fe^{++}}$ into the Nernst equation, we get

$$+1.06 = +0.68 - 0.059 \log \frac{[Fe^{++}]}{(0.05)}$$

$$+0.38 = -0.059 \log \frac{[Fe^{++}]}{(0.05)}$$

$$-\frac{0.38}{0.059} = -6.44 = \log \frac{[Fe^{++}]}{(0.05)}$$

$$\frac{[Fe^{++}]}{(0.05)} = 3.6 \times 10^{-7}$$

$$[Fe^{++}] = 1.8 \times 10^{-8} \, M$$

Beyond the equivalence point.   Points on the titration curve after the equivalence point can be most readily determined from the Nernst equation for the cerium(IV)-cerium(III) reaction. It is reasonable to assert that 2.500 millimoles of cerium(III) is present at and beyond the equivalence point, because this is the quantity formed upon oxidation of 2.500 millimoles of iron(II) by cerium(IV). The addition of cerium(IV) after the equivalence point simply introduces excess unreacted cerium(IV). For example, after the addition of a *total* of 26.00 ml of 0.1000 M cerium(IV) titrant, or 1.00 ml in excess of the volume needed to reach the equivalence point, the solution contains 2.500 millimoles of cerium(III) and 0.100 millimole of cerium(IV). The Nernst equation for the cerium(IV)-cerium(III) half-reaction has the form

$$E_{Ce^{++++},Ce^{+++}} = E^{o'}_{Ce^{++++},Ce^{+++}} - \frac{0.059}{n} \log \frac{[Ce^{+++}]}{[Ce^{++++}]}$$

$$E_{Ce^{++++},Ce^{+++}} = +1.44 - 0.059 \log \frac{(2.500)}{(0.100)} = +1.44 - 0.059 \log 25$$

$$= +1.44 - 0.08 = +1.36 \, v$$

After the addition of a grand total of 30.00 ml of the cerium(IV), there is still 2.500 millimoles of cerium(III) present, but the quantity of cerium(IV) is 0.500 millimole:

$$E_{Ce^{++++},\, Ce^{+++}} = E^{o\prime}_{Ce^{++++},\, Ce^{+++}} - \frac{0.059}{n} \log \frac{[Ce^{+++}]}{[Ce^{++++}]}$$

$$= +1.44 - 0.059 \log \frac{(2.500)}{(0.500)} = +1.44 - 0.059 \log 5$$

$$= +1.44 - 0.04 = +1.40 \text{ v}$$

After the addition of 40.00 ml of cerium(IV) titrant, $E_{Ce^{++++},Ce^{+++}} = +1.43$ v.

After the addition of 50.00 ml of cerium(IV) titrant, $E_{Ce^{++++},Ce^{+++}} = +1.44$ v. This is a special point on the titration curve, for the quantities of cerium(III) and cerium(IV) present are equal. Thus, the potential of the indicator electrode is identical to the formal potential for the cerium(IV)-cerium(III) half-reaction. There is one other special point on the titration curve which occurs halfway to the equivalence point. After the addition of exactly 12.50 ml of cerium(IV) titrant in the present titration, the quantity of iron(III) produced and the amount of untitrated iron(II) are the same, and so the potential of the platinum indicator electrode is identical to the formal potential (+0.68 v) for the iron(III)-iron(II) couple in 1 F sulfuric acid.

The complete titration curve for the iron(II)-cerium(IV) reaction is plotted in Figure 12-6. The general appearance of this curve is similar to that for an acid-base, precipitation, or complexometric titration. The potential changes very abruptly as the titration passes through the equivalence point. The potentials for this titration curve have all been calculated relative to the standard hydrogen electrode. If some other reference electrode is employed, the entire titration curve would be shifted up or down along the potential-axis or y-axis, depending on the relative standard potentials of the desired reference electrode and the standard hydrogen electrode. For practical titrations, the saturated calomel electrode (SCE) is almost always used as reference electrode instead of the standard hydrogen electrode. The saturated calomel electrode consists of metallic mercury in contact with a solution saturated with both mercurous chloride (Hg_2Cl_2) and potassium chloride, and its standard potential is +0.2415 v versus the hydrogen electrode. Figure 12-7 shows the relative positions on the scale of standard and formal potentials of the hydrogen electrode, the saturated calomel electrode, the iron(III)-iron(II) couple, and the cerium(IV)-cerium(III) couple. It can be seen that the formal potential for the iron(III)-iron(II) half-reaction is +0.68 v versus the hydrogen electrode, and it is (+0.68 − 0.24) or +0.44 v versus the calomel electrode. Similarly, although the formal potential for the cerium(IV)-cerium(III) half-reaction is +1.44 v with respect to the hydrogen electrode, it is only (+1.44 − 0.24) or +1.20 v

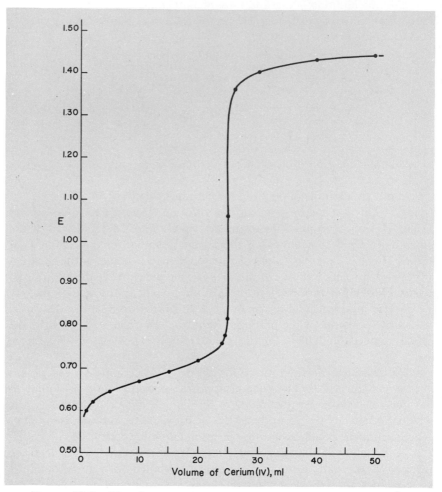

FIGURE 12-6.   Titration curve for the titration of 25.00 ml of 0.1000 M iron(II) with 0.1000 M cerium(IV) in a 1 F sulfuric acid medium.

against the calomel electrode. If the saturated calomel electrode were used as the reference electrode in the cerium(IV)-iron(II) titration, all the potentials on the titration curve in Figure 12-6 would be *decreased* by 0.24 v. Thus, the equivalence point potential, for example, would be $(+1.06 -0.24)$ or $+0.82$ v versus the saturated calomel electrode.

OXIDATION-REDUCTION INDICATORS

There are many ways in which the end point of an oxidation-reduction titration can be detected. Most of these techniques are common to all types of titrations. The well-defined titration curve of Figure 12-6 suggests that a good approach is to plot or record the complete titration curve. Then the end point can simply be taken as the midpoint of the steeply rising portion of the titration curve. Alternatively, if the theoretical equivalence point potential is known, it may be feasible to titrate carefully just to or very close to that potential. Any titration which is followed by measurement of the potential of an indicator electrode as a function of added titrant is termed a **potentiometric titration.** Potentiometric titrations will be discussed in detail in a later chapter.

A few titrants have such intense colors that they may serve as their own end point indicators. For example, even a small amount of potassium permanganate imparts a distinct purple tinge to an otherwise colorless solution, and so the appearance of the color due to the first slight excess of permanganate in a titration vessel marks the end point of the titration. However, it is evident that this method of end point detection will not be

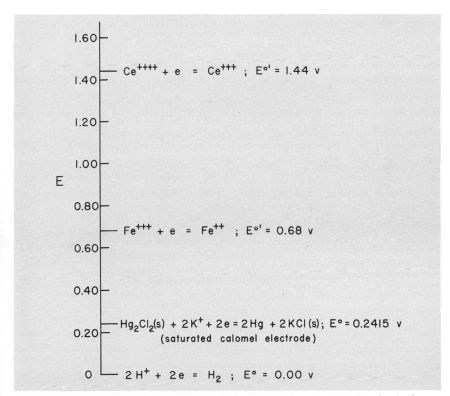

FIGURE 12-7. Relative positions of the standard potentials for the hydrogen electrode and the saturated calomel electrode, and the formal potentials for the iron(III)-iron(II) and cerium(IV)-cerium(III) half-reactions in a 1 F sulfuric acid solution.

applicable if the sample solution contains other highly colored substances. The colors of potassium dichromate and cerium(IV) are not intense enough to allow these titrants to function as their own indicators.

For some titrations, it is possible to add a species to the sample solution which reacts either with the substance being titrated or with the titrant to produce a sharp color change at the end point. Thus, starch is frequently used as an indicator in titrations involving iodine. Starch forms an intensely colored, dark blue complex with iodine which can serve to indicate the disappearance of the last trace of iodine in the titration of iodine with thiosulfate or the appearance of the first small excess of iodine in the titration of arsenic(III) with triiodide solution.

Redox indicators comprise another class of end point indicators for oxidation-reduction titrations. A **redox indicator** is a substance which can undergo an oxidation-reduction reaction and whose oxidized and reduced forms differ in color from each other. In many respects, this type of indicator is analogous to an acid-base indicator. The fundamental reaction which describes the behavior of a redox indicator may be represented by the half-reaction

$$\text{Ox} + n\text{e} \rightleftharpoons \text{Red}$$

(color A)   (color B)

where Ox is the oxidized form of the indicator with color A and Red is the reduced form of the indicator having a different color, B. This simple half-reaction implies that no hydrogen ions are involved in the conversion of the oxidized form of the indicator to the reduced form. Although such a conclusion is valid for some redox indicators, hydrogen ions do enter into the oxidation-reduction reactions of most indicators. However, in the general discussion which follows, it is permissible to neglect the protons involved in the indicator reaction. The main reason is that the concentration of indicator is always small and, therefore, the quantity of hydrogen ions produced or consumed by the oxidation or reduction of the indicator does not alter appreciably the pH of the sample solution.

We can write the Nernst equation corresponding to the above half-reaction as

$$E_{\text{Ox,Red}} = E^{\circ}_{\text{Ox,Red}} - \frac{0.059}{n} \log \frac{[\text{Red}]}{[\text{Ox}]}$$

where $E^{\circ}_{\text{Ox,Red}}$ is the standard potential for the indicator half-reaction. Ideally, the color intensity of a colored substance is directly proportional to its concentration, although some colors are naturally more easily perceived by the human eye. The Nernst equation may be rewritten as

$$E_{\text{Ox,Red}} = E^{\circ}_{\text{Ox,Red}} - \frac{0.059}{n} \log \frac{\text{intensity of color B}}{\text{intensity of color A}}$$

As in the case of acid-base or metallochromic indicators, the redox indicator will appear to be color A if the intensity of color A (the oxidized form) is at least 10 times greater than the intensity of color B (the reduced form). However, the indicator will have color B if the intensity of color B is 10 or more times greater than that of color A. From the preceding Nernst equation, we can conclude that color A will be seen when

$$E_{Ox,Red} = E^\circ_{Ox,Red} - \frac{0.059}{n} \log \frac{1}{10} = E^\circ_{Ox,Red} + \frac{0.059}{n}$$

On the other hand, color B will be observed if

$$E_{Ox,Red} = E^\circ_{Ox,Red} - \frac{0.059}{n} \log 10 = E^\circ_{Ox,Red} - \frac{0.059}{n}$$

At intermediate emf values, the indicator will appear to be a mixture of colors A and B. Thus, a redox indicator requires a potential change of $2 \times (0.059/n)$ or a maximum of about 0.12 v to change from one color form to the other. Theoretically, the range over which this color change occurs is centered on the standard potential value ($E^\circ_{Ox,Red}$) of the indicator. For many redox indicators, the number of electrons (n) involved in the half-reaction is 2, and so a potential change of only 0.059 v suffices to cause the indicator to change color.

In Table 12-2 are listed some common oxidation-reduction indicators

TABLE 12-2. SELECTED OXIDATION-REDUCTION INDICATORS

Indicator	Color of Reduced Form	Color of Oxidized Form	Standard Potential, E°
Indigo monosulfate	colorless	blue	0.26
Methylene blue	colorless	blue	0.36
1-naphthol-2-sulfonic acid indophenol	colorless	red	0.54
Diphenylamine	colorless	violet	0.76
Diphenylbenzidine	colorless	violet	0.76
Barium diphenylamine sulfonate	colorless	red-violet	0.84
Sodium diphenylbenzidine sulfonate	colorless	violet	0.87
Tris(2,2' bipyridine) iron(II) sulfate	red	pale blue	0.97
Erioglaucine A	green	red	1.00
Tris(5-methyl-1,10-phenanthroline) iron(II) sulfate (methyl ferroin)	red	pale blue	1.02
Tris(1,10-phenanthroline) iron(II) sulfate (ferroin)	red	pale blue	1.06
N-phenylanthranilic acid	colorless	pink	1.08
Tris(5-nitro 1,10-phenanthroline) iron(II) sulfate (nitroferroin)	red	pale blue	1.25
Tris(2,2'-bipyridine) ruthenium(II) nitrate	yellow	pale blue	1.25

along with their standard potentials and the colors of the oxidized and reduced forms. As pointed out previously, the oxidation-reduction reactions of most redox indicators involve hydrogen ions, and so the potentials at which these indicators change colors depend on pH. In addition, some redox indicator molecules have acidic functional groups which may be either protonated or deprotonated, depending on the pH value of the solution. The presence or absence of a proton on one of these functional groups can affect the color of the oxidized or reduced form of the indicator. The standard potentials and colors listed in Table 12-2 pertain to a hydrogen ion concentration (activity) of 1 M. One further general point should be mentioned. With certain redox indicators the oxidation-reduction process is not reversible. For example, after a period of time in the presence of excess oxidizing titrant (permanganate, cerium(IV), or dichromate), indicators such as diphenylamine, diphenylbenzidine, and erioglaucine are destructively oxidized and may not be converted back to their reduced forms. On the other hand, some redox indicators are metal complexes — a central metal ion surrounded by organic ligands — and appear to function by the simple oxidation and reduction of the metal cation. Generally, these latter indicators do behave in a reversible manner and may be oxidized and reduced repeatedly if necessary.

The redox indicator most frequently used for the iron(II)-cerium(IV) titration in 1 F sulfuric acid is tris(1,10-phenanthroline) iron(II) sulfate or **ferroin.** One prepares this indicator by dissolving small amounts of 1,10-phenanthroline and ferrous sulfate in a three-to-one ratio in water. The organic ligand, 1,10-phenanthroline or o-phenanthroline, has the structure

1,10-phenanthroline

Three of these ligands are coordinated to one iron(II) cation through the electron pairs on the nitrogen atoms to form the octahedral indicator complex, which is frequently abbreviated $Fe(phen)_3^{++}$. The structure of the ferroin indicator complex is shown in Figure 12-8. The reduced iron(II) form of the indicator has an intense red color, whereas the oxidized iron(III) indicator complex is a pale blue. The indicator half-reaction may be written

$$Fe(phen)_3^{+++} + e \rightleftharpoons Fe(phen)_3^{++}; \qquad E° = +1.06 \text{ v}$$

$$\text{(pale blue)} \qquad\qquad\qquad \text{(red)}$$

In the titration of iron(II) with cerium(IV) in a sulfuric acid medium, the ferroin indicator is initially in its reduced, red form. The end point is signaled by the sudden change to the pale blue color of the oxidized form. Actually, the combination of the blue color of the oxidized indicator and the yellow color of the first slight excess of cerium(IV) titrant imparts a green tinge to the solution at the end point. For the human eye to recognize that the redox indicator has become blue colored, it is necessary that the ratio of the concentration of the oxidized form to that of the reduced form be at least 10. Thus, we can write

$$E_{Fe(phen)_3^{+++},Fe(phen)_3^{++}} = E^{\circ}_{Fe(phen)_3^{+++},Fe(phen)_3^{++}} - 0.059 \log \frac{[Fe(phen)_3^{++}]}{[Fe(phen)_3^{+++}]}$$

$$= +1.06 - 0.059 \log \tfrac{1}{10} = +1.06 + 0.059 = +1.12 \text{ v}$$

This is the potential that a platinum indicator electrode would have (versus the standard hydrogen electrode) at the end point of the titration. Since the equivalence point potential is +1.06 v versus the hydrogen electrode and also since the titration curve shown in Figure 12-6 is very sharply defined, it is clear that a negligible titration error results when ferroin is used as an indicator for the iron(II)-cerium(IV) system.

Occasionally, cerium(IV) is determined by titration with a standard iron(II) solution. The pale-blue, oxidized form of ferroin is an excellent end point indicator, for it is very stable in the presence of cerium(IV) prior to the end point and undergoes a sharp color change at the end point to the red form. If we assume that the concentration of the reduced, red form must be 10 times greater than the concentration of the oxidized, blue form for us to recognize the end point, the potential of a platinum indicator electrode

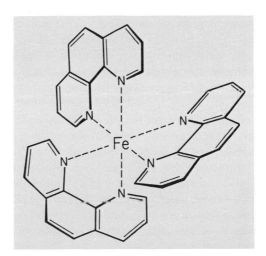

FIGURE 12-8. Structure of the tris(1,10-phenanthroline) iron(II) or ferroin redox indicator.

at this end point is given by

$$E_{\text{Fe(phen)}_3^{+++},\text{Fe(phen)}_3^{++}} = E^{\circ}_{\text{Fe(phen)}_3^{+++},\text{Fe(phen)}_3^{++}} - 0.059 \log \frac{[\text{Fe(phen)}_3^{++}]}{[\text{Fe(phen)}_3^{+++}]}$$

$$= +1.06 - 0.059 \log \tfrac{10}{1} = +1.06 - 0.059 = +1.00 \text{ v}$$

However, since the red form of the indicator is naturally more intensely colored than the pale-blue form, it is probable that the end point would be recognized when the ratio of the two forms is approximately unity. Thus, the end point potential should be very close to the theoretical equivalence point potential of $+1.06$ v.

Before leaving this discussion of indicators for oxidation-reduction titrations, we should mention one other interesting class of indicators, namely **fluorescent redox indicators.** Some redox indicators listed in Table 12-2 cannot be used in solutions containing highly colored substances because the indicator color change is obscured. For example, permanganate and other oxidation states of manganese, notably manganese(III) and manganese(VI), are so deeply colored that the end points of titrations involving these species cannot always be detected with ordinary redox indicators. However, the use of fluorescent redox indicators provides a novel method to overcome this problem. A fluorescent redox indicator behaves as any other oxidation-reduction indicator except that one of the forms of the indicator fluoresces. Tris(2,2'-bipyridine) ruthenium(II), the bottom entry in Table 12-2, has a yellow color, but becomes pale blue upon the one-electron oxidation to tris(2,2'-bipyridine) ruthenium(III). This color change is frequently unsatisfactory as an end point signal because the intensities of the individual colors are weak and because these colors are sometimes masked by other colored species in solution. On the other hand, if the titration vessel is placed inside a black box or if the titration is simply performed in a darkened room, the ruthenium(II) indicator complex exhibits a brilliant orange-red fluorescence when the solution is irradiated with violet light. As the end point is reached, the first tiny excess of titrant oxidizes the indicator to the corresponding ruthenium(III) complex which does not fluoresce. Thus, the end point is marked by the sudden disappearance of the orange-red fluorescence. The behavior of most fluorescent redox indicators is reversible, so tris(2,2'-bipyridine) ruthenium(III) could serve as the indicator in the titration of an oxidant with a standard reducing agent, and the end point would be the appearance of the orange-red fluorescence due to tris(2,2'-bipyridine) ruthenium(II).

In principle, any one of several different metal cations and an almost limitless number of organic ligands can be combined to yield fluorescent redox indicators. Suitable variations in the choice of metal ion and organic ligand, as well as modifications of substituent groups on the organic ligands, are capable of providing a fluorescent redox indicator of nearly any desired standard potential to meet the needs of a particular titration. In addition to ruthenium(II), another cation which forms fluorescent indicators is osmium-(II). Among the organic ligands which have been used to prepare fluorescent redox indicators are 2,2′-bipyridine; 4,4′-dimethyl-2,2′-bipyridine; 5,6-dimethyl-1,10-phenanthroline; and 2,2′-biquinoline.

2,2′-bipyridine

4,4′-dimethyl-2,2′-bipyridine

5,6-dimethyl-1,10-phenanthroline

2,2′-biquinoline

A few specific examples of fluorescent redox indicators are tris(4,4′-dimethyl-2,2′-bipyridine) ruthenium(II) which has a deep red-orange fluorescence, tris(5,6-dimethyl-1,10-phenanthroline) ruthenium(II) which exhibits orange fluorescence, dicyanobis(5,6-dimethyl-1,10-phenanthroline) osmium(II) which has a green fluorescence, and tris(2,2′-biquinoline) ruthenium(II) which exhibits an intense green fluorescence. The corresponding complexes containing ruthenium(III) and osmium(III) do not fluoresce.

FEASIBILITY OF TITRATIONS AND SELECTION OF INDICATORS

A titration curve provides direct information concerning whether a titration is feasible and, if so, what method of end point detection should be used. An important factor which determines the probable success of any proposed redox titration is the difference between the standard or formal potentials for the titrant and titrate systems. For example, we have already seen that the difference between the formal potentials in 1 F sulfuric acid for the cerium(IV)-cerium(III) couple ($E^{\circ\prime} = +1.44$ v) and the iron(III)-iron(II) couple ($E^{\circ\prime} = +0.68$ v) is large enough to yield a very well defined titration curve (see Fig. 12-6). This problem may be viewed in a slightly different way, if we recall that the emf for the cerium(IV)-iron(II) titration reaction is the difference between these formal potentials:

$$Ce^{++++} + Fe^{++} \rightleftharpoons Ce^{+++} + Fe^{+++}; \qquad E^{\circ\prime}_{overall} = +0.76 \text{ v}$$

The fundamental question to be asked may be posed in the following way: In order to obtain a sufficiently well defined titration curve, what is the minimum allowable difference in the standard or formal potentials for the titrant and titrate systems, or what is the smallest acceptable emf for the overall titration reaction?

We can gain some insight into this problem by inspecting the titration curves shown in Figure 12-9. These curves show what happens when

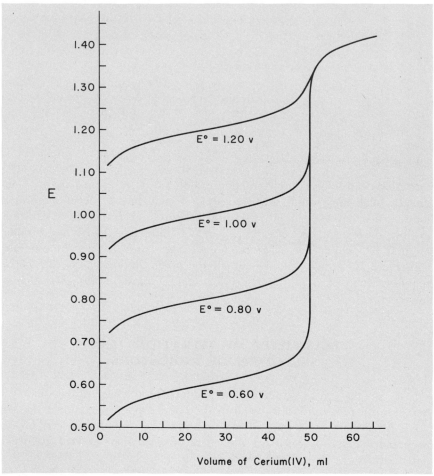

FIGURE 12-9.   Titration curves for the titrations of reducing agents of various strengths with 0.10 M cerium(IV) solution in a 1 F sulfuric acid medium. In each case, it is assumed that 50 ml of 0.10 M reducing agent is titrated and that each reducing agent undergoes a one-electron oxidation to its oxidized form. The pertinent standard potential for each species titrated is printed on the titration curve. The formal potential for the cerium(IV)-cerium(III) couple is +1.44 v versus NHE in a 1 F sulfuric acid solution.

cerium(IV) is used to titrate reducing agents of various strengths. For our discussion let us assume, first, that the titrant is 0.1 M cerium(IV) and, second, that each of the different reductants is at an initial concentration of 0.1 M and also that each undergoes a one-electron oxidation to its oxidized form. If we start with 50 ml of 0.1 M reducing agent, exactly 50 ml of 0.1 M cerium(IV) solution will be needed in each titration. We have calculated and plotted the titration curves of Figure 12-9 on the assumption that the solutions involved in these titrations are $1 F$ in sulfuric acid, and so the formal potential for the cerium(IV)-cerium(III) half-reaction ($E^{\circ\prime} = +1.44$ v versus NHE) is applicable. Standard potentials for the reductants being titrated are printed on the titration curves.

One fact emerges immediately from an inspection of Figure 12-9. The height or size of the emf change at the equivalence point of a titration is proportional to the *difference* between the formal potential for the cerium(IV)-cerium(III) half-reaction and the standard potential for the substance being titrated. If a species with a standard potential of $+0.60$ v (versus the hydrogen electrode) is titrated, the emf jumps at least 500 mv near the equivalence point. In the case of a substance with a standard potential of $+1.00$ v, the emf changes only about 150 mv near the equivalence point. With a species having a standard potential of $+1.20$ v, there is no very steep portion of the titration curve. The size and steepness of the vertical portion of a titration curve govern the accuracy and the precision with which the equivalence point can be located, and thereby govern the feasibility of a titration itself. When the vertical portion is large and steep, as it is for the two bottom titration curves in Figure 12-9, one may anticipate that the equivalence point can be easily determined. On the other hand, if the vertical portion is small and not sharply defined, as in the uppermost curve of Figure 12-9, the choice of colored redox indicator or other method for the location of the equivalence point is severely limited. Such general conclusions about the feasibility of a particular titration, as well as the best method of locating the equivalence point, can be decided more rigorously by calculations with appropriate Nernst equations.

Let us consider the titration of the reducing agent with an E° value of $+0.60$ v and let us assume that the maximal titration error which is acceptable is one part per thousand or ±0.1 per cent. In other words, an end point signal must be obtained between 99.9 and 100.1 per cent of the volume of cerium(IV) titrant needed to reach the exact equivalence point. Usually, the end point signal will be the change in color of a redox indicator. Before proceeding further, we should stop to recall the important rule discovered during our discussion of the cerium(IV)-iron(II) titration. That is, in order to correlate the results of Nernst equation calculations with an actual redox titration curve, it is convenient to write the half-reaction of interest as a *reduction* process. After the addition of 99.9 per cent of the theoretical volume of cerium(IV) solution, the emf or potential should be computed from the

Nernst equation for the species being titrated:

$$E_{\text{Ox,Red}} = E^{\circ}_{\text{Ox,Red}} - \frac{0.059}{1} \log \frac{[\text{Red}]}{[\text{Ox}]}$$

The ratio of the concentration of the reduced form to that of the oxidized form at this point is 1 to 999, or essentially 1 to 1000. Thus, we may write

$$E_{\text{Ox,Red}} = +0.60 - 0.059 \log \tfrac{1}{1000} = +0.60 + 0.18$$
$$= +0.78 \text{ v versus NHE}$$

After the addition of 100.1 per cent of the theoretical volume of cerium(IV) titrant, the cerium(III)-cerium(IV) concentration ratio is 1000, and so it is simple to calculate the emf from the relation

$$E_{\text{Ce}^{++++},\text{Ce}^{+++}} = E^{\circ\prime}_{\text{Ce}^{++++},\text{Ce}^{+++}} - \frac{0.059}{1} \log \frac{[\text{Ce}^{+++}]}{[\text{Ce}^{++++}]}$$

$$= +1.44 - 0.059 \log 1000 = +1.44 - 0.18 = +1.26 \text{ v versus NHE}$$

The two emf values derived from these calculations have considerable significance. If the experimental end point is obtained between $+0.78$ and $+1.26$ v versus NHE, we may be confident that the deviation from the theoretical equivalence point does not exceed one part per thousand. Several methods can be employed to locate the equivalence point, including the use of colored redox indicators. In an earlier discussion of redox indicators, it was pointed out that these indicators require an emf change of $2 \times (0.059/n)$ v to undergo their color changes. For indicator half-reactions involving only one electron, the emf must vary by approximately 0.12 v to cause the color change. It is essential that this interval of 0.12 v lie on the steep vertical portion of the titration curve, so that only a fraction of a drop or at most one drop of cerium(IV) titrant has to be added to produce a sharp color change.

In choosing suitable indicators for the titration of a reductant with an E° value of $+0.60$ v versus NHE, we can select one which exhibits the color of its reduced form at $+0.78$ v versus NHE and the color of its oxidized form at $+(0.78 + 0.12)$ or $+0.90$ v versus NHE. We may also pick an indicator which changes color in the interval from $+1.14$ to $+1.26$ v versus NHE. The standard potential for a redox indicator usually lies at the middle of the color-change interval. Thus, an indicator which exhibits the color of its reduced form at $+0.78$ v versus NHE and the color of its oxidized form at $+0.90$ v versus NHE should have a standard potential of $+0.84$ v. Similarly, an indicator which changes color in the interval from $+1.14$ to 1.26 v versus NHE has a standard potential near $+1.20$ v. Our final conclusion is that a suitable indicator for the proposed titration should have a standard potential between $+0.84$ and $+1.20$ v versus NHE. Seven indicators listed in Table 12-2 fulfill this requirement. However, the preferred indicators appear to be methyl ferroin and ferroin, since their E°

values are close to the theoretical equivalence point potential of $+1.02$ v versus NHE.

The titration curve for the titration of a reductant having an $E°$ value of $+0.80$ v with a cerium(IV) solution differs little from the preceding example. The only important difference is that the vertical portion of the curve is not as large as before, although the titration curve is still very well defined. It is necessary that the end point signal be obtained between $+0.98$ and $+1.26$ v versus NHE if the titration error is not to exceed ±0.1 per cent. Considerations such as those just made reveal that any redox indicator with a standard potential between $+1.04$ and $+1.20$ v versus NHE will be adequate for the titration.

An especially interesting situation is encountered when we consider the titration of a reductant whose standard potential is $+1.00$ v. It can be shown by means of calculations with the Nernst equation that the experimental end point must be taken between $+1.18$ and $+1.26$ v versus NHE to ensure a titration error of less than one part per thousand. Notice that this interval is only two thirds of that required to cause a complete color change of an indicator. (It must be remembered that the present discussion has been confined to indicator half-reactions which involve *one* electron; a redox indicator undergoing a *two-electron* oxidation would change color in the interval of only 0.059 v.)

It is appropriate to consider at this point how to calculate the titration error which results from the use of a redox indicator whose color-change interval does not coincide with the optimum value. Let us note first that the theoretical equivalence point potential for the titration of a reductant of $E° = 1.00$ v with cerium(IV) in $1\,F$ sulfuric acid $(E°' = +1.44\text{ v})$ is $+1.22$ v versus NHE if both half-reactions involve one electron. Suppose that ferroin is used to indicate the end point of this titration. Ferroin has a standard potential of $+1.06$ v, and will show a change in color from red to pale blue upon oxidation. We have already seen in the discussion of the cerium(IV)-iron(II) reaction that the color change of this indicator would be recognized when the emf reaches $+1.12$ v versus NHE. Thus, the end point would occur 100 mv prior to the equivalence point. We can compute the concentration ratio for the reduced and oxidized forms of the substance being titrated as follows:

$$E_{\text{Ox,Red}} = E°_{\text{Ox,Red}} - \frac{0.059}{1} \log \frac{[\text{Red}]}{[\text{Ox}]}$$

$$+1.12 = +1.00 - 0.059 \log \frac{[\text{Red}]}{[\text{Ox}]}$$

$$\log \frac{[\text{Red}]}{[\text{Ox}]} = -\frac{0.12}{0.059} = -2.03$$

$$\frac{[\text{Red}]}{[\text{Ox}]} = 9.3 \times 10^{-3}$$

This calculation demonstrates that approximately 0.93 per cent of the reductant would remain unoxidized at the end point. A similar calculation reveals that at the theoretical equivalence point ($E_{Ox,Red} = +1.22$ v) only 0.019 per cent of the reductant is unoxidized. Therefore, the titration error, which is essentially equal in magnitude to the difference between these percentages, is close to -0.91 per cent or nearly -1.0 per cent.

Another possible indicator for the same titration is nitroferroin. This redox indicator has a standard potential of $+1.25$ v and changes color from red to blue at the end point just as ferroin does. In practice, the appearance of the blue oxidized form of the indicator is usually recognized at a potential of $+1.31$ v versus NHE, which is 60 mv more positive or oxidizing than the indicator's standard potential. What is even more important, however, is the fact that the emf at the end point is 0.09 v greater than the equivalence point value, which means in this case we will incur a *positive* titration error. To calculate this error, we should use the Nernst equation for the cerium(IV)-cerium(III) half-reaction. At the *equivalence point*, we have

$$E_{Ce^{++++},Ce^{+++}} = E^{\circ'}_{Ce^{++++},Ce^{+++}} - \frac{0.059}{1} \log \frac{[Ce^{+++}]}{[Ce^{++++}]}$$

$$+1.22 = +1.44 - 0.059 \log \frac{[Ce^{+++}]}{[Ce^{++++}]}$$

$$\log \frac{[Ce^{+++}]}{[Ce^{++++}]} = \frac{0.22}{0.059} = 3.7$$

$$\frac{[Ce^{+++}]}{[Ce^{++++}]} = \frac{5000}{1}$$

If a similar calculation is performed for the *end point* situation, the results are

$$E_{Ce^{++++},Ce^{+++}} = +1.31 = +1.44 - 0.059 \log \frac{[Ce^{+++}]}{[Ce^{++++}]}$$

$$\log \frac{[Ce^{+++}]}{[Ce^{++++}]} = \frac{0.13}{0.059} = 2.2$$

$$\frac{[Ce^{+++}]}{[Ce^{++++}]} = \frac{160}{1}$$

At the equivalence point only about 0.02 per cent of the sum total of all cerium species is cerium(IV), whereas at the end point this figure has increased almost to 0.63 per cent. The excess of cerium(IV) corresponds to the quantity of titrant needed to increase the potential from $+1.22$ to $+1.31$ v versus NHE. The difference between the two percentages is essentially the titration error, $+0.61$ per cent. For the titration of 50 ml of $0.1\ M$ reductant with $0.1\ M$ cerium(IV) solution, this error amounts to 0.31 ml excess of titrant.

Several approaches might be used to decrease the titration error. One of these approaches is to select an indicator with a color-change interval which falls more nearly within the steep vertical portion of the titration curve. As mentioned earlier, an indicator which undergoes a two-electron oxidation, for example, changes color completely within a span of only 0.059 v. Such an indicator, if properly selected, would change color entirely within the steep vertical portion of the titration curve. An especially intriguing idea is to "tailor-make" a ferroin-type redox indicator that would change color close to the equivalence point potential of +1.22 v versus NHE. Table 12-2 indicates that the standard potential of ferroin itself is +1.06 v. However, if a methyl group (—CH$_3$) is placed in the 5-position of the 1,10-phenanthroline molecule, the resulting methyl ferroin indicator has a *lower* standard potential of +1.02 v. If, instead of a methyl group, the nitro group (—NO$_2$) is substituted at the 5-position, the nitroferroin indicator is obtained with a *higher* standard potential (+1.25 v). By correctly choosing the *nature* of the groups substituted, the *number* of groups substituted, and the *positions* at which they are substituted, one can synthesize a redox indicator of virtually any desired standard potential. The placement of either a chloro (—Cl) or a bromo (—Br) group at the 5-position of 1,10-phenanthroline molecule produces an indicator which changes color from red to pale blue at +1.18 v versus NHE. Two other methods by which the equivalence point can be accurately located involve the use of the technique of potentiometric titration. If the potential of a platinum indicator electrode versus some reference electrode is observed as a function of the volume of cerium(IV) solution added, one may either titrate to the exact equivalence point potential (+1.22 v versus NHE) or else record the entire titration curve and afterward determine the equivalence point by graphical or mathematical analysis of the titration data.

The upper titration curve of Figure 12-9 is not well enough defined to permit the use of redox indicators. The reason for this is that the vertical portion of the curve does not exhibit either the steepness or the size required for a redox indicator to undergo a sharp color change. Any color change would be very gradual and would occur over a range of titrant volumes of several milliliters. Nevertheless the titration is still feasible provided that some other means for locating the equivalence point is utilized. In the present case, the best method again is to determine a complete potentiometric titration curve and to establish the equivalence point by inspection or analysis of either this curve or the original data from which the titration curve is constructed. A discussion of potentiometric titrations and the procedures for handling experimental data is given in Chapter 17.

In regard to the upper curve in Figure 12-9, calculations with the Nernst equation seem to reveal a paradox. The titration of a reductant having an $E°$ value of +1.20 v with cerium(IV) in 1 F sulfuric acid has a theoretical equivalence point potential of +1.32 v versus NHE. At this equivalence point almost 1 per cent of the reductant remains unoxidized! Although this fact suggests that the titration error will be about 1 per cent, such a conclusion is definitely not correct. In principle, the degree of completeness of a reaction at the equivalence point (about 99 per cent in the present situation) has no direct relationship to the inherent accuracy of that titration. Titration accuracy relies upon the existence of a stoichiometric relation or reaction between the quantities of titrant and the substance being titrated. If this stoichiometric point or equivalence point can be located exactly, the titration should be ideally accurate. It is theoretically possible to conduct a titration in which virtually no reaction occurs, if one can accomplish the almost impossible feat of determining when stoichiometric quantities of substances have been brought together. The question of the completeness of a reaction enters this discussion in the following way: The degree of completeness of an overall reaction (which is proportional to its free-energy change, its equilibrium constant, or its emf as well as the *difference* between the emf values of the two half-reactions comprising the overall process) influences the size and sharpness of the vertical portion of the titration curve. The more complete a reaction is, the better defined the titration curve will be and the easier it will be to locate the equivalence point. Thus, completeness of reaction is related to the practical feasibility of a titration. The redox reactions which give rise to the bottom three titration curves in Figure 12-9 are so complete that no serious difficulty is encountered in locating their equivalence points. However, the reaction corresponding to the upper titration curve is sufficiently incomplete that great care must be exercised in determining the equivalence point. A deviation of only 10 mv from the theoretical potential of +1.32 v versus NHE at the equivalence point is enough to cause a titration error of about 0.5 per cent.

Let us now summarize the major conclusions of this section. It is generally recognized that a redox titration can be successfully performed if the *difference* between the standard or formal potentials for the titrant and titrate systems is 0.20 v or greater. For values between 0.20 and 0.40 v, it is preferable to follow the progress of a redox titration by means of potentiometric measurement techniques. On the other hand, when the difference between the formal or standard potentials for the titrant and titrate systems is larger than about 0.40 v, the use of either colored redox indicators or instrumental methods for the location of the equivalence point gives good results. It should be pointed out that these conclusions pertain strictly to half-reactions involving only one electron. However, it can be shown that these statements are essentially true for half-reactions involving two or even three electrons.

Sometimes the shape of a titration curve and thus the feasibility of a titration can be markedly improved by changes in the solution conditions. For example, the formal potentials for many half-reactions are altered when the concentration of acid or of some complexing agent is varied. The color-change intervals of redox indicators are also affected by changes in solution composition. Any prediction concerning the feasibility or success of a proposed titration must take account of the effects of the concentrations of solution components.

TITRATIONS OF MULTICOMPONENT SYSTEMS

Up to this point we have considered the titration of solutions containing only one reducing agent or one oxidizing agent. However, if a sample solution contains more than one reductant or oxidant, it may be possible to obtain a titration curve with a step corresponding to the titration of each species. Let us consider briefly the titration of a mixture of two reducing agents with a strong oxidant such as cerium(IV). In particular, if the two reducing agents happen to have standard potentials of $+0.60$ and $+1.00$ v, respectively, it can be seen from the plots of Figure 12-9 that the first one is completely titrated before the potential rises high enough to begin the titration of the second reductant. A stepwise titration curve would result, much like that for the titration of two acids of differing strengths with a strong base as described in Chapter 8. If, however, the two reducing agents had the same strength or same standard potential, they would be titrated simultaneously rather than successively. In order for one reducing agent to be titrated individually in the presence of another reducing agent, the standard potentials for these two must differ by at least 0.20 v. Notice that this is the same minimum difference in standard or formal potentials required for the successful titration of just one reductant with an oxidizing agent.

Mixture of Iron(II) and Thallium(I). Figure 12-10 shows a titration curve for the titration of a mixture of 1 millimole of iron(II) and 1 millimole of thallium(I) with $0.10\ M$ cerium(IV) in $1\ F$ sulfuric acid. Iron(II) undergoes a one-electron oxidation to iron(III), the formal potential for the iron(III)-iron(II) couple being given by

$$Fe^{+++} + e \rightleftharpoons Fe^{++}; \qquad E^{\circ\prime} = +0.68 \text{ v}$$

and thallium(I) is oxidized to thallium(III) in a two-electron step.

$$Tl^{+++} + 2\,e \rightleftharpoons Tl^{+}; \qquad E^{\circ} = +1.25 \text{ v}$$

The different number of electrons involved in these two half-reactions explains why the volume of titrant needed to react with thallium(I) is twice that required to oxidize the iron(II). As described earlier in this chapter, cerium(IV) is a good oxidizing agent in $1\ F$ sulfuric acid:

$$Ce^{++++} + e \rightleftharpoons Ce^{+++}; \qquad E^{\circ\prime} = +1.44 \text{ v}$$

Since iron(II) is the weaker of the two reducing agents, it is oxidized first. In the region of the first equivalence point, the titration curve is very well defined since the thallium and iron systems differ in their respective emf values by 0.57 v. However, although the second equivalence point is clearly visible, the titration curve is not especially steep at this point because the potentials for the cerium and thallium half-reactions differ by just 0.19 v.

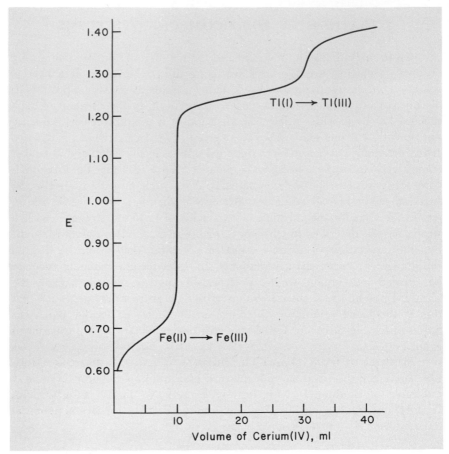

FIGURE 12-10.   Titration curve for the titration of a 1 F sulfuric acid solution containing 1.0 millimole of iron(II) and 1.0 millimole of thallium(I) with 0.10 M cerium(IV). The oxidation process occurring at each stage of the titration is indicated on the curve.

The accurate location of the first equivalence point could be easily accomplished with the aid of a suitable redox indicator, whereas the second equivalence point would undoubtedly have to be determined through the use of a potentiometric titration technique.

It should be evident that the shape of the titration curve up to the first equivalence point is governed by the Nernst equation for the iron(III)-iron(II) half-reaction:

$$E_{\mathrm{Fe^{+++},Fe^{++}}} = E^{\mathrm{o'}}_{\mathrm{Fe^{+++},Fe^{++}}} - 0.059 \log \frac{[\mathrm{Fe^{++}}]}{[\mathrm{Fe^{+++}}]}$$

The calculation of the potential at the *first* equivalence point requires several new considerations. The composition of the solution at the first equivalence point is identical to that obtained by mixing 1 millimole each of iron(III), thallium(I), and cerium(III). Two possible redox reactions can occur in such a solution,

$$2\ Fe^{+++} + Tl^+ \rightleftharpoons 2\ Fe^{++} + Tl^{+++}; \qquad E^{\circ\prime} = -0.57\ v$$

and

$$Fe^{+++} + Ce^{+++} \rightleftharpoons Fe^{++} + Ce^{++++}; \qquad E^{\circ\prime} = -0.76\ v$$

Although neither reaction is thermodynamically favored, the first reaction is at least *less* unfavorable. Hence, at equilibrium there will be very small concentrations of iron(II) and thallium(III) and, from the reaction stoichiometry, we can write

$$[Fe^{++}] = 2\ [Tl^{+++}]$$

Note that we are neglecting the iron(III)-cerium(III) reaction. Now, since the extent of the iron(III)-thallium(I) reaction is so slight, we will still have essentially 1 millimole of iron(III) and 1 millimole of thallium(I). Thus,

$$[Fe^{+++}] = [Tl^+]$$

At the first equivalence point, the Nernst equations for the iron and thallium half-reactions can be written as follows:

$$E_{ep} = E^{\circ\prime}_{Fe^{+++},Fe^{++}} - 0.059 \log \frac{[Fe^{++}]}{[Fe^{+++}]}$$

and

$$E_{ep} = E^{\circ}_{Tl^{+++},Tl^+} - \frac{0.059}{2} \log \frac{[Tl^+]}{[Tl^{+++}]}$$

If the last four equations are combined and manipulated according to the same procedure used in the discussion of the cerium(IV)-iron(II) titration earlier in this chapter, the result is

$$3\ E_{ep} = E^{\circ\prime}_{Fe^{+++},Fe^{++}} + 2\ E^{\circ}_{Tl^{+++},Tl^+} - 0.059 \log 2$$
$$3\ E_{ep} = +0.68 + 2(1.25) - 0.059(0.30)$$
$$E_{ep} = +1.05\ v\ versus\ NHE$$

It may be noted that, to a very close approximation, the equivalence point potential is just the *weighted* average of the iron(III)-iron(II) and thallium-(III)-thallium(I) potentials.

Beyond the first equivalence point and throughout the remainder of the titration, the shape of the titration curve is exactly that predicted for the titration of 1 millimole of thallium(I) with $0.10\ M$ cerium(IV). Between the first and second equivalence points, the titration curve can be calculated from the Nernst equation for the thallium(III)-thallium(I) couple, whereas the cerium(IV)-cerium(III) half-reaction governs the potential *after* the second equivalence point.

The potential exactly at the second equivalence point can be determined if we consider the overall titration reaction

$$2\ Ce^{++++} + Tl^+ \rightleftharpoons 2\ Ce^{+++} + Tl^{+++}$$

From the fundamental definition of equivalence point and from the preceding reaction stoichiometry, we can write

$$[Ce^{++++}] = 2\,[Tl^+] \qquad \text{and} \qquad [Ce^{+++}] = 2\,[Tl^{+++}]$$

Although the solution also contains 1 millimole of iron(III), its presence can be neglected. The two Nernst equations to be used in this calculation are

$$E_{ep} = E^{o\prime}_{Ce^{++++},Ce^{+++}} - 0.059\,\log\frac{[Ce^{+++}]}{[Ce^{++++}]}$$

and

$$E_{ep} = E^{o}_{Tl^{+++},Tl^+} - \frac{0.059}{2}\,\log\frac{[Tl^+]}{[Tl^{+++}]}$$

As before, the proper combination of the preceding four relations leads us to the following expression for the potential at the *second* equivalence point:

$$3\,E_{ep} = E^{o\prime}_{Ce^{++++},Ce^{+++}} + 2\,E^{o}_{Tl^{+++},Tl^+}$$
$$3\,E_{ep} = +1.44 + 2\,(1.25)$$
$$E_{ep} = +1.31 \text{ v versus NHE}$$

In this case, the potential at the second equivalence point is an *exact* weighted average of the cerium and thallium potentials.

Stepwise Oxidation of Vanadium(II). In addition to solutions which contain mixtures of two or more different elements, a solution containing only a single element can give a titration curve with two or more steps if that element exhibits several stable oxidation states. For example, uranium ions can exist in four different oxidation states — +3, +4, +5, and +6. In practice, if one titrates an acidic solution of uranium(III) with a moderately strong oxidizing agent, the titration curve will show two steps, representing the oxidation of uranium(III) to uranium(IV) and of uranium(IV) to uranium(VI), respectively. Both molybdenum(III) and tungsten(III) can be oxidized in two steps, first to the corresponding +5 state and then to the +6 state. Obviously, the procedure can be reversed, with uranium(VI), as an example, being reduced first to uranium(IV) and then to uranium(III).

We shall discuss in detail the stepwise oxidation of vanadium(II). From an inspection of Table 12-1, the following three entries, involving four different oxidation states of vanadium, may be found:

$$V^{+++} + e \rightleftharpoons V^{++}; \qquad\qquad E^{o} = -0.255 \text{ v}$$
$$VO^{++} + 2\,H^+ + e \rightleftharpoons V^{+++} + H_2O; \qquad E^{o} = +0.361 \text{ v}$$
$$VO_2^+ + 2\,H^+ + e \rightleftharpoons VO^{++} + H_2O; \qquad E^{o} = +1.000 \text{ v}$$

The large differences between the values for the standard potentials confirm the well-known fact that a pure solution of any one of the four oxidation states can be prepared. This conclusion also means that, if a solution originally containing only vanadium(II) is titrated with a strong oxidizing agent, three distinct steps will appear in the titration curve. These steps would correspond, respectively, to the oxidations of vanadium(II) to vanadium(III), of vanadium(III) to vanadium(IV), and of vanadium(V). A titration curve for the oxidation of 1 millimole of vanadium(II) with a 0.10 M cerium(IV) solution in $1\,F$ sulfuric acid is depicted in Figure 12-11.

The titration curve of Figure 12-11 comprises seven different regions or points of interest. The portion of the titration curve prior to the first equivalence point and the portions between the first and second equivalence points, between the second and third equivalence points, and after the third equivalence point can be described in terms of appropriate Nernst equations. Before the first equivalence point, the potential is governed by the vanadium(III)-vanadium(II) couple,

$$E_{V^{+++},V^{++}} = E^{\circ}_{V^{+++},V^{++}} - 0.059 \log \frac{[V^{++}]}{[V^{+++}]}$$

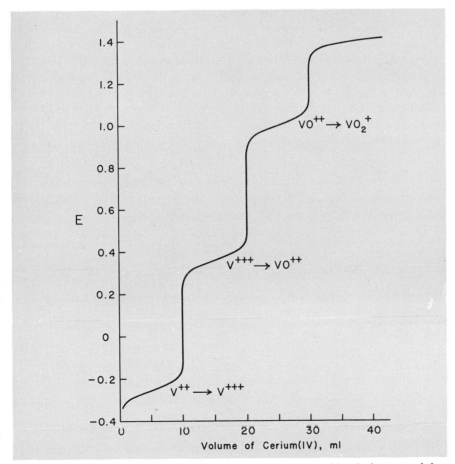

FIGURE 12-11. Stepwise titration of a $1\,F$ sulfuric acid solution containing 1.0 millimole of vanadium(II) with 0.10 M cerium(IV). The oxidation reaction occurring at each step of the titration is shown on the curve.

and the potential between the first and second equivalence points can be computed from the Nernst equation

$$E_{VO^{++},V^{+++}} = E^\circ_{VO^{++},V^{+++}} - 0.059 \log \frac{[V^{+++}]}{[VO^{++}][H^+]^2}$$

Between the second and third equivalence points, we can calculate the potential from the relation

$$E_{VO_2^+,VO^{++}} = E^\circ_{VO_2^+,VO^{++}} - 0.059 \log \frac{[VO^{++}]}{[VO_2^+][H^+]^2}$$

and beyond the third equivalence point, when excess cerium(IV) has been added, we would use the Nernst equation for the cerium(IV)-cerium(III) half-reaction. Note that the logarithmic terms in two of the preceding Nernst equations contain the square of the hydrogen ion concentration. Thus, the potential depends not only on the ratio of vanadium ion concentrations but on the pH of the solution as well.

Let us now focus our attention on the calculation of the three equivalence point potentials. The *first* equivalence point corresponds to that point at which vanadium(II) has been oxidized to vanadium(III); actually, the composition of the solution at this point is exactly the same as if one added 1 millimole of vanadium(III) to an appropriate volume of 1 F sulfuric acid. Here again, we can neglect the presence and effect of cerium(III). Vanadium(III) has a very slight tendency to disproportionate into vanadium(II) and vanadium(IV), as shown by the reaction

$$2 \, V^{+++} + H_2O \rightleftharpoons V^{++} + VO^{++} + 2 \, H^+; \qquad E^\circ = -0.616 \, v$$

By considering this equilibrium, we can calculate the equivalence point potential. Since the disproportionation of V^{+++} results in the formation of equal quantities of V^{++} and VO^{++}, we can write

$$[V^{++}] = [VO^{++}]$$

It is also true that the potential at the first equivalence point is given by either of the following two Nernst equations:

$$E_{ep} = E^\circ_{V^{+++},V^{++}} - 0.059 \log \frac{[V^{++}]}{[V^{+++}]}$$

or

$$E_{ep} = E^\circ_{VO^{++},V^{+++}} - 0.059 \log \frac{[V^{+++}]}{[VO^{++}][H^+]^2}$$

The second of these expressions can be rewritten as

$$E_{ep} = E^\circ_{VO^{++},V^{+++}} - 0.059 \log \frac{[V^{+++}]}{[VO^{++}]} - 0.059 \log \frac{1}{[H^+]^2}$$

and, if we substitute $[VO^{++}] = [V^{++}]$, this relation becomes

$$E_{ep} = E^\circ_{VO^{++},V^{+++}} - 0.059 \log \frac{[V^{+++}]}{[V^{++}]} - 0.059 \log \frac{1}{[H^+]^2}$$

or

$$E_{ep} = E^\circ_{VO^{++},V^{+++}} + 0.059 \log \frac{[V^{++}]}{[V^{+++}]} - 0.059 \log \frac{1}{[H^+]^2}$$

if the first logarithmic term is inverted. If we now combine the last expression
with the fourth preceding one, the result is

$$2 E_{ep} = E^{\circ}_{V^{+++},V^{++}} + E^{\circ}_{VO^{++},V^{+++}} - 0.059 \log \frac{1}{[H^+]^2}$$

or

$$E_{ep} = \frac{E^{\circ}_{V^{+++},V^{++}} + E^{\circ}_{VO^{++},V^{+++}}}{2} + 0.059 \log [H^+]$$

Assuming $[H^+] = 1\ M$ in a $1\ F$ sulfuric acid medium and substituting the
two standard-potential values into the latter equation, we obtain

$$E_{ep} = \frac{-0.255 + 0.361}{2} + 0.059 \log (1)$$

$$E_{ep} = +0.053 \text{ v versus NHE}$$

It should be noticed that the theoretical equivalence point potential depends
on the pH of the solution. At pH 1, $[H^+] = 0.1\ M$, it is -0.006 v versus
NHE; and at pH 2, $[H^+] = 0.01\ M$, the equivalence point potential is
predicted to be -0.065 v versus NHE. This effect of hydrogen ion concentration on the potential at the equivalence point can be important. For
some titrations, not necessarily the one we are discussing here, the pH of the
solution can be adjusted to bring the equivalence point potential into
coincidence with the color-change interval of a redox indicator. In other
situations, a change in pH can make the titration curve much more sharply
defined in the region of the equivalence point. At the same time, one must
always be aware of the fact that changes in pH may alter the nature of the
reactants and products or might cause the rate of reaction to vary.

The potential at the *second* equivalence point is calculated the same way,
except that at this point VO^{++} is the predominant vanadium species. In
addition, it is necessary to employ the Nernst equations for the vanad-
ium(IV)-vanadium(III) and vanadium(V)-vanadium(IV) half-reactions.
The result of this calculation may be stated as

$$E_{ep} = \frac{E^{\circ}_{VO^{++},V^{+++}} + E^{\circ}_{VO_2^{+},VO^{++}}}{2}$$

$$E_{ep} = \frac{0.361 + 1.000}{2}$$

$$E_{ep} = +0.681 \text{ v versus NHE}$$

The interesting observation is that the potential at the *second* equivalence
point is independent of the hydrogen ion concentration. This happens
because of the cancellation of two logarithmic terms containing $[H^+]$.
It is worth emphasizing again, however, that the potential at the second
equivalence point will be independent of pH only if the vanadium species
remain V^{+++}, VO^{++}, and VO_2^+. If a variation in the concentration of
hydrogen ion should cause a new species of vanadium to become predominant, the simple picture could be changed.

No new problems are encountered in the calculation of the potential at the *third* equivalence point. The reaction corresponding to the third step of the titration is

$$Ce^{++++} + VO^{++} + H_2O \rightleftharpoons Ce^{+++} + VO_2^+ + 2 H^+$$

Using the procedure described previously, one can show that the equivalence point potential is given by the general relation

$$E_{ep} = \frac{E^{\circ\prime}_{Ce^{++++},Ce^{+++}} + E^{\circ}_{VO_2^+,VO^{++}}}{2} + 0.059 \log [H^+]$$

and that in 1 F sulfuric acid

$$E_{ep} = \frac{1.44 + 1.000}{2} + 0.059 \log (1)$$

$$E_{ep} = +1.22 \text{ v versus NHE}$$

Before ending this discussion, we shall consider how to take advantage analytically of systems which contain elements having different oxidation states. Suppose it is necessary to determine the individual concentrations of both uranium and vanadium in an acidic solution of these two elements. Very likely, in the preparation of the sample solution, an oxidizing agent would be employed, and so let us assume that uranium and vanadium are both present in their highest oxidation states — UO_2^{++} and VO_2^+, respectively. If this sample solution were titrated with a standard titanium(III) titrant, the vanadium(V) would be quantitatively reduced to vanadium(IV).

$$VO_2^+ + Ti^{+++} \rightleftharpoons VO^{++} + TiO^{++}; \qquad E^{\circ} = +0.90 \text{ v}$$

From the volume of titanium(III) solution required to reach the first equivalence point (v_1), the amount of vanadium present could be calculated directly. If the addition of titanium(III) titrant were continued, a second equivalence point could be obtained, corresponding to the *combined* reductions of vanadium(IV) to vanadium(III) and uranium(VI) to uranium(IV).

$$VO^{++} + Ti^{+++} \rightleftharpoons V^{+++} + TiO^{++}; \qquad E^{\circ} = +0.26 \text{ v}$$
$$UO_2^{++} + 2 Ti^{+++} \rightleftharpoons U^{++++} + 2 TiO^{++}; \qquad E^{\circ} = +0.23 \text{ v}$$

Vanadium(IV) and uranium(VI) are titrated simultaneously because the standard potentials for the vanadium(IV)-vanadium(III) and uranium(VI)-uranium(IV) couples are very close together, being $+0.361$ and $+0.334$ v versus NHE, respectively. If the volume of titanium(III) solution required to go from the first to the second equivalence point is designated as v_2, the concentration of uranium(VI) originally present is proportional to $v_2 - v_1$.

Another approach to the same analytical problem involves the preliminary reduction of uranium and vanadium to U^{++++} and V^{+++}, respectively, with a reductant such as metallic lead or amalgamated lead. Then the solution is titrated with a suitable oxidizing agent — permanganate, cerium(IV), or dichromate. The resulting titration curve exhibits two steps, and the oxidation processes are the reverse of those just described. In other words, the first step corresponds to the combined oxidation of uranium(IV) and vanadium(III), whereas the second step represents the oxidation of vanadium(IV) alone.

QUESTIONS AND PROBLEMS

1. Balance the following oxidation-reduction equations:
   - (a) $Al + H^+ \rightleftharpoons Al^{+++} + H_2$
   - (b) $HAsO_2 + Ce^{++++} + H_2O \rightleftharpoons H_2AsO_4^- + Ce^{+++} + H^+$
   - (c) $SCN^- + MnO_4^- + H^+ \rightleftharpoons SO_4^- + CN^- + Mn^{++} + H_2O$
   - (d) $ClO_3^- + Cl^- + H^+ \rightleftharpoons Cl_2 + H_2O$
   - (e) $ClO_3^- + H_2S \rightleftharpoons S + Cl^- + H_2O$
   - (f) $H_2S + Br_2 + H_2O \rightleftharpoons SO_4^= + H^+ + Br^-$
   - (g) $Cr^{+++} + MnO_2 + H_2O \rightleftharpoons Mn^{++} + CrO_4^= + H^+$
   - (h) $Zn + OH^- \rightleftharpoons Zn(OH)_4^= + H_2$
   - (i) $BrO_3^- + I^- + H^+ \rightleftharpoons Br^- + I_2 + H_2O$
   - (j) $NO_2^- + Al + OH^- + H_2O \rightleftharpoons NH_3 + Al(OH)_4^-$
   - (k) $Cu(NH_3)_4^{++} + CN^- + OH^- \rightleftharpoons Cu(CN)_3^= + CNO^- + NH_3 + H_2O$
   - (l) $NO_3^- + Bi_2S_3 + H^+ \rightleftharpoons NO + Bi^{+++} + S + H_2O$
   - (m) $HOI + OH^- \rightleftharpoons IO_3^- + I^- + H_2O$
   - (n) $Cu^{++} + I^- \rightleftharpoons CuI + I_3^-$

2. Define or characterize each of the following terms: oxidation, reduction, oxidant, reductant, anode, cathode, galvanic cell, and electrolytic cell.

3. Describe clearly how the electromotive force or emf of a galvanic cell is measured experimentally.

4. Write the shorthand cell representation for each of the following galvanic cells:
   - (a) A metallic silver electrode in a $0.015\ F$ silver nitrate solution connected, through a potassium nitrate salt bridge to eliminate the liquid-junction potential, to a $0.028\ F$ nickel chloride solution into which a nickel metal rod is immersed.
   - (b) A platinum wire in a mixture of $0.10\ M$ cerium(IV) and $0.05\ M$ cerium(III) in a $1\ F$ sulfuric acid solution which is in contact through a permeable membrane with a $10\ F$ sodium hydroxide solution containing $0.05\ M$ permanganate ion (MnO_4^-) and $0.001\ M$ manganate ion $(MnO_4^=)$ in which a gold wire electrode is immersed.
   - (c) A palladium wire in a $0.025\ F$ hydrochloric acid solution which is saturated with hydrogen gas at a pressure of 0.5 atm and which is connected, through a potassium chloride salt bridge to minimize the liquid-junction potential, to another half-cell consisting of a zinc metal rod immersed in a $0.04\ F$ zinc nitrate solution.

5. Write the shorthand cell representation of a galvanic cell which could be employed to determine the solubility-product constant of silver chloride. In other words, construct a suitable cell in which the cell reaction is

$$AgCl(s) \rightleftharpoons Ag^+ + Cl^-$$

6. Write the shorthand cell representation of a galvanic cell which can be used to measure the ion-product constant for water. In other words, construct a cell for which the overall reaction is

$$H_2O \rightleftharpoons H^+ + OH^-$$

7. Write the shorthand cell representation for a suitable galvanic cell which might be used in the evaluation of the formation constant for the mercury(II)-EDTA

complex. In other words, construct a cell to study the reaction

$$Hg^{++} + Y^{-4} \rightleftharpoons HgY^{=}$$

where Y^{-4} represents the ethylenediaminetetraacetate ion.

8. Define or characterize each of the following terms: liquid-junction potential, platinum black, standard (or normal) hydrogen electrode, half-reaction, standard potential, and formal potential.

9. For each of the following galvanic cells: (a) Write the two half-reactions and the overall cell reaction, (b) calculate the actual emf for each cell from the Nernst equation, (c) calculate the equilibrium constant for each cell reaction, and (d) identify the anode and cathode and label the electrodes appropriately with either a $+$ or $-$ sign.

$Cu \mid CuSO_4(0.02\ F) \parallel Fe^{++}(0.2\ M),\ Fe^{+++}(0.01\ M),\ HCl(1\ F) \mid Pt$

$Pt \mid Pu^{++++}(0.1\ M),\ Pu^{+++}(0.2\ M) \parallel AgCl(s),\ HCl(0.03\ F) \mid Ag$

$Pt \mid KBr(0.2\ F),\ Br_3^-(0.03\ M) \parallel Ce^{++++}(0.01\ M),$
$$Ce^{+++}(0.002\ M),\ H_2SO_4(1\ F) \mid Pt$$

$Pt,\ Cl_2(0.1\ atm) \mid HCl(2.0\ F) \parallel HCl(0.1\ F) \mid H_2(0.5\ atm),\ Pt$

$Zn \mid ZnCl_2(0.02\ F) \parallel Na_2SO_4(0.1\ F),\ PbSO_4(s) \mid Pb$

$Pt \mid UO_2^{++}(0.005\ M),\ U^{++++}(0.1\ M),\ HClO_4(0.2\ F) \parallel HBr(0.3\ F),\ AgBr(s) \mid Ag$

10. Compute the equilibrium constant for the reaction

$$AuCl_4^- + 2\ Au + 2\ Cl^- \rightleftharpoons 3\ AuCl_2^-$$

from the standard potentials for the following half-reactions:

$$AuCl_2^- + e \rightleftharpoons Au + 2\ Cl^-; \qquad E^\circ = +1.154\ v$$
$$AuCl_4^- + 2\ e \rightleftharpoons AuCl_2^- + 2\ Cl^-; \qquad E^\circ = +0.926\ v$$

11. Given the information that

$$I_2(aq) + 2\ e \rightleftharpoons 2\ I^-; \qquad E^\circ = +0.6197\ v$$
and
$$I_2(s) + 2\ e \rightleftharpoons 2\ I^-; \qquad E^\circ = +0.5345\ v$$

where the symbol (aq) indicates unit activity of iodine in the aqueous phase and (s) denotes pure solid iodine at unit activity, calculate the solubility (moles/liter) of solid iodine in water.

12. Evaluate the equilibrium constant for the formation of the triiodide ion,

$$I_2(aq) + I^- \rightleftharpoons I_3^-$$

from the knowledge that

$$I_2(aq) + 2\ e \rightleftharpoons 2\ I^-; \qquad E^\circ = +0.6197\ v$$
and
$$I_3^- + 2\ e \rightleftharpoons 3\ I^-; \qquad E^\circ = +0.5355\ v$$

13. Calculate the solubility-product constant for copper(I) iodide,

$$CuI(s) \rightleftharpoons Cu^+ + I^-$$

given the following information:

$$Cu^{++} + e \rightleftharpoons Cu^+; \qquad E^\circ = +0.153\ v$$
and
$$Cu^{++} + I^- + e \rightleftharpoons CuI; \qquad E^\circ = +0.86\ v$$

14. Given that

$$Ag + 2\ CN^- \rightleftharpoons Ag(CN)_2^- + e; \qquad E^\circ = +0.31\ v$$
and
$$Ag \rightleftharpoons Ag^+ + e; \qquad E^\circ = -0.80\ v$$

calculate the equilibrium (dissociation) constant for the following reaction:

$$Ag(CN)_2^- \rightleftharpoons Ag^+ + 2\ CN^-$$

15. Given the information that

$$Cu^{++} + 2\ e \rightleftharpoons Cu; \qquad E^\circ = +0.34\ v$$

$$Cu^+ + e \rightleftharpoons Cu; \qquad E^\circ = +0.52\ v$$

$$Cu^{++} + Cl^- + e \rightleftharpoons CuCl(s); \qquad E^\circ = +0.54\ v$$

calculate the solubility-product constant for $CuCl(s)$.

16. Calculate the standard potential (E°) for the half-reaction

$$Au^+ + e \rightleftharpoons Au$$

from the following data:

$$Au^{+++} + 2\ e \rightleftharpoons Au^+; \qquad E^\circ = +1.41\ v$$
$$Au^{+++} + 3\ e \rightleftharpoons Au; \qquad E^\circ = +1.50\ v$$

17. Given the following data

$$MnO_4^- + 8\ H^+ + 5\ e \rightleftharpoons Mn^{++} + 4\ H_2O; \qquad E^\circ = +1.51\ v$$

$$Mn^{+++} + e \rightleftharpoons Mn^{++}; \qquad E^\circ = +1.51\ v$$

calculate the standard potential (E°) for

$$MnO_4^- + 8\ H^+ + 4\ e \rightleftharpoons Mn^{+++} + 4\ H_2O$$

18. Given that

$$Br_2 + 2\ H_2O \rightleftharpoons 2\ HOBr + 2\ H^+ + 2\ e; \qquad E^\circ = -1.59\ v$$

and

$$Br_2 + 6\ H_2O \rightleftharpoons 2\ BrO_3^- + 12\ H^+ + 10\ e; \qquad E^\circ = -1.52\ v$$

calculate E° for the half-reaction

$$BrO_3^- + 5\ H^+ + 4\ e \rightleftharpoons HOBr + 2\ H_2O$$

19. Consider the following galvanic cell:

$$Pt \mid PuO_2^{++}(0.01\ M),\ Pu^{++++}(0.001\ M),\ H^+(0.1\ M) \parallel Cu^{++}(0.001\ M) \mid Cu$$

   (a) Write the two pertinent half-reactions and the overall cell reaction.
   (b) Calculate the E° and the equilibrium constant for the overall cell reaction.
   (c) Calculate the actual emf of the galvanic cell.
   (d) Which electrode is the negative electrode?
   (e) A bar of pure copper metal weighing 127 gm was placed into 1 liter of a $0.0500\ F\ PuO_2(ClO_4)_2$ solution. The pH of this solution was maintained constant at exactly 3.00. What was the concentration of PuO_2^{++} at equilibrium?

20. Given the following data:

$$PtCl_4^= + 2\ e \rightleftharpoons Pt + 4\ Cl^-; \qquad E^\circ = +0.73\ v$$
$$PtCl_6^= + 4\ e \rightleftharpoons Pt + 6\ Cl^-; \qquad E^\circ = +0.72\ v$$

   (a) Calculate the E° and the equilibrium constant (to two significant figures) for the reaction

$$2\ PtCl_4^= \rightleftharpoons Pt + PtCl_6^= + 2\ Cl^-$$

(b) Suppose that a $1.00 F$ hydrochloric acid solution, which is initially $1.00 \times 10^{-6} M$ in $PtCl_4^=$ and $1.00 \times 10^{-6} M$ in $PtCl_6^=$, is equilibrated with a large piece of platinum foil. What will be the final equilibrium concentrations of $PtCl_4^=$ and $PtCl_6^=$?

(c) Calculate the $E°$ for the half-reaction

$$PtCl_4^= + 2\ Cl^- \rightleftharpoons PtCl_6^= + 2\ e$$

(d) If, in the experiment of part (b), electrical contact is made to the platinum foil and its potential measured versus a saturated calomel electrode (SCE) with a potentiometer, what will be the observed potential versus SCE?

21. Consider the following galvanic cell:

$$Pt \mid Fe^{+++}(0.01\ M),\ Fe^{++}(0.02\ M),\ H^+(1\ M) \parallel H^+(1\ M) \mid H_2(1\ atm),\ Pt$$

What will be the qualitative effect of each of the following upon the emf of this galvanic cell:

(a) The addition of 50 ml of $1\ M$ acid to the left half-cell?

(b) The addition of some soluble iron(II) salt to the left half-cell?

(c) The addition of a small amount of solid potassium permanganate to the left half-cell?

(d) The decrease of the pressure of hydrogen gas in the right half-cell?

22. Calculate the equilibrium constant for each of the following reactions:

(a) $Ce^{++++} + Fe(CN)_6^{\equiv} \rightleftharpoons Ce^{+++} + Fe(CN)_6^=$ ($1\ F\ HClO_4$ medium)

(b) $Pb + SnCl_6^= \rightleftharpoons Pb^{++} + SnCl_4^= + 2\ Cl^-$ ($1\ F\ HCl$ medium)

(c) $5\ Fe^{++} + MnO_4^- + 8\ H^+ \rightleftharpoons 5\ Fe^{+++} + Mn^{++} + 4\ H_2O$

(d) $Fe^{++} + Cu^{++} \rightleftharpoons Fe^{+++} + Cu^+$

23. Derive a general relation for the potential of a platinum indicator electrode versus the normal hydrogen electrode at the equivalence point of the titration of iron(II) with permanganate, according to the reaction

$$5\ Fe^{++} + MnO_4^- + 8\ H^+ \rightleftharpoons 5\ Fe^{+++} + Mn^{++} + 4\ H_2O$$

24. The determination of iron is frequently accomplished by means of the potentiometric titration of an iron(II) solution with a standard potassium dichromate solution

$$Cr_2O_7^= + 6\ Fe^{++} + 14\ H^+ \rightleftharpoons 2\ Cr^{+++} + 6\ Fe^{+++} + 7\ H_2O$$

If it is assumed that the hydrogen ion concentration is exactly $1\ M$, prove that the equivalence point potential is given by the expression

$$E_{ep} = \frac{E°_{Fe^{+++},\ Fe^{++}} + 6\ E°_{Cr_2O_7^=,\ Cr^{+++}}}{7} + \frac{0.059}{7} \log\left(\tfrac{2}{3}[Fe^{+++}]\right)$$

25. A 20.00 ml sample of $0.1000\ M$ uranium(IV) in a $1\ F$ sulfuric acid medium is titrated with $0.1000\ M$ cerium(IV) in $1\ F$ sulfuric acid, according to the reaction

$$2\ Ce^{++++} + U^{++++} + 2\ H_2O \rightleftharpoons 2\ Ce^{+++} + UO_2^{++} + 4\ H^+$$

Suppose that the progress of the titration is followed by means of the potentiometric measurement of the potential of a platinum indicator electrode versus a saturated calomel electrode (SCE).

(a) Calculate the potential of the platinum indicator electrode versus SCE at the equivalence point of the titration.

(b) What concentration of uranium(IV) remains unoxidized at the equivalence point?

(c) Calculate what volume of cerium(IV) titrant solution must be added to cause the potential of the platinum indicator electrode to become +0.334 v versus SCE.
(d) Calculate the potential of the platinum electrode versus SCE after the addition of 50.00 ml of cerium(IV) titrant.
(e) What would be the titration error, in per cent with the proper sign, if the titration were mistakenly terminated at an observed potential of +0.150 v versus SCE?

26. A sample of pure vanadium metal weighing 5.10 gm was treated with 500 ml of a 0.500 M VO_2^+ solution. Determine what vanadium species are present at equilibrium and calculate their concentrations. Assume that the solution is air free to prevent the extraneous oxidation of vanadium species, that the solution is maintained 1.00 F in perchloric acid, and that any reaction between hydrogen ion and vanadium species may be neglected.

27. Consider the titration of 20.00 ml of 0.05000 M iron(III) in a 1 F sulfuric acid medium with 0.02000 M titanium(III), also in 1 F sulfuric acid.

$$Fe^{+++} + Ti^{+++} + H_2O \rightleftharpoons Fe^{++} + TiO^{++} + 2\,H^+$$

(a) Calculate and plot the complete titration curve, taking enough points to define the titration curve smoothly.
(b) Calculate the concentration of iron(III) unreduced at the equivalence point of the titration.
(c) If methylene blue indicator (see Table 12-2), which undergoes a sharp color change from blue to colorless at a potential of +0.33 v versus the normal hydrogen electrode (NHE), is employed to signal the end point of this titration, what volume of titanium(III) titrant would be required to reach this end point?
(d) What would be the titration error, in per cent with the proper sign, if the methylene blue end point in part (c) was assumed to be the equivalence point?

28. Suppose that you perform a potentiometric study to evaluate the formation constants for the one-to-one complexes which mercury(II) and lead(II) form with a ligand Y^{-4}. Assume that the following three galvanic cells are constructed and that you measure the emf values for each cell, with the results indicated below.

$-Pt, H_2(1\text{ atm}) \mid H^+(1\ M) \parallel Hg^{++}(0.001\ M) \mid Hg+; \quad E_{cell} = 0.765$ v

$-Pt, H_2(1\text{ atm}) \mid H^+(1\ M) \parallel HgY^=(0.001\ M), Y^{-4}(0.001\ M) \mid Hg+;$
$$E_{cell} = 0.280\text{ v}$$

$-Pt, H_2(1\text{ atm}) \mid H^+(1\ M) \parallel HgY^=(0.001\ M), Pb^{++}(0.001\ M),$
$$PbY^=(0.001\ M) \mid Hg+; \quad E_{cell} = 0.581\text{ v}$$

From the results of these experiments, calculate values for the formation constants represented by the expressions

$$K_{HgY} = \frac{[HgY^=]}{[Hg^{++}][Y^{-4}]} \quad\text{and}\quad K_{PbY} = \frac{[PbY^=]}{[Pb^{++}][Y^{-4}]}$$

29. Calculate and plot the titration curves for each of the following:
(a) The titration of 20.00 ml of 0.02000 M tin(II) in a 1 F hydrochloric acid medium with 0.02000 M vanadium(V) in 1 F hydrochloric acid:

$$SnCl_4^= + 2\,VO_2^+ + 4\,H^+ + 2\,Cl^- \rightleftharpoons SnCl_6^= + 2\,VO^{++} + 2\,H_2O$$

    (b) The titration of 25.00 ml of 0.1000 M iron(III) in 1 F sulfuric acid with 0.05000 M chromium(II) in a 1 F sulfuric acid medium:

$$Fe^{+++} + Cr^{++} \rightleftharpoons Fe^{++} + Cr^{+++}$$

30. A 25.00 ml sample of 0.02000 M VO_2^+ in 1 F perchloric acid was titrated with 0.05000 M titanium(III) in 1 F perchloric acid according to the following reaction:

$$VO_2^+ + Ti^{+++} \rightleftharpoons VO^{++} + TiO^{++}$$

The titration was followed potentiometrically by measuring the potential between a platinum indicator electrode and a saturated calomel reference electrode (SCE). Determine the following information:

    (a) The equilibrium constant for the titration reaction.

    (b) The potential of the platinum indicator electrode versus the normal hydrogen electrode (NHE) at the equivalence point of the titration.

    (c) The concentration of VO_2^+ at the equivalence point.

    (d) The volume of titanium(III) titrant added at the point at which the potential of the platinum indicator electrode is $+1.00$ v versus the normal hydrogen electrode (NHE).

    (e) The potential of the platinum indicator electrode versus the saturated calomel electrode (SCE) after 8.00 ml of the titanium(III) had been added.

31. Calculate and plot the titration curves for each of the following:

    (a) The two-step titration of a 20.00 ml sample of 0.1000 M vanadium-(III) with 0.02000 M permanganate in a 1 F sulfuric acid medium:

$$5\ V^{+++} + MnO_4^- + H_2O \rightleftharpoons 5\ VO^{++} + Mn^{++} + 2\ H^+$$

and

$$5\ VO^{++} + MnO_4^- + H_2O \rightleftharpoons 5\ VO_2^+ + Mn^{++} + 2\ H^+$$

    (b) The titration of a mixture of 1.000 millimole of permanganate and 2.000 millimoles of plutonium(IV) in a 1 F sulfuric acid medium with 0.05000 M titanium(III) in 1 F sulfuric acid:

$$MnO_4^- + 5\ Ti^{+++} + H_2O \rightleftharpoons Mn^{++} + 5\ TiO^{++} + 2\ H^+$$

and

$$Pu^{++++} + Ti^{+++} + H_2O \rightleftharpoons Pu^{+++} + TiO^{++} + 2\ H^+$$

SUGGESTIONS FOR ADDITIONAL READING

Books

1. R. G. Bates: Electrode potentials. *In* I. M. Kolthoff and P. J. Elving, eds.: *Treatise on Analytical Chemistry*, Part I, Volume 1, Wiley-Interscience, New York, 1959, pp. 319–359.
2. H. A. Laitinen: *Chemical Analysis*, McGraw-Hill Book Company, New York, 1960, pp. 276–297, 326–341.
3. W. M. Latimer: *Oxidation Potentials*, second edition, Prentice-Hall, Inc., New York, 1952.
4. J. J. Lingane: *Electroanalytical Chemistry*, Wiley-Interscience, New York, 1958, pp. 1–70, 129–157.

Paper

1. F. C. Anson: Electrode sign conventions. J. Chem. Ed., *36*, 394 (1959).

Chapter Thirteen

Oxidation-Reduction Methods Using Permanganate, Dichromate, and Cerium(IV)

Among the most familiar titrants for oxidation-reduction methods of analysis are potassium permanganate, potassium dichromate, cerium(IV), and iodine. The first three of these substances will be considered as a group in this chapter; methods involving iodine as well as several other species will be described in the next chapter.

OXIDIZING STRENGTH

Although Table 12-1 in the preceding chapter reveals the existence of species covering a very wide range of oxidizing and reducing strengths, the selection of suitable oxidants for titrimetry is by no means trivial. For any particular titration which is contemplated, the oxidizing agent must fulfill several requirements. First, the oxidizing agent must be strong enough to react to practical completion with the substance being titrated. As discussed in Chapter 12, this requirement means that the standard potential for the half-reaction involving the oxidant, which we are assuming is the titrant, must be at least 0.2 v more positive than the standard potential for the half-reaction pertaining to the substance being titrated. Second, the oxidizing agent must not be so powerful that it is able to react with any component of the solution being titrated other than the desired species. Some oxidants, such as silver(II) and cobalt(III), easily satisfy the first requirement, but fail

523

to meet the second requirement because they quickly oxidize the solvent (water) in which they are dissolved. Third, the oxidizing agent must react rapidly with the substance being determined. A certain titration reaction may appear to be favorable from a thermodynamic point of view; that is, the emf for the overall reaction may be large in magnitude and positive in sign, but the mechanism of the redox process can be so complicated that the reaction may not occur at a convenient rate. The latter is often true if the redox reaction involves multiple electron transfer, or the formation or rupture of chemical bonds. Thus, the requirements for the selection of an oxidizing agent and for the performance of a successful redox titration differ little from those which must be met in other titrimetric methods of analysis.

Manganese may exist in a number of stable oxidation states. However, for the majority of oxidation-reduction titrations, the important states are manganese(VII), manganese(IV), and manganese(II). Furthermore, since potassium permanganate is the titrant in which we are interested, our attention should be focused specifically on the half-reactions involving manganese(VII). In Table 12-1, one finds the two half-reactions

$$MnO_4^- + 8\,H^+ + 5\,e \rightleftharpoons Mn^{++} + 4\,H_2O$$

and

$$MnO_4^- + 4\,H^+ + 3\,e \rightleftharpoons MnO_2 + 2\,H_2O$$

with standard potentials of $+1.51$ and $+1.695$ v versus NHE, respectively. The primary difference between these two half-reactions is the extent of reduction of the permanganate ion. The factors that govern which of the two reduction products, Mn^{++} or MnO_2, is actually formed are quite complex and involve consideration of both kinetics and thermodynamics. Suffice it to say here that, in neutral and alkaline media as well as in weakly acidic solutions, manganese dioxide is the product. In solutions having a hydrogen ion concentration of $0.5\,M$ or greater, permanganate is reduced all the way to manganous ion, Mn^{++}. Regardless of which half-reaction predominates, the permanganate ion is an excellent oxidizing agent.

In general, except for some reactions of permanganate with organic compounds, potassium permanganate is usually employed for titrations in strongly acidic media, in which manganous ion is the reduction product.

Two other oxidation states of manganese are involved to a limited extent in analytical applications of permanganate solutions. Although manganese(III) is normally unstable with respect to disproportionation into manganous ion and manganese dioxide,

$$2\,Mn^{+++} + 2\,H_2O \rightleftharpoons Mn^{++} + MnO_2 + 4\,H^+$$

the Mn^{+++} species can be stabilized by pyrophosphate and by fluoride. For example, permanganate may be reduced to the manganese(III)-pyrophosphate complex in a solution of pH 4 to 7 containing sodium pyrophosphate:

$$MnO_4^- + 3\,H_2P_2O_7^= + 8\,H^+ + 4\,e \rightleftharpoons Mn(H_2P_2O_7)_3^= + 4\,H_2O$$

The standard potential for this reaction ($+1.50$ v versus NHE) is almost identical to that for the permanganate-manganous ion couple. Unfortunately, the wine red color of the $Mn(H_2P_2O_7)_3^=$ complex resembles the color of permanganate so closely that visual end point detection is impossible.

The bright green manganate ion, $MnO_4^=$, is the reduction product of permanganate in strongly alkaline media:

$$MnO_4^- + e \rightleftharpoons MnO_4^=; \qquad E^\circ = +0.564 \text{ v}$$

In sodium hydroxide solutions which are more concentrated than about $2 F$, organic compounds reduce permanganate ion according to this half-reaction. However, the color intensity of manganate is so great that it can obscure the end point of the final titration. Frequently, barium ion is added to the solution in order to minimize this source of difficulty because it precipitates $MnO_4^=$ as barium manganate. Moreover, this expedient largely eliminates the tendency for manganate to be further reduced to manganese dioxide by the organic substances. Since the suspended barium manganate precipitate is green colored, this procedure still leaves much to be desired.

When we turn to the dichromate ion, we find that the only important reduction involving this species is

$$Cr_2O_7^= + 14 H^+ + 6 e \rightleftharpoons 2 Cr^{+++} + 7 H_2O; \qquad E^\circ - +1.33 \text{ v}$$

The standard potential is less than that for the permanganate-manganous ion half-reaction, but nevertheless signifies that dichromate ion is a strong oxidizing agent. Potassium dichromate is almost invariably employed as a titrant in acid media, for in neutral and alkaline solutions chromic ion, Cr^{+++} or $Cr(H_2O)_6^{+++}$, forms an insoluble hydrous oxide and dichromate is converted to the chromate ion:

$$Cr_2O_7^= + 2 OH^- \rightleftharpoons 2 CrO_4^= + H_2O$$

The simple half-reaction

$$Ce^{++++} + e \rightleftharpoons Ce^{+++}$$

which may be written to represent the one-electron reduction of cerium(IV) to cerium(III), conceals some fascinating and complicated chemistry. The fact that three different *formal* potentials are reported in Table 12-1 for the cerium(IV)-cerium(III) couple ($+1.70$ v in $1 F$ perchloric acid, $+1.61$ v in $1 F$ nitric acid, and $+1.44$ v in $1 F$ sulfuric acid) is a clear indication of the influence of the acid medium upon the oxidizing strength of cerium(IV). However, before we examine some of the specific chemical interactions which occur in cerium(IV) solutions, one important general principle should be introduced.

The Nernst equation for the cerium(IV)-cerium(III) half-reaction may take the form

$$E_{Ce^{++++},Ce^{+++}} = E^\circ_{Ce^{++++},Ce^{+++}} - 0.059 \log \frac{[Ce^{+++}]}{[Ce^{++++}]}$$

in which $E^{\circ}_{Ce^{++++}, Ce^{+++}}$ denotes the *standard potential* for the cerium(IV)-cerium(III) half-reaction for unit concentrations (activities) of the hydrated species $Ce(H_2O)_6^{++++}$ and $Ce(H_2O)_6^{+++}$. If $Ce(H_2O)_6^{++++}$ and $Ce(H_2O)_6^{+++}$ each undergo some chemical reaction with another component in the solution and if the extent of each reaction is different for $Ce(H_2O)_6^{++++}$ and $Ce(H_2O)_6^{+++}$, the *ratio* of the concentrations of $Ce(H_2O)_6^{++++}$ and $Ce(H_2O)_6^{+++}$ remaining unreacted will either increase or decrease, depending on which ion reacts more. If $Ce(H_2O)_6^{+++}$ reacts more completely than $Ce(H_2O)_6^{++++}$, the ratio $[Ce^{+++}]/[Ce^{++++}]$ will *decrease* and, according to the preceding Nernst equation, this should cause the actual emf for the half-reaction to become more positive or *more oxidizing*. Conversely, if $Ce(H_2O)_6^{++++}$ reacts more extensively than $Ce(H_2O)_6^{+++}$, the ratio $[Ce^{+++}]/[Ce^{++++}]$ will *increase* and the actual emf for the half-reaction will become less positive or *more reducing*.

Let us apply this reasoning as a means of interpreting the order of the *formal* potentials cited earlier. The formal potential for the cerium(IV)-cerium(III) couple in $1\,F$ sulfuric acid is $+1.44$ v, which is lower than the corresponding values for either $1\,F$ nitric acid or $1\,F$ perchloric acid. In simple terms, this observation means that the ratio $[Ce^{+++}]/[Ce^{++++}]$ is *higher* in sulfuric acid than in the other two media or that $Ce(H_2O)_6^{++++}$, *relative* to $Ce(H_2O)_6^{+++}$, reacts more completely with the components of a sulfuric acid solution than those of nitric or perchloric acid solutions. Similarly, the fact that the formal potential of the cerium(IV)-cerium(III) couple is highest in $1\,F$ perchloric acid means that the ratio $[Ce^{+++}]/[Ce^{++++}]$ is *lowest* in this medium or that the reaction of $Ce(H_2O)_6^{++++}$, *relative* to $Ce(H_2O)_6^{+++}$, is least with the components of perchloric acid. Note that the variations in the formal potentials only measure *differences* in the *relative* extents of reactions of $Ce(H_2O)_6^{++++}$ and $Ce(H_2O)_6^{+++}$ with the particular acid medium. The formal potentials provide no way to ascertain the absolute extent of reaction of either $Ce(H_2O)_6^{++++}$ or $Ce(H_2O)_6^{+++}$ with the acid medium.

From what has already been stated, it is apparent that the cerium(IV) ion does not exist simply as $Ce(H_2O)_6^{++++}$ and that $Ce(H_2O)_6^{+++}$ is definitely not the only form of cerium(III). In the discussion of the cerium(IV)-iron(II) titration in Chapter 12, it was pointed out that $Ce(H_2O)_6^{++++}$ is a strong acid and that proton-transfer reactions such as

$$Ce(H_2O)_6^{++++} + H_2O \rightleftharpoons Ce(H_2O)_5(OH)^{+++} + H_3O^+$$

and

$$Ce(H_2O)_5(OH)^{+++} + H_2O \rightleftharpoons Ce(H_2O)_4(OH)_2^{++} + H_3O^+$$

will occur regardless of what anions may be present in solution. In addition, the formation of dimeric species and perhaps higher polymers is known to occur. Analogous reactions prevail in the case of cerium(III), although the extent of such reactions is probably less, owing to the smaller positive charge of cerium(III). The kinds of reactions mentioned so far largely depend on the hydrogen ion concentration of the particular solution and on the total concentrations of cerium(IV) and cerium(III). Evidence, not always of a conclusive nature, has been obtained to indicate that both cerium(IV) and cerium(III) form complexes with anions of the mineral acids. Even the perchlorate ion, which is considered to be one of the poorest ligands with regard to complex formation, apparently coordinates with cerium(III) and cerium-(IV) to yield, respectively, $Ce(H_2O)_5(ClO_4)^{++}$ and $Ce(H_2O)_5(ClO_4)^{+++}$. In nitric acid solutions there seems to be definite interaction between nitrate and cerium(IV) leading to the formation of $Ce(H_2O)(NO_3)_5^-$ and $Ce(NO_3)_6^=$. The behavior of cerium(IV) and cerium(III) in sulfuric acid has been studied more extensively, and species such as $Ce(H_2O)_5(SO_4)^{++}$, $Ce(H_2O)_3(SO_4)_3^=$, and $Ce(H_2O)_5(SO_4)^+$ have been identified. In general, the order of increasing stability of cerium(IV) complexes *relative* to cerium(III) complexes seems to correlate well with the variations in the formal potentials mentioned previously. The behavior of cerium(IV) in hydrochloric acid should be discussed. The formal potential for the cerium(IV)-cerium(III) half-reaction in $1\ F$ hydrochloric acid is reported to be $+1.28$ v versus NHE. Although this potential is in accord with the known formation of cerium(IV) complexes such as $Ce(H_2O)_5Cl^{+++}$ and $Ce(H_2O)_4Cl_2^{++}$, the actual magnitude of the formal potential is subject to doubt because cerium(IV) spontaneously oxidizes chloride to chlorine gas. Consequently, hydrochloric acid solutions of cerium(IV) are not employed as standard titrants. In view of the varied and complicated chemistry of cerium(IV), as well as of cerium(III), it is understandable why the quadrivalent cerium ion is written as "cerium(IV)" to signify the oxidation state but to imply nothing specific about the actual ions which are present.

In summary, permanganate is a more powerful oxidizing agent than is dichromate, although pH influences the strength of both, and the oxidizing strength of cerium(IV) ranges from much greater than that of permanganate to slightly less than that of dichromate, depending upon the nature of the acid environment.

COLORS OF OXIDIZED AND REDUCED FORMS

The colors of the oxidized and reduced forms of a standard oxidizing agent are of significance in the detection of end points of titrations. If the color of a small amount of the oxidized form of the titrant can be detected in the presence of a much larger concentration of the reduced form, the reagent may serve as its own end point indicator when used to titrate other substances. Even if a colored redox indicator such as ferroin is employed to signal the end point, its color change must be detectable in the presence of the oxidized and reduced forms of the titrant, and so once again the colors of the oxidized and reduced forms of the standard oxidizing agent are significant. In any specific application, consideration must also be given to the possibility that the end point color change may be masked by some other colored substance in the solution being titrated.

Solutions of potassium permanganate are so intensely colored that a single drop of a $0.02\,F$ solution imparts a perceptible color to 100 ml of water. The reduction product of permanganate in an acid medium, Mn^{++}, is practically colorless at reasonable concentration levels. Usually, if the solution being titrated is colorless, the theoretical equivalence point in a titration with standard permanganate solution is the point just beyond which the first slight trace of unreacted permanganate ion persists in the titration vessel. Therefore, the appearance of the pale pink color imparted to the solution by the first trace of excess titrant may be taken as the theoretical equivalence point, permanganate thus serving as its own indicator.

The intense purple color of permanganate necessitates a different method for reading burets. In ordinary volumetric work, the lower part of the meniscus should be read but, with $0.02\,F$ potassium permanganate in the buret, the meniscus is not visible. Therefore, the position of the top of the solution is usually observed; however, if a flashlight is held behind the buret, the lower part of the meniscus may be seen. No appreciable error need be introduced in volume measurements if initial and final buret readings are made in the same manner.

Cerium(IV) is yellow in all mineral acid solutions, whereas its reduced form, cerium(III), is colorless. A cerium(IV) solution may serve as its own indicator, but only for relatively inexact work. The yellow color of cerium(IV) is not sufficiently intense for it to be recognized until an excessive amount is present, usually an excess of at least 1 per cent. In other words, the true equivalence point must be passed to an appreciable extent before the experimental end point is observed. The moderate yellow color of cerium(IV) does not interfere in the least with recognition of the color changes of redox indicators, and, as described in Chapter 12, numerous end point indicators are available for titrations involving cerium(IV). In addition, the technique of potentiometric titration can always be employed for redox titrimetry.

Both dichromate and its reduction product, chromium(III), are colored. Dichromate solutions have an orange-yellow color which resembles that of cerium(IV) solutions, whereas chromium(III) is usually either green or violet, depending upon the exact composition of the medium in which it is formed. The passing of the end point in a titration with dichromate is characterized by the persistence of the first trace of excess dichromate ion in the titration vessel, which doubtless gives a yellow coloration to the solution. Unfortunately, the yellow color due to excess dichromate is completely masked by the green or violet color of the chromium(III) formed earlier in the titration. Thus, dichromate cannot serve as its own end point indicator. Furthermore, any indicator which is used in titrations involving dichromate must be one whose color change is so distinct that it can be readily recognized in the presence of the other colored species in solution at and near the equivalence point. Suitable indicators are available for dichrome titrations and, alternatively, end points can be located by means of potentiometry.

PREPARATION AND STABILITY OF
STANDARD SOLUTIONS

Potassium Permanganate. Potassium permanganate is rarely, if ever, available in a sufficiently high state of purity to permit its direct use as a primary standard substance. Even reagent-grade potassium permanganate is almost invariably contaminated with small quantities of manganese dioxide. In addition, ordinary distilled water, from which potassium permanganate solutions are prepared, contains organic matter which can reduce permanganate to manganese dioxide.

From thermodynamic considerations, one would predict that permanganate solutions are inherently unstable because MnO_4^- is capable of oxidizing water spontaneously. The emf for the reaction

$$4\,MnO_4^- + 2\,H_2O \rightleftharpoons 4\,MnO_2 + 3\,O_2 + 4\,OH^-$$

is $+0.187$ v, which indicates that permanganate in a neutral medium should be reduced to manganese dioxide. Fortunately, the rate of this reaction is exceedingly slow if proper precautions are taken in the original preparation of the solution. The reaction between permanganate and water has been observed to be catalyzed by heat, light, acids, bases, manganese(II) salts, and especially by manganese dioxide itself. Thus, any manganese dioxide initially present in the potassium permanganate solution must be removed if a stable titrant is to be obtained. Since the reaction between permanganate and the organic matter in distilled water cannot conveniently be eliminated, it should be allowed to proceed to completion, or nearly so, prior to standardization of the solution. After the potassium permanganate is dissolved, the solution should be heated to hasten this decomposition reaction and allowed to stand so that the initially colloidal manganese dioxide can coagulate. Next, the manganese dioxide precipitate must be removed from the solution by filtration; otherwise, it would enter into further reaction when the titrant is subsequently used in an acid medium and, as already mentioned, it would tend to catalyze further decomposition of permanganate. The permanganate solution should be filtered through an asbestos mat contained in a Gooch crucible or Buchner funnel, or else through a sintered-glass filter funnel — but never through filter paper, because the paper itself could cause additional decomposition of the permanganate solution. Solutions of potassium permanganate should be stored in dark bottles and kept out of bright light and away from dust as much as is conveniently possible. Potassium permanganate solutions of a concentration not less than $0.02\,F$, when prepared and stored in the manner just described, are stable for many months.

A standard solution of any reducing agent which reacts quantitatively with permanganate may be used for standardization purposes. Among the primary standard substances which are suitable for this purpose are arsenious oxide (As_2O_3), sodium oxalate ($Na_2C_2O_4$), and pure iron wire.

In practice, arsenious oxide, which is commercially available as a primary-standard-grade solid, is initially dissolved in a sodium hydroxide solution,

$$As_2O_3 + 2\ OH^- \longrightarrow 2\ AsO_2^- + H_2O$$

which is subsequently acidified with hydrochloric acid and titrated with potassium permanganate according to the reaction*

$$2\ MnO_4^- + 5\ HAsO_2 + 6\ H^+ + 2\ H_2O \rightleftharpoons 2\ Mn^{++} + 5\ H_3AsO_4$$

However, this titration reaction does not proceed rapidly without a catalyst. One possible explanation for the slowness of this reaction is that permanganate is partially reduced to manganese(III) and manganese(IV) species, which are stabilized as arsenate complexes. Iodine monochloride has been recommended as an excellent catalyst for this titration, although in a hydrochloric acid solution, iodine monochloride actually exists as the species ICl_2^-. We can understand the catalytic ability of ICl_2^- by considering the following three half-reactions:

$$H_3AsO_4 + 2\ H^+ + 2\ e \rightleftharpoons HAsO_2 + 2\ H_2O; \qquad E^\circ = +0.559\ v$$
$$2\ ICl_2^- + 2\ e \rightleftharpoons I_2 + 4\ Cl^-; \qquad E^\circ = +1.06\ v$$
$$MnO_4^- + 8\ H^+ + 5\ e \rightleftharpoons Mn^{++} + 4\ H_2O; \qquad E^\circ = +1.51\ v$$

It is important to note that the reaction between $HAsO_2$ and ICl_2^-,

$$HAsO_2 + 2\ ICl_2^- + 2\ H_2O \rightleftharpoons H_3AsO_4 + I_2 + 2\ H^+ + 4\ Cl^-;$$

$$E^\circ = +0.50\ v$$

is a thermodynamically favorable process and that it does occur very rapidly. Furthermore, the iodine produced by this first reaction is quickly reoxidized to ICl_2^- by permanganate:

$$2\ MnO_4^- + 5\ I_2 + 20\ Cl^- + 16\ H^+ \rightleftharpoons 2\ Mn^{++} + 10\ ICl_2^- + 8\ H_2O$$

The emf under standard-state conditions for the latter reaction has a value of $+0.45$ v, which indicates that the oxidation of iodine by permanganate is quantitatively complete in a hydrochloric acid medium. Then, if the two preceding reactions are considered together, the desired titration reaction is realized. The requirements which must be fulfilled by a **redox catalyst** such as iodine monochloride may be summarized as follows: (1) The oxidized form of the catalyst must react rapidly with the reducing agent ($HAsO_2$ in this example); (2) the reduced form of the catalyst must react rapidly with

---

* Some authors use H_3AsO_3 as the formula of arsenious acid. We prefer to write $HAsO_2$ as the predominant form of arsenic(III) because arsenious acid behaves as a weak monoprotic acid in aqueous media.

the oxidizing agent (MnO_4^- in this example); and (3) the standard potential for the catalyst half-reaction should lie between the standard potentials for the half-reactions involving the desired reducing and oxidizing agents. With regard to the first of these requirements, it should be emphasized that the catalyst must convert the reducing agent to the same species as does the oxidizing agent. Thus, $HAsO_2$ must be oxidized to H_3AsO_4 by both permanganate and iodine monochloride. Similarly, permanganate must ultimately be reduced to manganous ion, whether by arsenic(III) or by iodine. The third requirement is necessary in order that the catalytically active species be able to react quantitatively with both the oxidizing agent and the reducing agent. As an illustration of this point, if the standard potentials for the arsenic(V)-arsenic(III) and ICl_2^--I_2 half-reactions happened to be identical, the catalyst would have little tendency to react with the arsenic(III) and, hence, the catalyst would probably behave sluggishly at best.

Sodium oxalate is another important substance used for the standardization of potassium permanganate solutions. It is available commercially in a very pure state, and it dissolves in sulfuric acid media with the resultant formation of undissociated oxalic acid molecules. The stoichiometry of the permanganate-oxalic acid reaction may be represented in the following way:

$$2\ MnO_4^- + 5\ H_2C_2O_4 + 6\ H^+ \longrightarrow 2\ Mn^{++} + 10\ CO_2 + 8\ H_2O$$

However, the mechanism by which this reaction proceeds is exceedingly complex, and analytical results that are reproducible and stoichiometric are obtained only when certain empirical conditions are fulfilled. Temperature plays a very important role in the success of the titration; usually, the titration is carried out at solution temperatures near $70°C$ so that the rate of reaction is conveniently fast. Another interesting feature of this redox process is that the first few drops of permanganate react very slowly, as evidenced by the fact that the permanganate color does not disappear for many seconds, but succeeding portions of titrant react more and more rapidly until the reaction becomes essentially instantaneous. This behavior is typical of an *autocatalytic process*, in which one of the reaction products functions as a catalyst. In the present situation, manganese(II) is this catalyst. As soon as the first few drops of permanganate solution are reduced to manganous ion, the latter quickly reacts with more permanganate, in the presence of oxalate, to form oxalate complexes of manganese(III),

$$4\ Mn^{++} + MnO_4^- + 15\ C_2O_4^= + 8\ H^+ \longrightarrow 5\ Mn(C_2O_4)_3^\equiv + 4\ H_2O$$

which subsequently decompose in several steps to yield manganese(II) and carbon dioxide:

$$2\ Mn(C_2O_4)_3^\equiv \longrightarrow 2\ Mn^{++} + 2\ CO_2 + 5\ C_2O_4^=$$

The sequence of reactions is even more complicated because manganese(IV) and manganese(VI) species are believed to be involved as transient intermediates. The net result of all these reactions is that oxalic acid is oxidized to carbon dioxide, permanganate is reduced to manganous ion, and the desired reaction stoichiometry is obeyed.

Ordinary iron wire is not pure enough for use as a primary standard, but a specially purified grade may be purchased for this purpose. A known weight of iron wire is dissolved in acid, converted to iron(II), and the iron(II) is titrated to iron(III) with the permanganate solution to be standardized. The reactions involved in the titration procedure will be discussed in detail later in this chapter when we consider the analysis of iron ores. Primary standard iron wire can be obtained with a sufficiently uniform cross section so that the quantity required for the standardization of a permanganate solution can be measured with a ruler instead of by weight. However, the regular weighing method is definitely recommended for the most accurate analytical work.

Potassium Dichromate.   Potassium dichromate may be obtained as a primary-standard substance which is suitable for the direct preparation, by weight, of standard solutions. Furthermore, potassium dichromate is readily soluble in water, and the resulting solutions are stable for many years if protected against evaporation. In addition, dichromate solutions can be boiled without the occurrence of any detectable decomposition. Occasionally, potassium dichromate solutions are standardized against known substances chemically similar to unknown samples which are to be analyzed later. The advantages of such an approach are that it eliminates any systematic errors inherent in the analytical procedure or the chemical reactions and that it compensates automatically for the volume of titrant needed to cause an end point indicator to undergo a color change.

Cerium(IV).   Ammonium hexanitratocerate(IV), $(NH_4)_2Ce(NO_3)_6$, is a good primary standard for the direct preparation of standard cerium(IV) solutions. However, cerium(IV) solutions are more commonly prepared from cerium(IV) bisulfate, $Ce(HSO_4)_4$; from ammonium sulfatocerate(IV), $(NH_4)_4Ce(SO_4)_4 \cdot 2 H_2O$; or from hydrous ceric oxide, $CeO_2 \cdot xH_2O$ — all of which are commercially available. The solution which is prepared must contain a high concentration of acid, usually 1 M or greater, in order to prevent the precipitation of hydrous ceric oxide. As discussed earlier in this chapter, cerium(IV) is a very acidic species and undergoes proton-transfer reactions such as

$$Ce(H_2O)_6^{++++} + H_2O \rightleftharpoons Ce(H_2O)_5(OH)^{+++} + H_3O^+$$

We may write the fourth member in the series of proton-transfer equilibria as

$$Ce(H_2O)_3(OH)_3^+ + H_2O \rightleftharpoons Ce(H_2O)_2(OH)_4 + H_3O^+$$

noting, in addition, that the cerium(IV) species on the right side of this equilibrium is one representation of hydrous ceric oxide. The latter reaction reaches virtual completion at pH values greater than 3, but precipitation of hydrous ceric oxide commences at pH values as low as 1.

Sulfuric acid solutions of cerium(IV) are stable indefinitely and, if necessary, they may even be heated for short periods of time. On the other hand, although solutions of cerium(IV) in nitric acid and in perchloric acid possess greater oxidizing strength, they are prone to undergo slow decomposition because of the reduction of cerium(IV) by water, a process which is light induced. Solutions of cerium(IV) in hydrochloric acid are decidedly unstable, owing to the oxidation of chloride ion to chlorine gas by cerium(IV). It is noteworthy, however, that no particular difficulty is experienced when one titrates species dissolved in hydrochloric acid with a sulfuric acid solution of cerium(IV). The reason for this is that the cerium(IV) reacts more readily with these other substances than with chloride prior to the equivalence point; whereas at and slightly beyond the equivalence point, cerium(IV) is stable long enough either to oxidize a redox indicator to a different colored form or to yield another kind of end point signal.

The general procedures used in the standardization of cerium(IV) titrants differ little from those used to standardize potassium permanganate solutions. Primary standard substances suitable for standardizing cerium(IV) solutions include the three already discussed for permanganate — namely, arsenious oxide, sodium oxalate, and iron wire.

As in the standardization of potassium permanganate described previously, a catalyst is required for rapid reaction between cerium(IV) and arsenic(III). If arsenic(III) is titrated in a hydrochloric acid medium, iodine monochloride may serve as the catalytic species; presumably, it behaves in this titration precisely as it does in the permanganate-arsenic(III) reaction. More commonly, after the solid arsenious oxide is initially dissolved in a sodium hydroxide medium, sulfuric acid rather than hydrochloric acid is used to acidify the solution, osmium tetroxide (OsO_4) is added as the catalyst, and the mixture is titrated with the cerium(IV) solution to be standardized. The mechanism of the catalysis by osmium tetroxide appears not to have been fully established. It is, of course, essential that arsenic(III) rapidly reduce osmium(VIII) to some lower oxidation state and that cerium(IV) immediately reoxidize the osmium species. When a few drops of osmium tetroxide catalyst are added to a solution of arsenic(III) in sulfuric acid, one observes the formation of a pale bluish-black color throughout the solution. Conceivably, arsenic(III) could reduce osmium tetroxide all the way to the elemental state since the emf for the reaction

$$4\ HAsO_2 + OsO_4 + 4\ H_2O \rightleftharpoons 4\ H_3AsO_4 + Os$$

is $+0.29$ v under standard-state conditions. However, since osmium exhibits other oxidation states — $+2$, $+3$, $+4$, and $+6$ — it is equally plausible that the bluish-black color is caused by a mixture of two different, intermediate oxidation states or, even more likely, by osmium(IV) which is known to exist as the colloidal blue-black hydrous oxide ($OsO_2 \cdot xH_2O$).

Pure sodium oxalate may be dissolved in perchloric acid and employed for the standardization at room temperature of cerium(IV) solutions in either nitric acid or perchloric acid. Interestingly, if one desires to standardize a cerium(IV) sulfate titrant by an analogous procedure, it is necessary to heat the oxalic acid solution to approximately 70°C so that the rate of the cerium(IV)-oxalic acid reaction will be adequately fast. At room temperature the presence of relatively stable and unreactive sulfate complexes of cerium(IV) inhibits the titration reaction. Once again, however, the use of iodine monochloride as a catalyst permits the room-temperature standardization of cerium(IV) sulfate solutions against oxalic acid in a hydrochloric acid medium.

In addition to pure iron wire, other substances for the standardization of cerium(IV) titrants include Oesper's salt, $FeC_2H_4(NH_3)_2(SO_4)_2 \cdot 2\ H_2O$, and Mohr's salt, $Fe(NH_4)_2(SO_4)_2 \cdot 6\ H_2O$. These compounds are available in exceptionally pure form and are readily soluble in water. They are suitable for the standardization of potassium permanganate and potassium dichromate solutions as well.

END POINT INDICATORS

For titrations with potassium permanganate, no indicator other than the titrant itself is required, unless the titrant happens to be very dilute, for example, $0.001\ F$ or less concentrated. If the titrant is too dilute to serve as its own indicator, tris(1,10-phenanthroline)iron(II), or ferroin, plus other substituted ferroin-type indicators discussed in Chapter 12 may be used. It should be recalled that many reactions involving permanganate, including the one with oxalic acid employed to standardize the titrant, proceed somewhat slowly. Thus, there may be a momentary appearance of the pink end point color before the true end point is reached. Furthermore, the end point color fades slowly, owing to the gradual reduction of permanganate by water, chloride ion, or other species, and so the point at which the first definite tinge of permanganate color persists in the titration vessel for 30 seconds is conventionally accepted as the end point.

Some common indicators, listed in Table 12-2, for cerium(IV) titrations are tris(1,10-phenanthroline)iron(II), tris(5-nitro-1,10-phenanthroline)iron-(II), and tris(5-methyl-1,10-phenanthroline)iron(II). Each of these indicators is a deep orange-red in its reduced form, but is oxidized to its pale blue iron(III) form by the first excess of cerium(IV) in the titration vessel. The standard-potential values for these three indicators range from $+1.02$ up to $+1.25$ v versus NHE, making one or more of them suitable for the titrations with cerium(IV) of iron(II), oxalic acid, arsenic(III), hydrogen peroxide, antimony(III), molybdenum(V), plutonium(III), tin(II), and numerous other species.

Potassium dichromate is not sufficiently strong as an oxidizing agent to permit the use of a colored redox indicator with a standard potential as high as those of the ferroin indicators, unless the hydrogen ion concentration is unduly high. The problem is that the theoretical equivalence point potentials for many titrations involving dichromate are well below the values at which ferroin indicators normally exhibit their color changes. Consequently, another family of redox indicators derived from the colorless compound diphenylamine has been developed. In the presence of an excess of an

diphenylamine

oxidant, such as potassium dichromate, diphenylamine undergoes an irreversible oxidative coupling reaction to yield diphenylbenzidine, which is also colorless. However, upon further oxidation, diphenylbenzidine is converted

diphenylbenzidine

to a bright purple compound, known as diphenylbenzidine violet, which owes its deep color to a system of conjugated double bonds. The purple color of

diphenylbenzidine violet

the completely oxidized indicator is sufficiently intense to be easily discernible even in the presence of green-colored chromium(III). It is highly significant that diphenylbenzidine and diphenylbenzidine violet are interconvertible, for it is this reversible reaction, with a standard potential of $+0.76$ v versus NHE, which provides the desired indicator behavior. In principle, either diphenylamine or diphenylbenzidine may be added to the solution being titrated, but diphenylbenzidine should be preferable because its oxidation to diphenylbenzidine violet consumes only one-half the quantity of dichromate needed to oxidize diphenylamine to the violet compound.

Unfortunately, both diphenylamine and diphenylbenzidine suffer from the disadvantage that they are relatively insoluble in aqueous media. These substances can be rendered water soluble, however, if the readily ionizable sulfonic acid derivatives are prepared. Thus, the diphenylamine sulfonate and diphenylbenzidine sulfonate ions, usually in the form of their barium or

diphenylamine sulfonate

diphenylbenzidine sulfonate

sodium salts, are soluble in acidic media and undergo exactly the same color change as the unsulfonated parent compounds. The only difference between the unsulfonated and sulfonated indicator species is the fact that the standard potentials of the latter are approximately 80 to 110 mv more positive (see Table 12-2).

SELECTED APPLICATIONS

The remainder of this chapter is devoted to an investigation of some of the typical quantitative determinations requiring the use of standard solutions of potassium permanganate, potassium dichromate, and cerium(IV). These applications involve both inorganic and organic substances and demonstrate most of the factors which must be considered in designing a titrimetric analytical procedure.

Determination of Iron

Iron may be the most frequently encountered element in industrial analysis, and so its accurate determination is of both practical and pedagogical interest. Several of the factors involved in the determination of iron are common to other redox titrations; therefore, a detailed understanding of the principles and rationale of the procedure is extremely valuable.

The volumetric determination of iron generally consists of four major steps: dissolution of the iron sample; quantitative reduction of iron(III) to iron(II) with a suitable reductant, followed by removal of the excess reducing agent; addition of special reagents, if needed, to ensure that the proper reaction will occur during the subsequent titration; and titration of the iron(II) solution with standard potassium permanganate, potassium dichromate, or cerium(IV). Some of the details of the individual steps differ according to which titrant is employed.

Dissolution of the Sample.   The steps taken to dissolve a sample must be selected to fit the particular specimen involved. Occasionally, a water-soluble iron salt is encountered, but the majority of iron-containing samples are either metal alloys or iron oxides which are insoluble in water. Metallic iron itself is soluble in nitric acid, hydrochloric acid, or sulfuric acid; and one or another of these solvents serves satisfactorily to dissolve most iron alloys.

The important iron ores, including hematite (Fe_2O_3), limonite $(2 Fe_2O_3 \cdot 3 H_2O)$, and magnetite (Fe_3O_4), can be effectively dissolved in hot hydrochloric acid, whereas neither nitric acid nor sulfuric acid is satisfactory. A sample that is finely pulverized dissolves much more readily than one in the form of larger granules. During the dissolution process, the hydrochloric acid should be boiled vigorously, but the solution should not be permitted to evaporate to dryness. A small amount of stannous chloride hastens the dissolution process, apparently by reducing the ferric ions to ferrous ions as rapidly as they pass into solution. In situations where the iron ore is highly refractory, fusion of a sample with a flux of sodium carbonate or potassium acid sulfate may be necessary to render the ore soluble.

Phosphoric acid dissolves most iron ore samples, but an insoluble iron phosphate precipitate of indefinite composition may form. A one-to-one mixture of perchloric and phosphoric acids is an excellent solvent for iron ores, a 15 minute period of heating near the boiling point being sufficient to dissolve the sample completely. Hot perchloric acid is a powerful oxidizing agent, and a reaction of explosive violence may occur when the concentrated acid is heated in the presence of organic material. Therefore, it is essential that the use of this reagent be limited to carefully prescribed procedures; however, no particular hazard is involved if perchloric acid is used properly.

Most iron ores contain some silica which will not dissolve upon treatment with hot hydrochloric acid. The siliceous residue is not harmful in the determination of iron, and it may be distinguished easily from any remaining particles of undissolved iron oxide because the silica is lighter than the iron oxide, both in color and in density.

After the sample is dissolved, the iron will exist either wholly or partly as iron(III). The dissolution of iron alloys and iron(II) oxides invariably yields some iron(III) through the process of air oxidation, unless the sample is dissolved in an oxygen-free environment.

Reduction of Iron(III) to Iron(II).   The eventual titration with the standard oxidant requires that all iron be present as iron(II). Therefore, the iron(III) formed during the dissolution of the sample must be quantitatively reduced to iron(II) prior to the start of the titration. Several different reducing agents have been used to accomplish this reduction.

It is of interest to consider what general properties of a reductant (or oxidant) make it suitable for use in adjusting the oxidation state of iron, or any other species to be determined. First, the reductant or oxidant must convert the iron or other species quantitatively to the desired oxidation state.

Second, it must be possible, as well as convenient, to remove the excess reductant or oxidant so that it will not react later with the titrant. Third, the reductant or oxidant should possess a certain degree of selectivity; for example, if a hydrochloric acid solution containing iron(III) and titanium(IV) is treated with a relatively strong reductant such as metallic zinc, iron(II) and titanium(III) are produced, but the so-called silver reductor selectively reduces only the iron(III).

Two gaseous substances which have been used to reduce iron(III) to iron(II) are hydrogen sulfide and sulfur dioxide. From a table of standard potentials, it is evident that the reduction of iron(III) should be quantitative in a hydrochloric acid medium with either reagent.

$$2\ Fe^{+++} + H_2S \rightleftharpoons 2\ Fe^{++} + S + 2\ H^+; \qquad E^\circ = +0.56\ v$$

$$2\ Fe^{+++} + H_2SO_3 + H_2O \rightleftharpoons 2\ Fe^{++} + SO_4^= + 4\ H^+; \qquad E^\circ = +0.53\ v$$

The excess of each gaseous reductant may be removed if one simply boils the solution, although care must be taken not to reoxidize the iron(II) in this process. The reduction of iron(III) by sulfur dioxide is somewhat slow, and the use of hydrogen sulfide does lead to the formation of colloidal sulfur which may react with strong oxidants.

Several solid reductants are commonly employed to convert iron(III) to iron(II). As already mentioned, metallic zinc is a potent reductant:

$$2\ Fe^{+++} + Zn \rightleftharpoons 2\ Fe^{++} + Zn^{++}; \quad E^\circ = +1.46\ v$$

Zinc metal may be employed in the form of a wire spiral or in the form of a **Jones reductor,** as shown in Figure 13-1. This reductor consists of a glass column, usually with a diameter two or three times that of an ordinary buret, which is packed with amalgamated, granulated zinc. The amalgamation of the zinc has no effect on the reduction of iron(III) but does minimize the undesirable reduction of water to hydrogen gas. The iron(III) solution to be reduced is simply poured through the column and is collected in the receiving flask as an essentially pure solution of iron(II). No special step is required to remove the excess reductant, because none of the metallic zinc passes through the column. Zinc ion formed in the reduction of iron(III) does accompany iron(II) into the receiving vessel, but it is completely innocuous in the subsequent titration. If a simple spiral of zinc wire is utilized as the reductant, it may be inserted into the iron(III) solution and withdrawn when the reduction is judged to be complete. The Jones reductor or the wire spiral should be washed to ensure that none of the iron(II) solution is lost and the washings should be added to the sample solution.

The silver reductor is extremely useful for a variety of applications, including the quantitative reduction of iron(III) to iron(II). A column, similar to that employed for the Jones reductor, is filled with high purity silver metal granules. When a hydrochloric acid solution of iron(III) is passed through the column, iron(II) is obtained quantitatively while the metallic silver, in the presence of chloride ion, is oxidized to silver chloride which coats the particles of silver:

$$Fe^{+++} + Ag + Cl^- \rightleftharpoons Fe^{++} + AgCl; \qquad E^\circ = +0.48 \text{ v}$$

Since silver metal in the presence of chloride ion is not as strong a reductant as metallic zinc, the use of a silver reductor may permit greater selectivity in the preferential adjustment of the oxidation state of one certain substance in a mixture of several species. Furthermore, the Nernst equation predicts that the reducing strength of a silver reductor depends directly on the concentration of chloride ion in the solution passed through the column. For example, it can be shown that the effective emf for the preceding reduction of iron(III) to iron(II) would be only $+0.36$ v in the presence of 0.01 M chloride ion. Although this emf still indicates that iron(III) would be quantitatively reduced, it is evident that appropriate variations of the chloride concentration in the original sample solution may provide additional selectivity in reduction processes. The only drawback to the use of a silver reductor

FIGURE 13-1.   Jones reductor assembly.

is that the metallic silver eventually becomes completely coated with a film of silver chloride. When this happens, the column can be treated with a strong reductant to regenerate elemental silver.

Other solid reductants, including cadmium, lead, and aluminum, may be employed either in the form of a column similar to the Jones reductor or in the form of a wire coil which is dipped into the sample solution and withdrawn after the desired reduction has been accomplished. A number of liquid amalgams have been employed to perform reductions in a manner analogous to the use of solid reductants. Thus, a solution of elemental lead, bismuth, or sodium in mercury may be shaken in an ordinary separatory funnel with the sample solution until the reduction is complete, the mercury and solution phases separated, and the aqueous medium subjected to appropriate titration or other chemical analysis.

Although all of the previously mentioned reductants function effectively for the quantitative reduction of iron(III), the use of each reducing agent is unnecessarily time-consuming. A simple, yet elegant, method for the reduction of iron(III) to iron(II) entails the addition of a very small excess of tin(II) chloride to the hot hydrochloric acid solution of the iron sample, followed by destruction of the excess tin(II) with mercury(II). The sequence of reactions is as follows:

$$2 \text{ Fe}^{+++} + \text{SnCl}_4^= + 2 \text{ Cl}^- \rightleftharpoons 2 \text{ Fe}^{++} + \text{SnCl}_6^=$$

$$\text{SnCl}_4^= + 2 \text{ HgCl}_4^= \rightleftharpoons \text{SnCl}_6^= + \text{Hg}_2\text{Cl}_2(s) + 4 \text{ Cl}^-$$

The quantity of tin(II) used in the first step is critical. Obviously, enough tin(II) must be introduced to cause complete reduction of iron(III); however, if the excess of tin(II) is too great, the second step will be replaced, at least partially, by the reaction

$$\text{SnCl}_4^= + \text{HgCl}_4^= \rightleftharpoons \text{SnCl}_6^= + \text{Hg}(s) + 2 \text{ Cl}^-$$

in which elemental mercury rather than mercurous chloride is formed. The occurrence of the latter process ruins the determination of iron because the metallic mercury, present in a finely divided colloidal state, reacts to a significant extent with the standard oxidizing agent in the subsequent titration. However, solid mercurous chloride (calomel) does not interfere with a successful titration, and so its presence is in no way harmful. Fortunately, iron(III) is yellow colored in hydrochloric acid media, owing to the presence of complexes such as $\text{FeCl}_4(\text{H}_2\text{O})_2^-$, and so a tin(II) solution may be added drop by drop until this yellow color just disappears. One or two drops more of the stannous chloride solution are then added to ensure that a slight excess of tin(II) is present. If the procedure is performed properly, a silky white precipitate of mercurous chloride appears when mercury(II) is introduced. On the other hand, if too much stannous chloride is used, the precipitate will be grayish or even black because of the presence of finely divided free mercury; the sample must be discarded if this error occurs.

The success of this procedure for adjusting the oxidation state of iron and for eliminating the excess tin(II) can be verified by means of equilibrium calculations. First, we will confirm that tin(II) does accomplish the quantitative reduction of iron(III) to iron(II). The formal potential for the overall reaction

$$2 \text{ Fe}^{+++} + \text{SnCl}_4^= + 2 \text{ Cl}^- \rightleftharpoons 2 \text{ Fe}^{++} + \text{SnCl}_6^=$$

can be calculated from the data in Table 12-1 to be $+0.56$ v, if we assume that formal potentials for half-reactions in $1 \ F$ hydrochloric acid apply to the actual sample solution, which has a hydrochloric acid concentration close to $6 \ F$. According to the concepts developed in the preceding chapter, the formal potential for the overall process just described corresponds to an equilibrium constant of 1.0×10^{19} at $25°C$. Thus,

$$\frac{[\text{Fe}^{++}]^2[\text{SnCl}_6^=]}{[\text{Fe}^{+++}]^2[\text{SnCl}_4^=][\text{Cl}^-]^2} = 1.0 \times 10^{19}$$

Taking the chloride concentration to be $6 \ M$ and assuming that only a 1 per cent excess of tin(II) is added, in which case $[\text{SnCl}_6^=]/[\text{SnCl}_4^=] = 100$, we calculate that

$$\frac{[\text{Fe}^{++}]^2}{[\text{Fe}^{+++}]^2} = 1.0 \times 10^{19} \frac{[\text{SnCl}_4^=][\text{Cl}^-]^2}{[\text{SnCl}_6^=]} = 1.0 \times 10^{19} \frac{(6)^2}{(100)} = 3.6 \times 10^{18}$$

$$\frac{[\text{Fe}^{++}]}{[\text{Fe}^{+++}]} = 1.9 \times 10^9$$

There is little doubt that the reduction of iron(III) to iron(II) is quantitative.

As a second step in this series of calculations, let us prove that the excess tin(II) is effectively removed from the scene of action by the addition of mercury(II). The formal potential for the overall reaction

$$\text{SnCl}_4^= + 2 \text{ HgCl}_4^= \rightleftharpoons \text{SnCl}_6^= + \text{Hg}_2\text{Cl}_2(s) + 4 \text{ Cl}^-$$

may be obtained if we combine the formal potentials for the following two half-reactions:

$$\text{SnCl}_4^- + 2 \text{ Cl} \rightleftharpoons \text{SnCl}_6^- + 2 \text{ e}$$

$$2 \text{ HgCl}_4^= + 2 \text{ e} \rightleftharpoons \text{Hg}_2\text{Cl}_2(s) + 6 \text{ Cl}^-$$

Unfortunately, the formal potential for the latter half-reaction is not listed in Table 12-1. However, it can be evaluated if we add the two half-reactions which follow and if we use the *free-energy relationships* discussed in Chapter 12. Accordingly,

$$2 \text{ HgCl}_4^= + 4 \text{ e} \rightleftharpoons 2 \text{ Hg} + 8 \text{ Cl}^-; \quad E° = +0.48 \text{ v}, \ nE° = +1.92 \text{ v}$$

$$2 \text{ Hg} + 2 \text{ Cl}^- \rightleftharpoons \text{Hg}_2\text{Cl}_2(s) + 2 \text{ e}; \quad E^{o\prime} = -0.27 \text{ v}, \ nE^{o\prime} = -0.54 \text{ v}$$

$$\overline{2 \text{ HgCl}_4^= + 2 \text{ e} \rightleftharpoons \text{Hg}_2\text{Cl}_2(s) + 6 \text{ Cl}^-; \quad nE^{o\prime} = +1.38 \text{ v}, \ E^{o\prime} = +0.69 \text{ v}}$$

Returning to the previous pair of half-reactions in this paragraph, we have

$$\text{SnCl}_4^= + 2\ \text{Cl}^- \rightleftharpoons \text{SnCl}_6^= + 2\ e; \qquad E^{o\prime} = -0.14\ \text{v}$$

and

$$2\ \text{HgCl}_4^= + 2\ e \rightleftharpoons \text{Hg}_2\text{Cl}_2(s) + 6\ \text{Cl}^-; \qquad E^{o\prime} = +0.69\ \text{v}$$

from which it follows that

$$\text{SnCl}_4^= + 2\ \text{HgCl}_4^= \rightleftharpoons \text{SnCl}_6^= + \text{Hg}_2\text{Cl}_2(s) + 4\ \text{Cl}^-; \qquad E^{o\prime} = +0.55\ \text{v}$$

The equilibrium constant for this reaction may be computed to be 4.5×10^{18}:

$$\frac{[\text{SnCl}_6^=][\text{Cl}^-]^4}{[\text{SnCl}_4^=][\text{HgCl}_4^=]^2} = 4.5 \times 10^{18}$$

In typical procedures, the quantity of mercury(II) added to oxidize the excess tin(II) corresponds to a concentration of 0.01 M. Therefore, if we assume that $[\text{HgCl}_4^=] = 0.01\ M$ and $[\text{Cl}^-] = 6\ M$,

$$\frac{[\text{SnCl}_6^=]}{[\text{SnCl}_4^=]} = 4.5 \times 10^{18} \frac{[\text{HgCl}_4^=]^2}{[\text{Cl}^-]^4} = 4.5 \times 10^{18} \frac{(0.01)^2}{(6)^4} = 3.5 \times 10^{11}$$

and the efficacy of the mercury(II) is confirmed.

There is one final point which should be considered. An inspection of the two half-reactions

$$\text{Fe}^{+++} + e \rightleftharpoons \text{Fe}^{++}; \qquad E^{o\prime} = +0.70\ \text{v}$$

and

$$2\ \text{HgCl}_4^= + 2\ e \rightleftharpoons \text{Hg}_2\text{Cl}_2(s) + 6\ \text{Cl}^-; \qquad E^{o\prime} = +0.69\ \text{v}$$

suggests that the mercury(II) added to destroy the excess tin(II) might cause some reoxidation of iron(II) to iron(III) according to the equilibrium

$$2\ \text{Fe}^{++} + 2\ \text{HgCl}_4^= \rightleftharpoons 2\ \text{Fe}^{+++} + \text{Hg}_2\text{Cl}_2(s) + 6\ \text{Cl}^-; \qquad E^{o} = -0.01\ \text{v}$$

The equilibrium expression and equilibrium constant for this reaction are

$$\frac{[\text{Fe}^{+++}]^2[\text{Cl}^-]^6}{[\text{Fe}^{++}]^2[\text{HgCl}_4^=]^2} = 0.46$$

If previously assigned values for the concentrations of $\text{HgCl}_4^=$ and Cl^- (0.01 and 6 M, respectively) are substituted into this relation, the result is

$$\frac{[\text{Fe}^{+++}]^2}{[\text{Fe}^{++}]^2} = 0.46 \frac{[\text{HgCl}_4^=]^2}{[\text{Cl}^-]^6} = 0.46 \frac{(0.01)^2}{(6)^6} = 9.9 \times 10^{-10}$$

or

$$\frac{[\text{Fe}^{+++}]}{[\text{Fe}^{++}]} = 3.1 \times 10^{-5}$$

This calculation (which, of course, is only an approximation) indicates that mercury(II) will not oxidize iron(II) to any significant extent under the experimental conditions employed.

Addition of Special Reagents. For some oxidation-reduction titrations, it is necessary to add certain special reagents to prevent the extraneous reaction of the oxidizing agent with species other than the desired substance and to ensure that the desired reaction proceeds quantitatively or that the end point color change of an indicator coincides with the theoretical equivalence point.

When iron(II) in a hydrochloric acid medium is titrated with one of the strong oxidizing agents — potassium permanganate, potassium dichromate, or cerium(IV) — two possible oxidation processes may occur. One of these reactions is the desired oxidation of iron(II), and the second possibility is the oxidation of chloride ion to chlorine. Dichromate is strong enough to oxidize iron(II) quantitatively, but the reaction between dichromate and chloride ions,

$$Cr_2O_7^= + 6\ Cl^- + 14\ H^+ \rightleftharpoons 2\ Cr^{+++} + 3\ Cl_2 + 7\ H_2O$$

has a standard potential of approximately -0.03 v and would not be expected to interfere with the determination of iron. It is interesting to note, however, that dichromate does oxidize chloride ion in very concentrated acid solutions. This behavior stems from the fact that the equilibrium constant for the reaction depends on the fourteenth power of the hydrogen ion concentration. The standard potential for the cerium(IV)-cerium(III) couple is low enough that only iron(II) is oxidized during the titration. In addition, it should be recalled that the accurate and precise results obtainable in the standardization of cerium(IV) titrants against arsenic(III) in a hydrochloric acid medium demonstrate that cerium(IV) does not rapidly oxidize chloride. Similarly, the standardization of potassium permanganate titrants against hydrochloric acid solutions of arsenic(III) is a reliable procedure; no significant oxidation of chloride occurs, even though permanganate is powerful enough as an oxidizing agent to react to some extent with chloride. However, when iron(II) in hydrochloric acid is titrated with permanganate, chloride ion is oxidized. The explanation for this unanticipated behavior is that the reaction between permanganate and iron(II) *induces* the oxidation of chloride to hypochlorous acid (HOCl). The mechanism of this induced reaction apparently involves the transient formation of an unstable higher oxidation state of iron, e.g., iron(IV) or iron(VI), or manganese(III) or manganese(IV) — any of which can subsequently oxidize chloride ion. Since hydrochloric acid is almost always needed as a solvent in the preparation of the sample solution, particularly for the dissolution of iron ores, there exists a potential source of error in the determination of iron with permanganate.

Two general methods have been devised for the elimination of this error. One approach is to remove the hydrochloric acid prior to the titration by evaporation with sulfuric acid. The latter acid has a high boiling point (360°C), and so hydrochloric acid is evolved when a solution containing both acids is partially evaporated. In this procedure, some sulfuric acid is added to the hydrochloric acid solution of the sample, and this solution is evaporated until dense white fumes of sulfur trioxide are evolved, at which time essentially all hydrochloric acid is absent. The second method employed to prevent the induced oxidation of chloride calls for the use of the Zimmermann-Reinhardt reagent followed by titration in the presence of the hydrochloric acid.

Zimmermann-Reinhardt reagent consists of manganous sulfate, phosphoric acid, and sulfuric acid. The exact reasons for the beneficial effect of these substances on the titration are not fully understood, but several facts are evident. The presence of manganese(II) prevents the accumulation of local excesses of the permanganate titrant as well as other intermediate oxidation states of manganese — notably manganese(IV), manganese(V), and manganese(VI). Phosphoric acid serves to weaken the strength of the active oxidizing agent, manganese(III), by forming complexes with it, so that chloride can no longer be oxidized. In addition, phosphoric acid forms colorless complexes with iron(III) which are more stable than iron(III)-chloride complexes and which do not obscure the appearance of the permanganate end point; the yellow iron(III)-chloride species do mask the end point.

In concluding this section on the addition of special reagents, we shall discuss briefly the iron(II)-dichromate titration in a $1 F$ hydrochloric acid medium. If the formal and standard potentials for the pertinent half-reactions are written

$$\text{Fe}^{+++} + e \rightleftharpoons \text{Fe}^{++}; \qquad E^{\circ\prime} = +0.70 \text{ v}$$

$$\text{Cr}_2\text{O}_7^= + 14 \text{ H}^+ + 6 e \rightleftharpoons 2 \text{ Cr}^{+++} + 7 \text{ H}_2\text{O}; \qquad E^\circ = +1.33 \text{ v}$$

and the theoretical titration curve is constructed, the result shown by curve A in Figure 13-2 is obtained. Note that the theoretical equivalence point potential is close to $+1.24$ v versus NHE. However, one of the curious and unexplained facts about dichromate is that it does not behave as if the standard potential for the chromium(VI)-chromium(III) couple is $+1.33$ v, but rather as if the standard potential were only approximately $+1.05$ v versus NHE. Curve B in Figure 13-2 depicts the titration curve when it is recalculated on this basis. In addition, we have shown the point at which diphenylbenzidine sulfonate is oxidized to diphenylbenzidine sulfonate violet. It is evident from a comparison of curve B with this color-change point that the indicator will change color too soon and that a negative titration error will arise. One of the steps taken to improve this situation involves the addition of phosphoric acid to the hydrochloric acid solution of iron(II). The effect of phosphoric acid is to render iron(II) a better reducing agent through complexation of iron(III); in a $1 F$ hydrochloric acid-$0.25 F$ phosphoric acid medium, the formal potential for the iron(III)-iron(II) couple is $+0.51$ v versus NHE. Therefore, the branch of the titration curve prior to the equivalence point is shifted downward to the position indicated by curve C, and the end point color change coincides much more closely with the steeply rising portion of the titration curve.

Another interesting point concerning the titration is that the oxidation of the indicator to its deep purple form is induced by the iron(II)-dichromate reaction and that dichromate by itself oxidizes the indicator only very slowly. Consequently, it is impossible to perform an indicator blank titration.

Titration.   The final titration of iron(II) may be performed with permanganate, dichromate, or cerium(IV). As indicated by the comparison of these reagents throughout this chapter, there are advantages and disadvantages of each, but excellent results are obtainable with all three titrants. The titration should be performed very soon after the reduction of

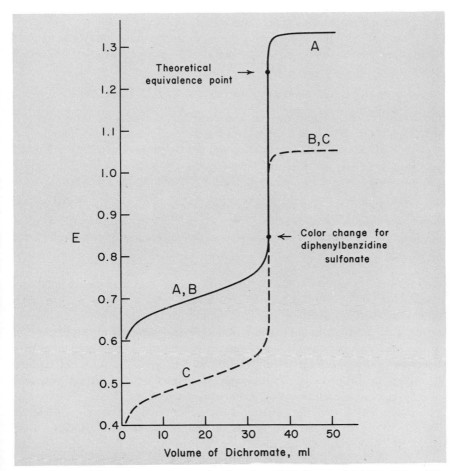

FIGURE 13-2.   Titration curves for titration of 35.00 ml of 0.1000 M iron(II) with 0.01667 F potassium dichromate. Curve A: theoretical titration curve for a 1 F hydrochloric acid medium based on tabulated standard and formal potentials. Curve B: actual titration curve for a 1 F hydrochloric acid medium based on apparent, rather than theoretical, oxidizing strength of dichromate. Curve C: actual titration curve for a 1 F hydrochloric acid-0.25 F phosphoric acid mixture.

iron(III) to iron(II), because solutions of the latter are slowly oxidized by atmospheric oxygen.

Determination of Calcium

The volumetric determination of calcium in limestone represents a useful type of indirect oxidation-reduction method of analysis. The principal components of dolomitic limestone are calcium carbonate and magnesium carbonate, although smaller percentages of calcium and magnesium silicates, plus carbonates and silicates of such elements as aluminum, iron, and manganese, are usually present. In addition, minor amounts of titanium, sodium, and potassium may exist in most specimens.

The first step of the procedure involves the preparation of the sample solution, which usually requires dissolution of a weighed portion of powdered limestone in hydrochloric acid:

$$CaCO_3 + 2 H^+ \longrightarrow Ca^{++} + CO_2 + H_2O$$

Occasionally, the sample can be rendered soluble only by fusion with a sodium carbonate flux. After the sample solution is obtained, the calcium is precipitated as calcium oxalate monohydrate under carefully adjusted conditions:

$$Ca^{++} + C_2O_4^{=} + H_2O \rightleftharpoons CaC_2O_4 \cdot H_2O$$

Then the precipitate is separated from its mother solution by filtration and is washed free of excess oxalate. Next, the calcium oxalate monohydrate is dissolved in sulfuric acid, the oxalate species being converted into oxalic acid,

$$CaC_2O_4 \cdot H_2O + 2 H^+ \rightleftharpoons Ca^{++} + H_2C_2O_4 + H_2O$$

and the oxalic acid solution is titrated with a standard potassium permanganate or cerium(IV) solution. Although calcium ion is not involved directly in the final titration, it is stoichiometrically related to the amount of oxalic acid titrated, each calcium ion corresponding to one molecule of oxalic acid. A number of other elements which form insoluble oxalate precipitates — zinc, cadmium, lead, cobalt, and nickel — may be determined according to the procedure. Obviously, these elements constitute potential interferences in the successful determination of calcium.

It is essential that the calcium oxalate monohydrate possess a perfectly defined composition and that it not be contaminated with coprecipitated oxalates. The precipitate obtained when an oxalate solution is added to the acidic sample solution of calcium ion and the mixture then slowly neutralized with aqueous ammonia is of higher purity than that obtained when the precipitate is formed by adding oxalate directly to a neutral or ammoniacal solution of calcium, because calcium oxalate monohydrate may be contaminated with calcium hydroxide or with a basic calcium oxalate if it is precipitated from a neutral or alkaline medium. The desired precipitate may contain coprecipitated magnesium and sodium oxalates when the quantities of these elements present are especially large or when the procedure for the determination of calcium is not rigorously followed. The coprecipitated substances can be effectively removed by the technique of reprecipitation. Furthermore, advantage may be taken of the tendencies for magnesium ion to form soluble oxalate complexes and for magnesium oxalate solutions to remain stable in the supersaturated state. Iron(III), aluminum(III), and manganese(II) do not interfere with the determination of calcium, owing to the formation of anionic oxalate complexes of these elements.

It is of interest to compare and contrast briefly the present procedure for the determination of calcium with other methods mentioned earlier in this text. However, it should be emphasized that the separation of calcium by precipitation of the oxalate compound is a necessary and accepted technique regardless of how the final determination is to be accomplished. The calcium oxalate monohydrate may be ignited at 500°C to pure calcium carbonate and can be weighed in the latter form. Alternatively, the calcium oxalate monohydrate may be redissolved and its calcium content determined by means of a complexometric titration, as described in Chapter 11. The latter approach has one advantage in that it is unnecessary to inquire about the purity of the calcium oxalate precipitate, since only total calcium is to be determined and since calcium can be titrated with EDTA in the presence of magnesium.

Determination of Higher Oxidation States of Manganese, Lead, Chromium, and Vanadium

Another important class of indirect oxidation-reduction methods of analysis pertains specifically to the determination of elements which are present in their higher oxidation states — manganese(VII) as MnO_4^-, manganese(IV) as MnO_2, lead(IV) as PbO_2 or Pb_3O_4, chromium(VI) as $Cr_2O_7^=$, and vanadium(V) as V_2O_5. If a known excess of a reducing agent is added to a sample solution of the desired element, an amount of reducing agent equivalent to that element is consumed and the unreacted reductant can be back-titrated with a standard solution of permanganate or cerium(IV).

For example, the manganese dioxide content of a pyrolusite ore may be determined if the sample is reduced with an excess of arsenic(III) in a sulfuric acid medium,

$$MnO_2 + HAsO_2 + 2\,H^+ \rightleftharpoons Mn^{++} + H_3AsO_4$$

and the resulting solution titrated with a standard solution of potassium permanganate to establish the quantity of unreacted arsenic(III):

$$5\,HAsO_2 + 2\,MnO_4^- + 6\,H^+ + 2\,H_2O \rightleftharpoons 5\,H_3AsO_4 + 2\,Mn^{++}$$

Similarly, it is possible to analyze an ore for lead dioxide by reaction of a sample with a measured excess of oxalic acid in sulfuric acid,

$$PbO_2 + H_2C_2O_4 + 2\,H^+ \rightleftharpoons Pb^{++} + 2\,CO_2 + 2\,H_2O$$

and by subsequent titration with cerium(IV):

$$H_2C_2O_4 + 2\,Ce^{++++} \rightleftharpoons 2\,CO_2 + 2\,Ce^{+++} + 2\,H^+$$

One frequently finds it convenient to determine species such as permanganate and dichromate by adding a known excess of iron(II) in the form of pure, solid ferrous ammonium sulfate, $Fe(NH_4)_2(SO_4)_2 \cdot 6\,H_2O$, to an acidic sample of the unknown and by back-titrating the unreacted iron(II) with a standard solution of permanganate, dichromate, or cerium(IV).

At least two reasons can be cited for the value of indirect titrimetric methods. First, standard solutions of certain reducing agents, such as chromium(II), titanium(III), or even iron(II), which are useful for direct titrations of higher oxidation states of manganese, lead, and chromium, are difficult to prepare and are unstable. Second, reactions of some of these higher oxidation states with reducing agents are not always conveniently rapid or precisely stoichiometric. As we shall see in Chapter 14, however, such difficulties can be avoided through the application of iodometric methods of analysis.

Determination of Organic Compounds

The quantitative oxidation of organic compounds has attracted no less attention than the determination of inorganic species. However, a major difficulty encountered in the development of routine procedures for the analysis of organic substances is their inherently slow rate of reaction with the various strong oxidizing agents such as permanganate, dichromate, and cerium(IV). Such behavior is understandable when it is realized that most organic compounds are eventually degraded to carbon dioxide and water, a process which usually involves the rupture of at least several carbon-carbon and carbon-hydrogen bonds. Furthermore, many organic compounds exhibit little or no specificity in the oxidation processes which they undergo, and so mixtures of organic substances may not always be analyzed. The occurrence of slow reactions can be overcome if the desired organic compound is treated with an excess of the oxidizing agent and if the reaction is allowed to proceed at an elevated temperature for extended periods of time. Unfortunately, these extreme conditions may lead to undesired side reactions and, therefore, to oxidation processes which appear to be nonstoichiometric. In spite of these problems, if reaction conditions are carefully controlled and reproduced, numerous valuable and practical determinations can be performed, some of which we will now describe.

In the introductory pages of this chapter, we mentioned that permanganate is reduced to the green-colored manganate ion by organic substances in concentrated sodium hydroxide solutions. This reaction serves as the basis of a quantitative method for the determination of a number of organic compounds, if the desired substance is dissolved in a known excess of strongly alkaline standard permanganate solution and allowed to react at room temperature for approximately 30 minutes. For example, glycerol is oxidized to carbonate, consuming 14 equivalents of permanganate in the process:

$$\begin{array}{ccc} H_2C & CH & CH_2 \\ | & | & | \\ OH & OH & OH \end{array} + 14\ MnO_4^- + 20\ OH^- \rightarrow$$

$$3\ CO_3^= + 14\ MnO_4^= + 14\ H_2O$$

The amount of glycerol in the original sample may be determined by acidification of the solution followed by titrimetric reduction of all higher oxidation states of manganese to manganese(II). The quantity of glycerol is computed from the *difference* between the total equivalents of permanganate originally taken and the total equivalents of higher oxidation states of manganese found in the final titration.

If a sample of an aqueous formic acid-acetic acid mixture is treated with a known volume of alkaline standard permanganate solution, only the formate ion undergoes oxidation,

$$HCOO^- + 2\ MnO_4^- + 3\ OH^- \longrightarrow CO_3^= + 2\ MnO_4^= + 2\ H_2O$$

whereas acetate remains completely unattacked. Therefore, subsequent acidification of the alkaline medium and titration of the higher oxidation states of manganese permit one to determine directly the quantity of formic acid in the original sample. If the result of the oxidation-reduction procedure is combined with a determination of the total acid content of a separate sample of the mixture, as obtained by titration with standard sodium hydroxide, the individual concentrations of both formic acid and acetic acid may be ascertained.

One other application of the alkaline permanganate procedure for organic compounds is the determination of methanol. In the presence of excess permanganate-sodium hydroxide solution, methanol is oxidized to carbonate according to the reaction

$$CH_3OH + 6\ MnO_4^- + 8\ OH^- \longrightarrow CO_3^= + 6\ MnO_4^= + 6\ H_2O$$

Instead of acidifying the solution, one can determine the excess, unreacted permanganate by adding barium ion and titrating the mixture with a standard solution of sodium formate. Formate reduces the permanganate only to manganate in an alkaline medium as shown previously, and the titration reaction is usually formulated as

$$2\ MnO_4^- + HCOO^- + 3\ Ba^{++} + 3\ OH^- \longrightarrow$$

$$2\ BaMnO_4(s) + BaCO_3(s) + 2\ H_2O$$

Notice that barium ion reacts with both manganate and carbonate ion to form insoluble precipitates and that, in particular, removal of the green-colored manganate ion from the solution phase aids considerably in helping one recognize the final disappearance of the permanganate color. The quantity of methanol in the sample is obtained if one subtracts the equivalents of formate needed for the titration from the total equivalents of permanganate used originally.

A partial list of other organic compounds which have been determined by means of the permanganate procedure includes glycolic acid, tartaric acid, citric acid, ethylene glycol, phenol, salicylic acid, formaldehyde, glucose, and sucrose.

Determinations of organic compounds by oxidation with dichromate are much too slow to be of any practical value. For example, the quantitative oxidation of glycerol in a potassium dichromate-sulfuric acid medium occurs according to the reaction

$$3 \;\; \begin{array}{ccc} H_2C\!\!-\!\!-\!\!CH\!\!-\!\!-\!\!CH_2 \\ | \quad\;\; | \quad\;\;\; | \\ OH \;\; OH \;\;\; OH \end{array} + 7\ Cr_2O_7^= + 56\ H^+ \rightarrow$$

$$9\ CO_2 + 14\ Cr^{+++} + 40\ H_2O$$

but the procedure entails a two hour heating period at about 95°C.

In early studies designed to test the suitability of cerium(IV) as an oxidant for organic compounds, it was logical to select a reaction medium consisting of cerium(IV) in 3 to $4\,F$ sulfuric acid because of the known stability of such a solution, even when boiled. However, in most instances the oxidation reactions proved to be extremely slow and failed to obey any simple stoichiometric relationships. Formic acid, which is readily oxidized by alkaline permanganate, showed no appreciable reaction with the hot cerium(IV)-sulfuric acid solution after two hours; tartaric acid, which consumes 10 equivalents of permanganate per mole, reacted with only 7.2 equivalents of cerium(IV).

The greater oxidizing strength of cerium(IV) in a perchloric acid medium overcomes both the slowness of the oxidation processes and the inexact stoichiometry encountered with cerium(IV) in sulfuric acid. Thus, cerium(IV) in $4\,F$ perchloric acid quantitatively oxidizes many organic substances, frequently within about 15 minutes at room temperature. Perhaps the most striking feature about the reactions between cerium(IV) and organic compounds is that the oxidation products depend on the nature of the organic substance. Some of the typical reactions may be summarized as follows:

1. A compound with *hydroxyl* groups on two or more adjacent carbon atoms has the bond between each of these carbon atoms cleaved, and each fragment is oxidized to a saturated carboxylic acid:

$$\begin{array}{ccc} H_2C\!\!-\!\!-\!\!CH\!\!-\!\!-\!\!CH_2 \\ | \quad\;\; | \quad\;\;\; | \\ OH \;\; OH \;\;\; OH \\ \text{glycerol} \end{array} + 3\ H_2O \rightarrow 3\ HCOOH + 8\ H^+ + 8\ e$$

$$\begin{array}{cc} H_2C\!\!-\!\!-\!\!CH\!\!-\!\!-\!\!CH_3 \\ | \quad\;\; | \\ OH \;\; OH \\ \text{1,2-propanediol} \end{array} + 2\ H_2O \rightarrow HCOOH + CH_3COOH + 6\ H^+ + 6\ e$$

2. A compound with an *aldehyde* group bound to a carbon atom also having a ketone group or a hydroxyl group has the bond between the two carbon atoms cleaved, and each fragment is oxidized to a saturated carboxylic acid:

$$H\!-\!\!\!\underset{\underset{\text{O}}{\|}}{C}\!-\!\!\underset{\underset{\text{OH}}{|}}{CH}\!-\!\!\underset{\underset{\text{OH}}{|}}{CH_2} + 3\,H_2O \rightarrow 3\,HCOOH + 6\,H^+ + 6\,e$$

glyceraldehyde

3. A compound with a *carboxyl* group bound to a carbon atom which also has a hydroxyl group, or a *carboxyl* group bound to an aldehyde group or another carboxyl group, has the bond between the two carbon atoms broken; each carboxyl group is oxidized to carbon dioxide, and the other fragments are oxidized to saturated carboxylic acids:

$$\underset{HO}{\overset{O}{\diagdown}}C\!-\!C\underset{OH}{\overset{O}{\diagup}} \rightarrow 2\,CO_2 + 2\,H^+ + 2\,e$$

oxalic acid

$$\underset{HO}{\overset{O}{\diagdown}}C\!-\!\underset{\underset{OH}{|}}{CH}\!-\!\underset{\underset{OH}{|}}{CH}\!-\!C\underset{OH}{\overset{O}{\diagup}} + 2\,H_2O \rightarrow$$

$$2\,CO_2 + 2\,HCOOH + 6\,H^+ + 6\,e$$

tartaric acid

4. A compound with a *ketone* group adjacent to a carboxyl group, an aldehyde group, or another ketone group — or a *ketone* group bound to a carbon atom with a hydroxyl group — has the bond between the two carbon atoms cleaved; each fragment with a ketone group is oxidized to a saturated carboxylic acid, and the other fragments are oxidized in accordance with previous rules:

$$H_3C\!-\!\underset{\underset{O}{\|}}{C}\!-\!\underset{\underset{O}{\|}}{C}\!-\!CH_3 + 2\,H_2O \rightarrow 2\,CH_3COOH + 2\,H^+ + 2\,e$$

biacetyl

$$H\!-\!\underset{\underset{O}{\|}}{C}\!-\!\underset{\underset{O}{\|}}{C}\!-\!CH_2\!-\!CH_3 + 2\,H_2O \rightarrow$$

$$HCOOH + CH_3CH_2COOH + 2\,H^+ + 2\,e$$

1,2-butanedione

5. A compound with an active *methylene* group ($-CH_2-$), i.e., a methylene group bound to two carboxyl groups, two aldehyde groups, two

ketone groups, or combinations of these groups, has each of the two carbon-carbon bonds broken; each methylene fragment is oxidized to formic acid, and each other fragment is oxidized in accordance with the preceding rules:

$$\underset{\text{malonic acid}}{\underset{\text{HO}}{\overset{\text{O}}{\diagdown}}C-CH_2-C\underset{\text{OH}}{\overset{\text{O}}{\diagup}}} + 2\ H_2O \rightarrow 2\ CO_2 + HCOOH + 6\ H^+ + 6\ e$$

$$\underset{\text{acetyl acetone}}{H_3C-\underset{\overset{\|}{O}}{C}-CH_2-\underset{\overset{\|}{O}}{C}-CH_3} + 4\ H_2O \rightarrow$$

$$2\ CH_3COOH + HCOOH + 6\ H^+ + 6\ e$$

In order to determine an organic compound, such as one of those just mentioned, the sample is added to a known excess of cerium(IV) in $4\ F$ perchloric acid and the reaction mixture is allowed to stand (or perhaps is heated at 50 to 60°C) for up to 20 minutes. The unreacted cerium(IV) can be back-titrated with a standard oxalic acid solution, and tris(5-nitro-1,10-phenanthroline)iron(II) will serve as the end point indicator.

A successful procedure has been developed by which organic compounds may be oxidized and determined quantitatively through the use of excess cerium(IV) in sulfuric acid. The key factor in the attainment of good analytical results is the concentration of sulfuric acid. Whereas the oxidation processes are incomplete in only 3 or $4\ F$ sulfuric acid, an increase in the acid concentration up to 10 or $12\ F$ promotes the complete oxidation of many organic compounds, although one cannot avoid boiling and refluxing the reaction mixture for at least one hour. It is significant that the oxidizing strength of cerium(IV) remains essentially unchanged for sulfuric acid concentrations between 4 and $12\ F$; so the increased acidity probably enhances the ease of protonation of an organic compound and, therefore, the *rate* of its oxidation. After the oxidation of the desired organic substance has reached completion, the mixture is cooled and the excess, unreacted cerium(IV) is titrated with a standard solution of a reducing agent, such as iron(II) or oxalic acid.

Tartaric acid, which is converted to two molecules of carbon dioxide and two molecules of formic acid by cerium(IV) in $4\ F$ perchloric acid, undergoes complete oxidation to four molecules of carbon dioxide in $12\ F$ sulfuric acid:

$$\underset{\text{HO}}{\overset{\text{O}}{\diagdown}}C-\underset{\overset{|}{OH}}{CH}-\underset{\overset{|}{OH}}{CH}-C\underset{\text{OH}}{\overset{\text{O}}{\diagup}} + 10\ Ce^{++++} + 2\ H_2O \rightarrow$$

$$4\ CO_2 + 10\ Ce^{+++} + 10\ H^+$$

Similarly, formic acid is unreactive toward cerium(IV) in perchloric acid, but is oxidized to carbon dioxide in a concentrated sulfuric acid medium:

$$HCOOH + 2\ Ce^{++++} \longrightarrow CO_2 + 2\ Ce^{+++} + 2\ H^+$$

In principle, it would be possible to analyze a mixture of tartaric acid and formic acid in the following way: One sample of the mixture can be oxidized with cerium(IV) in $4\ F$ perchloric acid, as a means of obtaining the quantity of tartaric acid present. A second sample could be oxidized in a cerium(IV)-sulfuric acid medium and the sum of the concentrations of tartaric and formic acids determined.

Some of the other organic compounds which can be oxidized, all of them to carbon dioxide, in $12\ F$ sulfuric acid with cerium(IV) are malonic acid, citric acid, benzoic acid, salicylic acid, fumaric acid, and phthalic acid.

Experiment 13-1

PREPARATION AND STANDARDIZATION OF A POTASSIUM PERMANGANATE SOLUTION

Purpose

This experiment provides for the preparation of 1 liter of $0.02\ F$ potassium permanganate and for the standardization of this solution against pure sodium oxalate.

Procedure

Preparation of a 0.02 F Potassium Permanganate Solution. Weigh approximately 3.3 gm of reagent-grade potassium permanganate into a clean 2 liter beaker and add 1 liter of distilled water to dissolve the solid. Heat the mixture to boiling over a burner or hot plate, stirring the solution until the potassium permanganate has dissolved completely. Cover the beaker with a large watch glass, and keep the solution near its boiling point for a period of 30 minutes.

The solution is maintained at its boiling point in order to ensure the complete oxidation of all organic matter in the distilled water. In addition, this period of heating promotes the coagulation of manganese dioxide, which is formed by the oxidation of organic matter and which may be present as an impurity in the potassium permanganate. It is highly desirable that the period of heating be extended to an hour or more, if time permits, and that the solution be allowed to stand overnight, if not longer, to ensure more complete oxidation of organic matter before the potassium permanganate solution is filtered and standardized.

Allow the potassium permanganate solution to cool to room temperature. Filter the solution directly into a clean 1 liter storage bottle, using a sintered-glass filter funnel or Buchner funnel which has been carefully cleaned prior to use; the previously cleaned storage bottle should be rinsed with the first portions of permanganate solution that pass through the filter, and the rinsings should be discarded. After all the permanganate solution has been filtered into the storage bottle, stopper the bottle and swirl it to mix the solution; then standardize the solution against sodium oxalate as described in the next section.

Since light and heat affect the stability of a potassium permanganate solution, it should be stored away from any source of heat or light. The storage bottle may be wrapped with a sheet of brown paper to protect the solution from light. Withdraw solution from the storage bottle with the aid of a clean pipet (rinsed with one or two small portions of the solution), rather than by pouring it, because the film of solution left on the ground-glass surfaces of the stopper and neck of the bottle will evaporate, leaving crystals of $KMnO_4$ (and sometimes MnO_2) which may later fall back into the solution.

Standardization of the Potassium Permanganate Solution.
Dry approximately 1 gm of primary-standard-grade sodium oxalate in an oven at 110°C for one hour, using a beaker-and-watch-glass arrangement as shown in Figure 2-1. After the sodium oxalate has been cooled in a desiccator, accurately weigh, to the nearest tenth milligram, 0.25 gm portions of the solid into each of three clean 600 ml beakers.

Dissolve the first sodium oxalate sample in 200 ml of 0.9 F sulfuric acid.

The sulfuric acid solution should be prepared in advance. Add 50 ml of concentrated (18 F) sulfuric acid to 950 ml of distilled water in a large flask, and boil the solution for 15 minutes. Cool the solution to room temperature prior to its use.

Heat the sodium oxalate solution to approximately 80 to 85°C by using a hot plate or by supporting the titration beaker on a tripod over a burner. Use a thermometer to measure the temperature and to stir the solution during the titration. Titrate the sample solution with the permanganate solution to be standardized, controlling the rate of addition of titrant so that it reacts completely before the next portion of titrant is introduced. Keep the solution temperature above 70°C throughout the titration. Continue the titration until the pink coloration due to excess permanganate persists for at least 30 seconds; note the approach of the end point by the fact that the pink permanganate color spreads fleetingly throughout the solution before disappearing. Record the volume of potassium permanganate used in the titration, using an appropriate procedure for reading the buret.

Perform a blank titration by diluting 200 ml of 0.9 F sulfuric acid in a 600 ml beaker with distilled water to give a solution volume equal to that at the end point of the preceding titration. Heat the solution to 70°C and titrate it with fractions of a drop of permanganate solution until the pink color matches the end point color in the actual titration. Subtract this volume of permanganate (which should not exceed about 0.05 ml) from the volume used in the titration of the sodium oxalate sample.

Repeat the same procedure for the titration of each of the other two sodium oxalate samples, and from the titration data calculate the average *formal* concentration of the potassium permanganate titrant. Replicate titrations should agree to within three parts per thousand.

When performing titrations with potassium permanganate, add the titrant directly into the solution being titrated and not down the side of the beaker or flask. A thin film of permanganate solution in contact with the hot glass surface may be reduced partially to manganese dioxide.

Experiment 13-2

PREPARATION OF A STANDARD POTASSIUM DICHROMATE SOLUTION

Purpose

The purpose of this experiment is to prepare directly a standard $0.017\ F$ solution of potassium dichromate.

Procedure

Transfer approximately 4.9 gm of reagent-grade potassium dichromate to a clean, dry weighing bottle; then dry the solid in an oven at 110°C for one hour. Use a beaker-and-watch-glass arrangement as shown in Figure 2-1. Cool the potassium dichromate and weighing bottle for at least 30 minutes in a desiccator.

Obtain the weight of the weighing bottle and its contents to the nearest milligram, transfer the potassium dichromate to a clean beaker, and reweigh the empty weighing bottle to the nearest milligram, in order to determine the weight of the potassium dichromate by difference.

Dissolve the potassium dichromate by adding a small volume of distilled water to the beaker. Transfer the solution quantitatively, with the aid of a glass funnel and stirring rod, to a clean 1 liter volumetric flask. Add distilled water to bring the solution volume up to the calibration mark, stopper the flask, and mix the solution thoroughly.

Finally, transfer the solution to a clean storage bottle, rinsing the bottle first with two or three small portions of the dichromate solution. From the weight of potassium dichromate taken, calculate the *formal* concentration of the solution.

Experiment 13-3

PREPARATION AND STANDARDIZATION OF A CERIUM(IV) SULFATE SOLUTION

Purpose

This experiment contains directions for the preparation of a standard $0.1\,F$ cerium(IV) solution in $1\,F$ sulfuric acid, starting with cerium(IV) bisulfate, and for the standardization of this solution against arsenious oxide.

Procedure

Preparation of a 0.1 F Cerium(IV) Solution in 1 F Sulfuric Acid. Weigh approximately 55 gm of reagent-grade cerium(IV) bisulfate, $Ce(HSO_4)_4$, into a 2 liter beaker and add 56 ml of concentrated $(18\,F)$ sulfuric acid. Cautiously add 100 ml of distilled water and stir the mixture to aid the dissolution of the solid. Continue to add distilled water, with good stirring between the additions, until the solution volume is 1 liter and all of the solid has dissolved. Cover the beaker with a large watch glass, and let the solution stand for at least several days.

The solution must be allowed to stand because commercially available cerium(IV) bisulfate apparently contains some phosphate or fluoride ions which cause a small precipitate of cerium(IV) phosphate or fluoride to form. This precipitate is permitted to form and to settle out before the solution is filtered and standardized.

An alternative procedure for the preparation of a standard cerium(IV) solution involves the use of ammonium hexanitratocerate(IV), $(NH_4)_2Ce(NO_3)_6$. This compound is available in a primary-standard form which may be employed for the direct preparation of a standard titrant. Accurately weigh 54.83 gm of $(NH_4)_2Ce(NO_3)_6$ (previously dried at 110°C for one hour) into a clean 1 liter beaker, and add 56 ml of concentrated sulfuric acid. Cautiously add 100 ml of distilled water, and stir the mixture to begin the dissolution of the solid. Add, in succession, five more 100 ml portions of distilled water, stirring the mixture thoroughly after each addition of water. When all the salt has dissolved, transfer the solution quantitatively to a 1 liter volumetric flask, dilute the solution to the mark with distilled water, and mix it thoroughly. The weight of salt prescribed, 54.83 gm, corresponds to an exactly $0.1000\,F$ cerium(IV) solution.

After the solution of cerium bisulfate has stood for several days, filter it directly into a clean storage bottle, using a coarse-porosity sintered-glass filter funnel. Rinse the storage bottle with the first portion of the filtrate, and discard the rinsing. When all the cerium(IV) solution has been filtered, stopper the bottle and mix the solution. Standardize the titrant against arsenious oxide as described in the next section.

Standardization of Cerium(IV) Solution. Dry approximately 1 gm of primary-standard-grade arsenious oxide (As_2O_3) in an oven for one hour at 110°C. Weigh accurately, to the nearest tenth milligram, individual 0.20 gm portions of the dried solid into each of three 250 ml Erlenmeyer flasks. Add 15 ml of 2 F sodium hydroxide solution to each flask, swirling the mixture gently to dissolve the arsenious oxide. When the arsenious oxide has dissolved add 25 ml of 3 F sulfuric acid, plus three drops of osmium tetroxide catalyst solution and two drops of ferroin indicator solution.

The osmium tetroxide solution should be prepared in advance. Dissolve 0.1 gm of osmium tetroxide per 40 ml of 0.1 F sulfuric acid. Osmium tetroxide (OsO_4) is volatile and reacts with the skin and eyes to form a deposit of metallic osmium; therefore, direct contact with the solid and its vapor should be avoided. A convenient method for the preparation of the osmium tetroxide solution is to drop a sealed glass ampoule containing the solid (this is the normal way in which OsO_4 is packaged and sold) into the desired volume of 0.1 F sulfuric acid contained in a thick-walled glass-stoppered bottle. Then shake the bottle until the glass ampoule breaks. No harm is done in leaving the broken glass inside the bottle.

Prepare the ferroin indicator solution by dissolving 0.70 gm of $FeSO_4 \cdot 7\ H_2O$ and 1.5 gm of 1,10-phenanthroline in 100 ml of distilled water.

Titrate the first arsenic(III) sample solution with cerium(IV) to the end point, which is marked by a color change from red-orange to pale blue. Record the volume of cerium(IV) solution used in the titration.

Actually, the blue color of the oxidized form of ferroin is so pale that the solution will probably appear to be colorless at the end point.

Repeat the titration with each of the other two arsenic(III) sample solutions. From the titration data, calculate the average concentration of the cerium(IV) solution. Replicate titrations should agree to within one or two parts per thousand.

Experiment 13-4

DETERMINATION OF IRON IN A WATER-SOLUBLE SALT OR AN ACID-SOLUBLE ORE

Purpose

This experiment demonstrates four major steps in a typical volumetric redox determination: the preparation of a sample solution, the adjustment of the oxidation state of the desired element, the utilization of special reagents to improve the titration, and the titration itself.

Procedure

Preparation of the Sample Solution. Transfer approximately 2 to 2.5 gm of the iron-containing sample to a clean, dry weighing bottle. Dry the sample in an oven at 110°C for about one hour. Weigh accurately, to the nearest tenth milligram, portions of the dried sample into each of three 500 ml Erlenmeyer flasks. Each weighed portion of sample should contain from 0.20 to 0.22 gm of iron.

Add 10 ml of distilled water and 10 ml of concentrated (12 F) hydrochloric acid to each flask, and warm each mixture gently over a burner. If the sample dissolves readily, proceed to the adjustment of the oxidation state of iron. However, if the sample does not dissolve readily, boil the solution until the sample is dissolved, keeping the solution volume at 20 to 25 ml through the addition of 6 F hydrochloric acid solution. Continue the boiling until no heavy dark solid particles remain; a residue of white or gray-white silica may be ignored.

Adjustment of the Oxidation State of Iron. Adjust the oxidation state of iron by means of either one of the two following methods. However, from this point on, carry each of the sample solutions separately and immediately through the final titration before returning to adjust the oxidation state of iron in the second, and then the third, sample solution.

Method I — use of stannous chloride. Heat the sample solution to boiling over a burner and add 0.5 F stannous chloride solution drop by drop, while swirling the flask, until the yellow color of iron(III) just disappears; then add one or two more drops of the stannous chloride solution.

The stannous chloride solution should be prepared in advance. Dissolve 110 gm of reagent-grade, iron-free $SnCl_2 \cdot 2\ H_2O$ in 250 ml of concentrated (12 F) hydrochloric acid. Then dilute the solution to 1 liter with distilled water. In order to minimize the air oxidation of tin(II) to tin(IV), also add 15 gm of spongy tin metal to the stannous chloride solution. Replenish the tin metal when it is exhausted.

Cool the solution to a temperature below 25°C and add *all at once* 10 ml of a 0.18 F mercury(II) chloride solution.

Prepare this mercury(II) chloride solution by dissolving 50 gm of reagent-grade $HgCl_2$ in 1 liter of distilled water.

A silky white precipitate should form. If it is gray or black or if no precipitate forms, an incorrect amount of stannous chloride solution was used and the sample must be discarded. After two or three minutes, but not longer, add 200 ml of distilled water and proceed immediately to the addition of special reagents and to the titration.

Method II — use of the Jones reductor. To prepare a Jones reductor, obtain a glass tube of the type illustrated in Figure 13-1, about 2 cm in diameter and long enough to hold a 30 cm column of zinc. Place a pad of glass wool at the bottom of the tube and a perforated porcelain plate upon that. Connect the outlet tube at the bottom of the column to a 500 ml Erlenmeyer flask through one hole of a two-hole rubber stopper. Fit a glass tube into the other hole of the stopper for connection to a vacuum line. In a separate beaker place 300 gm of granulated, pure zinc, and add 300 ml of water containing 6 gm of mercuric nitrate, $Hg(NO_3)_2$, plus 2 ml of concentrated (16 F) nitric acid. Stir the mixture for five to 10 minutes, and remove the liquid by decantation. The zinc should now be amalgamated and should have a bright, silvery luster. Wash the zinc several times by decantation with water. Fill the reductor tube with water, and slowly pour in the amalgamated zinc until the column is packed. Wash the column by pouring 500 ml of distilled water through it, and from this time on keep the column filled with water (or other liquid as needed). Prior to each use of the Jones reductor, wash the column with 1 F sulfuric acid until a 100 ml portion of the wash liquid does not decolorize two drops of standard 0.02 F potassium permanganate solution. During use of the reductor, apply enough suction to the column so that about 50 ml of liquid per minute is drawn through it.

To adjust the oxidation state of iron, add 15 ml of 9 F sulfuric acid to the hydrochloric acid sample solution. Heat the solution over a burner until the sulfuric acid begins to fume. Allow the solution to cool, and cautiously add a few milliliters of distilled water down the side of the flask; add a total of 100 ml of water. Drain the liquid in the reductor tube to within 1 or 2 cm of the top of the zinc; rinse the receiving flask with distilled water, and reconnect it to the column. Introduce the sulfuric acid solution of iron into the column, and draw this solution through the column at a rate of approximately 50 ml per minute. Stop the flow of the solution by closing the stopcock when the liquid level falls to within 1 or 2 cm above the zinc bed. Rinse the original sample flask with 50 ml of 1 F sulfuric acid and pass this liquid through the column. Repeat this operation with three more 50 ml portions of the acid, each time allowing the liquid level to fall to within a centimeter or two above the zinc. Disconnect the receiving flask from the column and immediately titrate its contents with either potassium permanganate or cerium(IV) as directed in the final titration step of this experiment.

Addition of Special Reagents. If the adjustment of the oxidation state of iron has been accomplished with the aid of stannous chloride solution, follow these directions regarding the use of special reagents.

If the iron(II) is to be titrated with dichromate, add 5 ml of concentrated (18 F) sulfuric acid, 10 ml of concentrated (85 per cent) phosphoric acid, and eight drops of barium diphenylamine sulfonate indicator solution.

The indicator solution should be prepared in advance. Dissolve 0.3 gm of barium diphenylamine sulfonate in 100 ml of distilled water. Add 0.5 gm of sodium sulfate, let the mixture stand, and decant the clear liquid for use as the indicator solution.

After addition of the indicator, titrate the iron(II) solution according to the directions that follow.

If the iron(II) is to be titrated with permanganate, add 25 ml of Zimmermann-Reinhardt reagent.

Prepare the Zimmermann-Reinhardt reagent as follows: Dissolve 70 gm of $MnSO_4 \cdot 4 H_2O$ in 500 ml of distilled water, adding 125 ml of concentrated (18 F) sulfuric acid and 125 ml of concentrated (85 per cent) phosphoric acid, and diluting the mixture to 1 liter.

After adding the Zimmermann-Reinhardt reagent, titrate the iron(II) solution as indicated in the next section.

If the iron(II) is to be titrated with cerium(IV), add 10 ml of concentrated (18 F) sulfuric acid.

Final Titration. Perform the titration of the iron(II) solution as indicated.

Use of dichromate. Titrate the solution with standard 0.0167 F potassium dichromate to an end point marked by the sudden permanent appearance of a deep violet color throughout the solution.

Use of permanganate. Titrate the solution with standard 0.02 F potassium permanganate to the appearance of a pink coloration which persists for at least 30 seconds.

Use of cerium(IV). Add to the solution to be titrated 10 ml of concentrated (85 per cent) phosphoric acid and two drops of ferroin indicator (see Experiment 13-3). Titrate with standard 0.1 F cerium(IV) solution until a permanent color change from red-orange to very pale blue (or colorlessness) occurs.

Repeat the steps of the procedure involving oxidation-state adjustment, addition of special reagents, and final titration for each of the other two sample solutions. From the experimental data, calculate and report the average percentage of iron in the original solid sample.

Experiment 13-5

INDIRECT VOLUMETRIC DETERMINATION OF CALCIUM

Purpose

This experiment serves as a typical example of an indirect procedure. Calcium ion is separated by precipitation as calcium oxalate monohydrate. The precipitate is washed free of excess oxalate and then dissolved in a sulfuric acid medium; the oxalate content of the precipitate, and thus calcium itself, is then determined by means of a permanganate titration. Therefore, this procedure combines separation by precipitation with volumetric analysis.

Procedure

Transfer about 2 gm of the solid sample to a clean, dry weighing bottle, and dry the material in an oven at 110°C for one hour, using a beaker-and-watch-glass arrangement such as shown in Figure 2-1.

After the sample material has been cooled in a desiccator, weigh accurately, to the nearest tenth milligram, portions of the sample which contain from 70 to 80 mg of calcium into each of three *wide-mouth* 250 ml Erlenmeyer flasks.

The mouth of each flask must be wide enough so that a sintered-glass filter crucible may be easily inserted. Therefore, the three flasks and the three filter crucibles should be properly selected at the outset of the experiment.

Add to each flask 10 ml of distilled water and 10 ml of concentrated $(12 F)$ hydrochloric acid. If the sample does not dissolve readily, heat the mixture gently over a burner to aid the dissolution of the solid. When the sample is dissolved completely, dilute the solution with distilled water to a volume of approximately 50 ml. Heat the solution almost to boiling and add slowly with good stirring about 100 ml of an aqueous solution containing 5 gm of ammonium oxalate monohydrate, $(NH_4)_2C_2O_4 \cdot H_2O$.

The ammonium oxalate solution must be perfectly clear before it is added to the calcium sample. If necessary, filter the ammonium oxalate solution prior to its use.

While keeping the solution temperature at 80 to 85°C, add a few drops of methyl orange indicator, and then add drop by drop with good stirring a 6 F aqueous ammonia solution until the indicator just changes color from red to yellow. Allow the solution to stand not longer than 30 minutes.

The relatively short digestion period is definitely required if the sample contains magnesium, since magnesium oxalate may coprecipitate or post-precipitate. If magnesium ion is absent or the sample contains only calcium along with alkali metals, the solution can be allowed to stand overnight.

Set up a suction-filtration apparatus, using one of the three sintered-glass filter crucibles, according to directions furnished by the laboratory instructor. Filter the calcium oxalate suspension, collecting the precipitate on the sintered-glass crucible. Wash the original precipitation flask and the precipitate in the filter crucible with eight to 10 small portions of ice-cold distilled water, passing the washings through the filter crucible. Remove the crucible from the filtering assembly and carefully rinse the outside of the crucible, as well as the bottom of the sintered-glass filter disc, to wash away any adhering ammonium oxalate solution. Insert the crucible with calcium oxalate precipitate into the flask in which the precipitation was originally performed.

Note that it is unnecessary to transfer all the precipitate to the crucible, since the crucible and precipitate are eventually returned to the flask. However, it is essential that the precipitate, crucible, and flask be washed thoroughly to remove excess oxalate.

Add 100 ml of distilled water and 6 ml of concentrated $(18 F)$ sulfuric acid to the flask. Heat the solution to about 75°C, swirl the flask to aid the dissolution of the calcium oxalate, and titrate the solution with standard $0.02 F$ potassium permanganate, following the procedure and observing the precautions described in Experiment 13-1. Leave the crucible in the titration flask throughout this part of the procedure.

Repeat the procedure with the other two samples and, from the experimental data, calculate and report the average percentage of CaO in the original sample material.

SUGGESTIONS FOR ADDITIONAL LABORATORY WORK

The following two references may be consulted for numerous other applications of redox methods involving potassium permanganate, potassium dichromate, and cerium(IV). These sources contain considerable information pertaining to the determination of organic compounds.

1. I. M. Kolthoff and R. Belcher: *Volumetric Analysis*, Volume 3, Wiley-Interscience, New York, 1957, pp. 33–198.
2. G. F. Smith: *Cerate Oxidimetry*, G. F. Smith Chemical Company, Columbus, Ohio, 1942.

QUESTIONS AND PROBLEMS

1. The formal potentials for the cerium(IV)-cerium(III) half-reaction (versus the normal hydrogen electrode) in various concentrations of perchloric acid, nitric

acid, and sulfuric acid are listed in the following table:

Acid Concentration, F	$HClO_4$	HNO_3	H_2SO_4
1	+1.70	+1.61	+1.44
2	1.71	1.62	1.44
4	1.75	1.61	1.43
6	1.82	1.56	—
8	1.87	—	1.42

Discuss the significance of these formal potentials in terms of the possible chemical interactions of cerium(IV) and cerium(III) with the acid media.

2. Discuss the advantages and disadvantages of potassium permanganate, potassium dichromate, and cerium(IV) as standard oxidizing agents.

3. Why must the manganese dioxide formed from the reaction of permanganate with organic matter be removed by filtration prior to standardization of a potassium permanganate solution?

4. What advantage does standardization of a dichromate solution against primary standard iron wire have over the direct use of potassium dichromate as a primary standard reagent?

5. Calculate the formality and the normality of a potassium dichromate solution 1.000 ml of which is equivalent to 0.005000 gm of iron.

6. Given the following information,

$$Cr_2O_7^= + 14 H^+ + 6 e \rightleftharpoons 2 Cr^{+++} + 7 H_2O; \qquad E° = +1.33 \text{ v}$$
$$Cr(OH)_3 \rightleftharpoons Cr^{+++} + 3 OH^-; \qquad K_{sp} = 6 \times 10^{-31}$$
$$CrO_4^= + H^+ \rightleftharpoons HCrO_4^-; \qquad K = 3.2 \times 10^6$$
$$2 HCrO_4^- \rightleftharpoons Cr_2O_7^= + H_2O; \qquad K' = 33$$

evaluate the standard potential for the half-reaction

$$CrO_4^= + 4 H_2O + 3 e \rightleftharpoons Cr(OH)_3 + 5 OH^-$$

7. State one advantage and one disadvantage of the volumetric determination of calcium based on the use of a potassium permanganate solution in comparison to a gravimetric procedure.

8. From standard-potential data for the half-reactions

$$MnO_4^- + 4 H^+ + 3 e \rightleftharpoons MnO_2 + 2 H_2O$$

and

$$MnO_4^- + e \rightleftharpoons MnO_4^=$$

calculate the equilibrium constant for the disproportionation of the manganate ion

$$3 MnO_4^= + 2 H_2O \rightleftharpoons 2 MnO_4^- + MnO_2 + 4 OH^-$$

and calculate what must be the minimum concentration of hydroxide ion required to prevent more than 1 per cent disproportionation of 0.01 M manganate ion.

9. Calculate the normality and the formality of a potassium permanganate solution, 35.00 ml of which is equivalent to 0.2500 gm of 98.00 per cent pure calcium oxalate.

10. In the determination of iron by titration with potassium permanganate solution, why is an acidic medium required? Why should excessive acidity be avoided?

11. Explain why the tris(1,10-phenanthroline)iron(II) complex is a good indicator for titrations with cerium(IV), but not for titrations involving potassium dichromate.

12. How many milligrams of hydrogen peroxide will react with 35.00 ml of a 0.02800 F potassium permanganate solution in an acidic medium?

13. If 40.32 ml of a solution of oxalic acid can be titrated with 37.92 ml of a 0.4736 F sodium hydroxide solution and if 30.50 ml of the same oxalic acid solution reacts with 47.89 ml of a potassium permanganate solution, what is the formality and the normality of the permanganate solution?

14. Barium ion is frequently added to the strongly alkaline reaction medium during the oxidation of organic compounds with potassium permanganate. How does barium ion influence the effective oxidizing strength of permanganate under these conditions? Explain your conclusion.

15. At what concentration of hydrogen ion would the effective emf values for the two half-reactions

$$Cr_2O_7^= + 14\,H^+ + 6\,e \rightleftharpoons 2\,Cr^{+++} + 7\,H_2O$$

and

$$MnO_4^- + 8\,H^+ + 5\,e \rightleftharpoons Mn^{++} + 4\,H_2O$$

be identical?

16. Calculate the per cent purity of a sample of impure $H_2C_2O_4 \cdot 2\,H_2O$ if 0.4006 gm of this material requires a titration with 28.62 ml of a potassium permanganate solution, 1.000 ml of which contains 5.980 mg of potassium permanganate.

17. Suggest a reason why, as indicated in Figure 13-2, the oxidizing strength of potassium dichromate appears to be considerably less than that predicted from the standard potential for the dichromate-chromic ion half-reaction.

18. A slag sample is known to contain all of its iron in the forms FeO and Fe_2O_3. A 1.000 gm sample of the slag was dissolved in hydrochloric acid according to the usual procedure, reduced with stannous chloride, and eventually titrated with 28.59 ml of a 0.02237 F potassium permanganate solution. A second slag sample, weighing 1.500 gm, was dissolved in a nitrogen atmosphere in order to prevent atmospheric oxidation of iron(II) during the dissolution process and, without any further adjustment of the oxidation state of iron, it was immediately titrated with the same potassium permanganate solution. If 15.60 ml of the permanganate solution was required in the second experiment, calculate (a) the total percentage of iron in the slag and (b) the individual percentages of FeO and Fe_2O_3.

19. A 20.00 ml aliquot of a mixture of formic acid and acetic acid was titrated with a 0.1209 F sodium hydroxide solution, 23.12 ml being required to reach a phenolphthalein end point. A second 20.00 ml sample of the acid mixture was pipetted into 50.00 ml of a strongly alkaline 0.02832 F potassium permanganate solution, and the reaction mixture was allowed to stand for 30 minutes at room temperature. Then the solution was acidified with sulfuric acid and titrated with a standard 0.1976 F iron(II) solution. The titration required 28.51 ml of the iron(II) solution. Calculate the molar concentrations of formic acid and acetic acid in the original acid mixture.

20. The quantity of glycerol in a sample solution was determined by reacting the glycerol with 50.00 ml of a strongly alkaline 0.03527 F potassium permanganate solution at room temperature for 25 minutes. After the reaction was complete, the mixture was acidified with sulfuric acid, and the excess unreacted permanganate was reduced with 10.00 ml of a 0.2500 F oxalic acid solution. Then the excess oxalic acid was back-titrated with a 0.01488 F potassium permanganate solution, 26.18 ml being required. Calculate the weight of glycerol in the original sample.

21. In the determination of the manganese dioxide content of a pyrolusite ore, a 0.5261 gm sample of the pyrolusite was treated with 0.7049 gm of pure sodium

oxalate, $Na_2C_2O_4$, in an acid medium. After the reaction had gone to completion, 30.47 ml of 0.02160 F potassium permanganate solution was needed to titrate the excess, unreacted oxalic acid. Calculate the percentage of manganese dioxide in the pyrolusite.

22. A 25.00 ml aliquot of a stock hydrogen peroxide solution was transferred to a 250.0 ml volumetric flask, and the solution was diluted and mixed. A 25.00 ml sample of the diluted hydrogen peroxide solution was acidified with sulfuric acid and titrated with 0.02732 F potassium permanganate, 35.86 ml being required. Calculate the number of grams of hydrogen peroxide per 100.0 ml of the original stock solution.

23. What weight of an iron ore should be taken for analysis so that the volume of 0.1046 F cerium(IV) sulfate solution used in the subsequent titration will be numerically the same as the percentage of iron in the ore?

24. Calculate the weight of potassium dichromate which must be used to prepare 1.000 liter of solution such that, when the solution is employed in iron determinations with 1.000 gm samples, the buret reading in milliliters will equal the percentage of iron in the sample.

25. A silver reductor was employed to reduce 0.01000 M uranium(VI) to uranium-(IV) in a 2.00 F hydrochloric acid medium according to the reaction

$$UO_2^{++} + 2\,Ag + 2\,Cl^- + 4\,H^+ \rightleftharpoons U^{++++} + 2\,AgCl + 2\,H_2O$$

Calculate the fraction of uranium(VI) which remains unreduced after this treatment.

26. What procedure would you employ to regenerate a silver reductor?

27. Calculate the normality of a solution, used as a standard oxidizing agent in acid media, which is prepared by dissolving 5.000 gm of $K_2Cr_2O_7$ and 5.000 gm of K_2CrO_4 in exactly 1 liter of distilled water.

28. Cerium(IV) in 4 F perchloric acid is an effective oxidant for many organic compounds. Write balanced half-reactions for the oxidation of each of the following organic substances:

(a) ethylene glycol

$$\begin{array}{cc} H_2C\text{——}CH_2 \\ | \qquad | \\ OH \quad OH \end{array}$$

(b) formaldehyde

$$H\text{—}C \overset{O}{\underset{H}{\diagup\diagdown}}$$

(c) citric acid

$$\begin{array}{c} OH \\ | \\ HOOC\text{—}CH_2\text{—}C\text{—}CH_2\text{—}COOH \\ | \\ COOH \end{array}$$

(d) malic acid

$$\begin{array}{c} HOOC\text{—}CH\text{—}CH_2\text{—}COOH \\ | \\ OH \end{array}$$

(e) 2,3-butanediol

$$\begin{array}{c} H_3C\text{—}CH\text{—}CH\text{—}CH_3 \\ | \qquad | \\ OH \quad OH \end{array}$$

(f) 2,3,5-hexanetrione

$$\begin{array}{c} H_3C\text{—}C\text{—}C\text{—}CH_2\text{—}C\text{—}CH_3 \\ \parallel \ \parallel \qquad \parallel \\ O \ \ O \qquad \ O \end{array}$$

29. A 20.00 ml aliquot of a $1 F$ hydrochloric acid solution containing iron(III) and vanadium(V) was passed through a silver reductor. The resulting solution was titrated with a $0.01020 F$ potassium permanganate solution, 26.24 ml being required to reach a visual end point. A second 20.00 ml aliquot of the sample solution was passed through a Jones reductor, proper precautions being taken to ensure that air oxidation of the reduced species did not occur. When the solution was titrated with the $0.01020 F$ permanganate solution, 31.80 ml was required for the titration. Calculate the concentrations of iron(III) and vanadium(V) in the original sample solution.

30. A potassium permanganate solution was standardized against 0.2643 gm of pure arsenious oxide. The arsenious oxide was dissolved in a sodium hydroxide solution; the resulting solution was acidified and finally titrated with the permanganate solution, of which 40.46 ml was used. Calculate the formality of the potassium permanganate solution.

31. A cerium(IV) sulfate solution was standardized against 0.2023 gm of 97.89 per cent pure iron wire. If 43.61 ml of the cerium(IV) solution was used in the final titration, calculate its normality.

32. A 10.00 ml sample of a mixture of tartaric acid and formic acid was boiled with 25.00 ml of $0.1625 F$ cerium(IV) in $10 F$ sulfuric acid for approximately one hour. The back-titration of the unreacted cerium(IV) required 3.41 ml of a $0.1009 F$ iron(II) solution. A second 10.00 ml sample of the acid mixture was treated for 15 minutes at room temperature with 20.00 ml of $0.1119 F$ cerium(IV) in $4 F$ perchloric acid. After the reaction was complete, the unreacted cerium(IV) was back-titrated with a $0.1031 F$ oxalic acid solution, 8.12 ml being required. Calculate the concentrations of tartaric acid and formic acid in the original mixture.

33. If 36.81 ml of a $0.1206 F$ sodium hydroxide solution is needed to neutralize the acid formed when 34.76 ml of a potassium permanganate solution is treated with sulfur dioxide,

$$2 \, MnO_4^- + 5 \, H_2SO_3 \rightleftharpoons 2 \, Mn^{++} + 4 \, H^+ + 5 \, SO_4^= + 3 \, H_2O$$

the excess sulfur dioxide being removed by boiling, what volume of $0.1037 M$ iron(II) solution would be oxidized by 38.41 ml of the potassium permanganate solution?

34. If 5.000 ml of a commercial hydrogen peroxide solution, having a density of 1.010 gm/ml, requires 18.70 ml of a $0.02416 F$ potassium permanganate solution for titration in an acid medium, what is the percentage by weight of hydrogen peroxide in the commercial solution?

35. Consider the titration of 50.00 ml of $0.06000 M$ iron(II) with $0.01000 F$ potassium dichromate in $1 F$ hydrochloric acid, assuming the validity of the following formal-potential data:

$Fe^{+++} + e \rightleftharpoons Fe^{++}$; $E^{\circ\prime} = +0.70$ v versus NHE

$Cr_2O_7^= + 14 \, H^+ + 6 \, e \rightleftharpoons 2 \, Cr^{+++} + 7 \, H_2O$; $E^{\circ\prime} = +1.05$ v versus NHE

Determine the following information:

   (a) The potential of a platinum indicator electrode versus a normal hydrogen electrode at the theoretical equivalence point of the titration.

   (b) The potential of a platinum indicator electrode versus a saturated calomel electrode (SCE) after the addition of 37.60 ml of the potassium dichromate titrant.

   (c) The per cent titration error, with the proper sign, if barium diphenyl-amine sulfonate, which changes to a violet color at $+0.84$ v versus NHE, is used as the end point indicator.

(d) Repeat the calculations of parts (a), (b), and (c), assuming that the titration is performed in a $1 F$ hydrochloric acid-$0.25 F$ phosphoric acid mixture in which the formal potential for the iron(III)-iron(II) couple is shifted to $+0.51$ v versus NHE.

SUGGESTIONS FOR ADDITIONAL READING

1. I. M. Kolthoff and R. Belcher: *Volumetric Analysis*, Volume 3, Wiley-Interscience, New York, 1957, pp. 33–198.
2. H. A. Laitinen: *Chemical Analysis*, McGraw-Hill Book Company, New York, 1960, pp. 326–392.
3. G. F. Smith: *Cerate Oxidimetry*, G. F. Smith Chemical Company, Columbus, Ohio, 1942.

Chapter Fourteen

Oxidation-Reduction Methods Involving Iodine

The element iodine exists in a number of analytically important oxidation states, which are represented in such familiar species as iodide, iodine (or triiodide ion), iodine monochloride, iodate, and periodate. Of particular significance are the oxidation-reduction processes involving the two lowest oxidation states, namely, iodide and iodine (or triiodide ion). It is of interest that the transfer or exchange of electrons between these substances may be expressed in terms of three different half-reactions listed in Table 12-1.

$$I_2(aq) + 2\ e \rightleftharpoons 2\ I^-; \qquad E° = +0.6197\ v$$
$$I_2(s) + 2\ e \rightleftharpoons 2\ I^-; \qquad E° = +0.5345\ v$$
$$I_3^- + 2\ e \rightleftharpoons 3\ I^-; \qquad E° = +0.5355\ v$$

The first of these half-reactions describes the redox properties of a chemical system consisting of dissolved molecular iodine and iodide ion. Thus the potential of a platinum indicator electrode immersed in a solution in which the concentrations (activities) of iodine and iodide are both 1 M should be $+0.6197$ v versus NHE. However, this prediction has only limited usefulness in any practical considerations of the behavior of an iodine-iodide mixture. It conceals the fact that the aqueous concentration of molecular iodine can never attain such a large value as 1 M, since the equilibrium solubility of iodine in pure water at 25°C is only 0.00133 M. Furthermore, in the presence of iodide, molecular iodine has a definite tendency to form the triiodide ion

$$I_2(aq) + I^- \rightleftharpoons I_3^-; \qquad K = 708$$

As soon as iodine and iodide are introduced into the same solution, a mixture of iodide, iodine, and triiodide results. Nevertheless, it should be stressed that the first half-reaction can be employed for making calculations and predictions if one is willing to compute the *correct* concentrations of $I_2(aq)$ and I^- by taking into account the solubility of iodine in water as well as the formation of the triiodide ion.

The second half-reaction listed differs from the first half-reaction because solid iodine replaces aqueous iodine as the oxidizing agent. However, it should be understood that when we indicate the presence of solid iodine, we automatically imply the concentration of dissolved molecular iodine, $I_2(aq)$, to be 0.00133 M. In addition, we cannot forget that the interaction between iodine and iodide to yield triiodide ion still occurs. The difference in the values of the standard potentials for the first and second half-reactions is directly related to the difference in the concentrations of $I_2(aq)$ present in the two systems. Thus, it is reasonable that the standard potential for the second half-reaction is less positive, or that there is a smaller driving force for the second process, because the concentration of $I_2(aq)$ is lower. Actually, the second half-reaction is rarely used to make predictions concerning the feasibility of titrations because very few practical oxidation-reduction methods of analysis ever involve the formation or presence of solid iodine. There is an important reason why this latter statement is true. The vapor pressure of solid iodine is sufficiently high that the loss of iodine vapor from the titration vessel may cause a significant error. The only common redox titrations which ordinarily result in the formation of solid iodine are those designed for the determination of iodide. The titration of an acidic solution of 0.05 M iodide with a standard solution of cerium(IV) is a good example of a procedure which provides a very accurate determination of iodide:

$$2\ Ce^{++++} + 2\ I^- \rightleftharpoons 2\ Ce^{+++} + I_2$$

During the early stages of this titration — but before enough dissolved molecular iodine has been produced to exceed the solubility of solid iodine — the solution contains unoxidized iodide, dissolved molecular iodine, and triiodide ion. Eventually, when most of the iodide has been oxidized and the formation of triiodide becomes unfavorable, solid iodine will precipitate. Only then does the chemical system conform to the second of the three half-reactions. Any loss of iodine vapor in this titration is of no consequence because iodine is a reaction product.

The third half-reaction gives the most realistic picture of the redox behavior of the iodine-iodide system because it includes the two predominant species, triiodide and iodide ions, encountered in practical situations. In virtually all of the direct and indirect procedures to be described in this chapter, one performs titrations *with* a standard solution of iodine containing a relatively high concentration of potassium iodide, or one performs titrations *of* iodine in the presence of a large excess of iodide. In either case, no solid iodine is formed and the concentration of aqueous iodine, $I_2(aq)$, is usually small compared to the triiodide concentration. This assertion can be verified by means of calculations. In typical experiments the iodide concentration ranges from approximately 0.05 to 1 M. At the lower iodide concentration, the ratio of the concentration of triiodide to that of aqueous iodine is given by the expression

$$\frac{[I_3^-]}{[I_2(aq)]} = 708[I^-] = 708(0.05) = 35.4$$

Therefore, less than 3 per cent of the *total* concentration of dissolved iodine — the sum of $[I_3^-]$ and $[I_2(aq)]$ — is present as molecular iodine. At the other extreme of the range of iodide concentrations, i.e., 1 M, we conclude that

$$\frac{[I_3^-]}{[I_2(aq)]} = 708[I^-] = 708(1) = 708$$

or that the concentration of $I_2(aq)$ is less than 0.2 per cent of the triiodide concentration.

Therefore, throughout the remainder of this chapter, we shall use the third half-reaction to describe the iodine-iodide system and to guide our predictions about the possible success of various titrations.

An interesting question can be asked as to why the standard potentials for the second and third half-reactions are nearly equal. The explanation is that the two standard potentials are similar because the two chemical systems designated by these half-reactions are almost the same. In order to confirm that this is true, let us compare the individual concentrations of iodide, iodine, and triiodide present in each system. First, consider the half-reaction

$$I_2(s) + 2\,e \rightleftharpoons 2\,I^-; \qquad E^\circ = +0.5345\text{ v}$$

According to the definition of a standard potential, the concentration (activity) of iodide ion is 1 M; and at 25°C the concentration of dissolved molecular iodine, $I_2(aq)$, in equilibrium with solid iodine is 0.00133 M. Knowing the concentrations of iodide and iodine, we can calculate the triiodide concentration from the relation

$$[I_3^-] = 708[I^-][I_2(aq)] = 708(1)(1.33 \times 10^{-3}) = 0.942\ M$$

This result shows how important triiodide ion is relative to iodine (even when the original half-reaction did not indicate the presence of triiodide) and serves as further justification for the use of I_3^- to represent the predominant form of iodine in aqueous iodide media.

If we turn our attention to the half-reaction

$$I_3^- + 2\,e \rightleftharpoons 3\,I^-; \qquad E^\circ = +0.5355\text{ v}$$

we can conclude immediately that the concentrations (activities) of iodide and triiodide are both 1 M. The concentration of molecular iodine is given by

$$[I_2(aq)] = \frac{[I_3^-]}{708[I^-]} = \frac{1}{(708)(1)} = 1.41 \times 10^{-3}\ M$$

These calculations definitely prove that the respective concentrations of the three species, I^-, $I_2(aq)$, and I_3^-, for the two systems are almost identical and, as a consequence, that the standard potentials are essentially the same. The slightly more positive standard potential for the triiodide-iodide half-reaction is consistent with the observation that the concentrations of the oxidizing agents, I_3^- and $I_2(aq)$, are somewhat larger in the latter than in the former system.

When the triiodide-iodide half-reaction is compared to other familiar half-reactions in a list of standard-potential data, such as Table 12-1, several important conclusions can be reached. The standard potential for the half-reaction

$$I_3^- + 2\,e \rightleftharpoons 3\,I^-; \qquad E° = +0.5355 \text{ v}$$

is far less than that for any of the three oxidizing agents discussed in the previous chapter, and it occupies a position near the middle of a table of standard potentials. Nevertheless, triiodide ion is a sufficiently good oxidizing agent to react quantitatively with a number of reductants. Furthermore, iodide is easily enough oxidized to permit its quantitative reaction with certain strong oxidizing agents. Accordingly, two major classifications of redox methods involving the use of this half-reaction have been developed. First, there are the so-called *direct* methods in which a solution of triiodide, or iodine dissolved in potassium iodide medium, serves as a standard oxidizing agent; some authors refer to these direct procedures as *iodimetric* methods of analysis. Second, many so-called *indirect* procedures are employed in which triiodide is formed through the reaction of excess iodide ion with some oxidizing agent; these indirect techniques are commonly designated as *iodometric* methods of analysis.

Direct Methods. Because triiodide ion is a relatively mild oxidant, it can react quantitatively only with substances which are easily oxidizable. It should be recalled from Chapter 12 that the emf of a proposed overall reaction must be at least $+0.2$ v in order for a successful titration to be performed. Among the substances which can be titrated directly with a standard iodine (triiodide) solution are hydrogen sulfide, tin(II), and sulfurous acid. These three reactions may be written as follows:

$$I_3^- + H_2S \rightleftharpoons 3\,I^- + S + 2\,H^+; \qquad E° = +0.395 \text{ v}$$
$$I_3^- + Sn^{++} \rightleftharpoons 3\,I^- + Sn^{++++}; \qquad E° = +0.382 \text{ v}$$
$$I_3^- + H_2SO_3 + H_2O \rightleftharpoons 3\,I^- + SO_4^= + 4\,H^+; \qquad E° = +0.37 \text{ v}$$

The observations that hydrogen sulfide, tin(II), and sulfurous acid do react quite completely with triiodide are in accord with the magnitudes of the emf values for these reactions. Of further importance from the viewpoint of analytical chemistry is the fact that all three species undergo a very rapid reaction with triiodide.

One of the most important iodimetric methods of analysis involves the arsenic(III)-triiodide reaction, which is used almost universally for the standardization of iodine or triiodide solutions:

$$HAsO_2 + I_3^- + 2\,H_2O \rightleftharpoons H_3AsO_4 + 3\,I^- + 2\,H^+$$

The standard potential for the arsenic(V)-arsenic(III) half-reaction*

$$H_3AsO_4 + 2\,H^+ + 2\,e \rightleftharpoons HAsO_2 + 2\,H_2O$$

is +0.559 v versus NHE, and is actually somewhat greater than that for the triiodide-iodide couple ($E° = +0.5355$ v versus NHE). Thus, the arsenic(III)-triiodide reaction has an emf of -0.023 v when all reactants and products have concentrations (activities) of unity, and it appears that the titration reaction would be far from complete. However, since hydrogen ion is a product of the arsenic(III)-triiodide reaction, it should be evident that the desired titration can be performed if the hydrogen ion concentration is significantly decreased below 1 M, because the effective emf or driving force for the reaction will increase. This approach is most successful, as the arsenic(III)-triiodide reaction proceeds quantitatively to completion in a neutral medium. We shall justify these statements concerning the arsenic(III)-triiodide system later in this chapter.

Such a qualitative discussion of the arsenic(III)-triiodide reaction emphasizes the caution which must be exercised when standard potentials alone are used to predict the feasibility of a titration. The tendency for any chemical process to occur is really governed by two factors: (1) the equilibrium constant for the reaction, as calculated, for example, from standard-potential data and (2) the actual concentrations (activities) of the reactant and product species. The practicing analytical chemist must be aware of each factor in reaching a final decision about the possible success of a proposed titration.

Indirect Methods.   Many strong oxidizing agents are capable of converting iodide quantitatively to free iodine, which in the presence of excess iodide forms the triiodide ion. Included among these substances are permanganate, dichromate, bromate, cerium(IV), and hydrogen peroxide, with the reactions proceeding as indicated by the following equations:

$$2\,MnO_4^- + 15\,I^- + 16\,H^+ \rightleftharpoons 2\,Mn^{++} + 5\,I_3^- + 8\,H_2O; \quad E° = +0.97\,v$$
$$Cr_2O_7^= + 9\,I^- + 14\,H^+ \rightleftharpoons 2\,Cr^{+++} + 3\,I_3^- + 7\,H_2O; \quad E° = +0.79\,v$$
$$BrO_3^- + 9\,I^- + 6\,H^+ \rightleftharpoons Br^- + 3\,I_3^- + 3\,H_2O; \quad E° = +0.91\,v$$
$$2\,Ce^{++++} + 3\,I^- \rightleftharpoons 2\,Ce^{+++} + I_3^-; \quad E° = +0.90\,v$$
$$H_2O_2 + 3\,I^- + 2\,H^+ \rightleftharpoons 2\,H_2O + I_3^-; \quad E° = +1.23\,v$$

These reactions, although thermodynamically favorable, are not ordinarily employed for the direct determination of such species as permanganate, dichromate, or hydrogen peroxide because of the lack of any suitable means for visual end point detection. Furthermore, the oxidation of iodide ion by

---

* Some authors use H_3AsO_3 as the formula of arsenious acid. We prefer to write $HAsO_2$ as the predominant form of arsenic(III) because arsenious acid behaves as a weak monoprotic acid in aqueous media.

dichromate is somewhat slow, and the hydrogen peroxide-iodide reaction requires a catalyst for best results. We indicated earlier in this chapter, however, that a standard solution of cerium(IV) may be used to titrate iodide. A similar procedure with potassium permanganate as the titrant is an accepted method for the direct determination of iodide, the end point in each of the latter two titrations being detected by potentiometric techniques. Instead of a direct titration with standard iodide solution, the *indirect* procedure for the determination of permanganate, dichromate, bromate, and similarly strong oxidizing agents involves a titration of the triiodide formed by the reaction of excess iodide with the particular oxidant. Since a stoichiometric relationship exists between the original quantity of oxidant and the amount of triiodide produced, a determination of triiodide provides data from which the concentration or quantity of oxidizing agent may be calculated. A standard solution of sodium thiosulfate is almost invariably used for the titration of triiodide,

$$I_3^- + 2\,S_2O_3^= \rightleftharpoons 3\,I^- + S_4O_6^=; \qquad E^\circ = +0.46\;v$$

but arsenic(III) or sulfite titrants might be employed in special situations. In applying the indirect or iodometric method of analysis, one must always be sure that the reaction between the strong oxidant and excess iodide has reached completion before beginning the titration with thiosulfate. Otherwise any strong oxidizing agent present at the start of the titration will probably oxidize thiosulfate to sulfur and sulfate as well as tetrathionate, thereby upsetting the stoichiometry of the desired triiodide-thiosulfate reaction.

The basic principles of the direct and indirect methods of analysis may now be summarized. Direct methods are designed for the determination of substances which are easily oxidized, the procedure consisting of a direct titration of the substance to be determined with a standard solution of iodine (triiodide). On the other hand, indirect methods are intended for the determination of substances which are themselves strong oxidizing agents, and the procedure consists of the preliminary reaction of that substance with an excess of iodide ion to yield triiodide, followed by the titration of the triiodide ion with a standard solution of sodium thiosulfate. The titration end point in a direct method is marked by the first permanent appearance of free iodine (triiodide) in the titration vessel, and, in an indirect method, by the final disappearance of free iodine.

PREPARATION AND STABILITY OF IODINE AND SODIUM THIOSULFATE SOLUTIONS

Iodine.   Iodine is generally not used as a primary standard substance because of the inconveniences which attend the preparation and weighing of the pure, dry solid. Some commercially available samples of solid iodine have a high degree of purity, so that standard titrant solutions may be prepared directly from a weighed portion of the reagent. In other instances, iodine can be purified by a sublimation procedure. Solid iodine has an appreciable vapor pressure (0.31 mm at room temperature), and so special precautions are necessary to prevent the loss of iodine during weighing and handling operations. Moreover, since iodine vapors are corrosive toward metals, any solid to be weighed on an analytical balance must be placed in a tightly stoppered weighing bottle. In practice, there is little need to weigh solid iodine accurately because one usually prepares an iodine (triiodide) solution of approximately the desired concentration and subsequently standardizes it against pure arsenious oxide.

Although solid iodine is sparingly soluble in water, its solubility is considerably enhanced in the presence of excess potassium iodide, owing to the formation of triiodide ion. It may be noted that there is evidence for the existence of species such as I_5^- and I_7^- in very concentrated solutions of iodine and potassium iodide. Solid iodine dissolves surprisingly slowly in dilute potassium iodide media. Therefore, in the preparation of an iodine or triiodide solution, it is advisable to mix the solid iodine and potassium iodide in a relatively small volume of water until the iodine is completely dissolved, and then to dilute the solution to the desired volume with water. In this manner, the iodine is initially dissolved in the presence of a very high concentration of iodide ion. Even after the iodine has dissolved, the final adjustment of the solution volume by addition of distilled water must be performed carefully. If water is added too rapidly, solid iodine may reprecipitate because of temporary local dilution of the iodide medium; once formed, the solid iodine redissolves very slowly.

Standard triiodide solutions are inherently unstable for at least two reasons. One cause of this instability is the volatility of iodine. Loss of iodine can occur in spite of the facts that excess potassium iodide is present and that most of the dissolved iodine really exists as the triiodide ion. However, if the standard solution is stored in a tightly stoppered bottle and the bottle is opened only on the occasions when a portion of the solution is withdrawn for use in a titration, there should be no significant loss of iodine for many weeks. A standard triiodide solution must be stored in a cool place, since heat markedly increases the volatility of iodine, and, of course, titrations involving iodine should be performed at room temperature.

Another reason why triiodide solutions may undergo gradual changes in concentration is that dissolved atmospheric oxygen causes the oxidation of iodide ion to iodine (triiodide) according to the reaction

$$6\,I^- + O_2 + 4\,H^+ \rightleftharpoons 2\,I_3^- + 2\,H_2O; \qquad E^\circ = +0.693\ v$$

Fortunately, this oxidation proceeds very slowly, even though the emf value, or the equilibrium constant, indicates that the forward reaction is strongly favored. As suggested by the fact that hydrogen ion is a reactant, the oxidation of iodide becomes more significant as the pH decreases, but the problem is not at all serious for essentially neutral triiodide solutions. Environmental factors, such as heat and light, induce the air oxidation of iodide, as does the presence of heavy metal impurities; so appropriate precautionary measures should be taken in the preparation, handling, and storage of triiodide titrants. Although not related directly to the question of the stability of triiodide solutions, it may be mentioned here that other redox processes can strongly induce the air oxidation of iodide under conditions for which the latter reaction would be expected to be insignificant. For example, the reaction between a known quantity of dichromate and an excess of iodide in an acid medium, liberating a known amount of iodine, is commonly employed as the basis of a successful method for the standardization of sodium thiosulfate solutions. It has been established that the dichromate-iodide reaction induces the oxygen-iodide reaction and that, in solutions having a hydrogen ion concentration greater than approximately 0.4 to 0.5 M, the induced air oxidation of iodide becomes a source of appreciable error.

Sodium Thiosulfate. Sodium thiosulfate pentahydrate, $Na_2S_2O_3 \cdot 5 H_2O$, is not usually regarded as a primary standard substance because of the tendency for this salt to effloresce or to lose some of its water of hydration. Although pure sodium thiosulfate pentahydrate of primary-standard quality may be crystallized and stored under carefully controlled conditions, it is more straightforward to prepare a solution of approximately the desired strength and to standardize it against a primary standard substance, such as potassium dichromate or potassium iodate, or a previously standardized iodine (triiodide) solution.

Sodium thiosulfate pentahydrate crystals are readily soluble in water, and so the preparation of a solution of this salt is simple. However, there are several factors which influence the stability of a thiosulfate solution: the pH of the solution, the presence of certain heavy metal impurities, and the presence of sulfur-consuming bacteria.

The effect of acidity on the stability of thiosulfate solutions is especially interesting. In a very dilute acid medium, such as might arise in an aqueous solution saturated with carbon dioxide, thiosulfate slowly decomposes with the resultant formation of elemental sulfur and hydrogen sulfite ion:

$$S_2O_3^= + H^+ \rightleftharpoons HS_2O_3^- \longrightarrow S + HSO_3^-$$

The rate of decomposition of thiosulfate becomes markedly greater as the concentration of acid increases. For example, in a $1 F$ hydrochloric acid medium, the formation of colloidal sulfur from thiosulfate is extensive within only a minute or two. In strongly acidic solutions, the hydrogen sulfite ion is protonated to form sulfurous acid. The production of hydrogen sulfite ion changes the effective concentration of thiosulfate titrants because the HSO_3^- ion reduces twice the amount of iodine (triiodide) that thiosulfate does, as can be seen from the equilibria

$$HSO_3^- + I_3^- + H_2O \rightleftharpoons SO_4^= + 3 I^- + 3 H^+$$

and

$$S_2O_3^= + \tfrac{1}{2} I_3^- \rightleftharpoons \tfrac{1}{2} S_4O_6^= + \tfrac{3}{2} I^-$$

Although thiosulfate is unstable in acidic media, nothing prevents its use as a titrant for iodine or triiodide in even relatively concentrated acid solutions, e.g., 2 to 3 M, provided that the titration is carried out in such a manner that no significant local excess of thiosulfate is present at any time.

Oxygen by itself has no particular effect on the stability of a thiosulfate solution, whereas traces of heavy metal impurities, in the presence of oxygen, cause the gradual oxidation of thiosulfate to tetrathionate ion. For example, this decomposition is promoted by copper(II) — an almost omnipresent impurity in distilled water — and appears to proceed through a two-step cyclic mechanism in which copper(II) first oxidizes thiosulfate to tetrathionate,

$$2 \, Cu^{++} + 2 \, S_2O_3^{=} \longrightarrow 2 \, Cu^{+} + S_4O_6^{=}$$

and then dissolved oxygen reoxidizes copper(I) back to copper(II) to reinitiate the sequence of reactions:

$$4 \, Cu^{+} + O_2 + 2 \, H_2O \longrightarrow 4 \, Cu^{++} + 4 \, OH^{-}$$

The most insidious cause of instability of thiosulfate solutions is the presence of sulfur-consuming bacteria in distilled water. These bacteria convert thiosulfate to a variety of products, including elemental sulfur, sulfite, and sulfate. In preparing standard thiosulfate titrants, one usually boils the distilled water in which the solid reagent is to be dissolved as a means of destroying the bacteria. Some workers have recommended that mercury(II) or chloroform be added to thiosulfate solutions as antibacterial agents. Furthermore, it is a common practice to introduce 50 to 100 mg of reagent-grade sodium bicarbonate into a liter of sodium thiosulfate titrant because bacterial action is minimal near pH 9 or 10. Finally, by boiling the distilled water and adding a small amount of sodium bicarbonate to the titrant solution, one also eliminates the presence of carbon dioxide and traces of other acidic substances which promote the acid-catalyzed decomposition of thiosulfate. When a slightly alkaline sodium thiosulfate solution is used to titrate iodine (triiodide), it is essential that the iodine solution contain at least enough acid to neutralize the small quantity of base in the thiosulfate titrant. Otherwise the stoichiometry of the iodine-thiosulfate reaction will be upset, as described in the following paragraphs.

The Iodine-Thiosulfate Reaction.   The reaction between thiosulfate and iodine or triiodide,

$$I_3^{-} + 2 \, S_2O_3^{=} \rightleftharpoons 3 \, I^{-} + S_4O_6^{=}$$

is unusual in that most other oxidizing agents convert thiosulfate to sulfite or sulfate, rather than to tetrathionate. In general, the iodine-thiosulfate reaction proceeds rapidly according to the preceding well-defined stoichiometry at all pH values between 0 and 7. In mildly alkaline media, however, even iodine oxidizes thiosulfate to sulfate,

$$4 \, I_3^{-} + S_2O_3^{=} + 10 \, OH^{-} \rightleftharpoons 2 \, SO_4^{=} + 12 \, I^{-} + 5 \, H_2O$$

although the reaction is by no means quantitative until the pH becomes very high. The nature of the iodine-thiosulfate reaction changes in alkaline solutions because iodine or triiodide is no longer the active oxidant. Above a pH of approximately 8 or 9, triiodide disproportionates into iodide and hypoiodous acid,

$$I_3^- + OH^- \rightleftharpoons 2\,I^- + HOI$$

the latter appearing to be the substance which most readily oxidizes thiosulfate to sulfate:

$$4\,HOI + S_2O_3^= + 6\,OH^- \rightleftharpoons 4\,I^- + 2\,SO_4^= + 5\,H_2O$$

However, the chemistry of iodine in alkaline media is complicated further by the disproportionation of hypoiodous acid into iodate and iodide:

$$3\,HIO + 3\,OH^- \rightleftharpoons IO_3^- + 2\,I^- + 3\,H_2O$$

Since side reactions such as these are not unique to the iodine-thiosulfate titration, the successful use of iodine or triiodide titrants is generally restricted to solutions having pH values less than about 8.

END POINT DETECTION

In our earlier classification of direct and indirect methods of analysis involving iodine, we pointed out that the end point for the former type of titration is marked by the first detectable and permanent excess of iodine in the titration vessel, whereas the disappearance of the last discernible quantity of iodine signals the end point in the latter class of titrations. Three different techniques are commonly employed for end point detection.

The appearance or disappearance of the iodine (triiodide) color is itself an extremely sensitive way to locate the end point of a titration, provided that iodine is the only colored substance in the system. Molecular iodine has a distinctive red-violet color in nonpolar solvents such as carbon tetrachloride and benzene; but, in polar solvents like water, dissolved iodine is characteristically orange-brown in color. Triiodide ion, which is the predominant form of iodine in aqueous iodide media, is yellow-brown colored. In a perfectly colorless solution, it is possible to detect visually a concentration of triiodide as low as $5 \times 10^{-6}\,M$ which, in a solution volume of 100 ml, corresponds to 1 μEq of titrant. In the *direct* titration of 50.00 ml of 0.05000 M arsenic(III) with 0.05000 M iodine (triiodide), the end point would be recognized as the first appearance of the yellow color of triiodide ion. If the minimum detectable concentration of triiodide is assumed to be $5 \times 10^{-6}\,M$, the titration error should be only $+0.02$ per cent.

Starch. Conventional redox indicators are not needed in iodine methods of analysis because of the availability of starch, a sensitive internal indicator which undergoes a highly specific interaction with iodine. Free iodine forms a very intense blue color with colloidally dispersed starch, and this coloration serves well as an indication of the presence of iodine. The end point of a titration with a standard triiodide solution is marked by the appearance of the blue starch-iodine color, and the blue color disappears at the end point of an indirect iodine procedure. The minimum concentration of iodine which can be detected with the aid of starch seems to depend on the amount of iodide ion present in solution. As little as $2 \times 10^{-7}\,M$ iodine gives a detectable blue color with starch under optimum conditions. In the presence of approximately $10^{-5}\,M$ iodide ion, one can readily see the blue starch-iodine color for a $5 \times 10^{-6}\,M$ iodine concentration, but in the absence of iodide the minimal detectable iodine concentration is 10 times greater.

One judges from these figures that the starch-iodine color does not provide appreciably greater sensitivity of end point detection than the color of iodine (triiodide) itself; however, the blue starch-iodine color is more distinctive, particularly in colored solutions. The structure of the starch-iodine complex has not been unambiguously established. However, one of the components of starches, amylose, consists of a long helical chain, inside of which (as shown by x-ray studies) linear iodine molecules lie. The effect of iodide concentration on the detectability of the starch-iodine color suggests that an interaction between the linear triiodide ion and amylose occurs.

Several general precautions should be taken in the use of starch as an indicator for iodine. The starch should not be present in the titrated solution until the free iodine concentration is rather low, because large amounts of iodine cause a starch suspension to coagulate and promote the decomposition of starch as well. Thus, the starch indicator solution should not be added until just prior to the end point in the titration of an indirect iodine method. This point may be ascertained through a preliminary rough titration or, in most instances, from the intensity of the natural color of iodine or triiodide in the solution. In a direct titration with standard triiodide solution, the starch indicator may be added at the start of the titration, since no iodine or triiodide ion exists in the titration vessel until the final end point is reached.

Starch suspensions must be stored in such a manner as to prevent undue exposure to air and to any possible source of bacteria, because the decomposition of starch is promoted by both oxygen and microorganisms. Various preservatives, such as mercuric iodide, thymol, and glycerol, help to minimize bacterially induced decomposition of starch. However, it should be noted that excessive amounts of these preservatives must be avoided, since they diminish the sensitivity of end point detection. Usually, it is preferable to prepare a fresh starch suspension at least within a day or two of the time it is to be used. Decomposed starch suspensions can usually be recognized by the fact that they yield a red or brown color which persists even after the normal blue starch-iodine color has disappeared; if decomposition of the starch is sufficiently extensive, the blue color may not develop at all. The starch indicator should be employed only at or near room temperature, as the sensitivity of the starch-iodine end point is markedly decreased in solutions at higher temperatures. Acid decomposes starch through a hydrolysis reaction, and so starch should not be used in strongly acidic media nor should it be allowed to remain very long in solutions of even moderate acidity.

Extraction Method. Another form of end point detection involves the addition of a few milliliters of a water-immiscible liquid, usually carbon tetrachloride or chloroform, to the titration vessel. Since molecular iodine is much more soluble in the nonpolar organic layer than in the aqueous phase, any iodine which may be present will tend to concentrate itself in the heavier, lower layer and will impart its violet color to this layer. In practice, one performs the titration with the aid of a ground-glass-stoppered flask. As the end point is approached, the titration flask is stoppered and the solution is thoroughly shaken after each addition of titrant. Then the flask is inverted so that the organic liquid collects in the narrow neck of the flask, and the organic phase is examined for the presence or absence of the iodine color before further addition of titrant. The extraction method of end point detection is less convenient and more time-consuming than is the use of starch, but both methods yield excellent results. The extraction method may be advantageously employed for titrations in strongly acidic media where the use of starch is not feasible.

STANDARDIZATION OF IODINE AND SODIUM THIOSULFATE SOLUTIONS

Iodine. Arsenious oxide is the primary-standard substance which is almost always used for the standardization of iodine or triiodide solutions. As in the standardization of a potassium permanganate solution discussed in the preceding chapter, the arsenious oxide is initially dissolved in a sodium hydroxide medium,

$$As_2O_3 + 2\ OH^- \longrightarrow 2\ AsO_2^- + H_2O$$

and the resulting solution is neutralized with hydrochloric acid prior to the titration of arsenic(III) with triiodide ion.

Earlier in this chapter we formulated the arsenic(III)-triiodide reaction as

$$HAsO_2 + I_3^- + 2\ H_2O \rightleftharpoons H_3AsO_4 + 3\ I^- + 2\ H^+$$

and reported that the emf for this equilibrium under standard-state conditions is -0.023 v. It is now of interest to prove, as stated, that this reaction can be made the basis of a highly accurate method for the standardization of triiodide solutions or, alternatively, for the direct determination of arsenic(III). The most critical aspect of the titration is to establish what the pH of the solution must be in order to guarantee a quantitatively complete reaction between arsenic(III) and triiodide ion.

We shall begin our consideration of this problem by using the emf value just cited to evaluate the pertinent equilibrium constant,

$$\log K = \frac{nE^\circ}{0.059} = \frac{(2)(-0.023)}{0.059} = -0.78$$

$$K = 0.166$$

and by writing the equilibrium expression for the arsenic(III)-triiodide reaction:

$$\frac{[H_3AsO_4][I^-]^3[H^+]^2}{[HAsO_2][I_3^-]} = 0.166$$

At least one careful experimental study of the arsenic(III)-triiodide reaction has been performed, from which it was concluded that the equilibrium constant is 5.5×10^{-2}. This latter value differs by a factor of three from the equilibrium constant just calculated, probably because activity coefficients were not considered in the experimental study. However, since our goal in making any equilibrium calculations is to arrive at reasonable chemical predictions — which must ultimately be corroborated by actual experiments — we shall continue to use the equilibrium constant (0.166) derived from standard-potential data.

By specifying values for the concentrations of all species, except hydrogen ion, at the end point of a successful arsenic(III)-triiodide titration, we can calculate what hydrogen ion concentration or pH is consistent with the attainment of these concentrations. Let us assume that we are titrating 50.00 ml of 0.04000 M arsenic(III) with 0.05000 F iodine (in 0.25 F potassium iodide) and that the total volume of solution at the end point of the titration is 100.0 ml. In addition, we can make the following statements regarding the concentrations of the various species at the end point:

1. Assuming that we use the appearance of the starch-iodine color to signal the end point, a reasonable triiodide concentration is 5×10^{-7} M.

2. The final iodide concentration is governed by two factors — the quantity of iodide produced by the arsenic(III)-triiodide reaction, plus the iodide introduced as potassium iodide from the titrant. Since 40.00 ml of titrant is required and since virtually all of the iodine ends up as iodide ion, we would obtain 4.000 millimoles of I^- from the iodine and another 10.00 millimoles of I^- from the potassium iodide. Therefore, in a volume of 100 ml the final iodide concentration would be 14.00/100 or 0.14 M.

3. Since we are really interested in the completeness of oxidation of arsenic(III), it suffices to specify the *concentration ratio* of arsenic(V) to arsenic(III) at the end point. If we desire the titration to be accurate to within one part per thousand, the ratio $[H_3AsO_4]/[HAsO_2]$ should be 1000. However, as a margin for safety, it is far better to propose a somewhat higher degree of completeness of reaction. We shall let the ratio $[H_3AsO_4]/[HAsO_2]$ be 10,000.

If the preceding equilibrium expression is solved for the hydrogen ion concentration,

$$[H^+]^2 = 0.166 \frac{[HAsO_2][I_3^-]}{[H_3AsO_4][I^-]^3}$$

and values for the concentration terms are substituted,

$$[H^+]^2 = \frac{(0.166)(5 \times 10^{-7})}{(1 \times 10^4)(0.14)^3}$$

we obtain

$$[H^+] = 5.5 \times 10^{-5} \, M, \quad \text{or} \quad pH = 4.26$$

On the basis of this calculation alone, one concludes that the arsenic(III)-triiodide reaction is feasible as a titrimetric method of analysis if the pH of the solution is not lower than approximately 4.3. However, such a prediction should always be subjected to an experimental test and, in this connection, the following observations concerning the arsenic(III)-triiodide reaction are especially pertinent. First, this reaction does proceed quantitatively to completion at pH 4.3, and even at pH values somewhat below 4, but at pH values less than 5 the *rate* of the reaction is so slow that fading, premature end points are obtained. Second, pH 7 to 9 is the optimum range for the arsenic(III)-triiodide reaction. Third, the upper pH limit is approximately 11; at this latter pH, some disproportionation of iodine (triiodide) into hypoiodous acid and iodide occurs, and hypoiodous acid smoothly oxidizes arsenic(III) to arsenic(V). Fourth, at still higher pH values, the hypoiodous acid disproportionates into iodide and iodate, the latter being extremely slow to react with arsenic(III). Finally, it is not sufficient that the initial pH of the solution being titrated merely lie between 7 and 9; the solution must be buffered within this pH range. If hydrogen ion which is produced during the titration is not neutralized by the buffer, the marked increase in the acidity of the solution can bring the arsenic(III)-triiodide reaction to a halt long before the true equivalence point is reached. Obviously, when the arsenic(III)-triiodide reaction ceases, further addition of the triiodide titrant will cause the very premature appearance of the blue starch-iodine color.

The proper solution conditions for the arsenic(III)-triiodide titration are usually attained in the following way: After a weighed portion of arsenious oxide is dissolved in a dilute sodium hydroxide medium, enough hydrochloric acid is added to neutralize or slightly acidify the solution. Next, several grams of reagent-grade sodium bicarbonate are added to provide a carbonic acid-bicarbonate buffer of pH 7 to 8; then starch indicator is added and the solution is titrated with iodine or triiodide.

Up to this point we have neglected one of the interesting features of the arsenic(III)-triiodide reaction, namely, the acid strengths of $HAsO_2$ and H_3AsO_4. Arsenious acid is extremely weak,

$$HAsO_2 \rightleftharpoons H^+ + AsO_2^-; \quad K = 6 \times 10^{-10}$$

whereas arsenic acid is a triprotic substance which undergoes the following ionizations:

$$H_3AsO_4 \rightleftharpoons H^+ + H_2AsO_4^-; \qquad K_1 = 6.0 \times 10^{-3}$$
$$H_2AsO_4^- \rightleftharpoons H^+ + HAsO_4^=; \qquad K_2 = 1.0 \times 10^{-7}$$
$$HAsO_4^= \rightleftharpoons H^+ + AsO_4^\equiv; \qquad K_3 = 3.0 \times 10^{-12}$$

An inspection of these ionization constants reveals that $HAsO_2$ and $HAsO_4^=$ are the predominant forms of arsenic(III) and arsenic(V), respectively, in the pH range from 7 to 9. Accordingly, the arsenic(III)-triiodide reaction should be represented by the equation

$$HAsO_2 + I_3^- + 2\ H_2O \rightleftharpoons HAsO_4^= + 3\ I^- + 4\ H^+$$

The equilibrium constant for this reaction should be expected to differ from that employed in earlier calculations, but it can be easily evaluated if we combine the following two equilibria:

$$HAsO_2 + I_3^- + 2\ H_2O \rightleftharpoons H_3AsO_4 + 3\ I^- + 2\ H^+; \qquad K = 0.166$$
$$H_3AsO_4 \rightleftharpoons 2\ H^+ + HAsO_4^=; \qquad K_1K_2 = 6.0 \times 10^{-10}$$

Thus, we may write

$$\frac{[HAsO_4^=][I^-]^3[H^+]^4}{[HAsO_2][I_3^-]} = KK_1K_2 = 1.0 \times 10^{-10}$$

Let us employ this new equilibrium constant, which is valid at pH 7, to determine the completeness of the oxidation of arsenic(III) to arsenic(V) at the end point of the titration. Taking $[H^+] = 10^{-7}\ M$ and assuming as before that $[I^-] = 0.14\ M$ and $[I_3^-] = 5 \times 10^{-7}\ M$, one obtains

$$\frac{[HAsO_4^=]}{[HAsO_2]} = 1.0 \times 10^{-10}\ \frac{[I_3^-]}{[I^-]^3[H^+]^4} = \frac{(1.0 \times 10^{-10})(5 \times 10^{-7})}{(0.14)^3(10^{-7})^4}$$
$$= 1.8 \times 10^{14}$$

The titration reaction is amply quantitative at pH 7.

Sodium Thiosulfate. A previously standardized iodine (triiodide) solution suffices well for the standardization of a sodium thiosulfate titrant. In addition, strong oxidizing agents, such as potassium dichromate and potassium iodate, may serve as primary standards for the standardization of thiosulfate solutions through the indirect method of analysis involving iodine. Finally, weighed portions of pure, solid iodine may be used to standardize sodium thiosulfate solutions. All of the procedures employed for the standardization of thiosulfate solutions ultimately involve the reaction between iodine (triiodide) and thiosulfate.

Because of the special techniques that must be used to handle and weigh highly volatile solid iodine, the standardization of a sodium thiosulfate solution against weighed portions of iodine is seldom employed in routine analytical work. Regardless of whether a thiosulfate solution is standardized against solid iodine or an aliquot of a standard triiodide solution, it is essential to acidify the iodine sample solution at least slightly. This procedure is necessary because the small quantity of sodium bicarbonate, which is normally added to a thiosulfate solution as an antibacterial agent, might cause the disproportionation of iodine to hypoiodous acid and iodide.

Potassium dichromate possesses the high purity and stability, plus the ideal physical properties, that make it an excellent reagent for the standardization of thiosulfate solutions. If excess potassium iodide is dissolved in an acidic dichromate solution, the latter oxidizes iodide to triiodide,

$$Cr_2O_7^= + 9\ I^- + 14\ H^+ \rightleftharpoons 2\ Cr^{+++} + 3\ I_3^- + 7\ H_2O$$

and the liberated iodine may be titrated with the sodium thiosulfate solution to a starch-iodine end point. However, the dichromate-iodide reaction is relatively slow and, in order for the oxidation of iodide to proceed quantitatively, careful control must be maintained over the experimental variables — the concentrations of acid and iodide, the time of reaction, and even the order in which the reagents are mixed. The effect of hydrogen ion concentration on the rate of oxidation of iodide is especially pronounced. At pH 2 or 3, for example, quantitative oxidation of iodide does occur, but the dichromate-iodide reaction does not become sufficiently rapid to have analytical usefulness until the acid concentration is at least $0.2\ M$. Experiments have demonstrated that the oxidation of iodide is quantitatively complete after approximately five minutes if the initial concentrations of hydrogen ion and iodide are 0.2 and $0.1\ M$, respectively. Although further increases in the hydrogen ion and iodide concentrations would be expected to enhance the rate of the dichromate-iodide reaction, such expedients are inadvisable because they promote the air oxidation of iodide. We pointed out previously that, in strongly acid media, iodide is oxidized by dissolved atmospheric oxygen,

$$6\ I^- + O_2 + 4\ H^+ \rightleftharpoons 2\ I_3^- + 2\ H_2O$$

and that, in addition, this process is induced by the dichromate-iodide reaction. In order to minimize this source of error in the standardization procedure, one should not exceed an acid concentration of $0.4\ M$ and the reaction time should be restricted to about 10 minutes. Nevertheless, if the various compromises are closely met, the standardization of a sodium thiosulfate solution against potassium dichromate is highly reliable.

Another substance which quantitatively oxidizes iodide to triiodide in an acid medium is potassium iodate:

$$IO_3^- + 8\ I^- + 6\ H^+ \rightleftharpoons 3\ I_3^- + 3\ H_2O$$

The iodine or triiodide produced by this reaction may be titrated with the sodium thiosulfate solution which is to be standardized. When compared to the dichromate-iodide reaction, the iodate-iodide system possesses several advantages, but it has one significant disadvantage. The iodate-iodide reaction occurs almost instantaneously, even in very dilute acid media, although in the standardization of thiosulfate the solution containing the iodate-iodide mixture is typically made 0.1 F in hydrochloric acid. Furthermore, there is apparently no induced oxidation of iodide by oxygen. Whereas the disappearance of the blue starch-iodine color is partially obscured by the green-colored chromic ion in the standardization of thiosulfate against potassium dichromate, the end point in the iodate procedure is signaled by a sharp change from blue to colorless. The disadvantage of potassium iodate as a primary-standard substance stems from the fact that its equivalent weight is low. For the standardization of a 0.1 F sodium thiosulfate solution, the required weight of potassium iodate is only about 0.12 gm, and so a typical weighing uncertainty of 0.1 mg exceeds the limit of error which is normally desired in a standardization procedure. This problem may be circumvented if one prepares a standard potassium iodate solution from a larger weight of the solid reagent; however, any weighing error incurred in this operation may remain undetected, since the standardization will be very precise, even if inaccurate.

SELECTED APPLICATIONS

Iodimetric and iodometric methods have very likely attracted more attention than any other class of titrimetric redox procedures. In beginning this section of the chapter, we shall mention briefly a few specific determinations which can be accomplished, and then we shall discuss several other procedures in somewhat greater detail.

Use of the Dichromate-Iodide Reaction. As discussed earlier in this chapter, the oxidation of iodide by dichromate in an acid medium yields triiodide, and the latter can be titrated with a standard sodium thiosulfate solution. The dichromate-iodide reaction serves as the basis for the determination of chromium as well as lead and barium.

Chromium(III), which is almost always obtained in the dissolution of various sample materials, can be quantitatively oxidized to dichromate or chromate by such diverse reagents as potassium chlorate in hot concentrated nitric acid, or argentic oxide in cold 4 F nitric acid, or hydrogen peroxide in sodium hydroxide solution. In each instance, the excess oxidizing agent is easily destroyed if the solution is heated or boiled, leaving dichromate or chromate which can be determined accurately according to the indirect iodometric procedure.

Both lead chromate and barium chromate are very slightly soluble, and so the addition of a modest excess of chromate to a sample solution containing either lead or barium ion causes the precipitation of $PbCrO_4$ or $BaCrO_4$ if the solution pH is correctly adjusted. The resulting precipitate may be washed free of excess chromate and dissolved in an acid solution to convert chromate to dichromate,

$$2\ CrO_4^= + 2\ H^+ \rightleftharpoons Cr_2O_7^= + H_2O$$

and the dichromate determined iodometrically. Alternatively, a known quantity of chromate greater than that required to precipitate quantitatively $PbCrO_4$ or $BaCrO_4$ may be added to a sample solution and, after separation of the solid and solution phases, the filtrate may be analyzed for excess, unreacted chromate.

Determination of Manganese. An indirect iodometric procedure, involving the oxidation of iodide to triiodide by either manganese dioxide or permanganate, can be employed for the determination of manganese:

$$2 \ MnO_4^- + 15 \ I^- + 16 \ H^+ \rightleftharpoons 2 \ Mn^{++} + 5 \ I_3^- + 8 \ H_2O$$

$$MnO_2 + 3 \ I^- + 4 \ H^+ \rightleftharpoons Mn^{++} + I_3^- + 2 \ H_2O$$

A titration of the liberated iodine with standard sodium thiosulfate solution provides data from which the quantity of MnO_2 or MnO_4^- may be calculated. Since it is manganese(II) that is usually encountered in an aqueous medium, several effective methods are available for the preliminary oxidation of manganous ion to manganese dioxide or permanganate. Argentic oxide quantitatively converts manganese(II) to permanganate in $4 \ F$ sulfuric acid, and manganous ion is smoothly oxidized to MnO_2 by potassium chlorate in boiling, concentrated nitric acid. After the excess argentic oxide or potassium chlorate is decomposed, the MnO_2 or MnO_4^- is subsequently treated with excess potassium iodide and the solution titrated to a starch-iodine end point.

Determination of Iron. Although the determination of iron is best accomplished through a titration of iron(II) with permanganate, dichromate, or cerium(IV), one may analyze a hydrochloric acid solution of iron(III) by taking advantage of the reaction

$$2 \ Fe^{+++} + 3 \ I^- \rightleftharpoons 2 \ Fe^{++} + I_3^-; \qquad E^{o\prime} = +0.16 \ v$$

In spite of the fact that this reaction has a small emf in a $1 \ F$ hydrochloric acid medium, a quantitatively complete reaction can be achieved if a relatively high iodide concentration is employed. In addition, the solution must be quite acidic in order to minimize the formation of brown-colored iron(III) species, such as $Fe(H_2O)_5(OH)^{++}$ and $Fe(H_2O)_4(OH)_2^+$, which obscure the end point and which react somewhat slowly with iodide. Finally, the removal of one of the reaction products, triiodide ion, by the sodium thiosulfate titrant further enhances the completeness of the iron(III)-iodide reaction.

Determination of Sulfides. The reaction between triiodide and hydrogen sulfide,

$$H_2S + I_3^- \rightleftharpoons S + 3 \ I^- + 2 \ H^+$$

provides a useful method for the determination of sulfide. However, at least two problems arise in the practical utilization of this reaction. First, hydrogen sulfide is quite volatile and may escape from neutral and acidic sample solutions. Second, although hydrogen sulfide is converted to nonvolatile HS^- in alkaline media, the triiodide titrant disproportionates into iodide and hypoiodous acid and partially oxidizes HS^- to sulfate at high pH values. Fortunately, there are several, simple procedural changes which permit the analysis to be successfully performed. For example, it is common practice to add an alkaline sulfide sample to an excess of acidified triiodide solution and to back-titrate the unreacted triiodide with standard sodium thiosulfate.

The same general procedure may be applied to the determination of cadmium or zinc in sulfide precipitates. In practice, the cadmium sulfide or zinc sulfide is separated from its mother solution by filtration or centrifugation and is washed free of excess sulfide. Next, the precipitate is suspended in a few milliliters of water to which is added several drops of acetic acid; the acetic acid does not dissolve the precipitate but does render the suspension of the precipitate slightly acidic to guard against the disproportionation of triiodide subsequently added and to prevent partial oxidation of sulfide to sulfate. Then, a measured excess of standard triiodide solution is introduced and the mixture is made approximately 2 to 3 F in hydrochloric acid. The cadmium or zinc sulfide precipitate immediately dissolves in the hydrochloric acid medium,

$$CdS + 2 H^+ \rightleftharpoons Cd^{++} + H_2S$$

the liberated hydrogen sulfide reacts rapidly and quantitatively with an equivalent amount of triiodide, and the unreacted triiodide is back-titrated with standard thiosulfate to a starch-iodine end point. The quantity of cadmium sulfide or zinc sulfide can be calculated from the difference between the amounts of standard triiodide and thiosulfate used in the determination.

Determination of Arsenic(V). Under certain conditions, the arsenic(III)-triiodide reaction (normally used in the standardization of iodine solutions) may be reversed such that arsenic(V) quantitatively oxidizes iodide to triiodide:

$$H_3AsO_4 + 3 I^- + 2 H^+ \rightleftharpoons HAsO_2 + I_3^- + 2 H_2O$$

An obvious consequence of this reverse process is that the triiodide ion formed in the reaction may be titrated with thiosulfate and the titration data can be employed to calculate the quantity of arsenic(V) originally present.

It is important to calculate what concentrations of iodide and hydrogen ion are needed to drive this reaction to quantitative completion, especially in view of the fact that the equilibrium constant for the proposed reaction is only 6.0.

$$\frac{[HAsO_2][I_3^-]}{[H_3AsO_4][I^-]^3[H^+]^2} = \frac{1}{0.166} = 6.0$$

Note that we have written $HAsO_2$ and H_3AsO_4, the fully protonated forms of arsenic(III) and arsenic(V), respectively, to anticipate the conclusion that the acidity of the solution must be very high if the reaction is to proceed quantitatively. We can arrive at a conclusion regarding the quantitativeness of the reduction of arsenic(V) to arsenic(III) in the following way: Let us assume certain reasonable values for the concentrations of hydrogen ion, iodide ion, and triiodide ion at the end point of the titration and then calculate the ratio of arsenic(III) to arsenic(V). For the first set of provisional concentration values, we shall let $[H^+] = 1\ M$, $[I^-] = 0.1\ M$, and $[I_3^-] = 5 \times 10^{-7}\ M$. When these values are substituted into the preceding equilibrium expression, we obtain

$$\frac{[HAsO_2]}{[H_3AsO_4]} = 6.0\ \frac{[I^-]^3[H^+]^2}{[I_3^-]} = \frac{(6.0)(0.1)^3(1)^2}{(5 \times 10^{-7})} = 1.2 \times 10^4$$

The result of this calculation immediately suggests that the reduction of arsenic(V) to arsenic(III) is adequately complete and that the titration should succeed if conditions pertaining to the iodide concentration and the acidity are achieved. Unfortunately, this computation fails to convey how critically the completeness of reaction depends on the concentrations of the various species. Let us repeat the calculation, assuming that $[H^+] = 0.5\ M$, $[I^-] = 0.05\ M$, and $[I_3^-] = 5 \times 10^{-7}\ M$. The concentrations of hydrogen ion and iodide are similar to the previous values, but they do reflect the typical fluctuations in experimental variables which might arise in an analytical procedure. Substituting these values into the equilibrium expression, one discovers that

$$\frac{[HAsO_2]}{[H_3AsO_4]} = 6.0\ \frac{[I^-]^3[H^+]^2}{[I_3^-]} = \frac{(6.0)(0.05)^3(0.5)^2}{(5 \times 10^{-7})} = 375$$

A comparison of these two calculations should leave little doubt that very careful control of the hydrogen ion and iodide concentrations is required in the arsenic(V)-iodide titration. Usually, to ensure that the reaction will definitely be complete, the initial hydrogen ion concentration is adjusted to between 4 and 5 M and enough solid potassium iodide is dissolved in the solution to provide an iodide concentration of at least 0.2 M. A final point concerning this titration is that, in 4 to 5 M acid, starch cannot be used as the indicator because it undergoes a rapid, acid-catalyzed decomposition. Therefore, the extraction method of end point detection may be employed, or one can simply watch for the disappearance of the yellow triiodide color.

Determination of Copper. When an excess of potassium iodide is added to an acidic solution of copper(II), two reactions occur simultaneously. First, the copper(II) oxidizes iodide to triiodide ion, being reduced to copper(I). Second, the copper(I) immediately reacts with iodide to form a precipitate of white copper(I) iodide. These two processes may be combined in the overall reaction

$$2\ Cu^{++} + 5\ I^- \rightleftharpoons 2\ CuI(s) + I_3^-; \qquad E^\circ = +0.32\ v$$

By titrating the triiodide with a standard sodium thiosulfate solution, one can achieve accurate determinations of copper in a variety of samples, including brasses and other alloys.

The success of this method for the determination of copper rests largely on the insolubility of copper(I) iodide. In the preceding chapter we discussed how the interactions of cerium(IV) and cerium(III) with different complexing agents can alter the effective oxidizing strength of cerium(IV). The copper(II)-iodide reaction may be viewed in an analogous fashion. If we write the half-reaction involving the simple hydrated copper(II) and copper(I) ions,

$$Cu^{++} + e \rightleftharpoons Cu^+; \qquad E^\circ = +0.153 \text{ v}$$

it is evident that, under ordinary conditions, copper(II) is a poor oxidant. However, since iodide reacts quite completely with copper(I) to precipitate CuI, the concentration of Cu^+ is greatly diminished relative to that of Cu^{++} and the effective oxidizing strength of copper(II) is thereby enhanced:

$$Cu^{++} + I^- + e \rightleftharpoons CuI(s); \qquad E^\circ = +0.86 \text{ v}$$

In practice, the presence of a relatively large amount of potassium iodide, approximately $0.25 F$, favors the copper(II)-iodide reaction not only by keeping the concentration of copper(I) very low but, in addition, by maintaining the concentration of one of the reactants, iodide, at a high value. Furthermore, the titration of triiodide with thiosulfate decreases the concentration of a product species, I_3^-, which further increases the completeness of the reaction.

   Although hydrogen ion does not appear as either reactant or product in the reaction of copper(II) with iodide, pH nevertheless exerts an influence on the rate of the reaction as well as on the accuracy of the determination. The hydrogen ion concentration must be greater than approximately $10^{-4} M$ in order to repress the occurrence of proton-transfer equilibria such as

$$Cu(H_2O)_4{}^{++} + H_2O \rightleftharpoons Cu(H_2O)_3(OH)^+ + H_3O^+$$

and

$$Cu(H_2O)_3(OH)^+ + H_2O \rightleftharpoons Cu(H_2O)_2(OH)_2 + H_3O^+$$

The $Cu(H_2O)_3(OH)^+$ and $Cu(H_2O)_2(OH)_2$ species react slowly with iodide. On the other hand, if the concentration of hydrogen ion exceeds $0.3 M$, the air oxidation of iodide is induced by the copper(II)-iodide reaction.

   A significant source of negative error in the titration arises from adsorption of triiodide ion by the CuI precipitate. Triiodide ion is held so tenaciously on the surface of the precipitate that the reaction between thiosulfate and triiodide is incomplete. The mechanism of the adsorption can undoubtedly be explained in terms of the phenomena discussed in Chapter 5; iodide ion probably comprises the primary adsorbed ion layer, and iodine molecules interact with the adsorbed iodide to form adsorbed triiodide ions. This simple picture seems to have some validity, because the ordinarily white CuI precipitate is distinctly yellow-brown colored in the presence of triiodide. The problem may be overcome in the following manner: As the end point is approached, a small excess of potassium thiocyanate is added to the mixture, which metathesizes copper(I) iodide to copper(I) thiocyanate:

$$CuI(s) + SCN^- \rightleftharpoons CuSCN(s) + I^-$$

Since solid copper(I) thiocyanate has almost no tendency to adsorb iodide ions, the previously adsorbed triiodide is released so that the thiosulfate titration can be finished. However, thiocyanate may not be added at the beginning of the titration, for triiodide slowly oxidizes thiocyanate.

Certain elements which accompany copper in brass, other alloys, and ores may interfere with the iodometric determination we have been describing. Copper alloys, including brass, contain zinc, lead, and tin as well as smaller amounts of iron and nickel, whereas iron, arsenic, and antimony are frequently found in copper-containing ores.

A hot, concentrated nitric acid treatment is almost invariably employed to dissolve brass and ore samples. Copper, zinc, lead, and nickel enter the nitric acid solution in their dipositive oxidation states, but the oxidizing properties of nitric acid cause the formation of iron(III), arsenic(V), and antimony(V). Tin behaves in a unique way in concentrated nitric acid, being precipitated as so-called metastannic acid, $SnO_2 \cdot xH_2O$; the presence of large amounts of antimony may result in the precipitation of some Sb_2O_5. Since zinc, nickel, and tin are innocuous insofar as the determination of copper is concerned, we shall disregard them in the remainder of this discussion.

After the sample has been dissolved in nitric acid, a small volume of concentrated sulfuric acid is added and the solution is boiled until fumes of sulfur trioxide are evolved. This operation serves to remove all nitrate and other oxides of nitrogen which, if allowed to remain, would later oxidize iodide to iodine. When the sulfuric acid solution is diluted with water and cooled, lead sulfate precipitates almost quantitatively and should be removed by filtration. Otherwise, when iodide is subsequently added for the determination of copper, the formation of large quantities of canary-yellow lead iodide (PbI_2) will obscure the end point of the titration.

We noted previously that, in strongly acidic media, both iron(III) and arsenic(V) oxidize iodide to triiodide. Furthermore, the chemical behavior of antimony(V) is remarkably similar to that of arsenic(V). Therefore, the procedure for the determination of copper must be appropriately modified to prevent these elements from oxidizing iodide. The tendencies for arsenic(V) and antimony(V) to oxidize iodide can be completely nullified if the pH of the sample solution is greater than approximately 3, but the solution pH must not exceed 4 for reasons stated earlier. If one adds some reagent which strongly complexes iron(III), it cannot oxidize iodide ion. When antimony and arsenic are absent, and acidity is not so critical, phosphoric acid may be used to complex iron(III). However, when antimony, arsenic, and iron are all present, a fluoride-hydrofluoric acid buffer is employed to adjust the solution pH to approximately 3.2 and to complex iron as FeF_4^- and similar species

Separation and Determination of Arsenic, Antimony, and Tin. The elements arsenic, antimony, and tin are commonly encountered together as sulfides — As_2S_3, As_2S_5, Sb_2S_3, Sb_2S_5, SnS, and SnS_2 — in the analysis of complex samples. Therefore, it is of interest to consider, first, the separation of these elements and, second, the individual determination of each element.

A satisfactory separation of these elements can be accomplished by means of distillation. Prior to the distillation, however, one must obtain a solution of only arsenic(III), antimony(III), and tin(IV). The adjustment of the oxidation states of these elements is readily achieved if the sulfides are dissolved in hot, concentrated sulfuric acid to which is added hydrazine sulfate. Next, the resulting solution is transferred to an all-glass distillation apparatus, concentrated hydrochloric acid is introduced, and $AsCl_3$ is distilled into a receiving flask. After the arsenic is removed, more hydrochloric acid and some phosphoric acid is added to the distilling flask and $SbCl_3$ is distilled into another receiving vessel; tin(IV) remains in the distilling flask as a phosphate complex. Finally, hydrobromic acid is introduced into the distilling flask and $SnBr_4$ is distilled into a third receiving vessel.

The determination of arsenic(III) in the first portion of distillate is carried out by direct titration at pH 7 to 8 with a standard triiodide solution. The procedure is identical to that employed for the standardization of an iodine (triiodide) titrant.

The antimony(III) present in the second distillate is amenable to determination through a direct titration in neutral medium with standard triiodide solution. With one exception, the general procedure resembles that for the analysis of an arsenic(III) solution. Unlike arsenic, antimony(III) and antimony(V) both form insoluble basic salts, such as SbOCl and SbO_2Cl, in slightly acidic and neutral solutions. Such behavior is not unexpected; since antimony is below arsenic in the periodic table, it exhibits a greater degree of metallic character. Fortunately, antimony(III) and antimony(V) can be kept in solution as complex ions, probably $SbOC_4H_4O_6^-$ and $SbO_2C_4H_4O_6^-$, by the addition of tartaric acid. The reaction between antimony(III) and triiodide is not adversely influenced by the presence of tartrate. The titration proceeds according to the equation

$$SbOC_4H_4O_6^- + I_3^- + H_2O \rightleftharpoons SbO_2C_4H_4O_6^- + 3\ I^- + 2\ H^+$$

with the hydrogen ions being removed, as formed, by the buffer ingredients.

Tin(IV) in the third portion of the distillate must be reduced to tin(II) prior to titration of the latter with a standard triiodide solution. Both the reduction of tin(IV) and the subsequent titration of tin(II) are performed in a moderately strong acid medium. Metallic lead and nickel are commonly employed as reductants, a coiled wire or strip of either metal being inserted directly into the flask which contains tin(IV). After a few minutes, when the reduction of tin(IV) is judged to be complete, the lead or nickel may be withdrawn from the flask and the titration of tin(II) performed immediately to a starch-iodine end point. One source of possible difficulty in this procedure is the ease with which tin(II) is reoxidized by atmospheric oxygen. However, this problem can be greatly minimized if the solution is blanketed with an inert gas, such as carbon dioxide or nitrogen, during the prereduction and titration steps.

POTASSIUM IODATE AS AN OXIDIZING AGENT

In our earlier discussion of the standardization of a sodium thiosulfate solution, potassium iodate was mentioned as an excellent primary-standard substance. Because of the ideal physical properties of potassium iodate, its availability in a high state of purity, and the stability of its aqueous solutions, many analytical uses of this reagent have been developed.

As already described, potassium iodate reacts quantitatively with iodide in an acid medium:

$$IO_3^- + 8\,I^- + 6\,H^+ \rightleftharpoons 3\,I_3^- + 3\,H_2O$$

However, the position of chemical equilibrium is strongly influenced by the pH of the solution and, in a neutral medium, iodate exhibits no tendency to oxidize iodide. Nevertheless, this reaction serves as an especially convenient source of iodine or triiodide, one needing only to add a known volume of standard potassium iodate solution to an excess of an acidic iodide medium. The liberated iodine may be employed in the standardization of a thiosulfate solution, for the determination of hydrogen sulfide, or for the determination of tin(II), to name just three representative uses. In the two latter situations, an excess of triiodide remains after the reaction of iodine with hydrogen sulfide or tin(II), and so the complete analytical procedure entails a final titration of the unreacted iodine with standard sodium thiosulfate solution.

A number of applications of potassium iodate as an oxidizing agent have been devised which do not fit into the normal classification of direct or indirect iodine methods. It has been observed that, if a suitable reductant is titrated with a standard potassium iodate solution in an acid medium, the initial portions of the iodate are reduced to free iodine,

$$2\,IO_3^- + 12\,H^+ + 10\,e \rightleftharpoons I_2 + 6\,H_2O; \qquad E^\circ = +1.20\ v$$

which, upon reaction with additional iodate, is oxidized to unipositive iodine. Although the species I^+ is unstable, iodine in the unipositive state is stabilized through the formation of complexes with chloride ion, bromide ion, and cyanide ion and through the formation of a compound with acetone. For example, in hydrochloric acid solutions ranging in concentration from 3 to 9 F, iodate oxidizes molecular iodine to the iodine dichloride complex:

$$IO_3^- + 2\,I_2 + 10\,Cl^- + 6\,H^+ \rightleftharpoons 5\,ICl_2^- + 3\,H_2O$$

In concentrated hydrobromic acid solutions, the species IBr_2 may be produced and, when hydrogen cyanide is present in 1 F hydrochloric acid or 2 F sulfuric acid, iodate can oxidize iodine to the iodine monocyanide molecule:

$$IO_3^- + 2\,I_2 + 5\,HCN + H^+ \rightleftharpoons 5\,ICN + 3\,H_2O$$

In addition, the titration of either iodide or iodine with iodate in an acidic acetone medium yields iodoacetone, according to the reaction

$$IO_3^- + 2\ I^- + 3\ (CH_3)_2CO + 3\ H^+ \longrightarrow 3\ CH_3COCH_2I + 3\ H_2O$$

Applications.   A brief consideration of two exemplary procedures in which potassium iodate has been employed directly as a titrant will indicate the general usefulness of such methods and will introduce some new ideas concerning end point detection.

Antimony(III) may be titrated with a standard solution of potassium iodate if the titration medium contains $3\ F$ hydrochloric acid. During the early stages of the titration, the reduction of iodate to molecular iodine occurs,

$$2\ IO_3^- + 5\ HSbO_2 + 2\ H^+ + 4\ H_2O \rightleftharpoons I_2 + 5\ H_3SbO_4$$

as evidenced by the accumulation of iodine in the titration vessel. However, after all of the antimony has been oxidized, further additions of the titrant cause the disappearance of iodine, owing to the formation of iodine dichloride:

$$IO_3^- + 2\ I_2 + 10\ Cl^- + 6\ H^+ \rightleftharpoons 5\ ICl_2^- + 3\ H_2O$$

The end point of the titration is signaled when the last detectable trace of molecular iodine is oxidized to the iodine dichloride complex, and the stoichiometric relationship between iodate and antimony(III) is readily obtained if the two preceding reactions are combined:

$$IO_3^- + 2\ HSbO_2 + 2\ H^+ + 2\ Cl^- + H_2O \rightleftharpoons 2\ H_3SbO_4 + ICl_2^-$$

The determination of tin(II) in concentrated hydrochloric acid by means of a direct titration with standard potassium iodate solution is especially interesting because of the fact that two different end points may be obtained. In distinct contrast to the antimony(III)-iodate system, no molecular iodine is formed in the first step of the iodate-tin(II) titration:

$$IO_3^- + 3\ SnCl_4^= + 6\ H^+ + 6\ Cl^- \rightleftharpoons I^- + 3\ SnCl_6^= + 3\ H_2O$$

Such behavior arises because tin(II) can reduce any transiently formed iodine to iodide,

$$SnCl_4^= + I_2 + 2\ Cl^- \rightleftharpoons SnCl_6^= + 2\ I^-$$

whereas antimony(III) is not a sufficiently strong reductant to have a similar capability. When tin(II) has been quantitatively oxidized, the next drop of potassium iodate titrant oxidizes iodide to iodine (triiodide), this end point being recognizable by the appearance of the yellow color of the latter. However, if one continues to add the iodate solution, all of the iodine is eventually oxidized to iodine dichloride; so the disappearance of the iodine color constitutes a second end point. At this second end point, the net titration reaction is represented as

$$IO_3^- + 2\ SnCl_4^= + 6\ H^+ + 6\ Cl^- \rightleftharpoons ICl_2^- + 2\ SnCl_6^= + 3\ H_2O$$

Among the other species which have been successfully titrated with a standard potassium iodate solution in concentrated hydrochloric acid medium are arsenic(III), iron(II), thallium(I), iodide, sulfurous acid — in fact, most of the substances that can be determined by the more classic iodimetric and iodometric methods of analysis. The major advantage of analytical applications based on the use of potassium iodate lies in the stability and ease of preparation of the titrant as compared to certain inconveniences encountered with iodine (triiodide) solutions.

Detection of End Points. Although iodate is ultimately reduced only to the unipositive state of iodine in the present family of oxidation-reduction methods, we have seen that molecular iodine is almost always formed as an intermediate substance during these titrations. Consequently, the disappearance of the last detectable quantity of iodine is usually employed to signal the end point of an iodate titration. The high acidity of the solutions encountered in iodate titrimetry precludes the use of starch in all but one system; a satisfactory starch-iodine end point may be obtained in titrations involving iodine monocyanide where the hydrogen ion concentration need be only 1 to 2 M. In general, the extraction method of end point detection is utilized in titrations with potassium iodate. A few milliliters of carbon tetrachloride or chloroform, introduced into the titration vessel at the beginning of the determination, serves well as the water-immiscible liquid. After each addition of potassium iodate titrant, the aqueous and organic phases are shaken together thoroughly, the phases are allowed to separate, and the organic layer is examined. Prior to the equivalence point of the titration, the carbon tetrachloride or chloroform will exhibit the red-violet color due to the presence of molecular iodine. However, the equivalence point, at which all of the molecular iodine has been oxidized to the unipositive state, is marked by the sudden disappearance of the red-violet color from the organic solvent.

Several organic dye molecules have been proposed as internal indicators for iodate titrimetry. In order to qualify for such a purpose, the indicator should be stable in the presence of molecular iodine, unipositive iodine, and rather high concentrations of hydrochloric acid; but it must undergo a distinct color change with the first excess of potassium iodate in the titration vessel. Colored indicators which have been successfully employed are amaranth, brilliant ponceau 5R, and naphthol blue black — the color of each substance undergoing a marked change near the equivalence point of the titration. Unfortunately, all of these compounds are destructively oxidized by iodate, and so the indicator action is irreversible.

PERIODIC ACID AS AN OXIDIZING AGENT

To the analytical chemist interested in the quantitative determination of organic compounds, the oxidizing properties of periodic acid have special significance because this reagent undergoes a number of highly selective reactions with organic functional groups. In fact, nearly all of the important applications of periodic acid have been made in the field of organic analysis.

Detailed studies have demonstrated that **paraperiodic acid, H_5IO_6,** is the parent compound in aqueous periodic acid solutions. In an aqueous medium paraperiodic acid behaves like a moderately weak diprotic acid,

$$H_5IO_6 \rightleftharpoons H^+ + H_4IO_6^-; \qquad K_1 = 5.1 \times 10^{-4}$$
$$H_4IO_6^- \rightleftharpoons H^+ + H_3IO_6^=; \qquad K_2 = 2.0 \times 10^{-7}$$

but there is some evidence to indicate that a third proton is ionizable in strongly alkaline solutions. Furthermore, the product of the first acid dissociation, $H_4IO_6^-$, may dehydrate to form the so-called **metaperiodate ion, IO_4^-:**

$$H_4IO_6^- \rightleftharpoons IO_4^- + 2\,H_2O; \qquad K = 40$$

Paraperiodic acid is a valuable reagent for the oxidation of organic compounds because it is an extremely powerful oxidant, the standard potential for the half-reaction

$$H_5IO_6 + H^+ + 2\,e \rightleftharpoons IO_3^- + 3\,H_2O$$

being in the neighborhood of $+1.6$ to $+1.7$ v versus NHE, although the precise value is unknown.

Preparation and Standardization of Solutions.   Periodate solutions may be prepared from paraperiodic acid, potassium metaperiodate, or sodium metaperiodate, all of which are commercially available, although the latter compound is most frequently employed because it exhibits high solubility and is easily purified. Despite the oxidizing strength of periodic acid and periodate salts, aqueous solutions containing these species are remarkably stable, and water is only slowly oxidized to oxygen and ozone. However, all organic matter must be rigorously excluded from periodate solutions.

At least two methods are useful for the standardization of periodate solutions. In one of these procedures, an aliquot of the periodate solution is added to an excess of potassium iodide dissolved in a bicarbonate or borate buffer of pH 8 to 9. In a neutral or slightly alkaline medium, periodate is reduced to iodate and an equivalent quantity of triiodide is liberated:

$$IO_4^- + 3\,I^- + H_2O \rightleftharpoons IO_3^- + I_3^- + 2\,OH^-$$

A standard solution of arsenic(III) can be employed to titrate the triiodide to a starch-iodine end point. Alternatively, a known volume of the periodate solution to be standardized is pipetted into an acidic iodide medium,

$$H_5IO_6 + 11\,I^- + 7\,H^+ \rightleftharpoons 4\,I_3^- + 6\,H_2O$$

and the triiodide produced in the reaction is titrated with a standard sodium thiosulfate solution.

Reactions with Organic Compounds. The development of a feasible analytical procedure for the determination of an organic compound must include consideration of such factors as the identity and reactivity of the organic functional groups of that substance, the nature of the solvent in which the compound is dissolved, and the possible presence of other oxidizable species. Since oxidations of organic molecules by periodic acid are slow, an excess of this reagent, as well as a reaction time ranging from a few minutes to several hours, is needed to achieve quantitative results. The majority of periodate oxidations are performed in an aqueous environment, although the limited solubility of the desired compound in water may require that ethanol or glacial acetic acid be used as the solvent. Furthermore, most oxidation processes are carried out at or below room temperature because undesired side reactions occur at elevated temperatures. An interesting aspect of periodate oxidations is that the rate of reaction with organic compounds is most rapid near pH 4, suggesting that $H_4IO_6^-$, or perhaps IO_4^-, is the active oxidant.

Organic compounds which have hydroxyl (—OH) groups on two adjacent carbon atoms are readily oxidized by periodic acid at room temperature. The oxidation process, known as the **Malaprade reaction,** always involves scission of the bond between these carbon atoms followed by conversion of each hydroxyl group to a carbonyl group. For example, ethylene glycol undergoes the reaction

$$
\begin{array}{cc}
H_2C\!-\!\!-\!CH_2 \\
|\quad\;\; | \\
OH\;\; OH
\end{array}
+ H_4IO_6^- \longrightarrow
\begin{array}{cc}
H_2C & CH_2 \\
\| & \| \\
O & O
\end{array}
+ IO_3^- + 3\,H_2O
$$

and 1,2-butanediol is oxidized to formaldehyde and propionaldehyde:

$$
\begin{array}{cccc}
H_2C\!-\!\!-\!CH\!-\!\!-\!CH_2\!-\!\!-\!CH_3 \\
|\quad\;\; | \\
OH\;\; OH
\end{array}
+ H_4IO_6^- \longrightarrow
$$

$$
\begin{array}{cc}
H_2C & HC\!-\!\!-\!CH_2\!-\!\!-\!CH_3 \\
\| & \| \\
O & O
\end{array}
+ IO_3^- + 3\,H_2O
$$

Many common organic substances are characterized by having a carbonyl group ($>C\!=\!O$) attached either to another carbonyl group or to a carbon atom with a hydroxyl group. Periodic acid reacts with these compounds to cleave the carbon-carbon bond and to oxidize a carbonyl group to a carboxyl group (—COOH) and a hydroxyl group to a carbonyl group. Thus, the oxidation of one mole of glyoxal yields two moles of formic acid,

$$
\begin{array}{cc}
H\!-\!C\!-\!C\!-\!H \\
\| \;\; \| \\
O \;\; O
\end{array}
+ H_4IO_6^- \longrightarrow
\begin{array}{cc}
H\!-\!C\!-\!OH \\
\| \\
O
\end{array}
+
\begin{array}{cc}
HO\!-\!C\!-\!H \\
\| \\
O
\end{array}
+ IO_3^- + H_2O
$$

and the oxidation of 2-hydroxy-3-pentanone results in the formation of propionic acid and acetaldehyde:

$$H_3C-CH_2-\underset{\underset{O}{\|}\underset{OH}{|}}{C}-CH-CH_3 + H_4IO_6^- \longrightarrow$$

$$H_3C-CH_2-\underset{\underset{O}{\|}}{C}-OH \quad + \quad \underset{\underset{O}{\|}}{HC}-CH_3 + IO_3^- + 2\,H_2O$$

A class of organic compounds which we have not previously discussed comprises those molecules in which a carbon atom with a primary or second-ary amine group is adjacent either to a carbonyl group or to a carbon atom with a hydroxyl group. As in other periodate oxidations, the bond between the adjacent carbon atoms is broken, a carbonyl group is oxidized to a carboxyl group, and a hydroxyl group is converted to a carbonyl group. However, the fate of an amine group differs from that of other groups. A *primary* amine group is lost as ammonia, and the carbon atom is transformed into an aldehyde. A *secondary* amine group is lost as a primary amine, and the carbon atom is converted to an aldehyde. Two typical reactions are

$$\underset{\underset{OH}{|}}{H_2C}-\underset{\underset{NH(CH_3)}{|}}{CH_2} + H_4IO_6^- \longrightarrow$$

N–methyl–ethanolamine

$$\underset{\underset{O}{\|}}{H_2C} + \underset{\underset{O}{\|}}{CH_2} + CH_3NH_2 + IO_3^- + 2\,H_2O$$

and

$$H_3C-\underset{\underset{OH}{|}}{CH}-\underset{\underset{NH_2}{|}}{CH}-COOH + H_4IO_6^- \longrightarrow$$

threonine

$$H_3C-\underset{\underset{O}{\|}}{CH} \quad + \quad \underset{\underset{O}{\|}}{HC}-COOH \quad + NH_3 + IO_3^- + 2\,H_2O$$

The latter reaction between threonine and periodate is of interest for another reason. Notice that glyoxylic acid,

$$\underset{\underset{O}{\|}}{HC}-COOH$$

which consists of a carboxyl group bound to an aldehyde group, is a stable product of the threonine-periodate reaction. Indeed, a carboxyl group adjacent to any of the functional groups mentioned so far displays little, if any, reactivity toward periodate. Moreover, a molecule such as ethylene-diamine,

$$\underset{\underset{NH_2}{|}}{H_2C}-\underset{\underset{NH_2}{|}}{CH_2}$$

with amine groups on two adjacent carbon atoms, reacts very slowly with periodic acid. Finally, it is of considerable significance to the success of periodate oxidations that organic compounds with single or isolated hydroxyl, carbonyl, or amine groups are unreactive *at room temperature*. It is impossible to overemphasize the important fact that *all* of the oxidation processes described in this section pertain to room temperature. At elevated temperatures, much of the selectivity of periodate oxidations is lost because carboxyl groups as well as the isolated functional groups will undergo reaction, and the simple rules for predicting the course of these reactions become invalid.

Situations may be encountered in which three or more adjacent functional groups are present in the same molecule, as, for example, in glycerol:

$$H_2C\text{---}CH\text{---}CH_2$$
$$\quad\,|\qquad|\qquad\;|$$
$$\quad\,OH\quad OH\quad OH$$

In attempting to establish what products should be formed in the oxidation of glycerol by periodate, one may apply two rules: (1) assume that chemical attack begins at two adjacent functional groups on one end of the molecule and progresses one carbon-carbon bond at a time toward the other end of the molecule, and (2) use information from previous examples to determine the nature of the products. In the case of glycerol, the first step of the oxidation,

$$H_2C\text{---}CH\text{---}CH_2 + H_4IO_6^- \longrightarrow$$

$$H_2C\quad HC\text{---}CH_2 + IO_3^- + 3\,H_2O$$
$$\;\|\; + \;\|\qquad\;|$$
$$\;O\qquad O\quad OH$$

is followed by the reaction

$$HC\text{---}CH_2 + H_4IO_6^- \longrightarrow HC\text{---}OH \quad CH_2 + IO_3^- + 2\,H_2O$$
$$\|\quad\;| \qquad\qquad\qquad\quad\| \quad + \;\|$$
$$O\quad OH \qquad\qquad\qquad\;\;O \qquad O$$

and so the overall oxidation of 1 mole of glycerol yields 1 mole of formic acid plus 2 moles of formaldehyde. A more complicated molecule, such as erythritol, can be envisaged to undergo the following sequence of oxidations, where the periodic acid, iodate, and water have been omitted for the sake of brevity:

$$H_2C\text{---}CH\text{---}CH\text{---}CH_2 \longrightarrow H_2C \quad HC\text{---}CH\text{---}CH_2$$

erythritol

$$H_2C \quad HC\text{---}OH \quad HC\text{---}OH \quad CH_2 \longleftarrow$$

$$H_2C \quad HC\text{---}OH \quad HC\text{---}CH_2$$

Two principal procedures are employed in the application of the Malaprade reaction to the determination of organic compounds. The first method requires a titrimetric measurement of the quantity of periodate consumed in the oxidation process; and the second, more elaborate technique involves a detailed analysis of the identities and quantities of the reaction products.

Determination of Ethylene Glycol.   Consider the analysis of an aqueous ethylene glycol solution. If a known excess of a standard sodium metaperiodate solution is added to the sample and the mixture set aside for one hour at room temperature, the ethylene glycol will be quantitatively oxidized to formaldehyde, and an equivalent quantity of periodate will be reduced to iodate. As described earlier, one may adjust the pH of the reaction mixture to 7 (employing a carbonic acid-bicarbonate buffer), add an excess of potassium iodide, and titrate the resulting triiodide with a standard arsenic(III) solution. The *difference* between the amount of periodate originally used in the reaction mixture and that found by means of the arsenic(III) titration is related to the quantity of ethylene glycol in the sample.

Determination of Glycerol in the Presence of Ethylene Glycol. When a mixture of glycerol and ethylene glycol is treated with an excess of periodic acid, the two compounds are oxidized according to the reactions

$$\underset{\text{glycerol}}{\underset{\overset{|}{\text{OH}}\quad\overset{|}{\text{OH}}\quad\overset{|}{\text{OH}}}{\text{H}_2\text{C}\!-\!\!-\!\text{CH}\!-\!\!-\!\text{CH}_2}} + 2\,\text{H}_4\text{IO}_6^- \longrightarrow$$

$$2\,\text{HCHO} + \text{HCOOH} + 2\,\text{IO}_3^- + 5\,\text{H}_2\text{O}$$

and

$$\underset{\text{ethylene glycol}}{\underset{\overset{|}{\text{OH}}\quad\overset{|}{\text{OH}}}{\text{H}_2\text{C}\!-\!\!-\!\text{CH}_2}} + \text{H}_4\text{IO}_6^- \longrightarrow 2\,\text{HCHO} + \text{IO}_3^- + 3\,\text{H}_2\text{O}$$

It is evident that formic acid arises only from the oxidation of glycerol. If the reaction mixture is titrated with a standard solution of sodium hydroxide after the periodate oxidation is concluded, the observed quantity of formic acid may be related to the concentration of glycerol in the sample. However, the titration data must be corrected for the amount of periodic acid present in the reaction mixture. In practice, one prepares a blank solution containing all of the reagents except the glycerol-ethylene glycol mixture. He then titrates this blank solution with sodium hydroxide and subtracts the volume of base used in the blank titration from that required in the titration of the actual sample.

The *sum* of the quantities of glycerol and ethylene glycol can be ascertained, if necessary, from a determination of the total amount of periodate consumed in the oxidation of the sample. Furthermore, once the latter information is known, one can obtain the concentration of ethylene glycol by combining the results of the sodium hydroxide titrations and the periodate measurements.

Analysis of a Mixture of Ethylene Glycol, 1,2-Propylene Glycol, and Glycerol.   The assortment of oxidation products obtained from a solution containing ethylene glycol, 1,2-propylene glycol, and glycerol allows a complete analysis of such a mixture to be accomplished. Treatment of the three-component sample with excess periodate causes the following reactions to occur:

$$\underset{\text{ethylene glycol}}{\overset{\displaystyle H_2C\text{------}CH_2}{\underset{\displaystyle OH\quad OH}{\big|\qquad\big|}}} + H_4IO_6^- \longrightarrow 2\ HCHO + IO_3^- + 3\ H_2O$$

$$\underset{\text{1,2-propylene glycol}}{\overset{\displaystyle H_2C\text{------}CH\text{------}CH_3}{\underset{\displaystyle OH\quad OH}{\big|\quad\big|}}} + H_4IO_6^- \longrightarrow$$

$$HCHO + CH_3CHO + IO_3^- + 3\ H_2O$$

$$\underset{\text{glycerol}}{\overset{\displaystyle H_2C\text{------}CH\text{------}CH_2}{\underset{\displaystyle OH\quad OH\quad OH}{\big|\quad\big|\quad\big|}}} + 2\ H_4IO_6^- \longrightarrow$$

$$2\ HCHO + HCOOH + 2\ IO_3^- + 5\ H_2O$$

As previously described, the quantity of glycerol in the mixture can be readily determined by means of a titration with a sodium hydroxide solution, although an appropriate blank correction is required.

The fact that acetaldehyde originates only from 1,2-propylene glycol is utilized in the determination of the latter substance. However, it is essential to separate acetaldehyde from the formaldehyde, which is an oxidation product of all three compounds in the mixture. In performing this separation, one passes a stream of carbon dioxide through the solution resulting from the periodic acid treatment. Highly volatile formaldehyde and acetaldehyde are both carried by the carbon dioxide gas through a closed system which includes several specific collecting solutions for the aldehydes. In particular, formaldehyde is preferentially absorbed as the aldehyde vapors bubble through a glycine solution,

$$HCHO + H_2N\text{---}CH_2\text{---}COOH \longrightarrow H_2C{=}N\text{---}CH_2\text{---}COOH + H_2O$$

then the pure acetaldehyde which remains is trapped in a sodium bisulfite medium:

$$CH_3CHO + NaHSO_3 \longrightarrow \underset{\displaystyle H}{\overset{\displaystyle SO_3H}{H_3C\text{---}\underset{\big|}{\overset{\big|}{C}}\text{---}O^-Na^+}}$$

The determination of the acetaldehyde is completed as follows: (1) The excess of the sodium bisulfite collecting solution is destroyed; (2) the acetaldehyde-bisulfite addition compound is decomposed; and (3) the liberated bisulfite (which is stoichiometrically equivalent to acetaldehyde) is titrated with a standard iodine solution.

Unfortunately, the oxidation of the third compound in the mixture, ethylene glycol, does not lead to any unique products, and so it is necessary to establish the ethylene glycol content of the mixture by an indirect method. Accordingly, the sum of all three components in the sample can be determined from the periodic acid consumed in the oxidation reactions; then the previously measured amounts of glycerol and 1,2-propylene glycol are subtracted from this sum to obtain the quantity of ethylene glycol.

Experiment 14-1

PREPARATION AND STANDARDIZATION OF AN IODINE (TRIIODIDE) SOLUTION

Purpose

This experiment provides for the preparation of a $0.05\ F$ iodine or triiodide solution and for its standardization against weighed portions of arsenious oxide.

Procedure

Preparation of a 0.05 F Iodine (Triiodide) Solution. Weigh approximately 40 gm of reagent-grade potassium iodide into a clean 500 ml Erlenmeyer flask, and dissolve the solid in about 25 ml of distilled water.

Weigh into a clean, dry 100 ml beaker 12.7 gm of analytical-reagent-grade iodine. Perform the weighing to the nearest 0.1 gm on a triple-beam balance. Transfer the solid iodine to the flask containing the potassium iodide solution, and swirl the mixture until the solid iodine has dissolved completely.

Slowly add 300 ml of distilled water to dilute the iodine solution, making sure that the solution is swirled continuously during this dilution.

Next, transfer the solution to a clean 1 liter storage bottle. Then, as before, slowly dilute the solution to a volume of approximately 1 liter with distilled water, continuously swirling the bottle as the dilution is performed.

Be sure that no undissolved solid iodine remains. If any doubt exists concerning the presence of undissolved iodine, especially in view of the dark color of the solution, it may be advisable to let the solution stand for several days to ensure the complete dissolution of the iodine.

Standardize the solution against arsenious oxide as described in the next section.

Standardization of the Iodine (Triiodide) Solution Against Arsenious Oxide. Transfer approximately 0.7 gm of primary-standard-grade arsenious oxide to a clean weighing bottle and dry the solid for one hour in an oven at 110°C. Use a beaker-and-watch-glass arrangement as shown in Figure 2-1, and cool the weighing bottle and arsenious oxide for 30 minutes prior to the weighing of individual samples for the standardization.

Weigh accurately, to the nearest tenth milligram, individual 0.2 gm portions of the arsenious oxide into each of three clean 500 ml Erlenmeyer flasks. Add 10 ml of a 2 F sodium hydroxide solution to each flask, and swirl the mixture gently until the arsenious oxide has completely dissolved. Dilute each sample solution to a volume of 75 ml by adding distilled water. Add two drops of a phenolphthalein indicator solution, then carefully neutralize each arsenic(III) solution with 6 F hydrochloric acid until the pink phenolphthalein color just disappears. Then add 1 ml more of the 6 F hydrochloric acid.

Carefully add solid reagent-grade sodium bicarbonate in small (0.1 gm) portions to each solution until effervescence due to carbon dioxide ceases. Then add 3 to 4 gm more of sodium bicarbonate to each flask. Add 5 ml of starch indicator solution and titrate the arsenic(III) sample in the first flask with the iodine (triiodide) solution until the blue or purple starch-iodine color persists for at least 30 seconds.

The starch indicator solution should be prepared in advance as follows: Prepare a starch paste by placing 2 gm of powdered soluble starch in a mortar, adding 25 ml of distilled water, and mixing the ingredients with a spatula. Slowly pour this paste into 1 liter of boiling water, and continue the heating until the starch dissolves. Cool the solution and store it in a clean bottle.

A commercial product, Thyodene, may be purchased from the Fisher Scientific Company for use as an indicator. One only has to add perhaps 100 mg of the solid directly to the solution to be titrated. The Thyodene dissolves instantly, exhibits ideal indicator action, and is, of course, stable indefinitely.

Titrate the other two arsenic(III) solutions in a similar manner. From the titration data and the weights of arsenious oxide used in the standardization, calculate the average concentration of the iodine (triiodide) solution. Replicate results should agree to within two parts per thousand.

Experiment 14-2

PREPARATION AND STANDARDIZATION OF A SODIUM THIOSULFATE SOLUTION

Purpose

This experiment demonstrates the preparation of a sodium thiosulfate solution and its standardization against potassium iodate.

Procedure

Preparation of a 0.1 F Sodium Thiosulfate Solution. Heat 1 liter of distilled water in a large flask, covered with a watch glass, to the boiling point. Boil the water for at least five minutes, and allow it to cool to room temperature. Weigh out approximately 25 gm of reagent-grade sodium thiosulfate pentahydrate ($Na_2S_2O_3 \cdot 5\ H_2O$) and 100 mg of reagent sodium bicarbonate. Dissolve the solids in the freshly boiled, but cooled, water. Transfer the solution to a clean 1 liter, ground-glass-stoppered storage bottle, and standardize the solution against potassium iodate as described in the next section.

Standardization of the Sodium Thiosulfate Solution Against Potassium Iodate. Transfer approximately 1.2 to 1.4 gm of reagent-grade potassium iodate to a clean, dry weighing bottle, and dry the solid in an oven at 120°C for one hour.

Accurately weigh, to the nearest tenth milligram, 1.2 to 1.4 gm of dried potassium iodate into a clean 400 ml beaker. Dissolve the solid in a minimal amount of distilled water, and transfer the solution into a 500 ml volumetric flask, using a glass funnel and stirring rod to direct the solution into the volumetric flask. Dilute the potassium iodate solution to the calibration mark with distilled water. Stopper the flask and mix the solution thoroughly. Calculate the concentration of the potassium iodate solution.

Pipet a 50.00 ml aliquot of the standard potassium iodate solution into each of three clean 250 ml Erlenmeyer flasks. Treat each aliquot separately from this point to the end of the procedure. To the first flask, add 3 gm of solid potassium iodide (KI), and swirl the solution to dissolve the solid. Next add 2 ml of 6 F hydrochloric acid, swirl the solution again, and titrate it immediately with the sodium thiosulfate solution to be standardized. Continue the titration until the yellow triiodide color is just barely visible, then add 5 ml of starch indicator (prepared as described in Experiment 14-1), and conclude the titration by adding titrant in drops and fractions of drops until the starch-iodine color just disappears.

Repeat the titration with the second and then the third aliquot of potassium iodate solution. From the experimental data, calculate the average concentration of the sodium thiosulfate solution. Replicate standardizations should agree to within one or two parts per thousand.

It is essential that the 50 ml pipet used to deliver the aliquots of the potassium iodate solution be exactly one tenth of the volume of the 500 ml volumetric flask, so that the weight of potassium iodate in each aliquot will be accurately known. The accuracy of calibration of most volumetric glassware should be adequate to ensure the correct one-to-ten volume relationship. If doubt exists, it is possible to calibrate the volumetric flask relative to the pipet as described in Experiment 2-2.

Experiment 14-3

DETERMINATION OF ANTIMONY IN A STIBNITE ORE BY IODINE TITRATION

Purpose

The determination of antimony in a stibnite ore demonstrates the application of the direct or iodimetric method of analysis. Some experience in the precautions to be taken in preventing loss of the desired component is provided.

Procedure

Transfer approximately 2 gm of the stibnite ore to a clean weighing bottle, and dry the material in an oven at 110°C for one hour. Weigh accurately, to the nearest tenth milligram, three portions of the stibnite ore into separate 500 ml Erlenmeyer flasks. The approximate weight of each portion, which contains antimony equivalent to 25 to 35 ml of 0.05 F iodine solution, must be calculated in advance from known information about the composition of the sample material.

Add 0.3 gm of solid potassium chloride and 20 ml of concentrated hydrochloric acid to each sample. Cover each flask with a small watch glass, place each flask on a sand bath or hot plate, and heat the sample solution to just below the boiling point. Maintain this temperature until no black particles of the stibnite ore remain undissolved and no more hydrogen sulfide gas is evolved. During the dissolution process, add 6 F hydrochloric acid, if necessary, to keep the bottom of each flask completely covered with liquid.

Stibnite is a naturally occurring ore containing antimony trisulfide, silica, and small amounts of other substances. The antimony sulfide is brought into solution by digestion of the sample with hydrochloric acid in the presence of excess potassium chloride:

$$Sb_2S_3 + 6\,H^+ + 8\,Cl^- \longrightarrow 2\,SbCl_4^- + 3\,H_2S$$

The excess chloride is necessary to prevent the loss of antimony as antimony trichloride, which is rather volatile. Silica will not dissolve completely, but its presence does not interfere with subsequent steps in the procedure. Hydrogen sulfide gas is one of the products of the dissolution process, and the cessation of its evolution is a convenient indication of complete solution of the antimony trisulfide. The solution must not be permitted to evaporate to dryness during the digestion step, lest the loss of volatile antimony trichloride become significant.

Add to each of the solutions 2.5 gm of powdered tartaric acid, plus 5 ml of 6 F hydrochloric acid, and heat the sample solutions on a sand bath or hot plate for 15 minutes. While swirling the solution in each flask continuously, add distilled water gradually until the solution volume is about 100 ml.

The dilution must be performed slowly to avoid the formation of SbOCl, which redissolves slowly once it is formed.

If all the hydrogen sulfide gas has not been expelled, orange-red antimony trisulfide, Sb_2S_3, may appear during the dilution. If it does, stop the dilution and heat the mixture gently to dissolve the antimony sulfide, adding more 6 F hydrochloric acid, if necessary, before resuming the dilution to 100 ml.

Add three drops of phenolphthalein indicator, then add 6 F sodium hydroxide solution until the pink color of the indicator appears. Next, add 6 F hydrochloric acid drop by drop until the pink color just disappears; then add 1 ml more. Introduce small portions of solid sodium bicarbonate until the effervescence ceases, and add 3 to 4 gm more of solid sodium bicarbonate. Finally, add 5 ml of starch indicator, and titrate the solution with standard 0.05 F iodine (triiodide) solution until the blue or purple starch-iodine color persists for at least 30 seconds.

Titrate the other two antimony(III) sample solutions in the same manner. From the experimental data, calculate and report the average percentage of antimony in the stibnite ore.

Experiment 14-4

IODOMETRIC DETERMINATION OF COPPER

Purpose

The determination of copper demonstrates the techniques used in dissolving alloys and ores and in eliminating the effects of possible interferences through appropriate preparation of the sample solution.

Procedure

If the sample is an ore, it should be dried in an oven at 110°C for one hour. However, if the sample material is a brass, it should be rinsed thoroughly with a few milliliters of reagent-grade acetone and warmed in an oven for several minutes to evaporate the acetone.

The purpose of the acetone rinse is to remove any film of grease or oil which may coat the brass; if the brass is known to be free of such contaminants, the rinsing with acetone may be omitted.

Weigh out accurately, into each of three 250 ml Erlenmeyer flasks, portions of the copper-containing sample which have about 200 mg of copper in them.

If no knowledge concerning the composition of the sample material is available, it may be necessary to analyze one sample completely before weighing out the other samples.

Add 10 to 15 ml of concentrated ($16 F$) nitric acid, and heat the mixture gently over a burner to decompose and dissolve the sample. Continue the heating until any residue, if one does remain, is white or only light gray.

If the sample is unusually slow to dissolve, add 5 milliliters of concentrated ($12 F$) hydrochloric acid and continue the heating as required.

When all of the sample appears to have dissolved (except for a residue of whitish silica or metastannic acid), add 10 ml of concentrated ($18 F$) sulfuric acid and evaporate the solution over a burner, swirling the solution continuously, until dense white fumes of sulfur trioxide are evolved. Cool the solution to room temperature. Cautiously add, 1 ml at a time and with gentle swirling after each addition, a total of 20 ml of distilled water. Use care to avoid having the concentrated sulfuric acid spatter as it is diluted.

If, and only if, antimony or arsenic are thought to be present, it is essential to convert them to their +5 oxidation states. Add to the diluted sulfuric acid solution 10 ml of a saturated aqueous bromine solution, and boil the sample solution vigorously in a hood for five minutes to expel the excess bromine. Cool the solution. The addition of bromine is completely unnecessary if antimony and arsenic are absent.

Swirl each of the flasks containing the cooled sulfuric acid-copper(II) solutions and add concentrated ($15 F$) aqueous ammonia until the first permanent deep blue copper(II)-ammine color is obtained. From this point to the end of the procedure, treat each sample solution individually.

Treat the ammonia solution of copper(II) according to *one* of the three following alternate procedures:

If iron, arsenic, and antimony are all absent, slowly add 3 F sulfuric acid until the blue copper-ammine color just disappears; then add 1 ml of 3 F sulfuric acid in excess. Cool the solution.

If iron is present but arsenic and antimony are both absent, slowly add 3 F sulfuric acid until the blue copper-ammine color just disappears, and then add 2 ml of concentrated (85 per cent) phosphoric acid. Swirl the solution to dissolve any iron(III) hydroxide; then cool the solution.

If arsenic or antimony may be present, and iron may be present, add 2 gm of solid ammonium hydrogen fluoride, NH_4HF_2, and swirl the solution until the ammonium hydrogen fluoride has dissolved and any precipitate of iron(III) hydroxide has redissolved. Cool the solution.

Next, add 4 gm of solid potassium iodide (KI) to the sample solution, swirl the solution to dissolve the solid, and immediately titrate the mixture with standard 0.1 F sodium thiosulfate solution. Continue the titration until the color of triiodide becomes indistinct. Add 5 ml of starch solution and titrate slowly until the starch-iodine color has become faint. Then dissolve 2 gm of solid potassium thiocyanate (KSCN) in the solution, and titrate the mixture to the complete disappearance of the starch-iodine color, the latter not returning for at least several minutes.

It is not always easy to ascertain when the starch should be added because the copper(I) iodide is brownish-colored owing to adsorbed triiodide. Sometimes it is helpful to let the CuI precipitate settle and to observe the color of the supernatant solution. When the KSCN is added, the starch-iodine color should intensify because of the release of adsorbed triiodide. If the starch-iodine color reappears too soon, iron(III) may be slowly oxidizing iodide, in which case more phosphoric acid or solid ammonium hydrogen fluoride should be added in the analysis of the remaining samples.

Repeat the last parts of the procedure with the other two samples. From the titration data and from the weights of the samples taken for analysis, calculate the average weight percentage of copper present in the sample material.

SUGGESTIONS FOR ADDITIONAL LABORATORY WORK

The following references may be consulted for many other applications of oxidation-reduction methods involving iodine, iodate, and periodate. In particular, these sources contain much information concerning the determination of organic compounds.

1. I. M. Kolthoff and R. Belcher: *Volumetric Analysis,* Volume 3, Wiley-Interscience, New York, 1957, pp. 199–596.
2. G. F. Smith: *Analytical Applications of Periodic Acid and Iodic Acid,* G. F. Smith Chemical Company, Columbus, Ohio, 1950.

QUESTIONS AND PROBLEMS

1. Calculate the equilibrium concentrations of H_5IO_6, $H_4IO_6^-$, $H_3IO_6^=$, and IO_4^- in a solution prepared by dissolving 0.0100 mole of sodium metaperiodate ($NaIO_4$) in 1 liter of a pH 7.00 buffer.

2. In the titration of 50.00 ml of 0.05000 M iodide ion with a 0.05000 M cerium(IV) solution, calculate what volume of cerium(IV) will be added before solid iodine just begins to precipitate. Take dilution into account.

3. What can be the maximal initial iodide concentration in 50.00 ml of solution such that solid iodine will not precipitate during a titration of the iodide with a 0.05000 M cerium(IV) solution?

4. From standard-potential data given in Appendix 4, calculate the solubility of bromine in water at 25°C and calculate the equilibrium constant for the reaction

$$Br_2(aq) + Br^- \rightleftharpoons Br_3^-$$

5. In order to gain some idea of the importance of pH control in the titration of arsenic(III) with a triiodide solution, consider the following situation: Assume that 50.00 ml of 0.04000 M arsenic(III) solution is mixed with 50.00 ml of 0.04000 M iodine (in 0.25 F potassium iodide) solution and that both solutions are initially unbuffered at pH 7.00. Using appropriate equilibrium considerations, calculate what fraction of arsenic(III) is oxidized when equilibrium is finally established.

6. From data given in Appendix 4, evaluate the standard potentials for each of the following half-reactions:

   (a) $3 IO_3^- + 18 H^+ + 16 e \rightleftharpoons I_3^- + 9 H_2O$

   (b) $IO_3^- + 6 H^+ + 2 Cl^- + 4 e \rightleftharpoons ICl_2^- + 3 H_2O$

   (c) $BrO_3^- + 6 H^+ + 6 e \rightleftharpoons Br^- + 3 H_2O$

7. Determine the equilibrium constant for the reaction

$$BrO_3^- + 5 Br^- + 6 H^+ \rightleftharpoons 3 Br_2 + 3 H_2O$$

and compute the concentration of free bromine in a solution of pH 7.00 containing 0.1000 F potassium bromate and 0.70 F potassium bromide.

8. If 37.12 ml of an iodine (triiodide) solution is required to titrate the sample solution prepared from 0.5078 gm of pure arsenious oxide, calculate the formality and the normality of the iodine (triiodide) solution.

9. A 0.1936 gm sample of primary-standard potassium dichromate was dissolved in water, the solution was acidified, and, after the addition of potassium iodide, the titration of the liberated iodine required 33.61 ml of a sodium thiosulfate solution. Calculate the formality and the normality of the thiosulfate solution.

10. The sulfur from a 5.141 gm steel sample was evolved as hydrogen sulfide and collected in an excess of an ammoniacal cadmium solution. The resulting cadmium sulfide precipitate was washed and suspended in water to which a few drops of acetic acid had been added. Then 25.00 ml of a 0.002027 F potassium iodate solution was added to the mixture, followed by 3 gm of potassium iodide and 10 ml of concentrated hydrochloric acid. The liberated iodine oxidized the hydrogen sulfide gas to sulfur, and the excess unreacted iodine was titrated with 0.1127 F sodium thiosulfate solution from a microburet, 1.085 ml being used. Calculate the percentage of sulfur in the steel.

11. What weight of a copper ore must be taken for analysis so that each 1.00 ml of a 0.1050 F sodium thiosulfate solution represents exactly 1.00 per cent copper in the sample?

12. From a 0.5635 gm sample of a copper ore, the copper was precipitated as copper(I) thiocyanate, CuSCN. The precipitate was treated with a 4 F hydrochloric acid solution and then titrated with a standard potassium iodate solution according to the reaction

$4 CuSCN + 7 IO_3^- + 18 H^+ + 14 Cl^-$
$$\rightleftharpoons 4 HCN + 4 Cu^{++} + 4 HSO_4^- + 7 ICl_2^- + 5 H_2O$$

If the standard potassium iodate solution contained 10.701 gm of KIO_3 per liter of solution and if 39.57 ml of this solution was required for the titration, calculate the percentage of copper in the ore.

13. A certain oxidizing agent has a molecular weight of 250.0. A 0.3125 gm sample of this compound was treated with excess potassium iodide in an acidic medium, and the liberated iodine (triiodide) was titrated with 20.00 ml of a $0.1250 F$ sodium thiosulfate solution. How many electrons per molecule are gained by the oxidizing agent in its reaction with iodide?

14. If 1.000 ml of a potassium dichromate solution is equivalent to 2.500 mg of iron and if 40.00 ml of the same dichromate solution liberates iodine from potassium iodide equivalent to 22.00 ml of a sodium thiosulfate solution, what is the formal concentration of the latter?

15. Write balanced equations showing all reactants and products for the oxidation of each of the following compounds with periodic acid at room temperature:

(a) acetoin

(b) biacetyl

(c) glycolic aldehyde

(d) gluconic acid

(e) fructose

(f) dihydroxyacetone

(g) serine

(h) β-hydroxyglutamic acid

16. If a solution of hydrogen sulfide in water required twice its volume of a $0.06045 F$ iodine (triiodide) solution to oxidize the hydrogen sulfide to elemental sulfur, how many grams of hydrogen sulfide were dissolved in 1 liter of the original solution?

17. A sample solution containing glycerol and ethylene glycol was transferred to a 100 ml volumetric flask, 50.00 ml of a standard $0.01913 F$ sodium metaperiodate solution was added, and the mixture was diluted to the calibration mark with distilled water. The reaction solution was allowed to stand at room temperature for one hour; then the following analyses were performed on aliquots of this reaction mixture:

A 25.00 ml aliquot was titrated with a $0.02041 F$ sodium hydroxide solution, 14.39 ml being required to reach a phenolphthalein end point.

In a blank titration, 24.90 ml of the sodium hydroxide solution was required to titrate a 25.00 ml portion of the *original* 0.01913 F sodium metaperiodate to the same end point.

A second 25.00 ml aliquot of the reaction mixture was neutralized with sodium bicarbonate to a pH of approximately 7, and potassium iodide was added. The liberated iodine was titrated with a 0.01029 F arsenic(III) solution to a starch-iodine end point, 5.47 ml being needed.
Calculate the total number of milligrams of glycerol and ethylene glycol in the original sample.

18. A 0.4191 gm sample of Paris green, an arsenic-containing insecticide, was treated with hydrochloric acid and a reducing agent; and the arsenic was distilled as arsenic trichloride ($AsCl_3$) into a receiving vessel which contained distilled water. The hydrogen chloride which accompanied the arsenic trichloride was neutralized with an excess of solid sodium bicarbonate and the solution was titrated with a 0.04489 F iodine (triiodide) solution, 37.06 ml being required. Calculate the percentage of arsenious oxide, As_2O_3, in the sample.

SUGGESTIONS FOR ADDITIONAL READING

1. I. M. Kolthoff and R. Belcher: *Volumetric Analysis*, Volume 3, Wiley-Interscience, New York, 1957, pp. 199–596.
2. H. A. Laitinen: *Chemical Analysis*, McGraw-Hill Book Company, New York, 1960, pp. 393–440.
3. G. F. Smith: *Analytical Applications of Periodic Acid and Iodic Acid*, G. F. Smith Chemical Company, Columbus, Ohio, 1950.

Chapter Fifteen

Radiant Energy Methods— Principles and Apparatus

Many analytical methods, both qualitative and quantitative, involve the interaction of matter and radiant energy. Some of these methods have been known and used for many years and others have received widespread application only recently. Some are among the methods which are most frequently encountered in modern analytical laboratories. Much current research and development work in analytical chemistry is centered upon radiant energy methods. Recent research studies have led to improved understanding of the underlying, fundamental principles as well as to the development of new and improved instrumentation for the exploitation of these principles for analytical purposes.

The purposes of this chapter are to describe briefly the nature of radiant energy and the principles and processes of interaction between matter and radiant energy and to describe the types of apparatus with which these interactions may be used in analytical chemistry. Some of the chemical factors underlying the analytical applications, along with several selected determinations, will be discussed in Chapter 16.

RADIANT ENERGY

Radiant energy may be defined as energy, the propagation and transfer of which are accomplished as a wave motion without transfer of matter. The term is generally used with reference to the energy of **electromagnetic**

radiation, and this is the context within which the term is employed throughout this chapter. In our consideration of the nature of radiant energy, we must pay attention both to the wave motion by which the energy is transmitted and to the energy content of this radiation. The transfer of radiant energy is accomplished without the transfer of matter, and the energy may even be transmitted through space which is free of matter.

The Electromagnetic Spectrum

The **wavelength,** λ, of the wave motion with which radiant energy is transmitted varies over an extremely wide range. The magnitude of this wavelength serves as a convenient means of classifying the various forms of electromagnetic radiation. A diagrammatic representation of the **electromagnetic spectrum** is shown in Figure 15-1, in which wavelength is shown on a logarithmic scale over a range from 10 meters to 1×10^{-10} cm. Even these extremely different wavelengths must not be considered as limits to the electromagnetic spectrum, for radiations of even longer and shorter wavelengths not only exist but may be exploited for a variety of purposes.

The spectrum in Figure 15-1 is labeled in several different ways in addition to the wavelength units. Such terms as *visible spectrum, infrared spectrum,* and *x-ray spectrum* are commonly used to designate various portions of the spectrum. It should be noted, however, that the electromagnetic

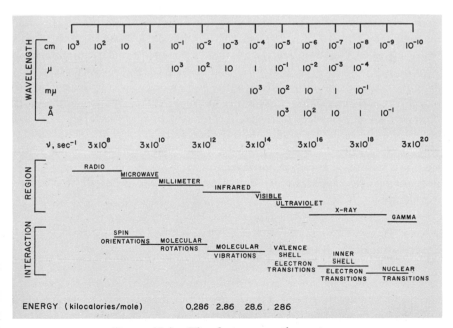

FIGURE 15-1. The electromagnetic spectrum.

spectrum is a continuum and that there are no sharp boundaries between any adjacent regions.

Frequency units are also shown in Figure 15-1. The wavelength, λ, and the frequency, expressed in cycles per second or simply reciprocal seconds ($\sec^{-1}$) and designated by the symbol ν, of any particular electromagnetic radiation are related to each other by the fundamental equation

$$c = \lambda \times \nu$$

in which c is the velocity of the radiation. This equation is simply a mathematical statement that the velocity, in units of length (distance) per unit of time, is equal to the number of waves passing a given point during one unit of time, multiplied by the length of each wave. The *velocity* with which all electromagnetic radiation is transmitted through a vacuum or free space is constant, about 3.00×10^{10} cm per second or approximately 186,000 miles per second. The velocity of radiation through air is essentially the same.

The other forms of the labeling of Figure 15-1 will become meaningful as we proceed through this chapter.

Radiant Energy as Wave Motion

We can consider the waves whereby radiant energy is transferred to consist of pulsating electric and magnetic displacements occurring at right angles to the direction of propagation. Herein lies the reason for use of the term "electromagnetic" in reference to this radiation. Both the electric and magnetic components of a given wave, in addition to being at right angles to the axis of propagation, are at right angles to each other. In the emanations from most types of sources, the radiation consists of many waves which may or may not be of the same wavelength; and the electric and magnetic displacements are in random directions around the axis of propagation. If, however, all of the electric displacements are in one plane as the wave progresses, the radiation is said to be **polarized.**

Electromagnetic radiation, all waves of which are of a single wavelength, is said to be **monochromatic,** literally, "one-colored." Conversely, **polychromatic radiation** consists of waves which are not all of the same wavelength.

Electromagnetic Radiation as Energy

Let us now turn our attention from the wave characteristics of radiant energy to its energy aspect. There can be no doubt that electromagnetic radiation is energy, because it exhibits properties characteristic of other forms of energy and can, in fact, be converted into other energy forms, such as heat and electricity. Furthermore, there can be no doubt that the energy of electromagnetic radiation consists of small bundles, called **photons** or **quanta.** The experimentally observed mechanisms of interaction between radiant energy and matter, some of which are discussed subsequently in this chapter, provide evidence that radiant energy, like matter itself, is not "continuous" but rather consists of minute, discrete quantities. The amount of energy per photon varies widely from one type of radiation to another, yet every photon of any one wavelength possesses exactly the same amount of energy as does any other photon of that same wavelength. Thus, monochromatic radiation is also monoenergetic radiation, and radiation which is polychromatic is also polyenergetic.

Let us now consider the relative magnitudes of the energies of photons throughout the electromagnetic spectrum. We do not need here to derive a mathematical relationship between energy and frequency or wavelength, but we must know what this relationship is before we can meaningfully study the mechanisms whereby radiant energy and matter interact with each other. This relationship may be expressed by the equation

$$E = h \times \nu$$

in which E is the energy per photon, ν is its frequency as already discussed, and h is a universal constant known as Planck's constant $(6.626 \times 10^{-27}$ erg sec). Thus, the energy per photon increases linearly with its frequency. This means that there is an inverse relationship between energy and wavelength. For example, a photon of ultraviolet radiation is of shorter wavelength and of higher energy than is a photon of infrared light. Figure 15-1 includes, as one of its forms of labeling, the energies of photons of radiation throughout the electromagnetic spectrum. Note on this figure that, along with the extremely wide ranges of wavelengths and of frequencies, there is also an extremely wide range of energies.

Let us summarize this brief consideration of the nature of radiant energy by stating that electromagnetic radiation consists of little bundles of energy, called photons, which travel with wavelike motion, each wave consisting of electric and magnetic displacements, and that electromagnetic radiation may be characterized by the wavelength, frequency, and energy quantities shown in Figure 15-1.

INTERACTIONS OF MATTER AND RADIANT ENERGY

Diffraction, Refraction, and Optical Rotation

There are several mechanisms of interaction of matter and radiant energy. Some of these phenomena arise from the wave nature of radiant energy, including three which are of particular significance in analytical chemistry: diffraction, refraction, and optical rotation.

Diffraction is the modification which any traveling waves undergo in passing by the edges of opaque bodies, in going through narrow slits or holes, or in being reflected from ruled surfaces. Those portions of the wavefront which pass on through the hole, for example, spread out and form in effect a new wavefront emerging from the hole. The phenomenon of diffraction of radiant energy is of particular significance in analysis in conjunction with grating monochromators for separating polychromatic radiation into its several wavelength components, as discussed later in this chapter. In addition, there are significant direct analytical applications of the diffraction of x-radiation.

Refraction is the bending, or changing of direction, of a beam of radiant energy as it passes obliquely from one medium into another medium of different density. This bending results from the slight difference in the velocity of electromagnetic radiation in the two media. Thus, the magnitude of refraction is dependent both upon what the media are and upon the wavelength of the radiation. Refraction is of considerable analytical significance in conjunction with the prism monochromators used in some of the analytical instruments discussed in this chapter. The phenomenon is also of direct analytical significance in the qualitative identification of substances which can be used as one of the media in a measurement of refraction and in the quantitative analysis of mixtures, especially of liquid mixtures. These latter methods of analysis will not be described further in this book.

Optical rotation is the phenomenon whereby the plane of polarization of polarized light is rotated during passage through a material medium. The qualitative and quantitative composition of the medium determines whether this rotation occurs and, if so, what its magnitude is. Some analytical application of this phenomenon is made, although these methods are not to be discussed subsequently in this book.

Absorption and Emission

Perhaps the most significant forms of interaction of matter and radiant energy, from the standpoint of the analytical chemist, are the phenomena of **absorption** and of **emission** of radiant energy by matter. Whenever an atom, a molecule, or any other particle of matter absorbs a photon, that particle of matter becomes more energetic; that is, the particle possesses more energy than it did prior to the interaction. Conversely, whenever a particle of matter emits a photon, the particle is left in a less energetic state. These two fundamental considerations underlie all analytical procedures which are based upon the absorption and emission of radiant energy.

The total energy of any particle of matter is the sum of numerous components. Three are of chief interest in the study of analytical chemistry — electronic energy, vibrational energy, and rotational energy. Let us now discuss each of these in turn.

Electronic Energy. The electrons in any atom normally occupy the electron orbitals of lowest energy. In an atom of lithium, for example, two electrons are normally in the 1s orbital and one is in the 2s orbital. This normal electronic condition of an atom is commonly referred to as its **ground state.** If that atom is supplied with just the appropriate amount of energy, the 2s electron can move into, for example, a 2p orbital; or, if a certain, but larger, amount of energy is provided, the electron may move into a 3s orbital. Similarly, a 1s electron can be moved into an orbital of higher energy. An atom which has one or more electrons in a higher energy orbital is referred to as being in an **excited state.** A definite amount of energy is required for each of the several conceivable electronic changes. Thus, there is a set of discrete amounts of energy which can be absorbed by lithium atoms, and photons which possess these amounts of energy are absorbed by lithium atoms in preference to photons of any other energy values.

The electronic configuration of a lithium atom differs from that of a sodium atom or that of an atom of any other element, and so the photon energy values which are preferentially absorbable differ from one element to another. Furthermore, the electronic configuration of a lithium ion differs from that of a lithium atom, and so the absorption characteristics of ions differ from those of their parent atoms. Therefore, the amount of energy change in any one absorption interaction of this type depends both upon what the atom or ion is and upon what electron orbitals in that atom or ion are involved in the change. Numerical values for many such transitions have been measured and reported in the literature. It is found that, in general, absorptions involving the outer electronic energy levels of atoms typically require energies corresponding to photons in the visible and ultraviolet regions of the electromagnetic spectrum. As the electron involved in a transition is initially located closer to the nucleus of the atom (that is, of lower principal quantum number) and as the atomic number of the atom increases, the requisite energies are greater, extending to photons in the far ultraviolet and x-ray regions of the electromagnetic spectrum. Photons in the infrared and longer wavelength regions do not possess sufficient energy to bring about any electronic changes from the normal, ground states of atoms.

There are other methods, in addition to the absorption of photons, whereby atoms are able to gain the energy required to change from the ground state to an excited state or from one excited state to a more highly excited state. The necessary energy can be supplied, for example, by heat or by placing the atoms in the midst of an electrical arc or spark discharge.

An atom seldom remains for long in an excited condition. Rather, it more commonly returns spontaneously to its normal, ground state. Typical "lifetimes" of atoms in electronically excited states are of the order of 10^{-8} second. The return to the ground state signifies, of course, a loss of energy from the atom. The law of conservation of energy is applicable, first to the excitation process and then to the de-excitation process. The energy lost by the atom in the latter process may appear in the form of heat energy. However, it is often in the form of an emitted photon of electromagnetic radiation.

It may seem that the net result of the combined processes of absorbing and emitting a photon is the same as if nothing had happened. It is true that the atom which goes through this process is restored to its initial condition. However, the emitted photon may travel in a direction different from the direction of the incident photon, a factor which is of considerable significance in the analytical applicability of the phenomenon.

Vibrational Energy. The electronic changes which we have been discussing so far in connection with atoms and ions are encountered when radiant energy interacts with molecules. In addition, however, molecules exhibit vibrational motions, each of which is associated with a definite amount of energy. Just as there are discrete energy levels associated with the electrons in an atom, so there are discrete energy levels associated with the vibrational motions within a molecule. A molecule can be excited, from one vibrational energy level to a higher one, by the absorption of a photon of just the requisite amount of energy. Therefore, molecules preferentially absorb photons, the energies of which correspond to the differences in possible vibrational energy levels within the molecules. A vibrationally excited molecule, like an electronically excited atom, typically returns quickly and spontaneously to its normal ground state, with the loss of energy.

Vibrations within complex, polyatomic molecules involve principally only localized portions of the molecules. Thus, certain vibrational energy levels and transitions are characteristic of —OH groups in molecules, the energies of which are largely, but not entirely, independent of what atoms the rest of the molecule includes. Therefore, the complete vibrational absorption spectrum of a molecule is a composite of all the possible vibrational transitions within the molecule.

Rotational Energy. A third mechanism whereby radiant energy may be absorbed by matter involves the rotational energy levels of an absorbing molecule. Consider, for example, a molecule of methanol,

H
|
H—C—O—H. Not only are there electronic energy levels associated with
|
H

all atoms, and vibrational motions and energy levels between each pair of adjacent atoms, but there are also rotations of the molecule as a whole. The energies associated with these motions are also quantized; that is, only specific energy levels of rotation are possible for a given molecule. An absorbing molecule can be excited from one rotational energy level to a higher one by absorption of a photon which provides precisely the necessary amount of energy, and a rotationally excited molecule can return to its ground state or to a less excited state by emitting a photon of electromagnetic radiation.

Not all kinds of molecules undergo rotational changes by the absorption of photons. These absorptions are most frequently encountered with molecules which have permanent electrical dipoles or permanent magnetic moments. The specific energies of the rotational absorptions which do occur are characteristic of the absorbing molecule as a whole, as contrasted to electronic absorptions characteristic of atoms or ions and to vibrational absorptions characteristic of functional groupings of atoms.

The amounts of energy associated with changes of rotational energy levels are generally quite small compared to electronic and vibrational transitions. Pure rotational absorption spectra are typically found in the far infrared and the microwave regions of the electromagnetic spectrum.

Combinations of Electronic, Vibrational, and Rotational Excitation. Thus far we have considered separately the three types of absorption: electronic, vibrational, and rotational. It is possible experimentally to observe pure rotational absorptions; however, it is generally not possible to obtain pure vibrational absorptions of molecules which can undergo rotational transitions. If incident polychromatic photons are sufficiently energetic to cause vibrational changes, they surely possess enough energy to accomplish rotational excitation as well. This does not necessarily imply that one photon causes a vibrational transition and another a rotational change, although this can occur. It does mean that a given photon, if its energy content matches the absorbing molecule suitably, can cause both a vibrational and a rotational change. It is also possible for an incident photon to be absorbed vibrationally by a molecule which is already in a rotationally excited state; this transition would require a slightly different amount of energy than the same vibrational change with some other initial or final rotational conditions. The net result of these several conceivable combinations is that a particular vibrational absorption is generally observable not simply as the absorption of one single wavelength of incident radiation but rather as a band consisting of several closely similar wavelengths. The overall wavelength of the band is an approximation to a pure vibrational absorption, and the differences among the closely spaced wavelengths within the band correspond to the several rotational transitions.

Similar reasoning leads to the conclusion that both rotational and vibrational absorptions are superimposed upon electronic absorptions. A given electronic absorption may consist experimentally not just of radiation of one wavelength only, but rather of a band of closely spaced wavelengths, all due to the superimposition of the various vibrational and rotational energy levels upon the electronic energy level.

The foregoing discussion has represented a rather idealized condition. Practical situations often differ from this ideal for one of several reasons. The experimental apparatus used in observing absorption spectra may not permit one to resolve, or to distinguish between or among, closely spaced wavelengths of absorbed radiation. Even with the best experimental apparatus, the number of possible combinations of rotational, vibrational, and

FIGURE 15-2.   Block diagram of apparatus for analytical methods based on the absorption of radiant energy.

electronic energy levels may be so great and the individual energy levels spaced so closely together that the absorption spectrum appears to be a virtually continuous band. Line absorption spectra and band spectra which are experimentally resolvable into discrete lines are more generally encountered with atoms than with complex molecules, and more with gases than with condensed liquid or solid phases. Interactions between atoms or molecules in a relatively dilute gas phase are much less severe than are similar interactions which occur in highly condensed states. Chemical species in the gas phase behave more or less independently of one another, whereas in liquids and solids the behaviors and structures of atoms and molecules are markedly affected by the presence of neighboring species.

Analytical Applicability

There are numerous ways in which the absorption and emission of radiant energy by matter can be used in analytical chemistry. Let us identify now, in broad categories, some of the most significant types of analytical methods. The experimental apparatus will be discussed in detail later in this chapter, and selected analytical applications will be described in Chapter 16.

Absorption Methods.   The most common type of analytical method based upon the interaction of matter and radiant energy is the straightforward absorption method in which measurement is made of the wavelengths or the intensities of electromagnetic radiation absorbed by the sample. We have already noted that the wavelengths of radiation which are preferentially absorbed are characteristic of the atoms, ions, or molecules which do the absorbing. This fact serves directly as the basis of many useful qualitative identifications. Furthermore, the number of photons absorbed is a direct function of the concentration or number of atoms, ions, or molecules which are the absorbing species, and this relationship provides the basis for many important quantitative determinations.

A block diagram is shown in Figure 15-2 of the apparatus used in making these measurements. The radiant energy from the source is generally polychromatic, literally, "many-colored"; that is, it includes photons of many different energies or wavelengths. This radiation may be used directly as polychromatic radiation in some analytical determinations, but it is usually necessary to employ a monochromator, which permits only a limited range of wavelengths of radiation to pass on to the test sample. The monochromator is almost invariably adjustable, usually continuously so, in order that various wavelengths of fairly monochromatic radiation may be selected. The sample, which is often in the form of a liquid solution but may be in some other physical state, interacts with the radiant energy. That portion of the radiation which is not absorbed, or otherwise removed, by the test sample passes on to the detector for measurement. For qualitative identifications, measurement must be made of what wavelengths are absorbed, whereas for quantitative purposes one measures the amount or fraction of radiation of a suitable wavelength which is absorbed. The components within each of the blocks of Figure 15-2 are described later in this chapter.

Various terms have come into common use to identify the instruments and procedures used for absorption methods of analysis. Some of these terms are quite long, but they are generally composites of shorter words and syllables, the meanings of which are almost self-evident. The following examples may be noted: "-meter" signifies an instrument for measuring some particular parameter or property; "-graph" means a recording or mapping obtained, for example, photographically or by a pen-and-ink recorder; "color-" or "colori-" denotes color or wavelength of radiant energy; "photo-" signifies radiant energy or, more specifically, the intensity of radiant energy; "spectro-" refers to a spectrum, such as is formed by dispersing a polychromatic beam of radiant energy into its component wavelengths with the aid of a prism or grating. Thus, for example, a "colorimeter" is an instrument for measuring the color or wavelength of radiant energy, and a "photometer" is a device for measuring the intensity of the radiation. Note that the phrase *intensity of radiation* refers essentially to the number of photons per unit time, not to the amount of energy per photon. A "spectrometer" is an instrument which disperses the radiant energy into a spectrum and provides for the measurement of the wavelengths of that radiation. A spectrometer may also provide intensity measurements, in which case it may also be designated a "spectrophotometer." The term "spectrograph" generally denotes a spectrometer or spectrophotometer in which the data are recorded photographically, although the words spectrometer and spectrograph are often used interchangeably. An additional word is often used, preceding the designation of the instrument, to signify what region of the electromagnetic spectrum is employed, such as "infrared spectrometer," "visible photometer," and "x-ray spectrometer."

Emission Methods. Measurements of the radiant energy emitted by excited atoms, ions, or molecules are useful for both qualitative and quantitative analysis. The energy required to raise these particles to excited states may be provided by any one of several methods, including heat. A block diagram for the essential apparatus is shown in Figure 15-3. Some of these blocks represent the same components shown in Figure 15-2. As in the methods based upon absorption of radiant energy, qualitative identifications

FIGURE 15-3.   Block diagram of apparatus for analytical methods based on the emission of radiant energy.

rely upon the measurement of wavelengths of radiation, and the intensity of the emitted radiation is measured in a quantitative determination.

The terminology used to designate instruments for emission methods of analysis is similar to that for absorption methods. For example, in an "emission spectrograph" the test sample is caused to emit radiant energy, which is then dispersed into a spectrum and recorded photographically.

Photon Scattering Methods.   Photon scattering methods of analysis may involve simple absorption of radiant energy followed by reëmission of photons of the same wavelength in another direction, or they may involve scattering of photons from the surfaces of colloidal particles. The actual mechanisms whereby these interactions of matter and radiant energy occur will not be discussed in this book, but some of the practical analytical consequences of these interactions should be noted. A block diagram of the necessary apparatus would be identical to that of Figure 15-2 with three simple variations: The test sample generally consists of a colloidal suspension rather than a true solution; the monochromator may be omitted; the detector may be situated either as shown in Figure 15-2 or at a right angle to the incident radiation. If the detector is placed as shown, it actually measures the intensity of radiant energy which remains unscattered or otherwise attenuated by the test sample, and the method of analysis is called a **turbidimetric method.** On the other hand, if the detector is positioned at right angles to the beam incident upon the sample, measurement is made of the photons which are scattered and the method is designated as a **nephelometric technique.** For certain special applications, the detector may be placed at other angles with respect to the incident beam of radiation.

Fluorescence and Phosphorescence Methods.   The processes of fluorescence and of phosphorescence consist of absorption of photons of one wavelength and reëmission of discrete portions of the absorbed energy as photons of *longer* wavelengths or *lower* energies. The remainder of the absorbed energy is dissipated in some other way, frequently by being transformed into thermal energy or heat. Both fluorescence and phosphorescence proceed by emission from the lowest vibrational level of an excited electronic state to a vibrationally excited state of the ground electronic level. Fluorescence differs from phosphorescence in that the absorption and reëmission are essentially simultaneous in the former, occurring in 10^{-8} to 10^{-7} second. In phosphorescence, however, a time delay of 10^{-3} second or longer occurs before reëmission of photons.

So far, we have discussed in this chapter the interactions of matter and radiant energy on the basis of modern concepts of the atomic and molecular structure of matter. It is interesting to note, however, that measurements upon absorption and emission of radiant energy have played a vital role in the historical development of these structural concepts.

QUANTITATIVE LAWS OF ABSORPTION

Quantitative methods of analysis based upon the absorption of radiant energy by matter involve the measurement of intensities of electromagnetic radiation. With reference to Figure 15-4, let us consider the factors which influence the intensity of radiation transmitted through an absorbing medium.

It is reasonable to expect that the value of the transmitted intensity, I, would be influenced by the incident intensity, I_0; by the thickness of the test solution, b; and by the concentration, c, of the absorbing solute. Unfortunately, it is experimentally difficult to make an absolute measurement of any single intensity of radiant energy. However, it is relatively simple to obtain a quantitative comparison of two intensities, such as measurement of the ratio I_0/I. As we shall see shortly, it is the intensity ratios, rather than any absolute intensity values, that we must ascertain in order to determine quantitatively the concentration of the desired substance in the test sample.

Lambert's Law

The Lambert law relates the *thickness of the test sample* to the *ratio of the intensities* of radiation transmitted through the sample and radiation incident upon the sample. It should be anticipated that, other factors being equal, the intensity of transmitted radiation should decrease as the thickness of the sample is increased. Accordingly, the Lambert law may be stated in words as follows: When monochromatic radiation passes through a transparent medium (i.e., a medium in which the portion of incident radiation which is

FIGURE 15-4. Diagram to show the relationship between the intensity of incident radiation (I_0), the intensity of the transmitted radiation (I), the thickness (or path length) of the test sample (b), and the concentration (c) of the absorbing species. The test sample is assumed in this instance to be in the form of a solution, the solute of which is the absorbing substance.

transmitted is too great to be negligible), the rate of decrease of intensity with the thickness of the medium is proportional to the intensity of the radiation.

This verbal statement of Lambert's law may be expressed mathematically by the differential equation

$$-\frac{dI}{dx} = kI$$

where I represents the intensity of the radiation at any point x in the absorbing medium and where k is a constant characteristic of the nature of the absorbing medium and of the wavelength of the radiation. Rearrangement of this expression yields

$$-\frac{dI}{I} = k \, dx$$

Upon integration, this relation becomes

$$-\int d \ln I = k \int dx$$

Now, if we stipulate that I_0 is the intensity of the incident radiation when $x = 0$ and that I represents the intensity of the transmitted radiation emerging from the absorbing medium at $x = b$, we may write definite integrals as follows:

$$-\int_{I_0}^{I} d \ln I = k \int_{0}^{b} dx$$

When this equation is solved, the result is

$$-\ln I + \ln I_0 = kb$$

One of the most useful forms of Lambert's law, and at the same time one of the simplest, is

$$\ln \frac{I_0}{I} = kb$$

which can be rewritten in base-ten logarithms as

$$\log \frac{I_0}{I} = k'b$$

where I_0, I, and b are identifiable from Figure 15-4. There are no known exceptions to Lambert's law.

Beer's Law

Beer's law applies to substances which absorb radiant energy by relating the *concentration of the absorbing species* to the *ratio of the intensities* of radiation transmitted through the absorbing medium and the radiation incident upon that medium. Any increase in the concentration of the absorbing species should increase the number of photons absorbed and, correspondingly, decrease the intensity of the transmitted radiation. The statement of Beer's law may be expressed as follows: When monochromatic radiation passes through a medium containing an absorbing substance, the rate of decrease of intensity with the concentration of absorbing species is directly proportional to the intensity of the radiation. Beer's law may be derived in the same straightforward manner described for Lambert's law, except that the starting equation is

$$-\frac{dI}{dc} = k''I$$

where c denotes the concentration of the absorbing species and k'' is a new proportionality constant which is characteristic of the system being studied. The fundamental integral equation is

$$-\int d \ln I = k'' \int dc$$

By stating that the intensity of transmitted radiation is I_0 when no absorbing species is present and that I signifies the intensity when the concentration is c, we can express Beer's law in the mathematical form

$$\ln \frac{I_0}{I} = k''c$$

or

$$\log \frac{I_0}{I} = k'''c$$

in which I_0, I, and c are as defined in Figure 15-4 and k''' is again a constant, the magnitude of which is determined by the nature of the absorbing substance and the wavelength of radiation employed.

Although there are few, if any, real failures of Beer's law, it is applicable only to certain concentration ranges for most substances and is not applicable at all to some practical systems. Apparent departures from this law are generally encountered when the absorbing substance undergoes a change in its degree of ionization, hydration, or complexation upon dilution or concentration. For example, the degree of dissociation of a weak acid changes with its concentration, and so it should be expected that Beer's law will not be applicable to a solution of a weak acid in which the photons are absorbed by the anion of the weak acid. Dilution or concentration of a potassium chromate solution causes a shift in the position of equilibrium between chromate ion and dichromate ion according to the reaction

$$2 \ CrO_4^= + 2 \ H^+ \rightleftharpoons Cr_2O_7^= + H_2O$$

so chromate solutions fail to follow Beer's law unless the solution pH is sufficiently high to keep essentially all of the anions in the chromate form.

The degree of complexation of a cation generally alters its radiation-absorbing characteristics; so Beer's law is not applicable if the degree of complexation varies throughout the range of concentrations studied. Furthermore, Beer's law is generally valid only for relatively dilute solutions of the absorbing substance, because interactions between neighboring species modify the absorption properties of the substance of interest. Still another important reason for the frequent inapplicability of the law arises from the fact that it specifies the use of monochromatic radiation, whereas the radiation employed experimentally is seldom perfectly monochromatic and frequently departs very widely from such a condition.

Combined Lambert-Beer Law

The Lambert law and the Beer law may be combined into a single relationship which serves as the basis for all practical quantitative determinations. This law may be stated mathematically as

$$\log \frac{I_0}{I} = abc$$

Since the intensity quantities, I_0 and I, appear in ratio form, any units of intensity may be used; even completely empirical units are fully satisfactory. If the thickness quantity, b, which is commonly called the **sample path length,** is expressed in centimeters and the concentration factor, c, in grams of absorbing substance per liter of solution, the constant a (which is a combination of k' and k''' from the two separate laws) is designated as the **absorptivity.**

Frequently, it is desirable to specify c in terms of molar concentration, with b remaining in units of centimeters. In the latter situation, the Lambert-Beer law is rewritten in the form

$$\log \frac{I_0}{I} = \epsilon bc$$

in which ϵ is called the **molar absorptivity.**

The quantity $\log (I_0/I)$ is defined as **absorbance** and given the symbol A. Some instruments are calibrated directly in absorbance units. The nonlogarithmic quantity (I/I_0) is called the **transmittance,** and $(I/I_0) \times 100$ is the **per cent transmittance.** It is not uncommon to find many commercial instruments calibrated directly in units of transmittance or per cent transmittance.

The Lambert-Beer law is applicable, of course, only when its component relations are valid. However, because there are no known exceptions to Lambert's law, all apparent deviations from the combined law are due to the concentration factor c. The applicability of the Lambert-Beer law may be tested for any particular system if one measures the absorbance for each of a series of solutions of known concentration of the absorbing species, for example. A plot of the experimental data in terms of absorbance A versus concentration c will yield a straight line passing through the origin if the Lambert-Beer law is obeyed. More often than not, a plot of the data over a wide range of concentration of an absorbing substance will give a graph such as that shown in Figure 15-5, indicating that the Lambert-Beer law is applicable only up to concentration c_1. Nevertheless, if a suitable calibration curve is prepared from a series of solutions or standards containing known concentrations of the absorbing species, it is still possible to determine the concentration of the absorbing substance in an unknown sample.

Some experimental procedures involve calculations based upon the Lambert-Beer law, and others do not. As already implied, it is frequently possible to conduct highly accurate quantitative determinations even when the chemical system departs from this fundamental law of absorption. The chief requirements in analysis are that the radiation-absorbing properties be measurable and that they be reproducible.

The test solution (see Fig. 15-4) may interact with the incident radiation by other mechanisms in addition to absorption of photons by the solute whose concentration is c. The solvent itself, or some additional undesired component, may absorb some radiation. Some reflection occurs at every interface between the wall of the sample container and the solution, and between the wall and the surrounding air. The errors from these extraneous interactions may be readily eliminated by taking as the I_0 value not the intensity of radiation incident upon the test solution but rather the intensity transmitted through a solution of zero concentration of the desired component held in the same or an equivalent cell and with radiation of the same intensity incident upon that cell. Thus, any apparent absorbance due either to the solvent or to the container is offset.

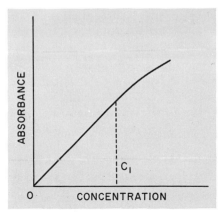

FIGURE 15-5. Relationship between absorbance and concentration of the absorbing substance.

SOURCES OF RADIANT ENERGY

Absorption Methods

In order to be suitable for an absorption method of analysis, the source of radiant energy must fulfill three main requirements. First, it must provide the *desired wavelength range* of radiant energy for the study or determination of the substance of interest. Second, the radiation provided by the source must possess *sufficient intensity* so that, in combination with the test sample and the detector, the measurements will provide analytical results of the desired precision and accuracy. An unduly intense radiation source should be avoided; it could cause harmful effects as a result of heating the sample or even chemically altering its composition. Third, the source must provide radiant energy of *constant intensity*, because most analytical determinations require more than one measurement. For example, measurements are usually made upon pure solvent and one or more standard solutions as well as upon the sample of the unknown, and separate measurements of intensities of transmitted radiation are not readily comparable if the intensity of incident radiation fluctuates from one measurement to the next. Some provision to minimize the possible error from this cause is incorporated into many complete instruments and procedures.

Visible Sources. Ordinary daylight is sometimes used for visible radiant energy; however, its lack of constant intensity is a serious disadvantage. It is much more common to use a glass-enclosed, tungsten filament incandescent light bulb. The output, with respect to its wavelength distribution, is determined primarily by the operating temperature of the filament. An ordinary 6 or 12 v automobile headlamp bulb is often used, even in some sophisticated commercial instruments. At a typical filament temperature of the order of magnitude of 2300°C, the emitted radiation is of peak intensity in the near infrared region of the electromagnetic spectrum with ample emission throughout the visible spectrum as well.

The intensity of the output of a tungsten filament lamp is highly dependent upon the lamp voltage. In order for the light output to be constant within a few tenths of 1 per cent, the voltage must typically be maintained within tolerances of a few thousandths of 1 v. Therefore, a storage battery or a well-regulated power supply must be used.

Infrared Sources. Common sources of infrared radiant energy are similar in principle to the tungsten filament lamp, which, as we have already noted, emits considerable energy in the near infrared region of the spectrum. Raising the filament temperature still higher would provide more radiant energy, including more at still longer wavelengths. However, neither the tungsten filament nor the glass bulb can withstand much higher temperatures for appreciable periods of time. Furthermore, the glass bulb does not transmit the longer wavelengths adequately. Therefore, other materials which can be heated sufficiently and which do not have to be housed within glass envelopes are preferable.

Two of the common types of practical infrared sources are the Nernst glower and the Globar. The **Nernst glower** consists of a mixture of zirconium and yttrium oxides, shaped into a hollow rod about 3 cm long, which is electrically heated to 1500–2000°C. The **Globar** is a rod of sintered silicon carbide about 5 cm long, which is heated to 1300–1700°C. Although both sources produce radiation which is of peak intensity within the wavelength range of 1 to 2 microns, each source emits radiation of usable intensity at much longer wavelengths as well.

Ultraviolet Sources. The most widely used source of ultraviolet radiation is the hydrogen discharge lamp. The long-wavelength limit of the continuous, polychromatic radiation from a hydrogen lamp is usually about 375 mμ. The limit on the short-wavelength side is set by the materials of which the lamp walls are made. Quartz walls transmit down to about 200 mμ and fused silica to about 185 mμ. The emission is more intense if deuterium gas is used within the discharge lamp rather than ordinary hydrogen.

Other ultraviolet light sources include mercury vapor lamps and xenon arcs. These sources yield radiant energy that is particularly intense at the wavelengths of the mercury or xenon emission spectra, respectively, although considerable "white" or polychromatic radiation is obtained also. Radiation from these sources includes wavelengths within the visible, as well as the ultraviolet, region of the electromagnetic spectrum.

For certain applications, such as the atomic absorption methods of analysis which will be discussed subsequently, the source of visible or ultraviolet radiant energy must be strictly monochromatic, and it must be of a proper wavelength. A gas discharge source, in which emission arises from excited atoms or ions of the desired element, must be used. Such a source is similar to one of the types used for emission methods of analysis.

X-ray Sources. A source of x-radiation generally consists of a two-electrode vacuum tube with associated electrical power supplies. A negatively charged, electrically heated cathode emits electrons which, after undergoing appreciable acceleration, strike a positively charged electrode. At the latter electrode, which is called the anode, much of the kinetic energy of the incident electrons is converted into heat which is of no practical value. However, some of the kinetic energy lost by the electrons which are stopped by the anode results in electronic excitation of the atoms of which the anode is composed. As these excited atoms spontaneously return to nonexcited, or less highly excited states, electromagnetic radiation is emitted. If the accelerating potential within the tube and the chemical composition of the anode have been chosen properly, much of this emitted radiation is within the x-ray region of the electromagnetic spectrum.

Some x-ray tubes are gas-filled rather than evacuated, and ionization fragments of the gas molecules contribute to the current flow within the tube.

In either type of x-ray tube, evacuated or gas-filled, the intensity (number of photons per unit time) is determined by the magnitude of electrical current striking the anode. The emission spectrum consists of some polychromatic radiation as well as relatively intense radiation at wavelengths corresponding to the electronic energy level differences within the atoms of which the anode is composed. It is important to note that the electron accelerating potential within the x-ray tube must be sufficient to bring about the appropriate electronic transitions within the anode atoms; otherwise, no x-radiation occurs.

Emission Methods

The source of radiant energy for emission methods of analysis differs from that for absorption methods principally in that the test sample itself must provide the photons. With this distinction, the general requirements which have been listed for sources of radiant energy for absorption methods of analysis may be modified for emission methods as follows: The source must produce both *sufficient intensity* and *constant intensity*. In both emission and absorption procedures, the source must emit radiation of sufficient intensity to provide, in conjunction with the detector and other portions of the apparatus, measurements which lead to analytical results of the desired accuracy and precision. In addition, the emitted radiation must be sufficiently constant over a series of measurements, including measurements on samples and on solvent or other reference materials, to permit meaningful comparison of one measured value with another in obtaining the desired analytical result. In emission methods, qualitative identifications are based upon the *specific wavelengths* of emitted radiation, and quantitative determinations require measurements of the intensities of the emission at those particular wavelengths, rather than of a broad-band polychromatic form. Electronic excitations are more frequently encountered in practical emission methods of analysis than are rotational or vibrational excitations, and the visible, ultraviolet, and x-ray regions are far more widely used than are the longer wavelength regions of the electromagnetic spectrum.

Visible and Ultraviolet Sources. There are five major sources of visible and ultraviolet radiation for use in emission methods of analysis: the d-c electrical arc, the a-c electrical spark, the flame, the laser beam, and the gas discharge tube.

The **d-c arc** is produced across the gap between two closely spaced electrodes, between which is established a potential difference of about 50 to 300 v. If the test sample can be used conveniently in the form of a solid metallic wire or rod, it is used directly as one of the electrodes. A powdered sample may be inserted into one of the electrodes — for example, in an indented region of one electrode placed so as to face the other electrode.

Liquid and gaseous specimens, although not commonly used with this kind of source, may be sprayed into the region between the two electrodes. Heat is caused by passage of electrical current through the gap, and this results in both vaporization of the sample and excitation of the vaporized atoms or ions. Some of the material comprising the electrodes is, of course, vaporized and excited along with the sample. The effective temperature within the gap region typically is of the order of 4000 to 8000°C, sufficient to cause electronic excitation of many elements.

The **a-c spark** also utilizes two electrodes and incorporates the sample either as, or on, one electrode or in the gap between the electrodes. An electrical spark discharge is developed across the gap by application of an a-c potential difference, often from 10 to 50 kv, between the two electrodes. The auxiliary electrical circuitry is designed to provide high current discharge through the gap during the instants of highest potential during each a-c pulse. The consequence is that the a-c spark provides greater excitation energy, with less overall heating effect, than the d-c arc.

There are numerous practical variations of the d-c arc and the a-c spark, both in the electrical circuitry and in the physical design and arrangement of the electrodes. The several forms differ in such factors as sensitivity for the excitation of trace components of the test sample, reproducibility over a period of time with a given sample, reproducibility from one sample to another of the same composition, adaptability to the excitation of low-melting alloys and of solutions, and origin of most of the emitted energy (i.e., whether it is from excited atoms or from excited ions).

The electrodes used in arc and spark emission spectrometry are usually made of graphitic carbon. Various shapes of electrodes, as well as various means of incorporating the sample, have been developed in order to render the discharges reproducible and the temperature as high as feasible. Because of the extreme sensitivity of this method of analysis, it is essential that the carbon electrodes be very pure.

The **flame** is also widely used as a means of exciting the sample. This type of source has been used for many years in qualitative analysis, but its widespread application in quantitative work is relatively recent. The main drawbacks of the flame for quantitative work have been in obtaining a flame of sufficiently constant emission intensity and in introducing the sample into the flame steadily and reproducibly for a period of time long enough for the necessary measurements to be made. These difficulties have been overcome sufficiently by good mechanical design of the experimental apparatus to permit considerable quantitative application of flame photometry in chemical analysis. The specimen is almost invariably prepared in the form of a solution, which is then sprayed into the flame of a burner. Several different physical forms for the burner have been designed and developed, and any one of several combinations of fuel and oxygen sources may be utilized. The flame temperatures normally achieved with some fuels are as follows: 1700°C with gas and air, 2100°C with hydrogen and air, 2200°C with acetylene and air, and 3050°C with acetylene and oxygen. Flame temperatures are somewhat lower than those of arc and spark sources; so excitation of fewer energy level transitions occurs.

A **laser beam** is of interest as the means of heating and thereby exciting the atoms or ions of a sample, particularly when the laser beam is focused to irradiate only a small area of the specimen. Solid specimen areas with dimensions as small as 50 microns may be readily analyzed. Even though a bit of the sample is vaporized, as with other types of emission sources, it may be so tiny with the laser source that the method may be classified as virtually nondestructive of the sample. Furthermore, it is possible to study the variations in composition from one small region of the sample to another, as contrasted to an average analysis for a larger mass of material generally obtained with other types of emission sources.

The **gas discharge tube** has already been mentioned in conjunction with sources of radiant energy for absorption methods of analysis. If a sample to be analyzed by the emission method is in the form of a gas, or can conveniently be vaporized, a gas discharge tube may be used in this type of analysis as well. Analytical application of this source is relatively limited, however, because of the problems in handling gases and in adjusting and maintaining the necessary pressure conditions, as contrasted to the relative simplicity of handling liquid and solid specimens.

X-ray Sources. In the qualitative and quantitative analytical application of x-ray emission spectra, the energy required to raise the atoms or ions of the test sample to their electronically excited states is generally obtained through bombardment of the sample with x-ray photons of even greater energy. The radiation which bombards the sample is obtained from an x-ray source of the exact same form as already described for x-ray absorption methods. In view of this method for exciting the atoms of the sample, this type of emission analysis is often called **x-ray fluorescence analysis.**

Alternatively, the test sample may be made the anode of the evacuated or gas-filled x-ray tube, although this method is much less convenient to use in the analytical laboratory.

MONOCHROMATORS

The purpose of a monochromator is to remove or reject all photons other than those of the desired wavelength. No monochromator is perfect in the sense that it can receive continuously polychromatic radiation and pass only purely monochromatic radiation. The degree to which this ideal must be approached varies considerably from one analytical situation to another.

A monochromator system may be evaluated on the basis of three quantities, all of which may be defined with reference to Figure 15-6. This figure shows a plot of per cent transmittance versus wavelength for the monochromator. These important quantities are (1) the **effective band-width,** which is defined as the width of the transmittance band at one-half the maximum transmittance value, (2) the **central wavelength** at the center of the effective bandwidth, and (3) the **peak per cent transmittance** at that central wavelength.

An ideally perfect monochromator would be one with an infinitely narrow effective bandwidth, a central wavelength as desired for the particular test sample, and 100 per cent transmittance at that central wavelength. It is immediately evident that this set of conditions is impossible to realize, because the ideals of infinitely narrow effective bandwidth and of 100 per cent transmittance are contradictory to each other. At the opposite extreme, a system which exhibits absolutely no monochromating effect would be one in which the effective bandwidth is infinitely wide. All practical monochromators fall somewhere between these two extremes.

There are three major types of monochromators: filter, prism, and grating. Each is usable in one form or another in various regions of the electromagnetic spectrum.

Filters

A filter is simply a physical object which absorbs electromagnetic radiation of some wavelengths to a greater extent than it does others, preferentially

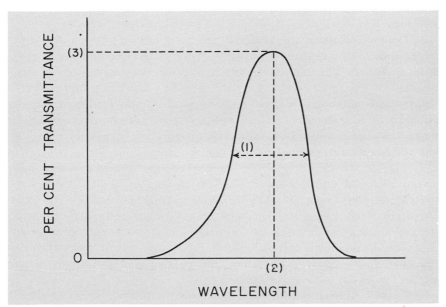

FIGURE 15-6. Plot of per cent transmittance versus wavelength for a monochromator system: (*1*), effective bandwidth; (*2*), central wavelength; (*3*), peak per cent transmittance.

transmitting photons of those wavelengths which are least absorbed. For example, a plate of colored glass can be used as a filter within the visible region of the spectrum. Typical effective bandwidths range from 30 to 50 mμ, and peak transmittances are often as low as 10 to 20 per cent. Narrow bandpass filters, based upon an interference principle, possess effective bandwidths as narrow as 10 mμ and peak transmittances as high as 60 per cent. A separate filter or combination of filters must be employed for each desired central wavelength.

Prisms and Gratings

A grating or prism is generally used as the monochromator in refined analytical work. Each serves effectively to separate or spread incident radiation into its component wavelengths. Radiation of all wavelengths follows the *same* path to the grating or prism, whereas the components of different wavelengths follow slightly *different* paths away from the grating or prism. A shield with a slit in it is placed in the path of radiation emerging from the monochromator so that only radiant energy of the desired wavelength passes on to the test sample and the detector. By means of proper rotation (or other physical movement) of the prism or grating relative to the exit slit, the analytical chemist may select any portion of the spectrum that he desires. This selection may be done either manually or continuously and automatically in synchronization with a recorder, which is connected to the detector.

The physical design and materials of construction of prisms and gratings vary considerably, depending on what region of the electromagnetic spectrum is desired. The relevant factors need not be discussed in detail here, although a few general comments are in order. The prism must actually transmit the radiation of interest, and so it must be fabricated from material which is quite transparent. Thus, ordinary glass prisms are adequate for visible, but not for ultraviolet, radiation; quartz prisms are suitable for both the visible and ultraviolet regions of the spectrum. Some forms of gratings also involve transmission of the radiant energy, although others more specifically involve surface reflection. The spacing between the rulings of a grating must be of approximately the same order of magnitude as the wavelengths involved; consequently, much closer spacing is required, for example, with x-rays than with visible or infrared radiation. The rulings are made mechanically on gratings for use with the longer wavelength regions. Crystals are used as gratings for x-radiation; the parallel planes of atoms or ions within the crystal serve as the rulings.

The effective bandwidth and peak transmittance of a prism or grating monochromator are determined jointly by the following main factors: physical dimensions of the prism or grating, optical characteristics of the prism or grating (e.g., index of refraction of a prism), the physical dimensions of the slit through which the polychromatic radiation enters the mono-chromating system, the physical dimensions of the exit slit, and the distances through which the radiation must pass between the prism or grating and each slit. For example, as an exit slit is made narrower, other factors being appropriate and equal, the effective bandwidth becomes more narrow. It is not feasible, however, for one to attempt to improve the monochromaticity by narrowing the slit below the value at which the intensity is barely sufficient for adequate measurement by the detector. Suffice it to state here that effec-tive bandwidths as narrow as 1 mμ and peak transmittances close to 100 per cent are not unusual in modern prism and grating instruments for use in the visible and ultraviolet regions.

There are no fundamental differences in monochromating systems for absorption and for emission work. However, for some emission work, the exit slit is omitted and the entire spectrum of radiation emerging from the prism or grating is detected and recorded simultaneously on photographic film.

TEST SAMPLE AND OPTICAL MATERIALS

The sample to be analyzed by a method based on the absorption of radiant energy may be placed either between the source of radiation and the monochromator or between the monochromator and the detector. However, the latter position, which is depicted in the block diagram of Figure 15-2, is generally preferable. This arrangement causes less radiation to fall upon the sample, thus minimizing the possibilities of errors through heating and other undesired interactions between radiant energy and the sample.

The sample in an absorption method of analysis is customarily in the form of a solution, not only for convenience in handling but for much more accurate and reproducible control of the path length or sample thickness (the b factor in Lambert's law) than can be achieved with a solid sample.

The walls of the container for the test solution must be constructed of a material which is transparent to the radiant energy that is used. The same consideration applies to a prism within a monochromator, as already men-tioned, and also to all lenses, windows, and other optical components through which the radiant energy must pass.

Ordinary glass transmits adequately within the approximate wavelength range from 350 to 2500 mμ, but other materials must be used for radiation of shorter and longer wavelengths. Corex glass and quartz, with lower wave-length limits of about 300 and 210 mμ, respectively, are particularly useful in the ultraviolet region of the spectrum. A somewhat lower cut-off value is exhibited by fused silica.

The air, or free space, through which the radiant energy passes must also be considered as an optical material. If ultraviolet radiation of wave-length less than about 210 mμ is to be used, oxygen must be removed from the optical paths, either by evacuation of the system or by replacement of air with a pure nitrogen or argon atmosphere. Even then the lower wavelength limit is about 180 mμ except in very special circumstances.

Optical materials suitable for use with infrared radiation, and the approximate long wavelength limit for each, include the following:

fused silica	4 microns
lithium fluoride	7 microns
calcium fluoride	10 microns
sodium chloride	17 microns
potassium bromide	25 microns
cesium iodide	40 microns

Some of these materials are water soluble, so they cannot be used to hold aqueous solutions. In addition, they should be kept in a dehumidified atmosphere.

Various plastics are quite transparent in the portion of the x-ray region which is most frequently used in analysis, ranging in wavelength approximately from 0.5 to 2 or 3 Å. Glass can also be used, although it is generally less transparent than are collodion, Parlodion, and similar plastics. The use of x-radiation longer than 2 or 3 Å generally requires an evacuated path through which the radiation passes. Radiation between 10 or 20 Å in the x-ray region and 180 mμ in the ultraviolet region has only very slight penetrating power and has not been used extensively as yet.

The solvent for the test solution must be one that does not significantly absorb radiant energy within the region of the electromagnetic spectrum which is being employed. Water and numerous organic solvents are suitable with visible radiation, but the choice is much more restricted in the ultraviolet and infrared regions of the spectrum. Extensive data have been compiled for many solvents, and the wavelength ranges over which each serves acceptably are listed in various reference books. Therefore, only a few examples will be mentioned here. In the ultraviolet region, some solvents and the approximate *lower* wavelength cut-off for each are as follows:

acetone	330 mμ
benzene	285 mμ
carbon disulfide	380 mμ
dioxane	220 mμ
ethyl ether	220 mμ
toluene	290 mμ

For use in the infrared region, water is of no value at wavelengths longer than about 2.5 microns. Carbon tetrachloride is reasonably acceptable at wavelengths up to about 10 microns. There are no organic solvents which are acceptable uniformly throughout the infrared region, because all exhibit some vibrational absorption frequencies. Fortunately, however, many organic solvents exhibit "windows" of high transmittance at certain wavelengths of the infrared region. Complete tabulations of data may be consulted or empirical observations may be made in the selection of a solvent suitable for any particular analytical need.

It is often desirable in infrared studies to perform measurements upon samples that are in solid form rather than in liquid solution. This procedure eliminates the need for the occasionally difficult selection of a mutually compatible solvent and material of which the sample container is made, but it does introduce other complications. It is generally not possible to obtain regular absorption spectra merely by placing a powdered sample in the optical path, because surface reflection of radiant energy incident upon the sample would overshadow the desired interaction by absorption. This difficulty may be largely circumvented, however, by either of two procedures. First, the test sample may be formed, under high pressure, into a homogeneous solid disk. A nonabsorbing diluent, such as potassium bromide, can be incorporated into the disk, in order that the "concentration" of the unknown substance, in conjunction with the thickness of the disk, will result in a measurable absorbance value. Second, a powdered unknown substance can be formed into a mull, for example with Nujol, which is a saturated hydrocarbon compound that exhibits relatively few absorptions in the infrared region of the electromagnetic spectrum.

Another technique, called **attenuated total reflectance,** has been developed for obtaining data on samples which can be placed as thin films on surfaces in contact with a specially designed prism. The radiant energy passes through the prism to the interface and is there reflected back into the prism. In this reflection process, however, the radiant energy passes into the sample, typically to a distance of no more than a few microns, and is reduced or attenuated in accordance with the absorption characteristics of the sample. Thus, the spectrum provides essentially the same type of information as does a regular absorption spectrum.

Gaseous samples are occasionally encountered in absorption methods of analysis. Relatively long sample cells, that is, cells with large b values, are generally desirable to provide a reasonable mass of sample within the optical path. Some gas cells are constructed so that the radiation is reflected back and forth several times through the cell in order to increase the b value.

DETECTORS

The human eye serves directly as the detector in some methods of analysis involving visible radiation. The eye is particularly effective in matching the colors or the intensities of two visible light beams. It cannot, however, make any meaningful quantitative measurements apart from direct comparisons, and it is subject to fatigue when engaged in close work over a continuous period of time.

Several types of photoelectric cells have been developed for use as detectors of visible and ultraviolet radiant energy. The overall sensitivity, reproducibility, and wavelength selectivity vary widely from one type to another and are influenced by such factors as the following: the basic type of cell, the chemical and physical characteristics of the light sensitive surface within the cell, the composition of the bulb or window through which the radiant energy must pass to reach the light sensitive surface, the electrical characteristics of the amplifying device, if any, used between the detector itself and the meter or recorder that is observed by the analyst, and the electrical characteristics of the power supplies and other associated electronic circuitry. Some photoelectric detectors yield output readings which are linearly related to the intensity of radiant energy, and others do not. This factor is of significance in the calibration of the apparatus for use in quantitative analytical determinations.

Thermal detectors are generally used for infrared radiation. The infrared energy is converted into heat and then measured as heat energy or, simply, as temperature. Thermocouples and thermistors are particularly useful. Another type of infrared detector is based upon the photoconductive effect, whereby the electrical conductivity of a certain type of substance decreases in accordance with the intensity of radiant energy striking it. For example, a photoconductive cell consisting of a thin layer of lead telluride on a glass surface serves well for the detection of infrared energy at wavelengths up to about 6 microns.

Photographic film is employed as the detector in some emission methods of analysis. The exit slit is omitted from the monochromator, and the entire spectrum of radiation emerging from the prism or grating is allowed to fall upon the photographic film. This type of detection was used almost invariably with arc and spark emission spectrographs for many years and is still used to an appreciable extent. The photographic film provides, for each wavelength of radiation, a summation of intensity over the period of time of the exposure. This feature is advantageous because of the randomly fluctuating intensity of an arc or spark source. The amount of blackening of a photographic film is a function of the number of photons which strike it, but this function is so complex that accurate calibration for quantitative work is rather difficult to establish and maintain.

X-rays are generally detected by photographic film, by a Geiger tube with its electrical power supplies and associated amplifying and counting circuitry, or by a fluorescent screen which absorbs x-ray photons and reëmits a portion of this energy as visible light for subsequent detection either by the human eye or by conventional photoelectric means.

COMPLETE INSTRUMENTS

The source of radiant energy, monochromator, test sample, and detector may be combined in many different ways to form complete instruments for the measurements of wavelength and of intensity of radiant energy. It is frequently possible for an analytical chemist to assemble a complete apparatus from inexpensive and readily available components. Alternatively, the several major blocks which comprise a complete instrument may be purchased from commercial firms and assembled in the laboratory as desired. Most frequently, however, the analytical measurements are made by means of manufactured complete instruments, many types of which are commercially available at prices ranging from a few dollars to many thousands of dollars.

Each complete instrument must be considered to be far more than a simple summation of the blocks of which it is constituted. Two reasons why this is true will be mentioned. First, the several blocks overlap somewhat in the functions which they perform. For example, we have already noted that the radiant energy emitted from some sources is predominantly of one or more discrete wavelengths. Lenses, windows, and other optical components may themselves absorb radiation selectively; and detectors exhibit a relatively greater response for some wavelengths of radiation than for others. Therefore, all of the major blocks of the instrument, not just the monochromator itself, contribute to the effective monochromaticity of the radiation. Second, the optical, electrical, and physical means by which the several blocks are interconnected are often as critical in determining the characteristics of the instrument as are the specific components within each block. This factor will become more evident as we consider a few of the typical instruments which are in common use.

The specific instruments described in the following paragraphs have been selected solely for their instructional value. Each one is representative of others which are likewise commercially available and which are also in practical use in many analytical laboratories.

Figure 15-7 shows an optical diagram of a complete instrument for absorption methods of analysis. It employs a filter and photoelectric cell as the monochromator and detector, respectively. A split-beam principle is used, with two detectors, to minimize error from the variable intensity of radiation emitted by the source. A small electric light bulb (*A*) emits visible radiation which passes through lens *B* and filter *C*. One half of the beam follows the

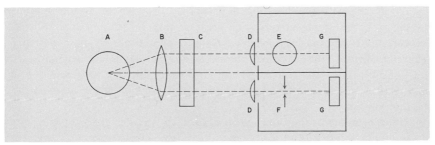

FIGURE 15-7. Optical diagram of a Klett-Summerson colorimeter. (See text for explanation.)

FIGURE 15-8.   Optical diagram of Bausch and Lomb Spectronic 20 colorimeter.
(See text for explanation.)

upper path through lens D and the test solution (E) to the upper photocell
(G). The electrical signals developed in the two photocells are applied to an
indicating meter in such a way that the meter reads zero only when the two
photocells are receiving radiation of equal intensity. The extent to which the
shutter (F) must be adjusted manually to render the two intensities equal is
a direct function of the absorbance of the test solution. Separate observations
must be made with the unknown solution and with a reference sample of
pure solvent in order to obtain the I and I_0 values, as defined earlier in this
chapter. It is not necessary that the shutter control be calibrated in terms of
absolute intensity units. Only a ratio of intensities is involved, regardless of
whether the results be calculated on the basis of the Lambert-Beer law and
measurement upon one standard solution or on the basis of an empirical
calibration plot prepared from measurements upon several standard solutions.

The colorimeter represented by Figure 15-8 employs a more refined
monochromator than the preceding instrument. Radiation from the incandescent source (A) passes through lens B to the monochromating system,
which consists of an entrance slit (C), focusing lens (D), reflection grating
(E), adjustable intensity controller (F), and exit slit (G). The monochromatic
radiation then passes through the test solution (H) and a supplementary
filter (I) to the phototube detector (J). Measurements may be made by
means of this instrument within and slightly beyond the visible region of
the electromagnetic spectrum. The grating may be rotated manually and
measurements are made at one wavelength at a time. By first inserting a
reference solution, usually consisting of the solvent alone, and then adjusting
the light intensity controller (F) and inserting the test solution, one can
obtain direct readings of the per cent transmittance or of the absorbance of
the test solution.

The instrument diagrammed in Figure 15-9 is designed for use in the
ultraviolet as well as the visible region of the electromagnetic spectrum.
However, two light sources and two detectors must be used to cover this
entire range. Radiant energy from the source (A) is reflected from two

mirrors (B and C) through entrance slit D, and from mirror E to the quartz prism (F). The prism may be rotated manually to select the wavelength of radiation which follows the indicated path back to mirror E and through the exit slit (D) to the test solution (G) and photocell detector (H). The entrance and exit slits are mounted one above the other; both are adjusted simultaneously and are of the same width. Measurement is made on one solution at a time. Again, a manual adjustment (of the slits, in this case) may be made with pure solvent in position as the test solution. This means that, when the test solution is subsequently inserted, a reading may be made of the per cent transmittance or of the absorbance of the test solution. This reading is obtained directly from a meter in the instrument shown in Figure 15-8. However, the spectrophotometer in Figure 15-9 utilizes a null-point principle to provide this reading. A potentiometer control is adjusted to cause a meter to indicate a fixed reference value, and the absorbance or per cent transmittance reading is then taken from the potentiometer dial.

The instrument shown in Figure 15-10 has many of the features which we have already discussed, but it incorporates two additional ones of particular significance. One major feature is the double monochromating system. A prism (E) and a grating (I) are arranged optically in series to provide a more effective separation of polychromatic light into its components of various wavelengths. In addition to the entrance slit (C) and exit slit (K), this monochromating system includes focusing mirrors (D, F, H, and J) and an intermediate slit (G) between the two sections. The other distinctive feature shown in Figure 15-10 is the beam splitting arrangement between the exit slit (K) and the detector (P). A rotating mirror (L) causes the beam to shift automatically and rapidly back and forth between two paths. The two paths are similar in that each involves mirrors (M and M', O and O'), but the paths differ in that the test solution (N) is placed in one and a reference solution or pure solvent (N') is placed in the other. If the two solutions absorb radiation equally, the intensity of illumination incident upon the detector is constant and its electrical output is a d-c signal. If, however, the two solutions (N and N') absorb unequally, the detector output is an a-c signal, the frequency of which is the same as the frequency at which the beam is shifted back and forth between the two solutions. The magnitude of

FIGURE 15-9. Optical diagram of Beckman model DU spectrophotometer. (See text for explanation.)

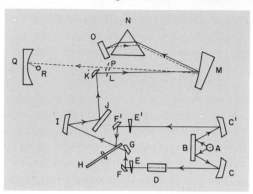

FIGURE 15-10. Optical diagram of Cary model 14 spectrophotometer. (See text for explanation.)

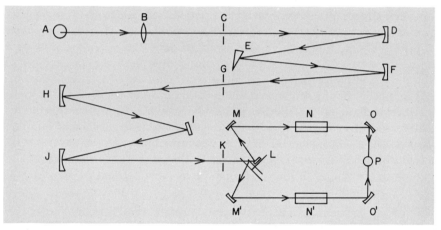

FIGURE 15-11. Optical diagram of Perkin-Elmer model 137B infrared spectrophotometer. (See text for explanation.)

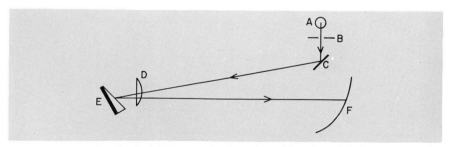

FIGURE 15-12. Optical diagram of a Bausch and Lomb emission spectrograph. (See text for explanation.)

this a-c signal is a function of the absorbance of the test solution compared to that of the reference solvent or solution. The instrument is designed to read, by means of an automatically balancing recording potentiometer, the magnitude of this absorbance ratio. The instrument is also designed to vary continuously the wavelength of radiation which passes from the mono-chromator to the sample, and thus to provide automatic recording of the complete absorbance spectrum of the test solution.

The optical diagram of a complete infrared spectrophotometer is shown in Figure 15-11. This instrument also employs a beam splitting device some-what similar to that of the preceding figure. Radiant energy from the source (A) is split by mirrors $B, C,$ and C' into a sample beam and a reference beam. The sample beam passes through the test sample (D), may be attenuated by the adjustable light controller (E), and is reflected by mirrors F and G to the rotating mirror (H). The reference beam passes through another adjustable light controller (E') and mirror (F') to rotating mirror H. The rotating mirror is shaped and rotated in such a way that it alternately passes on along the indicated path radiant energy either from the sample beam or from the reference beam. This beam is of constant or alternating intensity, as determined by the relative intensities of the reference and sample beams. It is then directed by mirrors $I, J,$ and K into the monochromating system, which consists of entrance slit L, prism N, and exit slit P, along with mirrors M and O. Finally, mirror Q focuses the radiation emerging from the mono-chromator onto the thermocouple detector (R). The prism may be rotated manually or automatically to vary the wavelength of radiation which follows the indicated path to the detector. The accompanying electrical circuitry (along with its mechanical linkages to the adjustable light controllers for intensity adjustment, to the prism for wavelength adjustment, and to the recorder) provide for automatically recording the absorption spectrum of the sample.

A complete instrument designed for emission methods of analysis using an arc or spark source and a photographic film as the detector is shown diagrammatically in Figure 15-12. The sample is introduced directly into the arc or spark (A), as already described. Radiant energy passes through entrance slit B and is reflected by mirror C through a lens (D) into the prism (E). The radiation is reflected back through prism E and again through lens D onto the photographic film (F). Radiation of all wavelengths from the source follows the same path to the prism, whereas the components of various wavelengths follow different paths from the prism to the film. No exit slit is used, and the entire spectrum falls simultaneously along the photographic film. This type of instrument is made with several different degrees of dispersion, dependent primarily upon the distance of the prism (E) from the film (F) and upon the physical dimensions and the composition of the prism. With relatively low dispersion, an entire spectrum from 200 to 800 mμ, for example, can be recorded on a single strip of photographic film. With larger instruments, the several wavelengths are more widely

FIGURE 15-13.   Optical diagram of a Perkin-Elmer model 290 atomic absorption spectrophotometer. (See text for explanation.)

dispersed, as much as a few millimeters per millimicron, and only a portion of the entire spectral range can be photographed on one strip of film.

Figure 15-13 is an optical diagram of one type of commercially available instrument designed for making quantitative determinations by the atomic absorption method. The source (A) is a lamp which is constructed partly of the same element which is to be determined and which emits radiant energy in the spectrum of that element. Mirror B and lens C direct this illumination to the sample. The sample is introduced by means of a flame (D), which is essentially the same as a flame source for emission methods of analysis. The unabsorbed photons then pass on through lens E and are reflected by mirrors F and G to the monochromator, which consists of an entrance slit (H), focusing mirror (I), grating (J), and exit slit (K). The radiation emerging from the monochromator strikes the detector (L). Separate source lamps are available for a variety of elements, and some multielement sources are available in certain combinations. This type of instrument, like many others, is readily adaptable to a high degree of automation.

QUESTIONS AND PROBLEMS

1. Define or explain each of the following terms: wavelength, frequency, monochromatic radiation, polarized light, photon, diffraction, refraction, optical rotation, absorption, emission, fluorescence, phosphorescence, Lambert-Beer law, absorptivity, molar absorptivity, absorbance, transmittance, flame photometry, monochromator, effective bandwidth, central wavelength, per cent peak transmittance.

2. Calculate the frequency, ν, in reciprocal seconds corresponding to each of the following wavelengths of electromagnetic radiation: (a) 222 mμ, (b) 530 mμ, (c) 17 Å, (d) 0.030 cm, (e) 1.30×10^{-7} cm, (f) 6.1 microns.

3. Calculate the wavelength, in centimeters and in millimicrons, corresponding to each of the following frequencies of electromagnetic radiation: (a) 1.97×10^{9} sec^{-1}, (b) 4.86×10^{15} sec^{-1}, (c) 7.32×10^{19} sec^{-1}.

4. Calculate the energy in ergs of a photon of each of the following wavelengths: (a) 803 mμ, (b) 3.68 microns, (c) 9.95 Å, (d) 11.5 cm.

5. Calculate the energy in ergs of a photon of wavelength 2615 Å. What is the total energy of a mole of such photons? If 1 mole of photons of wavelength

100 $m\mu$ has a total energy of 28.6 kcal, what is the energy in kilocalories of 1 mole of photons of wavelength 2615 Å? Calculate the number of ergs in 1 kcal.

6. Calculate the absorbance which corresponds to each of the following values of per cent transmittance: (a) 36.8 per cent, (b) 22.0 per cent, (c) 82.3 per cent, (d) 100.0 per cent, (e) 4.20 per cent.

7. Calculate the per cent transmittance which corresponds to each of the following absorbance values: (a) 0.800, (b) 0.215, (c) 0.585, (d) 1.823, (e) 0.057.

8. Suppose that the per cent transmittance of a solution containing an absorbing solute is observed to be 24.7 per cent in a spectrophotometer cell with a path length, b, of 5.000 cm. What will be the per cent transmittance of the same solution in a cell with each of the following path lengths: (a) 1.000 cm, (b) 10.00 cm, (c) 1.000 mm?

9. What experimental techniques may be employed to promote atoms and molecules to their excited states?

10. Why do absorption spectra for atomic species consist of discrete lines at specific wavelengths, whereas absorption spectra for molecules usually appear as relatively broad bands?

11. Describe the basic differences between absorption and emission methods of analysis.

12. Consider the following hypothetical absorption cell. Assume that the incident radiation is monochromatic, parallel, and of uniform intensity over the cross section of the cell. One half of the incident beam traverses thickness b_1 and the other half traverses thickness b_2. The absorbing substance is assumed to obey the Lambert-Beer law.

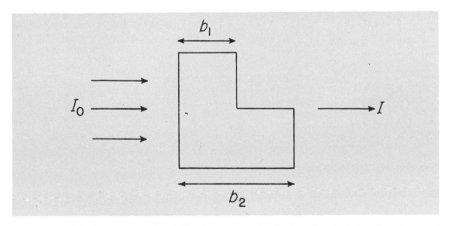

(a) Show that the following general relation is valid for the observed absorbance as a function of b_1 and b_2, the absorptivity a of the absorbing substance, and the concentration of the absorbing substance c:

$$A = -\log [10^{-ab_1c} + 10^{-ab_2c}]$$

(b) What will be the apparent slope of a plot of absorbance versus concentration for a situation in which c approaches 0 and one in which c approaches ∞?

13. List the requirements which must be fulfilled by a source of radiant energy for absorption methods of analysis. How do the requirements differ for a source employed in emission methods? Describe and compare the characteristics of

some common sources used for the visible, ultraviolet, and infrared regions of the spectrum.

14. Why do an infinitely narrow effective bandwidth and a 100 per cent peak transmittance contradict each other as characteristics of an ideal monochromator?

SUGGESTIONS FOR ADDITIONAL READING

1. L. H. Ahrens and S. R. Taylor: *Spectrochemical Analysis*, second edition, Addison-Wesley Publishing Company Inc., Reading, Massachusetts, 1961.
2. E. J. Bair: *Introduction to Chemical Instrumentation*, McGraw-Hill Book Company, New York, 1962.
3. L. S. Birks: *X-Ray Spectrochemical Analysis*, Wiley-Interscience, New York, 1959.
4. G. L. Clark, ed.: *The Encyclopedia of Spectroscopy*, Reinhold Publishing Corporation, New York, 1960.
5. R. T. Conley: *Infrared Spectroscopy*, Allyn & Bacon, Inc., Boston, 1966.
6. J. A. Dean: *Flame Photometry*, McGraw-Hill Book Company, New York, 1960.
7. I. M. Kolthoff and P. J. Elving, eds.: *Treatise on Analytical Chemistry*, Part I, Volumes 5 and 6, Wiley-Interscience, New York, 1959, pp. 2707–4217.
8. L. Meites and H. C. Thomas: *Advanced Analytical Chemistry*, McGraw-Hill Book Company, New York, 1958, pp. 231–344.
9. R. M. Silverstein and G. C. Bassler: *Spectrometric Identification of Organic Compounds*, John Wiley & Sons, Inc., New York, 1963.
10. H. A. Strobel: *Chemical Instrumentation*, Addison-Wesley Publishing Company Inc., Reading, Massachusetts, 1960, pp. 37–264.
11. F. J. Welcher, ed.: *Standard Methods of Chemical Analysis*, sixth edition, Volume 3-A, D. Van Nostrand Co., Inc., New York, 1966, pp. 3–282.
12. H. H. Willard, L. L. Merritt, Jr., and J. A. Dean: *Instrumental Methods of Analysis*, D. Van Nostrand Co., Inc., New York, 1965, pp. 32–456.

Chapter Sixteen

Analytical Applications of Radiant Energy Measurements

The purpose of this chapter is to evaluate the applicability in quantitative chemical analysis of the principles and apparatus described in Chapter 15. Particular attention is given to the chemical structures and reactions which are required in these methods and to an assessment of the overall role played in quantitative analysis by each of the types of methods which utilize the interactions of matter and radiant energy.

ABSORPTION METHODS — VISIBLE

One or more methods based upon the absorption of radiant energy have been developed for the quantitative determination of nearly every one of the elements and for many ionic and molecular groupings of atoms. Many of these procedures are of considerable practical usefulness in the analyses of both inorganic and organic substances. Even when we confine our discussion to the absorption of visible radiation, it becomes apparent that virtually every element and many ions and molecules are either colored, can react with a colored substance, or can react to form a colored substance. Each of these situations presents the possibility of a quantitative analytical determination.

Many of these methods are used to determine small amounts of substances. A solution concentration of 10^{-6} or even 10^{-7} M is frequently adequate for a determination, whereas conventional gravimetric and titrimetric methods are useless in dealing with such minute amounts of material. The need to determine small amounts of constituents may arise in practical situations for either of two reasons. First, the entire quantity of sample which is available for analysis may be very small, in which case these optical methods are useful for the determination of major constituents. Second, a larger amount of sample may be available, in which case trace constituents may be determined. With samples of the typical tenth-gram size range, it is frequently possible to identify and to determine trace constituents present to the extent of only one part per million. As a matter of fact, for tenth-gram samples, one ordinarily utilizes radiant energy measurements only for minor constituents present in amounts up to a few per cent, because more accurate titrimetric and gravimetric methods are generally available for determining major constituents. Moreover, the use of radiant energy methods of analysis may offer one advantage in eliminating the need for the separation of the desired substance.

The results of quantitative determinations by absorption procedures are typically accurate to within 1 or 2 per cent of the amount of constituent present. Some important practical procedures are of even less relative accuracy, and special techniques have been developed in a few instances to achieve greater accuracy.

Selection of Absorbing Substance

We noted in the preceding chapter that absorption of radiant energy in the visible region of the electromagnetic spectrum generally involves transitions to higher energy levels of electrons in the outer orbitals of the absorbing atoms, ions, or molecules. Therefore, test samples which selectively absorb visible radiation are substances possessing electron-deficient energy levels which differ by the appropriate amounts of energy from other levels already occupied. In addition, we pointed out that the absorption spectra of molecules and of polyatomic ions generally consist of rather broad bands, instead of being sharply defined, because of vibrational and rotational factors superimposed upon the electronic transitions. In a liquid or solid absorbing medium, the vibrations and rotations are affected by neighboring species, which tends to broaden the absorption bands even more.

Inorganic substances which absorb visible radiant energy selectively, and thus appear to be colored, may be single ions with incomplete outer electron shells, in which the several energy levels are very close together. For example, the transition metal and rare earth ions exhibit distinctive absorptions, many of which are in the visible region of the electromagnetic spectrum. Other colored substances, such as the permanganate ion and the dichromate ion, are polyatomic absorbing groups. However, the classification of inorganic substances into single ions and polyatomic species is, in a sense, an oversimplification, because even presumably simple cations are aquated or solvated and the coordinated solvent molecules definitely affect the characteristic absorptions of a cation. As some indication of the possible complexity of absorption processes involving visible radiation, let us consider the two following examples: The highly colored complex $FeSCN^{++}$, better represented as $Fe(H_2O)_5(SCN)^{++}$, is presumed to absorb a photon by an excitation process in which an electron is transferred from the thiocyanate ligand to the readily reducible ferric ion. The complex of ferrous and thiocyanate ions is colorless, because the ferrous ion is not readily reducible and cannot participate in such an electron transfer process. The complex formed between iron(II) and 1,10-phenanthroline (see Fig. 12-8) is another interesting species. It is possible that an electron can transfer from the ferrous ion to the 1,10-phenanthroline ligand. The necessary amount of energy for this process presumably equals that of a photon in one portion of the visible region of the electromagnetic spectrum, and a solution of this complex is colored a deep red. The same electron-transfer process does not occur in the complex formed between iron(III) and 1,10-phenanthroline, and this complex is not of the same deep red color.

Many organic substances selectively absorb visible light. Such compounds are characterized by a deficiency of electrons in appropriate energy levels, as, for example, in large molecules with a number of conjugated carbon-carbon double bonds. Thus, the β-carotene molecule, which has 11 conjugated double bonds, absorbs strongly in the 420 to 480 mμ region. Many other less highly unsaturated organic molecules exhibit absorptions in the ultraviolet region.

An unknown constituent which does not exhibit by itself sufficient absorption of visible radiation to be used directly in a quantitative determination may frequently be converted by a chemical reaction into a substance which is suitable. Thus, ferric ion may be readily determined by the absorption of radiant energy after reduction to the ferrous state and reaction with 1,10-phenanthroline to form the deep red complex mentioned previously. As with chemical reactions involved in many other quantitative procedures, the reaction between the unknown constituent and the color-producing reagents must go quantitatively to completion.

It is not even necessary that the colored substance actually contain the unknown constituent. It is sufficient that the colored species contain some component which is stoichiometrically related to the unknown. For example, calcium may be determined indirectly by the photometric measurement of the permanganate concentration remaining from a fixed volume of standard solution, after precipitation of the unknown as calcium oxalate and dissolution of the precipitate in an acidic standard solution of potassium permanganate.

It is frequently possible to choose among several different colored forms which are all suitable for measurement in an absorption method of analysis. Foremost among the factors which one must consider is the magnitude of the absorptivity relative to the required sensitivity and range. With a very intensely colored substance, as indicated by a high absorptivity at the appropriate wavelength, a relatively small amount of the colored form is detectable and a correspondingly small change in concentration is required to produce an easily measurable change in absorbance of the test solution. Thus, the greatest sensitivity is achievable with the colored form of the highest absorptivity.

The Photometric Error

Measurements of per cent transmittance obtained with most photometers and spectrophotometers are subject to an uncertainty because of random errors in the normal operation of these instruments. The reproducibility of the instrument control settings, the constancy of both detector response and intensity of radiant energy, the repeatability of filling the spectrophotometer cell and positioning it in the sample chamber, the stability of any auxiliary electrical circuitry, and the readability of the per cent transmittance meter or scale — all contribute to the overall accuracy of a spectrophotometric method of analysis. Accordingly, a variation or uncertainty in any of these factors may affect the observed per cent transmittance as well as the calculated concentration of the absorbing species. For most commercial instruments, the absolute uncertainty in the per cent transmittance falls within the approximate limits of 0.2 to 1.0 per cent. This range of values can be determined experimentally if one performs a series of measurements with a standard solution, each individual measurement involving a complete readjustment of all instrument controls and a fresh portion of the standard solution.

We shall use the larger figure for this error and illustrate what this uncertainty means in terms of concentrations of the unknown species, by assuming that transmittance readings of 5, 50, and 95 per cent are actually in error by 1.0 per cent and really signify transmittances of 6, 51, and 96 per cent, respectively. The absorbance values corresponding to each of these transmittances may be calculated from the basic definitions given in Chapter 15, namely,

$$\text{absorbance} = A = \log \frac{I_0}{I}$$

and

$$\text{transmittance} = T = \frac{I}{I_0}$$

The results are as follows:

Transmittance	Absorbance
0.05	1.301
0.06	1.222
0.50	0.301
0.51	0.292
0.95	0.022
0.96	0.018

Now, let us convert these absorbance values into relative uncertainties at each of the three levels of transmittance, as follows:

At the 5 per cent transmittance level, per cent relative uncertainty in absorbance

$$= \left(\frac{1.301 - 1.222}{1.301}\right) 100 = 7 \text{ per cent};$$

at the 50 per cent transmittance level, per cent relative uncertainty in absorbance

$$= \left(\frac{0.301 - 0.292}{0.301}\right) 100 = 3 \text{ per cent};$$

at the 95 per cent transmittance level, per cent relative uncertainty in absorbance

$$= \left(\frac{0.022 - 0.018}{0.022}\right) 100 = 18 \text{ per cent}.$$

Remembering from the Lambert-Beer law that the concentration of the absorbing species is directly and linearly related to the absorbance, we can conclude that these per cent errors in absorbance are equal to the per cent errors in concentration of the unknown constituent, all resulting from the constant 1 per cent uncertainty in transmittance.

We can reach the same conclusions in a more rigorous fashion by combining the basic definitions of absorbance and transmittance to obtain

$$A = \log \frac{1}{T}$$

or

$$A = \frac{1}{2.303} \ln \frac{1}{T} = 0.434 \ln \frac{1}{T}$$

If this equation is differentiated with respect to T, the result is

$$\frac{dA}{dT} = -\frac{0.434}{T}$$

or

$$dA = -\frac{0.434}{T} dT$$

In order to evaluate the *relative* error in the absorbance, it is necessary to divide each side of the preceding expression by absorbance (A). Thus,

$$\frac{\mathrm{d}A}{A} = -\frac{0.434}{TA}\mathrm{d}T = \frac{0.434}{T \log T}\mathrm{d}T$$

The latter equation shows that the relative error in absorbance ($\mathrm{d}A/A$) is governed by the absolute uncertainty in the observed transmittance ($\mathrm{d}T$) as well as by the reciprocal of a product of terms (T and $\log T$) involving the transmittance itself. In the present discussion, we shall still assume that the absolute error in the transmittance is 0.01, that is, that the per cent uncertainty is 1.0 per cent. Therefore, the per cent relative error in the absorbance can be computed from the following simple equation:

$$\text{per cent relative error in absorbance} = \frac{\mathrm{d}A}{A} \times 100 = \frac{0.434}{T \log T}$$

Next, let us evaluate the per cent relative error in absorbance which arises from a 1.0 per cent error in transmittance readings of 5, 50, and 95 per cent:

At the 5 per cent transmittance level

$$\frac{\mathrm{d}A}{A} \times 100 = \frac{0.434}{(0.05) \log (0.05)} = -6.7 \text{ per cent};$$

at the 50 per cent transmittance level

$$\frac{\mathrm{d}A}{A} \times 100 = \frac{0.434}{(0.50) \log (0.50)} = -2.9 \text{ per cent};$$

at the 95 per cent transmittance level

$$\frac{\mathrm{d}A}{A} \times 100 = \frac{0.434}{(0.95) \log (0.95)} = -20.5 \text{ per cent}.$$

Notice that the magnitudes of the relative uncertainties are essentially identical for this rigorous approach and for the somewhat empirical procedure given previously. The fact that the signs of the errors are reversed in the two treatments is immaterial since we are interested only in the sizes of these uncertainties. Obviously, the 1.0 per cent error in the transmittance can be either positive or negative and, consequently, the uncertainty in the absorbance or concentration has an equal probability of having a plus or a minus sign.

Results of a series of such calculations, based on the rigorous equation, of the per cent relative error in absorbance or concentration as a function of the per cent transmittance are presented graphically in Figure 16-1, from which three important conclusions may be drawn. First, the relative error in absorbance or concentration is *minimal* at 36.8 per cent transmittance or an absorbance of 0.434. Second, the error is reasonably *constant* between approximately 20 and 65 per cent transmittance or 0.7 to 0.2 absorbance units. Third, the error becomes extremely great at each end of the per cent transmittance scale. Therefore, for quantitative determinations of the highest accuracy, the instrument readings should be limited to the absorbance range from 0.7 to 0.2. Such a restriction can be easily met through appropriate variations in the sample path length, b, and the size or volume of the sample taken for analysis. It must be emphasized that the source of error just described is inherent in the spectrophotometric method of quantitative analysis. The unusual manner of variation of this error arises from the fact

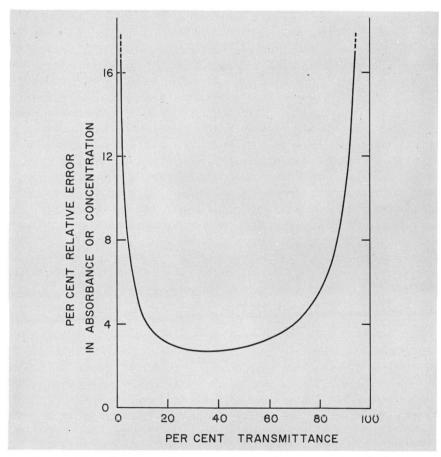

FIGURE 16-1. Per cent relative error in absorbance or in the calculated concentration of the absorbing species, as a function of per cent transmittance, due to a 1 per cent absolute error in the observed per cent transmittance.

that instruments measure transmittance, whereas concentrations are proportional to absorbance.

Selection of Wavelength

Some quantitative determinations are made using directly the polychromatic radiation from the source of radiant energy, with no monochromator of any type being employed. Much better selectivity and sensitivity are obtained, however, with radiation that is more narrowly restricted in its spectral distribution. Four factors are of significance in the selection of what wavelength to use for any particular quantitative determination.

1. The radiation should be restricted, insofar as feasible, to a band of wavelengths which are absorbed by the desired constituent. Consider the determination of a substance which absorbs blue light and transmits red and yellow. If all three colors of radiation are used, the observed response of the detector includes its response to red and yellow light, which is unaffected by the concentration of the desired substance. However, if only blue light is employed, the entire response of the detector is attributable to the intensity of transmitted blue light, and thus it is indicative of the concentration of the species being determined. In other words, any radiation which is of wavelengths other than those absorbable by the desired substance is simply "background" signal or noise, on top of which must be the entire range of desired response. This same factor is important in determining how wide a band of wavelengths is needed for a particular application. Inasmuch as the absorptions of visible radiation by components in solution are generally quite broad, there is no need to limit the range of wavelengths unduly, even though some degree of monochromaticity is desirable. For this reason, inexpensive filter monochromators are frequently as effective in procedures involving the absorption of visible radiation as are the more refined prism and grating devices.

2. The wavelength selected should be one at which the absorptivity results in a suitable compromise between sensitivity and concentration range of the desired substance. Not only does the analytical chemist frequently have several different colored species from which to choose, as already mentioned, but a given substance may exhibit more than one absorption band. The absorption spectrum for the dichromate ion $(Cr_2O_7^=)$ shown in Figure 16-2 illustrates these ideas. Dichromate ion has two absorption bands in the visible or near ultraviolet regions of the spectrum, one band located at approximately 350 mμ (A) with a molar absorptivity of 2270 liter mole^{-1} cm^{-1} and the other band at about 450 mμ (B) with a molar absorptivity of only 370 liter mole^{-1} cm^{-1}. If it is assumed that a spectrophotometer cell with a path length (b) of exactly 1 cm is employed for all measurements, we can calculate from the Lambert-Beer law what range of dichromate concentrations will

provide absorbance readings in the optimum 0.7 to 0.2 range at each of the two wavelengths.

For $\lambda = 350$ mμ and $A = 0.2$,

$$c = \frac{A}{\epsilon b} = \frac{0.200}{(2270)(1)} = 8.8 \times 10^{-5}\ M$$

For $\lambda = 350$ mμ and $A = 0.7$,

$$c = \frac{A}{\epsilon b} = \frac{0.700}{(2270)(1)} = 3.1 \times 10^{-4}\ M$$

For $\lambda = 450$ mμ and $A = 0.2$,

$$c = \frac{A}{\epsilon b} = \frac{0.200}{(370)(1)} = 5.4 \times 10^{-4}\ M$$

For $\lambda = 450$ mμ and $A = 0.7$,

$$c = \frac{A}{\epsilon b} = \frac{0.700}{(370)(1)} = 1.9 \times 10^{-3}\ M$$

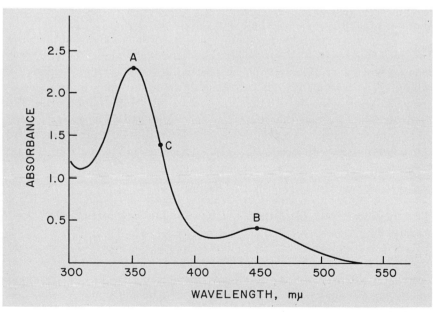

FIGURE 16-2.   Absorption spectrum for 0.001 M dichromate ion, $Cr_2O_7^{=}$, in a 1 F sulfuric acid medium and in a 1 cm spectrophotometer cell. [Redrawn, with permission, from the paper by J. J. Lingane and J. W. Collat: Anal. Chem., 22, 166 (1950).]

It is evident that an absorbance measurement at 350 mμ should be performed when the concentration of dichromate is between about 8×10^{-5} and 3×10^{-4} M because of the relatively greater sensitivity and accuracy at this wavelength. However, if information is available which indicates that the dichromate concentration lies within the range from 5.4×10^{-4} to 1.9×10^{-3} M, it is more straightforward and just as accurate to measure the absorbance of the solution at 450 mμ rather·than to dilute the solution so that a measurement at 350 mμ may be made. Moreover, the relative values of the molar absorptivities at 350 and 450 mμ, respectively, are such that, without dilution of the sample and with a 1 cm path length, one can determine dichromate at a concentration level ranging from 8×10^{-5} to 2×10^{-3} M by proper choice of the wavelength. It should be emphasized that, if the dichromate concentration is significantly lower than 8×10^{-5} M, it may be feasible to use a spectrophotometer cell with a longer path length in order to bring the absorbance into the optimum range. If this latter procedural change is made, it still remains to be decided whether the absorbance should be measured at 350 or 450 mμ. If the dichromate solution proves to be considerably more concentrated than about 1.9×10^{-3} M, it is possible either to utilize a spectrophotometer cell of shorter path length or to dilute appropriately the original solution for a subsequent absorbance measurement at 350 or 450 mμ. The significant conclusion to be drawn from this discussion is that wavelength can be an important variable, because one may obtain sensitivity on one hand and range on the other hand, without the need for dilution of the sample solution or for a change in the spectrophotometer cell.

3. The wavelength chosen should be one at which a slight shift in wavelength will not result in an appreciable change in molar absorptivity. If wavelength C in Figure 16-2 were to be selected, a slight random variation in adjusting the instrument to this wavelength would introduce an unnecessary source of error. Thus, it is better to select a wavelength at the peak of an absorption band rather than on the steeply rising or falling side of a band. This source of error is less significant with an instrument employing broadband filters than with one utilizing a monochromator of narrow effective bandwidth.

4. The wavelength chosen should ideally be one at which the unknown constituent is the only component of the test sample which absorbs radiation. This condition is often not attainable, but it should be approached as closely as feasible.

A direct application of these four factors to the selection of the wavelength to be used in a quantitative procedure necessitates that absorption spectra be obtained of the desired constituent and also of other potentially interfering substances. It is sometimes possible to make this selection of wavelength empirically, particularly in the use of filter instruments. A solution appears to the human eye to be of the color which that solution transmits preferentially, which in turn is complementary to the color that is absorbed; so the filter color should be complementary to the apparent solution color, as in the following table:

Solution Color	Filter Color
purple	green
orange to red	blue to blue-green
yellow	blue
violet to red	purple
blue	red

Interfering Substances

There are two principal types of substances which may interfere in quantitative determinations. The first type is any substance which causes the reactions used to produce the colored species to be less than stoichiometric. This is analogous to the requirements that the precipitation reaction must go quantitatively to completion in a gravimetric determination and that the reaction in a titrimetric procedure be stoichiometric. Furthermore, in a determination involving a calculation based upon the Lambert-Beer law, error may arise from the presence of any substance which causes the inapplicability of this law, as mentioned in Chapter 15. Empirical calibration may be used, but even this expedient is subject to appreciable error under conditions in which there are significant departures from the Lambert-Beer law.

The second type of interfering substance is any species which absorbs radiant energy of the same wavelength as that selected for the determination of the unknown constituent. If at all possible, this situation should be avoided by proper choices both of colored form for measurement and of wavelength to be employed. This ideal is often not realized, and other steps must frequently be taken to minimize the error.

If the interfering substance is present in fixed concentration in all samples of the unknown, the contribution of its absorbance to the total observed absorbance values is constant. No error arises from this source if the standard solutions used for calibration also contain the interfering substance in the same fixed concentration. However, the constant contribution toward total absorbance limits the range of unknown concentrations which can be covered within the optimum absorbance range of 0.7 to 0.2. A special instrumental calibration procedure permits this limitation to be overcome under certain conditions. In the usual calibration procedures, the instrument is adjusted to read zero absorbance (that is, 100 per cent transmittance) with pure solvent as the sample. In these special calibration procedures, this adjustment is made, not with pure solvent, but rather with a standard solution which is somewhat less in absorbance than is the least concentrated unknown solution. The overall sensitivity of the instrument sets a practical limit on the extent to which this technique can be employed.

If the interfering substance is present in varying concentrations from one sample of the unknown to another, it is still possible to carry out the analysis spectrophotometrically. It is even possible to determine the concentrations of each of two or more constituents with overlapping absorption spectra in the same test sample. The procedure is based upon the fact that if two or more constituents contribute to the absorbance at a fixed wavelength, the total absorbance equals the sum of the individual absorbances. Thus, if two components, x and y, contribute to the absorbance at wavelength λ_1, we can write

$$A_{\text{total } \lambda_1} = A_x + A_y \quad \text{(all at } \lambda_1\text{)}$$

Applying the Lambert-Beer law to each of the two components and letting the sample path length be equal to unity, we can rewrite the preceding relation as

$$A_{\text{total } \lambda_1} = a_{x_1} c_x + a_{y_1} c_y \quad \text{(all at } \lambda_1\text{)}$$

A similar equation can be written for the total absorbance at another wavelength λ_2,

$$A_{\text{total } \lambda_2} = a_{x_2} c_x + a_{y_2} c_y \quad \text{(all at } \lambda_2\text{)}$$

The numerical values of the absorptivities a_{x_1} and a_{x_2} can be determined at λ_1 and λ_2, respectively, by measurements upon a standard solution of x, that is, upon a solution in which c_x is known and c_y is zero. The numerical values of a_{y_1} and a_{y_2} at the same two wavelengths can be determined similarly with a standard solution of y. Note that, as long as the same sample cell is used throughout the procedure, no error arises from the assumption that the path length is equal to unity.

Then, when we measure the absorbances at the two wavelengths of an unknown mixture of the two components, we have two equations containing only c_x and c_y as unknowns, which may be solved simultaneously for the composition of the unknown sample. It is preferable for one of the wavelengths to be one at which x absorbs much more than y, and the other wavelength one at which y absorbs to a greater extent than does x. This entire procedure is another application of the principle of indirect analysis described in an earlier chapter. Two (or n) components can be determined without separation if one makes two (or n) measurements upon the mixture, writes the results of each measurement as a mathematical equation, and solves the equations for the desired information. The principle is applicable whether the measurements are gravimetric, titrimetric, of absorption of radiant energy, or of some other type; it is not even necessary that the two (or n) measurements be of the same type.

It is often desirable and sometimes necessary to perform a chemical or physical separation of the desired constituent from the interfering substances, rather than to attempt measurements in the presence of foreign substances which absorb radiant energy of the wavelengths employed in the determination of an unknown constituent. All of the usual methods of separation (including, among others, precipitation, extraction, distillation, and ion-exchange chromatography) find numerous practical applications for this purpose. In addition, the separation step may serve as a convenient means for adjusting the concentration of the unknown constituent to bring it within a range that is suitable for subsequent measurement.

Let us now review briefly the major conditions under which the greatest sensitivity and selectivity may be achieved: (1) The highest possible absorptivity provides for maximal sensitivity. (2) An extremely sharp, and therefore very distinctive, absorption band generally contributes to maximal selectivity. (3) To achieve experimentally this maximal sensitivity and selectivity, the radiant energy used in the measurement must be restricted to that particular wavelength band. The experimental technique in which these three conditions are met more closely than in possibly any other is in the **atomic absorption method** of analysis. The sample, which may be introduced into the complete instrument in the form of a solution, is converted into the atomic state in a flame. The electronic transitions which this atomized sample can undergo occur at very sharply defined wavelengths. Each absorbing species is an atom, and so it is free of the vibrational and rotational complexities of polyatomic ions and molecules. Furthermore, each atom is in the gaseous state, which means that it is free of the interactions with neighboring particles that broaden the absorption bands of matter in the liquid and solid states. The radiant energy produced by the source in the atomic absorption method of analysis is emitted from excited atoms of the same element which is to be determined; therefore, this radiant energy is precisely of the wavelengths which are absorbable by the atomized sample. With this type of sample and source, the effective absorptivities are high. Consequently, the atomic absorption method of analysis is virtually the ultimate technique, from the standpoints of sensitivity and selectivity, of all procedures based upon the absorption of radiant energy by matter.

Selected Determinations

Because there are many practical examples of useful determinations based upon the absorption of visible radiant energy, those procedures discussed here have necessarily been chosen arbitrarily. We shall consider the quantitative determinations of ammonia, iron, phosphate, lead, and nickel, as well as the simultaneous spectrophotometric analysis of a mixture of manganese and chromium. All the methods are of practical value in modern analytical laboratories, and each procedure possesses one or more features which are applicable to other determinations as well.

Colorimetric Determination of Ammonia. One of the classic methods for the quantitative determination of small amounts of ammonia is based upon the measurement of the intensity of the red-brown color produced when an alkaline solution of tetraiodomercurate(II), $HgI_4^=$ (called the **Nessler reagent**), is added to an aqueous solution containing ammonium ion or ammonia. The chemical reaction which occurs can be formulated as

$$2\,HgI_4^= + NH_3 + OH^- \longrightarrow NH_2Hg_2I_3 + 5\,I^- + H_2O$$
$$\text{(red-brown)}$$

The colored substance is actually colloidal in nature, and it eventually flocculates if the solution is permitted to stand for a period of time. Consequently, the colorimetric measurements must be performed within a relatively short time after the solutions are initially mixed — while the precipitate is still a uniformly dispersed colloid, but not too soon after the mixing because the reaction between $HgI_4^=$ and NH_3 is somewhat slow. The method is applicable to the determination of very small quantities of nitrogenous compounds, such as nitrates, nitrites, and proteins, which can be reduced to ammonia.

Ordinarily, a much more accurate procedure for the determination of ammonia, as well as other substances which can be reduced to ammonia, involves distillation of the ammonia into a known excess of standard hydrochloric acid followed by a back-titration with a standard sodium hydroxide solution. However, it is virtually impossible to distill quantitatively all ammonia from an aqueous solution, owing to its high solubility in water, a factor which is especially serious in the determination of trace quantities of ammonia. Therefore, the colorimetric method has definite analytical applicability in certain situations, although it clearly suffers from lack of accuracy.

Spectrophotometric Determination of Iron. Many color-producing reagents have been employed for the spectrophotometric determination of iron. Some procedures involve the direct determination of iron(III), whereas other methods take advantage of highly colored complexes formed between iron(II) and various organic ligands.

An interesting example of an iron(III) species that is suitable for spectrophotometric determination is the intensely blood-red-colored thiocyanate complex. The formation of this complex ion can be represented by the equilibrium

$$Fe(H_2O)_6^{+++} + SCN^- \rightleftharpoons Fe(H_2O)_5(SCN)^{++} + H_2O$$

However, this chemical system possesses at least two features which render it somewhat unsatisfactory for spectrophotometric work of the highest accuracy. First, in the presence of excess thiocyanate ion, the monothiocyanatoiron(III) complex may undergo further substitution with the resultant formation of such species as $Fe(H_2O)_4(SCN)_2^+$ and $Fe(H_2O)_3(SCN)_3$. Each of these species exhibits a characteristic absorption spectrum which differs from those spectra of the other members of this family of complexes with respect to wavelength and molar absorptivity. Therefore, unless the concentration of thiocyanate ion relative to the iron(III) concentration is carefully controlled, or the thiocyanate concentration is so large that only the most highly substituted complex, $Fe(SCN)_6^{\equiv}$, is stable, the analytical results may not be sufficiently accurate or reproducible. A second problem stems from the fact that iron(III) is a strong acid, undergoing proton-transfer reactions such as

$$Fe(H_2O)_6^{+++} + H_2O \rightleftharpoons Fe(H_2O)_5(OH)^{++} + H_3O^+$$

and

$$Fe(H_2O)_5(OH)^{++} + H_2O \rightleftharpoons Fe(H_2O)_4(OH)_2^+ + H_3O^+$$

Although $Fe(H_2O)_6^{+++}$ is a colorless cation, the product species of these proton-transfer reactions possess a variety of colors, ranging from yellow to brown. Obviously, these colors result from absorption of visible radiation which is of nearly the same wavelengths as the light absorbed by the iron(III)-thiocyanate complexes. Fortunately, the proton-transfer equilibria can be reversed if a relatively high concentration of acid is present. It should be pointed out that perchloric acid and nitric acid are preferable among the common mineral acids for acidification of the sample solution. The hydrogen sulfate ions in sulfuric acid form weak, colorless complexes with iron(III); chloride ion from hydrochloric acid forms yellow-colored complexes such as $FeCl_4(H_2O)_2^-$; and the phosphate species in phosphoric acid form quite stable, colorless complexes with iron(III).

Among the most important reagents for the spectrophotometric determination of iron are 1,10-phenanthroline (orthophenanthroline) and its substituted analogs, such as 4,7-diphenyl-1,10-phenanthroline (bathophenanthroline), plus several other related ligands.

1,10-phenanthroline   4,7-diphenyl-1,10-phenanthroline

These organic ligands react with iron(II) to yield intensely colored three-to-one complexes (see Fig. 12-8) and, in addition, they form relatively pale-colored complexes with iron(III). In practice, a sample solution containing iron, which is almost invariably present as iron(III), must be treated with an appropriate reducing agent to convert the iron(III) to iron(II), and an aqueous solution of the organic ligand must be added to form the desired complex. Hydroxylamine and hydroquinone are two of the common reductants used in these procedures. Bathophenanthroline forms a red complex with iron(II), its absorption maximum occurring at approximately 538 mμ, and the familiar iron(II)-orthophenanthroline complex has an absorption maximum at 510 mμ. The use of bathophenanthroline, as opposed to orthophenanthroline, for the determination of iron offers two important advantages.

First, the molar absorptivity of the iron(II)-bathophenanthroline complex, 22,350 liter mole^{-1} cm^{-1}, is almost exactly twice the value for the corresponding iron(II)-orthophenanthroline species. Second, the former complex can be extracted into water-immiscible solvents such as isoamyl alcohol and n-hexyl alcohol. This approach permits one to concentrate the iron(II)-bathophenanthroline complex into a small volume of the nonaqueous phase. Since the organic phase can be subjected directly to a spectrophotometric measurement, very high sensitivity can be achieved. Typically, one can detect 0.1 μg of iron per milliliter of solution by using orthophenanthroline, and as little as 0.005 μg per milliliter by employing bathophenanthroline. Needless to say, these methods are so sensitive that precautions must be taken to ensure that no iron is present as an impurity in the reagents used for the determination.

Colorimetric Determination of Phosphate. Phosphate ion in aqueous solution reacts with ammonium molybdate to form ammonium phosphomolybdate, $(NH_4)_3P(Mo_3O_{10})_4$. This compound can be reduced with a wide variety of reagents, including hydroquinone, tin(II), and iron(II), to yield an intensely colored substance called *molybdenum blue*, the concentration of which may be measured spectrophotometrically to provide a determination of phosphate. Molybdenum blue consists of a mixture of molybdenum(IV) and molybdenum(V), but it is not a stoichiometrically well-defined compound. It is interesting to note that compounds containing the same element in two different oxidation states display characteristically intense colors. Both of the two main reactions in this procedure, namely the formation of ammonium phosphomolybdate and the subsequent reduction to molybdenum blue, can yield incorrect products. Consequently, these reactions must be carried out under carefully prescribed conditions with respect to the acidity of the solution, the amount of ammonium molybdate reagent used, and the temperature of the reaction. Any excess ammonium molybdate remaining after the first reaction tends to be reduced partially to molybdenum blue in the second reaction, and so even the time allowed for the reduction step should be controlled reproducibly.

This procedure may be used to determine phosphate at concentration levels up to approximately 20 parts per million. Similar procedures may be employed for the determination of silicates, germanates, arsenates, and vanadates; and the entire technique may be reversed for the determination of molybdenum in unknown samples.

Determination of Lead After Separation by Extraction. One of the most powerful methods for the separation of one component from all others in a solution involves extraction of that species into a solvent which is immiscible with the original solvent. As discussed in Chapter 7, in order for the separation to be complete, the desired component should be removed quantitatively into the new solvent and all other components must remain quantitatively in the first phase. Several aspects of separation by extraction, in addition to those mentioned earlier in this book, may be illustrated by a brief consideration of one colorimetric procedure for the determination of lead.

Lead ion reacts with the organic reagent diphenylthiocarbazone to form a colored complex or chelate which can be extracted quantitatively from an aqueous medium into chloroform. The concentration of lead in the organic layer may be determined spectrophotometrically at 510 mμ; concentrations of lead as low as a few tenths of a microgram per milliliter of chloroform are readily determinable. The organic reagent, which is customarily designated by its shorter name, dithizone, has the structural formula

Dithizone reacts with a number of metal ions in addition to lead, including copper, zinc, silver, cadmium, and mercury; so the selectivity of the reaction is rather poor. However, the selectivity of the extraction step may be varied somewhat at will by judicious choice of the pH of the aqueous phase and of what organic solvent is used. For example, the mercury(II)-dithizone complex may be extracted at any pH above 2, whereas the lead-dithizone chelate is quantitatively extracted only within the pH range from 9 to 11. The selectivity of the extraction step may be enhanced further by the use of *masking agents*, which preferentially complex one or more components during the extraction and cause them to remain in the aqueous phase.

Dithizone is not directly soluble in water and is generally employed in the form of a chloroform solution, whose color is green. As might be expected from solubility considerations, excess dithizone which remains after the reaction with lead ion passes into the chloroform layer during the extraction of the lead-dithizone chelate. Therefore, the excess reagent must be removed prior to the spectrophotometric measurement of the chloroform phase, or compensation must be made for its presence by a procedure involving measurements at two different wavelengths of light.

The extraction of lead from aqueous media into chloroform can be reversed. If the organic liquid containing the lead-dithizone complex is shaken with an aqueous nitric acid solution, the lead is returned to the water phase because the dithizone accepts a proton. In addition, this procedure is useful if some type of measurement other than absorption of radiant energy is to follow the separation.

Spectrophotometric Determination of Nickel After Separation by Extraction. The formation of the intensely red-colored nickel dimethylglyoximate by the reaction between nickel and dimethylglyoxime in aqueous ammonia is very highly selective, palladium(II) being the only

other element which forms a precipitate with this reagent. Spectrophotometric measurement of the amount of nickel in a sample could be accomplished directly upon the aqueous suspension of the precipitate if no other
colored species were present. However, the elements which usually accompany nickel in real samples are colored. For example, the determination of
nickel in the presence of copper is of practical importance, but copper(II)
is intensely colored, especially in an ammonia solution where the royal-blue
cupric ammine species predominate. Fortunately, as discussed in Chapter 7,
nickel dimethylglyoxime can be extracted quantitatively and selectively
into an organic liquid such as chloroform. The solubility of nickel dimethylglyoximate in chloroform is approximately 50 μg per milliliter, the intense
red color is very stable, and the concentration of nickel dimethylglyoximate
may be determined by a spectrophotometric measurement at 366 $m\mu$.

**Simultaneous Spectrophotometric Determination of Chromium
and Manganese.** Another practical application of spectrophotometry is
the simultaneous determination of both manganese and chromium in steel
by means of measurements at two different wavelengths of the visible spectrum. The percentage ratio of manganese to chromium may vary widely.
Typical steel samples contain up to approximately 2 per cent manganese and
as much as 6 per cent chromium, although the chromium content of certain
kinds of steel may reach 20 per cent or more. Furthermore, these determinations may be successfully performed without the prior separation of other
elements — nickel, cobalt, iron, vanadium, copper, tungsten, and molybdenum — which commonly comprise most steel samples.

If a steel sample is dissolved in hot sulfuric acid and the solution is
subsequently treated with potassium persulfate and a catalytic amount of
silver nitrate, chromium(III) is oxidized quantitatively to dichromate ion,

$$S_2O_8^= + 2\ Ag^+ \longrightarrow 2\ SO_4^= + 2\ Ag^{++}$$
$$6\ Ag^{++} + 2\ Cr^{+++} + 7\ H_2O \longrightarrow 6\ Ag^+ + Cr_2O_7^= + 14\ H^+$$

and manganese(II) is converted to permanganate ion,

$$S_2O_8^= + 2\ Ag^+ \longrightarrow 2\ SO_4^= + 2\ Ag^{++}$$
$$5\ Ag^{++} + Mn^{++} + 4\ H_2O \longrightarrow 5\ Ag^+ + MnO_4^- + 8\ H^+$$

Although it is possible to write reactions showing the direct oxidation of
chromium(III) and manganese(II) by persulfate, there is much evidence
that the active oxidant is indeed silver(II). For example, if silver nitrate is
omitted from the reaction solution, the oxidations of chromium(III) and
manganese(II) scarcely proceed at all, and most of the persulfate is reduced
by water:

$$2\ S_2O_8^= + 2\ H_2O \longrightarrow O_2 + 4\ SO_4^= + 4\ H^+$$

It is interesting to note that silver(II) is commercially available in the
form of argentic oxide (AgO), a black powder, which can be used by itself
to accomplish the oxidations of chromium(III) and manganese(II). The

argentic oxide is added 'in successive small portions to a cold sulfuric acid solution containing these elements, each portion being allowed to react completely before the next one is introduced. When the oxidations of manganese(II) and chromium(III) are complete, the next portion of argentic oxide causes the solution to acquire the characteristic chocolate-brown color of the silver(II)-hydrogen sulfate complex. The excess silver(II) may be decomposed if the solution is gently warmed; however, one must be careful not to cause reduction of permanganate ion at the same time.

In the classic procedure involving the use of potassium persulfate, it is beneficial to employ potassium periodate as an auxiliary oxidizing agent. The latter compound oxidizes manganese(II) more efficiently than potassium persulfate:

$$5\ IO_4^- + 2\ Mn^{++} + 3\ H_2O \longrightarrow 5\ IO_3^- + 2\ MnO_4^- + 6\ H^+$$

More importantly, however, excess potassium periodate prevents the resulting permanganate ion from being slowly reduced by water, a process which does occur when either potassium persulfate or argentic oxide is used alone.

After the chromium(III) and manganese(II) have been quantitatively oxidized, absorbance measurements are usually made at wavelengths of 440 and 545 mμ, and two equations are solved simultaneously for the individual concentrations of permanganate and dichromate as discussed earlier in this chapter. Most of the absorption of radiant energy at 440 mμ is due to dichromate ion; however, permanganate does absorb at this wavelength, and so an appropriate correction is required. Similarly, although permanganate absorbs visible radiation at 545 mμ much more strongly than does dichromate, a small correction for the presence of the latter is usually desirable. The absorption band for dichromate ion shown in Figure 16-2 at 350 mμ would offer higher sensitivity for the determination of chromium in steel, but this band cannot be utilized because iron(III) produced by the dissolution of the steel sample absorbs radiation quite strongly at wavelengths below approximately 425 mμ.

ABSORPTION METHODS — ULTRAVIOLET

Much of our discussion of methods of analysis based upon absorption of visible radiation is equally applicable to ultraviolet absorption methods. The two classes of methods differ primarily in that the amount of energy provided by each photon for the excitation of the absorbing atom, ion, or molecule is greater in the ultraviolet region of the electromagnetic spectrum than in the visible region. Many substances which are colorless insofar as visible light is concerned readily undergo electronic excitations by the absorption of ultraviolet radiation. Transitions involving closely spaced vibrational and rotational levels are superimposed upon the electronic transitions, and many of the overall transitions in liquids and solids are influenced by the presence of neighboring molecules. Therefore, ultraviolet absorption spectra, similar to visible absorption spectra, generally consist of only one or a few broad absorption peaks throughout the region from 200 to 400 mμ. Gas phase samples and some liquids, such as benzene, exhibit more complex ultraviolet absorption spectra with numerous sharp absorption bands.

Among the inorganic substances which absorb ultraviolet radiant energy are the halide complexes of many metallic ions. For example, tellurium may be determined by measurement at 335 mμ of the absorbance of the $TeI_6^=$ complex. Complexes of metal cations with thiocyanate ion are also analytically useful, including for example the thiocyanate complexes of cobalt and uranium which have absorption maxima at 312 and 375 mμ, respectively. Some of the electronic transitions involving the closely spaced energy levels in the rare earth ions correspond to energies of photons in the ultraviolet region; others involve the visible region of the electromagnetic spectrum, as already mentioned. Other inorganic substances may be determined by ultraviolet absorption methods after conversion of the inorganic constituent to a complex with an organic ligand which imparts characteristic absorption. For example, aluminum may be determined by measurement at 390 mμ of its complex with 2-methyl-8-hydroxyquinoline, and measurement of the absorbance at 330 mμ of the complex formed between β-mercaptopropionic acid and nickel(II) provides a determination of the latter.

2-methyl-8-hydroxyquinoline β-mercaptopropionic acid

Most of the applications of the ultraviolet absorption method of analysis involve the determinations of organic compounds. The electronic transitions are generally associated with certain types of bonds within the absorbing molecule. A partial listing of the approximate wavelengths at which several common types of functional groups absorb ultraviolet radiation is given in Table 16-1.

Nearly all of the absorptions are fairly broad. There may be appreciable absorption at 220 and even 230 mμ from an aldehyde group (—CHO) which has an absorption maximum at 210 mμ. The position of each band in an ultraviolet spectrum varies somewhat in accordance with the structure of the rest of the molecule. For example, the absorption listed at 255 mμ for benzene, C_6H_6, is shifted to 262 mμ for toluene, $C_6H_5CH_3$, and to 265 mμ for chlorobenzene, C_6H_5Cl.

The wavelength range from approximately 220 to 400 mμ is most readily accessible with commercial ultraviolet spectrophotometers. Many of the absorptions listed in Table 16-1 occur at appreciably shorter wavelengths. If a qualitatively unknown organic compound exhibits no absorption of

TABLE 16-1. WAVELENGTHS OF MAXIMUM ABSORBANCE FOR
CERTAIN ORGANIC FUNCTIONAL GROUPS

Absorbing Group		λ_{max}, mμ
olefin:	$\ce{C=C}$	190
conjugated olefin:	$-(\ce{C=C})_2-$	210–230
	$-(\ce{C=C})_3-$	260
	$-(\ce{C=C})_4-$	300
	$-(\ce{C=C})_5-$	330
acetylene:	$-\ce{C#C}-$	175–180
benzene:		184, 202, 255
naphthalene:		220, 275, 312
ether:	—O—	185
thioether:	—S—	194, 215
amine:	$-\ce{NH2}$	195
nitro:	$-\ce{NO2}$	210
azo:	$-\ce{N=N}-$	285–400
ketone:	$\ce{C=O}$	195, 270–285
thioketone:	$\ce{C=S}$	205
aldehyde:	—CHO	210
carboxyl:	—COOH	200–210
bromide:	—Br	208
iodide:	—I	260

ultraviolet radiation of wavelengths longer than about 220 mμ, it is fairly
safe to conclude that the compound contains no conjugated unsaturated
groups, no aromatic (benzene-like) structures, no aldehyde or ketone group,
no nitro group, and no bromide or iodide atom. Most quantitative analytical
determinations within this wavelength range involve aromatic or conjugated
olefinic groups of atoms.

The lower wavelength limit in ultraviolet spectrophotometry may be
extended from 220 to about 180 mμ by appropriate choice of optical
materials, including the sample container, and by use of an evacuated or
purged optical path within the spectrophotometer. This makes the complete
spectrum more complex but also makes possible the analytical use of many
more absorbing groups of atoms, as is indicated by the data of Table 16-1.

Where more than one λ_{max} value is listed in Table 16-1 for a given
absorbing group, the one listed first is for the band of greater absorptivity.
An actual listing of absorptivities would reveal that the values are generally
much higher for aromatic groups than for the other groups. This is an
additional reason for the considerable practical usefulness of ultraviolet
absorption methods in the quantitative analytical determinations of aromatic
compounds.

Many organic substances appear yellowish when viewed by the human eye; this results from absorption of blue or violet light. Spectral measurements generally reveal an even greater absorption in the near ultraviolet region, with the visible absorption merely comprising a trailing edge of an absorption band which exhibits its peak in the ultraviolet region of the spectrum.

Quantitative determinations by measurement of ultraviolet absorption are not limited to unknown constituents which themselves undergo suitable electronic transitions. For example, no absorptions are found for alcohol groups, —OH, throughout the entire wavelength range from 200 to 1000 mμ. However, many alcohols can be caused to react stoichiometrically with phenyl isocyanate to form phenyl alkyl carbamates, which can be determined quantitatively by measurement of the absorbance at 280 mμ.

phenyl isocyanate   ethyl-N-phenylcarbamate

The same factors which we discussed in conjunction with the selection of absorbing form and of wavelength for measurement with visible radiation are applicable in ultraviolet radiant energy methods. The steps in establishing a quantitative procedure and in conducting analyses are similar in both regions of the electromagnetic spectrum.

ABSORPTION METHODS — INFRARED

Nearly every chemical compound exhibits selective absorption of radiant energy in the infrared region of the electromagnetic spectrum. Some of the absorptions which are found within the **near infrared region,** ranging approximately from 0.8 to 2.5 microns, result from electronic transitions within the absorbing molecules. Other absorptions, which are found in the **far infrared region** at wavelengths greater than about 50 microns, involve purely rotational excitation. In the intermediate infrared region, extending approximately from 2.5 to 50 microns and to which we will now limit our discussion, absorption arises primarily from elevation of the molecules of which the test sample is composed to excited vibrational energy levels. Rotational changes are superimposed upon the vibrational excitations. With liquid and solid test samples, this generally results in a broadening of the observed absorption band rather than in fine structure within the vibrational band.

Every polyatomic molecule is subject to interatomic vibrations. Consider, for example, a molecule of water. Each hydrogen atom vibrates back and forth, toward and away from the oxygen atom, much as if the two atoms were joined by means of a spring. This **stretching vibration** occurs only in discrete energy levels, and photons with precisely the correct amount of energy to raise the system from one of these vibrational levels to another are selectively absorbed. All molecules which have O—H bonds exhibit absorption due to stretching vibrations, and this occurs in the region of 2.8 to 3.3 microns. Other atoms, such as nitrogen or carbon, that are bonded to hydrogen atoms exhibit hydrogen stretching absorptions in the same general region of the infrared spectrum, usually between 2.6 and 4.1 microns. The exact wavelength at which any given molecule absorbs is determined in part by what other atoms are joined to either of the atoms involved in the immediate bond.

Other types of interatomic bonding result in characteristic absorption in other portions of the infrared region of the electromagnetic spectrum.

Double bonded carbon atoms, —C==C—, are typically marked by vibrational stretching absorptions in the region from 5.1 to 6.6 microns and triply bonded carbon atoms, —C≡C—, in the 4.1 to 5.1 micron region.

Stretching is only one of several forms of interatomic vibrations within molecules. Consider again a hydrogen atom bonded to oxygen in water or to a carbon atom in an organic compound. A **bending vibration** occurs at the H—O or H—C bond, either a bending back and forth within the same planar relationship to the rest of the molecule or into and out of that plane. Absorptions due to hydrogen bending vibrations are found at wavelengths greater than 6.6 microns. Vibrational absorption spectra are further complicated by interactions among vibrational modes of adjacent bonded atoms. For example, two hydrogen atoms on opposite sides of a carbon atom may undergo both symmetrical and unsymmetrical stretching, depending upon whether both hydrogen atoms move toward the carbon atom simultaneously or one moves toward it while the other moves away.

Not every conceivable vibrational transition results in the absorption of radiant energy. Each observable transition must result in a change in the electric dipole moment of the molecule. For example, no absorptions are observed in infrared spectra for hydrogen-hydrogen stretching in hydrogen molecules or for carbon-carbon stretching in ethylene, CH_2=CH_2, molecules. The reasons for these exceptions will not be discussed further here. Nevertheless, numerous vibrational transitions within most molecules, both inorganic and organic, do give rise to characteristic infrared absorptions.

One practical consequence of the fact that most molecules are subject to so many different vibrational conditions is that infrared spectra are quite complex, generally much more so than are the electronic absorption spectra which are observed for liquid and solid samples with visible and ultraviolet radiant energy. Each infrared spectrum is a composite of the vibrational absorptions arising from all chemical bonds within the absorbing molecules. Detailed tabulations of absorption bands and complete spectra for many compounds can be found in various reference sources.

The complexity of the spectrum is a distinct advantage in qualitative identifications and in elucidating the structures of compounds. The infrared spectrum is often referred to as a "fingerprint" of the compound. Accordingly, most of the practical applications of infrared measurements are in the realms of qualitative analysis and structure determination. In addition, however, practical procedures have been developed for the quantitative determinations of numerous organic substances and of some inorganic compounds as well. Most do not provide accuracies comparable to gravimetric and titrimetric procedures, and infrared methods are generally less sensitive than certain other procedures. Nevertheless, the distinctive nature of the vibrational transitions upon which the procedures are based does lend to some useful quantitative analyses.

As in visible and ultraviolet radiant energy methods, each infrared quantitative analytical determination consists of measuring the absorbance of one or more standards and of measuring the unknown sample at a suitable wavelength. The Lambert-Beer law is often applicable, at least over limited ranges of concentration, but the calibration is generally accomplished empirically through measurements of several standard samples. Overlapping spectra are frequently encountered in infrared absorption methods; the indirect analysis procedure consisting of measurements at two (or n) wavelengths is applicable, as described in conjunction with visible radiant energy methods.

EMISSION METHODS — VISIBLE AND ULTRAVIOLET

The spectra of radiant energy emitted by atoms and monatomic ions which have been raised to electronically excited energy levels are very useful in analytical chemistry. The wavelengths of emitted radiation are characteristic of the elements which comprise the sample, and the intensity of radiation at a specific wavelength is proportional to the concentration of the element. Therefore, emission spectra are useful both for qualitative identifications and for quantitative determinations.

These analytical methods are used principally for the detection and determination of metals and metal ions. Flame sources are usually used for the alkali and alkaline earth elements, but numerous other elements can also be excited in this type of source. Arc and spark sources are applicable to the determinations of nearly all of the metals and metal ions. It makes little or no difference whether the element of interest is present in the sample as free metal, as an alloy, or as a chemical compound.

Since quantitative determinations are based upon intensity measurements, all factors which affect the excitation of the sample and the detection of the emitted radiation should be held perfectly constant when one obtains the spectra of calibration standards and of the unknown sample. It is difficult to achieve even approximate constancy in some of the experimental conditions involved, so the **internal standard technique** is frequently employed.

In this method, a substance, called the *internal standard*, whose excitation and emission characteristics are similar to those of the element to be determined, is added in fixed concentration to each known and unknown sample. Then the emission intensity of the element to be determined is measured for each of these known and unknown samples at an appropriate wavelength. However, this emission intensity is not obtained in absolute units, but only relative to the intensity of the internal standard. The influence of a moderate variation in the conditions of excitation or of detection is effectively canceled, since the emission intensities of the internal standard and the element to be determined are affected to a similar extent. Whether the internal standard technique is employed or not, calibration data must be obtained with known samples before unknown samples can be determined quantitatively.

At best, the overall accuracy of quantitative determinations based upon the emission of radiant energy by the test sample is generally no better than about 5 per cent of the measured quantity. Many common gravimetric and titrimetric methods yield far better accuracy. The major analytical advantages of emission methods lie in factors other than accuracy. Foremost is the extreme sensitivity; elements present in minute traces, on the order of magnitude of a few parts per million in many cases and even less in others, can be detected and determined. Furthermore, a very small amount of sample is usually sufficient for an analysis, and relatively little chemical separation or other preparation is required prior to insertion of the sample into the instrument for measurement.

A single determination by an emission method would be rather time-consuming because of the necessary preparation of standards for calibration data. The method is very practical, however, for the routine analysis of large numbers of similar samples. Frequently, a determination that takes hours by the more classic chemical methods may be completed in a few minutes by this method once the necessary calibration experiments are done. Up to 10 or 12 constituents may be determined successfully from one spectrum of an unknown preparation.

TURBIDIMETRIC AND NEPHELOMETRIC METHODS

Turbidimetric and nephelometric methods differ from the absorption methods of analysis chiefly in two ways: First, the unknown substance is not in solution but rather is in colloidal suspension; and, second, some of the photons incident upon the sample are removed from the incident beam by scattering rather than by absorption. If the radiant energy which is transmitted through the suspension is measured, as in absorption procedures, the method is called a **turbidimetric** one. In a **nephelometric** method, measurement is made of the intensity of the scattered light. In either case, the measurement may involve the absolute intensity of the transmitted or scattered radiation, or it may involve a comparison to one or more standards.

The results obtained in turbidimetric and nephelometric determinations are generally not as accurate as those derived from absorption methods of analysis. In absorption work, the accuracy of the results is often limited only by the instrument itself. In turbidimetric and nephelometric procedures, however, a larger error generally arises from the difficulty of preparing and maintaining all standards and unknown suspensions in a uniform and reproducible degree of dispersion.

The determination of small amounts of sulfur after its precipitation as barium sulfate is one of the classic applications of turbidimetry. In order to provide results that are even reasonably accurate, the precipitation must be conducted by rigorous adherence to a predetermined rate of mixing the reagents, and the temperature and digestion time must be carefully controlled. The determination of trace amounts of hydrogen cyanide after conversion of the cyanide to insoluble silver cyanide and the determination of carbon dioxide after bubbling it through an alkaline solution of a barium salt to precipitate barium carbonate may be mentioned as other examples of useful turbidimetric and nephelometric procedures.

Turbidimetric measurements may be employed to follow the progress of a titration in which an insoluble precipitate is formed. At the start of the titration, no precipitate is present to scatter light, but, as the titration proceeds toward the equivalence point, the formation of a precipitate causes more scattering of the incident radiation. Beyond the equivalence point, no further precipitate is formed, and so the scattering should undergo no additional increase.

PHOTOMETRIC TITRATIONS

It is noteworthy that measurements of absorbance can be employed to monitor the progress of all types of titrations and that spectrophotometric end point detection is applicable when titration end points cannot be located by simpler procedures. Photometric titrimetry may be performed whenever (a) the substance being titrated, (b) the substance formed in the titration, or (c) the titrant itself exhibits distinctive absorption characteristics. Accordingly, the photometric titration curve involves a plot of absorbance as a function of added titrant, and it consists of two straight lines, the point of intersection being the equivalence point.

For example, in the titration of arsenic(III) in a neutral medium with a standard solution of iodine or triiodide ion,

$$HAsO_2 + I_3^- + 2\,H_2O \rightleftharpoons H_2AsO_4^- + 3\,I^- + 3\,H^+$$

the absorbance should remain virtually zero until the equivalence point is reached, as shown in Figure 16-3A, but beyond the equivalence point the absorbance increases linearly as excess I_2 or I_3^- is added. Such behavior, of course, presumes that we continuously observe the absorbance of the solution at a wavelength characteristic of the visible absorption of I_2 or I_3^-. Notice that, near the equivalence point, the experimental data do not fall perfectly on the two straight-line portions of the titration curve. This is typical of many spectrophotometric titrations and is due to the facts that no titration reaction is ever 100 per cent complete and that, in the present case, a small amount of unreacted iodine is present near the equivalence point of the titration. The extent to which the experimental data deviate from the straight lines will increase as the equilibrium constant or the driving force for the titration reaction decreases. Consequently, in a spectrophotometric titration, one always takes experimental data on each side of the equivalence point, well away from the curved region, and then extrapolates the straight-line portions to their point of intersection to obtain the equivalence point.

FIGURE 16-3. Photometric titration curves. Curve *A* results from the titration of a colorless substance with a colored titrant. Curve *B* corresponds to the titration of a colored species with a colorless titrant. Curve *C* depicts the behavior encountered when one of the products of the titration reaction is colored.

The application of spectrophotometric end point detection to complexometric titrations was described briefly at the end of Chapter 11, and a typical titration curve for such a system is shown in Figure 11-5.

Figure 16-3B depicts the spectrophotometric titration curve which results when the substance being determined is colored and when the titrant is either not colored at all or does not absorb visible radiation at the same wavelength as the species being titrated.

If the titration reaction results in the formation of a colored product, the absorbance of the solution should increase up to the equivalence point but remain constant beyond the equivalence point. Such a situation is represented by the spectrophotometric titration curve of Figure 16-3C.

Spectrophotometric titration curves may take other shapes, depending upon the particular absorption characteristics of the substance being titrated, the titrant, and the products of the titration reaction. In addition, even when none of the reactants or products is colored, one may use an end point indicator (an acid-base indicator, a metallochromic indicator, a redox indicator, or a fluorescent indicator) which does exhibit special absorption or emission properties. Finally, it should be mentioned that one must correct for the effects of dilution on the absorbance of the solution; otherwise, a spectrophotometric titration curve would show no straight-line portions.

FLUORESCENCE METHODS

Fluorescence methods of analysis are similar to absorption methods in that the test solution absorbs some of the incident photons of radiant energy, and they resemble nephelometric methods in that observation is often made of radiation emerging from the test solution at right angles to the beam of incident radiation. The mechanism of interaction between the radiant energy and the absorbing species was described in Chapter 15. Any substance capable of undergoing this interaction is called a fluorescent substance and may be determined quantitatively by the fluorescence method.

For any specific quantitative determination, one or more standard solutions of the fluorescent substance must be prepared and measured with the fluorescence meter to provide calibration data. Since a number of factors other than concentration may affect the intensity of fluorescent light, the standard and unknown solutions must be prepared, maintained, and measured under the same conditions. Among the variables which frequently must be carefully controlled are pH, temperature, foreign ion concentration, and intensity of incident radiant energy.

Fluorescence methods have been employed successfully for the determinations of certain organic and inorganic substances. Thiamine (vitamin B_1) may be determined quantitatively after its oxidation to the fluorescent substance, thiochrome. Riboflavin may be determined directly, after removal of any fluorescent impurities which may accompany it. Both of these determinations are useful even when the unknown concentration is as low as

0.1 μg per milliliter of solution. Aluminum yields a fluorescent compound when treated with the dye morin, and solutions containing as little as 0.1 to 1 μg of aluminum in each milliliter may be analyzed by a fluorescence procedure.

X-RAY METHODS

There are three major classes of analytical applications of x-rays — absorption, emission, and diffraction. The first two are similar in principle to absorption and emission methods involving radiant energy in other regions of the electromagnetic spectrum, except for differences arising from the considerably shorter wavelength and the much higher energy per photon of x-radiation. X-ray diffraction methods are quite distinct in their analytical applications, for they provide very useful measurements of characteristic distances between planes of atoms in crystalline substances.

Absorption of x-rays is largely an atomic phenomenon involving electronic transitions in inner orbitals. In general, elements of greater atomic number absorb x-radiation more readily, and at shorter wavelengths, than do those elements of lower atomic number. This is consistent with the fact that a given inner electron is bound more tightly to the nucleus in an atom of higher nuclear charge. Each element absorbs certain wavelengths of x-radiation more readily than others. However, most practical analytical applications of x-ray absorption use "white," or polychromatic, radiation and do not require an elaborate monochromator. Accordingly, most of the applications are in quantitative rather than in qualitative analysis.

The usefulness of the x-ray absorption method of analysis may be illustrated by a few examples. In commercial automotive gasoline, the lead in the tetraethyl lead is essentially the only component of high atomic number. Although all elements of which the gasoline is composed do contribute to its x-ray absorption characteristics, the overall absorption of any sample of gasoline is determined principally by the concentration of lead present. Therefore, tetraethyl lead in gasoline may be determined readily by x-ray absorption methods. Another example is encountered in the determination of sulfur in crude oils. Whenever sulfur is the heaviest element present in appreciable concentration, as it frequently is, a simple measurement of x-ray absorption suffices for its determination. It is likewise possible to determine the concentration of a single inorganic solute, such as silver nitrate in water, by x-ray absorption methods, but this type of determination can be performed much more accurately and satisfactorily by other methods. The emphasis in assessing the importance of any method of analysis should be placed upon what it can do that other methods cannot do or cannot do as satisfactorily.

When an unknown substance is caused to emit x-radiation, the emission spectrum may be used for analytical purposes, just as it is possible to use visible and ultraviolet emission spectra. In practice, the test specimen is usually bombarded with x-rays, and so the process is actually one of fluorescence. The bombarding x-rays must be of shorter wavelength (higher energy) than the characteristic x-rays emitted by the sample. The determination of tetraethyl lead in gasoline is one of the practical applications of this method. Since this determination may be accomplished by the x-ray absorption method, as previously discussed, it is of interest to compare performance of the two methods on the basis of this determination. X-ray absorption methods yield data on the overall absorption characteristics of the test specimen, and all of the elements comprising that specimen contribute to the measured quantity. On the other hand, x-ray fluorescence methods provide separate spectral information for each of the elements present in the sample. Thus, absorption methods in the tetraethyl lead determination yield accurate results only when the absorption due to lead atoms is far greater than that due to all other compounds combined or when the relative concentrations of other components are kept adequately uniform in all samples, both standard and unknown. However, the fluorescence method yields correct tetraethyl lead data, largely independently of what the remainder of the test sample may contain. Thus, one method involves measurement of an overall or cumulative property of the sample whereas the other technique yields individual data for separate elements present in the sample.

X-ray fluorescence methods have been found to be useful for determinations of the composition of some metal alloys. It is not necessary to dissolve or otherwise destroy the specimen in any way. In recent years numerous other useful applications have been developed for this method of analysis.

When a monochromatic beam of x-rays is passed through a powdered crystalline specimen, a spectrum of diffracted rays is obtained. Every crystalline compound exhibits a characteristic x-ray diffraction spectrum, and so the placement of lines or rings in the spectrum may be used as the basis of qualitative determinations. Furthermore, the diffraction spectrum of a mixture of substances is a simple combination of the various component spectra, and the relative intensities of the two or more component spectra are determined by the relative concentrations of the substances in the mixture. Therefore, intensity measurements permit quantitative determinations.

The necessary apparatus consists of a source of x-rays, a filter to render the rays essentially monochromatic, a specimen holder, and a detector. In analytical work the specimen is usually, but not necessarily, a powdered solid. The detecting device may involve a photographic film, a Geiger counter, or a scintillation counter. A typical photographically recorded diffraction pattern is shown in Figure 16-4. The diameters of the rings in this pattern are characteristic of what the crystalline specimen is.

It must be emphasized that the x-ray diffraction method provides analyses on the basis of crystalline compounds, not on the basis of elements or ions or atomic groupings as is the case with most other methods of analysis. For example, this method makes possible the determination of whether a certain mixture contains sodium chloride and potassium bromide or sodium bromide and potassium chloride. It is also possible to distinguish between different crystalline forms of the same substance. For example, titanium dioxide occurs in three distinct crystalline forms, one of which is far superior to the others as the white pigment in porcelain enamels. X-ray diffraction methods can reveal which crystalline forms are present in any sample of titanium dioxide.

X-ray diffraction analyses are nondestructive of the sample. Quantitative determinations are generally accurate only within 5 to 10 per cent, and any crystalline component present in an amount less than about 5 per cent of the total sample is usually not detected except with special techniques. This method of analysis is used primarily for the many analyses of crystalline substances which are not possible by other methods.

X-ray diffraction methods are very useful for many purposes other than straightforward qualitative and quantitative analysis. Since the diffraction characteristics of a crystalline specimen are determined by the geometrical arrangements of the atoms or ions within the crystals, it is possible with special techniques to arrive at ultimate structural information on crystalline substances. Other applications include the measurement of particle size of powdered materials and the detection of physical stress and strain in metals and plastics.

MASS SPECTROMETRY

The mass spectrometer is an instrument in which the molecules of a specimen are converted into ions and in which those ions are sorted according to their mass (actually mass to charge ratio, but in most cases each ion is singly charged) and are recorded as a **mass spectrum**. The main parts of a mass spectrometer are the following: a sampling system, in which a suitable quantity of gas or vapor is prepared for analysis; an ionizing region, in which molecules are ionized, usually by bombardment with a stream of electrons; an electrostatic accelerating region, in which the ions are caused to move in a fixed direction at suitable velocities, thus forming a beam of ions; a magnetic field, in which the incoming ion beam is, in effect, sorted

FIGURE 16-4. A typical x-ray powder diffraction pattern which has been recorded on photographic film. This is a pattern of a sample of calcium hydroxy phosphate, the main inorganic constituent of teeth and bones.

into separate beams for each mass of ion present; and a detector, by which the separated ion beams are located and measured.

Nearly every specimen which is a gas or can be converted to a gas may be analyzed both qualitatively and quantitatively by means of mass spectrometry, and countless practical examples have been found. For instance, traces of oxygen present as an impurity in tank nitrogen may be determined by measurement of the mass 32 intensity (due to singly-charged oxygen molecules) relative to that of mass 28 (due to singly-charged nitrogen molecules). As another example, the isotopic composition of hydrogen gas may be determined by the measurement of the mass 2, 3, and 4 intensities, which correspond to singly-ionized molecules of H_2, HD, and D_2, respectively (letting H represent the mass 1 isotope of hydrogen and D the mass 2 isotope).

Perhaps the largest field for the application of mass spectrometry is in hydrocarbon and organic analysis. This importance is based, in part, upon the fact that even molecules of the same molecular weight may be determined in the presence of each other because they can be caused to split apart into smaller fragments in the process of being ionized. For example, both butane,

$$CH_3$$
$$|$$

CH_3—CH_2—CH_2—CH_3, and isobutane, CH_3—CH—CH_3, have the same molecular weight. However, each will give its own characteristic fractions

$$CH_3$$
$$|$$

of ions of mass 15, CH_3^+; mass 29, CH_3—CH_2^+; mass 43, CH_3—CH^+ or CH_3—CH_2—CH_2^+; and mass 58, CH_3—CH_2—CH_2—CH_3^+ or

$$CH_3$$
$$|$$
$$CH_3—CH—CH_3^+.$$

Although the mass spectrometer is basically an instrument for gas analysis, it is readily used for analyzing liquid specimens merely by testing a portion of the liquid vapor. A vapor pressure of 10^{-7} mm Hg may be sufficient, although a somewhat higher vapor pressure is generally preferable. It is also possible to ionize solid specimens by heating to form sufficient vapor or even by direct electron bombardment of the solid itself.

Among the useful areas of application of mass spectrometry is the determination of molecular weight. The ion obtained with the highest mass number is generally that of the parent molecule. In some instances, however, no ionization occurs without fragmentation, in which cases the molecular weight is greater than the highest mass number obtained in the spectrum. Some modern instruments have such high resolving power that it is possible to determine molecular weights, not only to the nearest whole number, but so precisely that, for example, acetophenone, C_8H_8O (molecular weight 120.157) is distinguishable from ethyl toluene, C_9H_{12} (molecular weight 120.094).

It is interesting to note that the mass spectrometer has also been employed for purposes other than straightforward analyses. For example, instruments built on the principle of the mass spectrometer were used successfully during World War II to separate uranium, U^{235}, from its normal mixture with larger amounts of other isotopes of uranium. This application was possible because the mass spectrometer actually separates molecules, after ionization, in accordance with their mass numbers.

Experiment 16-1

COLORIMETRIC DETERMINATION OF AMMONIA

Purpose

This experiment provides for the determination of small amounts of ammonium ion through the use of an alkaline solution of tetraiodomercurate(II), $HgI_4^=$, which reacts with ammonia to form a red-brown-colored colloidal suspension. In addition, experience is gained in the critical visual comparison of the color intensities of standard and unknown solutions.

Preparation

It is important that the distilled water used to prepare the Nessler reagent, as well as the standard and unknown solutions, be essentially free of ammonia. If any doubt exists concerning the possible presence of ammonia, boil the distilled water to aid in the removal of ammonia, and check for its presence by testing the distilled water with the Nessler reagent. In the present experiment, however, the color of each unknown sample is compared to a series of standard solutions which are freshly prepared with the same distilled water as the unknown. Consequently, any ammonia which is present in the distilled water should cause the color intensities of all unknown and standard solutions to be uniformly higher, and no serious error should result. In view of the fact that the determination of ammonia by this procedure is only accurate to within a few per cent at best, the use of good laboratory distilled water should be acceptable.

Preparation of the Nessler Reagent. Dissolve approximately 50 gm of reagent-grade potassium iodide (KI) in 50 ml of cold distilled water which is contained in a clean 1 liter Erlenmeyer flask. Add portions of a saturated aqueous solution of mercuric chloride ($HgCl_2$), swirling the mixture after each addition, until a slight precipitate finally persists. Next add 400 ml of a *clear* 9 F sodium hydroxide (or potassium hydroxide) solution.

Concentrated sodium hydroxide solutions which have stood in contact with a glass container invariably contain a suspension of sodium silicate, which results from attack of the glass by sodium hydroxide. Any turbidity which is extraneous to the solutions ultimately examined in the determination of ammonia is a source of error, and must be avoided. One method which may be employed to prepare a clear 9 F sodium hydroxide soultion is similar to that described in Experiment 8-1 for the preparation of a carbonate-free sodium hydroxide titrant. If a stock solution of 50 per cent sodium hydroxide is available from Experiment 8-1, approximately 200 ml of that solution (which is close to 19 F in concentration) can be diluted with 200 ml of freshly boiled and cooled distilled water to obtain the desired 9 F sodium hydroxide solution.

Finally, dilute the Nessler reagent to a volume of 1 liter by adding more distilled water. Allow any residue in the solution to settle, and then decant the clear supernatant solution into a clean polyethylene bottle for storage.

It is also feasible to filter the Nessler reagent through a large sintered-glass filter funnel directly into the polyethylene storage container.

Procedure

Prepare a stock solution of ammonium chloride by dissolving the appropriate weight of the reagent-grade solid in distilled water and by diluting the solution to a known volume in a volumetric flask.

Throughout this experiment, it is necessary only to make measurements accurate to within ± 1 per cent.

Next, prepare a series of 11 solutions containing ammonium chloride, which correspond to a range of ammonia concentrations from 0.000 to 0.050 mg of ammonia per milliliter in increments of 0.005 mg per milliliter. These solutions should be prepared in 100 ml volumetric flasks by dilution of appropriate volumes of the original stock solution of ammonium chloride with distilled water.

It is advisable, for the sake of convenience in volume measurements, to prepare a second stock solution of ammonium chloride by dilution of the first stock solution. Then, in the preparation of the final standards, it will not be necessary to pipet or otherwise dispense very small volumes of ammonium chloride solution.

Place each standard and unknown solution, prepared as described in the preceding paragraphs, into a clean Nessler tube, which has been dried or rinsed with one or two small portions of the desired standard or unknown solution. Each Nessler tube should be filled exactly to the calibration mark.

Nessler tubes are made of especially clear glass tubing of uniform cross section, and they have polished, flat bottoms. Usually, one performs the subsequent color-matching procedure by arranging the tubes in a rack which is so constructed that light is reflected upward through the bottom of each tube. If Nessler tubes are unavailable, ordinary large test tubes of reasonable uniformity in diameter may be used as substitutes.

Pipet exactly 1 ml of the Nessler reagent into each of the tubes, and stir each solution with a clean, dry stirring rod. Allow the tubes to stand for 10 minutes, and then compare the color of the unknown with each of the standards by viewing the tubes lengthwise from above. Hold the tubes above a white surface which is placed so that light is reflected upward through them.

Determine which standard matches the unknown most closely, and report the concentration of the unknown in terms of the milligrams of NH_3 per milliliter.

If the unknown should happen to have a color which is more intense than the most concentrated standard, either prepare additional standards or quantitatively dilute another portion of the original unknown to bring it within the range of the standards. In addition, if more accurate results are desired, it is possible (once the approximate concentration of the unknown is established) to prepare a second series of standards with a smaller overall range of ammonia concentrations and with smaller increments between each standard.

Experiment 16-2

SPECTROPHOTOMETRIC DETERMINATION OF IRON WITH ORTHOPHENANTHROLINE

Purposes

Although the primary purpose of this experiment is to permit the determination of the concentration of iron in an unknown solution, experience is provided in the operation of a colorimeter (Bausch and Lomb Spectronic 20), in the recording of an absorption spectrum for the iron(II)-orthophenanthroline complex, in the selection of an optimum wavelength for a spectrophotometric measurement, and in the construction of a calibration curve for the determination of iron.

Procedure

Clean four 100 ml volumetric flasks, one of which should be submitted to your laboratory instructor, who will place in it the unknown iron solution to be analyzed. Into each of the other three flasks, pipet exactly 2.00, 5.00, and 10.00 ml, respectively, of a standard iron(III) solution containing 50 mg of iron per liter.

Numerous methods are available for the preparation of a standard iron(III) solution. In one of these, dissolve 0.3511 gm of analytical-reagent-grade ferrous ammonium sulfate, $Fe(NH_4)_2(SO_4)_2 \cdot 6 H_2O$, in 100 ml of distilled water and add 3 ml of concentrated (18 F) sulfuric acid. Then add (drop by drop and with good stirring) a dilute potassium permanganate solution until the first permanent pink color due to excess MnO_4^- is observed. Finally, dilute the solution with distilled water to exactly 1 liter in a volumetric flask.

Add approximately 50 ml of distilled water to each of the four volumetric flasks. Then drop by drop add a 2 F sodium acetate solution to each flask (less than 1 ml will be required) until the pH of the solution is determined with the aid of pH paper to be 3.5 $\pm$ 1.0. Stopper the volumetric flask and shake the solution after each addition of sodium acetate; then test the pH by touching a piece of wide-range pH paper to the solution which wets the stopper of the flask. Finally, add 4 ml of a 1 per cent hydroquinone solution and 4 ml of a 0.3 per cent solution of orthophenanthroline to each volumetric flask, dilute each solution to the calibration mark with distilled water, stopper and shake each flask, and allow the flasks to stand for 10 minutes.

Prepare the hydroquinone solution in advance of the experiment by dissolving 1 gm of the pure solid in 100 ml of a 1 F acetic acid-1 F sodium acetate buffer solution.

Prepare the orthophenanthroline solution by dissolving 300 mg of orthophenanthroline monohydrate in 100 ml of water. Warm the mixture, if necessary, to aid the dissolution of the orthophenanthroline.

Obtain the complete absorption spectrum of the iron(II)-orthophenanthroline complex, prepare a calibration curve, and determine the quantity of iron in the unknown sample in accordance with the following paragraphs.

General Operating Instructions for the Spectronic 20 Colorimeter. (1) Turn on the instrument by rotating the amplifier control (left knob on the front of the case), and allow the colorimeter to warm up for several minutes. (2) Adjust the amplifier control to bring the meter needle to zero on the per cent transmittance scale or to infinity on the absorbance (optical density) scale. (3) Insert a sample tube, containing water as the reference solution, into the sample holder; position the index line on the sample tube so that it is next to the index line on the sample holder, and close the cover of the sample compartment. (4) Set the wavelength dial to the desired value. (5) With water as the reference solution, adjust the lamp control (right knob on the front of the case) until the meter needle reads 100 on the per cent transmittance scale or zero on the absorbance (optical density) scale. (6) Replace the sample tube containing water with a tube containing the test solution, and read the absorbance (optical density) on the meter without making any further adjustments. (7) Reinsert the sample tube containing water into the sample compartment, and repeat steps (4), (5), and (6) for other desired wavelength values.

A Roto-Cell accessory is commercially available for the Bausch and Lomb Spectronic 20 colorimeter. It consists of two cells — one is filled with the reference solution and the other is filled with the test sample solution. The Roto-Cell attachment fits into the normal sample compartment of the colorimeter and can be rotated back and forth to place either the reference or test solution in the optical path. This eliminates the cumbersome and irreproducible technique in which test tubes must be alternately inserted and withdrawn.

Obtaining an Absorption Spectrum. Use one sample tube containing water and a second tube containing the most concentrated standard solution prepared earlier. Obtain the complete spectrum of the iron(II)-orthophenanthroline complex throughout the entire available wavelength region at 25 mμ intervals except in the region of an absorption maximum, where smaller wavelength intervals should be used to define the spectrum better. Record your data simultaneously in a laboratory notebook and on graph paper by plotting the observed values of absorbance (optical density) as a function of wavelength.

If the colorimeter has been allowed to warm up sufficiently, the amplifier control (left knob on the front of the case) should not require readjustment during the course of the experiment. However, the adjustment of the lamp control (right knob on the front of the case) with water as the sample must be repeated at each wavelength.

From your plot of the absorption spectrum for the iron(II)-orthophenanthroline complex, select the wavelength of maximal absorbance and use this wavelength alone for the remainder of the experiment.

Preparation of the Calibration Curve and Determination of the Unknown. Measure the absorbance (optical density) of each standard solution and of your unknown solution, all at the wavelength of maximal absorbance found from the work of the preceding part of the experiment. In order to ensure the highest precision, use the *same* sample tube for all absorbance measurements, rinsing it first with a portion of the solution to be studied. Perform duplicate or triplicate measurements with a given solution by emptying the sample tube and refilling it with a fresh portion of the test solution. From data obtained with the three standard solutions, prepare a calibration chart by plotting absorbance versus the concentration (or the number of milligrams) of iron in each sample solution. Then, from the measured absorbance of the unknown solution and the calibration chart, ascertain the concentration (or the number of milligrams) of iron in your unknown solution.

Experiment 16-3

SPECTROPHOTOMETRIC DETERMINATION OF NICKEL AFTER SEPARATION FROM COPPER BY EXTRACTION

Purposes

This experiment demonstrates the separation of nickel from copper by the extraction of nickel dimethylglyoximate into chloroform and the subsequent determination of nickel by a spectrophotometric measurement of the chloroform phase.

Preparation

The following two solutions should be prepared prior to the beginning of the experiment:

1. Prepare an acetic acid-sodium acetate buffer solution by dissolving 60 gm of reagent-grade sodium acetate in 200 ml of water which contains 1.2 ml of glacial acetic acid.

2. Prepare a dimethylglyoxime solution by dissolving 1 gm of the solid in 100 ml of 95 per cent ethanol.

Samples for analysis may consist of 10 ml portions of synthetic unknown solutions containing 25 to 50 mg of copper(II) and 0.1 to 0.4 mg of nickel(II). Alternatively, it may be of considerable interest to the student for him to prepare a solution containing known quantities of copper(II) and nickel(II) and to analyze the solution for nickel as a means of evaluating the accuracy of the experimental procedure.

Procedure

Clean four 50 ml Erlenmeyer flasks and obtain for each flask a tightly fitting rubber stopper. Pipet into three of the flasks 1.00, 2.00, and 4.00 ml, respectively, of a standard nickel(II) solution which contains 0.100 mg of nickel per milliliter.

The nickel(II) standard solution may be conveniently prepared from reagent-grade nickel nitrate, $Ni(NO_3)_2 \cdot 6\ H_2O$. Prepare this solution by dissolving 0.485 gm of nickel nitrate hexahydrate in distilled water and diluting the solution to exactly 1 liter in a volumetric flask.

To the fourth flask, introduce a quantity of the unknown nickel-copper mixture which contains approximately 0.1 to 0.4 mg of nickel.

To each of the four flasks, add in succession (with vigorous swirling of the flask) 0.5 gm of solid sodium tartrate, 2.5 gm of solid sodium thiosulfate pentahydrate, 5 ml of the acetic acid-sodium acetate buffer solution, 50 mg of solid hydroxylamine hydrochloride, and 2 ml of dimethylglyoxime solution.

Next, pipet 5.00 ml of chloroform into each flask, and stopper and shake each flask vigorously for one minute. Allow the flasks to stand until the chloroform and water layers separate. Transfer most of the chloroform phase to a colorimeter sample tube with the aid of a dropper. Obtain an absorption spectrum for nickel dimethylglyoximate in chloroform, prepare a calibration curve, and determine the quantity of nickel in the unknown sample in accordance with the procedures that follow.

General Operating Instructions for the Spectronic 20 Colorimeter. Follow the corresponding section in Experiment 16-2 with the single exception that pure chloroform rather than water should be used as the reference solvent.

Obtaining an Absorption Spectrum. Follow the corresponding section in Experiment 16-2, except substitute chloroform for water as the reference solvent.

Preparation of the Calibration Curve and Determination of the Unknown. Follow the corresponding section in Experiment 16-2. Report the concentration (or the total quantity in milligrams) of nickel in the sample solution.

Experiment 16-4

SIMULTANEOUS SPECTROPHOTOMETRIC DETERMINATION OF MANGANESE AND CHROMIUM

Purpose

The concentrations of manganese(II) and chromium(III) in a mixture may be determined by chemical oxidation of these species to permanganate and dichromate, respectively, followed by spectrophotometric measurement at two wavelengths. This experiment illustrates the principle of the additivity of absorbances due to two substances and shows how absorbance values at two different wavelengths are employed to calculate the concentrations of the two desired components.

Preparation

Standard solutions of manganese(II) and chromium(III) should be available so that individual spectra of MnO_4^- and $Cr_2O_7^=$ may be obtained. These standard solutions may serve for the preparation of manganese-chromium mixtures for subsequent spectrophotometric analysis.

Prepare a standard 0.010 M solution of chromium(III) in 1 F sulfuric acid as follows: Weigh to the nearest milligram 1.48 gm of reagent-grade potassium dichromate into a clean 500 ml Erlenmeyer flask. Dissolve the potassium dichromate in 100 ml of distilled water; then add 5 ml of concentrated (18 F) sulfuric acid and 25 ml of 3 per cent hydrogen peroxide. After the reduction of dichromate to chromium(III) has occurred, heat the solution to boiling for 15 to 20 minutes to decompose the excess hydrogen peroxide. Cool the solution and transfer it to a 1 liter volumetric flask. Add distilled water, along with 50 ml of concentrated sulfuric acid, to bring the volume precisely to the calibration mark. Mix the solution thoroughly, and calculate the exact concentration of chromium(III).

Prepare a standard 0.0010 M solution of manganese(II) in 1 F sulfuric acid as follows: Pipet exactly 50.00 ml of a previously standardized 0.020 F potassium permanganate solution into a clean 500 ml Erlenmeyer flask. Add 50 ml of distilled water, 5 ml of concentrated (18 F) sulfuric acid, and 10 ml of 3 per cent hydrogen peroxide. After the reduction of permanganate appears to be complete, heat the solution to boiling for 15 to 20 minutes to decompose the excess hydrogen peroxide. Cool the solution and transfer it quantitatively to a 1 liter volumetric flask. Add distilled water, plus 50 ml of concentrated sulfuric acid, to bring the volume to the calibration mark. Stopper the flask, mix the solution thoroughly, and calculate the exact concentration of manganese(II).

Procedure

Clean three 250 ml Erlenmeyer flasks. Into the first flask pipet 25.00 ml of the chromium(III) standard solution, and pipet the same volume of the standard manganese(II) solution into the second flask. Pipet a 25.00 ml aliquot of the unknown manganese-chromium mixture into the third flask.

The concentration of chromium(III) in the unknown mixture should preferably range from approximately 0.003 to 0.015 M, and the manganese(II) concentration from 0.0003 to 0.0015 M.

To each flask add 5 ml of concentrated sulfuric acid and 1 ml of a 0.1 F silver nitrate solution. Dilute each solution with distilled water to a volume of approximately 50 ml. Then dissolve 5 gm of reagent-grade potassium persulfate ($K_2S_2O_8$) in each solution; heat the solutions to boiling, and continue the boiling for about five minutes. Cool each solution slightly, and to each flask add 0.5 gm of reagent-grade potassium periodate (KIO_4). Again bring the solutions to boiling for a period of five minutes. Finally, cool each solution to room temperature, transfer each solution quantitatively to a clean 100 ml volumetric flask, and dilute the solutions with distilled water.

Obtain the complete absorption spectrum for each of the standard solutions as well as for the unknown solution in the wavelength region from about 375 to 600 mμ. Follow the general operating instructions for the Spectronic 20 colorimeter outlined in Experiment 16-2, using water as the reference solvent. Record your experimental data in a laboratory notebook and plot the results — absorbance versus wavelength — for all three solutions on the same graph. Since the wavelengths between about 420 and 475 mμ and between 520 and 570 mμ are of particular interest, be sure to obtain data at 5 mμ intervals for all *three* solutions in these wavelength regions.

Inspect the three absorption spectra in order to select the two wavelengths at which the mutual interferences between permanganate and dichromate appear to be least. From the data obtained with the pure permanganate and dichromate solutions, calculate an *apparent* molar absorptivity for each species at each desired wavelength.

Notice that only an *apparent* molar absorptivity may be calculated because the path length is not known, although *it does remain constant throughout the experiment*.

Using information discussed on page 656, calculate the concentrations (moles/liter) of chromium(III) and manganese(II) in the *original* sample solution.

SUGGESTIONS FOR ADDITIONAL LABORATORY WORK

1. C. E. Meloan and R. W. Kiser: *Problems and Experiments in Instrumental Analysis*, Charles E. Merrill Books, Inc., Columbus, Ohio, 1963, pp. 1–80.
2. R. W. Ramette: Formation of monothiocyanatoiron(III). J. Chem. Ed., *40*, 71 (1963).
3. C. N. Reilley and D. T. Sawyer: *Experiments for Instrumental Methods*, McGraw-Hill Book Company, New York, 1961, pp. 105–232.
4. J. Waser: *Quantitative Chemistry*, W. A. Benjamin, Inc., New York, 1964, pp. 351–359.
5. H. H. Willard, L. L. Merritt, Jr., and J. A. Dean: *Instrumental Methods of Analysis*, fourth edition, D. Van Nostrand Co., Inc., New York, 1965, pp. 104–111.

QUESTIONS AND PROBLEMS

1. Spectrophotometry is a valuable tool for the evaluation of equilibrium constants. For example, the equilibrium constant for the reaction

$$AuBr_4^- + 2\,Au + 2\,Br^- \rightleftharpoons 3\,AuBr_2^-$$

can be established by preparation of a mixture of $AuBr_4^-$ and $AuBr_2^-$ in contact with a piece of pure gold metal, followed by spectrophotometric measurement of the concentration of $AuBr_4^-$ from its absorption maximum at 382 mμ. In one experiment, a solution *initially* containing a *total* of 6.41×10^{-4} mEq per milliliter of dissolved gold (present as both $AuBr_4^-$ and $AuBr_2^-$) in 0.400 F hydrobromic acid was allowed to equilibrate in the presence of pure gold metal. The absorbance of the resulting solution was found to be 0.445 in a 1 cm cell at 382 mμ. In separate experiments, the absorbance of a 8.54×10^{-5} M $AuBr_4^-$ solution in 0.400 F hydrobromic acid was determined to be 0.410 at 382 mμ, and $AuBr_2^-$ was observed to exhibit no absorption at this wavelength.

   (a) Calculate the molar absorptivity of $AuBr_4^-$ at 382 mμ.
   (b) Calculate the equilibrium concentrations of $AuBr_4^-$ and $AuBr_2^-$.
   (c) Evaluate the equilibrium constant for the reaction, neglecting activity effects.
   (d) Predict how ionic strength will affect the magnitude of the equilibrium constant based on concentrations alone.

2. Compute the per cent relative uncertainty in the calculated concentration of a substance due to the photometric error, if the transmittance of the sample solution is 0.237 and if the absolute uncertainty in the transmittance reading is 0.3 per cent. If the preceding transmittance reading was obtained in a 1.00 cm spectrophotometer cell, calculate what the sample path length should have been to ensure the smallest possible uncertainty in the calculated concentration.

3. The titanium(IV)-peroxide complex has an absorption maximum at 415 mμ, whereas the analogous vanadium(V)-peroxide complex exhibits its absorption maximum near 455 mμ. When a 50 ml aliquot of 1.06×10^{-3} M titanium(IV) was treated with excess hydrogen peroxide and the final volume adjusted to exactly 100 ml, the absorbance of the resulting solution (containing 1 F sulfuric acid) was 0.435 at 415 mμ and 0.246 at 455 mμ when measured in a 1 cm cell. When a 25 ml aliquot of 6.28×10^{-3} M vanadium(V) was similarly treated and diluted to 100 ml, the absorbance readings were 0.251 at 415 mμ and 0.377 at 455 mμ in a 1 cm cell. A 20 ml aliquot of an unknown mixture of titanium(IV) and vanadium(V) was treated as the previous standard solutions were, including the dilution to 100 ml, and the final absorbance readings were 0.645 at 415 mμ and 0.555 at 455 mμ. What were the titanium(IV) and vanadium(V) concentrations in the original aliquot of the unknown solution?

4. The organic compound thioacetamide (CH_3CSNH_2) undergoes an acid-catalyzed hydrolysis to yield hydrogen sulfide gas which can be employed for the homogeneous precipitation of metal sulfides. The rate of hydrolysis in a solution containing a small concentration of thioacetamide and a relatively high concentration of acid may be expressed by the pseudo first-order equation

$$- \frac{d[CH_3CSNH_2]}{dt} = k'[CH_3CSNH_2]$$

The rate constant k' can be evaluated if the logarithm of the absorbance of thioacetamide solutions at 262 mμ is plotted as a function of time. In one experiment, a solution initially containing 1.00×10^{-4} F thioacetamide and 0.25 F hydrochloric acid was heated at 90°C, and the absorbance was measured as a function of time, the following data being obtained:

Time in Minutes	Absorbance
0	1.10
3	0.99
6	0.87
9	0.77
12	0.69
15	0.60

Evaluate the rate constant k', and calculate the *initial* rate of hydrolysis of thioacetamide in moles/liter·minute.

5. Construct the idealized photometric titration curve which would result from each of the following hypothetical situations. Ignore dilution effects, but be sure to show quantitatively (in a relative manner) how the absorbance varies with the volume of added titrant.

    (a) The titration of $0.0001\ M$ B with $0.01\ M$ A, according to the reaction

$$A + B \rightleftharpoons C + D$$

    Both the titrant A and the product D absorb at the chosen wavelength, but the molar absorptivity of A is exactly twice that of D.

    (b) The titration of $0.0001\ M$ B with $0.01\ M$ A, according to the reaction

$$A + B \rightleftharpoons C + D$$

    The substance being titrated (B) and the product C both absorb at the selected wavelength, but the molar absorptivity for B is twice that of C.

    (c) The titration of $0.0001\ M$ B with $0.01\ M$ A, according to the reaction

$$A + B \rightleftharpoons C + D$$

    The substance being titrated (B) and the titrant (A) both absorb at the selected wavelength, but the molar absorptivity of A is twice that of B.

6. A 5.00 ml aliquot of a standard iron(III) solution, containing 47.0 mg of iron per liter, was pipetted into a 100 ml volumetric flask, treated according to the procedure described in Experiment 16-2 to form the iron(II)-orthophenanthroline complex, and finally diluted to exactly 100 ml. The absorbance of the resulting solution was measured in a 1 cm spectrophotometer cell and found to be 0.467 at 510 mμ. Calculate the per cent transmittance of the solution and calculate the molar absorptivity of the iron(II)-orthophenanthroline complex.

7. A mixture of dichromate and permanganate ions in 1 F sulfuric acid was analyzed spectrophotometrically at 440 and 545 mμ as a means for the simultaneous determination of these two species, and the observed values of the absorbances were 0.385 and 0.653, respectively, at each wavelength for a 1 cm cell. Independently, the absorbance in a 1 cm cell of a $8.33 \times 10^{-4}\ M$ solution of dichromate in 1 F sulfuric acid was found to be 0.308 at 440 mμ and only 0.009 at 545 mμ. Similarly, a $3.77 \times 10^{-4}\ M$ solution of permanganate, placed in a 1 cm cell, exhibited an absorbance of 0.035 at 440 mμ and 0.886 at 545 mμ. Calculate the molar absorptivity of dichromate at 440 mμ, the molar absorptivity of permanganate at 545 mμ, and the concentrations of dichromate and permanganate in the unknown mixture.

8. The ionization constants for acid-base indicators can be evaluated by means of spectrophotometry. The ionization constant for methyl red was determined as follows: A known quantity of the indicator was added to each of a series of buffer solutions of various pH values, and the absorbance of each solution was measured at 531 mμ, at which wavelength only the red acid-form of the indicator absorbs

radiation. The experimental data were as follows:

pH of Buffer	Absorbance
2.30	1.375
3.00	1.364
4.00	1.274
4.40	1.148
5.00	0.766
5.70	0.279
6.30	0.081
7.00	0.017
8.00	0.002

Calculate the ionization constant for methyl red indicator.

9. The *method of continuous variations* is a procedure commonly used to determine the number of ligands coordinated to a metal ion. In this technique, the sum of the moles of metal ion and ligand is kept *constant*, as is the solution volume, but the individual quantities of metal and ligand are varied. A plot is constructed of the absorbance due to the metal-ligand complex as a function of the mole fraction of the metal ion. Such a plot consists of two straight-line portions, intersecting at a point which corresponds to the mole fraction of metal ion in the unknown complex. Suppose that the method of continuous variations was employed to establish the identity of the complex formed between iron(II) and 2,2'-bipyridine

2,2'-bipyridine

and that the following data were obtained:

Mole Fraction of Iron(II)	Absorbance
0.08	0.231
0.12	0.346
0.17	0.491
0.22	0.632
0.28	0.691
0.36	0.615
0.45	0.531
0.56	0.422
0.65	0.334
0.75	0.241
0.83	0.162
0.91	0.087

(a) Construct a plot of absorbance versus the mole fraction of iron(II).

(b) Determine the formula of the complex formed between iron(II) and 2,2'-bipyridine by extrapolating the two straight-line portions to their point of intersection and interpreting the result.

(c) If the sum of the concentrations of iron(II) and 2,2'-bipyridine (in all their forms in solution) in this experiment remained constant at $2.74 \times 10^{-4} M$ and all absorbances were measured in a 1 cm cell, calculate the molar absorptivity of the complex.

10. A $0.150\,F$ solution of sodium picrate in a $1\,F$ sodium hydroxide medium was observed to have an absorbance of 0.419, due only to the absorption by picrate anion. In the same spectrophotometer cell and at the same wavelength as in the previous measurement, a $0.300\,F$ solution of picric acid was found to have an absorbance of 0.581. Calculate the ionization constant for picric acid.

11. Suppose that you desire to determine spectrophotometrically the ionization constant for an acid-base indicator. A series of measurements is performed in which the *total* concentration of indicator is $0.000500\,F$. In addition, all of the spectrophotometric measurements are obtained with a cell of 1 cm path length and at the same wavelength. Other components, in addition to the indicator, are introduced as listed in the following table of data, but none of these exhibits any measurable absorption. Calculate the ionization constant for the indicator.

Solution Number	Other Component	Absorbance
1	$0.100\,F$ HCl	0.085
2	pH 5.00 buffer	0.351
3	$0.100\,F$ NaOH	0.788

12. A solution known to contain both ferrocyanide and ferricyanide ions was examined spectrophotometrically at a wavelength of 420 mμ where only ferricyanide absorbs. A portion of the solution was placed into a 1 cm cell and found to have a transmittance of 0.118. The molar absorptivity of ferricyanide at 420 mμ is 505 liter mole^{-1} cm^{-1}. A platinum indicator electrode was inserted into the solution of ferricyanide and ferrocyanide, and its potential was observed to be $+0.337$ v versus the normal hydrogen electrode. Calculate the concentrations of ferricyanide and ferrocyanide in the original solution.

13. A two-color acid-base indicator has an acid form which absorbs visible radiation at 410 mμ with a molar absorptivity of 347 liter mole^{-1} cm^{-1}. The base-form of the indicator has an absorption band with a maximum at 640 mμ and a molar absorptivity of 100 liter mole^{-1} cm^{-1}. In addition, the acid-form does not absorb significantly at 640 mμ and the base-form exhibits no measurable absorption at 410 mμ. A small quantity of the indicator was added to an aqueous solution, and absorbance values were observed to be 0.118 at 410 mμ and 0.267 at 640 mμ for a 1 cm spectrophotometer cell. Assuming that the indicator has a pK_{In} value of 3.90, calculate the pH of the aqueous solution.

SUGGESTIONS FOR ADDITIONAL READING

Books

1. R. P. Bauman: *Absorption Spectroscopy*, John Wiley & Sons, Inc., New York, 1962.
2. I. M. Kolthoff and P. J. Elving, eds.: *Treatise on Analytical Chemistry*, Part I, Volumes 5 and 6, Wiley-Interscience, New York, 1959, pp. 2707–4217.
3. L. Meites and H. C. Thomas: *Advanced Analytical Chemistry*, McGraw-Hill Book Company, New York, 1958, pp. 231–344.
4. M. G. Mellon, ed.: *Analytical Absorption Spectroscopy*, John Wiley & Sons, Inc., New York, 1950.
5. G. H. Morrison and H. Freiser: *Solvent Extraction in Analytical Chemistry*, John Wiley & Sons, Inc., New York, 1957, pp. 189–247.
6. E. B. Sandell: *Colorimetric Determination of Traces of Metals*, Wiley-Interscience, New York, 1959.
7. H. A. Strobel: *Chemical Instrumentation*, Addison-Wesley Publishing Company Inc., Reading, Massachusetts, 1960, pp. 37–264.

8. F. J. Welcher, ed.: *Standard Methods of Chemical Analysis*, sixth edition, Volume 3-A, D. Van Nostrand Co., Inc., New York, 1966, pp. 3–282.
9. H. H. Willard, L. L. Merritt, Jr., and J. A. Dean: *Instrumental Methods of Analysis*, D. Van Nostrand Co., Inc., New York, 1965, pp. 32–456.

Papers

1. C. L. Hiskey: Principles of precision colorimetry. Anal. Chem., *21*, 1440 (1949).
2. J. J. Lingane and J. W. Collat: Chromium and manganese in steel and ferroalloys. Anal. Chem., *22*, 166 (1950).
3. C. N. Reilley and C. M. Crawford: Principles of precision colorimetry. Anal. Chem., *27*, 716 (1955).

Chapter Seventeen

Potentiometric
and Conductometric
Methods of Analysis

In our discussion of the principles and theory of redox methods of analysis in Chapter 12, we observed that the electromotive force of a galvanic cell depends on the concentrations (activities) of the reducing and oxidizing agents in equilibrium with the electrodes. Such behavior may be exploited analytically in two distinct ways. First, in certain well-defined situations the magnitude of the electromotive force of a galvanic cell can be related by means of the Nernst equation to the concentration or activity of a single desired species, providing us with the procedure known as **direct potentiometry.** Second, the variation of the electromotive force of a galvanic cell in response to changes in the concentrations (activities) of chemical species can serve as a valuable method for following the progress of a titration, commonly referred to as the technique of **potentiometric titration.**

The method of potentiometric titration has enjoyed widespread popularity because it is applicable to every kind of chemical reaction and because the required instrumentation is relatively simple and inexpensive. In the past the use of direct potentiometry in chemical analysis has been largely restricted to pH measurements. However, within the last few years, the development of highly specific ion-selective electrodes has generated great enthusiasm among analytical chemists in the subject of potentiometry. In the present chapter, we shall describe the experimental apparatus needed

691

to perform potentiometric titrations as well as direct potentiometry and we shall explore some specific analytical applications of these techniques.

If the two electrodes which comprise a cell are connected to each other through an external circuit and if these electrodes have different potentials, the electrolyte solution in contact with the electrodes will conduct electricity because of the migration of cations and anions. All ionic species in a solution contribute to the ability of that solution to conduct electricity, the participation of each individual species depending upon both its concentration and its intrinsic mobility. This property of an electrolyte solution, called the **conductance,** is frequently nonspecific; when a solution contains a mixture of electrolytes, the concentrations of the individual ions can be varied in an infinite number of ways and the conductance can still have the same value. However, if a solution is known to contain only one ionic compound, a single measurement of the conductance may suffice for the determination of that substance. Alternatively, the *change* in the conductance of a solution during the course of a titration, like the variation in the electromotive force of a galvanic cell, can be employed to monitor the reaction and to signal the equivalence point. As we shall see later in this chapter, **conductometric titrations** possess some unique advantages in comparison to other methods of analysis.

POTENTIOMETRIC METHODS

Apparatus required for the performance of either direct potentiometry or potentiometric titrations involves the same components. Every potentiometric measurement requires that a suitable galvanic cell, consisting of a sensitive indicator electrode and a stable reference electrode, be constructed with the solution to be studied in direct electrolytic contact with the indicator electrode. The reference electrode may be inserted into the sample solution or it can be brought into contact with the sample solution through an appropriate salt bridge. To determine the absolute magnitude of the electromotive force of the galvanic cell or to follow the changes which occur in electromotive force as titrant is added during a potentiometric titration, a reliable potential-measuring instrument must be available.

Indicator Electrodes.   Although we shall consider specific types of indicator electrodes in detail later in this chapter, three general characteristics must be sought when one selects an indicator electrode for direct potentiometry or for a potentiometric titration. First, the potential of an indicator electrode should be related through the Nernst equation to the concentration (activity) of the species being determined. This requirement is especially critical in the technique of direct potentiometry. Second, it is desirable that an indicator electrode respond rapidly and reproducibly to variations in the concentration or activity of the substance of interest. Third, an indicator electrode should possess a physical form which permits one to perform measurements conveniently.

Reference Electrodes. As defined earlier in this text, a reference electrode is one whose potential remains constant during a single potentiometric measurement or throughout the course of a complete potentiometric titration. In principle, reference electrodes could be constructed to utilize many of the half-reactions listed in Table 12-1. Actually, the roster of suitable reference electrodes is very small, the selection being limited by several important practical considerations. From the standpoint of convenience, the preparation and maintenance of a reference electrode should be simple, and the components comprising the electrode must undergo no significant change when a small current is passed through the electrode during potentiometric measurements.

The most commonly used reference electrode is the **calomel electrode,** which is composed of metallic mercury and solid mercurous chloride (calomel) in contact with, and in equilibrium with, an aqueous solution of potassium chloride. Of course, some form of electrolytic contact must be provided between the solution which comprises the electrode proper and the solution to be analyzed. The electrochemical equilibrium which characterizes the behavior of a calomel electrode is represented by the half-reaction

$$Hg_2Cl_2(s) + 2\ e \rightleftharpoons 2\ Hg(s) + 2\ Cl^-$$

and the corresponding Nernst equation can be written as

$$E_{Hg_2Cl_2,Hg} = E^{\circ}_{Hg_2Cl_2,Hg} - \frac{0.059}{2} \log [Cl^-]^2$$

or

$$E_{Hg_2Cl_2,Hg} = E^{\circ}_{Hg_2Cl_2,Hg} - 0.059 \log [Cl^-]$$

An inspection of the preceding Nernst equation immediately reveals that the potential of a calomel reference electrode depends only on the chloride ion concentration (activity). Since mercurous chloride is very insoluble, the concentration of chloride ion is governed almost entirely by the amount of potassium chloride used in the preparation of the electrode. Three different calomel electrodes are commonly referred to in the chemical literature: the **saturated calomel electrode** (SCE), in which the aqueous solution in contact with metallic mercury and solid mercurous chloride is saturated with potassium chloride; the **normal calomel electrode,** in which the aqueous medium is $1\ F$ potassium chloride solution; and the **decinormal calomel electrode,** in which $0.1\ F$ potassium chloride solution is employed. The potentials of these three reference electrodes are $+0.2415$, $+0.280$, and $+0.334$ v versus NHE, respectively.

The saturated calomel electrode is almost invariably preferred in analytical chemistry because the preparation of a saturated potassium chloride solution is readily accomplished. However, the solubility of potassium chloride does depend on the temperature of the solution, and the potential of a saturated calomel electrode decreases about 0.76 mv for a one degree

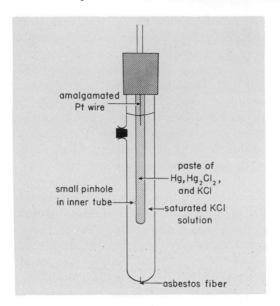

amalgamated
Pt wire

paste of
Hg, Hg_2Cl_2,
and KCl

small pinhole
in inner tube

saturated KCl
solution

FIGURE 17-1.   Common
form of commercially available
saturated calomel reference
electrode.

asbestos fiber

rise in temperature. Therefore, for highly accurate work, the temperature
of the electrode must be controlled. The normal and decinormal calomel
electrodes are not so temperature sensitive, but the care required to prepare
and, especially, to maintain the potassium chloride concentrations at the
desired values makes the routine use of these reference electrodes unappealing.

Saturated calomel electrodes are commercially available, one of the
most common varieties being depicted in Figure 17-1. This electrode consists
of two concentric tubes. The smaller, inner tube contains an amalgamated
platinum wire which leads eventually to the external circuit. In addition,
the inner tube is packed with a thick paste of metallic mercury, mercurous
chloride, and potassium chloride. The outer tube is filled with a saturated
potassium chloride solution; a few crystals of solid potassium chloride can
be added to ensure saturation at all times. Electrolytic contact between the
inner and outer compartments of this electrode is obtained by means of a
small pinhole in the side of the inner tube; sometimes the end of the inner
tube is left open but plugged tightly with glass wool. Finally, electrolytic
contact between the electrode itself and the sample solution is provided
through a porous asbestos fiber sealed into the tip of the outer tube.

One other reference electrode, the silver-silver chloride electrode
(Fig. 17-2), is worthy of mention. It is analogous to the calomel electrode,
except that silver metal and silver chloride replace the mercury and mercurous chloride, respectively, and the pertinent half-reaction is

$$AgCl(s) + e \rightleftharpoons Ag(s) + Cl^-$$

Once again, the potential of this reference electrode depends solely on the
concentration or activity of chloride ion in equilibrium with solid silver

chloride. Unlike the family of calomel reference electrodes, the silver-silver chloride electrode is invariably prepared with saturated potassium chloride solution, its potential under this condition being +0.197 v versus NHE at 25°C.

Potential-Measuring Instruments. As discussed in Chapter 12, a meaningful value of the electromotive force or potential of a galvanic cell can be obtained only if virtually no current flows through the cell during the experimental measurement. From our knowledge of electrochemical cells, it is evident that the passage of current through a galvanic cell will have two effects upon the magnitude of the observed electromotive force. First, the concentrations (activities) of the potential-determining species at the surface of each electrode change because of a small amount of electrolysis, thereby leading to an erroneous electromotive force. Second, every electrochemical cell possesses a certain internal resistance, R, and so the flow of a current i through the cell produces a voltage iR which, in turn, opposes the electromotive force of the cell, making the observed reading *less* than the true value.

Ag wire

saturated KCl + saturated AgCl

3 % agar in saturated KCl

sintered-glass disk

FIGURE 17-2. Silver-silver chloride reference electrode.

In the selection of an instrument for the measurement of electromotive force, the two phenomena named in the preceding paragraph must be kept in mind. The use of a simple magnetic-coil dial-face voltmeter, such as the familiar d'Arsonval meter, is generally unacceptable for electrochemical experiments, since the operation of these low-resistance instruments requires the passage of relatively large currents through the galvanic cell to be studied. The progress of a potentiometric titration, for which the change of the electromotive force of a galvanic cell is of primary concern and for which continuous observation of electromotive force is usually desirable, can be followed with the aid of a high-resistance vacuum tube voltmeter. Although we shall not discuss here the behavior or circuitry of a vacuum tube voltmeter, suffice it to say that such an instrument allows the accurate measurement of voltage without causing or permitting a significant current to flow through the system of interest. In fact, the current need not exceed 10^{-10} amp and may be even smaller. Vacuum tube voltmeters are usually incorporated into direct-reading pH meters. However, such instruments lack the highest attainable accuracy, not only because they do draw a tiny current from the galvanic cell but because the typical meter scale cannot be calibrated very precisely.

The most reliable values for the electromotive force of a galvanic cell are derived from measurements with a potentiometer, the general principles of which we discussed earlier in this book. The precision of any potentiometric measurement depends on the sensitivity with which one can balance the known, variable electromotive force against the electromotive force of the galvanic cell. Fundamentally, this sensitivity is governed by the device used to detect the tiny current which flows through the circuit when the two opposing potentials are not perfectly balanced. In Figures 12-4 and 12-5, the use of a galvanometer as a current-measuring instrument is depicted. Provided that the internal resistance of the galvanic cell and its associated circuitry does not exceed 1 megohm, it is feasible to employ a galvanometer for this purpose. However, for pH measurements, where the resistance of the glass membrane electrode itself may reach 100 megohms, one must replace the galvanometer with a direct-current amplifier in order to detect the very small currents which flow when the two opposing potentials are in a state of imbalance.

The potentiometric circuit discussed in Chapter 12 lacks the sophistication necessary for the accurate measurement of electromotive force. However, the introduction of several improvements provides the precision potentiometer shown in Figure 17-3. As before, the potentiometer is equipped with a uniform or linear slidewire (AB) which may be accurately calibrated from, for example, 0 to 1.5 v in 0.1 mv increments. It also has a source of voltage (V) which is typically a 3 v battery but the value of which need not be known exactly. It should be noted that most commercially available potentiometers have a large fraction of the slidewire replaced by fixed, precision resistors. The first step in the use of such an instrument is the standardization of the potentiometer circuit. To accomplish this standardization, one throws switch S to connect the Weston cell (to be discussed a little later) across the slidewire. Next, one sets the movable contact (C) to a scale reading along slidewire AB equal to the known electromotive force of the Weston cell. This electromotive force will be precisely known for any particular cell and will have a value of about 1.0186 v at 20°C. Then, by tapping the key (K) and observing the deflections of the galvanometer needle (G), one carefully adjusts the variable resistance (R) until the galvanometer indicates that no *net* current is flowing. The standardization procedure guarantees that, if one replaces the Weston cell with an unknown cell, keeps all other adjustments unchanged, and finds that no net current flows when contact C is moved to 1.0186 v on slidewire AB, the electromotive force of the unknown cell is 1.0186 v. Furthermore, since slidewire AB is linear, any other position to which C must be moved will give directly the electromotive force of the unknown cell. Therefore, an actual potentiometric measurement involves the following operations: (1) The potentiometer is standardized; (2) the unknown cell is switched into the circuit; (3) contact C and key K are, respectively, moved and tapped alternately until potentiometric balance is achieved; and (4) the final position of the sliding contact (C) is recorded.

Weston Cells. Standardization of potential-measuring instruments, including potentiometers, requires the availability of a galvanic cell whose

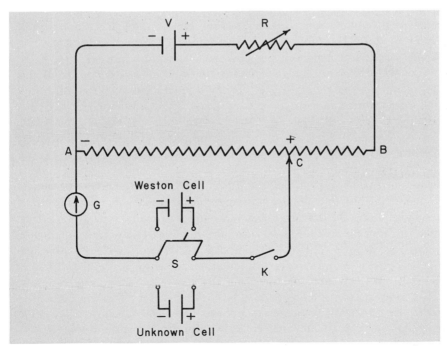

Figure 17-3. Circuit diagram of a simple potentiometer with a linear voltage divider.

FIGURE 17-4.   Saturated Weston standard cell.

electromotive force is known very accurately. The internationally accepted standard for calibration purposes is the Weston cell. The shorthand representation for this galvanic cell,

$$- \; Cd(Hg) \; | \; CdSO_4 \cdot \tfrac{8}{3} \, H_2O(s), \; Hg_2SO_4(s) \; | \; Hg \; +$$

should be interpreted to indicate that the anode is a saturated cadmium amalgam in equilibrium with an aqueous phase which is saturated with respect to both hydrated cadmium sulfate and mercurous sulfate. The cathode consists of a pool of pure mercury in equilibrium with the same aqueous phase. The cell usually contains excess cadmium sulfate crystals and solid mercurous sulfate to ensure that the aqueous phase will be saturated at all temperatures, in which case it is called a *saturated* Weston cell. Customarily, the Weston cell is fabricated in the form of an H-shaped glass vessel, as shown in Figure 17-4. At 20°C the electromotive force of the saturated Weston cell is 1.0186 v.

Passage of small currents through a Weston cell for even short periods of time must be avoided during the calibration or standardization of potential-measuring instruments. In addition, the electromotive force of a saturated Weston cell decreases 0.04 mv for each one degree rise in temperature, owing to the fact that the solubilities of cadmium sulfate and mercurous sulfate are temperature dependent. However, if a saturated Weston cell is not subjected to unnecessarily large currents or fluctuations in temperature, it will maintain a virtually constant potential for many years.

Weston cells encountered in a typical laboratory and employed for routine electrochemical measurements are almost always *unsaturated* with respect to cadmium sulfate. Such cells are prepared from a solution saturated with cadmium sulfate at approximately 4°C but, since no solid cadmium sulfate is added during the fabrication of the cell, the aqueous phase is somewhat less than saturated at room temperature. An unsaturated Weston cell usually exhibits an electromotive force between 1.0185 and 1.0195 v — the exact value being determined by potentiometric comparison to a saturated Weston cell.

Direct Potentiometry

Ideally, the direct potentiometric measurement of the electromotive force of a galvanic cell can be related through the Nernst equation to the activity of a single desired species, if the activities of all other oxidants and reductants in the system are known. Unfortunately, this ostensibly simple procedure is complicated by both practical and theoretical problems.

Suppose we wish to analyze a dilute aqueous solution of silver nitrate by means of potentiometry. A reasonable approach involves the construction of a galvanic cell consisting of a suitable reference electrode and an indicator electrode sensitive to silver ion, followed by the subsequent measurement of the electromotive force of the cell. The shorthand representation of a useful cell is

$$Hg \mid Hg_2Cl_2(s), \; KCl(s) \mid KNO_3(1\;F) \mid AgNO_3 \mid Ag$$

$$E_{Hg,Hg_2Cl_2} \qquad\qquad E_j \qquad\qquad E_j' \qquad E_{Ag^+,Ag}$$

The left-hand electrode is the familiar saturated calomel reference electrode, the electromotive force of which we designate E_{Hg,Hg_2Cl_2}. As an indicator electrode, we have selected a silver wire or foil, realizing that the electromotive force of this electrode, written as $E_{Ag^+,Ag}$, is related to the activity of silver ion in the sample solution by the expression

$$E_{Ag^+,Ag} = E_{Ag^+,Ag}^{\circ} - 0.059 \log \frac{1}{(Ag^+)}$$

at a temperature of 25°C. In addition, since the saturated calomel electrode contains chloride, which forms a precipitate with silver ion, it is essential to separate the calomel electrode from the silver nitrate solution by a salt bridge. Although numerous salt bridges could conceivably be employed, we have chosen one containing a $1\;F$ potassium nitrate solution.

Liquid-Junction Potentials. When two solutions containing dissimilar ions or identical ions at different concentrations are brought into contact with each other, a potential develops at the interface or boundary between these two media. The so-called **liquid-junction potential** arises because the various ionic species diffuse or migrate across the interface at characteristically different rates. In the preceding cell, which we have proposed for the potentiometric determination of silver ion, two liquid-junction potentials exist — one at the boundary between the saturated calomel electrode and the potassium nitrate salt bridge, E_j, and the other at the interface between the salt bridge and the silver nitrate test solution, E_j'. In order to understand what factors influence the magnitude of a liquid-junction potential, let us examine the phenomena which occur at the boundary between the saturated potassium chloride solution and the 1 F potassium nitrate medium. Schematically, this phase boundary may be depicted as

Since the potassium ion concentration in saturated potassium chloride medium is somewhat greater than 4 M, this ion will tend to diffuse toward the phase with the lower concentration of potassium ion, that is, from left to right across the boundary. Chloride ion, being present originally on only one side of the interface, will migrate from left to right, and nitrate will move from right to left. In view of the fact that the migrations of chloride and nitrate ions tend to counterbalance each other, the right side of the boundary acquires a small positive charge because of the transport of potassium ions across the boundary, whereas the left side of the liquid junction will become slightly negative because of the loss of potassium ions. Thus, it is the separation of charge which causes the liquid-junction potential. It should be emphasized that the liquid-junction potential cannot continue to increase beyond a certain equilibrium state. The presence of a tiny excess of positively charged ions on the right side of the phase boundary retards further migration of potassium ions and, simultaneously, accelerates the transport of chloride ion from left toward right to restore neutrality. An analogous situation prevails for the left side of the liquid junction, the negative charge hindering the movement of potassium ions and enhancing the migration of chloride ions from left to right.

The magnitudes of liquid-junction potentials encompass a large range, depending upon the charges, mobilities, and concentrations of the various ionic species and the nature of the solvent on each side of the boundary. At best, when the properties and concentrations of the two opposing solutions are similar, the liquid-junction potential may be only 1 or 2 mv. Such values are acceptably small for most electroanalytical measurements, but we shall see that the accuracy of direct potentiometry can be seriously affected by an uncertainty in a liquid-junction potential of only a few millivolts. Even though the liquid-junction potential is known for a particular pair of solutions, minor changes in the concentrations of the electrolytes markedly affect the liquid-junction potential. Furthermore, since almost every potentiometric measurement of analytical interest involves an unknown solution, the uncertainties in the values of liquid-junction potentials are unpredictable, but may easily reach 15 to 20 mv.

Returning to the galvanic cell described earlier for the determination of silver ion, we may conclude that the overall electromotive force of the cell, E_{cell}, is the sum of the potentials of the reference electrode and indicator electrode as well as the two liquid-junction potentials:

$$E_{cell} = E_{Hg,Hg_2Cl_2} + E_j + E_j' + E_{Ag^+,Ag}$$

A determination of the silver ion activity requires that the value of the electromotive force for the indicator electrode, $E_{Ag^+,Ag}$, be established. Thus, it is necessary to measure potentiometrically the overall electromotive force for the cell and to subtract from this experimental quantity the values of the reference electrode potential and the two liquid-junction potentials. Obviously, any uncertainties or variations in the liquid-junction potentials or the reference-electrode potential will be reflected in the values for $E_{Ag^+,Ag}$ and the silver ion activity calculated from the Nernst equation. Generally speaking, it is easy to obtain a saturated calomel reference electrode whose potential is known to within 1 mv or better. Therefore, uncertainties in liquid-junction potentials constitute one of the drawbacks to the widespread analytical use of direct potentiometry.

To reduce the liquid-junction potential between two solutions to no more than a few millivolts, it is common practice to interpose between these media a salt bridge containing a concentrated electrolyte solution. Usually, a saturated $(4.2\,F)$ potassium chloride solution is employed because potassium and chloride ions have similar mobilities and tend to migrate across the liquid junctions at nearly equal rates. This procedure is successful, however, only when the concentrations of all other ionic species at the solution boundaries are small compared to that of potassium chloride. If appreciable quantities of other ions are present, the liquid-junction potentials will be relatively large.

Calibration Techniques in Direct Potentiometry. Most successful analytical applications of direct potentiometry — notably pH measurements — rely upon an empirical calibration technique which minimizes the effects of variations or errors in the potential of the reference electrode and in the liquid-junction potentials. Assume we are interested in the determination of silver ion in unknown silver nitrate solutions, and let us prepare a series of solutions containing known concentrations of silver ion. In addition, each known solution must have the same concentration of all other species as the anticipated unknown samples so that activity coefficients will be constant. Next, the known solutions are transferred, one by one, into a galvanic cell such as that described earlier, and the overall electromotive force of the cell is measured potentiometrically for each solution. Finally, we construct a calibration curve, which is essentially a straight line, by plotting the overall electromotive force of the galvanic cell as a function of the logarithm of the silver ion concentration.

When an unknown silver ion solution is subsequently placed in the galvanic cell, the observed electromotive force can be interpreted directly in terms of the unknown concentration of silver ion by inspection of the calibration curve. Although the individual values of the reference-electrode potential and the liquid-junction potentials need not be known in this procedure, it is important that the values of these parameters remain constant during the establishment of the calibration curve and the measurement of the electromotive force of the galvanic cell containing the unknown solutions.

A consideration of the Nernst equation reveals that the activity, not the analytical concentration, of a desired substance governs the observed electromotive force of an indicator electrode. Notice, however, that calibration techniques in potentiometry eliminate this problem because the analytical concentration of a species may be determined directly.

Other Limitations of Direct Potentiometry. The logarithmic form of the Nernst equation places another restriction upon the inherent accuracy of direct potentiometry for analytical purposes. This statement may be illustrated through two hypothetical calculations. Suppose that the *true* potential of a silver indicator electrode immersed in a silver ion solution at 25°C is +0.5920 v versus NHE. The activity of silver ion can be calculated from the relation

$$E_{Ag^+,Ag} = E^\circ_{Ag^+,Ag} - 0.05915 \log \frac{1}{(Ag^+)}$$

Taking the standard potential for the silver ion-silver metal half-reaction to be +0.7995 v versus NHE, we may write

$$+0.5920 = +0.7995 - 0.05915 \log \frac{1}{(Ag^+)}$$

and

$$\log \frac{1}{(Ag^+)} = \frac{0.2075}{0.05915} = 3.508$$

$$\log (Ag^+) = -3.508 = 0.492 - 4.000$$

$$(Ag^+) = 3.11 \times 10^{-4} M$$

Now let us assume that the potential of the silver indicator electrode immersed in the same sample medium was *observed* to be +0.5930 v versus NHE, an error of only 1 mv. Although the *precision* of an electromotive force measurement is 0.1 mv or better, an *accuracy* of 1 mv is perfectly normal in direct potentiometry. Such an uncertainty may arise from a number of sources, including a change in the potential of the reference electrode, an error in the liquid-junction potentials, a variation in temperature, an undetected shift in the standardization of the potentiometer circuit, or an absence of electrochemical equilibrium at the surface of the indicator electrode. The silver ion activity based upon the *observed* electromotive force of the silver indicator electrode can be calculated in the manner of the preceding example, namely,

$$+0.5930 = +0.7995 - 0.05915 \log \frac{1}{(Ag^+)}$$

$$\log \frac{1}{(Ag^+)} = \frac{0.2065}{0.05915} = 3.491$$

$$\log (Ag^+) = -3.491 = 0.509 - 4.000$$

$$(Ag^+) = 3.23 \times 10^{-4} M$$

Thus, a 1 mv uncertainty in the experimental evaluation of the indicator-electrode potential leads to an error of just under 4 per cent in the activity of silver ion. When we recall that the possible uncertainties in liquid-junction potentials may easily exceed 10 mv, there can be little doubt that the attainment of accurate analytical results from direct potentiometry is frequently fortuitous and that the use of an empirical calibration technique is almost always necessary.

A practical problem in direct potentiometry is that an indicator electrode usually does not respond solely to the desired species. In other words, the nonavailability of highly selective indicator electrodes is one of the limiting factors in the development of potentiometry for analytical purposes. In order to appreciate a few of the difficulties, let us again consider briefly the determination of silver ion through the use of an indicator electrode of pure silver metal. First, solutions ordinarily contain dissolved molecular oxygen, which is capable of slowly oxidizing the silver indicator electrode to silver ion:

$$4 \, Ag + O_2 + 2 \, H_2O \longrightarrow 4 \, Ag^+ + 4 \, OH^-$$

Since the silver ions produced are localized near the surface of the electrode, the activity of silver ion at the electrode surface will be higher than in the bulk of the solution and the potential of the electrode will be more positive than anticipated. The situation is undoubtedly complicated even more by the precipitation of silver hydroxide or silver oxide upon the electrode surface. Second, the silver electrode can be responsive to the presence of dissolved oxygen, particularly when the silver ion activity is low. In this event, the silver indicator electrode may exhibit a **mixed potential** which is governed by the activities of both silver ion and oxygen. The reaction of oxygen with the silver indicator electrode undoubtedly takes place regardless of the original activity of silver ion in solution. However, it should be evident that this extraneous reaction cannot markedly alter the surface activity of silver ion or the potential of the indicator electrode if the initial silver ion activity is reasonably large.

Analytical Applications of Direct Potentiometry

Among the obvious virtues of direct potentiometry are that measurements can be performed on exceedingly small samples — much less than a milliliter — and that the sample solution is not altered or destroyed during the experimental measurements. In addition, potentiometry is suitable for the analysis of relatively dilute solutions. Two of the most exciting applications of potentiometry lie in the areas of continuous, automated analysis and bioanalytical chemistry. Because the technique of potentiometry involves the simple measurement of an electrical signal, the electromotive force of a galvanic cell, it is possible to insert suitable indicator and reference electrodes directly into chemical systems which might otherwise be inaccessible and to obtain valuable information concerning the composition of these systems. Thus, direct potentiometry may be employed to monitor industrial processes, nuclear reactors, and other remote or dangerous facilities. Moreover, the relatively recent development of reliable indicator electrodes sensitive to sodium and potassium ions permits the study of such phenomena as the binding of sodium ion in brain tissue, the diffusion of potassium and sodium ions through nerve and muscle membranes, and the composition of blood and cerebrospinal fluid.

Potentiometric Determination of pH.   The activity or concentration of hydrogen ion in a solution plays a critical role in biochemical processes, in the rates of many organic and inorganic reactions, and in a wide variety of separations and measurements in analytical chemistry. Furthermore, the hydrogen ion activity in aqueous and nonaqueous media may vary over an enormous range. Consequently, the determination of pH remains the most important practical application of direct potentiometry.

Theoretically, any electrode process leading to the formation or consumption of hydrogen ions could be made the basis of a potentiometric method for pH measurement. Closer examination of most of these half-reactions, however, reveals that other oxidizing and reducing agents besides hydrogen ion are involved as reactants and products and that these species affect the observed potential of the indicator electrode. For example, the permanganate-manganous ion couple,

$$MnO_4^- + 8\ H^+ + 5\ e \rightleftharpoons Mn^{++} + 4\ H_2O$$

contains hydrogen ion as a reactant. Unfortunately, in addition to pH, the activities of MnO_4^- and Mn^{++} have a profound influence upon the potential of a platinum, gold, or palladium electrode immersed in a particular sample solution.

Hydrogen Electrode.   A logical indicator electrode for the measurement of pH is the classic hydrogen electrode, a convenient form of which is incorporated into the galvanic cell shown in Figure 12-5. A hydrogen electrode consists of a piece of platinum, or some other noble metal such as palladium or gold, which is immersed in the solution whose pH is to be measured. In addition, the unknown solution must be saturated with very pure hydrogen gas at a known partial pressure and temperature.

The fundamental potential-determining half-reaction,

$$2\ H^+ + 2\ e \rightleftharpoons H_2$$

reaches equilibrium rather slowly unless the surface of the noble metal electrode is in an active state. A platinum electrode may be readily activated if one deposits on its surface a thin layer of finely divided platinum metal by polarizing the electrode cathodically in a dilute solution of chloroplatinic acid, H_2PtCl_6. Apparently, this *platinization* of the electrode provides a large surface area for the adsorption of hydrogen molecules and catalyzes the rupture of the hydrogen-hydrogen bond, and so hydrogen atoms can be readily oxidized to hydrogen ions. However, an excessive deposit of finely divided platinum should be avoided; otherwise, traces of numerous substances, including organic molecules, arsine, and hydrogen sulfide, tend to be adsorbed upon the electrode and cause the hydrogen electrode to perform erratically. Through repeated use, as well as through an aging process, the active surface of a platinized electrode eventually can no longer promote the hydrogen gas-hydrogen ion equilibrium, and so the old layer of finely divided metal must be dissolved with aqua regia and replaced with a fresh deposit. The hydrogen electrode can be employed only in media which contain no extraneous oxidizing and reducing agents because, as mentioned earlier, these species alter the potential of the electrode. Such stringent requirements regarding the preparation and handling of the hydrogen electrode place severe limitations on its usefulness in analytical chemistry, but highly important applications remain in the field of electrochemistry.

Glass Membrane Electrode. Of all the electrodes sensitive to hydrogen ions, the glass membrane electrode, or simply the glass electrode, is unique, because the mechanism of its response to hydrogen ion is totally different, involving an ion-exchange reaction rather than an electron-transfer process. Consequently, the glass electrode is not subject to interferences by oxidizing and reducing agents in the sample solution. Furthermore, the rapidity and accuracy with which the glass electrode responds to sudden changes in hydrogen ion activity make it the universal choice of indicator electrode for potentiometric acid-base titrations in aqueous solutions and in many nonaqueous media.

Glass electrodes may be purchased in a wide variety of sizes and shapes for such diverse purposes as the determination of the pH of blood and other biological fluids, the continuous measurement and recording of the hydrogen ion concentration (activity) in flowing solutions, or the evaluation of the pH of a single drop or less of solution. However, the most familiar form of the glass membrane electrode is depicted in Figure 17-5. A thin-walled bulb, fabricated from a special glass highly sensitive to the hydrogen ion activity of a solution, is sealed to the bottom of an ordinary glass tube. Inside the glass bulb is a dilute aqueous hydrochloric acid solution, usually $0.1 \, F$ in concentration. A silver wire coated with a layer of silver chloride is immersed into the hydrochloric acid medium. The silver wire is extended upward through the resin-filled tube to provide electrical contact to the external circuit. Thus, the glass electrode essentially comprises an inner silver-silver chloride reference electrode dipping into a dilute hydrochloric acid solution confined within a pH-sensitive glass bulb. Other inner reference electrodes, including the calomel electrode, are sometimes employed.

In order to appreciate how the glass electrode appears to function, when placed into a solution whose pH is to be determined, we must consider some aspects of the structure of the glass membrane itself. After a glass electrode

FIGURE 17-5.   Glass membrane electrode.

has been briefly exposed to an aqueous medium, the cross section of the glass membrane, including the hydrochloric acid solution and the unknown sample solution, is believed to have the general structure

$$
\text{0.1 } F \text{ HCl} \left| \begin{array}{c} \text{inner} \\ \text{hydrated} \\ \text{layer} \end{array} \right| \begin{array}{c} \text{dry} \\ \text{glass} \\ \text{layer} \end{array} \left| \begin{array}{c} \text{outer} \\ \text{hydrated} \\ \text{layer} \end{array} \right| \begin{array}{c} \text{unknown} \\ \text{solution} \end{array}
$$

$$
\underbrace{\hspace{6cm}}_{\text{glass membrane}}
$$

According to this simple picture, the glass membrane consists of a central layer of dry glass, perhaps 50 microns in thickness, sandwiched between inner and outer hydrated layers which are typically a few hundred angstroms thick.

The structure of glass has been characterized by x-ray studies as a three-dimensional framework in which each silicon atom is bound to four oxygen atoms. This framework contains interstitial holes which are normally occupied by somewhat loosely held sodium ions. In an aqueous medium, water molecules penetrate into the surface of the silicate lattice forming the inner and outer hydrated layers. In the process, sodium ions become aquated and can be exchanged for hydrogen ions,

$$
\text{Na}^+_{\text{glass}} + \text{H}^+_{\text{solution}} \rightleftharpoons \text{Na}^+_{\text{solution}} + \text{H}^+_{\text{glass}}
$$

by the same kind of mechanism as occurs with the cation-exchange resins discussed in Chapter 7. The presence of water in these inner and outer layers is essential as shown by the fact that the glass electrode begins to malfunction soon after it is immersed in a dehydrating medium such as concentrated sulfuric acid or anhydrous ethanol; however, the electrode is quickly restored to normal behavior by being returned to water for a short time. Nevertheless, a complete theory of the mechanism of operation of glass electrodes remains to be formulated.

If ion-exchange processes take place within the outer and inner hydrated layers, one may conclude that the quantity of hydrogen ion occupying the exchange sites on either side of the membrane is proportional to the activity of hydrogen ion in the adjacent solution. Next, one can propose that a so-called *phase-boundary potential* is associated with the inner and outer hydrated layers and that the magnitude of this potential is related directly to the quantity of hydrogen ion at the exchange sites. Finally, it is reasonable that the difference between the two phase-boundary potentials at the inner and outer hydrated layers is what one ultimately measures when he determines the pH of an unknown solution. It should be emphasized at this point that, in spite of the presence of the dry glass layer, electrical charge is readily transferred through the membrane to complete the potentiometric circuit because loosely bound, unhydrated sodium ions can move through the silicate framework.

Differences in the two phase-boundary potentials can be easily demonstrated, if we consider a special type of concentration cell,

$$\left.\begin{array}{l}\text{reference}\\\text{electrode}\end{array}\right| \text{H}^+ (a_1) \left|\begin{array}{l}\text{glass}\\\text{membrane}\end{array}\right| \text{H}^+ (a_2) \left|\begin{array}{l}\text{reference}\\\text{electrode}\end{array}\right.$$

which consists of identical reference electrodes immersed into each of two solutions having different hydrogen ion activities, a_1 and a_2, respectively, and being separated by a glass membrane. Under such conditions, the observed electromotive force of this galvanic cell is found experimentally to be governed by the relation

$$E_{\text{cell}} = k - 0.059 \log \frac{(a_2)}{(a_1)}$$

The constant k accounts for any inequality in the liquid-junction potentials between the reference electrodes and the solutions, as well as for any difference in the potentials of the two reference electrodes, although the latter are presumably equal to each other. In addition, k includes a parameter called the **asymmetry potential** of the glass membrane. The asymmetry potential — of perhaps 1 or 2 mv in magnitude — arises because the inner and outer hydrated layers of a glass membrane are not exactly the same, but exhibit small differences in their adsorptive power for hydrogen ions and water molecules. These differences result from strains in the membrane caused by unequal heating of the inner and outer surfaces of the glass bulb when the electrode is fabricated.

If we assume that the activity (a_1) of hydrogen ion on the left-hand side of the glass membrane is held constant, as is true for the inner compartment of the typical glass electrode shown in Figure 17-5, but that the hydrogen ion activity (a_2) on the right-hand side of the membrane is unknown, the preceding equation may be rewritten as

$$E_{cell} = k' - 0.059 \log (a_2)$$

where k' now incorporates the activity of hydrogen ion (a_1) inside the bulb of the glass electrode. Finally, the activity of hydrogen ion (a_2) in the unknown solution can be expressed in terms of the pH of that medium through the relation

$$E_{cell} = k' + 0.059 \text{ pH}$$

It is the latter equation which serves as the basis of all practical pH determinations.

Practical pH Measurements.   A glass membrane electrode in combination with the saturated calomel reference electrode provides the galvanic cell usually employed for practical pH measurements in the analytical chemical laboratory. The shorthand representation for such a cell is

$$\text{Ag} \left| \text{AgCl(s), HCl (0.1 } F) \right| \begin{array}{c} \text{glass} \\ \text{mem-} \\ \text{brane} \end{array} \left| \begin{array}{c} \text{sample} \\ \text{solution of} \\ \text{unknown pH} \end{array} \right| \text{Hg}_2\text{Cl}_2\text{(s), KCl(s)} \left| \text{Hg} \right.$$

Each vertical line in the present galvanic cell representation denotes a phase boundary across which an electromotive force or potential develops. Therefore, the overall electromotive force for this galvanic cell is composed of five parts: (1) the potential of the silver-silver chloride electrode, (2) the potential between the hydrochloric acid solution inside the glass electrode and the inner wall of the glass membrane, (3) the potential between the outer wall of the glass membrane and the solution of unknown pH, (4) the liquid-junction potential between the solution of unknown pH and the saturated calomel electrode, and (5) the potential of the saturated calomel electrode. An asymmetry potential is also included in the overall electromotive force of the galvanic cell. Fortunately, the first, second, and fifth sources of potential are virtually invariant since the composition of the solution inside the glass electrode remains constant and since the electromotive force of the saturated calomel electrode is fixed. Any shift in the observed overall electromotive force of the galvanic cell, as solutions of different pH are transferred into the sample compartment, can be attributed to three effects — small variations in the liquid-junction and asymmetry potentials and, most importantly, a change in potential at the interface between the outer wall of the glass membrane and the unknown sample solution.

Many careful experimental studies have led to the conclusion that the overall electromotive force, E_{cell}, for such a cell is related to the pH of the unknown sample by the expression

$$E_{cell} = K + 0.059 \text{ pH}$$

This equation is analogous to a relation given earlier, except that the constant K includes the first, second, and fifth sources of potential just listed, plus the liquid-junction and asymmetry potentials. The value of K can never be precisely known because the liquid-junction potential and the asymmetry potential are both uncertain. Therefore, all practical pH determinations necessarily involve a calibration procedure in which the pH of an unknown solution is compared to the pH of a standard buffer. If we transfer a portion of some standard buffer into the galvanic cell and measure the electromotive force of the cell, it follows that

$$(E_{cell})_s = K + 0.059 \ (pH)_s$$

where the subscript s pertains to the standard buffer. Similarly, if an unknown solution is present in the cell, we obtain

$$(E_{cell})_x = K + 0.059 \ (pH)_x$$

where the subscript x refers to the unknown solution. When the latter two relationships are combined, the result is

$$(pH)_x = (pH)_s + \frac{(E_{cell})_x - (E_{cell})_s}{0.059}$$

which has been adopted at the National Bureau of Standards as the *operational definition* of pH. Implicit in this operational or practical definition are two assumptions, namely that the pH of the standard buffer is accurately known and that K has the same value when either the standard buffer or the unknown sample is present in the galvanic cell.

The pH values for a selected group of standard buffers have been determined at the National Bureau of Standards from electromotive force measurements of galvanic cells *without* liquid-junction potentials. The galvanic cell usually employed for this purpose can be depicted as

$$\text{Pt, } H_2 \mid \text{standard buffer, NaCl, AgCl(s)} \mid \text{Ag}$$

In order to establish the pH value for a standard buffer, it is necessary to make reasonable assumptions concerning the activity coefficients for the buffer constituents. The details of this rather complicated procedure are discussed in several of the specialized references at the end of this chapter, but it can be stated here that the pH values of standard buffers are known with an accuracy of ± 0.005 pH unit at 25°C. A list of accepted pH values for various standard buffer solutions is presented in Table 17-1.

The operational definition of pH presumes that the liquid-junction and asymmetry potentials of the galvanic cell are the same when electromotive force measurements are performed with either the standard buffer or the unknown solution in the sample compartment. In other words, the value of K must remain constant if this definition of pH is to be truly valid. As discussed earlier in this chapter, liquid-junction potentials vary considerably for even small changes in solution composition. In practice, one attempts to overcome this difficulty by selecting a standard buffer with a pH as close as possible to that of the unknown sample. For example, if the unknown solution

TABLE 17-1. pH VALUES OF STANDARD BUFFERS*

Temperature, °C	Potassium Tetroxalate, 0.05 M	Potassium Hydrogen Tartrate, Saturated at 25°C	Potassium Acid Phthalate, 0.05 M	KH_2PO_4, 0.025 M; Na_2HPO_4, 0.025 M	Borax, 0.01 M
0	1.666	—	4.003	6.984	9.464
10	1.670	—	3.998	6.923	9.332
20	1.675	—	4.002	6.881	9.225
25	1.679	3.557	4.008	6.865	9.180
30	1.683	3.552	4.015	6.853	9.139
40	1.694	3.547	4.035	6.838	9.068
50	1.707	3.549	4.060	6.833	9.011

* Values taken with permission from R. G. Bates: *Determination of pH*, John Wiley & Sons, Inc., New York, 1964, p. 76. The uncertainties in these values are about ±0.005 unit at 25°C, but somewhat larger at other temperatures.

has a pH close to 4, it is preferable that the standard buffer be potassium acid phthalate, the latter having a pH of 4.01 at 25°C (Table 17-1).

Generally speaking, the ultimate accuracy of glass electrode pH measurements is dictated by the constancy of the parameter K in the preceding equations. For optimum conditions, when the pH values of the standard buffer and unknown sample are essentially identical and when any variations in the liquid-junction potential are minimized as much as possible, the uncertainty in the electromotive force of an appropriate galvanic cell can be reduced to approximately 1 mv. In turn, this corresponds to an expected error in the pH of the unknown solution of about ±0.02 pH unit. It is noteworthy that pH meters are available commercially from which one can read pH values with a precision of ±0.003 unit or better, a feature which is frequently useful for studying *changes* in the pH of a system under carefully controlled conditions. However, such precision must not be misconstrued, for the accuracy of the measurements is still no better than one or two hundredths of a pH unit.

Errors in Glass Electrode pH Measurements. Although the glass membrane electrode does not usually suffer from the interferences found with most pH-sensitive electrodes, such as the hydrogen gas electrode, the former exhibits several peculiarities which limit its application in certain kinds of media.

The composition of the glass membrane has an important bearing on the characteristics of the electrode. Only soft glass displays a satisfactory sensitivity toward hydrogen ion, and high-melting glass, such as Pyrex and Vycor, is unsuitable. Soda-lime glass, containing 22 per cent Na_2O, 6 per cent CaO, and 72 per cent SiO_2, is commonly used in commercially available glass electrodes and responds well between pH 0 and 9. At higher pH values, however, such an electrode exhibits a so-called **alkaline error,** in which the observed pH is *lower* than the true value by an amount increasing as the pH becomes greater. The alkaline error arises because cations other than hydrogen ion — particularly sodium ion and, to a lesser extent, potassium and lithium ions — compete for the exchange sites in the hydrated layers of the glass membrane, thereby altering the phase-boundary potential mentioned earlier. The size of the alkaline error varies with the nature and concentration of the extraneous cation as well as with temperature. For example, at pH 12 the observed pH is low by 1.0 unit at room temperature when the sodium ion concentration is 1 M, but it is low by only 0.4 unit for 0.1 M sodium ion. The alkaline error is slightly less than 0.2 pH unit when 1 M potassium ion is present at pH 12 or when 1 M sodium ion is present at pH 10. Considerable research has been directed toward the development of glasses containing little or no sodium oxide which do not exhibit large alkaline errors. Thus, a glass composed of 28 per cent Li_2O, 3 per cent La_2O_3, 4 per cent BaO, 2 per cent Cs_2O, and 63 per cent SiO_2 has an alkaline error of approximately 0.1 pH unit at pH 13 for 2 M sodium ion.

At the other end of the pH scale, the glass electrode exhibits an **acid error** which is opposite from that observed in alkaline solutions. In other words, in very strongly acidic media, the observed pH is *higher* than the true value. Although the cause of the acid error is not as well understood as that of the alkaline error, it appears that the variable activity of water in concentrated acid solutions results in a corresponding change in the water content of the hydrated layer of the glass membrane. However, the acid error is negligibly small down to at least pH 0, and so this source of uncertainty is rarely important in practical pH determinations.

Finally, it should be mentioned that a glass electrode does not respond rapidly when inserted into solutions which are poorly buffered, presumably because the rate of attainment of equilibrium in the outer hydrated layer is slow.

pH Meters. One of the chief characteristics of a glass membrane is its extraordinarily high resistance, which typically ranges from 1 to 100 megohms. This property adds a new problem to the experimental measurement of pH.

Recall from our brief description of potential-measuring instruments that all galvanic cells have a certain internal resistance, R, and that a current, i, inevitably flows through the cell during an electromotive force measurement. The product of these two quantities, iR, will always produce a voltage which opposes the electromotive force of the galvanic cell. Thus, if one does not wish to exceed the usual 1 mv error in potentiometric measurements, the quantity iR must be kept below this value. For galvanic cells employed in pH measurements, it is reasonable to assume that virtually all the internal resistance of the cell is provided by the glass membrane. If the largest permissible value of iR is 1 mv and R is taken to be 10 megohms, it follows that the maximal current which can flow through a galvanic cell during the determination of pH is 10^{-10} amp. Unfortunately, the minimal detectable deflection of an ordinary galvanometer, such as that indicated in the potentiometer circuit of Figure 17-3, corresponds to a current which is perhaps 10^{-9} amp, or 10 times greater than the acceptable value. Obviously, if one balances a potentiometric circuit but cannot detect any difference in the final potentiometer setting while a current of 10^{-9} amp flows through the cell, the error in the electromotive force measurement may be as large as 10 mv, and the pH of the solution can be uncertain by nearly 0.2 pH unit. For these reasons, an ordinary potentiometer is rarely used for pH determinations; however, two kinds of pH meters are employed.

The *direct-reading* pH meter is essentially a vacuum tube voltmeter in which the electromotive force of the galvanic cell is impressed across a very high resistance and the resulting current is amplified and passed through an ammeter whose dial face is calibrated directly in pH units. The *potentiometric* or *null-detector* instrument is the second type of pH meter. It incorporates a relatively straightforward potentiometer circuit, except that the usual galvanometer is replaced with a vacuum tube amplifier so that currents as small as 2×10^{-12} amp, instead of 10^{-9} amp, can be readily detected at potentiometric balance. A direct-reading pH meter is especially convenient for use in potentiometric acid-base titrations, where the variation of pH as a function of added titrant is more important than any individual value of pH. Direct-reading instruments are usually accurate to ± 0.1 pH unit. On the other hand, null-detector pH meters yield pH values with accuracies of 0.01 to 0.02 pH units, and consequently they are preferable for precise measurements. Both types of instruments must be standardized according to the operational definition of pH discussed earlier.

Ion-Selective Electrodes. For a long time the analytical uses of direct potentiometry were limited to the determination of pH, primarily because of the lack of sensitive and selective indicator electrodes. However, the last several years have witnessed the development of a number of interesting ion-selective electrodes. Such electrodes are starting to find important applications in the control and monitoring of industrial processes, in the analysis of water, in oceanography, and in the study of biochemical systems.

We have already seen that variations in the composition of a glass electrode affect the magnitude of the alkaline error in pH measurements because the ion-exchange sites in the hydrated layer of the membrane are modified. At the present time, it is impossible to predict in advance how the glass composition influences the selectivity of an electrode for a specific ion. However, it is clear that the response of glass membrane electrodes to different cations is markedly altered through only minor changes in the composition of the glass. For example, a glass composed of 27 per cent Na_2O, 5 per cent Al_2O_3, and 68 per cent SiO_2 exhibits a preferential response to potassium ions down to an activity of 10^{-4} M, the Nernst equation being applicable. If the composition is changed to 11 per cent Na_2O, 18 per cent Al_2O_3, and 71 per cent SiO_2, the glass electrode responds to sodium ion in preference to potassium ion. Interestingly, the latter glass electrode is even more highly selective with respect to silver ion, displaying a 1000-to-1 preference for silver ion over sodium ion. A glass containing 15 per cent Li_2O, 25 per cent Al_2O_3, and 60 per cent SiO_2 can be employed for the determination of lithium ion in the presence of both sodium and potassium ions. All of these different electrodes are available commercially.

Anion-selective indicator electrodes have been developed in which an insoluble precipitate containing the desired anion is impregnated into a solid matrix. For example, one can prepare an electrode for iodide ion by causing monomeric silicone rubber to polymerize in the presence of an equal weight of silver iodide particles. After the mixture has solidified, the uniform matrix is sealed to the bottom of a glass tube, and a potassium iodide solution and a silver electrode are placed into the tube. Similar electrodes have been fabricated from silver chloride, silver bromide, and barium sulfate. The mechanism by which precipitate electrodes respond is related to the tendency of a solid to adsorb preferentially the ions of which it is composed, as discussed in Chapter 5. A silver iodide-silicone rubber matrix tends to adsorb iodide ion in proportion to the activity of iodide in an unknown solution. In turn, this adsorption of iodide produces a phase-boundary potential which can be measured and related to the activity of iodide ion in the unknown solution by means of the Nernst equation. The silver iodide-silicone rubber electrode possesses a significant advantage over a silver-silver iodide indicator electrode, the latter consisting of a length of silver wire coated with a thin layer of silver iodide. The former electrode is unaffected by the presence of dissolved oxidants and reductants, whereas the potential of a silver-silver iodide indicator electrode is altered by many different species.

The use of liquid ion-exchange substances provides another important kind of highly specific indicator electrode. The direct potentiometric determination of calcium ion can be accomplished with the aid of a specially constructed electrode containing a calcium organophosphorous compound in liquid form and an inner silver-silver chloride reference electrode. The calcium organophosphorous liquid exchanger comes into contact with the sample solution through either a plastic membrane or a sintered-glass disk which holds the liquid ion-exchange material in place. The primary purpose of the plastic membrane or sintered-glass disk is to prevent the liquid exchanger from dissolving in the unknown sample solution and contaminating it. Such an electrode has been demonstrated to follow the Nernst equation for calcium ion concentrations as low as $5 \times 10^{-6} M$ and to exhibit marked specificity for calcium ion in the presence of strontium, magnesium, barium, sodium, and potassium ions. However, this electrode cannot be employed in solutions of pH 11 or higher, owing to the precipitation of calcium hydroxide. A similar liquid-liquid indicator electrode for the determination of copper(II) has been recently developed, and electrodes designed specifically for the measurement of chloride, nitrate, and perchlorate are available.

Potentiometric Titrations

Although the applications of direct potentiometry continue to gain in importance, most potentiometric methods of analysis involve titrimetry. In this section of the chapter, the techniques and uses of potentiometric titrations will be described. Basically, we may characterize a potentiometric titration as one in which the change of the electromotive force of a galvanic cell during a titration is recorded as a function of added titrant. The major goal of this procedure is the precise location of the equivalence point, although thermodynamic information, including dissociation constants for weak acids and stability constants for complex ions, may be deduced from potentiometric titration curves.

In comparison to other methods for the location of equivalence points in titrimetry, the technique of potentiometric titration offers a number of advantages. First, it is applicable to chemical systems which are so brightly colored that ordinary visual methods of end point detection are useless. Second, a potentiometric titration is especially useful when no internal indicator is available. Third, this experimental approach is valuable for titrations in nonaqueous media. Fourth, it eliminates subjective decisions concerning color changes of end point indicators as well as the need for indicator blank corrections. Fifth, potentiometric titrations may be used for acid-base, precipitation, complexometric, and oxidation-reduction reactions. The accuracy which may be achieved in potentiometric titrations is fully as good as with conventional end point indicators and, under certain conditions, may be even better.

The equipment required for the performance of potentiometric titrations is relatively simple. A titration vessel, which is usually no more than an open beaker, a buret containing the standard titrant, and suitable indicator and reference electrodes are the necessities. It is preferable that the solution be well stirred throughout the course of the titration, a magnetic stirring device being ideal because it permits ample room for the placement of the electrodes and buret into the titration vessel. For some titrations, the titration vessel must be closed, so that an inert gas such as nitrogen or helium may be bubbled through the solution to remove oxygen.

For most titrations the analytical chemist possesses knowledge in advance concerning the approximate volume of titrant required. Therefore, the titrant can be added rather rapidly at the beginning of the titration until the equivalence point is approached. Thereafter, until the equivalence point is passed, one should introduce the titrant in small increments and should wait for equilibrium to be established before recording the potential of the indicator electrode and the volume of titrant and adding more reagent. For reasons to be discussed, it is convenient if these small volume increments are equal in size. After the addition of each increment, sufficient time must be allowed for the indicator-electrode potential to become reasonably steady, so that it exhibits a drift of perhaps not more than 1 mv per minute.

In contrast to direct potentiometry, the measurement of the electromotive force of a galvanic cell does not require the highest possible accuracy, because only the rather large *changes* in the potential of an indicator electrode near the equivalence point of a titration have significance. It is unnecessary to know the potential of the reference electrode or the magnitudes of any liquid-junction potentials. Furthermore, any small variations in the values of these quantities have no effect upon the determination of the equivalence point.

Generally, one may perform potentiometrically almost any titration for which a procedure has been given in preceding chapters merely by inserting appropriate indicator and reference electrodes into the titration vessel and by measuring the potential between these electrodes at various points throughout the titration.

Precipitation Titrations.   The potentiometric method of end point detection is applicable to the various precipitation titrations mentioned in Chapter 10. The common chemical species involved in these determinations are cations such as silver(I), mercury(II), lead(II), and zinc(II) and anions such as chloride, bromide, iodide, thiocyanate, and ferrocyanide.

Indicator electrodes for potentiometric precipitation titrations are usually fabricated from the metal whose cation comprises the precipitate. In a few instances, however, the indicator electrode may be one whose potential is governed by the anion of the precipitate. For example, the progress of a titration of chloride ion with standard silver nitrate solution can be monitored if the potential of a silver indicator electrode versus a saturated calomel reference electrode is measured. The physical appearance of the titration apparatus is illustrated schematically in Figure 17-6. A shorthand representation of the galvanic cell shown in this diagram is

$$Hg \mid Hg_2Cl_2(s), KCl(s) \mid KNO_3 \ (1 \ F) \mid \text{chloride sample solution} \mid Ag$$

In the present example, a potassium nitrate salt bridge has been inserted between the sample solution and the saturated calomel electrode so that potassium chloride solution will not diffuse into the sample. As soon as a small volume of silver nitrate titrant is added, the solution becomes saturated with silver chloride and the indicator electrode behaves as a silver-silver chloride electrode,

$$AgCl(s) + e \rightleftharpoons Ag + Cl^-; \qquad E° = +0.2222 \ v$$

its potential being governed by the Nernst equation

$$E_{AgCl,Ag} = E°_{AgCl,Ag} - 0.059 \log (Cl^-)$$

If, for the convenience of this discussion, we neglect the liquid-junction potentials, the overall electromotive force of the preceding galvanic cell can be written as

$$E_{cell} = E_{Hg,Hg_2Cl_2} + E_{AgCl,Ag}$$

FIGURE 17-6. Apparatus for potentiometric titration of chloride with silver nitrate solution.

and, if the Nernst equation for the silver chloride-silver metal half-reaction is substituted into the latter relation, it becomes

$$E_{cell} = E_{Hg,Hg_2Cl_2} + E^{\circ}_{AgCl,Ag} - 0.059 \log (Cl^-)$$

When the respective values for E_{Hg,Hg_2Cl_2} and $E^{\circ}_{AgCl,Ag}$ (namely, -0.2415 and $+0.2222$ v versus NHE) are substituted into this equation, the result is

$$E_{cell} = -0.0193 - 0.059 \log (Cl^-)$$

or

$$E_{cell} = -0.0193 + 0.059 \; pCl$$

This expression is valuable because it reveals that a linear relationship exists between the values of pCl and the electromotive force of the galvanic cell. Accordingly, if one performs a potentiometric titration of chloride with silver nitrate solution and constructs a plot of electromotive force as a function of the volume of titrant, the titration curve would be similar to that shown in Figure 10-1. Equations analogous to those just derived can be obtained for the precipitation titrations of other anions which form insoluble silver salts.

It should be emphasized that the indicator electrode actually responds to changes in silver ion activity and that, in fact, the potential of the electrode is governed by an electron-transfer process involving silver ion and silver metal. Thus, any potentiometric titration involving the use of a silver indicator electrode can be interpreted in terms of the silver ion-silver metal half-reaction:

$$Ag^+ + e \rightleftharpoons Ag; \qquad E^\circ = +0.7995 \text{ v}$$

However, it is instructive to see the interrelationship between the treatments based on the silver chloride-silver metal and the silver ion-silver metal couples. Let us convert the equation

$$E_{cell} = E_{Hg,Hg_2Cl_2} + E^\circ_{AgCl,Ag} - 0.059 \log (Cl^-)$$

into an expression which contains the silver ion activity by using the thermo-dynamic activity product for silver chloride, namely,

$$(Ag^+)(Cl^-) = K_{ap}$$

Combination of these two relations, followed by rearrangement of the re-sulting equation, yields

$$E_{cell} = E_{Hg,Hg_2Cl_2} + E^\circ_{AgCl,Ag} - 0.059 \log K_{ap} + 0.059 \log (Ag^+)$$

The second and third terms on the right-hand side of this expression are equivalent to the standard potential for the silver ion-silver metal half-reaction, $E^\circ_{Ag^+,Ag}$, as may be verified from page 479, and so we can write

$$E_{cell} = E_{Hg,Hg_2Cl_2} + E^\circ_{Ag^+,Ag} + 0.059 \log (Ag^+)$$

Finally, if E_{Hg,Hg_2Cl_2} and $E^\circ_{Ag^+,Ag}$ are replaced by the values -0.2415 and $+0.7995$ v versus NHE, respectively, we have

$$E_{cell} = 0.548 + 0.059 \log (Ag^+)$$

or

$$E_{cell} = 0.548 - 0.059 \text{ pAg}$$

The latter relation could have been derived readily if, at the beginning of our discussion, we had proposed that the silver indicator electrode responds to silver ion. Above all, it is essential to understand that the equations involving pCl and pAg give exactly the same value for the overall electro-motive force of the galvanic cell and that the use of one or the other expression is a matter of choice and convenience.

Determination of Equivalence Points. As previously suggested, the technique of potentiometric titrimetry is especially advantageous for the location of equivalence points in all kinds of titrations. Having mentioned precipitation titrations, however, we shall consider the problem of equivalence point determination for the titration of chloride with silver nitrate, but the procedures to be described have general applicability.

A typical set of potentiometric titration data for the reaction between chloride and silver nitrate is presented in Table 17-2. The first column con-tains a list of the buret readings during the titration, and the second column shows the potential of a silver indicator electrode, measured against the

1 2 3   5 6   8   0   1 2 3 4 5 6 7 8 9 0

TABLE 17-2. POTENTIOMETRIC TITRATION DATA FOR
TITRATION OF 3.737 MILLIMOLES OF CHLORIDE
WITH 0.2314 *F* SILVER NITRATE

Volume of $AgNO_3$, ml	E versus SCE, v	$\Delta E/\Delta V$	$\Delta^2 E/\Delta V^2$
0	+0.063		
5.00	0.071		
10.00	0.086		
15.00	0.138		
15.20	0.145		
15.40	0.152		
15.60	0.161		
15.70	0.166		
15.80	0.172		
15.90	0.181		
		15	
16.00	0.196		+14
		29	
16.10	0.225		+35
		64	
16.20	0.289		−34
		30	
16.30	0.319		−13
		17	
16.40	0.336		
16.50	0.346		

saturated calomel electrode (SCE), corresponding to each volume reading. Notice that the volume increments are large near the beginning of the titration when the potential of the indicator electrode varies only slightly. However, in the region of the equivalence point, small and equal volume increments are introduced. Usually, prior experience with a particular titration or knowledge of the equivalence point potential alerts one to the fact that the equivalence point is being approached. Basically, three methods may be employed for determination of the equivalence point of a potentiometric titration.

One obvious procedure, known as the **graphical method,** involves inspection of the complete titration curve. If one plots the potential of the indicator electrode versus the volume of titrant, the resulting titration curve exhibits a maximal slope — that is, a maximal value of $\Delta E/\Delta V$. In turn, it is common practice to call the amount of titrant corresponding to this maximal slope the equivalence point volume. Figure 17-7A illustrates this simple approach with the experimental data in Table 17-2, although only that portion of the titration curve near the equivalence point is pictured. Quite clearly, the success of this method depends upon the time and care expended in plotting the data and upon the accuracy with which the maximal slope can be determined. For sharply defined titration curves, the uncertainty in the procedure is small, but considerable trouble may be encountered in less favorable situations.

A logical extension of the preceding technique entails actual preparation of a plot of $\Delta E/\Delta V$, the change in potential per volume increment of titrant, as a function of the volume of titrant. Such a graph, derived from the titration data of Table 17-2, is shown in Figure 17-7B. The values of $\Delta E/\Delta V$, as well as the titrant volumes, V, required for the construction of this curve are obtained in the following manner: (1) If the volume increments near the equivalence point are equal, one may simply take the difference in, for example, millivolts between each successive pair of potential readings as $\Delta E/\Delta V$; however, if the volume increments are unequal, it is necessary to normalize the data. (2) The volume, V, to which each value of $\Delta E/\Delta V$ pertains, is the *average* of the two volumes corresponding to the successive potential readings. For example, in Table 17-2 the change in potential, ΔE, is

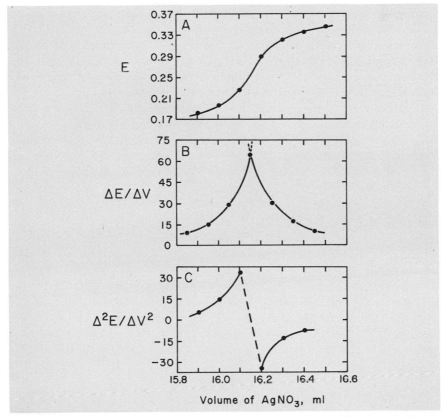

FIGURE 17-7. Titration curves for the titration of 3.737 millimoles of chloride with 0.2314 F silver nitrate. Curve A: normal titration curve, showing the region near the equivalence point. Curve B: first derivative titration curve. Curve C: second derivative titration curve. All data points are taken from Table 17-2.

29 mv as one proceeds from 16.00 to 16.10 ml of titrant added. Accordingly, the correct value of $\Delta E/\Delta V$ is 29 mv per 0.1 ml, whereas V should be taken as 16.05 ml. Notice that the graph in Figure 17-7B consists of two curves which must be extrapolated upward to a point of intersection; it is only a happenstance that one of the experimental points lies so close to this point of intersection. A vertical line drawn from the intersection point to the abscissa indicates the equivalence point volume. This graphical method is tedious, is subject to the same uncertainties as the previous approach, and, as a consequence, is rarely used.

A more rapid, accurate, and convenient procedure for the location of an equivalence point is the so-called **analytical method.** This technique relies upon the mathematical definition that the second derivative $(\Delta^2 E/\Delta V^2)$ of the titration curve is zero at the point where the first derivative $(\Delta E/\Delta V)$ is a maximum. The fourth column of Table 17-2 lists the individual values of $\Delta^2 E/\Delta V^2$ — the difference between each pair of $\Delta E/\Delta V$ values — for the titration of chloride with silver nitrate, and Figure 17-7C presents a graph of these results as a function of the volume of titrant. An inspection of either Table 17-2 or Figure 17-7C reveals that the second derivative $(\Delta^2 E/\Delta V^2)$ changes sign and passes through zero between volume readings of 16.10 and 16.20 ml and that the equivalence point volume must lie within this interval. Obviously, the equivalence point volume could be determined graphically from Figure 17-7C, if one draws a vertical line from the point at which $\Delta^2 E/\Delta V^2$ is zero to the volume axis. However, the *analytical method* is an interpolative technique, based on the premise that the ends of the upper and lower curves in Figure 17-7C can be joined by a straight line if the volume increments are small enough. Provided that this approach is valid, one can show mathematically that the equivalence point volume should be

$$16.10 + 0.10\left(\frac{35}{35 + 34}\right) = 16.15 \text{ ml}$$

It is important to recognize that the *analytical method* requires only experimental data similar to those listed in Table 17-2; no graphical constructions are necessary.

Implicit in the graphical and analytical methods just described is the assumption that the theoretical equivalence point for a titration coincides with the maximal value of $\Delta E/\Delta V$ for the titration curve. However, this requirement is fulfilled only for chemical processes in which the reactants combine in a one-to-one stoichiometric ratio, that is, for equilibria such as

$$Ag^+ + Cl^- \rightleftharpoons AgCl(s)$$

and

$$Fe^{++} + Ce^{++++} \rightleftharpoons Fe^{+++} + Ce^{+++}$$

which are *symmetrical.* On the other hand, when the reaction between the titrant and the substance being titrated involves unequal numbers of chemical species, an *asymmetric* titration curve results, the theoretical equivalence point will deviate from the region of maximal slope, and a significant titration error may arise in especially unfavorable situations if the graphical methods are used. The titration curve depicted in Figure 13-2 for the iron(II)-dichromate system,

$$6 \; Fe^{++} + Cr_2O_7^= + 14 \; H^+ \rightleftharpoons 6 \; Fe^{+++} + 2 \; Cr^{+++} + 7 \; H_2O$$

is an excellent example of such behavior, since six iron(II) ions react with a single dichromate anion. Notice that the theoretical equivalence point potential of $+1.24$ v versus NHE occurs well above the most steeply rising portion of the titration curve. It should be added here that the acid concentration is relatively large compared to that of either iron or chromium species, and it remains virtually constant throughout the titration. Therefore, hydrogen ion has no particular influence on the asymmetry of the titration curve. Moreover, the fact that one dichromate ion yields two chromium(III) species upon reduction builds into this system another source of asymmetry. For most of the titrations encountered in chemical analysis, the difference between the potential at which $\Delta E / \Delta V$ is a maximum and the theoretical equivalence point potential is small enough to be neglected, since other systematic errors in the procedures are usually much more important.

A third experimental method, **direct titration to the equivalence point,** is employed in potentiometric titrimetry. This procedure is applicable only if the equivalence point potential has been established from previous titrations or by means of theoretical calculations. This technique has the additional virtue that no titration data need be recorded; one simply introduces titrant — slowly as the equivalence point is approached — until the potential of the indicator electrode, as measured with an appropriate instrument, attains the desired value. Obviously, conditions must be controlled sufficiently well to ensure that the equivalence point potential is reasonably reproducible from one titration to another. In many instances, the titration curve rises so steeply near the equivalence point that a considerable latitude of potential values still guarantees highly accurate results.

Complexometric Titrations. Most present applications of complexometric titrations center on the reactions of metal ions with various members of the family of aminopolycarboxylic acids, notably ethylenediaminetetraacetic acid (EDTA). As emphasized in Chapter 11, a large number of metallic ions form stable one-to-one complexes with the ethylenediaminetetraacetate anion, and so there exists considerable interest in the use of potentiometric methods to monitor the progress of metal-EDTA titrations. It seems reasonable, at first glance, that one could follow the titration of a hypothetical metal ion M^{+n} with EDTA by using an indicator electrode of the parent metal M, because the potential of this electrode should be governed by the following Nernst equation:

$$E_{M^{+n},M} = E^\circ_{M^{+n},M} - \frac{0.059}{n} \log \frac{1}{(M^{+n})}$$

Unfortunately, remarkably few metal-metal ion electrode systems behave in accordance with the Nernst equation over a wide range of metal ion concentrations. Earlier in this chapter it was pointed out that a metallic electrode might not always respond correctly to the desired species. One source of difficulty is that the activity of the substance of interest can be altered by extraneous reactions at the electrode surface, and a second phenomenon is the existence of *mixed potentials*.

Elemental mercury in the presence of a small concentration of the very stable mercury(II)-EDTA complex provides a versatile and unique indicator-electrode system for many metal-EDTA titrations. Mercury is ideally suited for this application because it is a noble metal, being reasonably difficult to oxidize, and does not suffer from mixed-potential phenomena. In practice, the indicator electrode may consist of a pool of mercury in a small cup positioned inside the titration vessel, with some means for connecting the electrode to an external potentiometer circuit. A more convenient form of mercury indicator electrode can be prepared if a gold wire is amalgamated by immersion into mercury; the mercury-coated gold wire is especially easy to manipulate.

Suppose we wish to determine calcium ion in an unknown sample solution by means of a potentiometric EDTA titration. Into the titration vessel containing the sample, let us insert a mercury indicator electrode and a saturated calomel reference electrode. We shall then introduce a small concentration, perhaps approximately 10^{-4} M, of the mercury(II)-EDTA complex. Finally, let us titrate the mixture with a standard solution of EDTA, recording the potential of the mercury indicator electrode as a function of the titrant volume. If the potential of the indicator electrode is plotted versus the volume of titrant, a titration curve similar to that shown in Figure 11-3 will be obtained. Thus, the mercury indicator electrode exhibits a linear response to the negative logarithm of the calcium ion concentration or to pCa — behavior which must now be explained.

Once the addition of EDTA titrant has commenced, the sample solution will contain both calcium ion and the calcium-EDTA complex, as well as the mercury(II)-EDTA species; so the chemical system comprises a galvanic cell which may be represented by the shorthand notation

$$\text{Hg} \mid \text{Hg}_2\text{Cl}_2(s), \text{KCl}(s) \parallel \text{Ca}^{++}, \text{CaY}^=, \text{HgY}^= \mid \text{Hg}$$

where $Y^{\equiv}$ is the standard abbreviation for the ethylenediaminetetraacetate ion. A small concentration of this latter anion will, of course, be in equilibrium with the metal-EDTA complexes. Of particular interest is the electrode involving mercury and the mercury(II)-EDTA complex at the right-hand side of the cell. Throughout the titration this electrode ultimately responds to the concentration (activity) of Hg^{++}, since the potential-determining process is the electron transfer between mercury and dissolved mercury ions. Therefore, the Nernst equation,

$$E_{\text{Hg}^{++}, \text{Hg}} = E^{\circ}_{\text{Hg}^{++},\text{Hg}} - \frac{0.059}{2} \log \frac{1}{[\text{Hg}^{++}]}$$

is always obeyed. Dissociation of the mercury(II)-EDTA complex, present in solution during the titration, is the primary source of mercuric ion,

$$HgY^= \rightleftharpoons Hg^{++} + Y^\equiv$$

and the concentrations of these two species are related through the equilibrium expression for the formation of the mercury(II)-EDTA complex

$$K_{HgY} = \frac{[HgY^=]}{[Hg^{++}][Y^\equiv]} = 6.3 \times 10^{21}$$

If we solve this equilibrium expression for the mercuric ion concentration and substitute the result into the Nernst equation for the mercury indicator electrode, it follows that

$$E_{Hg^{++},Hg} = E^\circ_{Hg^{++},Hg} - \frac{0.059}{2} \log \frac{K_{HgY}[Y^\equiv]}{[HgY^=]}$$

For the titration reaction between calcium ion and EDTA,

$$Ca^{++} + Y^\equiv \rightleftharpoons CaY^=$$

the equilibrium expression has the form

$$K_{CaY} = \frac{[CaY^=]}{[Ca^{++}][Y^\equiv]} = 5.0 \times 10^{10}$$

If this relation is rearranged,

$$[Y^\equiv] = \frac{[CaY^=]}{[Ca^{++}]K_{CaY}}$$

and substituted into the previous modified Nernst equation, we have

$$E_{Hg^{++},Hg} = E^\circ_{Hg^{++},Hg} - \frac{0.059}{2} \log \frac{K_{HgY}[CaY^=]}{K_{CaY}[Ca^{++}][HgY^=]}$$

which becomes

$$E_{Hg^{++},Hg} = E^\circ_{Hg^{++},Hg} - \frac{0.059}{2} \log \frac{K_{HgY}[CaY^=]}{K_{CaY}[HgY^=]} + \frac{0.059}{2} \log [Ca^{++}]$$

or

$$E_{Hg^{++},Hg} = E^\circ_{Hg^{++},Hg} - \frac{0.059}{2} \log \frac{K_{HgY}[CaY^=]}{K_{CaY}[HgY^=]} - \frac{0.059}{2} pCa$$

In the second term of the right-hand member of the preceding equation are the formation constants for the calcium-EDTA and mercury(II)-EDTA complexes together with the concentrations of these two species. Since the mercury(II)-EDTA ion is very stable, its concentration remains virtually constant during the titration, if dilution effects are minimized through the use of a relatively concentrated titrant. Near the equivalence point, when most of the calcium ion has already been converted to its EDTA complex, the concentration of CaY= will undergo so little additional increase that it may be assumed to be constant. Accordingly, the first and second terms on the right-hand side of the latter relation both appear to be constant as the equivalence point is approached, with the result that

$$E_{\text{Hg}^{++},\text{Hg}} = K - \frac{0.059}{2}\,\text{pCa}$$

As depicted in Figure 11-3, the calcium ion concentration as well as the value of pCa changes abruptly at the equivalence point of an EDTA titration, and so the potential of the mercury indicator electrode will exhibit a similarly large variation. It should be noted that the potential of the indicator electrode is actually measured against a saturated calomel reference electrode, but this only means that the value of K in the previous equation is different and that the entire titration curve is shifted vertically along the potential axis.

Wide applicability of the potentiometric procedure stems from the fact that the mercury(II)-EDTA complex is unusually stable. Indeed, only metal cations whose EDTA complexes are *less* stable than the mercury(II)-EDTA species can be determined satisfactorily. However, Table 11-2 provides evidence that this requirement is met by many cations of analytical importance and, in accord with this observation, several dozen elements may be successfully titrated with EDTA.

Acid-Base Titrations.   Almost universal availability of glass electrodes, saturated calomel electrodes, and pH meters has rendered potentiometric acid-base titrations more convenient to perform than practically any other method of analysis. Particularly impressive is the increasing number of applications in the field of nonaqueous acid-base titrimetry, some of which were described in Chapter 9. Furthermore, potentiometric acid-base titrimetry is especially useful in situations where visual end point detection is precluded by the presence of colored species or turbidity.

Earlier in this chapter, we found that a linear relationship exists between the pH of a solution and the potential of a glass membrane electrode. Since most pH-measuring instruments are calibrated directly in pH units, it is more straightforward for potentiometric acid-base titrations to record pH versus the volume of titrant rather than to convert pH readings into values of potential. In addition, experimental pH data can be readily correlated with theoretical titration curves such as those calculated in Chapter 8. For similar reasons, in applying the *graphical* or *analytical* methods for the location of equivalence points in potentiometric acid-base titrimetry, one may employ $\Delta\text{pH}/\Delta V$ and $\Delta^2\text{pH}/\Delta V^2$, respectively, for the first and second derivatives of the titration curves.

Potentiometric acid-base titrimetry offers several additional advantages which other neutralization methods of analysis lack. First, the former technique allows the recording of complete titration curves, which is especially valuable for the study of mixtures of acids or bases in either aqueous or nonaqueous solvents. Second, the potentiometric procedure permits one to apply graphical or analytical methods for the location of equivalence points, an absolute necessity in the investigation of multicomponent systems. Third, quantitative information concerning the relative acid or base strengths of solute species can be obtained. For example, the titration of a sodium carbonate solution with standard hydrochloric acid produces a titration curve with two steps (see Fig. 8-7), corresponding to the consecutive reactions

$$CO_3^= + H^+ \rightleftharpoons HCO_3^-$$

and

$$HCO_3^- + H^+ \rightleftharpoons H_2CO_3 \rightleftharpoons CO_2 + H_2O$$

Halfway to the first equivalence point, the concentrations of carbonate and hydrogen carbonate anions are essentially equal, and so the second dissociation constant for carbonic acid can be obtained from the hydrogen ion concentration at this point,

$$[H^+] = K_2 \frac{[HCO_3^-]}{[CO_3^=]} = K_2$$

or, alternatively, the value of pK_2 is numerically equal to the measured pH of the solution. At the first equivalence point, we discovered in Chapter 8 that

$$[H^+] = \sqrt{K_1 K_2}$$

or

$$pH = \tfrac{1}{2}(pK_1 + pK_2)$$

to a very good approximation. Therefore, the pH at the first equivalence point, in combination with the previously determined value of pK_2, can be employed for the evaluation of pK_1. However, the value of pK_1 may be obtained directly from the pH midway between the first and second equivalence points. Similar reasoning applies to the titration curves for carbonic acid and phosphoric acid as well as many other acidic and basic species.

Oxidation-Reduction Titrations. Principles and applications of oxidation-reduction methods of analysis have been considered in detail in earlier chapters, and so it suffices to mention here that a large majority of the determinations outlined previously can be accomplished by means of potentiometric titrimetry. Most potentiometric redox titrations involve the use of a platinum indicator electrode, a saturated calomel reference electrode, and a suitable potential-measuring instrument. Unless chloride ion has a deleterious effect upon the desired oxidation-reduction reaction, the calomel reference electrode can be immersed directly into the titration vessel; otherwise, an appropriate salt bridge connecting the reference electrode to the solution in the titration vessel is required. Although a platinum wire or foil is almost invariably employed as the indicator electrode, gold, palladium, and carbon are occasionally used. If an indicator electrode responds reversibly to the various oxidants and reductants in the chemical system, titration curves recorded in practice may exhibit excellent agreement with theoretical curves derived according to procedures discussed in Chapter 12.

CONDUCTOMETRIC METHODS

Conductometric methods were among the earliest techniques employed by physical chemists to study the behavior of electrolyte solutions, to evaluate dissociation constants for weak acids, and to determine solubility products of insoluble salts. As emphasized in the introduction to this chapter, every dissolved ionic substance makes a contribution to the total conductance of a solution, and so measurements of conductivity lack the specificity encountered with some analytical procedures. Another deterrent to the widespread use of conductance methods in chemical analysis is that suitable equipment is not always readily available. In some situations, however, the distinctive changes in solution conductivity which occur during acid-base and precipitation titrations provide the only satisfactory means of end point detection. Conductometric titrations are especially valuable for reactions involving very dilute solutions or for reactions which are incomplete, such as the titration of a weak acid with a weak base. With the usual care taken in experimental measurements, the conductance of a solution can be determined with an accuracy of approximately 1 per cent, which is acceptable for practical applications. If special attention is paid to the careful manipulation of all apparatus, the uncertainty may be reduced to 0.1 per cent.

Fundamental Definitions and Relationships

Basically, the conductance of an electrolyte solution arises from the migration or movement of negatively charged ions toward the anode of an electrolysis cell and of positively charged species in the direction of the cathode. Obviously, in order for any solution to conduct electricity, ionic species must be capable of stable existence in the solvent of interest. Solutes such as sodium chloride or potassium nitrate, which dissociate almost completely in water, exist largely as nonconducting ion pairs in a solvent of low dielectric constant. The size of an ion (and, therefore, its ability to conduct electricity) is related to its charge and to the number and orientation of solvent molecules coordinated to that ion. Various properties of the solvent itself, including viscosity and structure, play an important role in the conductance of a solution. Finally, increases in temperature raise the conductivity of a solution because the viscosity of the solvent is lowered; the mobilities of ions are increased approximately 2 per cent for each one degree rise.

Specific Conductance. In beginning a quantitative treatment of conductance measurements, it is customary to consider a hypothetical situation in which a column of electrolyte solution of length l in centimeters and uniform cross-sectional area A in square centimeters is confined between two planar platinum electrodes. As is true for all conducting materials, the resistance R in ohms of this column of solution is, by definition, directly proportional to l and inversely proportional to A,

$$R = \rho \frac{l}{A}$$

the proportionality constant ρ being called the **specific resistance,** expressed in ohm $\cdot$ cm. Thus, the specific resistance is the resistance of a cube of liquid which is 1 cm in length and 1 cm^2 in cross-sectional area. The specific resistance of an electrolyte solution depends upon the various factors described qualitatively in the preceding paragraph.

For purposes of chemical analysis, it is much more convenient to introduce another term, the conductance L of an electrolyte solution, which is simply the reciprocal of resistance:

$$L = \frac{1}{R}$$

Values of conductance are usually reported in units of reciprocal ohms, or mhos. Combination of the two previous expressions yields the relation

$$L = \frac{A}{\rho l} = \kappa \frac{A}{l}$$

where κ, the **specific conductance** of a solution, is stated in units of ohm^{-1} $\cdot$ cm^{-1}, or mho $\cdot$ cm^{-1}, and is taken to be the reciprocal of specific resistance. For *dilute* aqueous solutions of *strong* electrolytes, such as hydrochloric acid and potassium chloride, a linear relationship exists between specific conductance and solute concentration. Eventually, however, a concentration level is reached beyond which the specific conductance increases less rapidly and in a non-linear manner, owing principally to the effects of interionic attractions on the mobilities of ions. The specific conductance of a solution containing a weak electrolyte, such as acetic acid, varies in a more complicated way than for strong electrolyte solutions, because the percentage or degree of dissociation of weak electrolytes is quite sensitive to concentration.

Equivalent Conductance. If we are interested solely in the performance of conductometric titrations, the relationships presented in the preceding section are entirely adequate for the interpretation of experimental data. As we shall see later, a successful conductometric titration requires only that *changes* in the total conductance L of a solution be measured as titrant is added. In fact, provided that the conductance cell employed in a titration has fixed geometry with respect to the areas (A) and the distance of separation (l) of the two electrodes, it is actually unnecessary to know either of these two parameters.

Quantitative measurements of equilibrium constants for solubility and acid-base reactions demand that still another term be introduced. This is the **equivalent conductance,** Λ, of an electrolyte, defined to be the conductance, L, of 1 gram-equivalent-weight of solute in a solution confined between two electrodes of equal area which are spaced 1 cm apart. However, the areas of these electrodes need not be specified. Alternatively, the equivalent conductance is the specific conductance, κ, of a solution containing 1 gram-equivalent-weight of electrolyte per cubic centimeter.

Values of equivalent conductance are determined from the results of specific-conductance measurements. Assuming the two electrodes in a conductance cell are separated by a distance of 1 cm, we can conclude that the area of each electrode in square centimeters required to confine 1 gram-equivalent-weight of solute is given by the relation

$$A = \frac{1000}{C}$$

where C is the solute concentration in equivalents per liter. Recalling that

$$L = \kappa \frac{A}{l}$$

we may write

$$L = \frac{1000\kappa}{lC}$$

However, in view of the definition of equivalent conductance, it follows that

$$\Lambda = \frac{1000\kappa}{C}$$

Equivalent conductance is expressed in terms of mho $\cdot$ cm^2.

Therefore, the equivalent conductance can always be determined from the previous equation if the specific conductance is measured experimentally and if the concentration of the desired solution is known. On the other hand, it should be emphasized that, if the equivalent conductance is established from independent experiments, measurements of specific conductance enable one to calculate the concentration of the solute — provided that just one electrolyte is present. The latter approach is utilized in the evaluation of solubility products and dissociation constants for weak acids and bases.

Variation of Equivalent Conductance with Concentration. Theoretically, if a solute exhibited ideal behavior, the specific conductance of a solution would be directly proportional to the concentration of the dissolved substance or to the number of charges per unit volume of solution. Thus, we might predict from the last preceding equation that the equivalent conductance should remain constant as the solute concentration is varied. However, as indicated earlier, the specific conductance does not increase with concentration in a perfectly linear manner, especially at high solute concentrations, and so the equivalent conductance does depend upon the concentration of solute. Figure 17-8 illustrates the variation of the equivalent conductance for typical strong and weak electrolytes as a function of solute concentration.

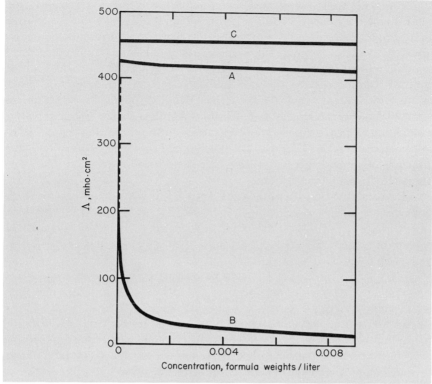

FIGURE 17-8. Variation of equivalent conductance with concentration. Curve
A: hydrochloric acid. Curve B: acetic acid. Curve C: ideal electrolyte.

At least two phenomena account for the behavior of a strong electrolyte
such as hydrochloric acid. First, increases in the concentration of hydrochloric acid are marked by an enhanced tendency for chloride ions to cluster
around a hydrogen ion, whereas hydrogen ions are attracted to chloride. In
each instance, the proximity of oppositely charged species impedes the
migration of an ion, and this *interionic attraction effect* causes the equivalent
conductance to decrease as the solute concentration increases. Second, the
so-called *electrophoretic effect* lowers the equivalent conductance as the concentration of an electrolyte increases because migration of solvated cations
toward the cathode is retarded by the movement of hydrated anions in the
direction of the anode.

For a weak electrolyte the unusually large variation in equivalent
conductance seen in Figure 17-8 cannot be adequately explained by interionic or electrophoretic effects, although these factors are still operative.
Instead, the rapid decrease in equivalent conductance is due mainly to the
fact that the fraction of dissociation of a weak electrolyte diminishes very
markedly as the solute concentration increases.

When a graph of equivalent conductance as a function of solute concentration for a strong electrolyte is extrapolated to infinite dilution — that is, to zero concentration — one obtains the **limiting equivalent conductance,** Λ_0, which represents the value of the equivalent conductance if the solute exhibited ideal behavior. For hydrochloric acid at 25°C, the limiting equivalent conductance, Λ_0, is 426.1 mho · cm². A determination of the limiting equivalent conductance for acetic acid by means of a similar extrapolation procedure is not feasible, however, since the equivalent conductance for a weak electrolyte varies so abruptly in the region of low solute concentration. For weak electrolytes, the limiting equivalent conductance may be evaluated through a consideration of equivalent conductances for individual ions.

Equivalent Conductances of Ions. By combining two relationships derived earlier,

$$L = \kappa \frac{A}{l}$$

and

$$\Lambda = \frac{1000\kappa}{C}$$

we can arrive at an equation which expresses the conductance of a solution containing a single electrolyte in terms of the equivalent conductance and the concentration of that electrolyte, as well as the parameters of the conductance cell employed in the experimental measurements:

$$L = \frac{\Lambda C A}{1000 l}$$

One of the most important concepts in the theory of ionic conductivity states that the total conductance of a solution containing an arbitrary number of electrolytes is the sum of the contributions from all individual species present. Accordingly, the preceding expression can be transformed into the more general relation

$$L = \frac{A}{1000 l} \sum_i \lambda_i C_i$$

where λ_i denotes the **equivalent ionic conductance** for a particular species and C_i is the concentration of that ion in equivalents per liter.

If these equations are applied to an aqueous solution of a simple binary salt, such as sodium chloride, it can be shown that

$$\Lambda_{NaCl} C_{NaCl} = \lambda_{Na^+} C_{Na^+} + \lambda_{Cl^-} C_{Cl^-}$$

However, since the concentration of sodium chloride and the concentrations of the individual ions are identical, it is apparent that

$$\Lambda_{NaCl} = \lambda_{Na^+} + \lambda_{Cl^-}$$

which indicates that the equivalent conductance for an electrolyte is the sum of the equivalent ionic conductances for the ions comprising the parent substance. When extended to the limiting equivalent conductance of sodium chloride, $(\Lambda_0)_{NaCl}$, this fundamental definition becomes

$$(\Lambda_0)_{NaCl} = \lambda^\circ_{Na^+} + \lambda^\circ_{Cl^-}$$

where $\lambda^\circ_{Na^+}$ and $\lambda^\circ_{Cl^-}$ are, respectively, the **limiting equivalent ionic conductances** of sodium ion and chloride ion at a specified temperature.

Equivalent ionic conductances, and the corresponding limiting values, can be evaluated if we stipulate that a certain portion of the total equivalent conductance of a salt is due to each ion. By convention, the fraction of the equivalent conductance of sodium chloride attributable to sodium ion is defined to be

$$t_{Na^+} = \frac{\lambda_{Na^+}}{\Lambda_{NaCl}}$$

in which t_{Na^+} is called the **transference number** of sodium ion. Similarly, the transference number of chloride ion is

$$t_{Cl^-} = \frac{\lambda_{Cl^-}}{\Lambda_{NaCl}}$$

Such a set of relationships always presumes, of course, that the sum of the transference numbers for the ions of a salt is unity; that is,

$$t_{Na^+} + t_{Cl^-} = 1$$

Provided that the transference numbers for the pertinent ions can be separately evaluated and provided that the equivalent conductance of sodium chloride is known, the equivalent ionic conductances for sodium and chloride ions are obtainable from the preceding equations. We shall not consider here the procedures employed to determine transference numbers, since details are available in most textbooks of physical chemistry.

We discovered earlier that the limiting equivalent conductance, Λ_0, for a strong electrolyte can be readily determined if a plot of equivalent conductance versus concentration (or square root of concentration) is extrapolated to infinite dilution (see Fig. 17-8). On the other hand, values of limiting equivalent ionic conductances, λ°, for single ions are established by means of a procedure consisting of two parts. Let us consider how to evaluate the limiting equivalent ionic conductance for the sodium ion. First, it is necessary to obtain the limiting equivalent conductance for sodium chloride, as described previously. Second, we measure the transference number of sodium ion for various sodium chloride concentrations and extrapolate the experimental data to zero concentration in order to find the infinite-dilution transference number of the sodium ion, $t^\circ_{Na^+}$. From these two pieces of information and from the fundamental equation

$$t^\circ_{Na^+} = \frac{\lambda^\circ_{Na^+}}{(\Lambda_0)_{NaCl}}$$

TABLE 17-3.   LIMITING EQUIVALENT IONIC
CONDUCTANCES AT 25°C

Cation	$\lambda°$, mho · cm²	Anion	$\lambda°$, mho · cm²
H^+	349.8	OH^-	198
Li^+	38.7	F^-	55
Na^+	50.1	Cl^-	76.3
K^+	73.5	Br^-	78.4
NH_4^+	73.4	I^-	76.8
Ag^+	61.9	NO_3^-	71.4
$\frac{1}{2} Mg^{++}$	53.1	IO_3^-	40.8
$\frac{1}{2} Ca^{++}$	59.5	HCO_3^-	44.5
$\frac{1}{2} Sr^{++}$	59.5	ClO_4^-	67.3
$\frac{1}{2} Ba^{++}$	63.6	CH_3COO^-	40.9
$\frac{1}{2} Cu^{++}$	54	$HCOO^-$	54.6
$\frac{1}{2} Pb^{++}$	73	$\frac{1}{2} CO_3^=$	69.3
$\frac{1}{2} Zn^{++}$	52.8	$\frac{1}{2} C_2O_4^=$	74.2
$\frac{1}{3} La^{+++}$	69.6	$\frac{1}{2} SO_4^=$	79.9

the limiting equivalent ionic conductance for sodium ion can be computed. In this manner, a whole series of limiting equivalent ionic conductances can be determined, a partial list being presented in Table 17-3. In this compilation, the fractions which appear before the multicharged ions simply serve as a reminder that the concentration of a species should be expressed in equivalents per liter.

Once the limiting equivalent ionic conductances for a few ions have been determined, values for other ionic species are more easily established. Thus, knowing the limiting equivalent conductance for sodium chloride, plus the limiting equivalent ionic conductance for the sodium ion, we can calculate the equivalent conductance for chloride at infinite dilution from the relation

$$\lambda°_{Cl^-} = (\Lambda_0)_{NaCl} - \lambda°_{Na^+}$$

Limiting equivalent conductances for weak electrolytes, such as acetic acid, cannot be evaluated by the graphical procedure suggested in Figure 17-8. However, since the limiting equivalent conductance of acetic acid is defined by the relationship

$$(\Lambda_0)_{CH_3COOH} = \lambda°_{H^+} + \lambda°_{CH_3COO^-}$$

the availability of values for the limiting equivalent ionic conductances of hydrogen and acetate ions in Table 17-3 allows us to calculate Λ_0 for this weak electrolyte:

$$(\Lambda_0)_{CH_3COOH} = 349.8 + 40.9 = 390.7 \text{ mho} \cdot \text{cm}^2$$

Alternatively, if data are available, the limiting equivalent conductances for three appropriate strong electrolytes may be combined to yield the limiting equivalent conductance for a weak electrolyte. Thus,

$$(\Lambda_0)_{CH_3COOH} = (\Lambda_0)_{HCl} + (\Lambda_0)_{NaCH_3COO} - (\Lambda_0)_{NaCl}$$

The second procedure is better from an experimental viewpoint; it is much easier to measure the limiting equivalent conductance for a strong electrolyte than to determine the limiting equivalent ionic conductance for a single ion.

Experimental Apparatus and Techniques

Conductometric titrations as well as absolute determinations of conductance always involve the measurement of resistance. Recalling, however, that the resistance and conductance of an electrolyte solution bear a reciprocal relationship to each other, one can easily calculate the latter quantity after the former is obtained. Accordingly, the most important item of equipment needed for conductometric methods of analysis is a suitable resistance bridge.

Measurement of Resistance or Conductance. In principle, one can determine the resistance of an electrolyte solution by passing a known direct current through a portion of the unknown sample, contained in an appropriate conductance cell, by measuring the difference in potential between the two electrodes of the cell, and by calculating the resistance of the solution from Ohm's law. Unfortunately, unless special care is exercised, the direct-current technique usually leads to experimental results which are meaningless, since the passage of a direct current through a solution causes the composition and, therefore, the resistance of that solution to change in the vicinity of the two electrodes. Consequently, practical conductance measurements almost invariably require the use of an alternating-current conductance bridge. With high-frequency alternating current, no net chemical reactions occur at the electrodes.

Most of the electrical circuits employed for the determination of solution resistances utilize a resistance-capacitance network called a Wheatstone bridge, one common variety being illustrated in Figure 17-9. An alternating voltage source, S, which operates within a frequency range of 1000 to 10,000 cycles per second (hertz) and at an amplitude of 6 to 10 v, is connected between points M and O. Frequently, this source is an audio frequency oscillator, although the ordinary 60 cycle alternating current from laboratory electrical outlets could be used. The Wheatstone bridge circuit includes three precision resistors, R_1, R_2, and R_3, which may be varied, and a variable capacitor, C, whose purpose is to allow one to compensate for the capacitance of the conductance cell and, thereby, to improve the sensitivity of the measurements. The unknown resistance of the sample solution is denoted by R_x. A null detector (ND) serves to indicate when no current flows between points N and P. The latter device can be a simple alternating-current meter, a set

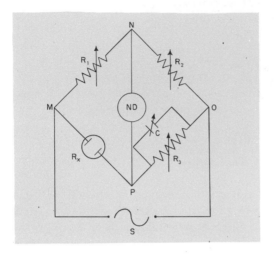

FIGURE 17-9. Wheatstone bridge circuit for conductance measurements.

of headphones for audio detection of frequencies in the kilocycle range, or a cathode ray oscilloscope.

In use, the Wheatstone bridge is turned on with the conductance cell containing the sample solution in place, and the variable resistors are adjusted until the null detector indicates that zero, or at least minimal, current is flowing between points N and P. When this condition prevails, the potentials at these two points must be equal, and an analysis of the electrical circuit leads to the conclusion that

$$\frac{R_x}{R_3} = \frac{R_1}{R_2}$$

or

$$R_x = \frac{R_1 R_3}{R_2}$$

Thus, the conductance of the unknown solution, L_x, is given by the relation

$$L_x = \frac{1}{R_x} = \frac{R_2}{R_1 R_3}$$

From the known values of R_1, R_2, and R_3, the desired conductance is calculated. Frequently, it is convenient to make resistances R_2 and R_3 equal, so that the value of R_1 is identical to the reciprocal of the conductance.

Numerous refinements may be made in the Wheatstone bridge circuit for highly accurate work, but even simple apparatus suffices for conductometric titrimetry. In some commercially available conductance bridges, resistances R_1 and R_2 are replaced by a uniform slidewire with a movable contact, as in a potentiometer. Moreover, the third resistor, R_3, is often a decade resistance box. Nevertheless, the experimental procedure still involves, fundamentally, an adjustment of three resistances until the bridge circuit is balanced.

Conductance Cells.   Two typical conductance cells are depicted in Figure 17-10. For some practical applications, the parameters of a conductance cell, namely the areas of the electrodes and their distance of separation, should be selected or adjusted so that the resistances or conductances to be measured have easily determinable values. Generally, platinum electrodes are employed and, if reproducible and accurate results are desired, the electrodes must be sealed into position. Figure 17-10A shows a cell which is suitable for the precise measurement of absolute conductances; the leads from the two electrodes are spaced far apart to minimize capacitance effects. The common dip-type cell illustrated in Figure 17-10B is particularly convenient to use for laboratory measurements of the conductivity of distilled water or dilute aqueous solutions, since the cell can be readily immersed into a beaker containing the desired sample.

It is customary in conductance work to coat the surface of each electrode with a thin layer of finely divided, spongy platinum metal (platinum black). This is done to increase the effective surface area of each electrode and to minimize the capacitance of the conductance cell. However, it is vitally important that the film of platinum black not be too thick; otherwise, errors may arise from surface adsorption of the species of interest as well as of impurities. Since the layer of platinum black has a tendency to deteriorate when permitted to dry out, a conductance cell should be stored with distilled water in contact with the electrodes. It should be stressed that good results

FIGURE 17-10.   Two types of conductance cells.

can be obtained for routine measurements with bright (unplatinized) electrodes.

As stated earlier, it is unnecessary to know the areas of the electrodes or the distance by which they are separated when conductometric titrations are performed. If the electrodes are fixed rigidly in their positions within a cell, any variations in conductance during a titration can be correlated with changes in the chemical system under investigation.

On the other hand, if one intends to evaluate the solubility product of an insoluble compound or the dissociation constant for a weak acid, accurate values of the specific conductance κ are needed. Since the specific conductance of an electrolyte solution is related to the total conductance by the expression

$$L = \kappa \frac{A}{l}$$

or

$$\kappa = L \frac{l}{A} = L\Theta$$

it is evident that the **cell constant,** Θ, together with the conductance, L, must be determined. Unfortunately, for most cells used in conductance measurements, the effective values of A and l bear no simple relationship to the actual physical dimensions of the cell. This is so because a solution usually surrounds the electrodes (see Fig. 17-10) and because the electric field near the electrodes is nonuniform. In practice, one evaluates the cell constant empirically with a solution whose specific conductance has been previously established in an ideal conductance cell. Thus, the solution of known specific conductance is placed into the cell to be calibrated; the conductance, L, is determined; and the cell constant is computed. Thereafter, the cell constant is assumed to have the calculated value, and so the specific conductances of unknown solutions can be obtained. Aqueous potassium chloride solutions have been adopted as calibration standards for conductance cells; specific conductances for three different concentrations of potassium chloride are listed in Table 17-4. For best results one should choose a potassium chloride solution having a specific conductance similar to that of the unknown sample.

TABLE 17-4. SPECIFIC CONDUCTANCES OF POTASSIUM CHLORIDE SOLUTIONS AT 25°C

Grams of KCl, Weighed in Air with Brass Weights, per Liter of Solution	κ, **mho · cm^{-1}**
76.401	0.11134
7.4569	0.012856
0.74405	0.0014088

Temperature Control.   It must be emphasized that the conductance of an electrolyte solution is a function of temperature, the mobilities of the majority of aqueous ions increasing approximately 2 per cent for a one degree rise in temperature. For absolute conductance measurements designed for the evaluation of solubility products and acid dissociation constants, the temperature should be regulated very closely. As we shall see, however, conductometric titrations require the determination of changes in conductance during the course of a reaction. In conductometric titrimetry it is unnecessary for the solution temperature to be adjusted to any particular value, or even for the temperature to be known; it has only to stay constant throughout the titration. Since many titration reactions are appreciably exothermic or endothermic, some form of temperature regulation is advisable for refined titration experiments. Generally, it is sufficient to immerse the conductance cell in a water bath at ambient temperature, although a thermostated oil bath is invariably needed for absolute conductance measurements.

Changes in Volume.   If the sample solution is inordinately diluted with titrant during the performance of a conductometric titration, the observed conductance undergoes an undesirable variation, in addition to the expected change due to chemical reaction. The dilution effect arises because the conductance of a solution depends upon the concentrations of all ionic species present. Customarily, one corrects for this effect by multiplying each conductance reading by the factor $(V + v)/V$, where V is the original volume of the sample and v is the volume of titrant introduced. Notice that this correction factor, being always greater than unity, increases each conductance reading to overcome the effect of dilution. This procedure is valid only insofar as conductance is a linear function of electrolyte concentration. Such a relationship is followed, however, if the changes in volume during a titration are reasonably small. Therefore, to minimize this problem in practical work, the concentration of the titrant should be at least 10 times greater than that of the species being determined, and the titrant itself may be delivered from a microburet or calibrated syringe.

Conductometric Titrations

Although conductance is a nonspecific physical property of electrolyte solutions — depending upon all ionic species present — the substitution of one ion for another will cause the conductance to change if the intrinsic mobilities of these two species differ. As shown in Table 17-3, the limiting equivalent ionic conductance for hydrogen ion is almost exactly seven times larger than that for sodium ion. Therefore, a certain quantity of hydrogen ion contributes approximately seven times as much to the conductance of an aqueous solution as does an identical concentration of sodium ion. Similarly, chloride ions conduct electricity somewhat better than nitrate anions. If a titration reaction leads to replacement of an ionic component of the sample solution by one of the ions of the titrant, and if these two species have different mobilities, the conductance of the solution will vary with added titrant. Thus, one performs a conductometric titration by measuring the conductance of a solution as titrant is introduced and plots the experimental data, after correcting for the dilution effect, to determine the equivalence point.

Conductometric titrimetry is intended primarily for the location of equivalence points of titrations. Since only the changes in conductance which occur during the course of a titration are significant, it is never necessary to evaluate the specific conductance of a solution. A suitable conductance cell may consist of nothing more than a beaker of appropriate size to contain the sample with two electrodes sealed into the beaker wall, plus a magnetic or motor-driven stirring device. Dip-type cells are frequently employed, although one must be careful to mix the solution thoroughly after each volume increment of titrant is added.

In principle, conductometric titrimetry is applicable to the determination of equivalence points for each of the four classes of volumetric methods of analysis — neutralization, precipitation, complex-formation, and oxidation-reduction processes. However, redox reactions rarely produce the adequately large changes in conductance desired for the accurate location of equivalence points, and the formation of a complex ion is often characteristically slow and may proceed in a series of steps. Most successful conductometric titrations involve acid-base chemistry, but several applications to precipitation reactions have been proposed.

Acid-Base Titrations.   Among the ionic species in aqueous media, hydrogen ion and hydroxide ion possess the highest mobilities. Therefore, large variations in solution conductance occur during an acid-base titration, making the conductometric method of equivalence point location especially sensitive.

A classic example of a conductometric procedure involves the titration of hydrochloric acid with sodium hydroxide, although the equivalence point of this particular titration can be easily located through the use of potentiometric titrimetry or internal acid-base indicators. Since both hydrochloric acid and sodium hydroxide are strong electrolytes, the titration reaction may be formulated as

$$\mathrm{H^+ + Cl^- + Na^+ + OH^- \rightleftharpoons Na^+ + Cl^- + H_2O}$$

and, as titrant is added, the conductance of the solution varies in the manner shown in Figure 17-11A. At the start of the titration, the conductance is relatively large, owing to the presence of the highly mobile hydrogen ions. However, the addition of sodium hydroxide titrant neutralizes hydrogen ions and replaces them with a stoichiometric quantity of sodium ion. In view of the much lower equivalent ionic conductance for sodium ion, compared to the proton, the solution conductance decreases rapidly — and linearly, if dilution is minimized or an appropriate correction is applied — as the equivalence point is approached. Beyond the equivalence point, however, the conductance of the solution rises again because of the introduction of excess sodium and hydroxide ions. Notice that the conductance changes less rapidly after than before the equivalence point, since the sum of the equivalent ionic conductances for sodium and hydroxide ions is smaller than the equivalent ionic conductance for hydrogen ion (see Table 17-3). Furthermore, if the volume of the solution remains essentially unchanged throughout the titration, the contribution of chloride ion to the total conductance will be constant.

Figure 17-11A reveals that the strong acid-strong base system produces a V-shaped titration curve, the equivalence point lying at the intersection of the two straight-line portions of this curve. However, it is noteworthy that

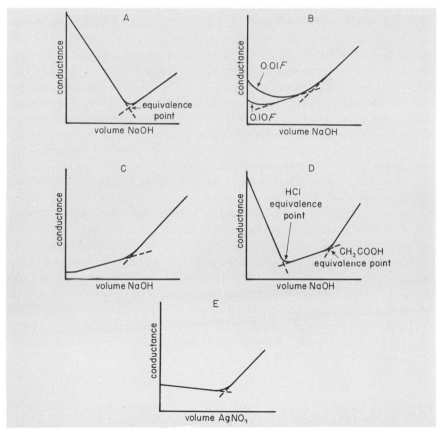

Figure 17-11. Representative conductometric titration curves for acid-base and precipitation titrations. Curve A: titration of hydrochloric acid with sodium hydroxide. Curve B: titration of acetic acid with sodium hydroxide. Curve C: titration of phenol with sodium hydroxide. Curve D: titration of hydrochloric acid-acetic acid mixture with sodium hydroxide. Curve E: titration of sodium chloride with silver nitrate.

the observed conductance departs from these straight lines near the equivalence point, and so the actual titration curve is somewhat rounded at the equivalence point. Such behavior results from the slight incompleteness of the neutralization reaction. Near the equivalence point, small concentrations of hydrogen ion and hydroxide ion remain unreacted and cause the true conductance to be a little larger than anticipated. Theoretically, if the acid-base reaction were absolutely complete, the conductometric titration curve would exhibit a sharp discontinuity at the equivalence point. In general, the extent of curvature in the vicinity of the equivalence point increases as the equilibrium constant for the titration reaction decreases and as the concentrations of the reagents diminish.

One special feature of conductometric titrimetry is that analytical results can be derived from experimental measurements which are relatively distant from the equivalence point of a titration. In practice, one makes two or three conductance measurements before the equivalence point and takes several more readings beyond the equivalence point in order to define the two straight-line portions of the curve. These lines are then extended to their point of intersection, and the equivalence point volume is determined graphically. Uncertainties due to the curved region of the graph are thereby avoided. Thus, conductometric titrimetry is well suited to chemical reactions having unfavorably small equilibrium constants or involving low concentrations of reactants. It is interesting to recall that spectrophotometric titrations offer a similar advantage. Clearly, the conductometric method for locating the equivalence point of a titration differs markedly from the potentiometric technique, in which measurements near and at the equivalence point are essential.

Another virtue of conductometric strong acid-strong base titrations is that the *relative* change in conductance is nearly the same regardless of the concentrations of the reagents. Therefore, the conductometric analysis of dilute solutions of strong acids or strong bases yields results which have similar accuracy to those obtained for relatively concentrated samples. This advantage should be contrasted against the problems encountered in the conventional volumetric analysis of a dilute solution of an acid or base.

Conductometric titrimetry is applicable to the reaction between a weak acid and a strong base, as in the titration of acetic acid with sodium hydroxide:

$$CH_3COOH + Na^+ + OH^- \rightleftharpoons Na^+ + CH_3COO^- + H_2O$$

As shown in Figure 17-11B, the experimental conductometric titration curve differs considerably from that for the preceding strong acid-strong base system. The original conductance of the sample solution is due mainly to the hydrogen ions resulting from dissociation of acetic acid, although acetate ions make a small contribution. When sodium hydroxide is added to the sample solution, the conductance falls because acetate ion, produced in the titration reaction, represses the dissociation of acetic acid. This decrease in conductance occurs in spite of increases in the sodium ion and acetate ion concentrations. However, as the titration is continued, the conductance passes through a minimum and then rises linearly up to the equivalence point as the concentrations of sodium and acetate ions build up. Beyond the equivalence point, the conductance increases even more rapidly because of the introduction of excess sodium hydroxide titrant. It is evident that the linear portions of the conductometric titration curve for a weak acid-strong base system do not intersect at a sharp angle, and so the equivalence point is more difficult to locate precisely than that for a strong acid-strong base reaction. Furthermore, the position and curvature of the minimum in a weak acid-strong base titration curve (see Fig. 17-11B), as well as the degree of curvature at the equivalence point itself, depend upon the concentrations of the reagents and the dissociation constant for the weak acid.

An excellent demonstration of the analytical value of conductometric titrimetry can be seen in Figure 17-11C, which depicts the titration curve for the reaction between phenol and sodium hydroxide.

Inspection of Figure 8-4 shows that phenol, having an acid dissociation constant of approximately 1×10^{-10}, could not possibly be titrated with an aqueous sodium hydroxide solution according to potentiometric or other classic techniques. However, phenol can be determined conductometrically with good accuracy. Prior to the addition of any sodium hydroxide, the conductance of the sample solution is quite small, simply because phenol is such an exceedingly weak acid. Once the titration is begun, the conductance exhibits an almost linear increase because of the formation of phenolate anion and the introduction of sodium ions from the titrant. As the equivalence point is reached and passed, the slope of the conductometric titration curve changes, since excess sodium hydroxide is being added. Fundamentally, the two straight-line portions of the titration curve have dissimilar slopes because the equivalent ionic conductances for phenolate and hydroxide ions are different.

In certain cases, the analysis of mixtures of acids can be accomplished more conveniently and accurately through conductometric titrimetry than by any other method. For example, we discovered earlier that the potentiometric titration curve for the titration with sodium hydroxide of a solution containing hydrochloric acid and acetic acid (see Fig. 8-6) lacks the good definition required for the precise determination of each component. On the other hand, when the progress of such a titration is followed conductometrically, we obtain the result illustrated in Figure 17-11D, which definitely permits the successful analysis of the acid mixture. It should be pointed out that conductometric and potentiometric methods might well be employed in combination for the analysis of a hydrochloric acid-acetic acid mixture. A conductometric titration yields a reliable value for the hydrochloric acid content of a sample, whereas potentiometric titrimetry would allow a highly accurate determination of the *sum* of the two acids from which the acetic acid concentration could be calculated by difference.

Precipitation Titrations. If we consider the precipitation titration of a sample solution containing sodium chloride with silver nitrate, the overall reaction may be represented as

$$Na^+ + Cl^- + Ag^+ + NO_3^- \rightleftharpoons AgCl(s) + Na^+ + NO_3^-$$

Up to the equivalence point, the addition of silver nitrate results in the precipitation of silver chloride and, in effect, chloride ion is replaced in solution by a stoichiometric quantity of nitrate ion. Since the limiting equivalent ionic conductance for nitrate is slightly less than that for chloride (see Table 17-3), the conductance of the solution will exhibit a small, but linear, decrease until the equivalence point is reached. Thereafter, as the concentration of excess silver nitrate increases, the conductance rises, as shown in Figure 17-11E.

Although the conductometric titration curve for a precipitation process is expected to display a positive slope beyond the equivalence point (because of the excess titrant), the straight-line portion of the graph prior to the equivalence point may have either a positive or negative slope, or perhaps no slope at all. If the mobility of the anion being precipitated is greater than that of the anion of the titrant, the titration curve will be V-shaped. Conversely, when the anion of the titrant has the greater equivalent ionic conductance, the conductance of the solution will increase up to the equivalence point. Finally, in the rare situation that the mobilities of the two anions happen to be identical, the initial portion of the conductometric titration curve will have zero slope. A similar set of relationships can be formulated if the cation in a sample medium is precipitated by the anion of the titrant and is, simultaneously, replaced in solution by the cation of that titrant. In general, since the determination of equivalence points is most easily accomplished for V-shaped titration curves, one should seek a titrant which will produce this result.

Conductometric precipitation titrations have not been employed as extensively as methods involving acid-base reactions. One reason is that changes in conductance during a precipitation reaction are relatively small compared to the large variations found with neutralization processes. Such behavior stems from the fact that, aside from hydrogen ion and hydroxide ion, the mobilities of most ionic species are comparable in magnitude. Other problems encountered in any method of analysis involving the formation of a precipitate include coprecipitation and the slow attainment of solubility equilibrium.

Experiment 17-1

*POTENTIOMETRIC TITRATION OF HALIDES AND
HALIDE MIXTURES*

Purpose

This experiment provides experience in the performance of potentiometric precipitation titrations.

Preparation

A standard $0.02\,F$ silver nitrate solution, prepared according to the procedure described in Experiment 10-1, should be available.

Prepare 250 ml of a standard $0.02\,F$ potassium chloride solution by accurately weighing out the required amount of analytical-reagent-grade potassium chloride which has been previously dried at 110°C for at least one hour. Dissolve the solid in distilled water, transfer the solution quantitatively to a 250 ml volumetric flask, and dilute and mix the solution.

Prepare 250 ml of a standard $0.02\,F$ potassium bromide solution in the manner indicated in the preceding paragraph.

Approximately 1 liter of a buffer solution containing $0.6\,F$ acetic acid and $0.6\,F$ sodium acetate is needed.

Procedure

Assemble the titration apparatus as illustrated in Figure 17-6. For the titration vessel, a 250 ml or 400 ml beaker is most convenient. Clean a 5- or 6-inch length of pure silver wire for the indicator electrode by dipping it for several seconds in $8\,F$ nitric acid and rinsing it thoroughly with distilled water. A commercial fiber-type calomel reference electrode may be employed, except that the reference electrode must be brought into contact with the sample solution through a 4 per cent agar-potassium nitrate salt bridge in order to prevent the leakage of potassium chloride from the reference electrode into the sample solution. The titration vessel should be equipped with a magnetic stirring bar. The potential-measuring instrument is preferably a direct-reading pH meter calibrated in voltage units.

Determination of Chloride. Pipet 25.00 ml of the $0.02\,F$ potassium chloride solution into a 250 ml beaker containing a magnetic stirring bar. Add approximately 75 ml of the acetic acid-sodium acetate buffer. Immerse the end of the silver indicator electrode and the tip of the salt bridge tube from the reference electrode into the sample solution, connect the electrodes to the potential-measuring instrument, and start the magnetic stirrer.

Titrate the sample with a standard $0.02\,F$ silver nitrate solution, recording the potential of the indicator electrode after each addition of titrant. Add relatively large increments of titrant (1 to 3 ml) at the beginning of the titration, waiting until the potential does not drift more than 1 or 2 mv per minute before introducing the next portion of titrant. Near the equivalence point of the titration, add the titrant in exact 0.1 ml increments. Continue the titration at least 1 ml beyond the equivalence point. Determine the equivalence point by means of one of the graphical or analytical procedures discussed in the text.

Determination of Bromide.   Repeat the procedure just described, using 25.00 ml of standard $0.02\,F$ potassium bromide instead of potassium chloride.

Determination of Chloride and Bromide in Mixtures.   Repeat the procedure, using a mixture of 10.00 ml of standard $0.02\,F$ potassium chloride and 10.00 ml of standard $0.02\,F$ potassium bromide.

Plot the experimental titration curves and tabulate the results of the titrations. For each titration, compare the number of millimoles of halide found with the number of millimoles taken for analysis. In the case of the halide mixtures, calculate the millimoles of bromide from the volume of silver nitrate titrant needed to reach the first "break" in the titration curve, calculate the millimoles of chloride from the difference in volume between the first and second "breaks" in the curve, and calculate the sum of the quantities of bromide and chloride from the total volume of titrant needed to reach the second "break." Compute the titration error, in per cent with the proper sign, for each determination.

Experiment 17-2

POTENTIOMETRIC TITRATION OF IRON(II)

Purpose

This experiment shows the application of potentiometric titrimetry to the iron(II)-cerium(IV) titration described in Experiment 13-4.

Preparation

A standard 0.1 F cerium(IV) solution, prepared as described in Experiment 13-3, is required. Alternatively, a standard 0.02 F potassium permanganate or 0.0167 F potassium dichromate solution may be employed as the titrant.

Follow the first three steps of the procedure given in Experiment 13-4 — (a) preparation of the sample solution, (b) adjustment of the oxidation state of iron, and (c) addition of special reagents, if needed, with the following major exception: If stannous chloride is used to reduce iron(III) to iron(II), omit addition of the mercury(II) chloride solution and instead, proceed immediately to titrate the iron(II) solution potentiometrically with the standard oxidant as described in the next section.

A suitable iron(II) sample solution can be prepared if an accurately weighed sample of analytical-reagent-grade ferrous ammonium sulfate, $Fe(NH_4)_2(SO_4)_2 \cdot$ 6 H_2O, is dissolved in 1 F sulfuric acid. This solution should be titrated without delay, as iron(II) undergoes slow air oxidation.

It should be noted that, when excess tin(II) remains in the sample solution after the reduction of iron(III), two steps or breaks will be observed in the subsequent titration curve — the first corresponding to oxidation of residual tin(II) to tin(IV) and the second to the desired oxidation of iron(II). However, the quantity of iron is readily related to the difference in the volumes of titrant required to reach the two equivalence points.

Procedure

Assemble a potentiometric titration apparatus similar to that shown in Figure 17-6 and mentioned in Experiment 17-1, except that a platinum wire indicator electrode should be used. The saturated calomel reference electrode can be inserted directly into the sample solution to be titrated.

Connect the electrodes to the potential-measuring instrument, and start the magnetic stirrer. Titrate the iron(II) sample with a standard 0.1 F cerium(IV) solution, or with potassium permanganate or potassium dichromate, recording the potential of the indicator electrode after each addition of titrant. As usual, add relatively large increments of titrant at the start of the titration. Near the equivalence point, introduce exactly 0.1 ml volumes of titrant to facilitate the precise location of the equivalence point, and continue the titration at least 1 ml beyond that point.

Plot the experimental titration curve, locate the equivalence point, and calculate and report the percentage or weight of iron in the sample. Replicate determinations should agree to within two or three parts per thousand.

In view of the effect of phosphoric acid on the titration curves for iron(II) with strong oxidants (see, for example, Fig. 13-2), it is of considerable interest to compare the results obtained with and without added phosphoric acid. Furthermore, if desired, the usual internal redox indicators may be added in order to compare the visual and potentiometric end points.

SUGGESTIONS FOR ADDITIONAL LABORATORY WORK

Potentiometric Titrimetry

Earlier in this text, procedures for two potentiometric acid-base titrations were presented in detail. Experiment 8-2 provides for the analysis of a carbonate-bicarbonate mixture in an aqueous medium, and Experiment 9-1 is an especially elegant demonstration of the applicability of nonaqueous acid-base reactions to chemical analysis.

In addition, attention should be called to experiments dealing with potentiometric titrations in the following laboratory textbooks:

1. C. E. Meloan and R. W. Kiser: *Problems and Experiments in Instrumental Analysis*, Charles E. Merrill Books, Inc., Columbus, Ohio, 1963.
2. C. N. Reilley and D. T. Sawyer: *Experiments for Instrumental Methods*, McGraw-Hill Book Company, New York, 1961.

Conductometric Titrimetry

A number of interesting experiments are contained in the two laboratory texts just mentioned. Generally, equipment and techniques for the performance of conductometric titrations tend to be diverse, and so specific instructions for such experiments are not presented here.

For the majority of routine titrations, a dip-type conductance cell and a commercially available conductance meter (such as that manufactured by Beckman Instruments, Inc., Cedar Grove Operations, Cedar Grove, N.J.) provide very satisfactory results. Obviously, a determination of the cell constant is unnecessary.

The titration vessel itself may be a beaker which can accommodate the conductivity cell and the buret containing the titrant. The advantages of a relatively concentrated titrant, delivered from a microburet, should be recalled. Stirring of the solution can be accomplished with the aid of a Teflon-covered magnetic bar, or the conductance cell and titration vessel can merely be swirled gently to effect mixing of the reactants.

As described in the text, it is important to obtain at least three or four reliable conductance readings before and after the equivalence point; variations of the conductance very near the equivalence point have less usefulness. A conductometric titration curve normally consists of a plot of conductance versus the volume of titrant, and the experimental data are treated graphically as discussed in the text.

Some suggested conductometric titrations are:

(a) 0.001 F hydrochloric acid with 0.1 F sodium hydroxide
(b) 0.01 F acetic acid with 0.1 F sodium hydroxide
(c) 0.001 F hydrochloric acid with 0.1 F aqueous ammonia
(d) 0.01 F acetic acid with 0.1 F aqueous ammonia
(e) 0.01 F hydrochloric acid plus 0.01 F acetic acid with 0.1 F sodium hydroxide
(f) 0.01 F sodium chloride with 0.1 F silver nitrate
(g) 0.01 F sodium chloride with 0.1 F silver acetate

QUESTIONS AND PROBLEMS

1. Suppose that the activity of copper(II) in an aqueous medium is to be determined through a direct potentiometric measurement with a copper metal indicator electrode, the pertinent half-reaction being

$$Cu^{++} + 2\,e \rightleftharpoons Cu$$

   (a) If an error of exactly 1 mv in the observed potential of the copper electrode is incurred, calculate the corresponding per cent uncertainty in the copper(II) activity.
   (b) If the error in the copper(II) activity is not to exceed 1 per cent, calculate the maximal tolerable uncertainty in the electromotive force of the copper indicator electrode.
2. The following data were observed during the potentiometric pH titration of a 25.00 ml aliquot of a solution containing a weak monoprotic acid with 0.1165 F sodium hydroxide:

Volume, ml	pH	Volume, ml	pH
0	2.89	15.60	8.40
2.00	4.52	15.70	9.29
4.00	5.06	15.80	10.07
10.00	5.89	16.00	10.65
12.00	6.15	17.00	11.34
14.00	6.63	18.00	11.63
15.00	7.08	20.00	12.00
15.50	7.75	24.00	12.41

   (a) Construct a plot of the experimental titration curve.
   (b) Construct the first derivative titration curve.
   (c) Construct the second derivative titration curve.
   (d) Calculate the concentration of the original acid solution.
   (e) Evaluate the dissociation constant for the weak acid and the pH at the equivalence point of the titration.
3. Consider the determination of zinc by titration with a standard potassium ferrocyanide solution, $K_4Fe(CN)_6$, according to the precipitation reaction

$$3\,Zn^{++} + 2\,K^+ + 2\,Fe(CN)_6^{-4} \rightleftharpoons K_2Zn_3[Fe(CN)_6]_2(s)$$

The solubility product for the precipitate is 1.0×10^{-17}. Assume that 50.00 ml of a 0.001000 M zinc ion solution, containing 0.001000 M ferricyanide ion, is titrated with 0.2000 F potassium ferrocyanide; the effect of dilution may be ignored. The progress of such a titration may be followed potentiometrically with the aid of a platinum indicator electrode and a saturated calomel reference electrode, the potential of the platinum electrode being governed by the ferricyanide-ferrocyanide half-reaction. Construct a theoretical plot of the potential of the platinum indicator electrode versus the saturated calomel electrode, on the assumption that the formal potential for the ferricyanide-ferrocyanide couple is +0.70 v versus NHE under the conditions of the titration. Neglect the existence of any liquid-junction potentials.
4. Describe in detail how the iodine-iodide couple, in conjunction with a platinum indicator electrode, might be used to follow the progress of the titration of silver ion with a standard potassium iodide solution.

5. Discuss the practical and theoretical limitations of direct potentiometry for analytical purposes.
6. Calculate the electromotive force of the following galvanic cell, assuming the absence of liquid-junction potentials:

$$\text{Hg} \mid \text{Hg}_2\text{Cl}_2(\text{s}), \text{KCl} \ (1.0 \ F) \ \| \ \text{Ag}^+ \ (0.00250 \ M) \mid \text{Ag}$$

7. Under what conditions may a glass electrode be employed as a reference electrode in potentiometric titrimetry?
8. Silver ion in 100.0 ml of a dilute nitric acid medium was titrated potentiometrically with a standard $2.068 \times 10^{-4} \ F$ potassium iodide solution, according to the reaction

$$\text{Ag}^+ + \text{I}^- \ \rightleftharpoons \ \text{AgI}(\text{s})$$

A silver iodide indicator electrode and a saturated calomel reference electrode were used, and the following titration data resulted:

Volume of KI, ml	E versus SCE, v
0	+0.2623
1.00	0.2550
2.00	0.2451
3.00	0.2309
3.50	0.2193
3.75	0.2105
4.00	0.1979
4.25	0.1730
4.50	0.0316
4.75	−0.0066

(a) Calculate the concentration of silver ion in the original sample solution.
(b) Compute the titration error, in per cent with the proper sign, if potassium iodide titrant is added until the potential of the indicator electrode reaches +0.0600 v versus SCE.

9. A 0.2479 gm sample of anhydrous sodium hexachloroplatinate(IV), Na_2PtCl_6, was analyzed for its chloride content by means of a potentiometric titration with standard silver nitrate. The weighed sample was decomposed in the presence of hydrazine sulfate, platinum(IV) being reduced to the metal, and the liberated chloride ion was titrated with 0.2314 F silver nitrate. A silver indicator electrode, a saturated calomel reference electrode, and a nitric acid salt bridge were used in the performance of the titration. The resulting experimental data were as follows:

Volume of AgNO$_3$, ml	E versus SCE, v
0	+0.072
13.00	0.140
13.20	0.145
13.40	0.152
13.60	0.160
13.80	0.172
14.00	0.196
14.20	0.290
14.40	0.326
14.60	0.340

Calculate the apparent percentage of chloride in the sample, the true percentage of chloride in sodium hexachloroplatinate(IV), and the per cent relative error between these two results.

10. If the electromotive force of the galvanic cell

$$- \text{Pt, H}_2 \text{ (0.5 atm)} \mid \text{solution of unknown pH} \mid \text{Hg}_2\text{Cl}_2\text{(s), KCl(s)} \mid \text{Hg} +$$

is 0.366 v, calculate the pH of the unknown solution, neglecting the liquid-junction potential.

11. The following galvanic cell was constructed for the measurement of the dissociation constant of a weak monoprotic acid, HA:

$$- \text{Pt, H}_2 \text{ (0.8 atm)} \mid \text{HA (0.5 } F\text{), NaCl (1.0 } F\text{), AgCl(s)} \mid \text{Ag} +$$

If the observed electromotive force of this cell was 0.568 v, what is the dissociation constant for the weak acid?

12. Explain why unsaturated potassium hydrogen tartrate buffers have essentially the same pH values as those shown in Table 17-1 for saturated potassium hydrogen tartrate buffers.

13. Using the limiting equivalent ionic conductances listed in Table 17-3, sketch qualitatively, but accurately, the conductometric titration curves for each of the following titrations:
    (a) hydrochloric acid with aqueous ammonia
    (b) silver nitrate with lithium chloride
    (c) phenol with aqueous ammonia
    (d) ammonium chloride with sodium hydroxide
    (e) acetic acid with aqueous ammonia
    (f) barium nitrate with sulfuric acid
    (g) silver nitrate with hydrochloric acid
    (h) a mixture of hydrochloric acid and acetic acid with aqueous ammonia.

14. A measurement of the specific conductance of a saturated solution of barium sulfate at 25°C gave a value of 4.332×10^{-6} mho $\cdot$ cm^{-1}, and the specific conductance of the distilled water used in the preparation of the saturated solution was 1.384×10^{-6} mho $\cdot$ cm^{-1}. Calculate the molar solubility as well as the solubility product of barium sulfate. Assume that the equivalent conductance for barium sulfate in this dilute solution is identical to the value at infinite dilution, and assume that the net specific conductance of barium sulfate is the difference between the stated values.

15. The limiting equivalent conductances for potassium nitrate (KNO$_3$), nitric acid (HNO$_3$), and potassium propionate (KC$_2$H$_5$COO) are 145.0, 421.2, and 109.3 mho $\cdot$ cm^2, respectively, at 25°C. In addition, the equivalent conductance of a $0.005000 \, F$ propionic acid (C$_2$H$_5$COOH) solution is 19.47 mho $\cdot$ cm^2 at the same temperature.
    (a) Calculate the limiting equivalent conductance for propionic acid.
    (b) Calculate the dissociation constant for propionic acid.

16. Consider the titration of 50.00 ml of $0.001000 \, F$ sodium hydroxide with $0.1000 \, F$ perchloric acid in a conductance cell whose constant (l/A) is 0.150 cm^{-1}. Calculate the conductance of the solution, neglecting dilution, after the addition of the following volumes (in milliliters) of titrant: (a) 0, (b) 0.1000, (c) 0.2000, (d) 0.4000, (e) 0.4500, (f) 0.5000, (g) 0.7500, and (h) 1.000. Assume the solution to be sufficiently dilute so that the equivalent ionic conductances for the various ions have the limiting values listed in Table 17-3. Construct a graph of the conductometric titration curve.

17. If the solubility product of lead iodate is 3.2×10^{-13}, what would be the resistance of a saturated solution of this salt, measured in a conductance cell having a

cell constant (l/A) of 0.3441 cm^{-1}? Neglect any correction for the solvent. Assume that the limiting equivalent conductance for lead iodate is applicable.

18. The resistance of a conductance cell, containing a dilute solution of potassium iodide and having a cell constant (l/A) of 0.318 cm^{-1}, was observed to be 5216 ohms at 25°C. Assuming that the equivalent ionic conductances for potassium and iodide ions in this dilute solution are essentially identical to the values at infinite dilution (Table 17-3), calculate the concentration of the potassium iodide solution. In view of the variation of the equivalent ionic conductance of an ion with concentration, how does the preceding calculated concentration of potassium iodide differ from the true concentration?

19. A 50.00 ml sample of a dilute acetic acid solution was titrated conductometrically with 0.2175 F aqueous ammonia, and the following resistance readings were obtained in the region of the equivalence point:

Volume of NH$_3$, ml	Resistance, ohms
0.350	892
0.400	841
0.450	794
0.500	738
0.550	690
0.600	650
0.650	629
0.700	621
0.750	617
0.800	616
0.850	615
0.900	614

Plot the titration data in terms of conductance versus volume of titrant, and determine the concentration of the acetic acid solution.

20. When a portion of potassium chloride solution, prepared by dissolving 0.7441 gm of the pure solid in enough distilled water to make 1 liter of solution at 25°C (Table 17-4), was used to fill a conductance cell, the observed resistance was 2.749 ohms. Later, when the same cell was filled with a perchloric acid solution, the resistance of the conductance cell was found to be 1073 ohms.

   (a) Calculate the specific conductance of the perchloric acid solution.

   (b) Assuming that the equivalent conductance of perchloric acid under the conditions of this experiment is virtually identical to the limiting equivalent conductance of this solute (Table 17-3), calculate the concentration of the acid. Assess the validity of the assumption involved in the calculation.

SUGGESTIONS FOR ADDITIONAL READING

Books

1. R. G. Bates: *Determination of pH*, John Wiley & Sons, Inc., New York, 1964.
2. R. G. Bates: Electrometric methods of pH determination. *In* F. J. Welcher, ed.: *Standard Methods of Chemical Analysis*, sixth edition, Volume 3-A, D. Van Nostrand Co., Inc., New York, 1966, pp. 521–532.
3. D. G. Davis: Potentiometric titrations. *In* F. J. Welcher, ed.: *Standard Methods of Chemical Analysis*, sixth edition, Volume 3-A, D. Van Nostrand Co., Inc., New York, 1966, pp. 283–296.

4. N. H. Furman: Potentiometry. *In* I. M. Kolthoff and P. J. Elving, eds.: *Treatise on Analytical Chemistry*, Part I, Volume 4, Wiley-Interscience, New York, 1959, pp. 2269–2302.
5. S. Glasstone: *An Introduction to Electrochemistry*, D. Van Nostrand Co., Inc., New York, 1942.
6. H. A. Laitinen: *Chemical Analysis*, McGraw-Hill Book Co., New York, 1960, pp. 22–27; 326–341.
7. J. J. Lingane: *Electroanalytical Chemistry*, second edition, Wiley-Interscience, New York, 1958, pp. 9–35; 71–195.
8. J. W. Loveland: Conductometry and oscillometry. *In* I. M. Kolthoff and P. J. Elving, eds.: *Treatise on Analytical Chemistry*, Part I, Volume 4, Wiley-Interscience, New York, 1959, pp. 2569–2629.
9. D. A. MacInnes: *The Principles of Electrochemistry*, Reinhold Publishing Corporation, New York, 1939.
10. L. Meites and H. C. Thomas: *Advanced Analytical Chemistry*, McGraw-Hill Book Co., New York, 1958, pp. 17–132.
11. J. W. Ross: Conductometric titrations. *In* F. J. Welcher, ed.: *Standard Methods of Chemical Analysis*, sixth edition, Volume 3-A, D. Van Nostrand Co., Inc., New York, 1966, pp. 297–322.
12. H. F. Walton: *Principles and Methods of Chemical Analysis*, Prentice-Hall, Inc., New York, 1964, pp. 220–244; 390–427.

Papers

1. G. A. Rechnitz: Ion-selective electrodes. Chem. Eng. News, *45*, 146 (June 12, 1967).
2. C. N. Reilley and R. W. Schmid: Chelometric titrations with potentiometric end-point detection: mercury as pM indicator electrode. Anal. Chem., *30*, 947 (1958).
3. C. N. Reilley, R. W. Schmid, and D. W. Lamson: Chelometric titrations of metal ions with potentiometric end-point detection: (ethylenedinitrilo)tetraacetic acid. Anal. Chem., *30*, 953 (1958).

Chapter Eighteen

Coulometric
and Polarographic
Methods of Analysis

Some of the most interesting and unique methods of chemical analysis are based upon the fact that one may cause a desired reaction to take place when an external voltage of appropriate magnitude and polarity is impressed across the electrodes of an electrochemical cell. In **controlled-potential coulometry,** the electromotive force of an anode or cathode is maintained constant so that only a single reaction occurs at that electrode. By integrating the current which flows as a function of time, one can determine the total quantity of electricity produced by the desired reaction and can calculate the amount of the species of interest according to Faraday's law. In contrast to the preceding method of analysis, **polarography** does not involve the exhaustive oxidation or reduction of a substance, since the electrode at which reaction proceeds has a maximal area of only several square millimeters. Instead, the latter technique requires the recording of a so-called current-potential curve, which is a plot of the instantaneous current (flowing as an electroactive substance reacts at the surface of a dropping mercury electrode) versus the electrode potential. The magnitude of the current is quantitatively related to the concentration of the electroactive species, and the characteristics of the current-potential curve provide qualitative information, if needed, concerning the identity of the substance. Another important technique — **coulometric titration** — is essentially a method in which a titrant, electrochemically generated at constant current, reacts with the substance to be determined. The size of the constant current is analogous to the concentration of a standard titrant solution, and the time required to complete the titration is equivalent to the volume of titrant; so the current-time product bears a direct relationship to the unknown quantity of substance.

In the present chapter, we shall investigate the consequences of the passage of current through electrochemical cells. On the basis of this fundamental knowledge, the evolution and applications of several prominent methods of electroanalysis, including coulometric titrations, controlled-potential coulometry, and polarography as well as a few closely related techniques, will be discussed.

BEHAVIOR OF ELECTROLYTIC CELLS

Several interrelated phenomena occur when current is caused to pass through an electrochemical cell. First, changes in the concentrations of chemical species may arise at one or both electrodes. Second, there is an ohmic potential drop which develops because current flows against the resistance of the cell. Third, special effects related to the kinetics of electron-transfer processes influence the behavior of a cell. In addition, it should be recalled that, if the electrochemical cell contains solutions which share a common interface, liquid-junction potentials exist.

Current-Voltage Curves

Let us consider the behavior of an electrochemical cell consisting of a pair of identical copper electrodes, both of which are immersed directly into the same solution of copper(II) sulfate, say, at a concentration level of 0.01 F. The shorthand representation for this cell may be written as

$$Cu \mid CuSO_4 \ (0.01 \ F) \mid Cu$$

If the two copper electrodes are connected by an external conducting wire, no net current will flow through this circuit because the potentials of the electrodes happen to be identical. Consequently, the overall electromotive force of this cell is zero.

However, when a source of small voltage is attached to the copper electrodes, a current will pass through the electrochemical cell. At one of the electrodes, namely the cathode, copper(II) ions are reduced to the elemental state and deposited in the form of copper crystals

$$Cu^{++} + 2 \ e \rightleftharpoons Cu$$

Simultaneously, the second electrode undergoes anodic dissolution according to the half-reaction

$$Cu \rightleftharpoons Cu^{++} + 2 \ e$$

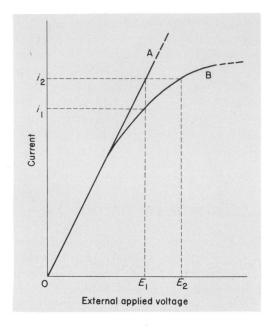

Current

O E_1 E_2

External applied voltage

FIGURE   18-1.   Current-applied voltage curves for the simple electrolytic cell

$$Cu \mid CuSO_4 \ (0.01 \ F) \mid Cu.$$

Curve A: variation of current with applied voltage for ideal situation in which the concentration of copper(II) is uniform throughout the solution. Curve B: variation of current with applied voltage, showing the effect of overpotential.

It should be noted that the present electrochemical cell behaves reversibly in the sense that a particular electrode may function as either anode or cathode, depending upon the polarity of the external voltage source. Moreover, observe that electrons flow from the external voltage source into the cathode at which copper(II) is reduced and that electrons are withdrawn from the anode where copper metal is oxidized. Therefore, *in an electrolytic cell, in which reactions are forced to occur through the imposition of an external voltage across the electrodes, the cathode is the negative electrode, whereas the positive electrode is the anode.* Exactly the opposite situation prevails for a galvanic cell, as emphasized in Chapter 12.

Since the processes occurring at the two copper electrodes are the reverse of each other, the *total* concentration of copper(II) in the solution will remain constant. However, because of electrolysis there is a tendency for some slight diminution in the concentration of copper(II) at the surface of the cathode and a corresponding small increase in the copper(II) concentration near the surface of the anode. Nevertheless, suppose that perfect homogeneity of the copper(II) solution is maintained, even in the vicinity of the electrodes, through highly efficient stirring. Under this special set of conditions, the current passing through the cell would show a linear dependence on the magnitude of the external voltage impressed across the electrodes, as depicted qualitatively by curve A of Figure 18-1. In other words, the electrochemical cell would act as a simple resistance, and the current, i, would be governed by Ohm's law,

$$i = \frac{E_{app}}{R}$$

where E_{app} is the voltage applied to the copper electrodes and R is the total resistance of the electrochemical cell. Such ideal behavior can be exhibited only if the potentials of the two copper electrodes remain absolutely the same — which means that the concentration of copper(II) must be uniform throughout the electrochemical cell and that no concentration gradients exist near the surfaces of the two electrodes.

According to the theory of hydrodynamics, a thin layer of stationary liquid is always present around a solid object immersed in a moving fluid, although the thickness of the immobile liquid film does decrease as the agitation of the fluid is increased. Therefore, no matter how efficiently the copper(II) sulfate solution is stirred, the copper(II) concentration at the surface of the anode is inevitably somewhat larger, and the concentration of copper(II) at the surface of the cathode invariably smaller, than the bulk concentration. Thus, it is unavoidable that the potential of the copper anode will be positive with respect to the cathode. The potential difference is completely analogous to the electromotive force of a galvanic cell consisting of two copper electrodes immersed in dissimilar copper(II) solutions connected by a salt bridge. More important is the fact that this electromotive force — called the **back emf** of the cell — opposes the external applied voltage. A plot of the current which flows through the electrochemical cell as a function of applied voltage actually appears as curve B in Figure 18-1. If one impresses a voltage E_1 across the two copper electrodes, the observed current will be i_1 instead of i_2 — smaller than expected because of the back emf of the cell. In fact, in order to realize a current of i_2, one must apply a voltage of E_2 to the electrochemical cell, the difference between E_2 and E_1 being the back emf of the cell. Notice that the back emf becomes greater and greater as the total applied voltage increases.

Electrochemical cells employed in analytical chemistry are seldom as simple in construction and behavior as the system described in the preceding paragraphs. The additional complexity arises because cells used in practical work usually consist of dissimilar electrodes immersed in two different electrolyte solutions which are connected by means of an ion-permeable membrane or a salt bridge. The zinc-copper cell discussed in Chapter 12 and represented here by the shorthand notation

$$\text{Zn} \mid \text{Zn(NO}_3)_2 \, (1 \, F) \parallel \text{CuSO}_4 \, (1 \, F) \mid \text{Cu}$$

is typical. Assuming, for purposes of this discussion, that the activity coefficients of zinc and cupric ions are unity, we can calculate an electromotive force of 1.100 v for this cell under the condition of zero current flow, the copper electrode being positive with respect to the zinc electrode. Suppose we connect an external voltage source to this zinc-copper cell — the positive terminal of the source to the copper electrode, the negative terminal to the zinc electrode.

If the magnitude of the applied voltage is precisely equal to the electromotive force of the zinc-copper cell — that is, 1.100 v — no current will pass

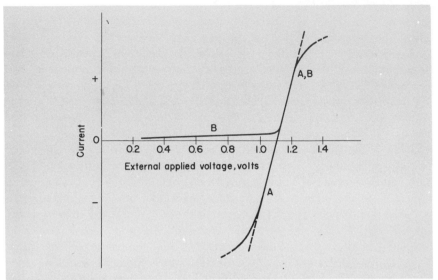

FIGURE 18-2.   Current-applied voltage curves for reversible and irreversible cells. Curve A: behavior of the reversible cell Zn | $Zn(NO_3)_2$ (1 F) || $CuSO_4$ (1 F) | Cu. Curve B: behavior of the irreversible cell Pt | $Zn(NO_3)_2$ (1 F) || $CuSO_4$ (1 F) | Cu.

through the cell and no net reaction can occur. When the applied voltage is increased above 1.100 v, the zinc-copper cell behaves as an electrolytic cell, the reaction

$$Zn^{++} + Cu \rightleftharpoons Zn + Cu^{++}$$

is forced to proceed, and the relationship between the applied voltage and the current which flows through the cell is depicted by the *upper* branch of curve A in Figure 18-2. On the other hand, if the magnitude of the applied voltage is less than 1.100 v, the zinc-copper cell acts as a galvanic cell, the overall reaction becomes

$$Zn + Cu^{++} \rightleftharpoons Zn^{++} + Cu$$

and the current-voltage curve is the *lower* branch of curve A in Figure 18-2. By convention, when an electrochemical cell operates nonspontaneously, the resulting current is positive, whereas the current is negative if an electrochemical cell functions spontaneously as a galvanic cell. In view of the fact that the zinc-copper cell behaves reversibly (the overall reaction can be made to go in either direction) the upper and lower branches of curve A are symmetrical about the point at which the applied voltage is 1.100 v. The two branches of curve A resemble curve B in Figure 18-1, owing to the combined effects of the resistance of the electrochemical cell and the changes in the surface concentrations of the various species.

Some electrochemical cells of practical interest behave irreversibly. As an example, consider the cell

$$Pt \mid Zn(NO_3)_2 \ (1\ F) \ \| \ CuSO_4 \ (1\ F) \mid Cu$$

in which the zinc electrode of the previous zinc-copper cell has been replaced by a platinum electrode. In contrast to the zinc-copper cell just described, the assignment of an electromotive force to the present cell is impossible; since the platinum electrode initially has no deposit of zinc metal on its surface, the potential of this electrode is undefined. Furthermore, the absence of zinc metal precludes the spontaneous discharge of this electrochemical cell, and so a plot of current versus voltage, such as the *lower* branch of curve *A* in Figure 18-2, is not obtainable. Let us examine and interpret the behavior of this cell when a variable voltage is impressed across the two electrodes, the negative side of the source being connected to the platinum electrode and the positive side of the source to the copper electrode. The qualitative dependence of the current upon the value of the applied voltage is represented by curve *B* of Figure 18-2. Provided that the applied voltage remains significantly below 1.100 v, the current is relatively small, although it increases more or less linearly as the applied voltage becomes larger. However, when the applied voltage reaches about 1.100 v, the current rises abruptly, and the current-voltage curve follows curve *A*.

The commencement of rapid deposition of metallic zinc upon the platinum electrode accounts for the sudden rise in current at approximately 1.100 v, and at higher applied potentials curve *B* coincides with curve *A* because sufficient zinc is plated on the platinum cathode to transform the latter into a zinc electrode. Some electrochemists designate the applied voltage at which zinc ion begins to be reduced as the **decomposition potential.** However, the concept of a decomposition potential lacks theoretical significance for an irreversible cell such as

$$Pt \mid Zn(NO_3)_2 \ (1\ F) \ \| \ CuSO_4 \ (1\ F) \mid Cu$$

because some zinc metal is deposited at all values of the applied voltage. Thus, it is preferable to regard the decomposition potential as the approximate applied voltage at which the cell current exhibits a rapid increase and beyond which reduction of zinc ion occurs at a convenient rate for practical applications. On the other hand, the decomposition potential for a reversible cell like

$$Zn \mid Zn(NO_3)_2 \ (1\ F) \ \| \ CuSO_4 \ (1\ F) \mid Cu$$

is virtually identical to the electromotive force of the cell at zero current flow; deposition of zinc metal begins just as soon as the applied voltage barely exceeds 1.100 v.

It remains for us to consider briefly why, in curve *B* of Figure 18-2, a small current — the **residual current** — flows through the cell long before the decomposition potential is reached. One cause of this residual current is the deposition of a very small quantity of zinc metal upon the platinum cathode, and the simultaneous oxidation of a very small amount of elemental copper to cupric ion, at applied voltages much less than the decomposition potential. Part of the residual current may be attributable to the reduction of dissolved oxygen to hydrogen peroxide or water at the platinum cathode.

Relationships Involving External Applied Voltage, Cell Resistance, Current, and Individual Electrode Potentials

From the preceding discussion, the most important conclusion is that the behavior of any electrolytic cell is determined primarily by the magnitude of the external voltage impressed across the electrodes. A minimal requirement for the operation of an electrolytic cell is that the external voltage be sufficiently large to overcome both the resistance and the back emf of the cell. Therefore, in starting a description of electroanalytical methods, it is helpful to derive an expression which shows quantitatively how the external applied voltage is related to the characteristics of the electrolytic cell and the electrode reactions.

One of the reversible cells already mentioned, namely

$$\text{Zn} \mid \text{Zn(NO}_3)_2 \ (1 \, F) \ \| \ \text{CuSO}_4 \ (1 \, F) \mid \text{Cu}$$

will serve as example for the present treatment. Throughout this discussion we shall assume that the solution in contact with each electrode is efficiently stirred. Under conditions of zero current flow, the concentrations of zinc and cupric ions will be uniform throughout their respective solutions, and the overall electromotive force of the cell is the sum of two contributions, one from the copper electrode and the other from the zinc electrode,

$$E_{\text{overall}} = E_{\text{Cu}^{++},\text{Cu}} + E_{\text{Zn},\text{Zn}^{++}}$$

if liquid-junction potentials are neglected. An alternate form of the previous equation is

$$E_{\text{overall}} = E_{\text{Cu}^{++},\text{Cu}} - E_{\text{Zn}^{++},\text{Zn}}$$

The latter relation possesses one advantage when compared to the former expression. In electroanalytical chemistry, it is often useful to describe the behavior of each electrode separately in terms of its potential with respect to a reference electrode, for example, the normal hydrogen electrode. According to the electrochemical sign conventions introduced in Chapter 12, we see that $E_{\text{Cu}^{++},\text{Cu}}$ denotes the potential of the copper electrode and $E_{\text{Zn}^{++},\text{Zn}}$ the potential of the zinc electrode, both measured against the same reference electrode. Although we shall employ the second of the two preceding equations, each relation gives an identical result when sign conventions are followed rigorously.

On the assumption that the activity coefficients of zinc and cupric ions in the previous electrochemical cell are unity, we can write

$$E_{\text{overall}} = E^{\circ}_{\text{Cu}^{++},\text{Cu}} - E^{\circ}_{\text{Zn}^{++},\text{Zn}} = 1.100 \text{ v}$$

As stated earlier, if the negative terminal of an external voltage source is connected to the zinc electrode and the positive terminal of the voltage source is attached to the copper electrode, the zinc-copper cell starts to behave as an electrolytic cell only when the applied voltage, E_{app}, exceeds 1.100 v.

Ohmic Potential Drop. Unfortunately, when the applied voltage is just slightly larger than 1.100 v, very little current will pass through the zinc-copper cell and the quantitative deposition of zinc — if this is the goal of the experiment — would take an impractically long time. Therefore, the magnitude of the applied voltage must be increased so that the flow of current and the rate of deposition of zinc will be reasonably large. Suppose we wish to deposit zinc metal at a rate corresponding to the passage of current i through the zinc-copper cell. Since the electrochemical cell has a finite resistance, R, it is necessary to increase the applied voltage above 1.100 v by an amount at least equal to iR in order to overcome the ohmic potential drop or the so-called **iR drop** of the cell.

Figure 18-3 illustrates the relationship between applied voltage and the iR drop. If the resistance of the zinc-copper cell remains constant, regardless of the magnitude of the applied voltage, the iR drop will be directly proportional to the current i, as indicated by the dashed straight line A. In fact, the slope of this straight line equals the reciprocal of the cell resistance.

Concentration Overpotential. When the zinc-copper cell behaves electrolytically, the overall reaction

$$Zn^{++} + Cu \rightleftharpoons Zn + Cu^{++}$$

FIGURE 18-3. Schematic relationship between cell current, applied voltage, ohmic potential drop, concentration overpotential, and activation overpotential for the electrolytic cell $Zn \mid Zn(NO_3)_2$ (1 F) $\parallel$ $CuSO_4$ (1 F) $\mid$ Cu.

occurs, and there is a tendency for the concentration (activity) of zinc ion to be smaller than $1\ M$ at the surface of the zinc cathode and for the concentration of cupric ion around the copper cathode to be somewhat larger than $1\ M$. Efficient stirring of the solution in contact with each electrode of the zinc-copper cell can minimize, but never eliminate, such concentration gradients, owing to the existence of a stationary film of solution around each electrode.

As mentioned earlier, in a practical electrolysis experiment, the voltage impressed across the anode and cathode of an electrolytic cell must be increased to compensate for the ohmic potential drop in the cell. We can show by means of simple calculations that the existence of concentration gradients at the surfaces of the electrodes creates a similar need — the applied voltage must be increased still more in order to cause the desired rate of electrolysis. With reference to Figure 18-3, let us adjust the applied voltage until a current i flows through the zinc-copper cell. Furthermore, let us assume arbitrarily that the surface concentration of zinc ion is reduced to $0.3\ M$ and that the surface concentration of cupric ion becomes $1.5\ M$. Actually, a priori knowledge concerning the surface concentrations of these species would not be available, other than the fact that, because of electrolysis, the surface concentrations of zinc and copper ions are smaller and larger than $1\ M$, respectively. The potential of the zinc electrode corresponding to a surface zinc ion concentration of $0.3\ M$ rather than $1.0\ M$ is

$$E_{Zn^{++},Zn} = E^{\circ}_{Zn^{++},Zn} - \frac{0.059}{2} \log \frac{1}{[Zn^{++}]}$$

$$E_{Zn^{++},Zn} = -0.763 - \frac{0.059}{2} \log \frac{1}{(0.3)} = -0.778\ v$$

and the copper electrode must be at a potential of

$$E_{Cu^{++},Cu} = E^{\circ}_{Cu^{++},Cu} - \frac{0.059}{2} \log \frac{1}{[Cu^{++}]}$$

$$E_{Cu^{++},Cu} = 0.337 - \frac{0.059}{2} \log \frac{1}{(1.5)} = 0.342\ v$$

if the surface concentration of cupric ion is to be $1.5\ M$.

Recall that the zinc-copper cell can function electrolytically only when the applied voltage at least exceeds a value corresponding to the difference in the potentials of the copper and zinc electrodes. For the impractical situation in which the current to be passed through the cell is very small, the applied voltage need be little more than $1.100\ v$. On the other hand, if current i is to flow through the zinc-copper cell, the *minimal* applied voltage should be

$$E_{Cu^{++},Cu} - E_{Zn^{++},Zn} = 0.342 - (-0.778) = 1.120\ v$$

and, of course, one must overcome the ohmic potential drop of the cell by making the applied voltage appropriately larger. The 20 mv difference, which we have calculated for the present hypothetical situation, is due solely to the fact that the surface concentrations of zinc and cupric ions at the electrodes deviate during electrolysis from their values in the bulk of each solution. In modern electrochemical literature, such a difference in electromotive force is designated the **concentration overpotential.**

In Figure 18-3, curve B depicts the current-voltage behavior of the zinc-copper cell, including an added contribution due to concentration overpotential. Notice that the magnitude of the concentration overpotential — for a given current, the horizontal distance between curves A and B in Figure 18-3 — becomes larger as the current passing through the cell increases. Characteristically, however, the concentration overpotential is not a linear function of the current. Since the concentration overpotential depends fundamentally upon the difference between the concentrations of chemical species at the surface of an electrode and in the bulk of the solution, it is of interest to examine briefly some of the factors which affect this concentration gradient.

Several processes can govern the transport of chemical species to and from the surface of an electrode. For controlled-potential coulometry and coulometric titrations, where efficient transport of a substance to an electrode surface is essential for the rapid performance of analytical determinations and separations, *mechanical stirring* of solutions is always employed. The movement of ionic species toward or away from the surface of an electrode may be subject to *electrical migration* effects. For example, anions in the vicinity of a negatively charged cathode have a tendency to be repelled, whereas cations, such as cadmium(II), copper(II), and zinc(II), are attracted to the surface of a negatively charged electrode. If a large excess of an innocuous salt — the supporting electrolyte — is introduced into the sample solution, the attraction or repulsion forces between the electrode and the particular ion of interest are virtually eliminated. Once a concentration gradient has been established at the surface of an electrode, a chemical species tends to undergo *diffusion* from a region of high concentration to one of lower concentration. For electrochemical experiments the rate of a diffusion-controlled process is roughly proportional to the difference in the concentrations of a substance at the surface of an electrode and in the bulk of the solution. It should be noted that the diffusion process occurring at each electrode of the zinc-copper cell acts to diminish concentration overpotential. Sometimes, when diffusion-controlled processes are studied, another mode of mass transfer, *natural convection*, is observed. If, as a consequence of electrolysis of an unstirred solution, the density of solution near an electrode becomes significantly different from the adjacent medium, the resulting density gradient may cause self-stirring or natural convection of the solution in the vicinity of that electrode.

As suggested before, even though the zinc nitrate and cupric sulfate solutions in contact with the zinc and copper electrodes are stirred as vigorously as possible, a stationary film of liquid remains in contact with each electrode. Thus, the movement of zinc ions to the surface of the cathode proceeds in two steps. Zinc ions are transported by the *stirring* of the solution to the edge of the thin film of immobile liquid, and then *diffuse* through the film to the electrode surface at which they react. At the copper anode, the cupric ions *diffuse* away from the electrode through the thin film of stationary liquid and, upon reaching the stirred solution, are *swept* into the main body of the cupric sulfate medium.

It is evident that the establishment of a concentration gradient depends not only on mass transport phenomena but upon the **current density,** that is, the current per unit of electrode area. If one is interested in minimizing concentration overpotential, the two most obvious requirements are to stir the solution efficiently and to employ a low current density. Unfortunately, a small current density tends to be incompatible with the performance of a rapid electrolysis.

Activation Overpotential.   Often an electrochemical process does not occur at a reasonable rate unless the voltage impressed across the electrolytic cell is substantially larger than the sum of the three parameters just discussed above — the zero-current electromotive force of the cell, the ohmic potential drop, and the concentration overpotential. This is so because, for many reactions, the mechanism of electron transfer between reactant and product species at the surface of an electrode involves a slow step with a high energy of activation. Therefore, it is necessary to supply the system with extra energy, in the form of higher applied voltage, so that the desired reaction will proceed rapidly. The additional voltage required to accomplish this practical goal is called the **activation overpotential.** In Figure 18-3 we have drawn curve C to illustrate schematically the overall current-voltage behavior of the zinc-copper cell, taking into consideration the zero-current electromotive force of the cell, the ohmic potential drop, and the two overpotential terms. The magnitude of the activation overpotential is represented, at a specified current, by the horizontal distance between curves B and C.

It is difficult, if not impossible, to predict the value of an activation overpotential, because this quantity is affected by a number of largely empirical factors. Nevertheless, it is worthwhile to emphasize a few of the general effects of experimental variables on the magnitudes of activation overpotentials. First, activation overpotential always increases, sometimes quite drastically, as the current density becomes larger or as the electrode reaction is forced to proceed more rapidly. Second, an elevation of temperature causes the activation overpotential to decrease, presumably because part of the energy of activation for the electron-transfer process is provided thermally. Third, the activation overpotentials are characteristically large for reactions resulting in liberation of gaseous products, in oxidation or reduction of organic molecules, and in multiple electron changes as in the reductions of iodate, dichromate, and permanganate. Fourth, the deposition of one metal upon the surface of a different metal usually proceeds with some overpotential until a complete layer of the desired metal has been plated out. Fifth, electrode processes occurring at the so-called *soft* metals, including tin, lead, zinc, bismuth, and mercury, usually show much larger activation overpotentials than at the more noble metals, such as platinum, palladium, gold, and iridium.

Table 18-1 lists some selected values of activation overpotentials for the

TABLE 18-1. ACTIVATION OVERPOTENTIALS FOR HYDROGEN AND OXYGEN EVOLUTION AT VARIOUS ELECTRODES AT 25°C *

Electrode Material	Overpotential, Volts							
	0.001 amp/cm²		0.01 amp/cm²		0.1 amp/cm²		1.0 amp/cm²	
	H_2	O_2	H_2	O_2	H_2	O_2	H_2	O_2
Pt, smooth	0.024	0.72	0.068	0.85	0.29	1.3	0.68	1.5
Pt, platinized	0.015	0.35	0.030	0.52	0.041	0.64	0.048	0.76
Au	0.24	0.67	0.39	0.96	—	—	0.80	1.6
Cu	0.48	0.42	0.58	0.58	0.80	0.66	1.3	0.79
Ni	0.56	0.35	0.75	0.52	1.1	0.64	1.2	0.85
Hg	0.9	—	1.0	—	1.1	—	1.2	—
Zn	0.72	—	0.75	—	1.1	—	1.2	—
Fe	0.40	—	0.56	—	0.82	—	1.3	—
Pb	0.52	—	1.0	—	1.2	—	1.3	—

* Data from International Critical Tables, *VI*, 339 (1929).

evolution of hydrogen and oxygen gases at different electrodes and current densities. These data illustrate the qualitative observations mentioned previously. It is evident that current density has a pronounced influence on the overpotentials for both hydrogen and oxygen evolution.

We have seen that for a practical electrolysis the voltage impressed across the electrodes of a cell must equal the sum of four terms: the zero-current electromotive force, the ohmic potential drop, the concentration overpotential, and the activation overpotential. This fact is illustrated in Figure 18-3. There are several ways in which this fundamental relationship can be expressed. With reference to the zinc-copper cell, a convenient equation is

$$E_{app} = E_{Cu^{++},Cu} - E_{Zn^{++},Zn} + iR + \omega$$

In this relation, E_{app} represents the total voltage impressed across the electrolysis cell; $E_{Cu^{++},Cu}$ is the potential of the copper electrode based on the bulk concentration of cupric ion; $E_{Zn^{++},Zn}$ is the potential of the zinc electrode predicted from the zinc ion concentration in the main body of the zinc nitrate solution; iR denotes the ohmic potential drop of the cell; and ω combines the concentration overpotential and activation overpotential for both the copper and zinc electrodes.

Noting that the copper electrode functions as the anode of the zinc-copper electrolytic cell and that the zinc electrode is the cathode, we can write a general equation for the applied voltage in any electrolysis experiment:

$$E_{app} = E_{anode} - E_{cathode} + iR + \omega$$

where E_{anode} and $E_{cathode}$ are the potentials of the two electrodes calculated from the bulk concentrations of the pertinent species. If we designate the experimentally determined anode and cathode potentials by E_a and E_c, respectively, an alternate form of the preceding expression is

$$E_{app} = E_a - E_c + iR$$

The parameters E_a and E_c both consist of a sum of three terms — the zero-current potential of the electrode, the concentration overpotential, and the activation overpotential.

Before concluding this section, we should make one more point. During an actual electrolysis, the various terms in the previous relation change as a function of time. For example, when the applied voltage, E_{app}, is held constant, the cell resistance, R, may increase as electrolysis proceeds, and the current, i, undoubtedly decreases as the reacting species are consumed. In any event, if the latter two quantities change unequally, the ohmic potential drop, iR, will vary, and so must the potentials of the anode (E_a) and cathode (E_c). Similarly, if one performs a constant-current electrolysis, it is necessary to readjust the applied voltage continuously as the resistance varies; but any variation in the applied voltage alters the anode and cathode potentials.

ELECTROGRAVIMETRY

Most early analytical applications of electrochemistry dealt with the deposition and subsequent weighing of metals. Such procedures relied upon either of two fundamental techniques, both of which are still successfully employed in modern laboratories. The first method is based upon the fact that a number of determinations and separations can be performed if the total voltage impressed across an appropriate cell is fixed. Alternatively, the external applied voltage is varied in such a manner that the current passing through an electrolytic cell remains constant.

Electrogravimetric methods of analysis usually involve the deposition of the desired metallic element upon a previously weighed cathode followed by the subsequent reweighing of the electrode plus deposit to obtain by difference the quantity of that substance. Among the metals which have been determined in this manner are cadmium, copper, nickel, silver, tin, and zinc.

However, a few substances may be oxidized at an appropriate anode to form an insoluble and adherent precipitate suitable for gravimetric measurement. The oxidation of lead(II) to lead dioxide at a platinum electrode in a nitric acid medium,

$$Pb^{++} + 2\,H_2O \rightleftharpoons PbO_2(s) + 4\,H^+ + 2\,e$$

is a well-known example of the latter procedure. In addition, certain analytical separations can be accomplished quickly and conveniently through a variation of electrogravimetry, in which easily reducible metallic ions are deposited into a mercury pool cathode, while difficultly reduced cations remain in solution. Thus, aluminum, vanadium, titanium, tungsten, and the alkali and alkaline earth metals are separated from iron, silver, copper, cadmium, cobalt, and nickel by deposition of the latter group of elements into mercury.

Electrolysis at Constant Applied Voltage

Representative of most electrogravimetric methods of analysis is the determination of copper. Suppose we desire to measure the quantity of copper(II) in a 1 F sulfuric acid medium by depositing the metal upon a previously weighed platinum electrode. Typical experimental apparatus, consisting of a large platinum gauze cathode and a smaller anode, is depicted in Figure 18-4. Generally speaking, both electrodes are immersed directly in

FIGURE 18-4. Schematic electrical circuit for deposition of metals by means of electrolysis at constant applied voltage or by means of constant-current electrolysis.

the solution to be electrolyzed, although some applications may require that the anode and cathode be in different compartments separated by a porous diaphragm or ion-permeable membrane to prevent gross interaction of the products formed at the anode with the metal deposit on the cathode. The electrical circuitry is exceedingly simple, a direct-current power supply (E) and a rheostat (R) enabling one to vary the voltage impressed across the anode and cathode. It is customary to incorporate both a voltmeter (V) and an ammeter (A) so that the magnitudes of the applied voltage and current can be monitored continuously. Efficient stirring of the solution is mandatory. A magnetic stirrer or a motor-driven propeller is commonly employed; sometimes, the anode has a design which permits it to be rotated with the aid of a synchronous motor and, more recently, ultrasonic agitation of the solution has proved especially valuable. This instrumentation serves equally well for electrolysis at constant applied voltage or for constant-current electrolysis.

In beginning our discussion of electrolysis at constant applied voltage, we shall assume that the original concentration of copper(II) is 0.01 M and that a voltage sufficient to cause rapid and quantitative deposition of copper is impressed across the electrochemical cell. An obvious problem concerns the selection of the external voltage required to accomplish the desired result. For a practical electrolysis, the minimal acceptable value for the applied voltage may be ascertained from the relation presented earlier; that is,

$$E_{app} = E_{anode} - E_{cathode} + iR + \omega$$

However, in order to utilize this equation, we must identify the electrode reactions which occur during the electrolysis of the copper(II)-sulfuric acid solution. As soon as the deposition of copper metal has commenced, the cathodic process is the reduction of cupric ion at a copper-plated platinum electrode,

$$Cu^{++} + 2\ e \rightleftharpoons Cu$$

whereas, at the anode, the oxidation of water is virtually the sole reaction:

$$2\ H_2O \rightleftharpoons O_2 + 4\ H^+ + 4\ e$$

Notice that steady evolution of oxygen gas during the electrolysis causes the solution around the anode to be saturated with this gas at a pressure of essentially 1 atm. Naturally, the hydrogen ion concentration will vary slightly as electrolysis proceeds, whereas the concentration of copper(II) will change markedly.

Returning to the expression for the applied voltage, we may write

$$E_{app} = E_{O_2,H_2O} - E_{Cu^{++},Cu} + iR + \omega$$

where E_{O_2,H_2O} and $E_{Cu^{++},Cu}$ are the zero-current potentials for the anode and cathode, respectively, based on the bulk concentrations of the various species. Accordingly,

$$E_{O_2,H_2O} = E^{\circ}_{O_2,H_2O} - \frac{0.059}{4} \log \frac{1}{(p_{O_2})[H^+]^4} = 1.23 \text{ v}$$

because the pressure of oxygen and the hydrogen ion concentration (activity) are close to unity. For the copper electrode,

$$E_{Cu^{++},Cu} = E^{\circ}_{Cu^{++},Cu} - \frac{0.059}{2} \log \frac{1}{[Cu^{++}]}$$

$$E_{Cu^{++},Cu} = 0.337 - \frac{0.059}{2} \log \frac{1}{(0.01)} = 0.278 \text{ v}$$

To ensure rapid completion of the deposition of copper, we shall assume the applied voltage to be adjusted so that the current at the start of the electrolysis is relatively high — 1 amp. If the cell resistance has a value of 0.5 ohm, the ohmic potential drop will be 0.5 v.

An accurate estimation of the combined concentration overpotential and activation overpotential term is virtually impossible. However, as a first approximation, let us propose that the concentration overpotential at each electrode is virtually eliminated through efficient stirring of the solution and that the activation overpotential for the reduction of cupric ions at a copper electrode is negligible. Next, on the assumption that the surface area of the platinum anode is 100 cm², the initial current density has a magnitude of 0.01 amp/cm² and, according to Table 18-1, the activation overpotential should have the rather large value of 0.85 v. Combining these results, we arrive at the conclusion that the applied voltage must be

$$E_{app} = 1.23 - 0.28 + 0.5 + 0.85$$

or approximately 2.3 v. As pointed out at the end of the preceding section, even though the voltage impressed across an electrolysis cell is maintained constant, the various parameters which comprise this overall voltage — the anode and cathode potentials, the ohmic potential drop, and the overpotentials — may change considerably throughout the duration of an electrolysis.

For several reasons, the zero-current anode potential undergoes little variation. Neither the hydrogen ion concentration nor the partial pressure of oxygen gas fluctuates appreciably during the electrolysis and, of course, there is an ample supply of water to be oxidized. Therefore, we shall regard the zero-current potential of the anode as essentially constant at 1.23 v.

More complicated behavior is exhibited by the copper electrode, for, as shown in Figure 18-5, the potential of the cathode drifts from an original value of +0.28 v versus NHE to somewhat below −0.44 v versus NHE. It should be stressed that the curve represents the experimentally observed potential of the copper cathode, including the concentration overpotential and activation overpotential terms. Basically, the potential-time behavior

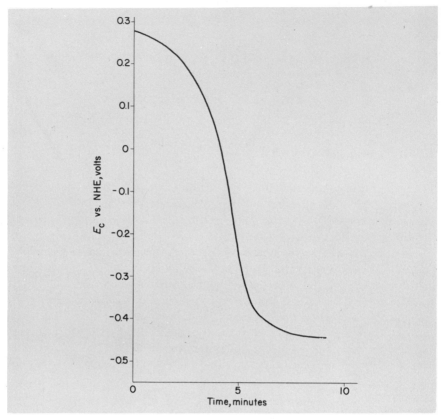

FIGURE 18-5.   Variation of potential of copper-plated platinum cathode during deposition of 0.01 M copper(II) by means of electrolysis at constant applied voltage.

of the copper electrode reflects the varying concentration (activity) of cupric ion at the electrode surface.

At the outset of the electrolysis, the surface concentration of cupric ion should be very nearly 0.01 M, because the solution is well stirred and concentration overpotential is minimal. Thus, for one or two minutes the potential of the copper cathode changes only slightly from its original value of $+0.28$ v versus NHE. Furthermore, efficient stirring, a relatively large cupric ion concentration, and a moderate current density all mean that the initial current of 1 amp is due entirely to the reduction of copper(II) to copper metal. Within several minutes, most of the cupric ion is reduced to the elemental state, and the concentration of cupric ion at the electrode surface and in the bulk of the solution begins to decrease rapidly. Therefore, the potential of the cathode would shift with some abruptness toward a value at which another reaction can maintain the current. As seen in Figure 18-5, the potential of the cathode decreases rapidly after about five minutes to approximately -0.3 v versus NHE and undergoes a slower drop to a final value near -0.44 v versus NHE. Any further shift of the cathode potential is halted by the more or less steady evolution of hydrogen gas at the copper-plated platinum electrode. Note that the reduction of hydrogen ion to hydrogen gas in 1 F sulfuric acid might be expected to occur close to 0 v versus NHE, except for an activation overpotential of between 0.4 and 0.5 v for hydrogen gas evolution at copper.

A large variation in the cathode potential cannot occur without an effect on the current which passes through the electrolytic cell. Assuming that $E_{O_2,H_2O} = 1.23$ v, $E_{Cu^{++},Cu} = -0.44$ v, $R = 0.5$ ohm, and $\omega = 0.5$ v, we can estimate the final current to be

$$i = \frac{E_{app} - E_{O_2,H_2O} + E_{Cu^{++},Cu} - \omega}{R}$$

$$i = \frac{2.3 - 1.23 - 0.44 - 0.5}{0.5} = 0.26 \text{ amp}$$

Since the activation overpotential for oxygen evolution decreases as the current density becomes smaller, we attempted to anticipate the result of the preceding calculation in choosing a lower value for the overpotential term (ω) than in previous computations. The final current is due almost exclusively to the reduction of hydrogen ion.

Feasibility of Determinations and Separations. That the electrodeposition of copper described in the preceding section is suitable for the attainment of highly accurate analytical results may be shown through a simple calculation. Suppose that no more than one part in 10,000 of the original quantity of copper(II) is to remain in solution at the termination of the electrolysis. Since the sulfuric acid medium initially contained cupric ion at a concentration of 0.01 M, the copper(II) concentration must be decreased to 10^{-6} M in order to achieve the desired completeness of separation. Using the Nernst equation

$$E_{Cu^{++},Cu} = E^{\circ}_{Cu^{++},Cu} - \frac{0.059}{2} \log \frac{1}{[Cu^{++}]}$$

we can arrive at the conclusion that, if the potential of the cathode has a value of

$$E_{Cu^{++},Cu} = 0.337 - \frac{0.059}{2} \log \frac{1}{(10^{-6})} = 0.160 \text{ v versus NHE}$$

or less when the electrolysis is finally interrupted, copper metal will have been deposited quantitatively. An inspection of Figure 18-5, showing the variation of the cathode potential as a function of time, reveals that this requirement is easily met, as the potential eventually reaches -0.44 v versus NHE.

Although the large negative shift of the cathode potential does ensure the quantitative deposition of copper, such an uncontrolled change in the potential is undesirable if separation of copper from other elements is to be accomplished. Any metal cations which happen to be present in the $1\,F$ sulfuric acid solution and which undergo even partial deposition at potentials more positive than -0.44 v versus NHE will be plated upon the cathode along with copper. Among the species which could interfere to a greater or lesser extent with the electrogravimetric determination of copper are antimony(III), bismuth(III), tin(II), cobalt(II), and cadmium(II), the pertinent half-reactions and standard potentials being:

$$SbO^+ + 2\,H^+ + 3\,e \rightleftharpoons Sb + H_2O; \qquad E° = +0.212\ v$$
$$BiO^+ + 2\,H^+ + 3\,e \rightleftharpoons Bi + H_2O; \qquad E° = +0.32\ v$$
$$Sn^{++} + 2\,e \rightleftharpoons Sn; \qquad E° = -0.136\ v$$
$$Co^{++} + 2\,e \rightleftharpoons Co; \qquad E° = -0.277\ v$$
$$Cd^{++} + 2\,e \rightleftharpoons Cd; \qquad E° = -0.403\ v$$

It is evident that codeposition of the latter three elements could be readily avoided if the electrolysis were stopped before the cathode potential became too negative. However, as commonly performed, electrolysis at constant applied voltage tends to be a "brute-force" technique in which one simply adjusts the voltage to a large enough value to separate metallic elements into two groups — those species which are more easily reduced than hydrogen ion or water and those elements which prove to be more difficult to reduce than hydrogen ion or the solvent under the extant experimental conditions. Therefore, this electroanalytical method lacks the selectivity desired of most techniques, although a number of specific applications are in common use.

An analytical chemist may often improve the selectivity of electrolysis at constant applied voltage by changing the pH of the sample solution or by adding appropriate complexing agents to alter the reduction potentials for the species of interest. Nevertheless, it remains true that electrogravimetric analysis with constant applied voltage is usually restricted to those chemical systems for which the metal ion of interest is the only reducible species other than hydrogen ion or water. In some situations, this procedure may be employed as a method of separation to precede another kind of physical measurement. Recall that the heavy metals — cobalt, copper, iron, and nickel — can be separated from titanium, aluminum, and the alkali and alkaline earth elements by means of electrolysis with a mercury cathode.

Constant-Current Electrolysis

As suggested previously, a second method by which electrogravimetric determinations are performed involves the use of constant-current electrolysis. In this technique one varies the external voltage impressed across an electrolytic cell by manual, servomechanical, or electronic means so that the current remains essentially constant during the course of the electrodeposition. If we refer to the copper(II)-sulfuric acid system described earlier, it should be clear that the potential-time behavior of the copper cathode resembles the curve shown in Figure 18-5, regardless of whether electrolysis at constant applied voltage or constant-current electrolysis is carried out, because the cupric ion concentration decreases with time. A consideration of the fundamental relation

$$E_{app} = E_{anode} - E_{cathode} + iR + \omega$$

shows that, in order to maintain constant current throughout an electrolysis, one must continually *increase* the applied voltage to compensate for the negative shift of the cathode potential. Here, we presume the anode potential, the overpotential, and, of course, the ohmic potential drop to be unchanged.

Much less time is needed to complete a constant-current electrodeposition than to accomplish the same determination by means of the constant-applied-voltage technique. The reason for this is that the former method permits the use of a relatively large as well as constant electrolysis current. However, if an unusually high current is demanded, it will be impossible for cupric ions alone to sustain the desired rate of electron transfer and, almost as soon as electrolysis commences, a significant fraction of the total current is due to evolution of hydrogen gas. As a result of this vigorous gas evolution, the physical properties of the metal deposit are frequently less optimum than those resulting from use of the slower constant-applied-voltage method. The formation of hydrogen gas can be eliminated through the use of a **cathodic depolarizer,** some substance more easily reduced than hydrogen ion but one that does not interfere with the smooth deposition of copper or another desired metal. Nitric acid is probably the most familiar cathodic depolarizer, since nitrate undergoes an eight-electron reduction at a copper cathode to ammonium ion:

$$NO_3^- + 10\ H^+ + 8\ e \rightleftharpoons NH_4^+ + 3\ H_2O$$

This process occurs at a more positive potential than does hydrogen evolution.

Regarding the usefulness of constant-current electrolysis for analytical separations, we may conclude that the rapid shift of the cathode potential, caused by a relatively large current, gives little selectivity to this procedure — even less than the constant-applied-voltage technique. At best, it is only realistic to consider the division of metals into two classes — those more readily and those less easily reduced than hydrogen ion.

Influence of Experimental Conditions on Electrolytic Deposits

In principle, quantitative separations and determinations based on electrodeposition closely resemble the more classic methods of gravimetric analysis and, therefore, must fulfill the same three requirements as other precipitation processes discussed in this text. First, the desired metal must be deposited completely. Second, the resulting metal deposit must be pure. Third, the plated metal must possess physical properties such that the subsequent washing, drying, and weighing operations will not cause significant mechanical loss or chemical alteration of the deposit. The quantitativeness or completeness of any electrodeposition is governed fundamentally by the potential of the cathode (or the anode for the deposition of PbO_2 or Co_2O_3) when the electrolysis is terminated relative to the initial potential of that electrode. By and large, the purity of an electrolytic deposit depends on the standard and formal potentials for half-reactions involving the desired substance and all other species which might undergo codeposition.

An analytical chemist must pay particular attention to the physical form of an electrolytic deposit. Above all, it is essential that experimental conditions be controlled or adjusted so that a lustrous, fine-grained, tightly adherent deposit of high density is produced. Unfortunately, some metal deposits tend toward brittleness; others fail to adhere well to the electrode surface and crumble or flake during and after the electrodeposition step of the procedure. Obviously, it is impossible to wash and weigh the latter kind of deposit because mechanical losses inevitably occur. In addition, spongy metal deposits, while still wet with electrolyte solution, are prone to form surface oxides by reaction with atmospheric oxygen. Such porous deposits are so difficult to wash thoroughly that significant amounts of impurities may be physically occluded. We shall now examine a few of the more important observations pertaining to the influence of experimental conditions on electrolytic deposits.

Current Density.   Generally speaking, the variable which has the greatest effect upon the physical state of an electrolytic deposit is its rate of formation — that is, the current density. Since metal deposition upon the surface of an electrode involves both nucleation and crystal growth, as in conventional precipitation processes, it follows that the size of individual crystals of the metal should decrease as the current density becomes larger. Although the production of small crystals does lead to a smooth metal plating, the use of excessively high current densities is definitely undesirable because the resulting electrolytic deposit has a tendency to consist of fragile whiskers or dendrites and because simultaneous evolution of hydrogen gas will cause spongy and porous deposits to form. As a rule, moderate current densities ranging from 0.005 to 0.05 amp/cm² yield metal deposits with optimum characteristics, but the choice of the proper current density for a specific application may necessitate trial-and-error experimentation.

Evolution of Gas.   As suggested in the preceding paragraph, liberation of a gas during the deposition of a metal invariably produces a rough, spongy solid, presumably because bubble formation creates nonuniform current density through physical blockage of the electrode surface. In addition, vigorous evolution of a gas may detach small fragments of the metal deposit from the electrode. Evolution of gas (which is nearly always hydrogen, since most deposition processes are cathodic reactions) can be eliminated or minimized in several ways, depending upon the particular electroanalytical technique employed. For constant-current electrolysis, the use of a depolarizer is almost mandatory because of the abrupt shift in the cathode potential toward the value at which hydrogen gas evolution occurs. The controlled-potential coulometric technique, which relies on the maintenance of an essentially constant cathode potential throughout the electrolysis, does not require a depolarizer, since gas evolution need never occur except in unusual situations.

Solution Composition. Metallic silver plated from an alkaline cyanide medium containing the species $Ag(CN)_2^-$, or from an ammonia solution in which $Ag(NH_3)_2^+$ is predominant, is characteristically smooth and shiny in appearance. On the other hand, a loosely adherent, dendritic or fibrous deposit of elemental silver is obtained from aqueous silver nitrate, where the simple hydrated argentous ion exists. This is a classic example of the profound differences in the physical properties of an electrolytic deposit resulting from the presence or absence of a ligand which strongly complexes the desired metal ion. Similar behavior is observed with practically every metallic element; reduction of a stable metal ion complex almost always yields a much smoother and more tightly adherent deposit than is obtainable from a solution of the aquated cation.

Effect of Electrode Surface Condition. Occasionally, deliberate roughening of an electrode surface is recommended so that metal deposits will be more adherent. However, on such an irregular electrode surface, the current density is nonuniform, causing evolution of gas as well as formation of an uneven, dendritic metal deposit. Therefore, a smooth, scrupulously clean electrode surface is usually preferable for production of a dense, fine-grained deposit. Closely related to the preceding phenomenon is the nature of the electrode material itself. It has been observed empirically that certain deposits adhere more tightly to one electrode material than to another. In some instances, the plated metal forms a surface alloy with the electrode material, which may improve the adherence of the deposit.

Apparatus for Electrogravimetric Determinations and Separations

Although previous reference has been made to the electrodes and other items of equipment required for electrodeposition methods of analysis, several additional points concerning experimental aspects of electrogravimetry should be mentioned.

Power supplies for the performance of electrolysis at constant applied voltage and constant-current electrolysis are available commercially in various degrees of sophistication. Furthermore, remarkably versatile equipment can be fabricated from electronic components commonly found in the laboratory. A cell vessel for an electrogravimetric analysis normally consists of a tall-form beaker which is covered with a watch glass, split in half to permit the stems of the cathode and anode to protrude above the top of the cell. Since vigorous gas evolution usually causes the solution to spray, the watch glass minimizes loss of the sample medium.

Platinum cathodes and anodes are generally employed for electrogravimetry, but copper, lead, and nickel cathodes have proved valuable in a number of practical applications. The principal virtues of platinum are that it is not readily attacked by acids or bases, that it can be easily cleaned with appropriate solvents to dissolve old metal deposits, and that, if necessary, it may be heated to dull redness in a flame to remove organic matter which might subsequently cause a poor or nonuniform deposit. Those metals, including zinc and cadmium, which form surface alloys with platinum should not be deposited directly upon a cathode of the latter material because dissolution of the metal film at a later time results in superficial etching of the platinum electrode itself. Consequently, when either zinc, cadmium, or lead is to be determined electrogravimetrically, the platinum cathode is customarily plated with a thin protective layer of copper or silver prior to the actual deposition of the desired element.

To meet the requirements of maximal surface area and minimal weight and to promote efficient circulation of the sample solution around the electrode, a platinum cathode is constructed in the shape of a gauze cylinder, typically ranging from 3 to 4 cm in diameter and from 4 to 6 cm in height; and a stout platinum wire, 10 to 12 cm in length, is welded to the gauze cylinder for the convenience of handling and weighing operations and for making electrical connections to the electrode. Not infrequently, the anode is another platinum gauze electrode with dimensions somewhat smaller than the cathode, the anode and cathode being positioned concentrically in the electrolysis cell. However, the anode may simply be a helical coil of stout platinum wire or a small platinum foil welded to a platinum wire.

Two properties of mercury render it unsuitable for use as a cathode in electrogravimetric methods of analysis. First, mercury possesses a sufficiently high vapor pressure that special procedures are required to prevent loss by volatilization during the various experimental manipulations. Second, the density of mercury is so great that the amount needed to prepare a cathode of adequately large surface area may easily approach 100 gm. The tremendous inconvenience of weighing this much mercury accurately, plus the fact that the deposited metal would undoubtedly constitute less than 1 per cent of the total weight, makes this technique most unattractive.

On the other hand, when a mercury pool cathode is employed in conjunction with either electrolysis at constant applied voltage or constant-current electrolysis, a number of useful separations can be accomplished. The unusually high activation overpotential for evolution of hydrogen gas at mercury (see Table 18-1) means, for example, that the reduction of hydrogen ion in 1 F hydrochloric acid or perchloric acid does not occur until the potential of the mercury cathode reaches approximately -1.0 v versus NHE. An inspection of a reasonably complete table of standard potentials indicates that, from a 1 F acid medium, all metal ions except aluminum(III), uranium(III), titanium(III), vanadium(II), the tripositive lanthanide and actinide cations, and the alkaline earth and alkali metal ions should be reduced to their elemental states and dissolved in the mercury. Manganese(II), not expected to undergo significant reduction even at -1.0 v versus NHE, may be deposited into mercury under certain conditions. Interestingly, molybdenum(III) and tungsten(III) remain in the aqueous phase in spite of predictions to the contrary.

An electrolysis cell incorporating a mercury pool cathode and a platinum wire anode is shown schematically in Figure 18-6. In such a cell the area of the cathode may vary from 10 to 50 cm². After the desired separation has been completed, the leveling bulb is lowered without interruption of the electrolysis until the level of mercury in the main vessel drops to the stopcock. This procedure is followed so that metals in the mercury phase cannot be reoxidized by oxygen present in the aqueous medium. Then the stopcock is turned to terminate the electrolysis and the solution is withdrawn from the cell. The electrolyzed solution can be subjected to other separation techniques or may be analyzed by suitable methods. Generally speaking, the metals dissolved in the mercury are not recovered, the impure mercury being saved for subsequent repurification and reuse.

FIGURE 18-6. Electrolysis cell incorporating a mercury pool cathode for separation of metal cations.

CONTROLLED-POTENTIAL COULOMETRY

Electrolysis at constant applied voltage, or constant-current electrolysis, possesses significant disadvantages for analytical separations and determinations. Most important is that both techniques lack selectivity because of variations in the potential of the cathode or anode at which the desired reaction is supposed to occur. As we have seen, any abrupt shift in the potential of the cathode or anode may cause other extraneous processes such as hydrogen gas evolution to take precedence over the reaction of interest. On the other hand, if the potential for a specific half-reaction is known and if no competitive process takes place at that potential, it should be possible to maintain the potential of an anode or cathode at the predetermined value so that only the desired reaction will proceed. Indeed, by controlling the potential of an electrode and by taking additional advantage of the influence of solution composition on the standard or formal potentials for half-reactions, one may achieve utmost specificity in electrochemical determinations and separations. This is the fundamental principle of controlled-potential coulometry.

Current-Electrode Potential Curves

In controlled-potential coulometry, primary attention is directed toward the behavior of the electrode — either anode or cathode, but usually known as the **working electrode** — at which the reaction of interest proceeds. Above all, it is necessary to establish the potential of the working electrode at a value which will cause the desired reaction to occur quantitatively without interference from other species in the sample solution. Information of this kind may be conveniently derived from current-electrode potential curves such as those illustrated schematically in Figure 18-7. A current-electrode potential curve consists of a plot of the current, which flows as a consequence of reactions at the working electrode, versus the potential of that electrode, measured against an appropriate reference electrode with a potentiometer. Notice that measurement of the working-electrode potential permits one to neglect the ohmic potential drop of the electrolytic cell. Furthermore, one need not be concerned about the reaction which takes place at the other electrode. The latter is commonly called the **auxiliary electrode** because it serves, along with the working electrode, to complete the electrolytic cell. Thus, a current-electrode potential curve depicts only the characteristics, including any activation overpotential, of processes which occur at the working electrode. Clearly, in order to be meaningful, a current-electrode potential curve, or simply a *current-potential curve*, should be recorded under conditions which correspond as closely as possible to those prevailing in an actual controlled-potential coulometric determination.

Figure 18-7 presents two idealized current-potential curves, one for the reduction of 0.01 M copper(II) in a 1 F sulfuric acid solution at a platinum cathode (curve A) and the other for reduction of 0.01 M antimony(III) under identical conditions (curve B). Both curves exhibit a small residual current until a potential is reached at which deposition of either copper or antimony metal commences. Such behavior parallels that displayed by the current-applied voltage curve in Figure 18-2. Since the half-reaction and standard potential for the two-electron reduction of cupric ion are

$$Cu^{++} + 2\,e \rightleftharpoons Cu; \qquad E° = 0.337 \text{ v}$$

it can be shown from the Nernst equation

$$E_{Cu^{++},Cu} = E°_{Cu^{++},Cu} - \frac{0.059}{2}\log\frac{1}{[Cu^{++}]}$$

that copper metal should theoretically begin to deposit from a 0.01 M copper(II) solution when the cathode potential attains a value of

$$E_{Cu^{++},Cu} = 0.337 - \frac{0.059}{2}\log\frac{1}{(0.01)}$$

or

$$E_{Cu^{++},Cu} = 0.278 \text{ v versus NHE}$$

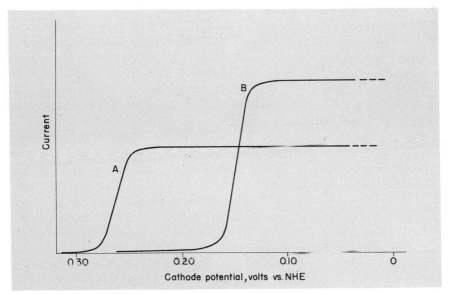

FIGURE 18-7.   Idealized current-potential curves. Curve A: reduction of 0.01 M copper(II) at a copper-plated platinum cathode in 1 F sulfuric acid medium. Curve B: reduction of 0.01 M antimony(III) at an antimony-plated platinum cathode in a 1 F sulfuric acid solution.

Similarly, from the antimony(III)-antimony metal half-reaction,

$$SbO^+ + 2\,H^+ + 3\,e \rightleftharpoons Sb + H_2O; \qquad E^\circ = 0.212\;v$$

we can predict for 0.01 M antimony(III) in 1 F sulfuric acid that metallic antimony starts to form when the cathode potential becomes

$$E_{SbO^+,Sb} = E^\circ_{SbO^+,Sb} - \frac{0.059}{3}\log\frac{1}{[SbO^+][H^+]^2}$$

$$E_{SbO^+,Sb} = 0.212 - \frac{0.059}{3}\log\frac{1}{(0.01)(1)^2}$$

$$E_{SbO^+,Sb} = 0.173\;v \text{ versus NHE}$$

Most current-potential curves exhibit another characteristic of special significance. Observe in Figure 18-7, for either curve A or curve B, that as the cathode potential becomes more and more negative a point is eventually reached beyond which the current no longer increases, but remains essentially constant. In the case of copper(II) reduction, for example, this so-called **limiting current** arises because, at cathode potentials more negative than approximately 0.22 v versus NHE, cupric ions undergo reduction immediately upon reaching the electrode surface. Hence, the limiting current is proportional to the rate at which cupric ions are transported to the surface of the cathode by the processes of convection, diffusion, and electrical migration. It may be recalled that, regardless of how efficiently any solution is agitated, a stationary film of liquid surrounds an electrode and that the reacting substance usually moves through this thin layer of solution by diffusion alone. For a well-stirred 0.01 M copper(II) medium, the concentration of cupric ion at the solution side of the thin layer of liquid should be essentially 0.01 M. However, according to the Nernst equation, if the potential of the cathode is 0.22 v versus NHE, the cupric ion concentration *at the surface of the electrode* is close to 10^{-4} M. The rate of diffusion of cupric ions across the thin film of solution is directly proportional to the *difference* between these two concentrations, but, since the surface concentration is small compared to the bulk concentration, it follows that the current is proportional to the bulk concentration of copper(II). All factors being held constant, the limiting current for a 0.001 M copper(II) solution should be one tenth of that for a 0.01 M copper(II) sample, and the limiting current is expected to be twice as great for a 0.02 M as a 0.01 M cupric ion solution.

A current-potential curve for the deposition of a metal upon a *solid* cathode is affected in two ways by the concentration of the cation in solution. First, as described in the previous paragraph, the magnitude of the limiting current is proportional to the metal ion concentration. Second, the position of a current-potential curve along the abscissa, or potential axis, depends on this concentration. For example, the current-potential curve in Figure 18-7 for the reduction of 0.01 M copper(II) shows a reasonably abrupt rise in current near 0.27 v versus NHE. However, if a platinum or copper electrode were used to record a current-potential curve for 10^{-4} M copper in 1 F sulfuric acid, one would not observe the characteristic rise in current until the cathode potential reached 0.22 v versus NHE, and, of course, the limiting current would only be 1 per cent of the value obtained with 0.01 M copper(II).

When both the reactant and product species are soluble, no shift of the current-potential curve along the abscissa is observed as the initial concentration of reactant is varied. In other words, the rising portion of the current-potential curve always appears at the same potential, regardless of the concentration of the substance being reduced or oxidized, if the redox process is reversible. The one-electron reduction of iron(III) at a platinum or gold cathode,

$$Fe^{+++} + e \rightleftharpoons Fe^{++}$$

is a typical example of a reaction in which the oxidant and reductant are both soluble in the aqueous phase. In contrast to this system, the reduction of cadmium ion into a mercury cathode,

$$Cd^{++} + Hg + 2\,e \rightleftharpoons Cd(Hg)$$

results in the formation of a cadmium amalgam. Again, the oxidized and reduced substances are soluble, except that the cadmium metal is dissolved in the electrode phase.

Current-potential curves may be recorded for mixtures of electroactive substances and, provided that the various species undergo reduction or oxidation at sufficiently different potentials, a separate *wave* appears for each reactant. If the current-potential behavior of a platinum electrode in a 1 F sulfuric acid solution containing 0.01 M copper(II) and 0.01 M antimony(III) were studied, curve A of Figure 18-7 would be followed exactly until the cathode potential approached 0.18 v versus NHE, whereupon the current would rise because of deposition of antimony metal. Thus, the overall current-potential curve would exhibit two steps or waves, one near 0.27 v corresponding to copper(II) reduction and another at about 0.16 v versus NHE caused by reduction of antimony(III).

Feasibility of Separations and Determinations

Once all of the current-potential curves pertinent to a given analytical problem have been established, it is usually straightforward to decide whether a particular separation can be accomplished by means of controlled-potential electrolysis and, if so, at what value the working-electrode potential should be set to achieve the proposed separation and determination of the desired substance.

Suppose we wish to separate and determine by means of controlled-potential coulometry with a platinum gauze cathode both copper(II) and antimony(III) in a 1 F sulfuric acid medium initially containing a 0.01 M concentration of each species. An inspection of Figure 18-7 as well as a consideration of the calculations performed previously reveals that the potential of the working electrode must not be more positive than 0.278 v versus NHE if deposition of copper is to occur. Furthermore, it is evident that the cathode potential cannot be less than 0.173 v versus NHE if codeposition of antimony is to be avoided. Let us decide to control the working-electrode potential at exactly 0.190 v versus NHE and calculate what residual concentration of copper(II) remains undeposited after the sample solution has been exhaustively electrolyzed. Using the Nernst equation, we can write

$$E_{Cu^{++},Cu} = E^{\circ}_{Cu^{++},Cu} - \frac{0.059}{2} \log \frac{1}{[Cu^{++}]}$$

$$0.190 = 0.337 - \frac{0.059}{2} \log \frac{1}{[Cu^{++}]}$$

$$\log [Cu^{++}] = \frac{2(0.190 - 0.337)}{0.059} = -4.98$$

$$[Cu^{++}] = 1.05 \times 10^{-5} M$$

Thus, little more than 0.1 per cent of the original copper(II) should be in solution when the electrolysis is terminated, a result which suggests that good accuracy for the determination of copper is obtainable.

At the conclusion of the first part of this procedure — signaled by the fact that the current falls practically to zero — the cathode could be removed from the electrolytic cell, and washed, dried, and weighed for the determination of copper. Prior to the deposition of antimony, the copper might be dissolved from the platinum cathode with nitric acid. Alternatively, the copper could be left on the electrode, and the latter simply returned to the electrolytic cell. The second step of the procedure calls for a readjustment of the cathode potential so that antimony(III) is reduced to the elemental state.

A prediction of the potential needed to ensure the quantitative deposition of antimony can be based on the Nernst equation

$$E_{SbO^{+},Sb} = E^{\circ}_{SbO^{+},Sb} - \frac{0.059}{3} \log \frac{1}{[SbO^{+}][H^{+}]^2}$$

Assuming a final antimony(III) concentration of $10^{-6} M$ to guarantee acceptable accuracy for the determination, we can show that the required cathode potential is

$$E_{SbO^{+},Sb} = 0.212 - \frac{0.059}{3} \log \frac{1}{(10^{-6})(1)^2}$$

or

$$E_{SbO^{+},Sb} = 0.094 \text{ v versus NHE}$$

If the cathode potential is maintained at 0.094 v versus NHE, the bulk concentration of antimony(III) decreases with time and the limiting current diminishes until it becomes almost zero — a very small residual current will probably continue to flow. At this point, the controlled-potential deposition of antimony may be regarded as complete, the cathode removed from the cell, and the plated antimony washed, dried, and weighed as usual.

However, the controlled-potential deposition of metals does not demand that any weighing operations actually be performed. In the event that proper control of the working-electrode potential is exercised and only one electrode reaction occurs, the total quantity of electricity produced by that reaction can be easily related to the weight or concentration of the original electroactive species through Faraday's law, as will be discussed subsequently.

One can achieve little improvement in the separation and determination of antimony by setting the potential to a more negative value than 0.094 v versus NHE. First, the deposition of antimony will not proceed any faster because 0.094 v is already in the limiting-current region of the current-potential curve for antimony(III) reduction. Second, the accuracy of the determination cannot be measurably improved, since a control potential of 0.094 v versus NHE permits 99.99 per cent of the antimony to be deposited. Third, it must be remembered that hydrogen ion reduction will occur at a more negative potential.

We have seen that 0.01 M copper(II) which starts to undergo reduction at 0.278 v versus NHE and 0.01 M antimony(III) which begins to be reduced at 0.173 v versus NHE are satisfactorily separated even though these two potentials differ by only 105 mv. It is worthwhile to consider in more general terms what the minimal difference in the standard or formal potentials for half-reactions involving two species must be to permit their quantitative separation by means of controlled-potential electrolysis. Suppose we desire to separate two substances, Ox_1 and Ox_2, which are reduced, respectively, to Red_1 and Red_2 according to the half-reactions

$$Ox_1 + n_1e \rightleftharpoons Red_1$$

and

$$Ox_2 + n_2e \rightleftharpoons Red_2$$

Furthermore, let us assume that the initial concentrations of Ox_1 and Ox_2 are identical, that Ox_1 is more easily reducible than Ox_2, that 99.9 per cent of Ox_1 should be reduced, but that no more than 0.1 per cent of Ox_2 undergoes reduction.

When all of the reactants and products are soluble in the aqueous phase and when both n_1 and n_2 are equal to one, the standard potentials for the two half-reactions must differ by at least 354 mv to accomplish the desired separation. Similarly, if $n_1 = n_2 = 2$, the difference in standard potentials need be only 177 mv; and, in the situation where n_1 and n_2 are both 3, the two standard potentials may differ by as little as 118 mv.

When both Ox_1 and Ox_2 are metal cations, are reduced to the elemental state, and are deposited at unit activity upon a solid electrode, the standard potentials for the reduction of two univalent metal ions to their elemental states should differ by a minimum of 177 mv for the desired separation of equimolar concentrations of the ions. The minimal permissible difference is 89 mv for separation of two divalent metal ions and 59 mv for the separation of a pair of trivalent cations. Naturally, in order to effect a more complete or sharper separation than just stipulated, these differences must be larger but can be readily calculated from appropriate assumptions about the desired completeness of the separation.

One may wonder why the recording of current-potential curves is necessary, in view of our apparent ability to make predictions on the basis of the Nernst equation. The explanation lies in the fact that real chemical systems are much more complicated than the idealized situations we have discussed, although calculations of this type can serve as useful guides to the selection of the control potential. For actual applications of controlled-potential coulometry, adequate data are rarely available concerning the effects of complexation, pH, temperature, ionic strength, and other variables on standard potentials. Furthermore, it is impossible to predict the magnitudes of activation overpotentials and concentration overpotentials for electrode reactions. Fortunately, a current-potential curve, if recorded under experimental conditions identical or at least very similar to those used in a practical controlled-potential separation and determination, does provide all of the information needed to help one choose the correct control potential.

Current-Time Curves and Faraday's Law

An important and analytically useful characteristic of controlled-potential electrolysis is the variation of current with time. To understand the significance of this statement, let us consider the deposition of copper metal upon a platinum cathode from a well-stirred 0.01 M solution of cupric ion in 1 F sulfuric acid. Suppose that the cathode potential is controlled at a value corresponding to the plateau region of the current-potential curve for copper(II) reduction — for example, 0.20 v versus NHE on curve A of Figure 18-7. At the moment the controlled-potential deposition begins, the current due to reduction of cupric ion has some initial value, i_0. When one half of the copper has been deposited, the current, being directly proportional to the bulk concentration of cupric ion as mentioned earlier, will have diminished to $0.5i_0$, provided that no other electrode reaction occurs at a potential of 0.20 v versus NHE. After 90 per cent of the cupric ion has undergone reduction, the current would be $0.1i_0$, and the current after 99 and 99.9 per cent of the copper is deposited should have a value of $0.01i_0$ and $0.001i_0$, respectively.

Under the ideal conditions described in the previous paragraph —

namely, that a single electrode process occurs with a current efficiency of 100 per cent — the current during a controlled-potential electrolysis decays in accordance with the exponential expression

$$i_t = i_0 e^{-kt}$$

where i_t is the instantaneous current at any specified time, t, and i_0 represents the initial current. The proportionality constant k is a combination of four parameters, as indicated by the relation

$$k = \frac{DA}{V\delta}$$

in which D is the diffusion coefficient of the reacting species in cm^2/second, A is the electrode area in cm^2, V is the volume of the sample solution in milliliters, and δ is the thickness in centimeters of the stationary film of solution at the surface of the electrode. It is noteworthy that the time required for quantitative completion of a controlled-potential electrolysis depends on the four terms named in the preceding equation — a larger value of k shortens the electrolysis time. Thus, if the diffusion coefficient of the electroactive substance is increased by, say, an elevation of temperature, or if the area of the electrode is made greater so that more of the reacting species can reach the electrode surface per unit time, the electrolysis can be performed more rapidly. On the other hand, the desired reduction or oxidation is carried out in less time if the sample medium is efficiently stirred to decrease the thickness of the immobile layer of solution at the electrode surface and if the solution volume is minimal.

For most controlled-potential electrolyses, as suggested previously, the current decays to a very small fraction of its original value. The nature of the exponential decay law, however, prevents the current from ever reaching exactly zero. Nevertheless, the magnitude of the final current relative to the initial current provides the most straightforward means to determine when an electrolysis has reached quantitative completion. For example, if 1 per cent uncertainty is adequate for a particular application, the controlled-potential electrolysis may be terminated when the current decreases to $0.01i_0$. When, as in most analyses, an error not exceeding one part per thousand is desired, the electrolysis should be continued until the current decays to 0.1 per cent of its initial value.

Despite the variation of current in the course of a controlled-potential electrolysis, the success of this analytical method demands that only the species being determined react at the working electrode. We can express such a requirement in an alternate manner by stating that the current efficiency for the process of interest should be 100 per cent; that is, the number of coulombs of electricity corresponding to oxidation or reduction of the desired substance must equal the total amount of electricity passed during the electrolysis. Obviously, any extraneous process should be insignificant within the limits of experimental accuracy; otherwise, the current efficiency for the desired reaction will fall below 100 per cent, and an appropriate correction for the side reaction may or may not be possible. For the purpose of simplicity in the remaining paragraphs of this section on controlled-potential coulometry, we shall assume that the requirement of 100 per cent current efficiency is closely met.

Assuming the potential of the working electrode is adjusted to, and maintained at, a value so that only the desired reaction takes place, we must now investigate briefly some of the experimental approaches employed to evaluate the quantity of electricity pertinent to that process. Fundamentally, the number of coulombs passed in any electrolysis is expressible in terms of the relation

$$Q = \int_0^t i_t \, dt$$

where Q is the quantity of electricity in coulombs, i_t is the current in amperes as a function of time, and t is the length of the electrolysis in seconds. For coulometric titrations, in which a constant current is used, the quantity of electricity is simply the current-time product,

$$Q = it$$

where i represents the constant current. On the other hand, in controlled-potential electrolysis the exponential decay of the current necessitates an integration of the current-time curve.

An electromechanical or all-electronic *current-time integrator*, with provision for direct readout of the number of coulombs of electricity passed during a controlled-potential electrolysis, can be incorporated into the electrical circuit. Alternatively, the quantity of electricity corresponding to the desired reaction can be determined by means of a *chemical coulometer* placed in series with the electrolysis cell. Chemical coulometers are themselves electrochemical cells in which specified reactions occur with 100 per cent current efficiency. For example, a silver coulometer entails the deposition of silver from a silver nitrate solution upon a platinum cathode, the latter being subsequently weighed to determine the amount of silver metal and, therefore, the number of coulombs passed during the electrolysis. A direct-reading hydrogen-oxygen or hydrogen-nitrogen coulometer will be described subsequently.

Once the quantity of electricity, Q, in coulombs has been measured, the weight, W, in grams of the substance being determined is obtainable from the expression

$$W = \frac{QM}{nF}$$

where M is the formula weight of the species which is oxidized or reduced, n is the number of faradays of electricity involved in the oxidation or reduction of one formula weight of substance, and F is the Faraday constant (96,487 coulombs). This relation is a mathematical statement of Faraday's law of electrolysis — namely, that the weight of a species which undergoes electrode reaction is proportional to the quantity of electricity which passes through the electrolysis cell.

Apparatus for Controlled-Potential Coulometry

Basic equipment and apparatus for controlled-potential coulometry comprises a cell and appropriate working, auxiliary, and reference electrodes; a coulometer; and a variable voltage source-potentiostat combination as illustrated schematically in Figure 18-8.

Voltage Source and Potentiostat. It may be recalled that one of the expressions for the total voltage, E_{app}, impressed across an electrolytic cell is

$$E_{app} = E_a - E_c + iR$$

where E_a and E_c denote the potentials (versus a reference electrode) of the anode and cathode, respectively, including activation overpotential and concentration overpotential terms, and where iR is the ohmic potential drop of the cell. On the basis of this relation, we should predict that the maintenance of a constant working-electrode potential requires continual variation of the applied voltage in order to compensate for changes in the potential of the auxiliary electrode and the ohmic potential drop. A consideration of the controlled-potential deposition of copper upon a platinum cathode will substantiate this statement. First, the ohmic potential drop decreases practically

FIGURE 18-8. Apparatus for controlled-potential coulometry.

to zero during the reduction of cupric ion as a result of the exponential current decay. Second, a decrease in the current causes the activation overpotential for evolution of oxygen — the likely anode reaction — to diminish so that the value of E_a becomes less positive. Therefore, the applied voltage must be continuously decreased throughout the electrolysis in order to keep the cathode potential constant. Similar reasoning pertains to controlled-potential coulometric experiments in which the anode potential is held constant, the total applied voltage being decreased during the course of the electrolysis.

In principle, one observes the potential of the working electrode versus a reference electrode, using a potentiometer, digital voltmeter, or other potential-sensing instrument. Simultaneously, the direct-current voltage source (which may consist of a variable autotransformer, a selenium rectifier bridge, and an inductor-capacitor filter network) is adjusted, perhaps with the aid of a rheostat or voltage-divider, so that the working-electrode potential does remain constant at the preselected value. A wide variety of servo-mechanical and electronic *potentiostats* have been designed, constructed, and sold — complete instruments performing automatically the observation of the working-electrode potential and the adjustment of the applied voltage without any effort on the part of the analytical chemist or technician.

Coulometers.   Reliable measurement of the quantity of electricity corresponding to oxidation or reduction of the desired substance is one factor which governs the analytical accuracy of controlled-potential coulometry. The use of chemical coulometers requires unusual care, plus a certain amount of inconvenience, and does not provide direct readout of the number of coulombs. The hydrogen-oxygen coulometer overcomes some of the objectionable features encountered in the measurement of quantities of electricity. This device, which is placed in series with the coulometric cell, involves the electrolysis of a dilute aqueous potassium sulfate solution between two platinum electrodes. At the anode, water is oxidized to oxygen,

$$2\,H_2O \rightleftharpoons O_2 + 4\,H^+ + 4\,e$$

and hydrogen gas is formed at the cathode:

$$4\,H_2O + 4\,e \rightleftharpoons 2\,H_2 + 4\,OH^-$$

The evolved gases are collected together in a closed chamber above the potassium sulfate solution, so that their volume may be determined at a known temperature and pressure. From the latter measurements, along with Faraday's law and the perfect gas law, the number of coulombs passed through the coulometric cell can be computed and correlated with the quantity of reaction at the working electrode. In practice, if the conditions under which the hydrogen-oxygen coulometer is operated are kept constant, one may simply prepare a calibration curve so that the observed gas volume can be translated immediately into the number of coulombs. Occasionally, a hydrazine sulfate solution is used instead of the potassium sulfate medium, in which case nitrogen gas is produced at the anode:

$$N_2H_4 \rightleftharpoons N_2 + 4\,H^+ + 4\,e$$

A number of mechanical and electronic current-time integrators have been developed for use in controlled-potential coulometry. One especially elegant, yet simple, device involves a precision capacitor which is charged by the current passing through the coulometric cell. Within certain broad limits, the charge, Q, in coulombs on a capacitor is directly proportional to the voltage, V, in volts across the plates of that capacitor, the proportionality constant, C, in coulombs per volt being the capacitance:

$$Q = CV$$

Invariably, one must calibrate the capacitor by transferring a known quantity of electricity or charge to the plates of the capacitor and by measuring the voltage difference developed across these plates. Subsequently, when the capacitor is used to obtain the current-time integral, one allows a charge, equal or at least proportional to the number of coulombs of electricity passed through the coulometric cell, to accumulate on the capacitor. Then V is measured with a potentiometer or digital voltmeter and Q is calculated from the previously determined value of C.

Coulometric Cells and Electrodes. As indicated in Figure 18-8, a coulometric cell consists of three electrodes: the working electrode, the auxiliary electrode, and the reference electrode. Usually, the auxiliary electrode is placed in a separate compartment of the cell, the auxiliary electrode and working electrode compartments being in electrolytic contact with each other through a sintered-glass disk or ion-permeable membrane. The auxiliary electrode is isolated in this manner to prevent electrode products, such as oxygen, formed at that electrode from being stirred to the working electrode at which they would react. Alternatively, an auxiliary electrode may be selected at which only innocuous substances are produced. The use of a separate auxiliary electrode compartment means that the species produced at the working electrode cannot subsequently react at the auxiliary electrode. For example, in the controlled-potential reduction of iron(III) to iron(II) at a platinum cathode, the usual platinum auxiliary anode must be isolated so that iron(II) is not reoxidized.

For the reference electrode, one almost always employs either a saturated calomel or silver-silver chloride reference half-cell, although a mercury-mercurous sulfate electrode proves satisfactory when chloride must be excluded from the system. In addition, the reference electrode can be brought into contact with the sample solution through a suitable salt bridge. Above all, it is important that the tip of the reference electrode or its salt bridge tube be as close as possible to the surface of the working electrode so that the potential at which the latter is controlled does not include an appreciable ohmic potential drop.

Two cells described previously in this chapter require only slight modification for controlled-potential coulometric analysis. The cell illustrated in Figure 18-4 is suitable for oxidation and reduction processes occurring at a platinum gauze working electrode. However, the auxiliary electrode would undoubtedly not be another gauze electrode. A short length of platinum wire placed in a separate compartment of the cell could be employed, although many other electrode materials, including gold and carbon, are appropriate. Ordinarily, a coulometric cell is closed with a stopper containing drilled holes for insertion of the various electrodes and other appurtenances. Provisions for efficient stirring of the sample solution and for removal of dissolved oxygen are essential.

Because of the vast amount of polarographic data concerning the electrochemical behavior of literally hundreds of inorganic and organic substances, the controlled-potential coulometric technique has been applied extensively to reactions at mercury pool cathodes. Frequently, one can find the desired control potential by looking at information listed in reference books and in the chemical literature. The coulometric cell depicted in Figure 18-6 is easily adapted to accurate coulometric work, if the auxiliary anode is situated in a separate compartment and if the cell is equipped with an air-tight cover and with inlet and outlet tubes so that nitrogen or helium can be bubbled through and passed over the sample solution during the electrolysis. In addition, a saturated calomel reference electrode with a salt bridge tube long enough to nearly touch the surface of the stirred mercury pool is needed.

Although platinum and mercury working electrodes have been employed almost exclusively for coulometry, electrodes fabricated from gold, carbon, and silver are preferable for a number of specific applications. The controlled-potential coulometric determination of individual halides as well as the analysis of halide mixtures can be performed with the aid of silver anodes, the primary reaction being

$$Ag + Cl^- \rightleftharpoons AgCl + e$$

in the case of chloride ion. Mercury is so easily oxidized that it can be used as an anode only for reactions of readily oxidizable substances. On the other hand, the exceptionally high activation overpotential for hydrogen gas evolution on mercury renders this electrode excellent for the study of cathodic processes. Regardless of the choice of working electrode, a current-potential curve should be recorded under experimental conditions identical to those expected for an actual coulometric analysis so that the correct control potential is selected.

Applications of Controlled-Potential Coulometry

Controlled-potential coulometry has been applied to the determination of both inorganic and organic substances. In addition, this technique has proved to be of inestimable value in the identification and study of unknown electrode processes and in the electrochemical generation of species which cannot be conveniently prepared by means of ordinary chemical methods. Generally speaking, analytical results derived from controlled-potential coulometry are accurate to within 0.5 to 1 per cent, although the uncertainty may be as small as 0.1 per cent in favorable situations. Furthermore, the controlled-potential method is best suited for the determination of 0.05 to 1 mEq of the desired substance in a solution volume of 50 to 100 ml.

Separation and Determination of Metals. One of the most elegant examples of the applicability of controlled-potential coulometry for the separation and determination of metal cations is the complete analysis of copper, bismuth, lead, and tin mixtures. These elements are commonly encountered together in alloys, and so their individual measurement has definite practical significance. After a weighed portion of the alloy has been dissolved in nitric acid (or perhaps a nitric acid-hydrochloric acid mixture), appropriate quantities of sodium tartrate, succinic acid, and hydrazine are introduced into the solution and the sample medium is adjusted to pH 6.0 through addition of sodium hydroxide. From this solution, copper can be deposited quantitatively upon a previously weighed platinum gauze cathode whose potential is maintained at -0.30 v versus SCE (saturated calomel electrode). After the cathode is rinsed, dried, and weighed to establish the quantity of copper, the copper-plated cathode is returned to the sample solution, and elemental bismuth is plated upon the electrode at a potential of -0.40 v versus SCE. Following the gravimetric determination of bismuth, the cathode is again returned to the coulometric cell for the deposition of lead at a control potential of -0.60 v versus SCE. Finally, when the weight of the lead deposit has been determined, the cathode is replaced in the cell, the solution is acidified with concentrated hydrochloric acid to decompose the stable tin(IV)-tartrate complex, the tin(IV)-chloride species is reduced to the elemental state at a potential of -0.60 v versus SCE, and the weight of tin metal is obtained. It should be noted that this procedure, as described, combines the techniques of controlled-potential separation and electrogravimetry; it does not involve measurement of the quantity of electricity corresponding to the deposition of each metal. Presumably, the latter approach would be a feasible one.

Separations and determinations similar to the procedure just outlined have been devised for one or more components of the following mixtures: lead, cadmium, and zinc; silver and copper; antimony and tin; nickel, zinc, aluminum, and iron; and rhodium and iridium.

A number of useful separations and determinations of metals have been accomplished with the aid of the mercury pool cathode. For example, lead(II) can be reduced from a $0.5 F$ potassium chloride medium into mercury, and separated from cadmium(II), if the cathode potential is controlled at -0.50 v versus SCE. Copper(II) and bismuth(III) in an acidic tartrate solution can be separated and determined by controlled-potential deposition into a mercury pool cathode. One of the few satisfactory procedures for the analysis of a mixture of nickel(II) and cobalt(II) entails the selective deposition of nickel from an aqueous pyridine solution of pH 6.5 into mercury at a potential of -0.95 v versus SCE. After the quantity of electricity corresponding to reduction of nickel has been obtained, the cathode potential is reset to -1.20 v versus SCE for the reduction of cobalt. Uranium(VI) may be accurately determined through controlled-potential reduction to uranium(IV) in a 1 F sulfuric acid medium at a mercury pool cathode whose potential is -0.60 v versus SCE.

Anodic Reactions at Platinum Electrodes.   Three representative examples of controlled-potential determinations which involve anodic processes at platinum electrodes are the oxidation of iron(II) to iron(III), the quantitative conversion of arsenic(III) to arsenic(V), and the deposition of thallium(III) oxide.

Quantities of iron(II) ranging from approximately 10 to 50 mg are determinable with an uncertainty of 1 per cent by means of controlled-potential oxidation at platinum in 1 F sulfuric acid. A similar procedure for the oxidation of arsenic(III) to arsenic(V) at a potential of 1.0 v versus SCE yields results of comparable accuracy. When the potential of a platinum electrode is maintained at 1.34 v versus SCE, thallium(I) in a 1 F sulfuric acid medium is oxidized quantitatively to thallium(III) oxide. Analytical results accurate to ± 0.3 per cent are attainable for amounts of thallium between 30 and 100 mg in a solution volume of 100 ml.

Determination and Preparation of Organic Compounds. Relatively few applications of controlled-potential coulometry to the analysis of organic compounds have been reported. The successful determination of picric acid through reduction to triaminophenol at a mercury pool cathode

suggests that more organic molecules should be studied to establish conditions for their determination. Polarographic information regarding the behavior of organic compounds indicates that the controlled-potential analysis of these substances both individually and in mixtures should prove especially valuable.

Another important use of controlled-potential coulometry involves the electrochemical preparation of organic compounds. For example, it has been demonstrated that the reduction of 9-(o-iodophenyl)acridine at a mercury cathode proceeds in two steps, namely, and

In an alkaline ethanol medium, the first step occurs at a potential of -1.32 v versus SCE, and the second two-electron reduction takes place at -1.62 v versus SCE. By controlling the potential of a mercury pool cathode at approximately -1.40 v versus SCE, one can quantitatively reduce the starting material according to the first step without incurring further reduction. On the other hand, attempts to perform the same synthesis by various chemical means are unsuccessful because of the occurrence of the overall four-electron reduction, of side reactions, or of no reaction at all. Again, preparative electrochemistry is a field which remains to be fully explored.

COULOMETRIC TITRATIONS

Another important method of analysis — coulometric titrimetry — is based upon the constant-current electrochemical generation of a titrant which reacts quantitatively with the substance to be determined. From the magnitude of the constant current as well as the time required to generate an amount of titrant stoichiometrically equivalent to the desired species, the weight or concentration of the substance of interest can be ascertained according to Faraday's law.

Principles of Coulometric Titrimetry

Several important aspects of coulometric titrimetry can be illustrated through consideration of a familiar reaction — the determination of cerium(IV) by reduction to cerium(III),

$$Ce^{++++} + e \rightleftharpoons Ce^{+++}$$

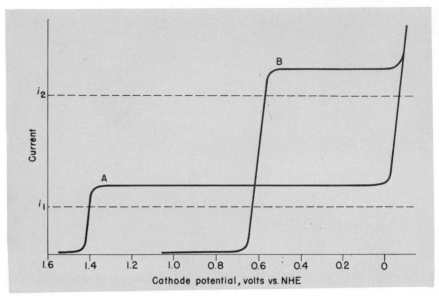

FIGURE 18-9. Schematic current-potential curves for reductions of cerium(IV), curve A, and iron(III), curve B, at a platinum cathode in 1 F sulfuric acid.

in a 1 F sulfuric acid medium. Assume that the cerium(IV)-sulfuric acid solution is contained in a coulometric cell equipped with a stirrer and with inlet and outlet tubes for introduction of nitrogen. Assume further that a platinum working electrode is immersed in the sample solution and that a platinum auxiliary electrode is situated in a separate compartment filled with pure sulfuric acid medium. By referring to a schematic current-potential curve for cerium(IV) reduction at platinum, let us review what happens when a constant current is passed through this electrolytic cell such that the working electrode is the cathode.

Curve A in Figure 18-9 is a current-potential curve for reduction of cerium(IV) to cerium(III). As expected, the current rises rapidly near the formal potential, 1.44 v versus NHE, for the cerium(IV)-cerium(III) couple in 1 F sulfuric acid. Thereafter, the current attains a limiting value as the cathode potential becomes more negative until, at approximately 0 v versus NHE, the current increases without apparent limit because of reduction of the relatively large concentration of hydrogen ion. If the constant current passing through the coulometric cell were adjusted to be i_1, it is evident from Figure 18-9 that this current level initially is sustained completely by reduction of cerium(IV), since the limiting current of curve A exceeds the selected current. However, as electrolysis proceeds, the limiting current for cerium(IV) reduction soon drops below i_1, at which time another electrode reaction — namely, hydrogen ion reduction — must occur to maintain the desired current.

As long as the limiting current for cerium(IV) reduction is equal to or greater than i_1, the current efficiency for this process is 100 per cent and the potential of the cathode remains at approximately 1.44 v versus NHE. Once the limiting current for reduction of cerium(IV) falls below i_1, the current efficiency for reduction of cerium(IV) becomes less than 100 per cent and the cathode potential shifts abruptly to about 0 v versus NHE. This situation resembles that described earlier for the electrodeposition of copper. Notice in Figure 18-9 that, if the constant current is chosen to be as large as i_2, the cathode potential immediately adopts a value at which hydrogen gas is evolved and the current efficiency for cerium(IV) reduction is much less than 100 per cent, even at the beginning of the electrolysis.

If, as quickly as it were produced, hydrogen gas reacted stoichiometrically and rapidly with cerium(IV),

$$2\ Ce^{++++} + H_2 \rightleftharpoons 2\ Ce^{+++} + 2\ H^+$$

all of the electricity passing through the coulometric cell would result in reduction of cerium(IV) to cerium(III). Thus, even though cerium(IV) might not undergo direct reaction at the platinum cathode, cerium(IV) would nevertheless be reduced chemically by hydrogen gas, and so the net result would be the same as if cerium(IV) had been reduced with 100 per cent current efficiency. Unfortunately, hydrogen gas does not react with cerium(IV) at a measurable rate, and so the constant-current coulometric titration of cerium(IV) fails under these conditions.

One excellent way to overcome the difficulty mentioned in the preceding paragraph involves addition to the cerium(IV)-sulfuric acid solution of some substance which is reduced at a platinum cathode more easily than hydrogen ion but less readily than cerium(IV) itself. Furthermore, the *reduced* form of this substance must undergo a quantitative and instantaneous reaction with cerium(IV). A reagent which fulfills these requirements excellently is iron(III), for reduction of this species yields a product, iron(II), that immediately reduces cerium(IV). To understand how the presence of iron(III) ensures the success of the constant-current coulometric titration of cerium(IV), we must refer to the current-potential curve for reduction of iron(III) at a platinum electrode in a 1 F sulfuric acid medium, as depicted by curve B in Figure 18-9. Since the formal potential for the iron(III)-iron(II) couple is 0.68 v versus NHE in 1 F sulfuric acid, very little current flows until the cathode potential reaches approximately this value. However, the onset of rapid reduction of iron(III) is marked by a large increase in current. A limiting-current region of the curve appears at potentials less positive than about 0.5 v versus NHE, with a final rise in current near 0 v versus NHE signaling the commencement of hydrogen gas evolution.

Let us now consider the effect of iron(III) on the coulometric titration of cerium(IV). We have already seen that, if a constant current i_1 is passed through the coulometric cell, cerium(IV) is initially reduced with 100 per cent current efficiency because the original limiting current for reduction of cerium(IV) is larger than i_1. Continued reaction of cerium(IV) causes the limiting current for curve A in Figure 18-9 to decrease below i_1, at which time the working-electrode potential must shift in a cathodic direction until some other current-sustaining process occurs. When a relatively large concentration of iron(III) is present, the cathode potential changes only to the value where the half-reaction

$$Fe^{+++} + e \rightleftharpoons Fe^{++}$$

takes place. However, the iron(II) produced at the electrode surface is stirred into the body of the sample solution and chemically reduces cerium(IV) to cerium(III):

$$Ce^{++++} + Fe^{++} \rightleftharpoons Ce^{+++} + Fe^{+++}$$

Since iron(II) is converted back to iron(III) almost immediately, the concentration of the latter stays constant as long as any cerium(IV) remains unreduced. Thus, the limiting current for iron(III) reduction is the same throughout the titration, and there is no danger that the cathode potential will shift to the value at which hydrogen ion is reduced. Therefore, only one net reaction occurs — *the quantitative reduction of cerium(IV)*. If a method of end point detection is available, such as a means to determine the first slight excess of electrogenerated iron(II), the quantity of cerium(IV) can be related through Faraday's law to the product of the constant current, i, and the electrolysis time, t.

There is no reason why the constant current should not have a much larger value than i_1, since the time required for a coulometric titration is inversely proportional to the electrolysis current. The only requirement is that the selected constant current not exceed the limiting current for iron(III) reduction. For example, if a constant current of magnitude i_2 were utilized (see Fig. 18-9), the current efficiency for cerium(IV) reduction is much less than 100 per cent at the start of the titration. However, because the limiting current for iron(III) reduction is greater than i_2, the cerium(IV) is nevertheless reduced quantitatively. Therefore, it is evident that as high a concentration of iron(III) as possible should be introduced into the sample solution. Accordingly, we may speak of the *coulometric titration of cerium(IV) with electrogenerated iron(II)*, where the latter species is called a **coulometric titrant.** Of course, it must be recognized that some of the cerium(IV) is reduced through direct electron transfer at the working electrode. The criteria for the selection of a coulometric titrant are much the same as in any other volumetric method of analysis.

Advantages of Coulometric Titrimetry

In comparison to conventional volumetric methods of analysis, coulometric titrimetry possesses a number of significant advantages. Not the least

among these virtues is the fact that the preparation, storage, and handling
of standard titrant solutions are completely eliminated. For the coulometric
titration of cerium(IV) with electrogenerated iron(II), the actual concentration of iron(III) from which the titrant is generated need not be known with
any great accuracy provided that enough iron(III) is present to sustain the
desired constant current. Closely related to the first advantage is the possibility that titrants which are unstable or otherwise troublesome to preserve
can be electrochemically generated in situ. Such uncommon reagents as
silver(II), manganese(III), titanium(III), copper(I), tin(II), bromine, and
chlorine can be conveniently prepared as coulometric titrants.

Coulometric titrimetry is inherently capable of much higher accuracy
than ordinary volumetric analysis because the two parameters of interest —
namely, current and time — can be determined experimentally with excep-
tional precision. Clearly, one need not be concerned about uncertainties in
volume and weight measurements or the preparation and purity of standard
substances used in classic procedures. In many instances, one can correct
for the presence of trace impurities in the supporting electrolyte solution or
in the substance from which the titrant is generated. This is accomplished
by a pretitration procedure in which a solution containing all reagents except
the sample is titrated to the desired end point prior to introduction of the
unknown. After the sample is added, the coulometric titration is carried out
until the same end point is reached. Still another advantage is that the solution is not diluted during the course of the titration. This feature has definite
value in the application of spectrophotometric and conductometric methods
of end point detection.

Perhaps the most important virtue of coulometric titrimetry is that
exceedingly small quantities of the titrant can be accurately generated. It
is not uncommon to perform coulometric titrations in which increments of
titrant are generated with a constant current of 10 ma flowing for 0.1 sec-
ond — which corresponds to only 1 millicoulomb or approximately 1×10^{-5} mEq. Such an amount of reagent would require the addition of 1 μl
of 0.01 N titrant from a buret.

Apparatus and Techniques of Coulometric Titrimetry

Basic equipment needed for the performance of coulometric titrations
includes a suitable source of constant current, an accurate timing device,
and a coulometric cell, as indicated schematically in Figure 18-10.

Constant-Current Sources.   In the majority of coulometric titrations, generating currents ranging from 5 to 20 ma are usually employed,
although the utilization of constant currents as large as 100 ma or as small
as 1 ma is occasionally desirable. In some of the earliest analytical applications of coulometric titrimetry, constant-current sources consisted of a bank

FIGURE 18-10. Diagram of essential apparatus for performance of constant-current coulometric titrations.

of heavy-duty radio B-batteries connected in series with a large current-limiting resistance. Thus, three or four 45 v batteries in series provide a voltage source which can deliver currents up to 10 ma with a constancy of ± 0.5 per cent. However, for coulometric titrations of the highest accuracy, such constant-current sources are inadequate because the voltage of a battery tends to decay during use, the current-limiting resistance changes because of heating effects, and the back emf of the coulometric cell (which opposes the voltage source) may vary with time. Electronic and servomechanical instruments, permitting current regulation to within ± 0.01 per cent and delivering currents of 200 ma or more, are commercially available but may be constructed from relatively inexpensive operational-amplifier components.

Many constant-current sources allow one to set the current at some preselected value prior to the beginning of a coulometric titration. A few instruments include integrators from which the current-time product may be read directly in coulombs or equivalents of the substance being titrated. However, it is preferable that one establish experimentally the exact magnitude of the current, as well as its constancy, by measuring the iR drop across a calibrated resistor (R) with a precision potentiometer (Fig. 18-10).

Measurement of Time. If constant currents precise to within ± 0.01 per cent are obtainable, it is apparent that the measurement of time must be accomplished with comparable accuracy in order to realize the full capabilities of coulometric titrimetry. Ordinarily, time is measured with the aid of an electric stopclock powered by a synchronous motor, which, in turn, is actuated through the same switch (S) used to start and stop the coulometric titration itself. In the performance of a coulometric titration, it is invariably necessary to open and close switch S a number of times as the equivalence point is approached so that small increments of titrant can be generated and permitted to react before the titration is either continued or terminated. This procedure parallels the manual closing and opening of a buret stopcock in classic volumetric analysis. Some electric timing devices exhibit a so-called start-stop error; that is, the synchronous motor tends to lag in starting or coast in stopping rather than starting and stopping abruptly. Thus, the cumulative timing uncertainty can become significant for a coulometric titration in which the switch S is opened and closed repeatedly. In precise work, one should employ an electric stopclock equipped with a solenoid brake to reduce the start-stop error to about 0.01 second for each separate operation of the switch. Nevertheless, the magnitude of the constant current used in coulometric titrimetry is usually adjusted to give a titration time of at least several hundred seconds so that timing errors are negligibly small.

Coulometric Cells. Figure 18-11 illustrates a cell which has been employed very successfully for the coulometric titration of acids with electrogenerated hydroxide. This application and cell will be described in more detail subsequently.

Every coulometric cell must contain a **generator electrode,** at which the titrant is produced, and the usual auxiliary electrode to complete the electrolysis circuit. In most instances, as we have mentioned before, the auxiliary-electrode reaction yields a substance which interferes chemically or electrochemically with the coulometric process. Therefore, one customarily isolates the auxiliary electrode from the main sample solution — although not for the cell shown in Figure 18-11 — by placing the auxiliary electrode in a tube containing electrolyte solution but closed at the bottom with a porous glass disk. The choice of a generator electrode is governed by the particular analytical application and is usually fabricated from platinum, gold, silver, or mercury. Generator electrodes typically range from 10 to 25 cm^2 in area, whereas the auxiliary electrode is probably a length of platinum wire. As for other coulometric methods of analysis, the sample solution must be well stirred. In addition, the coulometric cell may be closed with a fitted cover having an inlet tube for the continuous introduction of nitrogen, helium, argon, and sometimes carbon dioxide for removal and exclusion of dissolved oxygen from the sample solution. Depending upon the technique used to follow the progress of a coulometric titration, some cells are equipped with other electrodes. Thus, the cell pictured in Figure 18-11 contains a glass membrane *indicator* electrode and a salt bridge tube leading to a suitable reference electrode for potentiometric end point detection of the coulometric acid-base titration.

FIGURE 18-11. Coulometric cell employed for titration of acids. [Redrawn, with permission, from a paper by J. J. Lingane: Anal. Chim. Acta, *11*, 283 (1954).]

End Point Detection. Fundamentally, other than the mode by which titrant is added to the sample solution, there is remarkably little difference between coulometric titrimetry and the more familiar methods of classic volumetric analysis. Therefore, it is not surprising that all of the techniques discussed earlier in the text for end point detection are applicable.

Visual methods for location of titration equivalence points, including the use of colored acid-base and redox indicators, have been widely employed in coulometric titrimetry. Unfortunately, visual indicators lack the necessary sensitivity for end point detection in the titration of small amounts of a substance, as may be recalled, for example, from Chapter 8 where the titration of a *dilute* solution of strong acid with strong base was considered. Consequently, coulometric titrimetry has demanded that the analytical chemist pay special heed to the development and perfection of methods for equivalence point location.

Among the so-called instrumental techniques of end point detection are the spectrophotometric, potentiometric, and conductometric methods. Spectrophotometry has obvious applicability in conjunction with the use of visual indicators and, in addition, serves well for the location of equivalence points in coulometric titrations involving light-absorbing species such as iodine, bromine, cerium(IV), manganese(III), and titanium(III). Such a method of end point detection possesses some inconvenience in that the coulometric cell must be mounted in a spectrophotometer or colorimeter so that the light path is not obstructed by the stirrer and electrodes. Potentiometry is an obvious method of end point detection. In coulometric acid-base titrimetry, a glass membrane-calomel electrode pair is utilized, whereas a platinum or gold indicator electrode is the logical choice for redox reactions. The progress of complexometric titrations which involve the electrogeneration of ethylenediaminetetraacetate (EDTA) can be monitored with the aid of the mercury indicator electrode system described in the preceding chapter, whereas the equivalence point of a precipitation titration is normally located through the use of a silver or, possibly, a mercury indicator electrode. The conductometric method of end point detection is useful in a few situations, such as in the coulometric titrations of acids.

Analytical Applications of Coulometric Titrimetry

Every kind of titration — acid-base, precipitation, complex formation, and oxidation-reduction — has been successfully performed coulometrically, In principle, any titration which can be accomplished volumetrically is amenable to the coulometric technique. Coulometric titrations are best suited to the determination of quantities of a substance ranging from 1 μg or less up to about 100 mg, errors characteristically being on the order of 0.1 to 0.3 per cent as compared to the 1 per cent uncertainties encountered in controlled-potential coulometry.

Acid-Base Titrations. Oxidation and reduction of water provide the means for coulometric titrations of acids and bases. For the determination of both strong and weak acids, advantage may be taken of the fact that electroreduction of water at a platinum cathode yields hydroxide ions,

$$2\,H_2O + 2\,e \rightleftharpoons H_2 + 2\,OH^-$$

although, under some conditions, the hydrogen ion furnished by the acid is reduced directly at the electrode surface:

$$2\,H^+ + 2\,e \rightleftharpoons H_2$$

Regardless of which process occurs, however, the net result is neutralization of the acid with 100 per cent titration efficiency. If a platinum auxiliary anode is employed, it must be isolated from the main sample solution because oxidation of water,

$$2\,H_2O \rightleftharpoons O_2 + 4\,H^+ + 4\,e$$

produces hydrogen ion which would ruin the determination. However, the anodic generation of hydrogen ion can be eliminated entirely through the use of the coulometric cell shown in Figure 18-11. In this cell, a silver auxiliary anode is situated directly in the sample solution, the latter containing $0.04\,F$ sodium bromide in addition to the acid to be titrated. The anode reaction,

$$Ag + Br^- \rightleftharpoons AgBr + e$$

leads to formation of an innocuous coating of silver bromide upon the silver electrode. A significant advantage of the constant-current coulometric titration of acids with electrogenerated hydroxide ion is that one may avoid the nuisance of having to protect a standard base solution from atmospheric carbon dioxide.

Hydrogen ion, for the coulometric titration of bases, can be generated from the oxidation of water at a platinum anode in a manner analogous to the determination of acids mentioned in the preceding paragraph. Usually, it is necessary to isolate the auxiliary cathode so that the anodically formed hydrogen ion does not undergo subsequent reduction at the cathode.

By adding a very small amount of water to a nonaqueous solvent, one can electrogenerate hydrogen ions at a platinum anode for the titration of weak bases without seriously modifying the properties of the solvent system. One milligram samples of pyridine, benzylamine, and triethylamine have been determined with an error of less than 2 per cent in 100 ml of acetonitrile containing $0.05\,F$ lithium perchlorate trihydrate as the source of water as well as the supporting electrolyte.

Precipitation Titrations. If the glass membrane electrode is replaced with a silver wire indicator electrode for potentiometric end point detection, the coulometric cell of Figure 18-11 serves well for titrations with anodically generated silver ion. Individual halide ions can be accurately determined, and it is possible to analyze mixtures of these species as well. Thiourea has been titrated according to an indirect coulometric procedure, 0.4 to 4 mg amounts being determined with an uncertainty of only 0.01 mg. Mixtures of bromide and thiocyanate have been successfully titrated with electrogenerated silver ion in an aqueous acetone medium. An especially interesting application is the coulometric titration of mercaptans with silver ion, 3 μg quantities of mercaptans having been determined with an error of ±0.2 μg and larger samples with an uncertainty of 1 per cent or less.

A few studies have been reported in which electrogenerated mercury(I) is used to titrate chloride, bromide, and iodide individually and in mixtures.

Complexometric Titrations. Ethylenediaminetetraacetate is conveniently generated through reduction of the very stable mercury(II)-EDTA-ammine complex at a mercury pool cathode in an ammonia-ammonium nitrate buffer:

$$HgNH_3Y^= + NH_4^+ + 2\ e \rightleftharpoons Hg + 2\ NH_3 + HY^=$$

As soon as the EDTA species is liberated, it reacts rapidly with a metal ion, such as zinc(II), to form the corresponding metal-EDTA complex:

$$Zn(NH_3)_4^{++} + HY^= \rightleftharpoons ZnY^= + NH_4^+ + 3\ NH_3$$

End point detection is accomplished potentiometrically with the aid of a mercury indicator electrode as described in Chapter 17. The platinum auxiliary electrode must be enclosed in a separate compartment of the coulometric cell in order to prevent reduction of anodically formed oxygen at the mercury cathode, and the sample solution itself must be deaerated with pure nitrogen. This procedure has been applied to the titration of calcium(II), copper(II), lead(II), and zinc(II); and the analytical results are accurate to within ± 0.5 per cent for quantities of these species ranging from 2 to 40 mg. Very likely the technique can be extended to the determination of many other metal ions which form stable EDTA complexes.

Oxidation-Reduction Titrations. Coulometric titrimetry has been applied more extensively to redox processes than to all other kinds of reactions combined. The constant-current generation of halogens (chlorine, bromine, and iodine) is useful for a wide variety of determinations. Among the substances titrated coulometrically with electrogenerated chlorine are iodide and arsenic(III). Coulometric titrations of arsenic(III), antimony(III), iodide, thallium(I), uranium(IV), ammonia, thiodiglycol, 8-hydroxyquinoline, phenol, salicylic acid, and aniline have been successfully accomplished either directly or indirectly with electrogenerated bromine. Procedures have been developed for the determination with electrogenerated iodine or triiodide of arsenic(III), antimony(III), thiosulfate, selenium(IV), and hydrogen sulfide.

A number of methods have been perfected for the coulometric titrations of iron(II), ferrocyanide, titanium(III), arsenic(III), uranium(IV), iodide, and hydroquinone with anodically formed cerium(IV). Several techniques are available for the generation of manganese(III) and silver(II) — both very powerful oxidants — such species as oxalic acid, iron(II), arsenic(III), and vanadium(IV) having been titrated with these reagents. The electrogeneration of reducing agents, including iron(II), copper(I), uranium(IV), and titanium(III), has been employed as a means for the coulometric titration of many different oxidants.

POLAROGRAPHY

Polarography derives its analytical importance from the special characteristics of current-potential curves or polarograms obtained with a dropping mercury electrode. First, the position of a polarogram along the

FIGURE 18-12.   Dropping mercury electrode assembly and H-cell for polarographic measurements. [Redrawn, with permission, from a paper by J. J. Lingane and H. A. Laitinen: Ind. Eng. Chem., Anal. Ed., *11*, 504 (1939).]

potential axis may indicate the identity of the substance which undergoes electron transfer. Second, under experimental conditions which are easily achieved, the polarogram exhibits a diffusion-controlled limiting current whose magnitude is governed by the quantity of electroactive substance present. Consequently, polarography permits qualitative identification of a substance as well as quantitative measurement of the concentration of that species.

Characteristics and Advantages of the Dropping Mercury Electrode

Some of the apparatus used in the performance of polarographic measurements is pictured in Figure 18-12. A so-called H-cell, comprised of two compartments separated by a sintered-glass disk and an agar-saturated potassium chloride plug, is commonly employed. The dropping mercury electrode (DME) consists of a length of thin-bore capillary tubing attached to the bottom of a stand tube and a mercury reservoir. Under the influence of gravity, mercury emerges from the orifice of the capillary in a continuous series of individual and identical droplets, approximately one-half millimeter in diameter. By adjusting the height of the mercury column, one may vary the **drop time** — that is, the time required for a fresh drop of mercury to grow and fall from the tip of the capillary. Typical drop times range from three to six seconds with mercury reservoir heights of 30 cm or more. The dropping mercury electrode should always be immersed in the sample solution with mercury flowing from the tip of the capillary so that solution cannot back up into and clog the capillary. Since oxygen undergoes stepwise reduction at a mercury cathode,

$$O_2 + 2\,H^+ + 2\,e \rightleftharpoons H_2O_2$$

and

$$H_2O_2 + 2\,H^+ + 2\,e \rightleftharpoons 2\,H_2O$$

nitrogen or some other inert gas is bubbled through the sample solution to remove oxygen prior to the recording of a polarogram and is passed over the surface of the solution during the actual measurements.

A reference electrode of moderately large area is situated in the second compartment of the H-cell. In practically every instance, a saturated calomel electrode is utilized. It is important that the size of the reference electrode be great relative to the area of a mercury drop, because the former serves as the auxiliary electrode. Currents resulting from electrode processes at the surface of the dropping mercury electrode are so small — on the order of several microamperes — that the potential of the saturated calomel electrode remains virtually unchanged by the passage of this tiny current. Therefore, a single saturated calomel electrode may function well as both auxiliary electrode and reference electrode, and the potential of the dropping mercury electrode can be reliably measured.

As mentioned earlier in this chapter, other microelectrodes, particularly those fabricated from platinum wire, have been employed in the measurement and recording of current-potential curves, but the dropping mercury electrode possesses at least three unique advantages. First, the continuous growth and fall of mercury droplets means that a fresh electrode surface is presented to the sample solution every few seconds. Consequently, there is no accumulation of electrolysis products either at the surface of the electrode or in the electrode phase, and the reaction being studied is not adversely affected by the course of electrolysis at previous drops. Second, the activation overpotential for hydrogen gas evolution at mercury is unusually large (see Table 18-1), rendering the dropping mercury electrode especially valuable for the study of cathodic processes — most notably, the reduction of metal ions. Third, as we shall discover, with the dropping mercury electrode it is possible to obtain a reproducible diffusion-controlled limiting current which is quantitatively related to the concentration of the reacting species.

Mercury has one serious drawback as an electrode because of its relative ease of oxidation. For example, a dropping mercury electrode begins to undergo free anodic dissolution in a noncomplexing medium, such as perchloric acid, at a potential of approximately $+0.5$ v versus NHE. By way of comparison, platinum and gold anodes can be polarized in a 1 F perchloric acid solution to potentials well above $+1.2$ v versus NHE. In the presence of 1 M chloride ion, mercury is oxidized to insoluble mercury(I) chloride at about $+0.2$ v versus NHE, whereas dissolution of mercury as a cyanide complex, probably $Hg(CN)_4^=$, occurs at -0.5 v versus NHE in a 1 F sodium cyanide medium. Clearly, the dropping mercury electrode is largely restricted to the study of cathodic processes, although some easily oxidized species can be determined polarographically.

Nature of a Polarogram

Suppose an air-free 1 F potassium chloride solution containing 5.00×10^{-4} M copper(I) is transferred into a polarographic cell. If the potential of the dropping mercury electrode is scanned in a cathodic direction from 0 to -0.6 v versus SCE, the polarogram shown as curve A in Figure 18-13 is observed. This current-potential curve was obtained with the aid of a **polarograph,** an instrument which automatically increases the voltage impressed across the polarographic cell and, simultaneously, records the current on moving chart paper. Except for the current oscillations due to the periodic growth and fall of the mercury drops, this current-potential curve closely resembles those described earlier in the chapter.

According to polarographic convention, currents resulting from cathodic processes are designated as positive, whereas anodic currents are taken to be negative. Thus, we see in Figure 18-13 that a relatively tiny anodic current flows at 0 v versus SCE. As the potential of the dropping mercury electrode becomes more negative, however, the current attains a value of zero near -0.1 v. Further cathodic changes in the potential of the dropping mercury electrode cause a rapid increase in current between -0.1 and -0.3 v, followed by the attainment of a limiting-current region at potentials more negative than -0.35 v versus SCE. Although not shown in Figure 18-13, if the cathodic scan were continued, an almost limitless rise in current would occur near -2.0 v versus SCE because of the reduction of potassium ions to form a potassium amalgam.

A complete plot of current as a function of the dropping-electrode potential is termed a **polarogram,** and the rapidly ascending portion of the curve, as appears around -0.2 v versus SCE in Figure 18-13, is known as a **polarographic wave.** Reduction of the chlorocuprous ion with the resultant formation of a copper amalgam,

$$CuCl_2^- + e + Hg \rightleftharpoons Cu(Hg) + 2\ Cl^-$$

is responsible for this polarographic wave. It should be recognized that copper(I) is oxidizable to copper(II):

$$CuCl_2^- + Cl^- \rightleftharpoons CuCl_3^- + e$$

Indeed the negative or anodic current seen in the polarogram of Figure 18-13 is due in part to the commencement of copper(I) oxidation, but no well-defined polarographic wave for this latter process can be obtained

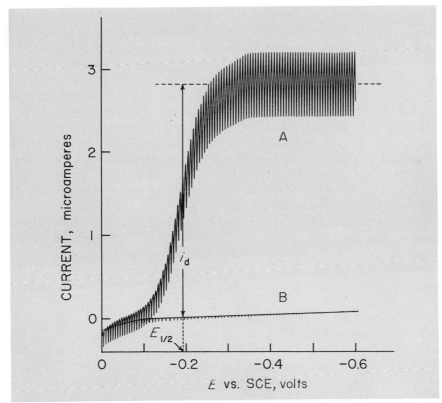

FIGURE 18-13. A representative polarogram. Curve A: polarogram for reduction of $5.00 \times 10^{-4}\ M$ copper(I) in a $1\ F$ potassium chloride medium containing 0.003 per cent maximum suppressor (Triton X-100). Curve B: schematic residual current for a $1\ F$ potassium chloride solution with maximum suppressor.

because, in a $1\,F$ potassium chloride medium, the dropping mercury electrode itself undergoes oxidation to insoluble mercurous chloride at approximately $+0.05$ v versus SCE.

Residual Current

Even when copper(I) is excluded from the potassium chloride solution, a small **residual current** flows through the polarographic cell, as may be seen in curve B of Figure 18-13. We have previously described residual currents as originating from the reduction or oxidation of traces of impurities in the distilled water and chemical reagents used to prepare a sample solution.

However, in polarography a major component of the residual current arises from charging of the so-called electrical double-layer at the surface of the mercury electrode. The mercury-solution interface behaves essentially as a tiny capacitor; in order for the mercury to acquire the potential demanded by the external applied voltage, electrons move either toward or away from the mercury surface depending on the required potential and on the nature of the solution. For example, in a $0.1\,F$ potassium chloride medium, a mercury drop is positively charged with respect to the solution at potentials more positive than approximately -0.53 v versus SCE. On the other hand, the mercury surface acquires a net negative charge at more cathodic potentials than the preceding value, but is neutral with respect to the solution at exactly -0.53 v versus SCE. The potential at which the mercury drop is uncharged is designated the **electrocapillary maximum.** Since each new mercury drop emerging from the orifice of the capillary must be charged to the proper potential, a continuous flow of current results. The greater the difference between the actual potential of a mercury drop and the electrocapillary maximum, the larger will be the charging current. It is interesting to note that the charging current is positive when the potential of the dropping mercury electrode is negative with respect to the electrocapillary maximum — electrons being forced to accumulate on the surface of the electrode. The converse is true at potentials positive to the electrocapillary maximum.

It is important to realize that the residual current sets the lower concentration limit accessible to accurate polarographic determination. In the majority of situations, the charging current comprises an appreciable fraction of the total observed limiting current when the concentration of the electroactive substance is approximately $10^{-4}\,M$ or less. However, if care is taken to correct for the charging current, analytical results precise to within ± 2 per cent are attainable. Several sophisticated modifications of polarography have been developed in which the residual current can be almost eliminated or canceled. These techniques permit concentrations as low as $10^{-7}\,M$ to be determined with respectable accuracy.

Polarographic Diffusion Current

In our discussion of concentration overpotential, we identified three mechanisms whereby an electroactive substance, such as copper(I), may reach the surface of an electrode — *migration* of a charged species under the influence of an electrical field, *convection* caused by stirring or agitation of the solution or electrode, and *diffusion* arising from a concentration gradient. Successful polarographic measurements demand that the electroactive species reach the surface of a mercury drop only by diffusion, this being the only process amenable to straightforward mathematical treatment. To eliminate electrical migration of an ion, one introduces into the sample solution a 50- to 100-fold excess of an innocuous **supporting electrolyte** — for example, potassium chloride — which lowers the transference number of the reacting species virtually to zero. Convective transfer of a substance to the electrode surface is effectively prevented if the sample solution is unstirred and if the polarographic cell is mounted in a vibration-free environment.

Of particular interest in many electroanalytical techniques, including polarography, is the **diffusion layer,** the very thin film of quiescent solution bounded on one side by the surface of the electrode and extending perhaps 0.05 mm away from the electrode. With reference to the reduction of copper(I) in a potassium chloride medium (see curve A, Fig. 18-13), let us consider the phenomena that occur at the surface of the dropping mercury electrode as the potential of the latter is varied. At approximately -0.1 v versus SCE, little, if any, copper(I) is reduced, as verified by the observation that the current is close to zero. However, if the potential of the dropping mercury electrode is suddenly shifted to about -0.2 v versus SCE, a significant fraction of the copper(I) at the electrode surface is reduced to copper metal, the latter being soluble in the mercury, and a finite current flows through the polarographic cell. Furthermore, as a consequence of this electrolysis, a concentration gradient is established, causing copper(I) to diffuse from the bulk of the solution toward the electrode surface. If copper(I) did not diffuse toward the electrode, the current would fall almost instantaneously to zero because the surface concentration of copper(I) would drop to the value governed by the electrode potential and would change no more. However, the current is, in fact, sustained by diffusion of additional copper(I) toward the electrode under the influence of the concentration gradient.

According to the simplest model for a diffusion-controlled process, the observed current is directly related to the rate of transport of electroactive substance to the electrode surface, or to the difference between the concentration of the electroactive species in the bulk of the sample solution, C, and at the surface of the electrode, C_{surface}. Thus, we may write

$$i = k(C - C_{\text{surface}})$$

where k, a proportionality constant, includes the Faraday constant (F), the electrode area (A), the diffusion coefficient (D) of the reacting substance, and the number of electrons (n) involved in the pertinent half-reaction. It is evident from this relation that any factor which decreases the surface concentration of the electroactive species will increase the rate of diffusion as well as the observed current. If the concentration of the reacting substance is essentially zero at the electrode surface, the current attains a limiting value. For the polarogram presented in Figure 18-13, the limiting-current region extends from approximately -0.35 v versus SCE up to the potential at which potassium ion is reduced, namely -2.0 v versus SCE.

It is customary to designate the limiting current of a polarogram, after the residual current has been subtracted, as the **diffusion current** for the species of interest and to denote this parameter by the symbol i_d (see Fig. 18-13). From the standpoint of analytical chemistry, the direct relationship between the diffusion current and the bulk concentration of the electro-active substance, that is

$$i_d = kC,$$

has considerable significance.

Polarograms obtained with a dropping mercury electrode may be characterized as smooth current-potential curves upon which are super-imposed current oscillations due to the periodic renewal of the electrode. Actually, the variations in current during the lifetime of a single drop are considerably larger than suggested by the fluctuations shown in Figure 18-13. At the beginning of each drop lifetime, the area of the electrode is essentially equal to the cross section of the capillary orifice. Accordingly, the current at this moment should be practically zero because the total quantity of electroactive substance reaching the electrode surface is exceedingly small. However, as a mercury drop expands, greater surface area is exposed to the sample solution and the current increases. Just before the drop detaches from the tip of the capillary, the current attains a maximal value. In view of these facts, the current oscillations might be expected to range from almost zero up to the maximal current value. Such large and rapid fluctuations in current are difficult and inconvenient to observe in practice unless a cathode ray oscilloscope is employed. Usually, the current is monitored and recorded with the aid of a damped galvanometer or other current-measuring instru-ment. Therefore, the oscillations of the galvanometer are much less than the actual current fluctuations at the dropping mercury electrode. Nevertheless, the average of the galvanometer excursions is virtually identical to the average current flowing through the polarographic cell.

Ilkovic Equation. As yet, no completely rigorous mathematical solution to the complicated diffusion process at the dropping mercury electrode has been formulated. Serious complexities are involved in the solution of this problem. First, it is necessary to account for the fact that the thickness of the diffusion layer *increases* because of continued electrolysis during the lifetime of a single drop. Second, one must consider the expansion of a drop, both outward and downward, into regions of the sample solution not originally in contact with the electrode — a phenomenon which tends to *decrease* the thickness of the diffusion layer in a nonuniform way. In the polarographic diffusion-controlled process, the current should decrease as the diffusion layer becomes thicker because the concentration gradient is diminished under these conditions. On the other hand, the outward growth of a mercury drop has the tendency to counteract the decrease in current. Despite these difficulties, the time-average current oscillations are amazingly reproducible at each potential, and so it is possible to predict with excellent quantitativeness the magnitude of the diffusion current as well as the effects of different experimental variables on this parameter.

Analytical applications of polarography are based upon the Ilkovic equation, which expresses the dependence of the diffusion current upon the concentration of the electroactive species, the characteristics of the capillary, and two other properties of the reacting substance. This fundamental relation is usually written as

$$i_d = 607nD^{1/2}Cm^{2/3}t^{1/6}$$

where i_d is the time-average diffusion current in microamperes which flows during the lifetime of a single mercury drop, n is the number of faradays of electricity per mole of electroactive substance, D is the diffusion coefficient (cm²/second) of the reactant, C is the bulk concentration of the electroactive species in millimoles per liter, m is the rate of flow of mercury in milligrams per second, and t is the drop time in seconds. Among other terms, the numerical constant 607 incorporates the value of the faraday (96,487 coulombs).

Factors Affecting the Diffusion Current. Although the Ilkovic equation establishes the dependence of the diffusion current on several experimental variables, some of these parameters are, in turn, affected by the composition of the sample solution, the potential of the dropping mercury electrode, and the temperature.

Diffusion coefficients are especially sensitive to variations in the composition and viscosity of the sample medium, the temperature, and the size and charge of the diffusing species. Generally speaking, since the diffusion coefficient of a substance increases approximately 2 per cent for every one degree rise in temperature, the polarographic cell should be thermostated to within one-tenth degree for accurate work. In addition, the effective sizes and diffusion coefficients of metal ions are markedly altered by formation of complexes with large ligands such as citrate, tartrate, and ethylenediaminetetraacetate (EDTA).

It is evident from the Ilkovic equation that the capillary characteristics — that is, the mercury flow rate m and the drop time t — affect the magnitude of the diffusion current. As might be anticipated, the rate at which mercury flows through the orifice of the capillary is directly proportional to the height of the mercury column in the stand-tube. On the other hand, the drop time is inversely related to the first power of the mercury height. When these two individual effects are considered together, it can be shown that $m^{2/3}t^{1/6}$, the so-called **capillary constant,** depends on the square root of the mercury column height. This relationship pertains only to diffusion-controlled reactions and is one criterion employed in the identification of such systems.

Another factor which influences the characteristics of the capillary is the potential of the dropping mercury electrode, the latter having a significant effect on the interfacial tension between mercury and the sample solution. The drop time attains a maximal value at the potential of the electro-capillary maximum but decreases at more positive and more negative potentials. For example, in a $0.1 F$ potassium nitrate medium, the electro-capillary maximum occurs at -0.53 v versus SCE. If the drop time should happen to be 3.8 seconds at this potential, one might observe drop times of approximately 3.5 seconds at 0 v versus SCE and 1.9 seconds at -2.0 v versus SCE. Since only the one-sixth power of the drop time appears in the Ilkovic equation, the diffusion current is not too seriously affected. Nevertheless, for accurate polarographic measurements, it is essential to determine the drop time and the diffusion current at the same potential. The mercury flow rate is much less influenced by changes in the applied potential. Although m has a minimal value at the electrocapillary maximum and increases as the potential of the dropping mercury electrode becomes more cathodic or more anodic, the overall variation is relatively small. In fact, the mercury flow rate changes less than 1 per cent between potentials of 0 and -1.5 v versus SCE.

Polarographic Maxima

If one records the polarogram for a very pure solution of $1 F$ potassium chloride containing $5.00 \times 10^{-4} M$ copper(I), the resulting current-potential curve will not appear as in Figure 18-13. Instead, as the potential of the dropping mercury electrode approaches -0.2 v versus SCE, the current rises above 5 μa and oscillates rapidly and erratically in spite of the continued regular growth and fall of the mercury droplets. Finally, when the electrode potential reaches approximately -0.4 v versus SCE, the erratic current fluctuations diminish until the well-behaved diffusion-controlled current is observed. Generally speaking, these unexpected current fluctuations describe a sharp peak or broad hump, called a **polarographic maximum,** at the top of the rising portion of the normal polarographic wave.

A polarographic current in excess of the limiting value of approximately 3 μa in Figure 18-13 can arise only if copper(I) is transported to the electrode surface by processes other than diffusion. High-speed motion picture photography has substantiated that the occurrence of a current maximum is associated with streaming or swirling of solution around the dropping mercury electrode. Such convective motion of the sample medium causes more electroactive substance to reach the electrode surface than would be anticipated on the basis of diffusion alone. However, the reasons why this rapid movement of solution occurs are not understood.

Fortunately, a polarographic maximum can be eliminated through addition to the sample medium of small concentrations of a **maximum suppressor,** some substance which is specifically adsorbed upon the surface of the mercury electrode. Among the most popular species for the suppression of current maxima are gelatin, methyl red, and Triton X-100, the latter being a commercially available surface-active substance. In general, the concentration of maximum suppressor should be as small as possible — a concentration of 0.005 per cent is usually sufficient — because the indiscriminate use of large amounts of a surface-active substance diminishes the magnitude of the diffusion current.

Equation of the Polarographic Wave

We have seen that the diffusion current is directly proportional to the bulk concentration of the electroactive species — a relationship which endows polarography with quantitative analytical usefulness. At the same time, the electrode potential corresponding to the appearance of a polarographic wave may be valuable in the qualitative identification of the reacting substance.

If we assume that a species originally present in the sample solution undergoes reversible reduction to some substance which is soluble either in the solution or in the mercury phase,

$$Ox + n\,e \rightleftharpoons Red$$

the concentrations (activities) of the reactant and product at the solution-electrode interface are related to the potential of the dropping mercury electrode through the Nernst equation:

$$E_{Ox,Red} = E^{\circ}_{Ox,Red} - \frac{0.059}{n} \log \frac{[Red]_{surface}}{[Ox]_{surface}}$$

In this expression, $E_{Ox,Red}$ and $E^{\circ}_{Ox,Red}$ represent, respectively, the potential of the dropping mercury electrode and the standard potential for the pertinent half-reaction, each measured with respect to the same reference electrode. Moreover, the observed potential of the dropping mercury electrode, as well as the surface concentrations of the oxidized and reduced species, must be average values during the lifetime of a mercury drop.

It can be demonstrated, although we shall not present the derivation in this text, that the potential of the dropping mercury electrode is related to the observed current, i, and the diffusion current, i_d, by the expression

$$E_{Ox,Red} = E_{1/2} - \frac{0.059}{n} \log \frac{i}{i_d - i}$$

TABLE 18–2.   HALF-WAVE POTENTIALS FOR
COMMON METAL IONS*

Half-Reaction	Supporting Electrolyte Solution	$E_{1/2}$ versus SCE, v
Bi(III) → Bi(Hg)	1 F HCl	−0.09
Cd(II) → Cd(Hg)	0.1 F KCl	−0.60
Co(II) → Co(Hg)	1 F KCl	−1.20
Cu(II) → Cu(Hg)	0.1 F KNO$_3$	+0.02
Cu(II) → Cu(I)	1 F KCl	+0.04
Cu(I) → Cu(Hg)	1 F KCl	−0.19
Pb(II) → Pb(Hg)	0.1 F KNO$_3$	−0.39
Tl(I) → Tl(Hg)	0.1 F KNO$_3$	−0.46
Zn(II) → Zn(Hg)	1 F KCl	−1.00

* Data excerpted from L. Meites: *Polarographic Techniques*, second edition, Wiley-Interscience, New York, 1965, pp. 615–670. This reference work contains a wealth of information pertaining to the polarographic behavior of inorganic and organic compounds.

where the **half-wave potential,** $E_{1/2}$, is defined as the potential of the dropping mercury electrode when the observed current is exactly one half of the diffusion current; that is, $E_{Ox,Red} = E_{1/2}$ for $i = i_d/2$. This is the most familiar form of the equation for a polarographic wave. Many polarographic studies involve the construction of plots of $E_{Ox,Red}$ versus $\log i/(i_d - i)$. If the electrode reaction proceeds reversibly, such a graph consists of a straight line with a reciprocal slope of $0.059/n$. Conversely, when this plot does yield a linear relationship, one can conclude that the electrode reaction is reversible. In addition, the slope of the straight line permits evaluation of n, the number of electrons involved in the electrode process. Finally, it should be noted that the value of the half-wave potential, corresponding to the point at which $\log i/(i_d - i)$ is zero, can be determined from an inspection of the graph.

Provided that the reactant and product species are completely soluble in either the solution or mercury phase, the half-wave potential is independent of the concentration of the reactant and may serve to identify an unknown polarographic wave. A brief list of half-wave potentials for reduction reactions of some common metal cations is presented in Table 18-2. As indicated in this compilation and by the polarogram shown in Figure 18-13, the half-wave potential for the reduction of copper(I) to copper amalgam in a 1 F potassium chloride medium is −0.19 v versus SCE. Furthermore, the half-wave potential for a reaction involving both a soluble reactant and product is very close to the standard potential for the reaction of interest.

Experimental Techniques of Polarography

Although polarographic measurements are usually accomplished with the aid of instruments which automatically and continuously record complete current-potential curves, experimental data of excellent accuracy can be obtained manually.

Polarographic Cells.   As suggested earlier in this section, the H-cell depicted in Figure 18-12 is especially popular for polarographic measurements. The compartment which contains the sample solution can be designed to accommodate volumes as small as 1 ml, but 15 to 25 ml capacities are most common. Some special polarographic cells have been constructed for the analysis of a single drop of solution. Usually, a saturated calomel electrode performs a dual role as both auxiliary and reference electrode. However, in some situations where chloride ion must be excluded from a chemical system, a mercury-mercurous sulfate electrode is utilized. After a series of polarographic measurements is completed, the sample compartment should always be cleaned and filled with an electrolyte solution of similar composition to that in the reference electrode compartment — for example, saturated potassium chloride solution. Such an expedient minimizes deterioration and contamination of the agar plug and the reference electrode.

Dropping Mercury Electrodes. Capillary tubing suitable for the fabrication of a dropping mercury electrode is available commercially. Typically, a 10 to 12 cm length of so-called marine barometer tubing, with an internal diameter of 0.06 mm, provides an electrode having a drop time of 3 to 5 seconds for a mercury reservoir height of 40 cm. To ensure capillary characteristics that are both uniform and reproducible, the end of the marine barometer tubing should be perfectly flat and horizontal, and the capillary tubing must not deviate from a vertical position by more than approximately five degrees. Obviously, attention must be devoted to the proper mounting of the dropping mercury electrode and polarographic cell in a stable and vibration-free location.

If several precautions are observed with regard to the care and handling of a dropping mercury electrode, it will behave reproducibly for many months. Above all, the mercury column should always be high enough so that a positive flow of mercury results. At the conclusion of an experiment, the tip of the capillary should be washed thoroughly with distilled water, while the mercury is still flowing, and allowed to stand in air or dipped into a small container of mercury for storage.

Analytical applications of polarography based upon use of the Ilkovic equation require knowledge of the capillary characteristics. A determination of the rate of mercury flow (m) involves collection of mercury for a definite length of time followed by a weight measurement. The drop time (t) is

FIGURE 18-14. Schematic
diagram of circuitry for manual
performance of polarographic
measurements. [Redrawn, with
permission, from a paper by J. J.
Lingane: Anal. Chem., *21*, 45
(1949).]

readily calculated if one employs a stop watch and measures the total time
required for a certain number of drops to fall. Since the capillary characteristics vary with the potential of the dropping mercury electrode, the mercury
flow rate and the drop time should preferably be evaluated for the potential
at which one intends to measure the diffusion current.

Electrical Circuitry for Manual Measurements. Two requirements must be fulfilled in the design of electrical apparatus for polarography.
First, it is necessary to impress variable and known voltages ranging in
magnitude from 0 to 2 v across the polarographic cell. Furthermore, the
potential of the dropping mercury electrode versus the reference electrode
should be determined with a precision of 10 mv. Second, it is desirable to
measure the cell current, which usually encompasses a range from 0.1 to
100 μa, with an accuracy of ± 0.01 μa.

A simple electrical circuit which can perform the functions mentioned
in the previous paragraph is illustrated in Figure 18-14. As a voltage source,
two ordinary 1.5 v batteries connected in series are satisfactory, the magnitude of the electromotive force applied to the polarographic cell being
varied through adjustment of a movable contact along the slidewire R_1. The
potential of the dropping mercury electrode with respect to the saturated

calomel electrode can be determined with the aid of a potentiometer if the double-pole double-throw switch in Figure 18-14 is thrown to the right-hand position. For measurement of the cell current, the switch is thrown to the left-hand position and the iR drop across a precision 10,000 ohm resistor (R_2) is obtained by means of the potentiometer. Usually, a galvanometer is incorporated into the potentiometer circuit as a null-point indicator in a manner similar to that described in Chapter 17. However, the galvanometer must be damped by placement of an appropriate resistor across its terminals so that the potentiometer can be balanced in spite of the current oscillations caused by the growth and fall of the dropping mercury electrode.

In operation, the position of the contact along the slidewire of this simple manual polarograph is varied systematically, and a series of readings of the potential of the dropping mercury electrode as well as the current flowing through the polarographic cell is recorded. Although the circuitry depicted in Figure 18-14 is excellent insofar as the accuracy of the potential and current measurements is concerned, the manual point-by-point plotting of a polarogram is unnecessarily tedious. Furthermore, unless considerable effort is expended, a polarogram obtained according to the manual technique is simply not a continuous current-potential curve, and small features and peculiarities may remain undetected. With only slight modification, the manual circuit of Figure 18-14 can be converted into an automatic recording polarograph. For example, the slidewire may be replaced by a motor-driven, 100 ohm, 10 turn potentiometer which varies the applied voltage in a known and linear fashion. Similarly, the current may be recorded in synchronization with the change in applied voltage, if a strip-chart potentiometer recorder is connected across resistor R_2.

Measurement of Diffusion Currents. Several methods are commonly employed for the determination of diffusion currents from recorded polarograms, the choice of procedure depending on the concentration level of the reactant. In the majority of polarographic studies, one measures the average of the current oscillations, since the latter correspond closely to the time-average diffusion current if the current fluctuations caused by growth and fall of the mercury droplets are adequately damped.

When the concentration of the electroactive substance is $10^{-3}\ M$ or higher, the residual current is negligible compared to the diffusion current. Therefore, the height of the polarographic wave is essentially equal to the diffusion current. The measurement procedure requires that the cell current be determined at two potentials. One potential, E_1, is chosen to be on the flat portion of the current-potential curve prior to the polarographic wave; and the other potential, E_2, is selected to be on the horizontal, limiting-current region of the polarogram. If i_1 and i_2 are the average currents measured at the first and second potentials, respectively, the average diffusion current is represented by the difference between the two current readings; that is, $i_d = i_2 - i_1$.

Correction for residual current becomes essential in the polarographic analysis of solutions containing approximately 10^{-4} M or lower concentrations of electroactive species. The most reliable procedure entails the recording of separate current-potential curves for the unknown solution and for a solution identical in all respects to the sample except for the desired substance. Next, one selects a potential at which the diffusion current is to be evaluated and measures the difference in current between the two curves. For example, Figure 18-13 shows a complete polarogram for the reduction of 5.00×10^{-4} M copper(I) in a 1 F potassium chloride medium along with the residual current curve for the potassium chloride solution. Since the polarogram for copper(I) reduction (curve A) has a limiting-current plateau which is perfectly horizontal, we have drawn a dashed line to indicate the average of the current oscillations. To obtain the true diffusion current at the half-wave potential (-0.19 v versus SCE), it is necessary to subtract the magnitude of the residual current (curve B) at the same potential from the total average current. Similarly, if one desired to evaluate the diffusion current for the reduction of copper(I) at -0.60 v versus SCE, he would subtract the residual current from the overall average current at the latter potential. As a general rule, the limiting-current region of the polarogram for the desired substance and the residual current curve have unequal slopes, and so the diffusion current varies slightly as a function of potential. However, this difference need not detract from the accuracy of polarographic measurements, if systematic procedures are followed.

Determination of Concentration.   We shall now turn our attention to the procedures used to evaluate the concentration of an electroactive substance from polarographic data.

In spite of the facts that the mercury flow rate (m) and the drop time (t) can be determined experimentally and that n is usually known for a particular reaction, the Ilkovic equation,

$$i_d = 607\ nD^{1/2}Cm^{2/3}t^{1/6}$$

is seldom used to calculate the concentration of the reactant, principally because of uncertainty in the values of most diffusion coefficients. On the other hand, a variation of the preceding absolute technique has been proposed which relies upon the so-called **diffusion current constant,** I, defined as

$$I = 607\ nD^{1/2} = \frac{i_d}{Cm^{2/3}t^{1/6}}$$

In practice, one measures the diffusion current for a known concentration of the desired substance in a carefully specified supporting electrolyte solution. If these data are combined with separate determinations of the mercury flow rate and the drop time, the diffusion current constant is obtainable. Later, when the concentration of the same electroactive species in an unknown sample is sought, experimental values for the diffusion current, mercury flow rate, and drop time are substituted, along with the previously evaluated diffusion current constant, into the expression

$$C = \frac{i_d}{Im^{2/3}t^{1/6}}$$

to calculate the concentration of the substance of interest. The success of this method demands that the composition of the known and unknown supporting electrolyte solutions be similar so that the diffusion coefficient of the electro-active species does not change.

It is unnecessary to describe in detail the analytical technique in which a calibration curve is constructed. This approach involves the preparation of a series of standard solutions, the measurement of the diffusion current for each sample, and the presentation of the data in the form of a graph of observed diffusion current versus concentration. The concentration of the desired substance in an unknown solution is determined from a single measurement of the diffusion current with the aid of the calibration curve. Obviously, the composition of the supporting electrolyte solution must be the same for both the standards and the unknown.

Another procedure for determination of the concentration of an electro-active species is called the **method of standard addition.** Suppose a polarogram is recorded for a solution containing an unknown concentration, C_u, of the desired substance and the observed diffusion current is $(i_d)_1$. Without knowing the drop time, the mercury flow rate, or the diffusion coefficient, we can state that

$$(i_d)_1 = kC_u$$

If an aliquot V_s of a standard solution of the electroactive substance of known concentration C_s is added to a volume V_u of the unknown solution, the diffusion current will attain a new value $(i_d)_2$ which is governed by the expression

$$(i_d)_2 = k\frac{C_sV_s + C_uV_u}{V_s + V_u}$$

When these two relations are combined to eliminate the proportionality constant, k, and are solved for the concentration of the unknown sample, the result is

$$C_u = \frac{C_sV_s(i_d)_1}{(V_u + V_s)(i_d)_2 - V_u(i_d)_1}$$

A virtue of the technique of standard addition is that the capillary characteristics need not be determined. However, the procedure does require preparation of one standard solution whose supporting electrolyte concentration, pH, and ionic strength are similar, if possible, to the unknown solution. Nevertheless, the volume of standard solution added should be small in order to avoid any changes in the composition of the unknown sample.

Finally, highest accuracy is achieved if the diffusion currents, $(i_d)_1$ and $(i_d)_2$, differ by at least a factor of two.

Some Analytical Applications of Polarography

A wide variety of inorganic and organic substances have been subjected to polarographic investigation, and many procedures for the analysis of individual species and mixtures of compounds have been developed — several of which will be mentioned in the paragraphs that follow. As suggested earlier, the optimum concentration range for polarography is 10^{-4} to $10^{-2} M$, although the lowest concentration amenable to accurate analysis may be $10^{-7} M$ if special instrumentation is employed to compensate for the residual current. The upper concentration limit is set by the requirement that a large excess of supporting electrolyte must be present and by the fact that polarographic maxima become especially severe. For routine determinations, analytical results precise to within ± 2 per cent are usually attainable. With special care, and for certain kinds of chemical systems, the uncertainty of a polarographic analysis may be as small as a few tenths of 1 per cent.

Determination of Metal Ions. Through an appropriate choice of supporting electrolyte, pH, and other complexing ligands, practically any metal ion can be reduced at the dropping mercury electrode to an amalgam or to a soluble lower oxidation state. In the majority of situations, one obtains polarographic waves and diffusion currents suitable for quantitative determination of these species. Common divalent cations such as cadmium, cobalt, copper, lead, manganese, nickel, tin, and zinc can be determined in many different complexing and noncomplexing media. The alkaline earth ions — barium, calcium, magnesium, and strontium — exhibit well-defined polarographic waves at approximately -2.0 v versus SCE in solutions containing tetraethylammonium iodide as the supporting electrolyte. Cesium, lithium, potassium, rubidium, and sodium undergo reduction between approximately -2.1 and -2.3 v versus SCE in aqueous and alcoholic tetraalkylammonium hydroxide media. Polarographic characteristics of the tripositive states of aluminum, bismuth, chromium, europium, gallium, gold, indium, iron, samarium, uranium, vanadium, and ytterbium in a number of supporting electrolytes have been reported.

Determination of Inorganic Anions. Polarographic studies of the reductions of chromate, iodate, molybdate, selenite, tellurite, and vanadate, as well as the anionic chloride complexes of tungsten(VI), tin(IV), and molybdenum(VI), are included among the list of analytically useful procedures.

In the presence of bromide ion, the dropping mercury electrode is oxidized to insoluble mercurous bromide,

$$2\,Hg + 2\,Br^- \rightleftharpoons Hg_2Br_2(s) + 2\,e$$

and a polarographic diffusion current proportional to the bulk concentration of the anion is observed. Other species, including chloride, iodide, sulfate, and thiocyanate, exhibit analogous behavior. In addition, cyanide and thiosulfate both form soluble complex ions with mercury(II):

$$Hg + 4 \, CN^- \rightleftharpoons Hg(CN)_4^= + 2 \, e$$

$$Hg + 2 \, S_2O_3^= \rightleftharpoons Hg(S_2O_3)_2^= + 2 \, e$$

An anodic polarogram for the oxidation of mercury in a dilute sodium cyanide medium shows a limiting current governed by diffusion of cyanide to the surface of the dropping mercury electrode.

Analysis of Mixtures. Solutions containing two or more electro-active substances may be analyzed polarographically provided certain requirements are satisfied. Clearly, the half-wave potentials for the species of interest must differ significantly if the resulting polarogram is to exhibit a distinct polarographic wave and limiting-current region for each component. The minimal difference in the half-wave potentials may be established as was done previously for controlled-potential coulometry.

A mixture of cadmium(II), zinc(II), and cobalt(II) in a 1 F potassium chloride medium can be resolved and analyzed by means of polarography, since Table 18-2 indicates that the respective half-wave potentials for these elements are -0.60, -1.00, and -1.20 v versus SCE. However, difficulty in the accurate analysis of such a mixture can be encountered if the relative concentrations of the three cations are widely disparate. For example, if a small quantity of zinc is present in a solution containing relatively large amounts of cadmium and cobalt, the polarographic wave for reduction of zinc will appear as a tiny hump on top of the cadmium wave and will be closely followed by another large rise in current because of cobalt(II) reduction. One remedy for this situation involves polarographic measurement of cadmium(II) and subsequent removal of most, if not all, of this ion by controlled-potential separation. Then, zinc may be more accurately determined because the interference from cadmium is eliminated. Furthermore, if cadmium(II) is separated quantitatively and a very low concentration of zinc(II) is present, one may measure the height of the polarographic wave for the cobalt(II)-zinc(II) mixture and calculate the concentration of cobalt by ignoring the small diffusion current due to zinc reduction.

Another procedure for the polarographic analysis of mixtures takes advantage of the fact that half-wave potentials, like standard and formal potentials, for reductions of metal ions change in the presence of complexing agents. As an example, the individual determinations of lead(II) and thallium(I) in a mixture cannot be accomplished if the supporting electrolyte solution is 0.1 F potassium nitrate because the half-wave potentials are too close together, being -0.39 and -0.46 v versus SCE, respectively (see Table 18-2). However, in a 1 F sodium hydroxide medium containing a small amount of maximum suppressor, the reduction of thallium(I) yields a well-developed polarographic wave at -0.48 v versus SCE, whereas reduction of lead(II) occurs at a half-wave potential of -0.76 v versus SCE. Under such conditions, both species may be determined accurately. It should be noted that the half-wave potential for thallium(I) reduction shifts very little, suggesting the absence of strong complex formation in either potassium nitrate or sodium hydroxide media. On the other hand, the large change in the half-wave potential for the lead(II) wave is in agreement with the known fact that the hydrogen plumbite anion, $HPbO_2^-$, is formed in alkaline solution.

Polarography of Organic Compounds. In contrast to inorganic substances, the reactions of organic compounds at the dropping mercury electrode are usually irreversible and proceed in several steps. Polarographic data pertaining to organic molecules are often difficult to interpret, owing to the effect of pH on the rate, mechanism, and products of an organic electrode process, the influence of solvent on the course of the reaction, the importance of the nature and concentration of the supporting electrolyte, and the occurrence of side reactions involving partially oxidized and reduced species. Nevertheless, a number of striking applications of polarography to the elucidation of organic reaction mechanisms and molecular structures have been reported.

A carbon-carbon double bond in conjugation with another double bond, an aromatic ring system, or another unsaturated group is reducible at the dropping mercury electrode. For example, the reduction of stilbene has been proposed to occur according to the following sequence of reactions:

Organic halogen compounds undergo reduction with the consequent replacement of the halogen with hydrogen, as exemplified by the reaction of ethyl iodide:

$$CH_3CH_2I + H^+ + 2\,e \longrightarrow CH_3CH_3 + I^-$$

Carbonyl compounds, including aldehydes, ketones, ketosteroids, and sugars are irreversibly reduced at a mercury cathode, whereas the reduction of quinones and the oxidation of hydroquinones proceed reversibly. A

classic example of the latter set of reactions is the interconvertibility of
p-benzoquinone and p-benzohydroquinone:

Dicarboxylic acids, keto acids, aldehydo acids, and halogenated acids can be
reduced. Many compounds containing carbon-nitrogen, nitrogen-nitrogen,
and nitrogen-oxygen bonds, as well as nitrogen heterocyclic compounds, are
electroactive. Finally, organic molecules with oxygen-oxygen, sulfur-sulfur,
and carbon-sulfur bonds exhibit characteristic behavior at the dropping
mercury electrode.

Experiment 18-1

*CONSTANT-CURRENT ELECTROLYSIS: SEPARATION
AND DETERMINATION OF COPPER IN BRASS*

Purpose

This experiment demonstrates one of the methods used to perform a
quantitative electrodeposition.

Procedure

Preparation of the Sample Solution. Weigh accurately into clean
250 ml beakers two 0.4 to 0.6 gm samples of the brass. To each weighed
sample, add approximately 5 ml of distilled water and then, in two or three
portions, add about 8 ml of concentrated nitric acid. Cover the beakers with
watch glasses to prevent spray loss of the sample solutions. Perform these
operations in a well-ventilated hood.

When decomposition of each brass sample appears to be complete, as
indicated by the observation that no dark or metallic residue remains,
carefully dilute the sample solutions to 50 ml with distilled water. Boil the
solutions gently for several minutes to remove nitrogen oxides and, if a

white residue of metastannic acid $(SnO_2 \cdot xH_2O)$ is present, digest the solutions on a steam bath to coagulate the precipitate. Remove the residue by filtration through a paper filter, collecting the filtrate in a tall-form electrolysis beaker. Wash the paper filter thoroughly with 100 ml of hot distilled water containing 1 ml of concentrated nitric acid; collect the wash liquid in the beaker containing the sample solution.

Electrodeposition of Copper. Obtain two sets of platinum electrodes and prepare each platinum cathode by placing it in concentrated nitric acid for one minute and in 8 F nitric acid for 10 minutes. Rinse each cathode thoroughly with distilled water and then finally with a small volume of *pure* acetone. Place the cathodes in clean dry beakers, and dry the electrodes in an oven at approximately 100°C for several minutes. Remove the electrodes from the oven, allow them to cool for at least 15 minutes, and determine the weight of each cathode accurately. Avoid unnecessary handling of the electrodes, since grease can cause uneven and nonadherent copper deposits to form.

Mount each tall-form beaker in the electrodeposition apparatus. Cover the beakers with the two halves of a split watch glass, add sufficient distilled water to cover the platinum cathodes completely, and start the stirring device. Introduce into each sample solution approximately 1 to 2 gm of urea to remove any residual traces of nitrogen oxides.

Connect the voltage source to the electrodes, and adjust the applied voltage so that a current of 1.5 to 2.0 amp passes through the electrolytic cell.

If it is necessary or desirable to continue the electrolysis overnight, adjust the applied voltage so that a current of only 0.2 to 0.3 amp is flowing, and add some extra urea.

After the solution becomes colorless, use distilled water from a wash bottle to rinse the droplets of solution sprayed on the inside of the watch glass cover and the wall of the beaker back into the solution. In addition, rinse down the stem of the platinum cathode, add 0.5 gm of urea, and continue the electrolysis for approximately 30 minutes *after* the solution has become colorless.

To discontinue the electrolysis, remove the beaker cover and, *without interrupting the current flow,* slowly lower the beaker away from the electrodes while a stream of distilled water from a wash bottle is directed upon the cathode. After the beaker has been completely lowered from the electrodes and rinsing of the electrodes is done, *turn off the electrolysis apparatus.*

If the electrolysis apparatus is turned off before the beaker is lowered and the electrodes are rinsed, some of the deposited copper may redissolve in the nitric acid medium.

Disconnect the electrodes from the electrolysis apparatus, and carefully immerse the copper-plated cathode in a beaker of distilled water. Finally, rinse each cathode with a minimal volume of pure acetone and dry the cathodes in an oven at 100°C for a few minutes. Cool the electrodes for 15 to 20 minutes in air, reweigh each cathode to determine the weight of deposited copper, and compute the percentage of copper in the brass.

After the experiment is finished, clean the copper-plated cathode with nitric acid according to the procedure described earlier.

SUGGESTIONS FOR ADDITIONAL LABORATORY WORK

Many excellent and highly instructive experiments dealing with electroanalytical methods of analysis are contained in the following laboratory textbooks:

1. C. E. Meloan and R. W. Kiser: *Problems and Experiments in Instrumental Analysis*, Charles E. Merrill Books, Inc., Columbus, Ohio, 1963, pp. 142–202.
2. C. N. Reilley and D. T. Sawyer: *Experiments for Instrumental Methods*, McGraw-Hill Book Company, New York, 1961, pp. 51–101.

QUESTIONS AND PROBLEMS

1. When a silver electrode is polarized anodically in a solution containing a halide ion, X^-, the following reaction occurs:

$$Ag + X^- \rightleftharpoons AgX + e$$

   (a) Suppose a silver electrode is to be polarized anodically in the controlled-potential electrolysis of an aqueous solution initially $0.02\,F$ in sodium bromide (NaBr) and $1\,F$ in perchloric acid. What is the minimal potential versus NHE (normal hydrogen electrode) at which the silver anode must be controlled in order to ensure an accuracy of at least 99.9 per cent in the determination of bromide?
   (b) Construct a qualitatively correct graph to show the behavior of the current versus time for the above typical controlled-potential electrolysis.

2. A weighed platinum gauze electrode is placed in an electrolysis cell containing 100 ml of a solution which is $0.050\,F$ in lead chloride ($PbCl_2$) and $0.020\,F$ in tin(IV) chloride ($SnCl_4$). The pH of the solution is buffered at exactly 3.00. If the solution is well stirred (to prevent polarization) and if a current of 1.00 amp is passed through the cell for exactly 25.0 minutes, what will be the gain in weight of the platinum electrode? (Assume that the platinum electrode is the cathode and that the anode is isolated by a salt bridge so that the cathode and anode products do not migrate and mix. In addition, assume that the activation overpotential for evolution of hydrogen at the cathode is 0.22 v.)

3. In a $1\,F$ potassium chloride medium, the polarographic half-wave potential for the reduction of zinc ion to a zinc amalgam is -1.00 v versus SCE. However, the half-wave potential for the reduction of the zinc-ammine complex, $Zn(NH_3)_4^{++}$, to a zinc amalgam is -1.18 v versus SCE in a $0.1\,F$ ammonia-$1\,F$ ammonium chloride buffer. In each instance, the reduction proceeds reversibly. Calculate the formation constant for the zinc-ammine complex.

4. In a $1\,F$ sodium hydroxide medium, the reduction of the tellurite anion, $TeO_3^=$, yields a single, well-developed polarographic wave. With a dropping mercury electrode whose m value was 1.50 mg/second and whose drop time was 3.15

seconds, the observed diffusion current was 61.9 μa for a 0.00400 M solution of the tellurite ion. If the diffusion coefficient of tellurite anion is 0.75×10^{-5} cm²/second, to what oxidation state is tellurium reduced under these conditions?

5. Define clearly each of the following terms: decomposition potential, residual current, iR drop, concentration overpotential, activation overpotential, cathodic depolarizer, working electrode, auxiliary electrode, limiting current, electrocapillary maximum, maximum suppressor, and method of standard addition.

6. Suppose it is desired to separate copper(II) from antimony(III) by controlled-potential deposition of copper upon a platinum cathode from a 1 F perchloric acid medium originally containing 0.010 M copper(II) and 0.075 M antimony-(III). At what potential versus the saturated calomel electrode must the platinum cathode be controlled to cause 99.9 per cent deposition of copper? What fraction of the antimony(III) will be codeposited? If the volume of the solution is 100 ml, what will be the total gain in weight of the cathode?

$$Cu^{++} + 2\,e \rightleftharpoons Cu; \qquad E^\circ = +0.337 \text{ v versus NHE}$$
$$SbO^+ + 2\,H^+ + 3\,e \rightleftharpoons Sb + H_2O; \qquad E^\circ = +0.212 \text{ v versus NHE}$$

7. If a 1 F perchloric acid solution which is 0.0300 M in antimony(III) and 0.0200 M in bismuth(III) is subjected to electrolysis at constant applied voltage in a cell containing two platinum electrodes, what will be the equilibrium concentration of bismuth(III) when the cathode potential shifts to the value at which antimony(III) is reduced? Assume that the stirring of the solution is highly efficient.

$$SbO^+ + 2\,H^+ + 3\,e \rightleftharpoons Sb + H_2O; \qquad E^\circ = +0.212 \text{ v versus NHE}$$
$$BiO^+ + 2\,H^+ + 3\,e \rightleftharpoons Bi + H_2O; \qquad E^\circ = +0.32 \text{ v versus NHE}$$

8. Assume that the half-reactions pertaining to the reduction of two substances, Ox_1 and Ox_2, are as follows:

$$Ox_1 + 3\,e \rightleftharpoons Red_1; \qquad E^\circ_{Ox_1, Red_1}$$
$$Ox_2 + 2\,e \rightleftharpoons Red_2; \qquad E^\circ_{Ox_2, Red_2}$$

If all oxidized and reduced species are soluble, if Ox_1 is more easily reducible than Ox_2, and if Ox_1 and Ox_2 are both initially present at the same concentration level, what is the minimal permissible difference between the standard potentials for the two half-reactions if one desires to reduce 99.9 per cent of Ox_1, yet not reduce more than 0.1 per cent of Ox_2, during a controlled-potential electrolysis?

9. An unknown cadmium(II) solution was analyzed polarographically according to the method of standard addition. A 25.00 ml sample of the unknown solution was found to yield a diffusion current of 1.86 μa. Next, a 5.00 ml aliquot of a $2.12 \times 10^{-3} M$ cadmium(II) standard solution was added to the unknown sample, and the resulting mixture gave a diffusion current of 5.27 μa. Calculate the concentration of cadmium(II) in the unknown solution.

10. In an aqueous ammonia solution, copper(II) can be reduced at a mercury cathode in a stepwise fashion according to the following half-reactions:

$$Cu(NH_3)_4{}^{++} + e \rightleftharpoons Cu(NH_3)_2{}^+ + 2\,NH_3; \qquad E^\circ = -0.22 \text{ v versus SCE}$$
$$Cu(NH_3)_2{}^+ + e + Hg \rightleftharpoons Cu(Hg) + 2\,NH_3; \qquad E^\circ = -0.51 \text{ v versus SCE}$$

(a) Suppose that you are interested in preparing a solution of copper(I) in 1 F aqueous ammonia by the controlled-potential reduction of copper(II) to copper(I) at a large mercury pool cathode. Furthermore, suppose that you begin with 0.010 M copper(II) and that you desire to minimize the concentration of copper(II) unreduced as well as the concentration of metallic copper in the mercury (amal-gam) phase. What potential would you employ to optimize the generation of copper(I)? What would be the ratio of copper(I) to copper(II) at the termination of the electrolysis? *Hint:* Assume that the species present in solution are $Cu(NH_3)_4^{++}$ and $Cu(NH_3)_2^{+}$, that the free ammonia concentration is 1 M, and that concentrations (rather than activities) are applicable. Moreover, assume that the volume of mercury is equal to that of the aqueous phase.

(b) Suppose that in an experiment of the preceding type you had wanted to reduce at least 99.9 per cent of the copper(II) to copper(I), while at the same time you wished to avoid the reduction of more than 0.1 per cent of the copper(I) to the copper amalgam. What is the *minimal difference* (in millivolts) between the standard potentials for the copper(II)-copper(I) and copper(I)-copper(0) half-reactions necessary to achieve this goal?

(c) What possible advantage or advantages does controlled-potential electrolysis possess as a preparative technique over conventional chemical preparations? What disadvantage or disadvantages can you name?

11. An unknown sample of hydrochloric acid was titrated coulometrically with hydroxide ion electrogenerated at a constant current of 20.34 ma, a total genera-tion time of 645.3 seconds being required to reach the equivalence point. Calcu-late the number of millimoles of hydrochloric acid in the sample.

12. Copper(II) may be titrated coulometrically with electrogenerated tin(II) in a 4 F sodium bromide medium according to the following reaction:

$$2 \, CuBr_3^- + SnBr_4^= \rightleftharpoons 2 \, CuBr_2^- + SnBr_6^=$$

In the titration of one sample, a constant generating current of 67.63 ma was employed and the titration time was 291.7 seconds. Calculate the weight of copper present in the unknown sample.

13. A 9.14 mg sample of pure picric acid was dissolved in 0.1 F hydrochloric acid and subjected to a controlled-potential coulometric reduction at -0.65 v versus SCE. A coulometer in series with the electrolysis cell registered 65.7 coulombs of electricity. Calculate the number of electrons involved in the reduction of picric acid.

14. A substance is known to undergo a reversible reduction at a dropping mercury electrode to give a stable product. Describe three independent methods, including important mathematical relationships, which might be employed to determine the number of faradays of electricity corresponding to the reduction of 1 mole of this species.

SUGGESTIONS FOR ADDITIONAL READING

1. R. N. Adams: Voltammetry at electrodes with fixed surfaces. *In* I. M. Kolthoff and P. J. Elving, eds.: *Treatise on Analytical Chemistry*, Part I, Volume 4, Wiley-Interscience, New York, 1959, pp. 2381–2416.

2. M. Březina and P. Zuman: *Polarography in Medicine, Biochemistry, and Pharmacy*, Wiley-Interscience, New York, 1958.

3. G. Charlot, J. Badoz-Lambling, and B. Trémillon: *Electrochemical Reactions*, Elsevier Pub. Co., Amsterdam, 1962.

4. D. D. DeFord and J. W. Miller: Coulometric analysis. *In* I. M. Kolthoff and P. J. Elving, eds.: *Treatise on Analytical Chemistry*, Part I, Volume 4, Wiley-Interscience, New York, 1959, pp. 2475–2531.

5. J. Doležal and J. Zýka: Amperometric titrations. *In* F. J. Welcher, ed.: *Standard Methods of Chemical Analysis*, sixth edition, Volume 3-A, D. Van Nostrand Co., Inc., New York, 1966, pp. 377–403.

6. I. M. Kolthoff and J. J. Lingane: *Polarography*, second edition, Wiley-Interscience, New York, 1952.

7. J. J. Lingane: *Electroanalytical Chemistry*, second edition, Wiley-Interscience, New York, 1958.

8. L. Meites: *Handbook of Analytical Chemistry*, McGraw-Hill Book Company, New York, 1963.

9. L. Meites: *Polarographic Techniques*, second edition, Wiley-Interscience, New York, 1965.

10. L. Meites: Voltammetry at the dropping mercury electrode (polarography). *In* I. M. Kolthoff and P. J. Elving, eds.: *Treatise on Analytical Chemistry*, Part I, Volume 4, Wiley-Interscience, New York, 1959, pp. 2303–2379.

11. L. Meites and H. C. Thomas: *Advanced Analytical Chemistry*, McGraw-Hill Book Company, New York, 1958.

12. G. W. C. Milner: *Principles and Practice of Polarography and Other Voltammetric Processes*, Longmans, Green & Co. Ltd., London, 1957.

13. W. C. Purdy: *Electroanalytical Methods in Biochemistry*, McGraw-Hill Book Company, New York, 1965.

14. G. A. Rechnitz: *Controlled-Potential Analysis*, The Macmillan Company, New York, 1963.

15. C. N. Reilley: Fundamentals of electrode processes. *In* I. M. Kolthoff and P. J. Elving, eds.: *Treatise on Analytical Chemistry*, Part I, Volume 4, Wiley-Interscience, New York, 1959, pp. 2109–2162.

16. C. N. Reilley and R. W. Murray: Introduction to electrochemical techniques. *In* I. M. Kolthoff and P. J. Elving, eds.: *Treatise on Analytical Chemistry*, Part I, Volume 4, Wiley-Interscience, New York, 1959, pp. 2163–2232.

17. W. B. Schaap: Polarography. *In* F. J. Welcher, ed.: *Standard Methods of Chemical Analysis*, sixth edition, Volume 3-A, D. Van Nostrand Co., Inc., New York, 1966, pp. 323–376.

18. W. D. Shults: Coulometric methods. *In* F. J. Welcher, ed.: *Standard Methods of Chemical Analysis*, sixth edition, Volume 3-A, D. Van Nostrand Co., Inc., New York, 1966, pp. 459–492.

19. N. Tanaka: Electrodeposition. *In* I. M. Kolthoff and P. J. Elving, eds.: *Treatise on Analytical Chemistry*, Part I, Volume 4, Wiley-Interscience, New York, 1959, pp. 2417–2473.

20. H. H. Willard, L. L. Merritt, Jr., and J. A. Dean: *Instrumental Methods of Analysis*, fourth edition, D. Van Nostrand Co., Inc., New York, 1965.

21. P. Zuman: *Organic Polarography*, The Macmillan Company, New York, 1964.

APPENDICES

827

Appendix 1

Solubility Product Constants*

(All values are valid at or near room temperature.)

Substance	Formula	K_{sp}
Aluminum hydroxide	$Al(OH)_3$	2×10^{-32}
Barium arsenate	$Ba_3(AsO_4)_2$	7.7×10^{-51}
Barium carbonate	$BaCO_3$	8.1×10^{-9}
Barium chromate	$BaCrO_4$	2.4×10^{-10}
Barium fluoride	BaF_2	1.7×10^{-6}
Barium iodate	$Ba(IO_3)_2 \cdot 2H_2O$	1.5×10^{-9}
Barium oxalate	$BaC_2O_4 \cdot H_2O$	2.3×10^{-8}
Barium sulfate	$BaSO_4$	1.08×10^{-10}
Beryllium hydroxide	$Be(OH)_2$	7×10^{-22}
ªBismuth hydroxide	$BiOOH$	4×10^{-10}
Bismuth iodide	BiI_3	8.1×10^{-19}
Bismuth phosphate	$BiPO_4$	1.3×10^{-23}
Bismuth sulfide	Bi_2S_3	1×10^{-97}
Cadmium arsenate	$Cd_3(AsO_4)_2$	2.2×10^{-33}
Cadmium hydroxide	$Cd(OH)_2$	5.9×10^{-15}
Cadmium oxalate	$CdC_2O_4 \cdot 3H_2O$	1.5×10^{-8}
Cadmium sulfide	CdS	7.8×10^{-27}
Calcium arsenate	$Ca_3(AsO_4)_2$	6.8×10^{-19}
Calcium carbonate	$CaCO_3$	8.7×10^{-9}
Calcium fluoride	CaF_2	4.0×10^{-11}
Calcium hydroxide	$Ca(OH)_2$	5.5×10^{-6}
Calcium iodate	$Ca(IO_3)_2 \cdot 6H_2O$	6.4×10^{-7}
Calcium oxalate	$CaC_2O_4 \cdot H_2O$	2.6×10^{-9}
Calcium phosphate	$Ca_3(PO_4)_2$	2.0×10^{-29}
Calcium sulfate	$CaSO_4$	1.9×10^{-4}
Cerium(III) hydroxide	$Ce(OH)_3$	2×10^{-20}
Cerium(III) iodate	$Ce(IO_3)_3$	3.2×10^{-10}
Cerium(III) oxalate	$Ce_2(C_2O_4)_3 \cdot 9H_2O$	3×10^{-29}
Chromium(II) hydroxide	$Cr(OH)_2$	1.0×10^{-17}
Chromium(III) hydroxide	$Cr(OH)_3$	6×10^{-31}
Cobalt(II) hydroxide	$Co(OH)_2$	2×10^{-16}
Cobalt(III) hydroxide	$Co(OH)_3$	1×10^{-43}
Copper(II) arsenate	$Cu_3(AsO_4)_2$	7.6×10^{-36}
Copper(I) bromide	$CuBr$	5.2×10^{-9}
Copper(I) chloride	$CuCl$	1.2×10^{-6}
Copper(I) iodide	CuI	5.1×10^{-12}

* See footnotes at end of table.

Substance	Formula	K_{sp}
Copper(II) iodate	$Cu(IO_3)_2$	7.4×10^{-8}
Copper(I) sulfide	Cu_2S	2×10^{-47}
Copper(II) sulfide	CuS	9×10^{-36}
Copper(I) thiocyanate	$CuSCN$	4.8×10^{-15}
Gold(III) hydroxide	$Au(OH)_3$	5.5×10^{-46}
Iron(III) arsenate	$FeAsO_4$	5.7×10^{-21}
Iron(II) carbonate	$FeCO_3$	3.5×10^{-11}
Iron(II) hydroxide	$Fe(OH)_2$	8×10^{-16}
Iron(III) hydroxide	$Fe(OH)_3$	4×10^{-38}
Lead arsenate	$Pb_3(AsO_4)_2$	4.1×10^{-36}
Lead bromide	$PbBr_2$	3.9×10^{-5}
Lead carbonate	$PbCO_3$	3.3×10^{-14}
Lead chloride	$PbCl_2$	1.6×10^{-5}
Lead chromate	$PbCrO_4$	1.8×10^{-14}
Lead fluoride	PbF_2	3.7×10^{-8}
Lead iodate	$Pb(IO_3)_2$	2.6×10^{-13}
Lead iodide	PbI_2	7.1×10^{-9}
Lead oxalate	PbC_2O_4	4.8×10^{-10}
bLead oxide	PbO	1.2×10^{-15}
Lead sulfate	$PbSO_4$	1.6×10^{-8}
Lead sulfide	PbS	8×10^{-28}
Magnesium ammonium phosphate	$MgNH_4PO_4$	2.5×10^{-13}
Magnesium arsenate	$Mg_3(AsO_4)_2$	2.1×10^{-20}
Magnesium carbonate	$MgCO_3 \cdot 3H_2O$	1×10^{-5}
Magnesium fluoride	MgF_2	6.5×10^{-9}
Magnesium hydroxide	$Mg(OH)_2$	1.2×10^{-11}
Magnesium oxalate	$MgC_2O_4 \cdot 2H_2O$	1×10^{-8}
Manganese(II) hydroxide	$Mn(OH)_2$	1.9×10^{-13}
cMercury(I) bromide	Hg_2Br_2	5.8×10^{-23}
cMercury(I) chloride	Hg_2Cl_2	1.3×10^{-18}
cMercury(I) iodide	Hg_2I_2	4.5×10^{-29}
dMercury(II) oxide	HgO	3.0×10^{-26}
cMercury(I) sulfate	Hg_2SO_4	7.4×10^{-7}
Mercury(II) sulfide	HgS	4×10^{-53}
cMercury(I) thiocyanate	$Hg_2(SCN)_2$	3.0×10^{-20}
Nickel arsenate	$Ni_3(AsO_4)_2$	3.1×10^{-26}
Nickel carbonate	$NiCO_3$	6.6×10^{-9}
Nickel hydroxide	$Ni(OH)_2$	6.5×10^{-18}
Nickel sulfide	NiS	3×10^{-19}
Palladium(II) hydroxide	$Pd(OH)_2$	1×10^{-31}
Platinum(II) hydroxide	$Pt(OH)_2$	1×10^{-35}
Radium sulfate	$RaSO_4$	4.3×10^{-11}
Silver arsenate	Ag_3AsO_4	1×10^{-22}
Silver bromate	$AgBrO_3$	5.77×10^{-5}
Silver bromide	$AgBr$	5.25×10^{-13}
Silver carbonate	Ag_2CO_3	8.1×10^{-12}
Silver chloride	$AgCl$	1.78×10^{-10}
Silver chromate	Ag_2CrO_4	2.45×10^{-12}
Silver cyanide	$Ag[Ag(CN)_2]$	5.0×10^{-12}
Silver iodate	$AgIO_3$	3.02×10^{-8}
Silver iodide	AgI	8.31×10^{-17}
Silver oxalate	$Ag_2C_2O_4$	3.5×10^{-11}

Substance	Formula	K_{sp}
[e]Silver oxide	Ag_2O	2.6×10^{-8}
Silver phosphate	Ag_3PO_4	1.3×10^{-20}
Silver sulfate	Ag_2SO_4	1.6×10^{-5}
Silver sulfide	Ag_2S	2×10^{-49}
Silver thiocyanate	$AgSCN$	1.00×10^{-12}
Strontium carbonate	$SrCO_3$	1.1×10^{-10}
Strontium chromate	$SrCrO_4$	3.6×10^{-5}
Strontium fluoride	SrF_2	2.8×10^{-9}
Strontium iodate	$Sr(IO_3)_2$	3.3×10^{-7}
Strontium oxalate	$SrC_2O_4 \cdot H_2O$	1.6×10^{-7}
Strontium sulfate	$SrSO_4$	3.8×10^{-7}
Thallium(I) bromate	$TlBrO_3$	8.5×10^{-5}
Thallium(I) bromide	$TlBr$	3.4×10^{-6}
Thallium(I) chloride	$TlCl$	1.7×10^{-4}
Thallium(I) chromate	Tl_2CrO_4	9.8×10^{-13}
Thallium(I) iodate	$TlIO_3$	3.1×10^{-6}
Thallium(I) iodide	TlI	6.5×10^{-8}
Thallium(I) sulfide	Tl_2S	5×10^{-21}
[f]Tin(II) oxide	SnO	1.4×10^{-28}
Tin(II) sulfide	SnS	1×10^{-25}
Titanium(III) hydroxide	$Ti(OH)_3$	1×10^{-40}
[g]Titanium(IV) hydroxide	$TiO(OH)_2$	1×10^{-29}
Zinc arsenate	$Zn_3(AsO_4)_2$	1.3×10^{-28}
Zinc carbonate	$ZnCO_3$	1.4×10^{-11}
Zinc ferrocyanide	$Zn_2Fe(CN)_6$	4.1×10^{-16}
Zinc hydroxide	$Zn(OH)_2$	1.2×10^{-17}
Zinc oxalate	$ZnC_2O_4 \cdot 2H_2O$	2.8×10^{-8}
Zinc phosphate	$Zn_3(PO_4)_2$	9.1×10^{-33}
Zinc sulfide	ZnS	1×10^{-21}

Although water appears in the formulas of a number of substances, it is not included in the solubility-product expression.

[a] $BiOOH \rightleftharpoons BiO^+ + OH^-$; $K_{sp} = [BiO^+][OH^-]$

[b] $PbO + H_2O \rightleftharpoons Pb^{++} + 2\,OH^-$; $K_{sp} = [Pb^{++}][OH^-]^2$

[c] All mercury(I) compounds contain the dimeric species Hg_2^{++}. Therefore, the solubility reaction and solubility-product expression are represented in general by:

$$(Hg_2)_mX_n \rightleftharpoons m\,Hg_2^{++} + n\,X^{-2m/n}; \quad K_{sp} = [Hg_2^{++}]^m[X^{-2m/n}]^n$$

[d] $HgO + H_2O \rightleftharpoons Hg^{++} + 2\,OH^-$; $K_{sp} = [Hg^{++}][OH^-]^2$

[e] $\frac{1}{2}Ag_2O + \frac{1}{2}H_2O \rightleftharpoons Ag^+ + OH^-$; $K_{sp} = [Ag^+][OH^-]$

[f] $SnO + H_2O \rightleftharpoons Sn^{++} + 2\,OH^-$; $K_{sp} = [Sn^{++}][OH^-]^2$

[g] $TiO(OH)_2 \rightleftharpoons TiO^{++} + 2\,OH^-$; $K_{sp} = [TiO^{++}][OH^-]^2$

More comprehensive tables of solubility-product data are given in the following references:

1. J. Bjerrum, G. Schwarzenbach, and L. G. Sillén: *Stability Constants of Metal-Ion Complexes, with Solubility Products of Inorganic Substances.* Part I: Organic Ligands; Part II: Inorganic Ligands. Chem. Soc. (London), Spec. Publ. No. 6 (1957); No. 7 (1958).

2. L. Meites, ed.: *Handbook of Analytical Chemistry*, McGraw-Hill Book Company, New York, 1963.

Appendix 2

Ionization Constants for Acids and Bases*

(All values are valid at or near room temperature.)

Acids

Acid	Ionization Equilibrium	
Acetic	$CH_3COOH \rightleftharpoons CH_3COO^- + H^+$;	$K = 1.75 \times 10^{-5}$
Alanine	$\underset{\underset{+NH_3}{\mid}}{CH_3CHCOOH} \rightleftharpoons \underset{\underset{+NH_3}{\mid}}{CH_3CHCOO^-} + H^+$;	$K_1 = 4.5 \times 10^{-3}$
	$\underset{\underset{+NH_3}{\mid}}{CH_3CHCOO^-} \rightleftharpoons \underset{\underset{NH_2}{\mid}}{CH_3CHCOO^-} + H^+$;	$K_2 = 1.3 \times 10^{-10}$
Arsenic	$H_3AsO_4 \rightleftharpoons H_2AsO_4^- + H^+$;	$K_1 = 6.0 \times 10^{-3}$
	$H_2AsO_4^- \rightleftharpoons HAsO_4^{--} + H^+$;	$K_2 = 1.0 \times 10^{-7}$
	$HAsO_4^{--} \rightleftharpoons AsO_4^{---} + H^+$;	$K_3 = 3.0 \times 10^{-12}$
[a]Arsenious	$H_3AsO_3 \rightleftharpoons H_2AsO_3^- + H^+$;	$K_1 = 6 \times 10^{-10}$
	$H_2AsO_3^- \rightleftharpoons HAsO_3^{--} + H^+$;	$K_2 = 3 \times 10^{-14}$
Benzoic		$K = 6.3 \times 10^{-5}$
[b]Boric	$H_3BO_3 \rightleftharpoons H_2BO_3^- + H^+$;	$K = 6.4 \times 10^{-10}$
Bromoacetic	$BrCH_2COOH \rightleftharpoons BrCH_2COO^- + H^+$;	$K = 1.38 \times 10^{-3}$
n-Butyric	$CH_3CH_2CH_2COOH \rightleftharpoons CH_3CH_2CH_2COO^- + H^+$;	$K = 1.48 \times 10^{-5}$
[c]Carbonic	$H_2CO_3 \rightleftharpoons HCO_3^- + H^+$;	$K_1 = 4.47 \times 10^{-7}$
	$HCO_3^- \rightleftharpoons CO_3^{--} + H^+$;	$K_2 = 4.68 \times 10^{-11}$
Chloroacetic	$ClCH_2COOH \rightleftharpoons ClCH_2COO^- + H^+$;	$K = 1.54 \times 10^{-3}$
Chromic	$H_2CrO_4 \rightleftharpoons HCrO_4^- + H^+$;	$K_1 = 0.18$
	$HCrO_4^- \rightleftharpoons CrO_4^{--} + H^+$;	$K_2 = 3.3 \times 10^{-6}$
Citric	$\underset{\underset{COOH}{\mid}}{HOOCCH_2\overset{\overset{OH}{\mid}}{C}CH_2COOH} \rightleftharpoons \underset{\underset{COO^-}{\mid}}{HOOCCH_2\overset{\overset{OH}{\mid}}{C}CH_2COOH} + H^+$;	
		$K_1 = 7.4 \times 10^{-4}$

* See footnotes at end of table.

	Acids (continued)
Acid	*Ionization Equilibrium*

Citic (*cont'd*)

$$\underset{\underset{COO^-}{|}}{\overset{\overset{OH}{|}}{HOOCCH_2CCH_2COOH}} \rightleftharpoons \underset{\underset{COO^-}{|}}{\overset{\overset{OH}{|}}{HOOCCH_2CCH_2COO^-}} + H^+;$$

$$K_2 = 1.7 \times 10^{-5}$$

$$\underset{\underset{COO^-}{|}}{\overset{\overset{OH}{|}}{HOOCCH_2CCH_2COO^-}} \rightleftharpoons \underset{\underset{COO^-}{|}}{\overset{\overset{OH}{|}}{^-OOCCH_2CCH_2COO^-}} + H^+;$$

$$K_3 = 4.0 \times 10^{-7}$$

[d]Ethylenediamine-
tetraacetic (H_4Y)

$H_4Y \rightleftharpoons H_3Y^- + H^+;$ $K_1 = 1.00 \times 10^{-2}$
$H_3Y^- \rightleftharpoons H_2Y^{--} + H^+;$ $K_2 = 2.16 \times 10^{-3}$
$H_2Y^{--} \rightleftharpoons HY^{---} + H^+;$ $K_3 = 6.92 \times 10^{-7}$
$HY^{---} \rightleftharpoons Y^{----} + H^+;$ $K_4 = 5.50 \times 10^{-11}$

Formic $HCOOH \rightleftharpoons HCOO^- + H^+;$ $K = 1.76 \times 10^{-4}$

Glycine $^+NH_3CH_2COOH \rightleftharpoons {^+NH_3CH_2COO^-} + H^+;$
                        $K_1 = 4.5 \times 10^{-3}$
    $^+NH_3CH_2COO^- \rightleftharpoons NH_2CH_2COO^- + H^+;$
                        $K_2 = 1.7 \times 10^{-10}$

Hydrazoic $HN_3 \rightleftharpoons N_3^- + H^+;$ $K = 1.9 \times 10^{-5}$

Hydrocyanic $HCN \rightleftharpoons CN^- + H^+;$ $K = 7.2 \times 10^{-10}$

Hydrofluoric $HF \rightleftharpoons F^- + H^+;$ $K = 6.7 \times 10^{-4}$

Hydrogen sulfide $H_2S \rightleftharpoons HS^- + H^+;$ $K_1 = 9.1 \times 10^{-8}$
    $HS^- \rightleftharpoons S^{--} + H^+;$ $K_2 = 1.2 \times 10^{-15}$

Hypochlorous $HClO \rightleftharpoons ClO^- + H^+;$ $K = 1.1 \times 10^{-8}$

Iodic $HIO_3 \rightleftharpoons IO_3^- + H^+;$ $K = 0.2$

Lactic $\underset{\underset{OH}{|}}{CH_3CHCOOH} \rightleftharpoons \underset{\underset{OH}{|}}{CH_3CHCOO^-} + H^+;$ $K = 1.4 \times 10^{-4}$

Malonic $HOOCCH_2COOH \rightleftharpoons HOOCCH_2COO^- + H^+;$
                        $K_1 = 1.38 \times 10^{-3}$
    $HOOCCH_2COO^- \rightleftharpoons {^-OOCCH_2COO^-} + H^+;$
                        $K_2 = 2.00 \times 10^{-6}$

Nitrous $HNO_2 \rightleftharpoons NO_2^- + H^+;$ $K = 5.1 \times 10^{-4}$

Oxalic $H_2C_2O_4 \rightleftharpoons HC_2O_4^- + H^+;$ $K_1 = 6.5 \times 10^{-2}$
    $HC_2O_4^- \rightleftharpoons C_2O_4^{--} + H^+;$ $K_2 = 6.1 \times 10^{-5}$

Phenol

$$\underset{}{\overset{\overset{OH}{|}}{\bigcirc}} \rightleftharpoons \underset{}{\overset{\overset{O^-}{|}}{\bigcirc}} + H^+; \qquad K = 1.1 \times 10^{-10}$$

Phosphoric $H_3PO_4 \rightleftharpoons H_2PO_4^- + H^+;$ $K_1 = 7.5 \times 10^{-3}$
    $H_2PO_4^- \rightleftharpoons HPO_4^{--} + H^+;$ $K_2 = 6.2 \times 10^{-8}$
    $HPO_4^{--} \rightleftharpoons PO_4^{---} + H^+;$ $K_3 = 4.8 \times 10^{-13}$

Acids (continued)

Acid	Ionization Equilibrium

Phosphorous

$$H_3PO_3 \rightleftharpoons H_2PO_3^- + H^+; \qquad K_1 = 5 \times 10^{-2}$$
$$H_2PO_3^- \rightleftharpoons HPO_3^{--} + H^+; \qquad K_2 = 2.6 \times 10^{-7}$$

o-Phthalic

[benzene ring]—COOH, —COOH $\rightleftharpoons$ [benzene ring]—COO$^-$, —COOH $+ H^+$; $K_1 = 1.2 \times 10^{-3}$

[benzene ring]—COO$^-$, —COOH $\rightleftharpoons$ [benzene ring]—COO$^-$, —COO$^-$ $+ H^+$; $K_2 = 3.1 \times 10^{-6}$

Picric

[benzene ring with O$_2$N, NO$_2$, NO$_2$ substituents and OH] $\rightleftharpoons$ [benzene ring with O$_2$N, NO$_2$, NO$_2$ substituents and O$^-$] $+ H^+$; $K = 0.42$

Propionic

$$CH_3CH_2COOH \rightleftharpoons CH_3CH_2COO^- + H^+; \quad K = 1.3 \times 10^{-5}$$

Salicylic

[benzene ring with COOH and OH] $\rightleftharpoons$ [benzene ring with COO$^-$ and OH] $+ H^+$; $K = 1.0 \times 10^{-3}$

Succinic

$$HOOCCH_2CH_2COOH \rightleftharpoons HOOCCH_2CH_2COO^- + H^+;$$
$$K_1 = 6.2 \times 10^{-5}$$
$$HOOCCH_2CH_2COO^- \rightleftharpoons {}^-OOCCH_2CH_2COO^- + H^+;$$
$$K_2 = 2.3 \times 10^{-6}$$

Sulfamic

$$NH_2SO_3H \rightleftharpoons NH_2SO_3^- + H^+; \qquad K = 0.10$$

Sulfuric

$$H_2SO_4 \rightleftharpoons HSO_4^- + H^+; \qquad K_1 \gg 1$$
$$HSO_4^- \rightleftharpoons SO_4^{--} + H^+; \qquad K_2 = 1.2 \times 10^{-2}$$

Sulfurous

$$H_2SO_3 \rightleftharpoons HSO_3^- + H^+; \qquad K_1 = 1.7 \times 10^{-2}$$
$$HSO_3^- \rightleftharpoons SO_3^{--} + H^+; \qquad K_2 = 6.5 \times 10^{-8}$$

Tartaric

$$HOOCCH{-}CHCOOH \rightleftharpoons HOOCCH{-}CHCOO^- + H^+;$$
(with OH, OH on the two central carbons)
$$K_1 = 1.1 \times 10^{-3}$$
$$HOOCCH{-}CHCOO^- \rightleftharpoons {}^-OOCCH{-}CHCOO^- + H^+;$$
(with OH, OH on the two central carbons)
$$K_2 = 6.9 \times 10^{-5}$$

Bases

Base	Ionization Equilibrium

Ammonia

$$NH_3 + H_2O \rightleftharpoons NH_4^+ + OH^-; \qquad K = 1.80 \times 10^{-5}$$

Aniline

[benzene ring]—NH$_2$ $+ H_2O \rightleftharpoons$ [benzene ring]—$^+$NH$_3$ $+ OH^-$; $K = 4.0 \times 10^{-10}$

	Bases (continued)
Base	*Ionization Equilibrium*

Diethylamine	$(CH_3CH_2)_2NH + H_2O \rightleftharpoons (CH_3CH_2)_2NH_2^+ + OH^-$; $K = 8.5 \times 10^{-4}$
Dimethylamine	$(CH_3)_2NH + H_2O \rightleftharpoons (CH_3)_2NH_2^+ + OH^-$; $K = 5.9 \times 10^{-4}$
Ethanolamine	$HOCH_2CH_2NH_2 + H_2O \rightleftharpoons HOCH_2CH_2NH_3^+ + OH^-$; $K = 3.2 \times 10^{-5}$
Ethylamine	$CH_3CH_2NH_2 + H_2O \rightleftharpoons CH_3CH_2NH_3^+ + OH^-$; $K = 4.3 \times 10^{-4}$
Ethylenediamine	$NH_2CH_2CH_2NH_2 + H_2O \rightleftharpoons NH_2CH_2CH_2NH_3^+ + OH^-$; $K_1 = 8.5 \times 10^{-5}$
	$NH_2CH_2CH_2NH_3^+ + H_2O \rightleftharpoons {}^+NH_3CH_2CH_2NH_3^+ + OH^-$; $K_2 = 7.1 \times 10^{-8}$
Hydrazine	$H_2NNH_2 + H_2O \rightleftharpoons H_2NNH_3^+ + OH^-$; $K = 1.3 \times 10^{-6}$
Hydroxylamine	$HONH_2 + H_2O \rightleftharpoons HONH_3^+ + OH^-$; $K = 9.1 \times 10^{-9}$
Methylamine	$CH_3NH_2 + H_2O \rightleftharpoons CH_3NH_3^+ + OH^-$; $K = 4.8 \times 10^{-4}$

Piperidine

$+ H_2O \rightleftharpoons$ ... $+ OH^-$; $K = 1.3 \times 10^{-3}$

Pyridine

$+ H_2O \rightleftharpoons$ ... $+ OH^-$; $K = 1.7 \times 10^{-9}$

Triethylamine	$(CH_3CH_2)_3N + H_2O \rightleftharpoons (CH_3CH_2)_3NH^+ + OH^-$; $K = 5.3 \times 10^{-4}$
Trimethylamine	$(CH_3)_3N + H_2O \rightleftharpoons (CH_3)_3NH^+ + OH^-$; $K = 6.3 \times 10^{-5}$
Tripropylamine	$(CH_3CH_2CH_2)_3N + H_2O \rightleftharpoons (CH_3CH_2CH_2)_3NH^+ + OH^-$; $K = 5.5 \times 10^{-4}$
Tris(hydroxymethyl)-aminomethane	$(HOCH_2)_3CNH_2 + H_2O \rightleftharpoons (HOCH_2)_3CNH_3^+ + OH^-$; $K = 1.2 \times 10^{-6}$

It is common practice to designate the above reactions of acids and bases as ionization equilibria. However, it is much more correct to consider them as *proton-transfer* equilibria, because all such reactions involve the transfer of a proton from a Brönsted-Lowry acid to a Brönsted-Lowry base.

All acid ionizations listed above pertain to water as solvent, the latter acting as the Brönsted-Lowry base (proton acceptor). Thus, the complete proton-transfer reaction for acetic acid should be written as

$$CH_3COOH + H_2O \rightleftharpoons CH_3COO^- + H_3O^+; \quad K = 1.75 \times 10^{-5}$$

to show clearly the true nature of this equilibrium. Other equilibria for acids can be similarly written.

On the other hand, correct proton-transfer reactions are listed above for the various bases, although it should be noted that water acts as a Brönsted-Lowry acid by donating one of its protons to the base.

ᵃ The extent of the second ionization of arsenious acid is so exceedingly small in water that only the first ionization step is of any significance. Sometimes the ionization of arsenious acid is written

$$HAsO_2 \rightleftharpoons AsO_2^- + H^+; \quad K = 6 \times 10^{-10}$$

to indicate that arsenious acid behaves strictly as a monoprotic acid in water.

ᵇ Boric acid behaves as a monoprotic acid in water. To convey this behavior, the ionization of boric acid is frequently written

$$HBO_2 \rightleftharpoons BO_2^- + H^+; \quad K = 6.4 \times 10^{-10}$$

ᶜ Carbonic acid (H_2CO_3) is really a much stronger acid than the value for K_1 indicates, because only a small fraction of the carbon dioxide dissolved in water exists as H_2CO_3. A discussion of the acid strength of carbonic acid is given on page 302.

ᵈ Ethylenediaminetetraacetic acid is a tetraprotic acid with the structural formula

$$\begin{array}{ccc}
HOOC-CH_2 & & CH_2-COOH \\
& \diagdown \!\!\!\ddot{N}-CH_2-CH_2-\ddot{N}\!\!\!\diagup & \\
HOOC-CH_2 & & CH_2-COOH
\end{array}$$

but, for purposes of brevity, it is usually represented as H_4Y.

Comprehensive data concerning acid-base equilibria are given in the following references:

1. L. Meites, ed.: *Handbook of Analytical Chemistry*, McGraw-Hill Book Company, New York, 1963.
2. S. Bruckenstein and I. M. Kolthoff: Acid-base strength and protolysis curves in water. In I. M. Kolthoff and P. J. Elving, eds.: *Treatise on Analytical Chemistry*, Part I, Volume 1, Wiley-Interscience, New York, 1959, pp. 421–465.

Appendix 3

Stepwise and Overall Formation Constants for Metal Ion Complexes*

(All values are valid at or near room temperature.)

Acetate, CH_3COO^-

$Cd^{++} + CH_3COO^- = CdCH_3COO^+$	$K_1 = 20$
$CdCH_3COO^+ + CH_3COO^- = Cd(CH_3COO)_2$	$K_2 = 10$
$Cu^{++} + CH_3COO^- = CuCH_3COO^+$	$K_1 = 160$
$CuCH_3COO^+ + CH_3COO^- = Cu(CH_3COO)_2$	$K_2 = 13$
$Hg^{++} + 2\ CH_3COO^- = Hg(CH_3COO)_2$	$\beta_2 = 2.5 \times 10^8$
$Pb^{++} + CH_3COO^- = PbCH_3COO^+$	$K_1 = 500$
$PbCH_3COO^+ + CH_3COO^- = Pb(CH_3COO)_2$	$K_2 = 32$

Ammonia, NH_3

$Ag^+ + NH_3 = AgNH_3^+$	$K_1 = 2.5 \times 10^3$
$AgNH_3^+ + NH_3 = Ag(NH_3)_2^+$	$K_2 = 1.0 \times 10^4$
$Cd^{++} + NH_3 = CdNH_3^{++}$	$K_1 = 400$
$CdNH_3^{++} + NH_3 = Cd(NH_3)_2^{++}$	$K_2 = 130$
$Cd(NH_3)_2^{++} + NH_3 = Cd(NH_3)_3^{++}$	$K_3 = 25$
$Cd(NH_3)_3^{++} + NH_3 = Cd(NH_3)_4^{++}$	$K_4 = 8$
$Cd(NH_3)_4^{++} + NH_3 = Cd(NH_3)_5^{++}$	$K_5 = 0.5$
$Cd(NH_3)_5^{++} + NH_3 = Cd(NH_3)_6^{++}$	$K_6 = 0.02$
$Co^{++} + NH_3 = CoNH_3^{++}$	$K_1 = 130$
$CoNH_3^{++} + NH_3 = Co(NH_3)_2^{++}$	$K_2 = 40$
$Co(NH_3)_2^{++} + NH_3 = Co(NH_3)_3^{++}$	$K_3 = 10$
$Co(NH_3)_3^{++} + NH_3 = Co(NH_3)_4^{++}$	$K_4 = 5$
$Co(NH_3)_4^{++} + NH_3 = Co(NH_3)_5^{++}$	$K_5 = 1$
$Co(NH_3)_5^{++} + NH_3 = Co(NH_3)_6^{++}$	$K_6 = 0.2$
$Co^{+++} + NH_3 = CoNH_3^{+++}$	$K_1 = 2.0 \times 10^7$
$CoNH_3^{+++} + NH_3 = Co(NH_3)_2^{+++}$	$K_2 = 5.0 \times 10^6$
$Co(NH_3)_2^{+++} + NH_3 = Co(NH_3)_3^{+++}$	$K_3 = 1.3 \times 10^6$
$Co(NH_3)_3^{+++} + NH_3 = Co(NH_3)_4^{+++}$	$K_4 = 4.0 \times 10^5$
$Co(NH_3)_4^{+++} + NH_3 = Co(NH_3)_5^{+++}$	$K_5 = 1.3 \times 10^5$
$Co(NH_3)_5^{+++} + NH_3 = Co(NH_3)_6^{+++}$	$K_6 = 2.5 \times 10^4$
$Cu^+ + NH_3 = CuNH_3^+$	$K_1 = 8.0 \times 10^5$
$CuNH_3^+ + NH_3 = Cu(NH_3)_2^+$	$K_2 = 8.0 \times 10^4$
$Cu^{++} + NH_3 = CuNH_3^{++}$	$K_1 = 1.3 \times 10^4$
$CuNH_3^{++} + NH_3 = Cu(NH_3)_2^{++}$	$K_2 = 3.2 \times 10^3$
$Cu(NH_3)_2^{++} + NH_3 = Cu(NH_3)_3^{++}$	$K_3 = 800$

* See footnotes at end of table.

Ammonia, NH_3 (continued)

$Cu(NH_3)_3^{++} + NH_3 = Cu(NH_3)_4^{++}$	$K_4 = 130$
$Cu(NH_3)_4^{++} + NH_3 = Cu(NH_3)_5^{++}$	$K_5 = 0.32$
$Hg^{++} + NH_3 = HgNH_3^{++}$	$K_1 = 6.3 \times 10^8$
$HgNH_3^{++} + NH_3 = Hg(NH_3)_2^{++}$	$K_2 = 5.0 \times 10^8$
$Hg(NH_3)_2^{++} + NH_3 = Hg(NH_3)_3^{++}$	$K_3 = 10$
$Hg(NH_3)_3^{++} + NH_3 = Hg(NH_3)_4^{++}$	$K_4 = 8$
$Ni^{++} + NH_3 = NiNH_3^{++}$	$K_1 = 630$
$NiNH_3^{++} + NH_3 = Ni(NH_3)_2^{++}$	$K_2 = 160$
$Ni(NH_3)_2^{++} + NH_3 = Ni(NH_3)_3^{++}$	$K_3 = 50$
$Ni(NH_3)_3^{++} + NH_3 = Ni(NH_3)_4^{++}$	$K_4 = 16$
$Ni(NH_3)_4^{++} + NH_3 = Ni(NH_3)_5^{++}$	$K_5 = 5$
$Ni(NH_3)_5^{++} + NH_3 = Ni(NH_3)_6^{++}$	$K_6 = 1$
$Zn^{++} + NH_3 = ZnNH_3^{++}$	$K_1 = 190$
$ZnNH_3^{++} + NH_3 = Zn(NH_3)_2^{++}$	$K_2 = 210$
$Zn(NH_3)_2^{++} + NH_3 = Zn(NH_3)_3^{++}$	$K_3 = 250$
$Zn(NH_3)_3^{++} + NH_3 = Zn(NH_3)_4^{++}$	$K_4 = 110$

Bromide, Br^-

$Bi^{+++} + Br^- = BiBr^{++}$	$K_1 = 2.0 \times 10^4$
$BiBr^{++} + Br^- = BiBr_2^+$	$K_2 = 18$
$BiBr_2^+ + Br^- = BiBr_3$	$K_3 = 2.2$
$BiBr_3 + Br^- = BiBr_4^-$	$K_4 = 85$
$Cd^{++} + Br^- = CdBr^+$	$K_1 = 56$
$CdBr^+ + Br^- = CdBr_2$	$K_2 = 3.9$
$CdBr_2 + Br^- = CdBr_3^-$	$K_3 = 9.5$
$CdBr_3^- + Br^- = CdBr_4^{--}$	$K_4 = 2.4$
$Hg^{++} + Br^- = HgBr^+$	$K_1 = 1.1 \times 10^9$
$HgBr^+ + Br^- = HgBr_2$	$K_2 = 1.9 \times 10^8$
$HgBr_2 + Br^- = HgBr_3^-$	$K_3 = 260$
$HgBr_3^- + Br^- = HgBr_4^{--}$	$K_4 = 18$
$Pb^{++} + Br^- = PbBr^+$	$K_1 = 14$
$PbBr^+ + Br^- = PbBr_2$	$K_2 = 5.9$
$PbBr_2 + 2\,Br^- = PbBr_4^{--}$	$K_3K_4 = 13$
$Zn^{++} + Br^- = ZnBr^+$	$K_1 = 0.25$

Chloride, Cl^-

$Bi^{+++} + Cl^- = BiCl^{++}$	$K_1 = 270$
$BiCl^{++} + Cl^- = BiCl_2^+$	$K_2 = 100$
$BiCl_2^+ + Cl^- = BiCl_3$	$K_3 = 25$
$BiCl_3 + Cl^- = BiCl_4^-$	$K_4 = 2.5$
$BiCl_4^- + Cl^- = BiCl_5^{--}$	$K_5 = 3.2$
$Cd^{++} + Cl^- = CdCl^+$	$K_1 = 22$
$CdCl^+ + Cl^- = CdCl_2$	$K_2 = 2.7$
$CdCl_2 + Cl^- = CdCl_3^-$	$K_3 = 2.5$
$Cu^+ + 2\,Cl^- = CuCl_2^-$	$\beta_2 = 5.0 \times 10^4$
$Fe^{+++} + Cl^- = FeCl^{++}$	$K_1 = 30$
$FeCl^{++} + Cl^- = FeCl_2^+$	$K_2 = 4.5$
$FeCl_2^+ + Cl^- = FeCl_3$	$K_3 = 0.10$
$Hg^{++} + Cl^- = HgCl^+$	$K_1 = 1.9 \times 10^5$
$HgCl^+ + Cl^- = HgCl_2$	$K_2 = 3.2 \times 10^7$
$HgCl_2 + Cl^- = HgCl_3^-$	$K_3 = 14$
$HgCl_3^- + Cl^- = HgCl_4^{--}$	$K_4 = 10$
$Pb^{++} + Cl^- = PbCl^+$	$K_1 = 44$
$PbCl^+ + 2\,Cl^- = PbCl_3^-$	$K_2K_3 = 1.7$

Cyanide, CN^-

$Ag^+ + 2\ CN^- = Ag(CN)_2^-$	$\beta_2 = 1.26 \times 10^{21}$
$Cd^{++} + CN^- = CdCN^+$	$K_1 = 3.5 \times 10^5$
$CdCN^+ + CN^- = Cd(CN)_2$	$K_2 = 1.2 \times 10^5$
$Cd(CN)_2 + CN^- = Cd(CN)_3^-$	$K_3 = 5.0 \times 10^4$
$Cd(CN)_3^- + CN^- = Cd(CN)_4^{--}$	$K_4 = 3.6 \times 10^3$
$Co^{++} + 6\ CN^- = Co(CN)_6^{----}$	$\beta_6 = 1.0 \times 10^{19}$
$Cu^+ + 2\ CN^- = Cu(CN)_2^-$	$\beta_2 = 1.0 \times 10^{21}$
$Cu(CN)_2^- + CN^- = Cu(CN)_3^{--}$	$K_3 = 3.9 \times 10^4$
$Hg^{++} + CN^- = HgCN^+$	$K_1 = 1.0 \times 10^{18}$
$HgCN^+ + CN^- = Hg(CN)_2$	$K_2 = 5.0 \times 10^{16}$
$Hg(CN)_2 + CN^- = Hg(CN)_3^-$	$K_3 = 6.3 \times 10^3$
$Hg(CN)_3^- + CN^- = Hg(CN)_4^{--}$	$K_4 = 1.0 \times 10^3$
$Ni^{++} + 4\ CN^- = Ni(CN)_4^{--}$	$\beta_4 = 1.0 \times 10^{22}$
$Zn^{++} + 3\ CN^- = Zn(CN)_3^-$	$\beta_3 = 3.2 \times 10^{17}$
$Zn(CN)_3^- + CN^- = Zn(CN)_4^{--}$	$K_4 = 500$

Ethylenediamine, $H_2NCH_2CH_2NH_2$ (en)

$Ag^+ + en = Ag(en)^+$	$K_1 = 5.0 \times 10^4$
$Ag(en)^+ + en = Ag(en)_2^+$	$K_2 = 1.4 \times 10^3$
$Cd^{++} + en = Cd(en)^{++}$	$K_1 = 3.0 \times 10^5$
$Cd(en)^{++} + en = Cd(en)_2^{++}$	$K_2 = 3.6 \times 10^4$
$Cd(en)_2^{++} + en = Cd(en)_3^{++}$	$K_3 = 120$
$Co^{++} + en = Co(en)^{++}$	$K_1 = 7.8 \times 10^5$
$Co(en)^{++} + en = Co(en)_2^{++}$	$K_2 = 6.9 \times 10^4$
$Co(en)_2^{++} + en = Co(en)_3^{++}$	$K_3 = 1.3 \times 10^3$
$Co^{+++} + 3\ en = Co(en)_3^{+++}$	$\beta_3 = 4.9 \times 10^{48}$
$Cu^+ + 2\ en = Cu(en)_2^+$	$\beta_2 = 6.3 \times 10^{10}$
$Cu^{++} + en = Cu(en)^{++}$	$K_1 = 3.5 \times 10^{10}$
$Cu(en)^{++} + en = Cu(en)_2^{++}$	$K_2 = 1.1 \times 10^9$
$Hg^{++} + 2\ en = Hg(en)_2^{++}$	$\beta_2 = 2.5 \times 10^{23}$
$Ni^{++} + en = Ni(en)^{++}$	$K_1 = 4.6 \times 10^7$
$Ni(en)^{++} + en = Ni(en)_2^{++}$	$K_2 = 2.5 \times 10^6$
$Ni(en)_2^{++} + en = Ni(en)_3^{++}$	$K_3 = 3.4 \times 10^4$
$Zn^{++} + en = Zn(en)^{++}$	$K_1 = 5.1 \times 10^5$
$Zn(en)^{++} + en = Zn(en)_2^{++}$	$K_2 = 4.6 \times 10^4$
$Zn(en)_2^{++} + en = Zn(en)_3^{++}$	$K_3 = 51$

Ethylenediaminetetraacetate, $(^-OOCCH_2)_2NCH_2CH_2N(CH_2COO^-)_2$ or (Y^{-4})

$Al^{+++} + Y^{-4} = AlY^-$	$K_1 = 1.35 \times 10^{16}$
$Ba^{++} + Y^{-4} = BaY^{--}$	$K_1 = 5.75 \times 10^7$
$Cd^{++} + Y^{-4} = CdY^{--}$	$K_1 = 2.88 \times 10^{16}$
$Ca^{++} + Y^{-4} = CaY^{--}$	$K_1 = 5.01 \times 10^{10}$
$Co^{++} + Y^{-4} = CoY^{--}$	$K_1 = 2.04 \times 10^{16}$
$Cu^{++} + Y^{-4} = CuY^{--}$	$K_1 = 6.30 \times 10^{18}$
$Ga^{+++} + Y^{-4} = GaY^-$	$K_1 = 1.86 \times 10^{20}$
$In^{+++} + Y^{-4} = InY^-$	$K_1 = 8.91 \times 10^{24}$
$Fe^{++} + Y^{-4} = FeY^{--}$	$K_1 = 2.14 \times 10^{14}$
$Fe^{+++} + Y^{-4} = FeY^-$	$K_1 = 1.3 \times 10^{25}$
$Pb^{++} + Y^{-4} = PbY^{--}$	$K_1 = 1.10 \times 10^{18}$
$Mg^{++} + Y^{-4} = MgY^{--}$	$K_1 = 4.90 \times 10^8$
$Mn^{++} + Y^{-4} = MnY^{--}$	$K_1 = 1.10 \times 10^{14}$
$Hg^{++} + Y^{-4} = HgY^{--}$	$K_1 = 6.30 \times 10^{21}$

Ethylenediaminetetraacetate,
($^-$OOCCH$_2$)$_2$NCH$_2$CH$_2$N(CH$_2$COO$^-$)$_2$ or (Y^{-4}) (continued)

Ni^{++} + Y^{-4} = NiY^{--}	$K_1 = 4.16 \times 10^{18}$
Sc^{+++} + Y^{-4} = ScY$^-$	$K_1 = 1.3 \times 10^{23}$
Ag$^+$ + Y^{-4} = AgY^{---}	$K_1 = 2.09 \times 10^7$
Sr^{++} + Y^{-4} = SrY^{--}	$K_1 = 4.26 \times 10^8$
Th^{++++} + Y^{-4} = ThY	$K_1 = 1.6 \times 10^{23}$
Ti^{+++} + Y^{-4} = TiY$^-$	$K_1 = 2.0 \times 10^{21}$
TiO^{++} + Y^{-4} = TiOY^{--}	$K_1 = 2.0 \times 10^{17}$
V^{++} + Y^{-4} = VY^{--}	$K_1 = 5.01 \times 10^{12}$
V^{+++} + Y^{-4} = VY$^-$	$K_1 = 8.0 \times 10^{25}$
VO^{++} + Y^{-4} = VOY^{--}	$K_1 = 5.89 \times 10^{18}$
Y^{+++} + Y^{-4} = YY$^-$	$K_1 = 1.23 \times 10^{18}$
Zn^{++} + Y^{-4} = ZnY^{--}	$K_1 = 3.16 \times 10^{16}$

Fluoride, F$^-$

Al^{+++} + F$^-$ = AlF^{++}	$K_1 = 1.4 \times 10^6$
AlF^{++} + F$^-$ = AlF$_2$$^+$	$K_2 = 1.1 \times 10^5$
AlF$_2$$^+$ + F$^-$ = AlF$_3$	$K_3 = 7.1 \times 10^3$
AlF$_3$ + F$^-$ = AlF$_4$$^-$	$K_4 = 570$
AlF$_4$$^-$ + F$^-$ = AlF$_5$$^{--}$	$K_5 = 42$
AlF$_5$$^{--}$ + F$^-$ = AlF$_6$$^{---}$	$K_6 = 3.0$
Ce^{+++} + F$^-$ = CeF^{++}	$K_1 = 1.6 \times 10^3$
Fe^{+++} + F$^-$ = FeF^{++}	$K_1 = 1.9 \times 10^5$
FeF^{++} + F$^-$ = FeF$_2$$^+$	$K_2 = 1.1 \times 10^4$
FeF$_2$$^+$ + F$^-$ = FeF$_3$	$K_3 = 580$

^{a}Hydroxide, OH$^-$

Al^{+++} + OH$^-$ = AlOH^{++}	$K_1 = 7 \times 10^8$
Al^{+++} + 4 OH$^-$ = Al(OH)$_4$$^-$	$\beta_4 = 2 \times 10^{33}$
Bi^{+++} + OH$^-$ = BiOH^{++}	$K_1 = 3 \times 10^{12}$
Cd^{++} + OH$^-$ = CdOH$^+$	$K_1 = 5 \times 10^4$
Co^{++} + OH$^-$ = CoOH$^+$	$K_1 = 1 \times 10^5$
Cu^{++} + OH$^-$ = CuOH$^+$	$K_1 = 1 \times 10^6$
Fe^{++} + OH$^-$ = FeOH$^+$	$K_1 = 3 \times 10^4$
Fe^{+++} + OH$^-$ = FeOH^{++}	$K_1 = 1 \times 10^{11}$
FeOH^{++} + OH$^-$ = Fe(OH)$_2$$^+$	$K_2 = 5 \times 10^{10}$
Hg^{++} + OH$^-$ = HgOH$^+$	$K_1 = 2 \times 10^{10}$
Ni^{++} + OH$^-$ = NiOH$^+$	$K_1 = 2 \times 10^3$
Pb^{++} + OH$^-$ = PbOH$^+$	$K_1 = 7 \times 10^7$
Pb^{++} + 3 OH$^-$ = Pb(OH)$_3$$^-$	$\beta_3 = 2 \times 10^{13}$
Zn^{++} + OH$^-$ = ZnOH$^+$	$K_1 = 2 \times 10^4$
Zn^{++} + 3 OH$^-$ = Zn(OH)$_3$$^-$	$\beta_3 = 2 \times 10^{14}$
Zn(OH)$_3$$^-$ + OH$^-$ = Zn(OH)$_4$$^{--}$	$K_4 = 10$

Iodide, I$^-$

Bi^{+++} + 6 I$^-$ = BiI$_6$$^{---}$	$\beta_6 = 2.5 \times 10^{19}$
Cd^{++} + I$^-$ = CdI$^+$	$K_1 = 190$
CdI$^+$ + I$^-$ = CdI$_2$	$K_2 = 44$
CdI$_2$ + I$^-$ = CdI$_3$$^-$	$K_3 = 12$
CdI$_3$$^-$ + I$^-$ = CdI$_4$$^{--}$	$K_4 = 13$
Cu$^+$ + 2 I$^-$ = CuI$_2$$^-$	$\beta_2 = 5.8 \times 10^8$
Hg^{++} + I$^-$ = HgI$^+$	$K_1 = 7.4 \times 10^{12}$
HgI$^+$ + I$^-$ = HgI$_2$	$K_2 = 8.9 \times 10^{10}$
HgI$_2$ + I$^-$ = HgI$_3$$^-$	$K_3 = 6.0 \times 10^3$
HgI$_3$$^-$ + I$^-$ = HgI$_4$$^{--}$	$K_4 = 170$

Iodide, I^- (continued)

$Pb^{++} + I^- = PbI^+$	$K_1 = 20$
$PbI^+ + I^- = PbI_2$	$K_2 = 30$
$PbI_2 + I^- = PbI_3^-$	$K_3 = 4$
$PbI_3^- + I^- = PbI_4^{--}$	$K_4 = 3$

Oxalate, $C_2O_4^{--}$

$Al^{+++} + 2\ C_2O_4^{--} = Al(C_2O_4)_2^-$	$\beta_2 = 1.0 \times 10^{13}$
$Al(C_2O_4)_2^- + C_2O_4^{--} = Al(C_2O_4)_3^{---}$	$K_3 = 6.3 \times 10^3$
$Cd^{++} + 2\ C_2O_4^{--} = Cd(C_2O_4)_2^{--}$	$\beta_2 = 5.9 \times 10^5$
$Co^{++} + 2\ C_2O_4^{--} = Co(C_2O_4)_2^{--}$	$\beta_2 = 1.3 \times 10^7$
$Cu^{++} + 2\ C_2O_4^{--} = Cu(C_2O_4)_2^{--}$	$\beta_2 = 2.0 \times 10^{10}$
$Fe^{++} + 2\ C_2O_4^{--} = Fe(C_2O_4)_2^{--}$	$\beta_2 = 4.0 \times 10^9$
$Fe^{+++} + C_2O_4^{--} = FeC_2O_4^+$	$K_1 = 2.5 \times 10^9$
$FeC_2O_4^+ + C_2O_4^{--} = Fe(C_2O_4)_2^-$	$K_2 = 6.3 \times 10^6$
$Fe(C_2O_4)_2^- + C_2O_4^{--} = Fe(C_2O_4)_3^{---}$	$K_3 = 1.0 \times 10^4$
$Mg^{++} + 2\ C_2O_4^{--} = Mg(C_2O_4)_2^{--}$	$\beta_2 = 2.4 \times 10^4$
$Mn^{++} + 2\ C_2O_4^{--} = Mn(C_2O_4)_2^{--}$	$\beta_2 = 6.3 \times 10^5$
$Ni^{++} + 2\ C_2O_4^{--} = Ni(C_2O_4)_2^{--}$	$\beta_2 = 3.3 \times 10^6$
$Pb^{++} + 2\ C_2O_4^{--} = Pb(C_2O_4)_2^{--}$	$\beta_2 = 3.5 \times 10^6$
$Zn^{++} + 2\ C_2O_4^{--} = Zn(C_2O_4)_2^{--}$	$\beta_2 = 2.3 \times 10^7$

Pyridine, C_5H_5N (py)

$Ag^+ + py = Ag(py)^+$	$K_1 = 100$
$Ag(py)^+ + py = Ag(py)_2^+$	$K_2 = 130$
$Cd^{++} + py = Cd(py)^{++}$	$K_1 = 20$
$Cd(py)^{++} + py = Cd(py)_2^{++}$	$K_2 = 6.3$
$Co^{++} + py = Co(py)^{++}$	$K_1 = 12$
$Co(py)^{++} + py = Co(py)_2^{++}$	$K_2 = 2.5$
$Cu^{++} + py = Cu(py)^{++}$	$K_1 = 330$
$Cu(py)^{++} + py = Cu(py)_2^{++}$	$K_2 = 73$
$Cu(py)_2^{++} + py = Cu(py)_3^{++}$	$K_3 = 20$
$Cu(py)_3^{++} + py = Cu(py)_4^{++}$	$K_4 = 7.1$
$Hg^{++} + py = Hg(py)^{++}$	$K_1 = 1.3 \times 10^5$
$Hg(py)^{++} + py = Hg(py)_2^{++}$	$K_2 = 8.0 \times 10^4$
$Ni^{++} + py = Ni(py)^{++}$	$K_1 = 63$
$Ni(py)^{++} + py = Ni(py)_2^{++}$	$K_2 = 12$
$Zn^{++} + py = Zn(py)^{++}$	$K_1 = 10$
$Zn(py)^{++} + py = Zn(py)_2^{++}$	$K_2 = 3$

Thiocyanate, SCN^-

$Ag^+ + 2\ SCN^- = Ag(SCN)_2^-$	$\beta_2 = 3.7 \times 10^7$
$Ag(SCN)_2^- + SCN^- = Ag(SCN)_3^{--}$	$K_3 = 320$
$Ag(SCN)_3^{--} + SCN^- = Ag(SCN)_4^{---}$	$K_4 = 10$
$Cu^+ + 2\ SCN^- = Cu(SCN)_2^-$	$\beta_2 = 1.3 \times 10^{12}$
$Cu(SCN)_2^- + SCN^- = Cu(SCN)_3^{--}$	$K_3 = 1.5 \times 10^5$
$Fe^{III} + SCN = FeSCN^{++}$	$K_1 = 130$
$FeSCN^{++} + SCN^- = Fe(SCN)_2^+$	$K_2 = 20$
$Hg^{++} + 2\ SCN^- = Hg(SCN)_2$	$\beta_2 = 3.1 \times 10^{17}$
$Hg(SCN)_2 + 2\ SCN^- = Hg(SCN)_4^{--}$	$K_3K_4 = 5.8 \times 10^3$

Thiosulfate, $S_2O_3^{--}$

$Ag^+ + S_2O_3^{--} = AgS_2O_3^-$	$K_1 = 6.6 \times 10^8$
$AgS_2O_3^- + S_2O_3^{--} = Ag(S_2O_3)_2^{---}$	$K_2 = 4.4 \times 10^4$
$Cd^{++} + S_2O_3^{--} - CdS_2O_3$	$K_1 = 8.3 \times 10^3$

Thiosulfate, $S_2O_3^{--}$ (continued)

$$CdS_2O_3 + S_2O_3^{--} = Cd(S_2O_3)_2^{--} \qquad K_2 = 330$$
$$Cu^+ + S_2O_3^{--} = CuS_2O_3^{-} \qquad K_1 = 1.9 \times 10^{10}$$
$$CuS_2O_3^{-} + S_2O_3^{--} = Cu(S_2O_3)_2^{---} \qquad K_2 = 90$$
$$Hg^{++} + 2\,S_2O_3^{--} = Hg(S_2O_3)_2^{--} \qquad \beta_2 = 2.8 \times 10^{29}$$
$$Hg(S_2O_3)_2^{--} + S_2O_3^{--} = Hg(S_2O_3)_3^{----} \qquad K_3 = 290$$
$$Pb^{++} + 2\,S_2O_3^{--} = Pb(S_2O_3)_2^{--} \qquad \beta_2 = 1.3 \times 10^5$$

Discussions of the formulation and significance of stepwise (K_n) and overall (β_n) formation constants are presented in Chapters 4 and 11.

[a] Reactions involving metal cations and hydroxide ions do not fit into the usual classification of complex formation equilibria but should be thought of as examples of simple Brönsted-Lowry proton-transfer reactions.

Each metal ion species in the above tabulation is represented by the general symbol M^{+n}, where n is the charge of the metal cation. However, it should be understood that a metal ion is hydrated (solvated). For example, although the iron(III) ion is abbreviated as Fe^{+++}, the actual species may be more reasonably written as $Fe(H_2O)_6^{+++}$. A usual set of complexation equilibria involves the stepwise substitution of a (hypothetical monodentate) ligand, L, for one of the water molecules, as in the following reactions:

$$Fe(H_2O)_6^{+++} + L = Fe(H_2O)_5L^{+++} + H_2O$$
$$Fe(H_2O)_5L^{+++} + L = Fe(H_2O)_4L_2^{+++} + H_2O \ldots$$
$$\ldots Fe(H_2O)L_5^{+++} + L = FeL_6^{+++} + H_2O$$

In the case of reactions between a metal ion such as $Fe(H_2O)_6^{+++}$ and OH^-, however, one should visualize a process in which the hydroxide ion (Brönsted-Lowry base) accepts a proton from one of the water molecules (Brönsted-Lowry acid) coordinated to iron(III), e.g.,

$$Fe(H_2O)_6^{+++} + OH^- = Fe(H_2O)_5OH^{++} + H_2O$$

or

$$Fe(H_2O)_5OH^{++} + OH^- = Fe(H_2O)_4(OH)_2^{+} + H_2O$$

If the water molecules coordinated to iron(III) are omitted from these last two equilibria, they assume the forms given in the table above:

$$Fe^{+++} + OH^- = FeOH^{++}$$

and

$$FeOH^{++} + OH^- = Fe(OH)_2^{+}$$

Clearly, no actual exchange or substitution of OH^- for H_2O is involved in such equilibria.

It may be noted that the so-called acid ionization constants for several metal cations can be calculated from data in this table. Thus, the first step in the acid ionization of $Fe(H_2O)_6^{+++}$ can be formulated as

$$Fe(H_2O)_6^{+++} + H_2O = Fe(H_2O)_5OH^{++} + H_3O^+$$

or, in abbreviated form, as

$$Fe^{+++} + H_2O = FeOH^{++} + H^+$$

The equilibrium constant for this acid dissociation of iron(III) may be calculated as follows:

$$Fe(H_2O)_6^{+++} + OH^- = Fe(H_2O)_5OH^{++} + H_2O; \quad K_1 = 1 \times 10^{11}$$
$$2\,H_2O = H_3O^+ + OH^-; \qquad K_w = 1 \times 10^{-14}$$

$$Fe(H_2O)_6^{+++} + H_2O = Fe(H_2O)_5OH^{++} + H_3O^+; \quad K_a = K_1K_w = 1 \times 10^{-3}$$

or

$$Fe^{+++} + OH^- = FeOH^{++}; \quad K_1 = 1 \times 10^{11}$$
$$H_2O = H^+ + OH^-; \qquad K_w = 1 \times 10^{-14}$$

$$Fe^{+++} + H_2O = FeOH^{++} + H^+; \quad K_a = K_1K_w = 1 \times 10^{-3}$$

Notice that the acid strength of $Fe(H_2O)_6^{+++}$ or Fe^{+++} in water is greater than that of acetic acid, for example, and almost as great as the second ionization constant for sulfuric acid ($K_2 = 1.2 \times 10^{-2}$).

Good sources of information about formation constants for metal ion complexes are:

1. J. Bjerrum, G. Schwarzenbach, and L. G. Sillén: *Stability Constants of Metal-Ion Complexes, with Solubility Products of Inorganic Substances.* Part I: Organic Ligands; Part II: Inorganic Ligands. Chem. Soc. (London), Spec. Publ. No. 6 (1957); No. 7 (1958).
2. K. B. Yatsimirskii and V. P. Vasil'ev: *Instability Constants of Complex Compounds* (translated from Russian), Consultants Bureau, New York, 1960.
3. L. Meites, ed.: *Handbook of Analytical Chemistry*, McGraw-Hill Book Company, New York, 1963.

Appendix 4

Standard and Formal Potentials for Half-Reactions*

(All values pertain to 25°C and are quoted in volts with respect to the normal hydrogen electrode, taken to have a standard potential of zero.)

Half-Reaction	$E°$
Aluminum	
$Al^{+++} + 3\,e = Al$	-1.66
$Al(OH)_4^- + 3\,e = Al + 4\,OH^-$	-2.35
Antimony	
$Sb_2O_5 + 6\,H^+ + 4\,e = 2\,SbO^+ + 3\,H_2O$	$+0.581$
$Sb + 3\,H^+ + 3\,e = SbH_3$	-0.51
Arsenic	
$H_3AsO_4 + 2\,H^+ + 2\,e = HAsO_2 + 2\,H_2O$	$+0.559$
$HAsO_2 + 3\,H^+ + 3\,e = As + 2\,H_2O$	$+0.248$
$As + 3\,H^+ + 3\,e = AsH_3$	-0.60
Barium	
$Ba^{++} + 2\,e = Ba$	-2.90
Beryllium	
$Be^{++} + 2\,e = Be$	-1.85
Bismuth	
$BiCl_4^- + 3\,e = Bi + 4\,Cl^-$	$+0.16$
$BiO^+ + 2\,H^+ + 3\,e = Bi + H_2O$	$+0.32$
Boron	
$H_2BO_3^- + 5\,H_2O + 8\,e = BH_4^- + 8\,OH^-$	-1.24
$H_2BO_3^- + H_2O + 3\,e = B + 4\,OH^-$	-1.79
Bromine	
$2\,BrO_3^- + 12\,H^+ + 10\,e = Br_2 + 6\,H_2O$	$+1.52$
$Br_2(aq) + 2\,e = 2\,Br^-$	$+1.087$[a]
$Br_2(l) + 2\,e = 2\,Br^-$	$+1.065$[a]
$Br_3^- + 2\,e = 3\,Br^-$	$+1.05$
Cadmium	
$Cd^{++} + 2\,e = Cd$	-0.403
$Cd(CN)_4^{--} + 2\,e = Cd + 4\,CN^-$	-1.09
$Cd(NH_3)_4^{++} + 2\,e = Cd + 4\,NH_3$	-0.61

* See footnotes at end of table.

Half-Reaction	$E°$
Calcium	
$Ca^{++} + 2\ e = Ca$	-2.87
Carbon	
$2\ CO_2 + 2\ H^+ + 2\ e = H_2C_2O_4$	-0.49
Cerium	
$Ce^{++++} + e = Ce^{+++}$ $(1\ F\ HClO_4)$	$+1.70$
$Ce^{++++} + e = Ce^{+++}$ $(1\ F\ HNO_3)$	$+1.61$
$Ce^{++++} + e = Ce^{+++}$ $(1\ F\ H_2SO_4)$	$+1.44$
Cesium	
$Cs^+ + e = Cs$	-2.92
Chlorine	
$Cl_2 + 2\ e = 2\ Cl^-$	$+1.3595$
$2\ ClO_3^- + 12\ H^+ + 10\ e = Cl_2 + 6\ H_2O$	$+1.47$
$ClO_3^- + 2\ H^+ + e = ClO_2 + H_2O$	$+1.15$
$HClO + H^+ + 2\ e = Cl^- + H_2O$	$+1.49$
$2\ HClO + 2\ H^+ + 2\ e = Cl_2 + 2\ H_2O$	$+1.63$
Chromium	
$Cr_2O_7^{--} + 14\ H^+ + 6\ e = 2\ Cr^{+++} + 7\ H_2O$	$+1.33$
$Cr^{+++} + e = Cr^{++}$	-0.41
$Cr^{++} + 2\ e = Cr$	-0.91
$CrO_4^{--} + 4\ H_2O + 3\ e = Cr(OH)_3 + 5\ OH^-$	-0.13
Cobalt	
$Co^{+++} + e = Co^{++}$	$+1.842$
$Co(NH_3)_6^{+++} + e = Co(NH_3)_6^{++}$	$+0.1$
$Co(OH)_3 + e = Co(OH)_2 + OH^-$	$+0.17$
$Co^{++} + 2\ e = Co$	-0.277
$Co(CN)_6^{---} + e = Co(CN)_6^{----}$	-0.84
Copper	
$Cu^{++} + 2\ e = Cu$	$+0.337$
$Cu^{++} + e = Cu^+$	$+0.153$
$Cu^{++} + I^- + e = CuI$	$+0.86$
$Cu^{++} + 2\ CN^- + e = Cu(CN)_2^-$	$+1.12$
$Cu(CN)_2^- + e = Cu + 2\ CN^-$	-0.43
$Cu(NH_3)_4^{++} + e = Cu(NH_3)_2^+ + 2\ NH_3$	-0.01
$Cu^{++} + 2\ Cl^- + e = CuCl_2^-$	$+0.463$
$CuCl_2^- + e = Cu + 2\ Cl^-$	$+0.177$
Fluorine	
$F_2 + 2\ e = 2\ F^-$	$+2.87$
Gold	
$Au^{+++} + 2\ e = Au^+$	$+1.41$
$Au^{+++} + 3\ e = Au$	$+1.50$
$Au(CN)_2^- + e = Au + 2\ CN^-$	-0.60
$AuCl_2^- + e = Au + 2\ Cl^-$	$+1.15$
$AuCl_4^- + 2\ e = AuCl_2^- + 2\ Cl^-$	$+0.926$
$AuBr_2^- + e = Au + 2\ Br^-$	$+0.959$
$AuBr_4^- + 2\ e = AuBr_2^- + 2\ Br^-$	$+0.802$

Half-Reaction	$E°$
Hydrogen	
$2 H^+ + 2 e = H_2$	0.0000
$2 H_2O + 2 e = H_2 + 2 OH^-$	-0.828
Iodine	
$I_2(aq) + 2 e = 2 I^-$	$+0.6197^b$
$I_3^- + 2 e = 3 I^-$	$+0.5355$
$I_2(s) + 2 e = 2 I^-$	$+0.5345^b$
$2 IO_3^- + 12 H^+ + 10 e = I_2 + 6 H_2O$	$+1.20$
$2 ICl_2^- + 2 e = I_2 + 4 Cl^-$	$+1.06$
Iron	
$Fe^{+++} + e = Fe^{++}$	$+0.771$
$Fe^{+++} + e = Fe^{++}$ $\quad$ (1 F HCl)	$+0.70$
$Fe^{+++} + e = Fe^{++}$ $\quad$ (1 F H_2SO_4)	$+0.68$
$Fe^{+++} + e = Fe^{++}$ $\quad$ (0.5 F H_3PO_4 $-$ 1 F H_2SO_4)	$+0.61$
$Fe(CN)_6^{---} + e = Fe(CN)_6^{----}$	$+0.36$
$Fe(CN)_6^{---} + e = Fe(CN)_6^{----}$ $\quad$ (1 F HCl or $HClO_4$)	$+0.71$
$Fe^{++} + 2 e = Fe$	-0.440
Lead	
$Pb^{++} + 2 e = Pb$	-0.126
$PbSO_4 + 2 e = Pb + SO_4^{--}$	-0.3563
$PbO_2 + SO_4^{--} + 4 H^+ + 2 e = PbSO_4 + 2 H_2O$	$+1.685$
$PbO_2 + 4 H^+ + 2 e = Pb^{++} + 2 H_2O$	$+1.455$
Lithium	
$Li^+ + e = Li$	-3.045
Magnesium	
$Mg^{++} + 2 e = Mg$	-2.37
$Mg(OH)_2 + 2 e = Mg + 2 OH^-$	-2.69
Manganese	
$Mn^{++} + 2 e = Mn$	-1.18
$MnO_4^- + 4 H^+ + 3 e = MnO_2 + 2 H_2O$	$+1.695$
$MnO_4^- + 8 H^+ + 5 e = Mn^{++} + 4 H_2O$	$+1.51$
$MnO_2 + 4 H^+ + 2 e = Mn^{++} + 2 H_2O$	$+1.23$
$MnO_4^- + e = MnO_4^{--}$	$+0.564$
$Mn^{+++} + e = Mn^{++}$ $\quad$ (8 F H_2SO_4)	$+1.51$
Mercury	
$2 Hg^{++} + 2 e = Hg_2^{++}$	$+0.920$
$Hg^{++} + 2 e = Hg$	$+0.854$
$Hg_2^{++} + 2 e = 2 Hg$	$+0.789$
$Hg_2SO_4 + 2 e = 2 Hg + SO_4^{--}$	$+0.6151$
$HgCl_4^{--} + 2 e = Hg + 4 Cl^-$	$+0.48$
$Hg_2Cl_2 + 2 e = 2 Hg + 2 Cl^-$ $\quad$ (0.1 F KCl)	$+0.334$
$Hg_2Cl_2 + 2 e = 2 Hg + 2 Cl^-$ $\quad$ (1 F KCl)	$+0.280$
$Hg_2Cl_2 + 2 K^+ + 2 e = 2 Hg + 2 KCl(s)$	$+0.2415$
$\quad$ (saturated calomel electrode)	
Molybdenum	
$Mo^{+6} + e = Mo^{+5}$ $\quad$ (2 F HCl)	$+0.53$
$Mo^{++++} + e = Mo^{+++}$ $\quad$ (4 F H_2SO_4)	$+0.1$

Half-Reaction	$E°$
Neptunium	
$Np^{++++} + e = Np^{+++}$	$+0.147$
$NpO_2^+ + 4 H^+ + e = Np^{++++} + 2 H_2O$	$+0.75$
$NpO_2^{++} + e = NpO_2^+$	$+1.15$
Nickel	
$Ni^{++} + 2 e = Ni$	-0.24
$NiO_2 + 4 H^+ + 2 e = Ni^{++} + 2 H_2O$	$+1.68$
Nitrogen	
$NO_2 + H^+ + e = HNO_2$	$+1.07$
$NO_2 + 2 H^+ + 2 e = NO + H_2O$	$+1.03$
$HNO_2 + H^+ + e = NO + H_2O$	$+1.00$
$NO_3^- + 4 H^+ + 3 e = NO + 2 H_2O$	$+0.96$
$NO_3^- + 3 H^+ + 2 e = HNO_2 + H_2O$	$+0.94$
$NO_3^- + 2 H^+ + e = NO_2 + H_2O$	$+0.80$
$N_2 + 5 H^+ + 4 e = N_2H_5^+$	-0.23
Osmium	
$OsO_4 + 8 H^+ + 8 e = Os + 4 H_2O$	$+0.85$
$OsCl_6^{--} + e = OsCl_6^{---}$	$+0.85$
$OsCl_6^{---} + e = Os^{++} + 6 Cl^-$	$+0.4$
$Os^{++} + 2 e = Os$	$+0.85$
Oxygen	
$O_3 + 2 H^+ + 2 e = O_2 + H_2O$	$+2.07$
$H_2O_2 + 2 H^+ + 2 e = 2 H_2O$	$+1.77$
$O_2 + 4 H^+ + 4 e = 2 H_2O$	$+1.229$
$H_2O_2 + 2 e = 2 OH^-$	$+0.88$
$O_2 + 2 H^+ + 2 e = H_2O_2$	$+0.682$
Palladium	
$Pd^{++} + 2 e = Pd$	$+0.987$
$PdCl_6^{--} + 2 e = PdCl_4^{--} + 2 Cl^-$	$+1.288$
$PdCl_4^{--} + 2 e = Pd + 4 Cl^-$	$+0.623$
Phosphorus	
$H_3PO_4 + 2 H^+ + 2 e = H_3PO_3 + H_2O$	-0.276
$H_3PO_3 + 2 H^+ + 2 e = H_3PO_2 + H_2O$	-0.50
Platinum	
$PtCl_6^{--} + 2 e = PtCl_4^{--} + 2 Cl^-$	$+0.68$
$PtBr_6^{--} + 2 e = PtBr_4^{--} + 2 Br^-$	$+0.59$
$Pt(OH)_2 + 2 H^+ + 2 e = Pt + 2 H_2O$	$+0.98$
Plutonium	
$PuO_2^+ + 4 H^+ + e = Pu^{++++} + 2 H_2O$	$+1.15$
$PuO_2^{++} + 4 H^+ + 2 e = Pu^{++++} + 2 H_2O$	$+1.067$
$Pu^{++++} + e = Pu^{+++}$	$+0.97$
$PuO_2^{++} + e = PuO_2^+$	$+0.93$
Potassium	
$K^+ + e = K$	-2.925
Radium	
$Ra^{++} + 2 e = Ra$	-2.92

Half-Reaction	$E°$

Rubidium

$Rb^+ + e = Rb$ -2.925

Selenium

$SeO_4^{--} + 4\,H^+ + 2\,e = H_2SeO_3 + H_2O$	$+1.15$
$H_2SeO_3 + 4\,H^+ + 4\,e = Se + 3\,H_2O$	$+0.740$
$Se + 2\,H^+ + 2\,e = H_2Se$	-0.40

Silver

$Ag^+ + e = Ag$	$+0.7995$
$Ag^{++} + e = Ag^+$ $(4\,F\,HNO_3)$	$+1.927$
$AgCl + e = Ag + Cl^-$	$+0.2222$
$AgBr + e = Ag + Br^-$	$+0.073$
$AgI + e = Ag + I^-$	-0.151
$Ag_2O + H_2O + 2\,e = 2\,Ag + 2\,OH^-$	$+0.342$
$Ag_2S + 2\,e = 2\,Ag + S^{--}$	-0.71

Sodium

$Na^+ + e = Na$ -2.714

Strontium

$Sr^{++} + 2\,e = Sr$ -2.89

Sulfur

$S + 2\,H^+ + 2\,e = H_2S$	$+0.141$
$S_4O_6^{--} + 2\,e = 2\,S_2O_3^{--}$	$+0.08$
$SO_4^{--} + 4\,H^+ + 2\,e = H_2SO_3 + H_2O$	$+0.17$
$S_2O_8^{--} + 2\,e = 2\,SO_4^{--}$	$+2.01$
$SO_4^{--} + H_2O + 2\,e = SO_3^{--} + 2\,OH^-$	-0.93
$2\,H_2SO_3 + 2\,H^+ + 4\,e = S_2O_3^{--} + 3\,H_2O$	$+0.40$
$2\,SO_3^{--} + 3\,H_2O + 4\,e = S_2O_3^{--} + 6\,OH^-$	-0.58
$SO_3^{--} + 3\,H_2O + 4\,e = S + 6\,OH^-$	-0.66

Thallium

$Tl^{+++} + 2\,e = Tl^+$	$+1.25$
$Tl^+ + e = Tl$	-0.3363

Tin

$Sn^{++} + 2\,e = Sn$	-0.136
$Sn^{++++} + 2\,e = Sn^{++}$	$+0.154$
$SnCl_6^{--} + 2\,e = SnCl_4^{--} + 2\,Cl^-$ $(1\,F\,HCl)$	$+0.14$
$Sn(OH)_6^{--} + 2\,e = HSnO_2^- + H_2O + 3\,OH^-$	-0.93
$HSnO_2^- + H_2O + 2\,e = Sn + 3\,OH^-$	-0.91

Titanium

$Ti^{++} + 2\,e = Ti$	-1.63
$Ti^{+++} + e = Ti^{++}$	-0.37
$TiO^{++} + 2\,H^+ + e = Ti^{+++} + H_2O$	$+0.10$
$Ti^{++++} + e = Ti^{+++}$ $(5\,F\,H_3PO_4)$	-0.15

Tungsten

$W^{+6} + e = W^{+5}$ $(12\,F\,HCl)$	$+0.26$
$W^{+5} + e = W^{+4}$ $(12\,F\,HCl)$	-0.3
$W(CN)_8^{---} + e = W(CN)_8^{----}$	$+0.48$
$2\,WO_3(s) + 2\,H^+ + 2\,e = W_2O_5(s) + H_2O$	-0.03
$W_2O_5(s) + 2\,H^+ + 2\,e = 2\,WO_2(s) + H_2O$	-0.043

Half-Reaction	$E°$
Uranium	
$U^{++++} + e = U^{+++}$	-0.61
$UO_2^{++} + e = UO_2^{+}$	$+0.05$
$UO_2^{++} + 4 H^+ + 2 e = U^{++++} + 2 H_2O$	$+0.334$
$UO_2^{+} + 4 H^+ + e = U^{++++} + 2 H_2O$	$+0.62$
Vanadium	
$VO_2^{+} + 2 H^+ + e = VO^{++} + H_2O$	$+1.000$
$VO^{++} + 2 H^+ + e = V^{+++} + H_2O$	$+0.361$
$V^{+++} + e = V^{++}$	-0.255
$V^{++} + 2 e = V$	-1.18
Zinc	
$Zn^{++} + 2 e = Zn$	-0.763
$Zn(NH_3)_4^{++} + 2 e = Zn + 4 NH_3$	-1.04
$Zn(CN)_4^{--} + 2 e = Zn + 4 CN^-$	-1.26
$Zn(OH)_4^{--} + 2 e = Zn + 4 OH^-$	-1.22

The *standard potential* for a redox couple is defined on page 465 as the emf or potential (sign and magnitude) of an electrode consisting of that redox couple under standard-state conditions measured in a galvanic cell against the normal hydrogen electrode at 25°C.

Formal potentials, properly designated by the symbol $E°'$ and defined on page 471, are italicized in the above table. The solution condition to which each formal potential pertains is written in parentheses following the half-reaction.

[a] The half-reaction and standard potential

$$Br_2(aq) + 2 e = 2 Br^-; \quad E° = +1.087 \text{ v}$$

pertain to the system in which the activity of dissolved molecular bromine, Br_2, as well as the activity of the bromide ion, is unity in water. Actually, this is an impossible situation because the solubility of Br_2 in water is only about 0.21 M at 25°C.

On the other hand, the half-reaction and standard potential

$$Br_2(l) + 2 e = 2 Br^-; \quad E° = +1.065 \text{ v}$$

apply to an electrode system in which excess *liquid* bromine is in equilibrium with an aqueous solution containing bromide ion at unit activity. It follows that an aqueous solution in equilibrium with liquid bromine will be saturated with respect to molecular bromine at a concentration (activity) of 0.21 M.

Thus, these two standard potentials are different because the former refers to the (hypothetical) situation in which the concentration (activity) of $Br_2(aq)$ is taken to be unity, whereas the latter refers to the physically real situation for which the concentration (activity) of $Br_2(aq)$ is only 0.21 M.

[b] The reason for the difference between the two entries

$$I_2(aq) + 2 e = 2 I^-; \quad E° = +0.6197 \text{ v}$$

and

$$I_2(s) + 2 e = 2 I^-; \quad E° = +0.5345 \text{ v}$$

is essentially the same as that stated in the preceding footnote. The first half-reaction requires (hypothetically) an aqueous molecular iodine concentration or activity of unity, whereas the second half-reaction specifies that excess *solid* iodine be in equilibrium with an aqueous, iodide solution of unit activity. Since the solubility of molecular iodine in water at 25°C is approximately 0.00133 M, it is impossible to ever have an aqueous solution containing 1 M molecular iodine. Thus, the standard potential for the second half-reaction will be considerably less oxidizing or less positive than the value for the first half-reaction.

Among the best sources of standard and formal potentials are the following references:

1. W. M. Latimer: *Oxidation Potentials*, second edition, Prentice-Hall, Inc., New York, 1952.
2. J. J. Lingane: *Electroanalytical Chemistry*, second edition, Wiley-Interscience, New York, 1958, pp. 639–651.
3. L. Meites, ed.: *Handbook of Analytical Chemistry*, McGraw-Hill Book Company, New York, 1963.

Appendix 5

Answers to Numerical Problems

Only the numerical portions of the answers are listed here. The complete answer to each problem must include an indication of the units. In some instances, no particular units are specified in the problem, and several different units may be equally valid. Consequently, some numerical answers other than those listed here may also be correct.

Chapter 2

14. $+0.52$
15. 0.26
16. 0.999906; 19.2642
17. 16.1545
18. 14.8154
19. 0.9983
20. 13.547
21. 0.9990
28. 25.02
29. $+0.05$

Chapter 3

3. 60.10; 0.26; 0.43
4. -0.56; 0.92
5. 12.0104; 0.0012; 12.0104 ± 0.0012
6. no; 39.02 ± 0.36; 0.31; 7.9
7. no; 0.0975 ± 0.0003; 0.0975 ± 0.0011
8. yes
9. inconclusive
10. 1.383
11. 396.0
12. $+4.1$
13. 51.82
14. 30.06
15. 0.09676; 2.622
16. 0.3635
17. 6.967; 85.21
18. 62.79; $C_3H_6Cl_2$
19. 31.2
20. 55.1; 44.9
21. $34.6/65.4$
22. 0.340; 0.238; 0.300
23. 34.2; 49.0; 16.69
24. 24.50
25. 58.17
26. $+3$
27. 0.4044
28. 6.808; 6.540

Chapter 4

1. 0.027; 0.1732; 0.040; 5.55×10^4
2. 0.0053
5. 1.4×10^{-4}
7. 5.0×10^{-12}
8. 2.53×10^{-5}
9. 2.07×10^{-5}
10. 1.08×10^{-16}
11. 1.38×10^{-2}
12. 6.53×10^{-5}
13. 1.82×10^{-4}; 6.05×10^{-7}; 1.82×10^{-4}

14. 1.7×10^{-2}
15. 0.20
16. 7.95×10^{-5}
17. 7.29×10^{-4}

18. 1.65×10^{-4}; 7.94×10^{-6}; 1.81×10^{-4}; 2.26
19. 4.8×10^{-4}
20. 1.8×10^{-4}; 4.3×10^{-3}; 4.4×10^{-3}; 8.8×10^{-5}
21. 1.0×10^{-8}

22. 0.7; 4.00×10^{-6}; 1.77×10^5; 1.32×10^{-10}; 5.3×10^{-7}; 2.0×10^{-3}; 6.3×10^{-8}
23. 2×10^{-17}; 2.5×10^{-4}; 5.0×10^6
24. 8.17×10^{-6}; 8.69×10^{-6}
25. 1.61×10^{-3}; 2.30×10^{-5}
26. 1.1×10^{-13}
27. 5.3×10^{-3}; 6.5×10^{-3}; 1.73×10^{-4}
28. AgCl; 5.05×10^{-6}; 50
29. 7.2×10^{-4}; 1.24×10^{-7}; 1.45×10^{-3}

30. 2.09×10^{-3}
31. 6.07×10^{-12}
32. $Cr(OH)_3$; 7.30; 4.48; $5.48 - 7.30$
33. 5.0×10^{-5}; 7.0×10^{-3}
34. 0.018
35. 1.31×10^{-6}
36. 3.2×10^{-10}; 2.6×10^{-6}
37. 1.4×10^{-9}
38. 0.26
39. 0.033
40. 2.15×10^{-2}

Chapter 6

7. 11.98
8. 16.18
9. 31.65
10. 46.80
11. 25.74
12. 0.327; 0.673
13. 31.2
14. 1.38; 2.67
15. 77.8; 0.0197

Chapter 7

3. 0.976
6. 67; 84
7. 4
8. 4.0; 3
11. 331; 320; 0.124; 310; 0.090
12. 86.99; 750

Chapter 8

4. 1.00; 0.40; 11.73; 12.40; −0.14; 7.00; 3.38; 2.72; 4.92; 9.20; 5.13; 8.88
5. 1.30
6. 4.76
7. 1.0 to 27.8
8. 1.0 to 7.2
9. 0.11; 0.47
10. 1.62×10^{-7}; 6.79
21. 1.158; 1.242
22. 180.0
23. 0.4049
24. 0.3449
25. 118.7
26. 4.804
27. 0.1835; 0.06805
28. 6.005
29. 35.52
30. 0.2932
33. 1.24; 6.2×10^{-8}
34. 4.5×10^{-12}; 2.2×10^{-3}; 0.265
35. 0.283; 7.86×10^{-7}; 3.70
36. 1.86×10^{-3}; 1.86×10^{-3}; 0.265
37. 0.340; 1.3×10^{-6}; 10.30
38. 9.33
39. 5.06
40. 1.20; 6.5×10^{-8}
41. 1.58×10^{-2}; 1.58×10^{-2}; 0.484
42. 0.100; 1.31×10^{-8}; 10.17

43. 12.00; 11.78; 11.52; 11.16; 8.40; 7.00; 2.95

44. 0.0078; 0.0078; 0.092
45. 0.67; 3.15×10^{-6}; 8.50

46. 4.00; 4.11; 4.32; 5.74; 6.96; 7.00; 9.00; 9.25
47. 0.0260; 6.9×10^{-4}; 1.45×10^{-11}; 6.9×10^{-4}

48. −0.99, 8.43; 0.0836
49. 0.14; 0.16
50. 336; 1.25×10^{-5}; 8.76
51. 1.84×10^{-5}

52. 2.54; 4.36; 6.15; 8.14; 11.12; 12.22; −0.23; +0.12
54. 3; 4.4; 8.2
55. 3.00; 3.10; 3.28; 3.72; 5.72; 7.00; 10.28

56. 28.00   58. 0.048; 0.024
60. 0.120; 0.0137
61. 11.32; 9.86; 9.43; 9.08; 8.65; 5.08; 1.65; 1.24; +0.64; −0.056

Chapter 9
14. 3.45×10^{-3}; 2.51

Chapter 10
9. 13.61   10. 0.08592
11. 91.00   12. 26.22
13. 22.70   14. 0.09824; 0.1330
15. 66.02; 30.22; 3.76   16. 4.45×10^{-4}
17. 8.1×10^{-5} 19. 2.241×10^{-5}
23. 1.00×10^{-5}; 5.00; −47.9; +5.9   24. 4.3×10^{-3}; 0.12
25. 6.5×10^{-7}; 2.0×10^{-2}; −64.8; 0.0864

Chapter 11
6. 0.41; 0.27; 0.15; 0.13; 0.04; 4.1×10^{-4}; 2.7×10^{-4}; 1.5×10^{-4};
   1.3×10^{-4}; 4.0×10^{-5}
9. 30.63   10. 0.008832
11. 0.01922   12. 0.0844
15. 9.56; 1.74×10^{-20}; 6.32×10^{-13}; 4.96×10^{-6}; 1.25×10^{-2}; 2.50×10^{-3}
16. 4.00×10^{-4}; 1.44×10^{-4} 17. +0.45

Chapter 12
9. +0.398; 2.5×10^{14}; copper electrode is anode.
   −0.64; 2×10^{-13}; platinum electrode is cathode.
   +0.414; 1.59×10^{13}; left-hand platinum electrode is anode.
   −1.361; 8.0×10^{-47}; left-hand platinum electrode is cathode.
   +0.507; 2.88×10^{14}; zinc electrode is anode.
   −0.109; 1.4×10^{-9}; platinum electrode is cathode.
10. 1.9×10^{-8} 11. 1.29×10^{-3}
12. 708   13. 1.0×10^{-12}
14. 1.48×10^{-19} 15. 3.6×10^{-7}
16. +1.68   17. +1.51
18. +1.50
19. −0.72; 4.0×10^{-25}; −0.72; copper electrode is negative; 1.0×10^{-15}
20. +0.010; 4.8; 3.0×10^{-6}; 4.3×10^{-11}; −0.71; +0.33
22. 6.3×10^{16}; 1.4×10^{9}; 8.0×10^{61}; 3.6×10^{-11}
25. +0.46; 1.30×10^{-14}; 40.00; +1.24; −1.06
26. 0.100; 0.600
27. 2.55×10^{-7}; 50.0057; +0.011
28. 2.5×10^{19}; 6.5×10^{14}
30. 1.78×10^{15}; +0.55; 3.35×10^{-10}; 5.00; +0.723

Chapter 13
5. 0.01492; 0.08953   6. −0.136
8. 31.6; 2.9   9. 0.1093; 0.02186
12. 83.35   13. 0.05676; 0.2838
15. 1.41×10^{4} 16. 85.24
18. 17.86; 8.359; 16.25   19. 0.03617; 0.1036
20. 37.93   21. 59.73
22. 3.332   23. 0.5842
24. 8.780   25. 2.81×10^{-6}
27. 0.1792   29. 0.0385; 0.0142
30. 0.02642   31. 0.08130

32. 0.00940; 0.139   33. 118.3
34. 0.7607
35. $+0.99$; $+0.49$; -0.42; $+0.96$; $+0.30$; -0.00025

Chapter 14

1. 4.57×10^{-8}; 2.33×10^{-4}; 4.65×10^{-4}; 9.30×10^{-3}
2. 27.74   3. 0.002810
4. 0.180; 18.0   5. 0.9575
6. $+1.174$; $+1.24$; $+1.45$ 7. 4.90×10^{36}; 0.00435
8. 0.1383; 0.2766   9. 0.1175; 0.1175
10. 0.05668   11. 0.6672
12. 12.75   13. 2
14. 0.08138   16. 4.120
17. 14.59; 25.73   18. 39.26

Chapter 15

2. 1.35×10^{15}; 5.66×10^{14}; 1.76×10^{17}; 1.00×10^{12}; 2.31×10^{17}; 4.92×10^{13}
3. 15.2; 1.52×10^{8}; 6.17×10^{-6}; 61.7; 4.10×10^{-10}; 4.10×10^{-3}
4. 2.48×10^{-12}; 5.40×10^{-13}; 2.00×10^{-9}; 1.73×10^{-17}
5. 7.602×10^{-12}; 109.4; 4.186×10^{10}
6. 0.434; 0.658; 0.0846; 0; 1.377
7. 15.8; 61.0; 26.0; 1.50; 87.7
8. 75.6; 6.10; 97.2
12. $\frac{1}{2}a(b_1 + b_2)$; ab_1

Chapter 16

1. 4800; 9.27×10^{-5}; 3.63×10^{-4}; 3.23×10^{-6}
2. 0.88; 0.694   3. 2.74×10^{-3}; 6.38×10^{-3}
4. 0.040; 4.0×10^{-6} 6. 34.1; 1.11×10^{4}
7. 370; 2.35×10^{3}; 9.73×10^{-4}; 2.73×10^{-4}
8. 7.98×10^{-6} 9. $Fe(C_{10}H_8N_2)_3{}^{++}$; 1.05×10^{4}
10. 0.470   11. 6.08×10^{-6}
12. 1.84×10^{-3}; 4.51×10^{-3} 13. 4.80

Chapter 17

1. 8.1; 0.128   2. 0.07304; 4.32×10^{-6}; 9.01
6. 0.367   8. 9.064×10^{-6}; $+1.5$
9. 46.67; 46.87; -0.43 10. 2.25
11. 3.08×10^{-12} 14. 1.027×10^{-5}; 1.055×10^{-10}
15. 385.5; 1.34×10^{-5}
16. 0.001654; 0.001480; 0.001305; 0.000958; 0.000871; 0.000783; 0.002173;
    0.003564
17. 3.51×10^{4} 18. 4.06×10^{-4}
19. 0.00272   20. 3.61×10^{-6}; 8.65×10^{-6}

Chapter 18

1. $+0.350$ 2. 1.094 (0.956 and 0.138)
3. 1.26×10^{10} 4. -2
6. -0.053; 0.0986; 154 (64 and 90)   7. 9.55×10^{-8}
8. 0.148   9. 1.77×10^{-4}
10. -0.365; 288; 354   11. 0.1360
12. 13.01   13. 17

Index